D1545134

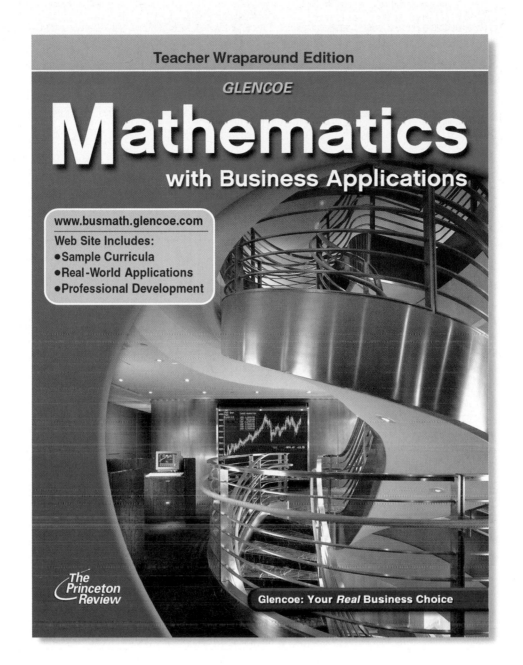

Teacher Wraparound Edition

GLENCOE

Mathematics
with Business Applications

www.busmath.glencoe.com
Web Site Includes:
- Sample Curricula
- Real-World Applications
- Professional Development

The Princeton Review

Glencoe: Your *Real* Business Choice

Fifth Edition

Walter H. Lange
The University of Toledo

Temoleon G. Rousos
The University of Toledo

www.busmath.glencoe.com

McGraw Hill **Glencoe**

New York, New York   Columbus, Ohio   Chicago, Illinois   Peoria, Illinois   Woodland Hills, California

Program Components

For the Teacher

Assessment Binder
    Exam*View® Pro Test Generator* CD-ROM
    Reproducible Tests
    Alternative Assessment Strategies
Interactive Lesson Planner CD-ROM
Mathematics with Business Applications, Teacher Wraparound Edition
Mathematics with Business Applications Web Site (www.busmath.glencoe.com)
PowerPoint® Presentations CD-ROM
Student Activity Workbook, Teacher Annotated Edition
Teacher Resource Binder
    Blackline Masters
    Lesson Plans
    Internet Resources

For the Student

Mathematics with Business Applications Web Site (www.busmath.glencoe.com)
School-to-Home Activity Workbook
Student Activity Workbook

Glencoe

The McGraw-Hill Companies

Copyright © 2004, 1998, 1993 by Glencoe/McGraw-Hill, a division of the McGraw-Hill Companies. All rights reserved. Copyright © 1986, 1984, 1981 by Houghton-Mifflin Company. Except as permitted under the United States Copyright Act of 1976, no part of this publication may be reproduced or distributed in any form or by any means, or stored in a database or retrieval system, without prior written permission of the publishers, Glencoe/McGraw-Hill.

Printed in the United States of America.

Send all inquires to:
Glencoe/McGraw-Hill
21600 Oxnard Street, Suite 500
Woodland Hills, California 91367

ISBN 0-07-829806-7 (Student Edition)
ISBN 0-07-831372-4 (Teacher Wraparound Edition)

2 3 4 5 6 7 8 9 027 08 07 06 05 04

Contents FOR TEACHER WRAPAROUND EDITION

Content Consultants

Table of Contents

Teaching Strategies

Content Consultants

Consultants and Accuracy Editors

Diane Culpepper
Mathematics Writer and Editor
Lake Mary, Fla.

Denise A. Heban, M.Ed.
Mathematics Teacher
Swanton, Ohio

Heidi Kinney
Mathematics Editor and Writer
Norton, Mass.

Christine Ann Francom
Mathematics Teacher
Newbury, Calif.

Gary M. Good, M. Ed.
Former Mathematics Teacher and
Department Head
Mesa, Ariz.

Don J. Guerrieri, Ph.D.
Former Business Education Teacher
Greensburg, Pa.

R. Jonathan Louvar, C.P.A.
Accounting Supervisor
Calabasas, Calif.

Amee Peterson
Mathematics Writer and Editor
Kingston, New York

Tabitha Ratcliffe
Business Teacher and Instructor
South Milwaukee, Wisc.

John Salerno
Business Education Teacher
Newington, Conn.

Linda Smoucha
English Teacher
Arlington Heights, Ill.

Teacher Reviewers

Teresa L. Adams
Edison High School
Huntington Beach, Calif.

Hal S. Bradford
Etowah High School
Woodstock, Ga.

Isaac Bristow
Fairfield High School
Fairfield, Calif.

David S. Emery
Soldotna High School
Soldotna, Alaska

Mary Pat Guinane
Webster Schroeder High School
Webster, N.Y.

Mary Henderson
Proctor High School
Utica, N.Y.

Kathy Hernandez
Sand Creek High School
Colorado Springs, Colo.

Dorothy Kurtz
Monmouth Regional High School
Tinton Falls, N.J.

Paul Lango
Bartlett High School
Webster, Mass.

Denise Leib
Monmouth Regional High School
Tinton Falls, N.J.

LaVerne B. Lundy
Griffin High School
Griffin, Ga.

Dale Miller
Formerly of Sand Creek High School
Colorado Springs, Colo.

Joyce Neal
Southside High School
Muncie, Ind.

Sherice L. Palmer
East Iberville High School
St. Gabriel, La.

Kim Peterson
Fortuna Union High School
Fortuna, Calif.

Vicki Potter
Evergreen High School
Seattle, Wash.

Evelyn Rock
Thomas Jefferson High School
Council Bluffs, Iowa

Susan Spivey
Fitzgerald High School
Fitzgerald, Ga.

Willard Steverson
Holmes County High School
Bonifay, Fla.

Brenda L. Touchinski
Luxemburg-Casco High School
Luxemburg, Wisc.

Lynn M. Williams
Windham Regional Vocational
Technical School
Willimantic, Conn.

Field Test Schools

Glencoe/McGraw-Hill wishes to thank the following schools that field-tested the textbook. They are instrumental in providing feedback and verifying the accuracy of the program.

Ann Cheman
Seneca Valley Senior High School
Harmony, Pa.

Anne Huffer
Governor Thomas Johnson High
   School
Frederick, Md.

Jim Keefe
Aurora Central High School
Aurora, Colo.

Dr. Ed Murphy
Will C. Wood High School
Vacaville, Calif.

Elisa Yukstas
Woodland Hills Senior High School
Pittsburgh, Pa.

Robin Carline
Teacher
East Iberville High School
Saint Gabriel, La.

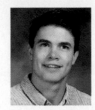

Loren Holthaus
Marketing Teacher
Big Lake Middle School
Big Lake, Minn.

Naomi Harwood
Teacher
Rutherfordton Spindle High School
Rutherfordton, N.C.

Margaret Colvin
Business Teacher
Southern Regional High School
Manahawkin, N.J.

Eric Matsuoka
Assistant Professor of Mathematics
University of Hawaii-Leeward CC
Pearl City, Hawaii

Elaine Peeters
Business Teacher
North Rose-Wolcott High School
Wolcott, N.Y.

Eddie Davidson
Teacher
East Union High School
Manteca, Calif.

Doug McCreath
Dean of Students
East Union High School
Manteca, Calif.

Tracy Plesek
Teacher
Lincoln-Way East High School
Frankfort, Ill.

Marge Garneau
Teacher
Central High School
Grand Junction, Colo.

Barbara Motley McGill
Teacher
T. Wingate Andrews High School
High Point, N.C.

Marilyn A. Evans Sanderson
Teacher
Ovtiz Middle School
Houston, Tex.

Contents in Brief

TABLE OF Contents

TABLE OF Contents

TABLE OF Contents

TABLE OF Contents

TEACHING Strategies

Instructional Design

The dependable instructional approach to the lessons strengthens student learning. The three-pronged approach—Workshops, Chapters, Reference Files—aids student performance and assessment.

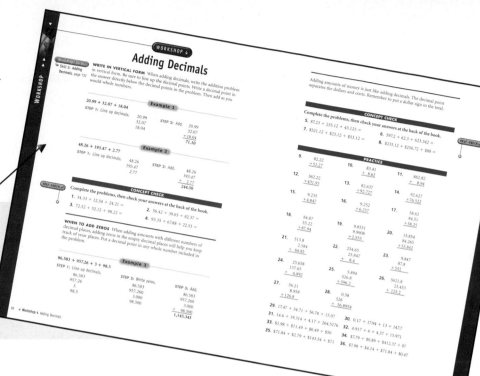

WORKSHOP Review the basic math skills here. These 42 Workshops cover the numerous mathematical functions students are asked to perform in this course. The detailed step-by-step instruction to the specific skills allows them to master the math skills required for success in the real world.

REFERENCE FILES At the end of the textbook, Skills File and Applications File comprise the Reference Files. The Skills File has 32 computational review parts. The Applications File has 26 common real-world applications. Call outs to these Reference Files are positioned throughout the textbook. (See the margins under "Need Help? Go to....")

COLOR CODING Before you know how to calculate a problem's answer, you need to learn the steps involved in that calculation. Therefore, pay attention to the content in blue. The blue indicates step-by-step instructions for you. You might also see blue content enclosed in parentheses. This is a special note for you to read and remember as you work through problems.

You might have noticed when you opened this textbook that some pages have red on the outside margin and others have green. The red designates Part 1 Basic Math Skills: Workshops and green designates Your Reference Files.

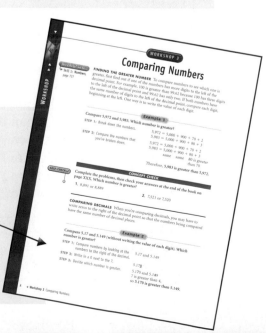

Instructional Design

Part Opener

PRACTICING LIFE SKILLS LAB
Use the part openers to engage in the Practicing Life Skills Lab—a hands-on approach to applying math to the real world.

Chapter Opener

WHAT YOU'LL LEARN This is a running list of the chapter's section objectives. These direct your reading as you progress through the chapter.

WHEN WILL YOU EVER USE THIS?
In each section, it answers how the concept is relevant in the real world.

KEY WORDS TO KNOW Use this at the beginning of every section. Key words are printed in boldface and highlighted in yellow when introduced and defined in the text. (You can also find the key words in the Glossary.)

MATHEMATICS ONLINE Extend the course work on the book-specific Web site. Students have access to games, study guides, and study tips. Teachers have access to professional development tools, ALEKS, online activities, and sample course curricula.

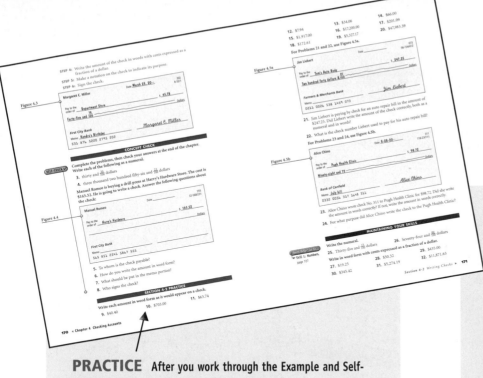

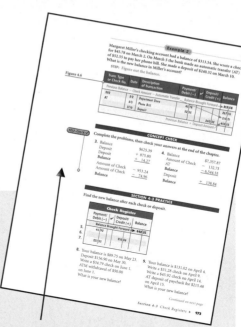

SELF-CHECK The problems let students practice the concept and formula before beginning the Practice problems. The Self-Check Answers are available in each chapter before the end-of-chapter Study Guide and Assessment starts.

PRACTICE After you work through the Example and Self-Check, complete the Practice. These problems are arranged to apply gradually in difficulty. Use the answers in the back of the book to check your work.

Features

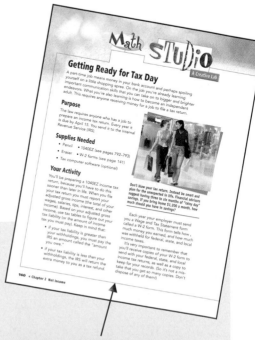

LIVING IN THE REAL WORLD
Each chapter starts and ends with a story about its content. The story is weaved through each section. Its application broadens the concept into a real-world situation.

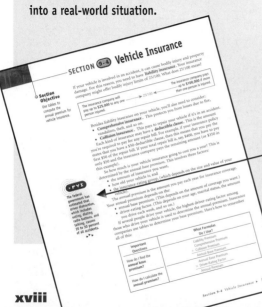

FYI These real-world tidbits are placed in the margins for your consideration.

MATH STUDIO There are seven different hands-on, group oriented projects. These creative labs bring in students' reading, writing, communication, and mathematical skills.

Efficient Program Resources

Assessment

Mathematics with Business Applications gives you all the tools you need to assess students' performance. With multi-tiered writing and accuracy checking processes and the help of The Princeton Review, tests have been prepared to help students' performance on standardized tests and course tests.

In the student edition, Glencoe offers multiple methods of reviewing and testing your students' comprehension and application of the concepts taught in *Mathematics with Business Applications*.

STUDY GUIDE AND ASSESSMENT At the end of each chapter, students' will review the content in the Study Guide and Assessment. This reviews Living in the Real World, key words, and practice of the sections.

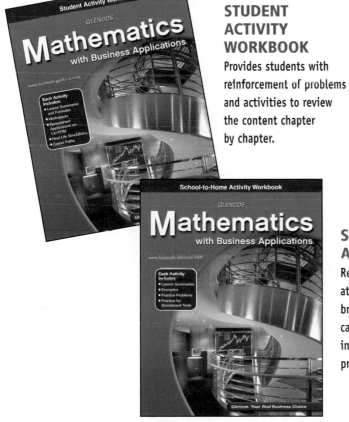

STUDENT ACTIVITY WORKBOOK

Provides students with reinforcement of problems and activities to review the content chapter by chapter.

CUMULATIVE TEST PREP Use this as preparation for a standardized, chapter, or part test. The Princeton Review evaluated these tests for accountability, accuracy, and clarity.

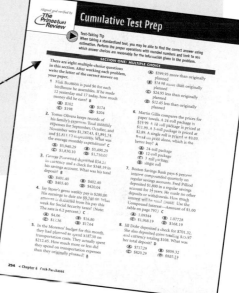

SCHOOL-TO-HOME ACTIVITY WORKBOOK

Review and practice the concepts at home. This is set up with a brief review so family members can understand and reinforce the instruction. They can work on the practice problems together.

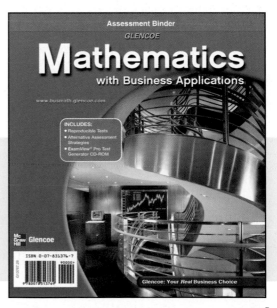

ASSESSMENT BINDER Use Exam*View*® *Pro Test Generator* CD-ROM to select from more than 1,800 questions to create a test for the class. This test bank on a CD-ROM allows you to customize the types of questions by difficulty level. In the *Assessment Binder*, *Reproducible Tests* are available to be photocopied. Diagnostic, chapter, part, midterm, and final tests have been created. Find the answer key after the tests. Lastly, use the *Alternative Assessment Strategies* to evaluate performance by applying it to the outlined rubrics.

Application and Reinforcement

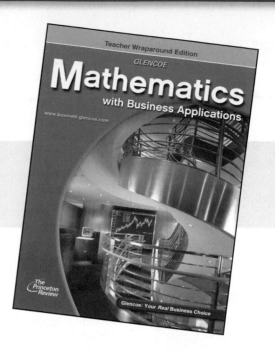

TEACHER WRAPAROUND EDITION Find extra review questions in this integral course supplement for chapter sections, such as Motivate the Lesson, In-Class Examples, and Reinforcement.

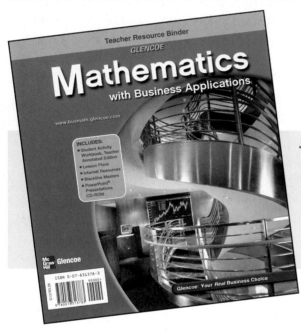

TEACHER RESOURCE BINDER Glencoe offers a *Student Activity Workbook, Teacher Annotated Edition,* which provides the answers to the section reviews, simulations, career paths, and spreadsheet applications. Also, the *Lesson Plans* offers chapter-by-chapter checklists of program components to help in planning. *Blackline Masters* and *Internet Resources* round out the packed binder full of extra content.

INTERACTIVE LESSON PLANNER CD-ROM This course management, interactive tool allows short- and long-term lesson planning. It's a practical device to organize and use the program components.

POWERPOINT® PRESENTATIONS CD-ROM More than 2,500 slides provide high-interest instruction. Introduce and walk-through a concept, with examples, charts, and tables.

Introduction to Styles and Needs

One of your greatest challenges as a teacher is to provide a positive learning environment for all students in your classroom. Because each student has his or her own unique set of abilities, perceptions, and needs, the learning styles and the physical abilities of your students may vary widely.

Assisting Students with Individual Needs

In order to help you provide all your students with a positive learning experience, this textbook provides a variety of activities. This diversity will stimulate student interest, motivate learning, and facilitate understanding.

TEACHING ENGLISH LANGUAGE LEARNERS (ELL)

Classrooms are increasingly populated with students who face the considerable challenge of mastering English as a second language. As you help your students overcome this language barrier, it is important to honor the richness of diversity and cultural heritage they bring to your school. Providing a wide variety of ways to learn, apply, and be assessed on the concepts of your course is the best method for reaching your English language learners (ELL).

Visual clues, hands-on tasks, questioning strategies, and cooperative learning are just some of the many ways in which you can make your ELL students feel more comfortable and experience successful learning. Explore the following organizations' Web sites for resources on the topic of teaching ELL:

- National Clearinghouse for English Language Acquisition and Language Instruction Educational Programs (NCELA) www.ncela.gwu.edu
- U.S. Department of Education: The Office of English Language Acquisition, Language Enhancement, and Academic Achievement for Limited English Proficient Students (OELA) www.ed.gov/offices/OBEMLA/index.html
- Center for Applied Linguistics www.cal.org
- California Association for Bilingual Education www.bilingualeducation.org/news.htm

TEACHING STUDENTS WITH SPECIAL NEEDS

Students in your classroom may have orthopedic impairments. They may have hearing or vision impairments, learning disabilities, or behavior disorders—all of which may interfere with their ability to learn. The learning styles of your students may also vary. Some students may be visual learners; others may learn more effectively through hands-on activities. Some students may work well independently, while others need the interaction of others. Students may come from a variety of cultural backgrounds and some may be second language learners.

Once you determine the special needs of your students, you can identify the areas in the curriculum that may present barriers to them. In order to remove those barriers, you may need to modify your teaching methods.

On the following pages are two charts. The first chart, Meeting Individual Needs, describes some of the special needs you may encounter with students in your classroom and identifies sources of information. Also provided are tips for modifying your teaching style to accommodate the special needs of your students.

The second chart on page xxiv, Eight Ways of Learning, will help you identify your students' learning styles. The chart gives a description of each type of learner; describes the likes of each type, what each type is good at, and how each learns best; and names some famous learners. Once you have identified each student's learning style, you can modify your teaching strategies to best suit his or her needs.

TEACHING Strategies

Meeting Individual Needs

Subject	Description	Sources of Information
Second Language Learners	Certain students often speak English as a second language, or not at all. Customs and behavior of people in the majority culture may be confusing for some of these students. Cultural values may inhibit some of these students from full participation in the classroom.	• *Teaching English as a Second Language* • *Mainstreaming and the Minority Child*
Behavior Disorders	Children with behavior disorders deviate from standards or expectations of behavior and impair the functioning of others and themselves. These children may also be gifted or have learning disabilities.	• *Exceptional Children* • *Journal of Special Education*
Visual Impairments	Children with visual impairments have partial or total loss of sight. Individuals with visual impairments are not significantly different from their sighted peers in ability range or personality. However, blindness may affect cognitive, motor, and social development.	• *Journal of Visual Impairment and Blindness* • *Education of Visually Handicapped* • *American Foundation for the Blind*
Hearing Impairments	Children with hearing impairments have partial or total loss of hearing. Individuals with hearing impairments are not significantly different from their peers in ability range or personality. However, the chronic condition of deafness may affect cognitive, motor, social, and speech development.	• *American Annals of the Deaf* • *Journal of Speech and Hearing Research* • *Sign Language Studies*
Physical Impairments	Children with physical impairments fall into two categories—those with orthopedic impairments (use of one or more limbs severely restricted) and those with other health impairments.	• *The Source Book for the Disabled* • *Teaching Exceptional Children*
Gifted	Although no formal definition exists, these students can be described as having above average ability, task commitment, and creativity. They rank in the top 5 percent of their classes. They usually finish work more quickly than other students and are capable of divergent thinking.	• *Journal for the Education of the Gifted* • *Gifted Child Quarterly* • *Gifted Creative/Talented*
Learning Disabilities	All students with learning disabilities have a problem in one or more areas, such as academic learning, language, perception, social-emotional adjustment, memory, or ability to pay attention.	• *Journal of Learning Disabilities* • *Learning Disability Quarterly*

Meeting Individual Needs

Tips for Instruction

- Remember that students' ability to speak English does not reflect their academic ability.
- Try to incorporate students' cultural experiences into your instruction. The help of a bilingual aide may be effective.
- Include information about different cultures in your curriculum to help build students' self-image.
- Avoid cultural stereotypes.
- Encourage students to share their cultures in the classroom.

- Work for long-term improvement; do not expect immediate success.
- Talk with students about their strengths and weaknesses; clearly outline objectives.
- Structure schedules, rules, room arrangement, and safety for a pleasant environment.
- Model appropriate behavior for students and reinforce proper behavior.

- Modify assignments as needed to help students become independent.
- Teach classmates how to serve as guides for the visually impaired.
- Tape lectures and reading assignments for the visually impaired.
- Encourage students to use their sense of touch; provide tactile models whenever possible.
- Verbally describe people and events as they occur in the classroom for students with visual impairments.

- Limit unnecessary noise in the classroom.
- Provide favorable seating arrangements so students with hearing impairments can see speakers and read their lips (or interpreters can assist); avoid visual distractions.
- Write out all instructions on paper or on the board; overhead projectors enable you to maintain eye contact while writing.
- Avoid standing with your back to the window or light source.

- With the student, determine when you should offer aid.
- Help other students and adults understand students with physical impairments.
- Learn about special devices or procedures and if any special safety precautions are needed.
- Allow students to participate in all activities including field trips, special events, and projects.

- Emphasize concepts, theories, relationships, ideas, and generalizations.
- Let students express themselves in a variety of ways including drawing, creative writing, or acting.
- Make arrangements for students to work on independent projects.
- Make arrangements for students to take selected subjects early.

- Provide assistance and direction; clearly define rules, assignments, and duties.
- Allow for pair interaction during class time; utilize peer helpers.
- Practice skills frequently. Distribute outlines of material presented to class.
- Allow extra time to complete tests and assignments.

Eight Ways of Learning

Type	Description	Likes To...
Verbal/Linguistic Learner	Intelligence is related to words and language, written and spoken.	read, write, tell stories, play word games, and tell jokes and riddles.
Logical/Mathematical Learner	Intelligence deals with inductive and deductive thinking and reasoning, numbers, and abstractions.	perform experiments, solve puzzles, work with numbers, ask questions, and explore patterns and relationships.
Visual/Spatial Learner	Intelligence relies on the sense of sight and being able to visualize an object, including the ability to create mental images.	draw, build, design, and create things, daydream, do jigsaw puzzles and mazes, watch videos, look at photos, and draw maps and charts.
Naturalistic Learner	Intelligence has to do with observing, understanding, and organizing patterns in the natural environment.	spend time outdoors and work with plants, animals, and other parts of the natural environment; good at identifying plants and animals and at hearing and seeing connections to nature.
Musical/Rhythmic Learner	Intelligence is based on recognition of tonal patterns, including various environmental sounds, and on sensitivity to rhythm and beats.	sing and hum, listen to music, play an instrument, move body when music is playing, and make up songs.
Bodily/Kinesthetic Learner	Intelligence is related to physical movement and the brain's motor cortex, which controls bodily motion.	learn by hands-on methods, demonstrate skill in crafts, tinker, perform, display physical endurance, and challenge self-physically.
Interpersonal Learner	Intelligence operates primarily through person-to-person relationships and communication.	talk to people, join groups, play cooperative games, solve problems as part of a group, and volunteer when others need help.
Intrapersonal Learner	Intelligence is related to inner states of being, self-reflection, metacognition, and awareness of spiritual realities.	work alone, pursue own interests, daydream, keep a personal diary or journal, and thinks about starting own business.

Eight Ways of Learning

Is Good At...	Learns Best By...	Famous Learners
memorizing names, dates, places, and trivia; spelling; using descriptive language; and creating imaginary worlds.	saying, hearing, and seeing words.	Maya Angelou—poet Abraham Lincoln—U.S. President and statesman Jerry Seinfeld—comedian Mary Hatwood Futrell—international teacher, leader, orator
math, reasoning, logic, problem solving, computing numbers, moving from concrete to abstract, thinking conceptually.	categorizing, classifying, and working with abstract patterns and relationships.	Stephen Hawking—physicist Albert Einstein—theoretical physicist Marilyn Burns—math educator Alexa Canady—neurosurgeon
understanding the use of space and how to get around in it, thinking in three-dimensional terms, and imagining things in clear visual images.	visualizing, dreaming, using the mind's eye, and working with colors and pictures.	Pablo Picasso—artist Maria Martinez—Pueblo Indian famous for black pottery Faith Ringgold—painter, quilter, and writer I.M. Pei—architect
measuring, charting, mapping, observing plants and animals, keeping journals, collecting, classifying, participating in outdoor activities.	visualizing, hands-on activities, bringing outdoors into the classroom, relating home/classroom to the natural world.	George Washington Carver—agricultural chemist Rachel Carson—scientific writer Charles Darwin—evolutionist John James Audubon—conservationist
remembering melodies, keeping time, mimicking beat and rhythm, noticing pitches, rhythms, and background and environmental sounds.	rhythm, melody, and music.	Henry Mancini—composer Marian Anderson—contralto Midori—violinist Paul McCartney—singer, songwriter, and musician
physical activities, such as sports, dancing, acting, and crafts.	touching, moving, interacting with space, and processing knowledge through bodily sensations.	Marcel Marceau—mime Jackie Joyner-Kersee—Olympic gold medalist in track and field Katherine Dunham—modern dancer Dr. Christian Barnard—cardiac surgeon
understanding people and their feelings, leading others, organizing, communicating, manipulating, and mediating conflicts.	sharing, comparing, relating, cooperating, and interviewing.	Jimmy Carter—U.S. President and statesman Eleanor Roosevelt—former first lady Lee Iacocca—president of Chrysler Corporation Mother Teresa—winner of Nobel Peace Prize
understanding self, focusing inward on feelings/dreams, following instincts, pursuing interests, and being original.	working alone, doing individualized projects, engaging in self-paced instruction.	Marva Collins—educator Maria Montessori—educator and physician Sigmund Freud—psychotherapist Anne Sexton—poet

SCANS Correlations

A variety of student text features and instructional tools located in the *Teacher Wraparound Edition* provide opportunities for students to improve foundation and workplace skills identified by the U.S. Secretary of Labor's Commission on Achieving Necessary Skills. The Commission's fundamental purpose is to encourage a high-performance economy characterized by high-skill, high-wage employment.

FOUNDATION SKILLS

Basic Skills

Reading
- What You'll Learn
- Why It's Important
- Key Word Review
- Living in the Real World
- Did You Know...
- Think about This
- Business Notes
- Motivating the Lesson
- Cooperative Learning
- Problem Solving
- Alternative Assessment
- Communication Skills
- Reteach/Enrichment
- Global Perspective
- Thinking Critically
- Technology Power
- Using Calculators
- Study Guide and Assessment
  - Quick Quiz, Reinforcement, Math Studio, Cumulative Test Prep

Writing
- Key Word Review
- Living in the Real World
- Business Notes
- Cooperative Learning
- Problem Solving
- Alternative Assessment
- Communication Skills
- Reteach/Enrichment
- Global Perspective
- Thinking Critically
- Technology Power
- Study Guide and Assessment
  - Math Studio, Cumulative Test Prep

Math
- Living in the Real World
- Business Notes
- Motivating the Lesson
- Cooperative Learning
- Problem Solving
- Alternative Assessment
- Communication Skills
- Reteach/Enrichment
- Global Perspective
- Thinking Critically
- Technology Power
- Using Calculators
- Study Guide and Assessment
  - Quick Quiz, Reinforcement, Math Studio, Cumulative Test Prep

Listening
- What You'll Learn
- Why It's Important
- Key Word Review
- Living in the Real World
- Did You Know...
- Think about This
- Business Notes
- Motivating the Lesson
- Cooperative Learning
- Problem Solving
- Alternative Assessment
- Communication Skills
- Reteach/Enrichment
- Global Perspective
- Thinking Critically
- Technology Power
- Using Calculators
- Study Guide and Assessment
  - Quick Quiz, Reinforcement, Math Studio, Cumulative Test Prep

Speaking
- Key Word Review
- Living in the Real World
- Think about This
- Business Notes
- Motivating the Lesson
- Cooperative Learning
- Problem Solving
- Alternative Assessment
- Communication Skills
- Reteach/Enrichment
- Global Perspective
- Thinking Critically
- Technology Power
- Study Guide and Assessment
  - Quick Quiz, Reinforcement, Math Studio, Cumulative Test Prep

Personal Qualities

Responsibility
- What You'll Learn
- Why It's Important
- Key Word Review
- Study Guide and Assessment
  - Math Studio, Cumulative Test Prep

Self-Esteem
- Key Word Review
- Living in the Real World
- Study Guide and Assessment
  - Math Studio, Cumulative Test Prep

Sociability
- Key Word Review
- Living in the Real World
- Business Notes
- Motivating the Lesson
- Cooperative Learning
- Problem Solving
- Alternative Assessment
- Communication Skills
- Reteach/Enrichment
- Global Perspective
- Thinking Critically
- Study Guide and Assessment
  - Math Studio

Self-Management
- What You'll Learn
- Why It's Important
- Key Word Review
- Living in the Real World
- Did You Know...
- Think about This
- Business Notes
- Motivating the Lesson
- Cooperative Learning
- Problem Solving
- Alternative Assessment
- Communication Skills
- Reteach/Enrichment
- Global Perspective
- Thinking Critically
- Technology Power
- Using Calculators
- Study Guide and Assessment
  - Quick Quiz, Reinforcement, Math Studio, Cumulative Test Prep

Integrity/Honesty
- What You'll Learn
- Why It's Important
- Key Word Review
- Assessment
  - Quick Quiz, Reinforcement, Math Studio, Cumulative Test Prep

FOUNDATION SKILLS, continued

WORKPLACE COMPETENCIES

Thinking Skills

Creative Thinking
- Key Word Review
- Living in the Real World
- Think about This
- Business Notes
- Motivating the Lesson
- Cooperative Learning
- Problem Solving
- Alternative Assessment
- Communication Skills
- Reteach/Enrichment
- Global Perspective
- Thinking Critically
- Technology Power
- Study Guide and Assessment
  - Math Studio, Cumulative Test Prep

Decision Making
- Key Word Review
- Living in the Real World
- Think about This
- Business Notes
- Motivating the Lesson
- Cooperative Learning
- Problem Solving
- Alternative Assessment
- Communication Skills
- Reteach/Enrichment
- Global Perspective
- Thinking Critically
- Technology Power
- Study Guide and Assessment
  - Quick Quiz, Reinforcement, Math Studio, Cumulative Test Prep

Problem Solving
- Key Word Review
- Living in the Real World
- Did You Know...
- Business Notes
- Motivating the Lesson
- Cooperative Learning
- Problem Solving
- Alternative Assessment
- Communication Skills
- Reteach/Enrichment
- Global Perspective
- Thinking Critically
- Technology Power
- Using Calculators
- Study Guide and Assessment
  - Quick Quiz, Reinforcement, Math Studio, Cumulative Test Prep

Seeing Things in the Mind's Eye
- What You'll Learn
- Why It's Important
- Key Word Review
- Living in the Real World
- Did You Know...
- Think about This
- Study Guide and Assessment
  - Math Studio, Cumulative Test Prep

Knowing How to Learn
- What You'll Learn
- Why It's Important
- Key Word Review
- Living in the Real World
- Did You Know...
- Think about This
- Study Guide and Assessment
  - Quick Quiz, Reinforcement, Math Studio, Cumulative Test Prep

Reasoning
- What You'll Learn
- Why It's Important
- Key Word Review
- Living in the Real World
- Did You Know...
- Think about This
- Business Notes
- Motivating the Lesson
- Cooperative Learning
- Problem Solving
- Alternative Assessment
- Communication Skills
- Reteach/Enrichment
- Global Perspective
- Thinking Critically
- Technology Power
- Using Calculators
- Study Guide and Assessment
  - Quick Quiz, Reinforcement, Math Studio, Cumulative Test Prep

Resources

Allocating Time
- What You'll Learn
- Why It's Important
- Key Word Review

Allocating Money
- What You'll Learn
- Why It's Important
- Key Word Review
- Living in the Real World
- Did You Know...
- Think about This
- Business Notes
- Motivating the Lesson
- Cooperative Learning
- Problem Solving
- Alternative Assessment
- Communication Skills
- Reteach/Enrichment
- Global Perspective
- Thinking Critically
- Technology Power
- Using Calculators
- Study Guide and Assessment
  - Quick Quiz, Reinforcement, Math Studio, Cumulative Test Prep

Allocating Material and Facility Resources
- Living in the Real World
- Assessment
  - Quick Quiz, Reinforcement, Math Studio, Cumulative Test Prep

Allocating Human Resources
- Living in the Real World
- Study Guide and Assessment
  - Math Studio, Cumulative Test Prep

Systems

Understanding Systems
- Technology Power
- Using Calculators

Monitoring and Correcting Performance
- What You'll Learn
- Why It's Important
- Key Word Review
- Did You Know...
- Think about This

Improving and Designing Systems
- Technology Power
- Using Calculators

SCANS Correlations, continued

WORKPLACE COMPETENCIES, continued

Information

Acquiring and Evaluating Information
- What You'll Learn
- Why It's Important
- Key Word Review
- Living in the Real World
- Did You Know...
- Think about This
- Business Notes
- Motivating the Lesson
- Cooperative Learning
- Problem Solving
- Alternative Assessment
- Communication Skills
- Reteach/Enrichment
- Global Perspective
- Thinking Critically
- Technology Power
- Using Calculators
- Study Guide and Assessment
  - Quick Quiz, Reinforcement, Math Studio, Cumulative Test Prep

Organizing and Maintaining Information
- Living in the Real World
- Motivating the Lesson
- Cooperative Learning
- Problem Solving
- Reteach/Enrichment
- Thinking Critically
- Study Guide and Assessment
  - Quick Quiz, Reinforcement, Math Studio, Cumulative Test Prep

Interpreting and Communicating Information
- What You'll Learn
- Why It's Important
- Key Word Review
- Living in the Real World
- Did You Know...
- Think about This
- Business Notes
- Motivating the Lesson
- Cooperative Learning
- Problem Solving
- Alternative Assessment
- Communication Skills
- Reteach/Enrichment
- Global Perspective
- Thinking Critically
- Technology Power
- Using Calculators
- Study Guide and Assessment
  - Quick Quiz, Reinforcement, Math Studio, Cumulative Test Prep

Using Computers to Process Information
- Living in the Real World
- Business Notes
- Motivating the Lesson
- Cooperative Learning
- Problem Solving
- Alternative Assessment
- Communication Skills
- Reteach/Enrichment
- Global Perspective
- Thinking Critically
- Technology Power
- Using Calculators
- Study Guide and Assessment
  - Quick Quiz, Reinforcement, Math Studio, Cumulative Test Prep

Technology

Selecting Technology
- Technology Power
- Using Calculators
- Study Guide and Assessment
  - Math Studio

Applying Technology to Task
- Key Word Review
- Living in the Real World
- Business Notes
- Motivating the Lesson
- Cooperative Learning
- Problem Solving
- Alternative Assessment
- Communication Skills
- Reteach/Enrichment
- Global Perspective
- Thinking Critically
- Technology Power
- Using Calculators
- Study Guide and Assessment
  - Math Studio

Maintaining and Troubleshooting Technology
- Living in the Real World
- Technology Power
- Using Calculators

Interpersonal Skills

Participating as Members of a Team
- Key Word Review
- Living in the Real World
- Business Notes
- Cooperative Learning
- Communication Skills
- Study Guide and Assessment
  - Quick Quiz, Reinforcement, Math Studio, Cumulative Test Prep

Teaching Others
- Key Word Review
- Living in the Real World
- Cooperative Learning
- Alternative Assessment
- Communication Skills
- Study Guide and Assessment
  - Math Studio

Serving Clients
- Living in the Real World
- Study Guide and Assessment
  - Math Studio

Exercising Leadership
- Key Word Review
- Living in the Real World
- Cooperative Learning
- Problem Solving
- Alternative Assessment
- Communication Skills
- Reteach/Enrichment
- Study Guide and Assessment
  - Math Studio

Negotiating to Arrive at a Decision
- Key Word Review
- Living in the Real World
- Cooperative Learning
- Problem Solving
- Communication Skills
- Reteach/Enrichment
- Global Perspective
- Thinking Critically
- Study Guide and Assessment
  - Quick Quiz, Reinforcement, Math Studio, Cumulative Test Prep

Working with Cultural Diversity
- Business Notes
- Cooperative Learning
- Alternative Assessment
- Communication Skills
- Global Perspective
- Thinking Critically

Program Validation:
Checked and Tested for High Achievement

AUTHORS, REVIEWERS, AND CONSULTANTS

Glencoe assembles a diverse panel of accuracy checkers to verify the exactness of the content and problems in *Mathematics with Business Applications*. Each problem was mulled over to hone its clarity and intent. You can find a complete listing of the reviewers and consultants on page iv in the *Teacher Wraparound Edition*. The role of each reviewer and consultant is to provide an in-depth analysis of the manuscript. Their comments and suggestions improved the effectiveness and validity of *Mathematics with Business Applications*.

Students' success in mathematics is often measured in the practice problems and end-of-chapter study guide. Glencoe formed an alliance with The Princeton Review to align and verify the textbook's Cumulative Test Prep and Test-Taking Tips.

National Council of Teachers of Mathematics Principles and Standards

APPLYING THE PRINCIPLES AND STANDARDS

Encourage fellow teachers and supervisors to examine this course for academic credit. Glencoe *Mathematics with Business Applications* embraced the National Council of Teachers of Mathematics (NCTM) during the development of this standards-based revision. Notice that the fundamentals of mathematics apply to real-world scenarios and the assessment sections.

National Council of Teachers of Mathematics Principles	Glencoe *Mathematics with Business Applications, Fifth Edition*
Equity. Excellence in mathematics education requires equity—high expectations and strong support for all students.	Glencoe's product line encourages high achievement. The program components that accompany this course promote not only honing mathematical skills, but also furthering students' reading, writing, and researching skills.
Curriculum. A curriculum is more than a collection of activities; it must be coherent, focused on important mathematics, and well articulated across the grades.	Glencoe and the authors developed a scope and sequence to pace building, practicing, and applying the concepts. Use the real-word scenarios (Living in the Real World) and hands-on labs (Practicing Life Skills Lab and Math Studio) to extend the content.
Teaching. Effective mathematics teaching requires understanding what students know and need to learn and then challenging and supporting them to learn it well.	Select from over 10 course-specific supplements to assist teaching the class. The *Teacher Wraparound Edition* offers numerous opportunities to teach, reinforce, and extend the concepts.
Learning. Students must learn mathematics with understanding, actively building new knowledge from experience and prior knowledge.	Mastery of math requires carefully reviewing lots of examples and practicing problems. Each section in the textbook has been developed to break down the concepts into detailed examples.
Assessment. Assessment should support the learning of important mathematics and furnish useful information to both teachers and students.	Glencoe heavily revised and created new assessment opportunities. The extended Study Guide and Assessment and Cumulative Test Prep prepare students for chapter, part, midterm, final, and standardized tests. Student workbooks and the *Assessment Binder* are chock-full of practice problems and test questions to assess your students' performance.
Technology. Technology is essential in teaching and learning mathematics; enhances students' learning.	The *Student Edition* and *Teacher Wraparound Edition* offer many opportunities to use calculators, create spreadsheets, and explore the Internet. Use the book-specific Web site (www.busmath.glencoe.com) to enhance the learning experience beyond the classroom.

NATIONAL COUNCIL OF TEACHERS OF MATHEMATICS STANDARDS: SCOPE AND SEQUENCE

The Standards portion of the National Council of Teachers of Mathematics Principles and Standards for School Mathematics focuses upon ten areas of mathematics curriculum development. The number assigned to each standard is for easy reference and is not part of each standard's official title.

Instructional programs from prekindergarten through grade 12 should enable all students to:

1. Numbers and Operations	• understand numbers, ways of representing numbers, relationships among numbers, and number systems • understand meanings of operations and how they relate to one another • compute fluently and make reasonable estimates	pp. 4-9, 26-27, 54-55, 76-77, 80-81, 92-107, 116-118, 122-125, 128-131, 146-155, 166-187, 196-219, 232-233, 258-271, 284-303, 314-335, 344-363, 394-411, 424-445, 458-475, 486-507, 518-539, 552-569, 582-601, 610-623, 634-649, 658-673, 682-697, 706-719, 727-733
2. Algebra	• understand patterns, relations, and functions • represent and analyze mathematical situations and structures using algebraic symbols • use mathematical models to represent and understand quantitative relationships • analyze change in various contexts	pp. 60-61, 74-81, 94-98
3. Geometry	• analyze characteristics and properties of two- and three-dimensional geometric shapes and develop mathematical arguments about geometric relationships • specify locations and describe spatial relationships using coordinate geometry and other representational systems • apply transformations and use symmetry to analyze mathematical situations • use visualization, spatial reasoning, and geometric modeling to solve problems	pp. 70-71, 84-85, 472-475, 582-584, 610-613, 640-641, 772-773
4. Measurement	• understand measurable attributes of objects and the units, systems, and process of measurement • apply appropriate techniques, tools, and formulas to determine measurements	pp. 44-59, 166-187, 196-219, 232-247, 258-271, 284-303, 314-335, 344-363, 394-411, 458-460, 463-465, 764-766
5. Data Analysis and Probability	• formulate questions that can be addressed with data and collect, organize, and display relevant data to answer them • select and use appropriate statistical methods to analyze data • develop and evaluate inferences and predictions that are based on data • understand and apply basic concepts of probability	pp. 8-9, 26-27, 30-31, 34-43, 54-55, 62-63, 68-73, 558-560, 752,760-761, 770
6. Problem Solving	• build new mathematical knowledge through problem solving • solve problems that arise in mathematics and in other contexts • apply and adapt a variety of appropriate strategies to solve problems • monitor and reflect on the process of mathematical problem solving	pp. 60-87, 92-93, 99-107, 116-131, 146-155, 168-187, 196-198, 202-219, 232-247, 258-271, 284-303, 314-335, 344-363, 394-411, 424-445, 458-462, 466-475, 486-507, 518-539, 552-569, 582-601, 610-611, 634-649, 658-673, 682-697, 706-719, 757-759
7. Reasoning and Proof	• recognize reasoning and proof as fundamental aspects of mathematics • make and investigate mathematical conjectures • develop and evaluate mathematical arguments and proofs • select and use various types of reasoning and methods of proof	pp. 12-27, 740-741, 742-746, 772-773
8. Communication	• organize and consolidate their mathematical thinking through communication • communicate their mathematical thinking coherently and clearly to peers, teachers, and others • analyze and evaluate the mathematical thinking and strategies of others • use the language of mathematics to express mathematical ideas precisely	pp. 168-187, 196-219, 232-247, 284-303, 314-335, 344-363, 394-411, 424-445, 458-475, 486-507, 518-539, 552-569, 582-601, 610-623, 634-649, 658-673, 682-697
9. Connections	• recognize and use connections among mathematical ideas • understand how mathematical ideas interconnect and build on one another to produce a coherent whole • recognize and apply mathematics in contexts outside of mathematics	pp. 60-63, 70-87, 94-107, 119-121, 126-127, 199-219, 232-247, 258-271, 282-303, 314-335, 344-363, 394-411, 706-719
10. Representation	• create and use representations to organize, record, and communicate mathematical ideas • select, apply, and translate among mathematical representations to solve problems • use representations to model and interpret physical, social, and mathematical phenomena	pp. 60-87, 196-198, 558-560

Part Overview

Part 1, Basic Math Skills: Workshops, offers a remedial mathematics review for students as they progress throughout the course. If students need to brush up on the basics, there are 42 workshops from basic adding and subtracting to converting international currency to using problem-solving strategies. You can extend the workshops by also referring to and assigning problems from the Reference Files in the back of the textbook.

Key to Descriptive Icons

The following designations will help you decide which activities are appropriate for your students.

L1 **Level 1** activities should be within the ability range of all students.

L2 **Level 2** activities should be within the ability range of the average to above-average students.

L3 **Level 3** activities are designed for the ability range of above-average students.

ELL Activities should be within the ability range of the **English Language Learner.**

LS **Learning Styles** designation represents activities designed to address different learning styles.

CL **Cooperative Learning** activities are designed for small group work.

P **Portfolio** designation represents student products that can be placed into a best-work portfolio.

Teacher Resources

Incorporating Technology

Do you need a little extra help in the classroom? Take a look at the program resources that might make your life easier. These program resources are correlated to technology standards, with your time and efficiency in mind.

Teacher Program Resources

Technology Standard	Technology Resources				
	Mathematics Online	Interactive Lesson Planner	Exam View Pro Test Generator	Student Activity Workbook, TAE CD-ROM	PowerPoint Presentations
Proficiency in operating equipment	✓			✓	✓
Using technology for research	✓	✓	✓	✓	
Problem solving and collaboration	✓	✓	✓	✓	
Using computers and software to support lessons	✓	✓	✓	✓	✓

Part 1 Intervention and Assessment

Type	Student Edition	Teacher Program Resources
Continuing Needs	pp. 2–86	Student Activity Workbook, Teacher Annotated Edition w/ CD-ROM Mathematics Online www.busmath.glencoe.com Teacher Resource Binder, Blackline Masters Teacher Resource Binder, Lesson Plans Teacher Resource Binder, Internet Resources
Open-Ended Assessment	See Mathematics Online www.busmath.glencoe.com	Assessment Binder, Alternative Assessment Strategies
Assessment	See Mathematics Online www.busmath.glencoe.com	Student Activity Workbook School-to-Home Activity Workbook Exam View® Pro Test Generator Assessment Binder, Reproducible Tests
Alternative Assessment	See Mathematics Online www.busmath.glencoe.com	Assessment Binder, Alternative Assessment Strategies Teacher Resource Binder, Internet Resources

Introduction

Before tackling chapters, you might want to review basic math skills or problem-solving strategies. Use the workshops as practice before, during, or after teaching the chapter content. Throughout the chapters, workshops are cross-referenced for your students.

Assessment Options

Part 1 Diagnostic Test

See the diagnostic test in the *Assessment Binder.* Select from the following diagnostic tests on workshops, skills, and applications. Gauge the students' skills on the fundamentals.

PART 1
Basic Math Skills: Workshops

Using Math in Unexpected Places

An elephant spends about 16 hours a day eating. Therefore, on average, what fraction of the day does an elephant spend eating? A baseball line drive travels about 100 yards in 4 seconds. How many feet did that baseball just travel in those 4 seconds? Whether its zoology or sports, business or history, you'll find facts and stories use math.

Practicing Life Skills LAB

Procedure

1. The Anthropologist Inside You want to know about your ancestors, but not necessarily the ones that might have traveled by boat to reach a distant land. You want to know about the ones before the family tree, such as human beings' beginning. But you'll need to go back a couple million years. Read the chart below, which breaks down the major discoveries about human ancestors.

2. Research Use the Internet or library to do research on one of the human ancestors. Find out as much information as possible. (Notice how anthropologists used math in their research.)

3. Compose Write a report on your findings. Create maps and charts to illustrate your research. Highlight what math skills an anthropologist uses to conduct research and draw conclusions on human discoveries.

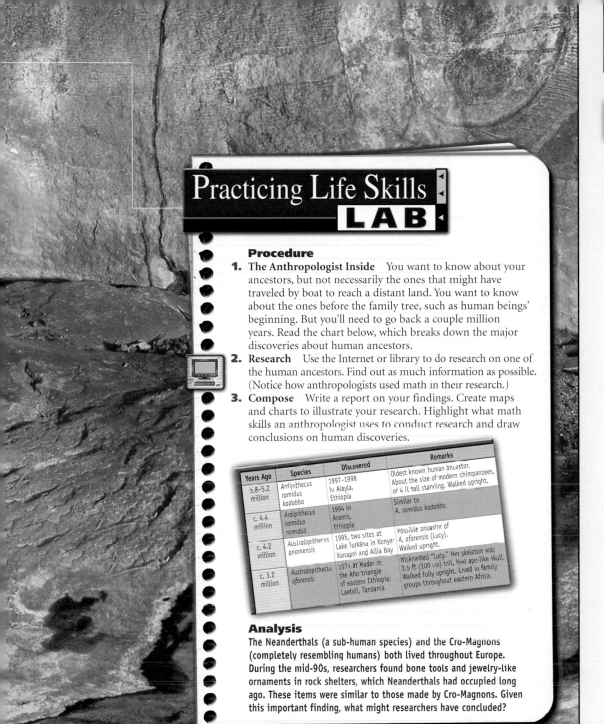

Years Ago	Species	Discovered	Remarks
5.8–5.2 million	Ardipithecus ramidus kadabba	1997–1998 in Alayla, Ethiopia	Oldest known human ancestor. About the size of modern chimpanzees, or 4 ft tall standing. Walked upright.
c. 4.4 million	Ardipithecus ramidus ramidus	1994 in Aramis, Ethiopia	Similar to A. ramidus kadabba.
c. 4.2 million	Australopithecus anamensis	1995, two sites at Lake Turkana in Kenya- Kanapoi and Allia Bay	Possible ancestor of A. afarensis (Lucy). Walked upright.
c. 3.2 million	Australopithecus afarensis	1974 at Hadar in the Afar triangle of eastern Ethiopia; Laetoli, Tanzania	Nicknamed "Lucy." Her skeleton was 3.5 ft (100 cm) tall. Had ape-like skull. Walked fully upright. Lived in family groups throughout eastern Africa.

Analysis

The Neanderthals (a sub-human species) and the Cro-Magnons (completely resembling humans) both lived throughout Europe. During the mid-90s, researchers found bone tools and jewelry-like ornaments in rock shelters, which Neanderthals had occupied long ago. These items were similar to those made by Cro-Magnons. Given this important finding, what might researchers have concluded?

3

Practicing Life Skills LAB

Teaching Suggestion
This activity allows students to apply math to research and science. Ask them if they're interested in learning about where they came from—whether it's their genealogy or evolution.

Analysis Answer
Use problem solving on this question. The Neanderthals might have lived in areas once inhabited by Cro-Magnons. They believe that these two species may have coexisted. The two species might have traded artifacts.

VOCABULARY BUILDER

Tell students building vocabulary requires digging to find the meaning (whether it's in context in the sentence or paragraph or looking in the dictionary). Have students uncover a new math function they have just learned. Have them write out the mathematical process in words. Students understand a concept when he or she can explain it in his or her own words.

1 FOCUS

Objectives

1. To read and write numbers as words and words as numbers.
2. To identify the place value of numbers.

2 TEACH

The key concept underlying the skills of this workshop is place value. Work with students on correctly identifying the place value of each digit in a number. Example: use the number 444 to illustrate that each 4 has a different value. Extend this example by using 44,444 and then 44,444,444.

Stress the importance of memorizing the names of each place in a number, using the example in **Figure W1.1**. Point out how the decimal point separates whole numbers and decimal numbers. Write the number 6,276,491.358 on the board. **Have students identify the name of each place you select randomly.**

Writing and Reading Numbers

WRITING NUMBERS The number system you use is based on *tens* and has ten digits that you use to write the numbers. Use the ten digits 1, 2, 3, 4, 5, 6, 7, 8, 9 and 0 and a decimal point to write any number.

Need Help? Go to...
Skill 1: Numbers, page 727

Example 1

Write the following using digits:

a. Twenty-one

b. Fifteen thousand four hundred fifty-six

c. Forty-six and thirty-five hundredths

STEP: Read the number and write it.

   a. Read the number *twenty-one* but write it using digits as **21.**

   b. Read the number *fifteen thousand four hundred fifty-six* but write it as **15,456.**

   c. Read the number *forty-six and thirty-five hundredths* but write it as **46.35.**

PLACE VALUE You read numbers from *left to right*. However, you usually learn the names of the place values from *right to left*. The place-value chart shows the place of each digit in the number 5,647,210.392. A decimal point separates the whole numbers (to the left of the decimal point) and the decimal numbers (to the right of the decimal point). The place-value chart can help you write numbers. The whole-number part is separated into groups of three digits with a comma. The name of each group is used to read the number.

Figure W1.1

Millions		Thousands			Hundreds				Decimals		
Ten Millions	Millions	Hundred Thousands	Ten Thousands	Thousands	Hundreds	Tens	Ones	Decimal	Tenths	Hundredths	Thousandths
5	6	4	7	2	1	0	.	3	9	2
					← Whole Numbers				Decimals →		

Example 2

Give the place value for each of the following:

a. The digit 5   b. The digit 7   c. The digit 3   d. The digit 9

STEP: Find the place value for the given digit.

   a. The digit 5 is in the **millions place.**

   b. The digit 7 is in the **thousands place.**

   c. The digit 3 is in the **tenths place.**

   d. The digit 9 is in the **hundredths place.**

WORKSHOP NOTES

READING AND WRITING WHOLE NUMBERS AND DECIMALS Here are some ways to read and write numbers:

	Whole Numbers	Decimals
Standard Form	5,647,210	0.392
Word Form	five million, six hundred forty-seven thousand, two hundred ten	three hundred ninety-two thousandths
Short Word Form	5 million, 647 thousand, 210	392 thousandths
Expanded Form	5,000,000 + 600,000 + 40,000 + 7,000 + 200 + 10	0.3 + 0.09 + 0.002
Point Form	five six four seven two one zero point	zero point three nine two

[Note: The point form is used when you proofread a business document and want to stress the placement of the "decimal point."]

CONCEPT CHECK

Complete the problems, then check your answers at the end of the book on page 802. On a separate piece of paper, fill in the blank.

1. Read the number *twenty-four thousand three hundred sixty-six* but write it as ___**24,366**___ .

2. Read the number *four hundred thirty-six and seven hundred eighty-five thousandths* but write it as ___**436.785**___ .

3. (Refer to Figure W1.1 on page 4 for this question.) The digit 2 is in the **hundreds** place and the **thousandths** place.

4. Write 5 thousand, 456 and 68 hundredths in standard form, word form, and point form.

5. Write 50 + 6 + 0.8 + 0.01 + 0.007 in standard form, word form, and point form.

6. Write $875.48 in word form.

6. Word form: eight hundred seventy-five and forty-eight one hundredth dollars or eight hundred seventy-five and $\frac{48}{100}$ dollars or eight hundred seventy-five dollars and forty-eight cents

PRACTICE

Use the number 98,045,132.706 to fill in the blanks.

7. The digit 8 is in the ___**millions**___ place.

8. The digit 1 is in the ___**hundreds**___ place.

Write each number in word form and short form.

9. 543,698   10. 45,987,159.9

Write each number in standard form and word form.

11. 654 thousand, 321   12. five six point nine nine

Write each number in expanded form.

13. 4,678
    4,000 + 600 + 70 + 8

14. 98,438
    90,000 + 8,000 + 400 + 30 + 8

Workshop 1 Writing and Reading Numbers ▶ **5**

---

4. Standard form: 5,456.68; Word form: five thousand four hundred fifty-six and sixty-eight hundredths; Point form: five four five six point six eight

5. Standard form: 56.817; Word form: fifty-six and eight hundred seventeen thousandths; Point form: five six point eight one seven

(SELF-CHECK ✓)

9. Word form: five hundred forty-three thousand, six hundred ninety-eight; Short word form: 543 thousand, 698

10. Word form: forty-five million nine hundred eighty-seven thousand one hundred fifty-nine and nine tenths; Short word form: 45 million, 987 thousand, 159 and 9 tenths

11. Standard form: 654,321; Word form: six hundred fifty-four thousand, three hundred twenty-one

12. Standard form: 56.99; Word form: fifty six and ninety-nine hundredths

WORKSHOP 1

③ ASSESS

A typical error that students make when writing numbers as words, or simply reading a number, is to use the word *and* in the wrong place. For example, they may write 647 as *six hundred and forty-seven* instead of *six hundred forty-seven*. Stress that *and* is used only to replace the decimal point.

Stress also that numbers from 21 to 99, other than multiples of 10, should be hyphenated when written in word form.

Example: write the number 4,523,978.436 on the board. Ask students to write this number in word form, short word form, expanded form, and point form. Review students' work to check their understanding.

④ CLOSE

The Practice problems can be assigned for class work and the answer checked in class to help students master the objective of the lesson.

WRAP-UP

Go over any problem for which a wrong answer is given.

Assignment Guide
  Basic: 7–8
  Average: 9–14

20 min.

WORKSHOP 2

1 FOCUS

Objectives

1. To round whole numbers.
2. To round decimals.
3. To round dollars and cents to the nearest cent.

2 TEACH

Write the following whole numbers on the board: 47; 293; 5,214. Have students name each place value. Explain that rounding numbers requires two steps: (1) identify the place value to be rounded and (2) read the number to the right of the place value to be rounded. If the number to the right is 5 or more, round up. If it is less than 5, round down.

Have students round 47 to the nearest ten; 293 to the nearest hundred; and 5,214 to the nearest thousand.

Write the decimal 0.5182 on the board. **(Review the place value of each digit.)** To round 0.5182 to the nearest tenth, first find the digit in the tenths place (0.5182). Second, read the number to the right (0.5182). Since 1 is less than 5, round down the number in the tenths place and drop the digits to the right (0.5). To round to the nearest hundredth, first find the digit in the hundredths place (0.5182). Second, read the number to the right (0.5182). Since 8 is more than five, round up and drop the digits to the right **(0.52)**.

Rounding Numbers

Need Help? Go to... Skill 2: Rounding Numbers, page 729

PLACE VALUE The place-value chart shows the value of each digit in the number 5,647,210.392. Place value is used in rounding numbers. If the digit to the right of the place value you want to round is 5 or more, round up by adding 1 to the number in the place value and then change all the digits to the right of the place value to zeros. If the number is 4 or less, round down by changing all the numbers to the right of the place value to zeros.

Figure W2.1

Millions		Thousands			Hundreds				Decimals		
Ten Millions	Millions	Hundred Thousands	Ten Thousands	Thousands	Hundreds	Tens	Ones	Decimal	Tenths	Hundredths	Thousandths
	5	6	4	7	2	1	0	.	3	9	2
					← Whole Numbers				Decimals →		

Example 1

Round 7,862 to the nearest hundred.

STEP 1: Find the digit in the hundreds place. 7,862

STEP 2: Read the number to the right of the digit in the hundreds place. If the digit is five or more then you'll want to round up. 7,862

STEP 3: Add 1 to the hundreds place. Change the digits to the right to zeros. 7,900

Example 2

Round 0.637 to the nearest tenth.

STEP 1: Find the digit in the tenths place. 0.637

STEP 2: Read the number to the right of the digit in the tenths place. If the digit is four or less, then you'll want to round down. 0.637

STEP 3: Do not change the tenths digit. Drop the digits to the right. 0.6

WORKSHOP NOTES

CONCEPT CHECK

Complete the problems, then check your answers at the end of the book on page 802. Round 5,693.251 to the place value given.

SELF-CHECK ✓

1. thousands	2. tenths	3. hundreds	4. ones
6,000	**5,693.3**	**5,700**	**5,693**

ROUNDING TO THE NEAREST PLACE VALUE Dollar and cents amounts are often rounded to the nearest cent, or the hundredths place. Begin with the digit in the hundredths place.

Example 3

Round to the nearest cent.

STEP 1: Find the digit in the hundredths place. $112.4<u>1</u>7

STEP 2: Read the number to the right of the digit in the hundredths place. If the number is five or more, then you'll want to round up. $112.41<u>7</u>

STEP 3: Round up the hundredths digit. Do not change the tenths digit.   **$112.42**

CONCEPT CHECK

Complete the problems, then check your answers at the end of the book on page 802. Round to the nearest cent.

SELF-CHECK ✓

5. $21.277	6. $967.461	7. $138.7836	8. $647.555
$21.28	**$967.46**	**$138.78**	**$647.56**

PRACTICE

Round 15,748,516 to the place value given.

9. millions	10. ten millions	11. thousands
16,000,000	**20,000,000**	**15,749,000**
12. hundreds	13. ten thousands	14. hundred thousands
15,748,500	**15,750,000**	**15,700,000**

15. Amy Cole records the attendance data for the sporting events at the Glass Bowl. Round each number to the amount indicated.

	Football Game	Number	Nearest Thousand	Nearest Hundred	Nearest Ten
a.	Austin Peavey	18,971	**19,000**	**19,000**	**18,970**
b.	Bowling Green	25,687	**26,000**	**25,700**	**25,690**
c.	Ohio University	20,119	**20,000**	**20,100**	**20,120**
d.	Western Michigan	24,567	**25,000**	**24,600**	**24,570**
e.	Central Michigan	19,424	**19,000**	**19,400**	**19,420**

WORKSHOP 2

WORKSHOP

3 ASSESS

Write the following three problems on the board:

1. Round 37,867 to the nearest ten, hundred, thousand, and ten thousand.
2. Round 0.4357 to the nearest tenth, hundredth, and thousandth.
3. Round $1,726,455.926 to the nearest cent.

If students make a mistake, ask them to explain their thought process. **In step one, they may identify the wrong place value to be rounded. In step two, they may read the place value to be rounded instead of the number to the right of the place value. Remind them that when the digit to the right of the place value being rounded is 5 or more, round up. If the number is 4 or less, round down.**

4 CLOSE

The Practice problems can be assigned for class work and the answers checked in class to help students master the objective of the lesson.

WRAP-UP

Go over any problem for which a wrong answer is given.

Assignment Guide
 Basic: 9–14
Average: 15

20 min.

7

1 FOCUS

Objectives

1. To compare whole numbers to see which one is greater.
2. To compare decimals to see which one is greater.

2 TEACH

The use of a whole number line can help those students having difficulty comparing numbers. Start with some simple examples using whole numbers and make sure students understand that the larger number is always to the right.

Example: ask students to compare 9.84 and 9.67 by using a number line.

Have them start with 9.00 and arrange: 9.10, 9.20, 9.30, . . . 9.90, 10.0 on their number lines.

Before discussing the examples in the book, review the concept of place value. Without an understanding of place value, the comparison of numbers (particularly decimals) becomes a rote and meaningless process.

WORKSHOP

Need Help? Go to...
► Skill 1: **Numbers,** page 727

Comparing Numbers

FINDING THE GREATER NUMBER To compare numbers to see which one is greater, first find out if one of the numbers has more digits to the left of the decimal point. For example, 100 is greater than 99.62 because 100 has three digits to the left of the decimal point and 99.62 has only two. If both numbers have the same number of digits to the left of the decimal point, compare each digit, beginning at the left. One way is to write the value of each digit.

Example 1

Compare 5,972 and 5,983. Which number is greater?

STEP 1: Break down the numbers.

$5{,}972 = 5{,}000 + 900 + 70 + 2$
$5{,}983 = 5{,}000 + 900 + 80 + 3$

STEP 2: Compare the numbers that you've broken down.

$5{,}972 = 5{,}000 + 900 + 70 + 2$
$5{,}983 = 5{,}000 + 900 + 80 + 3$
           same   same   80 is greater than 70

Therefore, **5,983 is greater than 5,972.**

CONCEPT CHECK

Complete the problems, then check your answers at the end of the book on page 802. Which number is greater?

1. 8,891 or 8,889 **8,891**

2. 7,521 or 7,520 **7,521**

COMPARING DECIMALS When you're comparing decimals, you may have to write zeros to the right of the decimal point so that the numbers being compared have the same number of decimal places.

Example 2

Compare 5.17 and 5.149 (without writing the value of each digit). Which number is greater?

STEP 1: Compare numbers by looking at the numbers to the right of the decimal.

5.17 and 5.149

STEP 2: Write in a 0 next to the 7.

5.17**0**

STEP 3: Decide which number is greater.

5.170 and 5.149
7 is greater than 4,
so **5.170 is greater than 5.149.**

WORKSHOP NOTES

CONCEPT CHECK

Complete the problems, then check your answers at the end of the book on page 802. Which number is greater?

(SELF-CHECK ✓)

3. 284.4 or 284.396 **284.4**

4. 0.06 or 0.006 **0.06**

PRACTICE

Which number is greater?

5. 26 or 29 **29**

6. 4,201 or 4,210 **4,210**

7. 2.65 or 2.56 **2.65**

8. 0.696 or 0.695 **0.696**

9. 0.4 or 0.04 **0.4**

10. 0.1 or 0.9 **0.9**

11. 0.03 or 0.003 **0.03**

12. 2.234 or 2.244 **2.244**

Write the numbers in order from least to greatest.

13. 1.37, 1.36, 1.39 **1.36, 1.37, 1.39**

14. 5.11, 5.09, 5.10 **5.09, 5.10, 5.11**

15. 7.18, 7.38, 7.58 **7.18, 7.38, 7.58**

16. 5.86, 5.95, 5.81 **5.81, 5.86, 5.95**

17. 40.004, 40.04, 40.4
40.004, 40.04, 40.4

18. 121.012, 121.021, 121.210
121.012, 121.021, 121.210

19. 365.15, 365.51, 365.490
365.15, 365.490, 365.51

20. 0.1234, 0.1342, 0.1423
0.1234, 0.1342, 0.1423

21. Janet Swick works part-time shelving books in the school library. Arrange the following library call numbers from least to greatest.
a. Science: 513.12, 519.03, 532.626, 571.113, 587.41
b. Literature: 94.79, 32.615, 11.7, 67.192, 34.9
c. Religion: 46.94, 18.7, 15.04, 71.21, 26.311
d. Language: 22.5, 67.21, 48.275, 38.9, 93.047

a. Science: **513.12, 519.03, 532.626, 571.113, 587.41**
b. Literature: **11.7, 32.615, 34.9, 67.192, 94.79**
c. Religion: **15.04, 18.7, 26.311, 46.94, 71.21**
d. Language: **22.5, 38.9, 48.275, 67.21, 93.047**

22. Swick also files the cards from checked-out books according to the card numbers. Between which two cards would she file the checked-out books?
a. Card number of the checked-out book is 874.192.
Filed cards are: 872.41, 873.15, 877.142, 879.190. **873.15 and 877.142**
b. Card number of the checked-out book is 332.75.
Filed cards are: 309.8, 311.75, 332.075, 332.749, 333.54. **332.749 and 333.54**

3 ASSESS

Ask those students who continue to get wrong answers to explain what they are doing. **Their explanations may provide a clue to why they cannot compare numbers successfully.**

Also observe students' written work. Carelessness in arranging numbers vertically can result in errors. **(Tell students that decimal points must be aligned vertically to compare decimals. Then all they have to do is to look for the place where the digits are different to find the greater number.)** Using Example 2 in the text, ask students *why* 5.17 is greater than 5.149. Try to elicit an answer based upon an understanding of place value.

4 CLOSE

The Practice problems can be assigned for class work and the answers checked in class to help students master the objective of the lesson.

WRAP-UP

Ask other students if they see any errors and, if so, to correct them.

Assignment Guide
 Basic: 5–20
Average: 21–22

20 min.

1 FOCUS

Objectives

1. To add decimals with the same number of decimal places.
2. To add decimals with a different number of decimal places.
3. To add amounts of money.

2 TEACH

Work a few problems with whole numbers before having students add decimals. Start with the following example:

1,473
+ 2,609
4,082

Then change the problem to adding 14.73 and 40.82. Ask students to read the decimals 14.73 and 40.82 and have them name each place in both decimals.

Write the following decimals on the board and ask students if they are equal: 42.76 and 42.760. Use similar examples and ask students why the zero does not change the value of the decimal. Review place value concepts from Workshop 1.

WORKSHOP

Need Help? Go to...
➤ Skill 5: **Adding Decimals,** page 732

Adding Decimals

WRITE IN VERTICAL FORM When adding decimals, write the addition problem in vertical form. Be sure to line up the decimal points. Write a decimal point in the answer directly below the decimal points in the problem. Then add as you would whole numbers.

Example 1

20.99 + 32.07 + 18.04

STEP 1: Line up decimals.	STEP 2: Add.
20.99	20.99
32.07	32.07
18.04	+18.04
	71.10

Example 2

48.26 + 193.47 + 2.77

STEP 1: Line up decimals.	STEP 2: Add.
48.26	48.26
193.47	193.47
2.77	+ 2.77
	244.50

CONCEPT CHECK

SELF-CHECK✓

Complete the problems, then check your answers at the back of the book on page 802.

1. 34.33 + 12.34 + 24.21 = **70.88**
2. 56.42 + 39.65 + 82.37 = **178.44**
3. 72.52 + 52.12 + 98.22 = **222.86**
4. 93.35 + 67.88 + 22.53 = **183.76**

WHEN TO ADD ZEROS When adding amounts with different numbers of decimal places, adding zeros in the empty decimal places will help you keep track of your places. Put a decimal point in any whole number included in the problem.

Example 3

86.583 + 957.26 + 3 + 98.5

STEP 1: Line up decimals.	STEP 2: Write zeros.	STEP 3: Add.
86.583	86.583	86.583
957.26	957.260	957.260
3.	3.000	3.000
98.5	98.500	+ 98.500
		1,145.343

WORKSHOP NOTES

Adding amounts of money is just like adding decimals. The decimal point separates the dollars and cents. Remember to put a dollar sign in the total.

CONCEPT CHECK

Complete the problems, then check your answers at the back of the book on page 802.

5. 87.23 + 235.12 + 43.125 = **365.475** **6.** 597.2 + 62.3 + 623.342 = **1,282.842**

7. $521.12 + $23.12 + $53.12 = **$597.36**

8. $235.12 + $256.72 + $88 = **$579.84**

PRACTICE

9.	82.22 +51.27 **133.49**	**10.**	83.41 + 8.62 **92.03**	**11.**	862.82 + 8.94 **871.76**

12. 362.22
 +431.93
 794.15

13. 82.637
 +92.727
 175.364

14. 92.627
 +76.522
 169.149

15. 9.235
 +4.847
 14.082

16. 9.252
 +6.257
 15.509

17. 58.62
 84.51
 +58.25
 201.38

18. 84.87
 55.22
 +87.94
 228.03

19. 9.8551
 9.9908
 +2.555
 22.4009

20. 15.854
 84.265
 +55.842
 155.961

21. 513.8
 2.584
 + 84.85
 601.234

22. 254.65
 25.847
 + 8.4
 288.897

23. 9.847
 87.8
 +552
 649.647

24. 25.658
 157.65
 + 6.892
 190.2

25. 5.894
 526.8
 +596.2
 1,128.894

26. 5621.8
 23.453
 + 125.2
 5,770.453

27. 56.21
 8.958
 +126.8
 191.968

28. 0.58
 526
 + 56.8954
 583.4754

29. 17.47 + 34.71 + 56.78 + 15.07
 124.03

30. 0.17 + 17.94 + 13 + 147.7
 178.81

31. 14.6 + 19.314 + 4.17 + 264.5176
 302.6016

32. 4.917 + 6 + 4.37 + 15.971
 31.258

33. $1.98 + $71.49 + $0.49 + $50
 $123.96

34. $7.79 + $0.89 + $412.37 + $7
 $428.05

35. $71.84 + $2.79 + $143.54 + $71
 $289.17

36. $7.98 + $4.14 + $71.84 + $0.47
 $84.43

3 ASSESS

Write the following decimals on the board and ask students to write them in vertical form so they can be added:
    107.42
    63.971
    4.063
Stress that the decimals must be aligned vertically when adding decimals, like this:
107.42
 63.971
  4.063
Ask students to write 9 as a decimal. Accept any of the following answers: 9.0, 9.00, 9.000, and so on. Then have students add the following numbers: 12.42, 7, 13.06, 8.4, and 159. Review students' written work if they did not get the correct answer **(199.88)** to see what kinds of errors they are making.

4 CLOSE

The Practice problems can be assigned for class work and the answer checked in class to help students master the objective of the lesson.

WRAP-UP

Go over any problem for which a wrong answer is given.

Assignment Guide
  Basic: 9–28
Average: 29–36

20 min.

WORKSHOP 5

① FOCUS

Objectives

1. To subtract decimals with the same number of decimal places.
2. To subtract decimals with a different number of decimal places.
3. To subtract amounts of money.

② TEACH

Use the examples in the text to reteach the subtraction of decimals. Ask for a few volunteers to work some problems at the board. Then read the following decimals to students and tell them to arrange the decimals in vertical form and subtract:

1. 72.69
    − 48.32
    24.37

2. 104.7
    − 39.46
    65.24

3. 15
    − 8.98
    6.02

4. 8.901
    − 3.79
    5.111

Ask students to read out loud their answers to check for misunderstandings in reading decimals.

Subtracting Decimals

Need Help? Go to...
► Skill 6: Subtracting Decimals, page 733

ALIGNING THE DECIMALS When you're subtracting decimals, write the subtraction problem in vertical form. Be sure to line up the decimal points. Write a decimal point in the answer directly below the decimal points in the problem. Then subtract as you would with whole numbers.

Example 1

Subtract 85.29 − 34.72.

STEP 1: Line up decimals.

85.29
34.72

STEP 2: Subtract.

85.29
− 34.72
50.57

WRITING ZEROS AS PLACE HOLDERS When subtracting amounts with different numbers of decimal places, you may want to write zeros in the empty decimal places. Put a decimal point in any whole number included in the problem.

Example 2

Subtract 838.5 − 39.248.

STEP 1: Put in zeros.

838.5<u>00</u>

STEP 2: Subtract.

838.500
− 39.248
799.252

CONCEPT CHECK

SELF-CHECK✔

Complete the problems, then check your answers at the end of the book on page 802.

1. $87.86 − 34.25 = $ **53.61**
2. $125.9 − 87.6 = $ **38.3**
3. $675.4 − 65.32 = $ **610.08**
4. $76.76 − 8 = $ **68.76**

PRACTICE

5.   94.7
    − 31.4
    63.30

6.   98.6
    − 88.5
    10.1

7.   19.87
    − 8.54
    11.33

8.   7.93
    − 2.03
    5.90

9.   49.64
    − 10.34
    39.30

10.   96.13
    − 12.37
    83.76

11.   38.065
    − 33.426
    4.639

12.   68.111
    − 9.648
    58.463

WORKSHOP NOTES

13.	$99.85	14.	$75.67	15.	$953.22	16.	$506.37
	− 32.16		− 28.30		− 287.32		− 243.70
	$67.69		**$47.37**		**$665.90**		**$262.67**

17.	$347.	18.	$275.	19.	$55,553.65	20.	$47,005.45
	− 82.97		− 85.12		− 38,872.58		− 3,257.64
	$264.03		**$189.88**		**$16,681.07**		**$43,747.81**

21. 335.4 − 217.9 **117.5**   22. 148.1 − 132.5 **15.6**

23. 5.21 − 0.71 **4.50**   24. $434.66 − $51.43 **$383.23**

25. $3,479.31 − $2,616.16 **$863.15**   26. $6,000 − $4,333.83 **$1,666.17**

27. You work as a cashier in a restaurant. Compute the correct change for each of the following orders.

	Customer's Order	Customer Gives You	Change
a.	$ 6.94	$ 7.00	**$0.06**
b.	9.12	10.00	**$0.88**
c.	16.97	17.00	**$0.03**
d.	3.42	5.42	**$2.00**
e.	5.01	5.01	**$0.00**
f.	23.11	25.00	**$1.89**
g.	41.97	42.07	**$0.10**
h.	27.42	30.00	**$2.58**
i.	20.13	21.13	**$1.00**
j.	150.84	151.00	**$0.16**

28. The marketing department for Jackson Sporting Goods Company prepared a comparison sheet that shows sales projections and actual sales for ten products. Find the difference between the projected sales and the actual sales by subtracting actual sales from projected sales.

	Jackson Sporting Goods Company			
	Product	Sales Projections	Actual Sales	Difference
a.	Electric motors	$ 3,000.00	$ 2,749.67	**$250.33**
b.	Fishing tackle	32,000.00	31,897.40	**$102.60**
c.	Wilderness boots	6,500.00	5,607.15	**$892.85**
d.	Boat moccasin	950.00	571.28	**$378.72**
e.	Campware sets	400.00	339.67	**$60.33**
f.	Geodesic dome tent	6,400.00	5,379.58	**$1,020.42**
g.	Backpacking tent	2,500.00	1,999.40	**$500.60**

3 ASSESS

Many errors that students make when subtracting decimals are computational errors in subtraction. If this is the case with your students, you will need to review the subtraction of whole numbers. A thorough understanding of place value concepts can help students having difficulty subtracting whole numbers and decimals. Also, a discussion of examples involving dollar and cent amounts can make the subtraction of decimals more understandable to many students.

4 CLOSE

The Practice problems can be assigned for class work and the answers checked in class to help students master the objective of the lesson.

WRAP-UP

Work the problems with the class by calling upon individual students to do each part.

Assignment Guide
  Basic: 5–20
  Average: 21–28

20 min.

1 **FOCUS**

Objectives

1. To multiply decimals.
2. To multiply amounts of money.
3. To multiply decimals by 10, 100, or 1,000.

2 **TEACH**

Remind students that multiplication of decimals is similar to multiplying whole numbers. Emphasize the need for setting the problems up neatly and properly aligning the numbers in columns. Neatness is very important. Discuss the rule for finding the number of decimal places in the answer.

In Example 2, make sure the students start at the right of the product in computing decimal places and place any needed zeros at the left of the product.

Stress that multiplication by 10, 100, 1,000, or 10,000 is simply a matter of counting zeros and moving the decimal point that many places to the right.

WORKSHOP

Need Help? Go to...
→ Skill 8: Multiplying Decimals, page 735

WORKSHOP 6

Multiplying Decimals

LINE UP LIKE WHOLE NUMBERS When multiplying decimals, multiply as if the decimal numbers were whole numbers. Then count the total number of decimal places to the right of the decimals in the factors. This number will be the number of decimal places in the product.

Example 1

Multiply as if whole numbers, then count the total number of decimal places to put in the product.

$$
\begin{array}{r}
18.1 \leftarrow \text{factor} \\
\times\ 0.35 \leftarrow \text{factor} \\
\hline
905 \\
543 \\
\hline
6335 \leftarrow \text{product}
\end{array}
$$

STEP: Multiply.

$$
\begin{array}{r}
18.1 \leftarrow \text{1 decimal place} \\
\times\ 0.35 \leftarrow +\text{ 2 decimal places} \\
\hline
905 \\
543 \\
\hline
6.335 \leftarrow \text{3 decimal places}
\end{array}
$$

WHEN TO WRITE ZEROS If the product doesn't have enough digits to place the decimal in the correct position, you'll need to write in zeros. Start at the right of the product in counting the decimal places and write zeros at the left.

Example 2

$$
\begin{array}{r}
0.72 \\
\times\ 0.03 \\
\hline
216
\end{array}
$$

STEP: Count the decimal places, and write zeros at the left.

$$
\begin{array}{r}
0.72 \leftarrow \text{2 decimal places} \\
\times\ 0.03 \leftarrow +\text{ 2 decimal places} \\
\hline
0.0216 \leftarrow \text{4 decimal places}
\end{array}
$$

CONCEPT CHECK

Complete the problems, then check your answers at the end of the book on page 802.

1.	2.	3.	4.
$\begin{array}{r} 24.7 \\ \times\ 0.33 \\ \hline 8.151 \end{array}$	$\begin{array}{r} 41.8 \\ \times\ 2.14 \\ \hline 89.452 \end{array}$	$\begin{array}{r} 0.78 \\ \times\ 0.11 \\ \hline 0.0858 \end{array}$	$\begin{array}{r} 0.74 \\ \times\ 0.08 \\ \hline 0.0592 \end{array}$

WHEN TO ROUND THE ANSWER When you're multiplying amounts of money, you'll want to round the answer off to the nearest cent. Remember to put a dollar sign in the answer.

14 ◄ **Basic Math Skills: Workshops**

WORKSHOP NOTES

Example 3

$3.35 **STEP:** Round to the nearest cent. Put the dollar sign in the answer.
× 4.5
15075

$3.35 ◄──── 2 places $3.35 × 4.5 = $15.075
× 4.5 ◄──── +1 place   = **$15.08** (rounded to
15.075 ◄──── 3 places   the nearest cent)

MOVING THE DECIMAL POINT When multiplying by 10, 100, or 1,000, count the number of zeros and then move the decimal point to the right the same number of spaces.

Example 4

a. 6.7 × 10   **b.** 5.24 × 100

STEP: Count the number of zeros. Move the decimal point accordingly.
a. 6.7 × 10 = 6.7 = **67**   10 has 1 zero; move decimal 1 place.
b. 5.24 × 100 = 5.24 = **524**   100 has 2 zeros; move decimal 2 places.

CONCEPT CHECK

Complete the problems, then check your answers at the end of the book on page 802.

 SELF-CHECK ✔

5. $4.15 × 8.5   **6.** 71.4 × 10 **714**   **7.** 41.861 × 100 **4,186.1**
$35.275 – **$35.28**

PRACTICE

8.   41.3   **9.**   78.4   **10.**   84.8   **11.**   51.7
   × 0.2   × 0.3   ×0.25   ×0.72
   8.26   **23.52**   **21.2**   **37.224**

12.   97.8   **13.**   51.7   **14.**   0.41   **15.**   0.74
   ×0.31   ×0.67   ×0.02   ×0.08
   30.318   **34.639**   **0.0082**   **0.0592**

16.   0.51   **17.** $5.15   **18.** $5.85   **19.** $3.35
   ×0.06   ×   85   ×   3.5   ×   7.6
   0.0306   **$437.75**   **$20.475 =**   **$25.46**
                                          $20.48

Multiply by 10.   **20.** 31.7 **317**   **21.** 5.71 **57.1**

Multiply by 100.   **22.** 32.85 **3,285**   **23.** 41.786 **4,178.6**

Multiply by 1,000.   **24.** 72.716 **72,716**   **25.** 7.1956 **7,195.6**

Multiply by 10,000.   **26.** 6.9178 **69,178**   **27.** 3.42876 **34,287.6**

Workshop 6 Multiplying Decimals ▶ **15**

③ ASSESS

Review students' written work to identify the kinds of errors they may be making. Very often errors in the basic multiplication facts are common. If this is the case, ask students to write out the multiplication tables, starting with the two times table and going through the nine times table. Review their tables to find and correct the errors in them.

④ CLOSE

The Practice problems can be assigned for class work and the answers checked in class to help students master the objective of the lesson.

WRAP-UP

Ask five students to show their work for a few problems on the board.

Assignment Guide
  Basic: 8–19
  Average: 20–27

20 min.

WORKSHOP 7

WORKSHOP

① FOCUS

Objectives

1. To divide decimals.
2. To divide an amount of money by a whole number.
3. To divide by 10, 100, or 1,000.

② TEACH

Dividing decimals requires a distinct series of steps in order to get the correct answer. Work through each example very carefully. Then review students' work on the Self-Check.

Ask students why the decimal point is moved the same number of places in both the divisor and the dividend. To help students remember how to divide decimals, you might wish to type the steps given in the first paragraph of the workshop in list form and reproduce copies for all students. For example: (1) check if there is a decimal point in the divisor; and (2) if there is, move the decimal point to the right to make the divisor a whole number. **Continue the list until you have four steps.**

Need Help? Go to...

▶ Skill 9: **Dividing (Fractional Remainder),** page 736

▶ Skill 10: **Dividing (Decimal Remainder),** page 737

▶ Skill 11: **Dividing Decimals,** page 738

Dividing Decimals

DIVIDING DECIMALS When you're dividing decimals, it's important to keep these steps in mind:

1. Check if there is a decimal point in the divisor. If there is, move the decimal point to the right to make the divisor a whole number.
2. Move the decimal point in the dividend to the right the same number of places you moved the decimal point in the divisor.
3. Write the decimal point in the quotient directly above the decimal point in the dividend.
4. Divide as with whole numbers.

$$\text{divisor} \longrightarrow 3\overline{)693} \longleftarrow \text{dividend} \quad 231 \longleftarrow \text{quotient}$$

Example 1

$23.78 \div 5.8$ or $5.8\overline{)23.78}$

STEP: Divide.

$$5.8\overline{)23.78}$$

$$\begin{array}{r} 4.1 \\ 58\overline{)237.8} \\ -232 \\ \hline 58 \\ -58 \end{array}$$

ADDING ZEROS TO DECIMAL POINT Add zeros to the right of the decimal point in the dividend if needed.

Example 2

$0.147 \div 0.42$ or $0.42\overline{)0.147}$

STEP: Divide.

$$0.42\overline{)0.147}$$

$$\begin{array}{r} 0.35 \\ 42\overline{)14.70} \\ -126 \\ \hline 210 \\ -210 \end{array} \quad \text{(zero added)}$$

CONCEPT CHECK

SELF-CHECK ✓

Complete the problems, then check your answers at the end of the book on page 802.

1. $35.96 \div 5.8$ **6.2**

2. $12.9\overline{)55.341}$ **4.29**

3. $0.052\overline{)1.872}$ **36**

DIVIDEND AS AMOUNT OF MONEY When the dividend is an amount of money, remember to place the dollar sign in the quotient and round the answer to the nearest cent.

WORKSHOP NOTES

─ Example 3 ─

$47.56 ÷ 24

STEP: Divide. $24\overline{)\$47.560}^{\,1.981}$ or **$1.98**   (rounded to nearest cent)

DIVIDING BY 10, 100, OR 1,000 When dividing by 10, 100, or 1,000, count the number of zeros in 10, 100, or 1,000 and move the decimal point to the left the same number of places.

─ Example 4 ─

9.3 ÷ 10

STEP: Divide. 9.3 ÷ 10 = 09.3 = **0.93**   (10 has 1 zero. Move decimal 1 place.)

─ Example 5 ─

742.64 ÷ 100

STEP: Divide. 742.64 ÷ 100 = 742.64   (100 has 2 zeros. Move decimal 2 places.)
= **7.4264**

─ Example 6 ─

13,436.1 ÷ 1,000

STEP: Divide. 13,436.1 ÷ 1,000 = 13436.1   (1,000 has 3 zeros. Move decimal
= **13.4361**   3 places.)

CONCEPT CHECK

Complete the problems, then check your answers at the end of the book on page 802.

 (SELF-CHECK ✔)

4. $16.32 ÷ 12   **5.** 7.9 ÷ 10   **6.** 138.9 ÷ 100   **7.** 9,862.8 ÷ 1,000
$1.36   0.79   1.389   9.8628

PRACTICE

Divide. Round answers to the nearest tenths.

8. $5.3\overline{)9.54}$ 1.8   **9.** $3.2\overline{)11.2}$ 3.5   **10.** $2.6\overline{)24.18}$ 9.3

Divide. Round answers to the nearest hundredths.

11. $4.3\overline{)7.871}$ 1.83   **12.** $5.9\overline{)5.343}$ 0.905 =   **13.** $7.36\overline{)88.34}$ 12.002 = 12.00
                                                0.91

Divide by 10.

14. 9.3 **0.93**   **15.** 14.42 **1.442**   **16.** 726.81 **72.681**

Divide by 100.

17. 429.8 **4.298**   **18.** 133.39 **1.3339**   **19.** 8,462.65 **84.6265**

Divide by 1,000.

20. 5,896.9 **5.8969**   **21.** 321.29 **0.32129**   **22.** 22.098 **0.022098**

Divide by 10,000.

23. 63,652.18 **6.365218**   **24.** 3,879.19 **0.387919**   **25.** 415.49 **0.041549**

Workshop 7 Dividing Decimals ▶ **17**

WORKSHOP

(3) ASSESS

Students can make a variety of errors when dividing decimals. Those errors must be analyzed individually and corrected. Some types of errors are the following:

• moving the decimal point incorrectly;

• not moving the decimal point in the dividend;

• errors in basic multiplication facts;

• subtracting incorrectly;

• forgetting to put a zero in the quotient; and

• not completing the division to arrive at the correct quotient.

(4) CLOSE

The Practice problems can be assigned for class work and the answers checked in class to help students master the objective of the lesson.

WRAP-UP

Work out the complete solutions to a few of the Practice problems on the board.

Assignment Guide
   Basic: 8–13
   Average: 14–25

20 min.

1 FOCUS

Objectives

1. To multiply fractions.
2. To multiply fractions and whole numbers.
3. To simplify fractions.
4. To change a mixed number to an improper fraction.
5. To multiply mixed numbers.

2 TEACH

Write $\frac{2}{5} \times \frac{4}{9}$ on the board. Ask students to identify the numerators and the denominators. Explain that to multiply fractions, multiply the numerators together and then multiply the denominators. **(Write the answer as a fraction: $\frac{2}{5} \times \frac{4}{9} = \frac{2 \times 4}{5 \times 9} = \frac{8}{45}$)**

Write the whole number 36 and the fraction $\frac{36}{1}$ on the board. Explain that the value of each is the same because every whole number has a denominator of 1. Have students multiply $\frac{1}{4} \times 36$. **($\frac{1}{4} \times 36 = \frac{1}{4} \times \frac{36}{1} = \frac{36}{4} = 9$)**

Write $\frac{7}{8} \times \frac{2}{3}$ on the board. Ask students: Of the numbers 2, 3, 7, and 8, which is not a prime number? Have students list the prime factors of 8. Rewrite the problem using the prime factors: $\frac{7 \times 2}{2 \times 2 \times 2 \times 3}$. To simplify, cancel the common factors, like this: $\frac{7 \times 2}{2 \times 2 \times 2 \times 3} = \frac{7}{2 \times 2 \times 3} = \frac{7}{12}$

Before students multiply mixed numbers, practice changing mixed numbers to improper fractions. Tell them to multiply the whole number times the denominator in the fraction. Then add the numerator. Write the answer over the denominator. $6\frac{1}{3} = [(6 \times 3) + 1] = \frac{19}{3}$

Need Help? Go to...
→ Skill 20:
Multiplying Fractions/Mixed Numbers, page 747

1. $\frac{3}{4} \times \frac{5}{8} = \frac{3 \times 5}{4 \times 8}$
   $= \frac{15}{32}$

SELF-CHECK ✓

2. $\frac{7}{8} \times \frac{3}{8} = \frac{7 \times 3}{8 \times 8}$
   $= \frac{21}{64}$

3. $\frac{2}{3} \times 600 =$
   $\frac{2}{3} \times \frac{600}{1} =$
   $\frac{1200}{3} = 400$

METHOD TO MULTIPLICATION When multiplying fractions, first multiply the numerators and then multiply the denominators. The product of the numerators is placed over the product of the denominators to give the answer in the form of a fraction.

Example 1

$\frac{2}{3} \times \frac{4}{5}$ **STEP: Multiply.** $\frac{2}{3} \times \frac{4}{5} = \frac{8}{15}$ ← product of numerators
← product of denominators

A WHOLE NUMBER'S DENOMINATOR When multiplying a fraction and a whole number, note that every whole number has a denominator of 1.

Example 2

$\frac{4}{5} \times 300$ **STEP: Multiply.** $\frac{4}{5} \times 300 = \frac{4}{5} \times \frac{300}{1} = \frac{1200}{5} = 240$

CONCEPT CHECK

Complete the problems, then check your answers at the end of the book on page 802. Multiply.

1. $\frac{3}{4} \times \frac{5}{8}$ 2. $\frac{7}{8} \times \frac{3}{8}$ 3. $\frac{2}{3} \times 600$

SIMPLIFYING FRACTIONS It is customary business practice to reduce all fractions to lowest terms. Reducing a fraction to lowest term is also called *simplifying the fraction*. To simplify a fraction, you can use prime factorization and then cancel the common factors. To review, prime factorization is a composite number (a whole number that has more than two factors, such as 4, 6, 8, and 9) that is expressed as a product of prime factors (a whole number that has exactly two factors, 1 and itself). For example, the prime factorization of 63 is as follows:

Example 3

$\frac{5}{6} \times \frac{3}{7}$ **STEP: Multiply. Write the product in simplest form.**

$\frac{5}{6} \times \frac{3}{7} = \frac{5 \times 3}{2 \times 3 \times 7} = \frac{5}{14}$

WORKSHOP NOTES

_____

_____

_____

_____

_____

_____

_____

CONCEPT CHECK

Complete the problems, then check your answers at the end of the book on page 802. Multiply.

SELF-CHECK ✓

4. $\frac{3}{4} \times \frac{5}{9}$

5. $\frac{2}{15} \times \frac{5}{8}$

6. $\frac{5}{6} \times 180$

MULTIPLYING MIXED NUMBERS When multiplying mixed numbers, first change the mixed number to an improper fraction and then multiply and simplify.

Example 4

$2\frac{1}{2} \times 4$

$1\frac{4}{5} \times 2\frac{2}{9}$

$3\frac{1}{2} \times 2\frac{1}{3}$

STEP: Multiply the mixed numbers.

$$2\frac{1}{2} \times 4 = \frac{5}{2} \times \frac{4}{1} = 10$$

$$1\frac{4}{5} \times 2\frac{2}{9} = \frac{9}{5} \times \frac{20}{9} = \frac{20}{5} = 4$$

$$3\frac{1}{2} \times 2\frac{1}{3} = \frac{7}{2} \times \frac{7}{3} = \frac{49}{6} = 8\frac{1}{6}$$

CONCEPT CHECK

Complete the problems, then check your answers at the end of the book on page 802. Multiply and simplify.

7. $4\frac{1}{2} \times 8$

8. $3\frac{3}{5} \times 2\frac{2}{9}$

9. $4\frac{1}{2} \times 3\frac{1}{3}$

PRACTICE

Multiply and simplify.

10. $\frac{3}{4} \times \frac{7}{8}$ $\frac{21}{32}$

11. $\frac{7}{5} \times \frac{3}{8}$ $\frac{21}{40}$

12. $\frac{3}{11} \times \frac{7}{2}$ $\frac{21}{22}$

13. $\frac{9}{10} \times \frac{3}{5}$ $\frac{27}{50}$

14. $\frac{5}{8} \times 80$ **50**

15. $\frac{3}{4} \times 20$ **15**

16. $\frac{3}{5} \times 300$ **180**

17. $\frac{2}{3} \times 660$ **440**

18. $\frac{7}{8} \times 248$ **217**

19. $\frac{9}{10} \times \frac{5}{3}$ $1\frac{1}{2}$

20. $\frac{9}{12} \times \frac{3}{15}$ $\frac{3}{20}$

21. $\frac{12}{35} \times \frac{21}{30}$ $\frac{6}{25}$

22. $5\frac{3}{4} \times 288$ **1,656**

23. $8\frac{1}{2} \times 3\frac{1}{4}$ $27\frac{5}{8}$

24. $6\frac{3}{4} \times 2\frac{2}{3}$ **18**

25. $12\frac{1}{2} \times 4\frac{3}{4}$ $59\frac{3}{8}$

26. $12\frac{3}{4} \times 8\frac{2}{3}$ $110\frac{1}{2}$

27. $27\frac{1}{5} \times 8\frac{3}{4}$ **238**

Workshop 8 Multiplying Fractions ▶ **19**

SELF-CHECK ✓

4. $\frac{3}{4} \times \frac{5}{9} = \frac{3 \times 5}{4 \times 9} =$

$$\frac{3 \times 5}{2 \times 2 \times 3 \times 3} =$$

$$\frac{5}{12}$$

5. $\frac{2}{15} \times \frac{5}{8} =$

$$\frac{2 \times 5}{3 \times 5 \times 2 \times 2 \times 2}$$

$$= \frac{1}{3 \times 2 \times 2} = \frac{1}{12}$$

6. $\frac{5}{6} \times 180$

$$= \frac{5}{6} \times \frac{180}{1} =$$

$$\frac{5 \times 6 \times 30}{6} = 150$$

7. $4\frac{1}{2} \times 8 = \frac{9}{2} \times \frac{8}{1} =$

$$\frac{9 \times 2 \times 4}{2} = 36$$

8. $3\frac{3}{5} \times 2\frac{2}{9} = \frac{18}{5} \times \frac{20}{9}$

$$= \frac{2 \times 9 \times 5 \times 4}{5 \times 9} =$$

$$\frac{8}{1} = 8$$

SELF-CHECK ✓

9. $4\frac{1}{2} \times 3\frac{1}{3} = \frac{9}{2} \times \frac{10}{3}$

$$= \frac{3 \times 3 \times 2 \times 5}{2 \times 3}$$

$$= 15$$

---

③ ASSESS

Review students' written work to assess the kinds of mistakes they are making. They may have forgotten to simplify a fraction, or incorrectly changed a mixed number to an improper fraction, or made computational mistakes in multiplication. Identify the type of error and have students correct their mistakes.

④ CLOSE

The Practice problems can be assigned for class work and the answer checked in class to help students master the objective of the lesson.

WRAP-UP

Go over any problem for which a wrong answer is given.

Assignment Guide

Basic: 10–13

Average: 14–22

20 min.

 FOCUS

Objectives

1. To find the reciprocal of a fraction.
2. To divide fractions.

2 TEACH

Introduce a reciprocal by writing the fraction $\frac{7}{8}$ on the board. Have students identify the numerator and the denominator. Ask students to switch the number in the numerator with the number in the denominator. **(The answer, $\frac{8}{7}$, is the reciprocal of the fraction $\frac{7}{8}$. Be sure students know that *reciprocal* means any number multiplied by its reciprocal is 1.)**

Write the mixed number $2\frac{1}{4}$ on the board. Ask students how they might find the reciprocal. Explain that they must first change the mixed number to an improper fraction. Review how to do this. Then ask, what is the reciprocal of $\frac{9}{4}$? Work through Example 1 a–d in the text.

(Review the idea that a *divisor* is the number you are dividing by. The *dividend* is the number to be divided.) For example, in $\frac{8}{3}$, the divisor is 3; the dividend is 8. Next, write on the board the following steps for dividing fractions.

1. Change any mixed numbers to improper fractions.
2. Change the divisor to its reciprocal.
3. Multiply the fractions.
4. Simplify the fraction.

Dividing Fractions

Need Help? Go to...
► Skill 21: **Dividing Fractions/Mixed Numbers,** page 748

FINDING THE RECIPROCAL Dividing fractions involves finding the reciprocal of the divisor. The reciprocal of a fraction is found by interchanging the numerator and the denominator.

Example 1
---

a. $\frac{2}{3}$ b. $\frac{5}{8}$

c. 4 d. $1\frac{3}{4}$

STEP: Find the reciprocal.

a. $\frac{2}{3} \times \frac{3}{2}$ $\frac{3}{2}$ is the reciprocal

b. $\frac{5}{8} \times \frac{8}{5}$ $\frac{8}{5}$ is the reciprocal

c. $\frac{4}{1} \times \frac{1}{4}$ $\frac{1}{4}$ is the reciprocal

d. $1\frac{3}{4} = \frac{7}{4} \times \frac{4}{7}$ $\frac{4}{7}$ is the reciprocal

CONCEPT CHECK

SELF-CHECK ✓

Complete the problems, then check your answers at the end of the book on page 802. Write the reciprocal for each number.

1. $\frac{5}{3}$ $\frac{3}{5}$ 2. $\frac{7}{8}$ $\frac{8}{7}$

3. 10 $\frac{1}{10}$ 4. $2\frac{1}{2}$ $\frac{2}{5}$

CHANGING THE DIVISOR TO ITS RECIPROCAL To divide fractions, first change the divisor to its reciprocal, multiply the resulting fraction, and simplify.

Example 2
---

a. $\frac{3}{4} \div \frac{1}{2}$ b. $\frac{8}{5} \div \frac{4}{3}$

c. $\frac{2}{3} \div 6$ d. $4\frac{1}{2} \div 1\frac{3}{4}$

STEP: Divide.

a. $\frac{3}{4} \div \frac{1}{2} = \frac{3}{4} \times \frac{2}{1} = \frac{6}{4} = 1\frac{1}{2}$

b. $\frac{8}{5} \div \frac{4}{3} = \frac{8}{5} \times \frac{3}{4} = \frac{24}{20} = 1\frac{4}{20} = 1\frac{1}{5}$

c. $\frac{2}{3} \div 6 = \frac{2}{3} \times \frac{1}{6} = \frac{2}{18} = \frac{1}{9}$

d. $4\frac{1}{2} \div 1\frac{3}{4} = \frac{9}{2} \div \frac{7}{4} = \frac{9}{2} \times \frac{4}{7} = \frac{36}{14} = 2\frac{4}{7}$

WORKSHOP NOTES

CONCEPT CHECK

Complete the problems, then check your answers at the end of the book on page 802. Divide and simplify.

5. $\frac{5}{8} \div \frac{3}{4}$ $\frac{5}{6}$

6. $\frac{9}{16} \div \frac{3}{2}$ $\frac{3}{8}$

7. $\frac{4}{5} \div 2$ $\frac{2}{5}$

8. $8\frac{1}{3} \div 1\frac{2}{3}$ 5

PRACTICE

Write the reciprocal.

9. $\frac{3}{4}$ $\frac{4}{3}$

10. $\frac{5}{8}$ $\frac{8}{5}$

11. $\frac{3}{16}$ $\frac{16}{3}$

12. $\frac{21}{2}$ $\frac{2}{21}$

13. $\frac{1}{10}$ $\frac{10}{1}$

14. 9 $\frac{1}{9}$

15. 15 $\frac{1}{15}$

16. 7 $\frac{1}{7}$

17. $1\frac{1}{2}$ $\frac{2}{3}$

Divide and simplify.

18. $\frac{3}{5} \div \frac{2}{3}$ $\frac{9}{10}$

19. $\frac{1}{3} \div \frac{8}{7}$ $\frac{7}{24}$

20. $\frac{9}{16} \div \frac{1}{4}$ $2\frac{1}{4}$

21. $\frac{7}{8} \div \frac{1}{3}$ $2\frac{5}{8}$

22. $7 \div \frac{7}{6}$ 6

23. $12 \div \frac{3}{4}$ 16

24. $\frac{5}{8} \div 2$ $\frac{5}{16}$

25. $\frac{7}{16} \div 8$ $\frac{7}{128}$

26. $1\frac{7}{8} \div \frac{3}{4}$ $2\frac{1}{2}$

27. $6\frac{2}{3} \div \frac{5}{3}$ 4

28. $15\frac{1}{2} \div 1\frac{1}{2}$ $10\frac{1}{3}$

29. $12\frac{7}{8} \div 1\frac{5}{8}$ $7\frac{12}{13}$

30. It takes $1\frac{1}{4}$ ounces of oatmeal to make 1 serving. How many servings are contained in a 16-ounce box? $12\frac{4}{5}$ **servings**

31. You work in a bulk food store. How many $\frac{1}{4}$ pound bags of redskin peanuts can you package from a $24\frac{1}{2}$ pound box? **98 bags**

32. How many pieces of wire, each $12\frac{1}{2}$ feet long, can an electrician cut from a 100-foot coil? **8 pieces of wire**

33. A quart of milk is equal to $\frac{1}{4}$ of a gallon. How many quarts of milk are in $\frac{7}{8}$ of a gallon? $3\frac{1}{2}$ **quarts**

3 ASSESS

Students can make a variety of errors when dividing fractions, such as: (1) incorrectly changing a mixed number to an improper fraction; (2) not changing the divisor to its reciprocal; (3) mistakenly changing the dividend to its reciprocal; (4) multiplying incorrectly; or (5) forgetting to simplify a fraction. Errors must be analyzed individually and corrected.

4 CLOSE

The Practice problems can be assigned for class work and the answer checked in class to help students master the objective of the lesson.

WRAP-UP

Go over any problem for which a wrong answer is given.

Assignment Guide
  Basic: 9–29
Average: 30–33

20 min.

WORKSHOP 10

Adding Fractions

FRACTIONS WITH A COMMON DENOMINATOR To add fractions which have a common denominator, the numerators are summed and the sum is placed over the common denominator.

Need Help? Go to...
▶ **Skill 15:** Adding Fractions, Like Denominators, page 742
▶ **Skill 16:** Adding Fractions, Unlike Denominators, page 743

Example 1

$\frac{3}{8} + \frac{1}{8} + \frac{5}{8}$

STEP: Find the sum. $\frac{3}{8} + \frac{1}{8} + \frac{5}{8} = \frac{(3 + 1 + 5)}{8} = \frac{9}{8}$ or $1\frac{1}{8}$

CONCEPT CHECK

SELF-CHECK ✔

Complete the problems, then check your answers at the end of the book on page 802.

1. $\frac{2}{3} + \frac{1}{3} = \frac{3}{3}$ or 1

2. $\frac{11}{18} + \frac{5}{18} + \frac{7}{18} = \frac{23}{18}$ or $1\frac{5}{18}$

3. $\frac{5}{7} + \frac{1}{7} + \frac{2}{7} + \frac{6}{7} = \frac{14}{7}$ or 2

4. $\frac{4}{9} + \frac{2}{9} + \frac{1}{9} + \frac{5}{9} = \frac{12}{9}$ or $1\frac{1}{3}$

FRACTIONS WITHOUT A COMMON DENOMINATOR To add fractions which do not have common denominators, each fraction is expressed in terms of the least common denominator, the numerators are then summed, and the sum is placed over the least common denominator.

Example 2

$\frac{3}{4} + \frac{5}{6} + \frac{1}{2}$

STEP: Find the sum.

To find the least common denominator, find the prime factors of the denominators 4, 6, and 2. Write the denominator 4 as 2×2, the denominator 6 as 2×3, and the denominator 2 as 2×1. The least common denominator must contain two factors of 2 and one factor of 3. To add two fractions without a common denominator, first find the least common denominator. This is the lowest number that can be evenly divided by each denominator. Therefore, the least common denominator is $2 \times 2 \times 3$ or 12.

$\frac{3}{4} + \frac{5}{6} + \frac{1}{2} = \frac{(3 \times 3)}{(3 \times 4)} + \frac{(2 \times 5)}{(2 \times 6)} + \frac{(6 \times 1)}{(6 \times 2)} = \frac{9}{12} + \frac{10}{12} + \frac{6}{12} = \frac{25}{12}$ or $2\frac{1}{12}$

CONCEPT CHECK

SELF-CHECK ✔

Complete the problems, then check your answers at the end of the book on page 802.

5. $\frac{1}{2} + \frac{1}{4} + \frac{3}{8} = \frac{9}{8}$ or $1\frac{1}{8}$

6. $\frac{1}{3} + \frac{5}{6} + \frac{2}{3} = \frac{11}{6}$ or $1\frac{5}{6}$

7. $\frac{2}{5} + \frac{2}{3} + \frac{7}{10} = \frac{53}{30}$ or $1\frac{23}{30}$

8. $\frac{3}{4} + \frac{2}{5} + \frac{1}{6} = \frac{79}{60}$ or $1\frac{19}{60}$

WORKSHOP 10

① FOCUS

Objectives

1. To add fractions with a common denominator.
2. To add fractions without a common denominator.
3. To find the least common denominator.

② TEACH

Write the problem $\frac{2}{7} + \frac{3}{7} + \frac{1}{7}$ on the board. Ask students to name the denominator in each fraction. Explain that when the denominators are the same, simply add the numerators $(2 + 3 + 1)$ and then write the sum over the common denominator. For example: $\frac{2}{7} + \frac{3}{7} + \frac{1}{7} = \frac{6}{7}$

Write the problem $\frac{2}{3} + \frac{3}{5} + \frac{4}{9}$ on the board. Ask students to identify the denominators. Explain that to add two fractions without a common denominator, first find the least common denominator. **(The *least common denominator* is the lowest number that can be evenly divided by each denominator.)** In this example, the least common denominator is the lowest number that can be evenly divided by 3, 5, and 9.

To find the least common denominator of 3, 5, and 9, list the prime factors of each denominator:

$3 = 3 \times 1$
$5 = 5 \times 1$
$9 = 3 \times 3$

Then, multiply the factors together, but do not repeat factors: $3 \times 3 \times 5 = 45$. Here (3×3) are the factors of 9; (5×1) are the factors of 5, but since any number multiplied by 1 is itself, it is not necessary to multiply by 1. The factors of 3 are (3×1), but 3 is not repeated in multiplying the factors together. The least common denominator is $3 \times 3 \times 5$, or 45.

WORKSHOP NOTES

PRACTICE

9. $\frac{2}{3} + \frac{4}{5} = \frac{22}{15}$ or $1\frac{7}{15}$ **10.** $\frac{1}{2} + \frac{3}{4} = \frac{5}{4}$ or $1\frac{1}{4}$ **11.** $\frac{5}{6} + \frac{2}{9} = \frac{19}{18}$ or $1\frac{1}{18}$

12. $\frac{1}{2} + \frac{1}{4} + \frac{1}{3} = \frac{13}{12}$ or $1\frac{1}{12}$ **13.** $\frac{5}{7} + \frac{2}{3} + \frac{1}{6} = \frac{65}{42}$ or $1\frac{23}{42}$ **14.** $\frac{5}{8} + \frac{5}{12} + \frac{5}{18} = \frac{95}{72}$ or $1\frac{23}{72}$

15. $\frac{8}{11} + \frac{3}{4} = \frac{65}{44}$ or $1\frac{21}{44}$ **16.** $\frac{5}{8} + \frac{3}{5} = \frac{49}{40}$ or $1\frac{9}{40}$ **17.** $\frac{5}{7} + \frac{2}{9} = \frac{59}{63}$

18. $\frac{3}{5} + \frac{2}{3} + \frac{4}{7} = \frac{193}{105}$ or $1\frac{88}{105}$ **19.** $\frac{7}{8} + \frac{2}{5} + \frac{1}{3} = \frac{193}{120}$ or $1\frac{73}{120}$ **20.** $\frac{3}{4} + \frac{3}{11} + \frac{2}{3} = \frac{223}{132}$ or $1\frac{91}{132}$

21. $\frac{3}{5} + \frac{2}{15} + \frac{1}{3} = \frac{16}{15}$ or $1\frac{1}{15}$ **22.** $\frac{3}{8} + \frac{1}{4} + \frac{1}{2} = \frac{9}{8}$ or $1\frac{1}{8}$ **23.** $\frac{3}{4} + \frac{2}{6} + \frac{7}{12} = \frac{13}{6}$ or $2\frac{1}{6}$

24. $\frac{2}{5} + \frac{1}{3} + \frac{7}{10} = \frac{43}{30}$ or $1\frac{13}{30}$ **25.** $\frac{5}{8} + \frac{1}{6} + \frac{11}{12} = \frac{41}{24}$ or $1\frac{17}{24}$ **26.** $\frac{1}{2} + \frac{1}{3} + \frac{1}{5} = \frac{31}{30}$ or $1\frac{1}{30}$

27. $\frac{3}{4} + \frac{5}{9} + \frac{5}{6} = \frac{77}{36}$ or $2\frac{5}{36}$ **28.** $\frac{3}{4} + \frac{4}{5} + \frac{5}{6} = \frac{143}{60}$ or $2\frac{23}{60}$ **29.** $\frac{8}{11} + \frac{2}{3} + \frac{3}{22} = \frac{101}{66}$ or $1\frac{35}{66}$

30. $\frac{1}{2} + \frac{1}{3} + \frac{1}{4} + \frac{1}{5} + \frac{1}{6} =$ **31.** $\frac{3}{7} + \frac{5}{6} + \frac{2}{3} + \frac{1}{2} + \frac{3}{4} = \frac{89}{28}$ or $3\frac{5}{28}$
$\frac{29}{20}$ or $1\frac{9}{20}$

32. Tom, Kwasi, and Juan purchased a large pizza to share. If Tom ate $\frac{1}{3}$ of the pizza, Kwasi ate $\frac{1}{4}$ of the pizza, and Juan ate $\frac{1}{6}$ of the pizza, what fractional part of the pizza was eaten? $\frac{3}{4}$

33. On the Jones farm, a large cylindrical container is used to catch rain water. If $\frac{1}{2}$ of the container was filled in one rainfall, $\frac{4}{5}$ of the container was filled in a second rainfall, and $\frac{7}{10}$ of the container was filled in a third rainfall, how many containers were filled in the three rainfalls? **2**

34. Zeno started to walk from his home to work. After walking $\frac{1}{2}$ of the way he got tired and stopped for a rest. He then walked $\frac{1}{4}$ of the way and rested again. After walking $\frac{1}{8}$ of the way, he rested again. After walking $\frac{1}{16}$ of the way, he rested again. How far towards his place of work had he walked? $\frac{15}{16}$

35. A nickel is $\frac{1}{20}$ of a dollar. A dime is $\frac{1}{10}$ of a dollar and a quarter is $\frac{1}{4}$ of a dollar, while a fifty cent piece is $\frac{1}{2}$ of a dollar. If you had a nickel, a dime, a quarter, and a fifty cent piece, what fractional part of a dollar would you have? $\frac{9}{10}$

36. John spent $\frac{1}{4}$ of his life as a boy growing up, $\frac{1}{6}$ of his life in college, and $\frac{1}{2}$ of his life as a teacher before he retired. What fractional part of his life did he spend before he retired? $\frac{11}{12}$

37. Luis Delgado owns $\frac{2}{5}$ of the Terrytown Restaurant. His brother, Juan, owns $\frac{1}{3}$ and his daughter Angel owns $\frac{1}{4}$. What fractional part of the restaurant do the Delgados own? $\frac{59}{60}$

38. About $\frac{11}{12}$ of a golf course is fairways, $\frac{1}{18}$ greens, and the rest tees. What fractional part of the golf course is fairways and greens? $\frac{35}{36}$

Workshop 10 Adding Fractions ▶ **23**

WRAP-UP

Go over any problem for which a wrong answer is given.

Assignment Guide
Basic: 9–31
Average: 32–38

20 min.

To add $\frac{2}{3} + \frac{3}{5} + \frac{4}{9}$, change each fraction to its equivalent form with 45 as the least common denominator. $\frac{2}{3} = \frac{30}{45}$ because $\frac{45}{3} = 15$, and $15 \times 2 = 30$; $\frac{3}{5} = \frac{27}{45}$ because $\frac{45}{5} = 9$, and $9 \times 3 = 27$; $\frac{4}{9} = \frac{20}{45}$ because $\frac{45}{9} = 5$, and $5 \times 4 = 20$. Now add the numerators of the equivalent fractions: $30 + 27 + 20 = \frac{77}{45}$ or $1\frac{32}{45}$

③ ASSESS

Students may have difficulty adding fractions without a common denominator. Recall the example: $\frac{2}{3} + \frac{3}{5} + \frac{4}{9}$. **(You may wish to introduce another way to find the least common denominator.)** Start with the highest denominator (9) and multiply it by 2. **(9 × 2 = 18.)** Can 18 be evenly divisible by 3? **(Yes.)** Can 18 be evenly divisible by 5? **(No, therefore, 18 is not the least common denominator.)**

Next, try 9×3. $9 \times 3 = 27$. Can 27 be evenly divisible by 3? **(Yes.)** Can 27 be evenly divisible by 5? **(No; therefore, 27 is not the least common denominator.)** Next, try $9 \times 4 = 36$. Can 36 be evenly divisible by 3? **(Yes.)** Can 36 be evenly divisible by 5? **(No; therefore, 36 is not the least common denominator.)** Next, try 9×5. Can 45 be evenly divisible by 3? **(Yes.)** Can 45 be evenly divisible by 5? **(Yes.)** Can 45 be evenly divisible by 9? **Yes, therefore, 45 is the least common denominator of 3, 5, and 9.**

④ CLOSE

The Practice problems can be assigned for class work and the answers checked in class to help students master the objective of the lesson.

WORKSHOP 11

① FOCUS

Objectives

1. To subtract fractions with a common denominator.
2. To subtract fractions without a common denominator.
3. To subtract mixed fractions.

② TEACH

Work through Example 1 in the text with students. Remind students to simplify the answer.

Write the problem $\frac{5}{8} - \frac{1}{6}$ on the board. Ask students to identify the denominators. **(Find the *least common denominator*, that is, the lowest number that can be evenly divided by each denominator.)** In this example, the least common denominator is the lowest number that can be evenly divided by 8 and 6.

To find the least common denominator of 8 and 6, list the prime factors of each denominator:

$8 = 2 \times 2 \times 2$
$6 = 2 \times 3$

Then, multiply the factors together, but do not repeat factors of the other denominator: $2 \times 2 \times 2 \times 3 = 24$. The factors of 8 are $(2 \times 2 \times 2)$; (2×3) are the factors of 6, but do not repeat the factor 2. The least common denominator is $2 \times 2 \times 2 \times 3$, or 24.

To subtract $\frac{5}{8} - \frac{1}{6}$, change each fraction to its equivalent form with 24 as the least common denominator.

$\frac{5}{8} = \frac{?}{24}$
$\frac{5}{8} = \frac{15}{24}$ because $\frac{24}{8} = 3$
  and $3 \times 5 = 15$
$\frac{1}{6} = \frac{?}{24}$
$\frac{1}{6} = \frac{4}{24}$ because $\frac{24}{6} = 4$
  and $4 \times 1 = 4$

Subtracting Fractions

Need Help? Go to...
- Skill 17: Subtracting Fractions, Like Denominators, page 744
- Skill 18: Subtracting Fractions, Unlike Denominators, page 745
- Skill 19: Subtracting Mixed Numbers, Borrowing, page 746

FRACTIONS WITH A COMMON DENOMINATOR To subtract fractions which have a common denominator, the numerators are subtracted and the difference is placed over the common denominator.

Example 1

$\frac{7}{8} - \frac{3}{8}$

STEP: Find the difference between the fractions.

$\frac{7}{8} - \frac{3}{8} = \frac{4}{8}$, which simplifies to $\frac{1}{2}$

CONCEPT CHECK

SELF-CHECK ✓

Complete the problems, then check your answers at the end of the book on page 802.

1. $\frac{3}{4} - \frac{1}{4} = \frac{1}{2}$ 2. $\frac{5}{6} - \frac{1}{6} = \frac{2}{3}$ 3. $\frac{12}{17} - \frac{1}{17} = \frac{11}{17}$ 4. $\frac{13}{29} - \frac{11}{29} = \frac{2}{29}$

FRACTIONS WITHOUT A COMMON DENOMINATOR To subtract fractions which do not have common denominators, each fraction is expressed in terms of the least common denominator, the numerators are then subtracted, and the difference is placed over the least common denominator.

Example 2

$\frac{5}{6} - \frac{1}{4}$

STEP: Find the difference between fractions without a common denominator.

To find the least common denominator, write the prime factors of the denominators 6 and 4 ($6 = 2 \times 3$ and $4 = 2 \times 2$). The least common denominator must contain two factors of 2 and one factor of 3. Therefore, the least common denominator is $2 \times 2 \times 3$ or 12.

$\frac{5}{6} - \frac{1}{4} = \frac{(5 \times 2)}{(6 \times 2)} - \frac{(1 \times 3)}{(4 \times 3)} = \frac{10}{12} - \frac{3}{12} = \frac{7}{12}$

CONCEPT CHECK

SELF-CHECK ✓

Complete the problems, then check your answers at the end of the book on page 802.

5. $\frac{3}{4} - \frac{1}{2} = \frac{1}{4}$ 6. $\frac{5}{8} - \frac{1}{6} = \frac{11}{24}$ 7. $\frac{5}{12} - \frac{3}{10} = \frac{7}{60}$ 8. $\frac{5}{6} - \frac{7}{20} = \frac{29}{60}$

WORKSHOP NOTES

SUBTRACTING MIXED FRACTIONS To subtract mixed numbers it is sometimes necessary to borrow one from the whole number in the minuend and convert it to a fraction. Here's an example to review minuend and subtrahend:

$$\begin{array}{r} 500 \quad \longleftarrow \quad \text{minuend} \\ -\ \ 30 \quad \longleftarrow \quad \text{subtrahend} \\ \hline 470 \end{array}$$

This is necessary when the fraction in the minuend is less than the fraction in the subtrahend. This can be determined after the fractions have been converted to the least common denominator.

Example 3

$4\frac{3}{8} - 2\frac{5}{8}$

STEP: Find the difference by subtracting mixed fractions.

Borrow 1 from the whole number 4 in the minuend. Next, add 1 to the fraction $\frac{3}{8}$ in the minuend. Change 1 to $\frac{8}{8}$ and add it to the fraction in the minuend. Then subtract: $3\frac{11}{8} - 2\frac{5}{8}$.

$4\frac{3}{8} - 2\frac{5}{8} = [(3 + 1) + \frac{3}{8}] - 2\frac{5}{8} = [3 + (1 + \frac{3}{8})] - 2\frac{5}{8} =$
$[3 + (\frac{8}{8} + \frac{3}{8})] - 2\frac{5}{8} = 3\frac{11}{8} - 2\frac{5}{8} = 1\frac{6}{8} \text{ or } 1\frac{3}{4}$

CONCEPT CHECK

Complete the problems, then check your answers at the end of the book on page 802.

SELF CHECK ✔

9. $5\frac{6}{7} - 2\frac{3}{7} = 3\frac{3}{7}$ **10.** $7\frac{2}{3} - 3\frac{1}{6} = 4\frac{1}{2}$ **11.** $12\frac{3}{8} - 4\frac{3}{4} = 7\frac{5}{8}$ **12.** $1 - \frac{15}{16} = \frac{1}{16}$

PRACTICE

13. $\frac{11}{12} - \frac{7}{12} = \frac{1}{3}$ **14.** $\frac{7}{9} - \frac{2}{9} = \frac{5}{9}$ **15.** $\frac{14}{17} - \frac{3}{17} = \frac{11}{17}$ **16.** $\frac{3}{4} - \frac{1}{2} = \frac{1}{4}$

17. $\frac{5}{8} - \frac{5}{12} = \frac{5}{24}$ **18.** $\frac{5}{6} - \frac{2}{15} = \frac{7}{10}$ **19.** $\frac{7}{8} - \frac{2}{3} = \frac{5}{24}$ **20.** $\frac{4}{5} - \frac{1}{4} = \frac{11}{20}$

21. $\frac{5}{7} - \frac{2}{9} = \frac{31}{63}$ **22.** $\frac{1}{2} - \frac{3}{10} = \frac{1}{5}$ **23.** $\frac{9}{10} - \frac{7}{15} = \frac{13}{30}$ **24.** $\frac{7}{12} - \frac{5}{18} = \frac{11}{36}$

25. $3\frac{2}{3} - 1\frac{1}{4} = 2\frac{5}{12}$ **26.** $7\frac{5}{6} - 2\frac{7}{10} = 5\frac{2}{15}$ **27.** $23\frac{4}{5} - 16\frac{1}{2} = 7\frac{3}{10}$ **28.** $8\frac{1}{5} - 3\frac{1}{3} = 4\frac{13}{15}$

29. Alice ran $\frac{7}{8}$ of the way home while Meredith ran $\frac{5}{6}$ of the way home. What fractional part more of the distance home did Alice run? $\frac{1}{24}$

30. Juan got $\frac{3}{4}$ of the problems correct on the last test. Julio got $\frac{5}{8}$ of the problems correct on the last test. What fractional part more of the test questions did Juan get correct than Julio? $\frac{1}{8}$

31. Megan completed $\frac{1}{6}$ of the church quilt while Samanthia completed $\frac{1}{4}$. What fractional part more of the church quilt did Samanthia complete than Megan? $\frac{1}{12}$

32. It $2\frac{1}{2}$ inches of rain fell on Monday and $1\frac{3}{4}$ inches of rain fell on Tuesday, how much more rain fell on Monday? $\frac{3}{4}$

33. Akili had a quarter and a dime. Recall that a quarter is $\frac{1}{4}$ of a dollar and a dime is $\frac{1}{10}$ of a dollar. Duhon had a dime and a nickel. Recall that a nickel is $\frac{1}{20}$ of a dollar. What fractional part more of a dollar did Akili have than Duhon had? $\frac{1}{5}$

Workshop 11 Subtracting Fractions ▶ **25**

Rewrite the problem as $\frac{15}{24} - \frac{4}{24}$. Now subtract the numerators of the equivalent fractions and write the difference over the least common denominator. ($\frac{5}{8} - \frac{1}{6}$ is $\frac{11}{24}$)

When subtracting mixed numbers, the key idea is to borrow 1 from the whole number in the minuend and write it as a fraction. Ask students for various ways to write the value of 1 as a fraction, such as $\frac{4}{4}$ or $\frac{9}{9}$. In the problem $7\frac{2}{7} - 3\frac{5}{7}$, change the minuend to $6\frac{9}{7}$ and then subtract $3\frac{5}{7}$.

③ ASSESS

You may wish to introduce another way to find the least common denominator. Recall the example, $\frac{5}{8} - \frac{1}{6}$. Start with the highest denominator (**8**). Can 8 be evenly divided by the other denominator? (**No; therefore, 8 is not the least common denominator.**) Next, multiply 8×2 to get 16. Can 16 be evenly divided by 6? (**No, therefore, 16 is not the least common denominator.**) Next, try 8×3. $8 \times 3 = 24$. Can 24 be evenly divisible by 3? **Yes; therefore, 24 is the least common denominator of 8 and 6.**

④ CLOSE

The Practice problems can be assigned for class work and the answers checked in class to help students master the objective of the lesson.

WRAP-UP

Go over any problem for which a wrong answer is given.

Assignment Guide
  Basic: 13–28
Average: 29–33

20 min.

1 FOCUS

Objectives

1. To compare fractions with a common denominator.
2. To compare fractions without a common denominator.

2 TEACH

Write $\frac{7}{8}$ and $\frac{5}{8}$ on the board. Explain that you will compare these fractions. Ask students to name the numerators and the denominators. Explain that since both denominators are 8, just compare the numerators to find the smaller fraction. ($\frac{5}{8} < \frac{7}{8}$ because 5 < 7)

Write Example 2 from the text on the board. Have students identify the numerators and the denominators. Explain that one way to compare two fractions with unlike denominators is to multiply the numerator and the denominator of each fraction you are comparing by 1. However, write the value of 1 as a fraction using the denominator of the other fraction. For example, to compare $\frac{7}{11}$ and $\frac{13}{21}$, first multiply $\frac{7}{11}$ by $\frac{21}{21}$: $\frac{7}{11} \times \frac{21}{21} = \frac{147}{231}$. Now multiply $\frac{13}{21}$ by $\frac{11}{11}$: $\frac{13}{21} \times \frac{11}{11} = \frac{143}{231}$.

Since $\frac{21}{21}$ is equal to 1 and $\frac{11}{11}$ is equal to 1, you are not changing the value of $\frac{7}{11}$ or $\frac{13}{21}$. However, you are changing the fractions to their equivalent forms. That means the fractions now have a common denominator so you can easily compare them. Compare $\frac{147}{231}$ and $\frac{143}{231}$. ($\frac{143}{231} < \frac{147}{231}$ because 143 < 147)

Remember that $\frac{7}{11} = \frac{147}{231}$ and $\frac{13}{21} = \frac{143}{231}$. **Therefore, $\frac{13}{21} < \frac{7}{11}$**

Comparing Fractions

FRACTIONS WITH A COMMON DENOMINATOR To compare fractions having common denominators, simply compare their numerators. The fraction having the smaller numerator is the smaller fraction.

Example 1

$\frac{5}{7}$ and $\frac{4}{7}$

STEP: Compare these fractions $\frac{4}{7} < \frac{5}{7}$ because 4 < 5

CONCEPT CHECK

Complete the problems, then check your answers at the end of the book on page 802.

1. Compare $\frac{5}{8}$ and $\frac{7}{8}$. $\frac{5}{8} < \frac{7}{8}$
2. Compare $\frac{11}{12}$ and $\frac{7}{12}$. $\frac{11}{12} > \frac{7}{12}$
3. Compare $\frac{2}{3}$ and $\frac{1}{3}$. $\frac{2}{3} > \frac{1}{3}$
4. Compare $\frac{49}{50}$ and $\frac{41}{50}$. $\frac{49}{50} > \frac{41}{50}$

FRACTIONS WITHOUT A COMMON DENOMINATOR To compare fractions having different denominators, one approach is to get a common denominator and then compare numerators.

Example 2

Compare the fractions without a common denominator.
$\frac{7}{11}$ and $\frac{13}{21}$

STEP 1: One way to compare two fractions with unlike denominators is to multiply the numerator and the denominator of each fraction you are comparing by 1. However, write the value of 1 as a fraction using the denominator of the other fraction.

$\frac{7}{11}$ and $\frac{13}{21}$ $\frac{7}{11} \times \frac{21}{21} = \frac{147}{231}$ $\frac{13}{21} \times \frac{11}{11} = \frac{143}{231}$

STEP 2: Change the fractions to equivalent form.

Since $\frac{21}{21}$ is equal to 1 and $\frac{11}{11}$ is equal to 1, you're not changing the value of $\frac{7}{11}$ or $\frac{13}{21}$. However, you are changing the fractions to their equivalent forms. That means the fractions now have a common denominator so you can easily compare them.

$\frac{143}{231} < \frac{147}{231}$ because 143 < 147

Remember that $\frac{7}{11} = \frac{147}{231}$ and $\frac{13}{21} = \frac{143}{231}$ so $\frac{13}{21} < \frac{7}{11}$

WORKSHOP NOTES

Complete the problems, then check your answers at the end of the book on page 802. Compare fractions.  **SELF-CHECK✔**

5. $\frac{5}{6}$ and $\frac{7}{8}$ $\quad\frac{5}{6} < \frac{7}{8}$ **6.** $\frac{7}{12}$ and $\frac{5}{9}$ $\quad\frac{7}{12} > \frac{5}{9}$ **7.** $\frac{3}{7}$ and $\frac{7}{15}$ $\quad\frac{3}{7} < \frac{7}{15}$ **8.** $\frac{45}{47}$ and $\frac{89}{93}$ $\quad\frac{45}{47} > \frac{89}{93}$

9. $\frac{8}{11}$ and $\frac{15}{19}$ **10.** $\frac{1}{23}$ and $\frac{2}{45}$ **11.** $\frac{5}{13}$ and $\frac{9}{25}$ **12.** $\frac{147}{347}$ and $\frac{440}{1,039}$

$\quad\frac{8}{11} < \frac{15}{19}$ $\qquad\frac{1}{23} < \frac{2}{45}$ $\qquad\frac{5}{13} > \frac{9}{25}$ $\qquad\frac{147}{347} > \frac{440}{1,039}$

WORKSHOP (vertical tab)

PRACTICE

Compare the following fractions.

13. $\frac{4}{5}$ and $\frac{3}{5}$ **14.** $\frac{8}{13}$ and $\frac{10}{13}$ **15.** $\frac{347}{498}$ and $\frac{299}{498}$ **16.** $\frac{1}{4}$ and $\frac{1}{5}$

17. $\frac{5}{8}$ and $\frac{11}{18}$ **18.** $\frac{4}{9}$ and $\frac{7}{12}$ **19.** $\frac{43}{45}$ and $\frac{22}{23}$ **20.** $\frac{91}{97}$ and $\frac{45}{49}$

21. $\frac{14}{19}$ and $\frac{27}{37}$ **22.** $\frac{7}{15}$ and $\frac{15}{31}$ **23.** $\frac{23}{25}$ and $\frac{45}{49}$ **24.** $\frac{57}{59}$ and $\frac{115}{119}$

25. $\frac{3}{11}$ and $\frac{7}{23}$ **26.** $\frac{5}{34}$ and $\frac{9}{67}$ **27.** $\frac{12}{17}$ and $\frac{26}{37}$ **28.** $\frac{132}{235}$ and $\frac{260}{463}$

29. The Clothing Hut advertised $\frac{1}{3}$ off its summer clearance items while Apparel Outlet advertised $\frac{1}{4}$ off. Which store was taking the most off? **Clothing Hut**

30. The newspaper reported that on the "big board," where 1.24 billion shares were traded, 1,366 stocks fell and 1,788 rose. On the NASDAQ, where 1.76 billion shares were traded, 1,587 fell and 2,068 rose. Comparing the fractions of stocks that fell to stocks that rose, which market had the largest fraction? **NASDAQ**

31. The newspaper reported that the Dow Jones Industrials have had a low of 8,062 and a high of 11,350. The Dow Jones Transportation index has had a low of 1,942 and a high of 3,157. Comparing the fraction of low to high for the year, did the Dow Jones Industrials or the Dow Jones Transportation index have the largest fraction? **Dow Jones Industrials**

32. The Tampa Bay Buccaneers completed 18 passes out of 40 attempts. The Chicago Bears completed 14 out of 29. Which team had the greatest fractional part of attempted passes completed? **Bears**

33. Data from a recent *Environmental Almanac* indicates that Illinois was generating approximately 13,100,000 tons of waste per year, and of that amount, 786,000 tons were being recycled. Texas, on the other hand, was generating approximately 18,000,000 tons of waste per year, and of that amount, 1,440,000 million tons were being recycled. Which state had the higher recycling rate? **Texas**

13. $\frac{4}{5} > \frac{3}{5}$

14. $\frac{8}{13} < \frac{10}{13}$

15. $\frac{347}{498} > \frac{299}{498}$

16. $\frac{1}{4} > \frac{1}{5}$

17. $\frac{5}{8} > \frac{11}{18}$

18. $\frac{4}{9} < \frac{7}{12}$

19. $\frac{43}{45} < \frac{22}{23}$

20. $\frac{91}{97} > \frac{45}{49}$

21. $\frac{14}{19} > \frac{27}{37}$

22. $\frac{7}{15} < \frac{15}{31}$

23. $\frac{23}{25} < \frac{45}{49}$

24. $\frac{57}{59} < \frac{115}{119}$

25. $\frac{3}{11} < \frac{7}{23}$

26. $\frac{5}{34} > \frac{9}{67}$

27. $\frac{12}{17} > \frac{26}{37}$

28. $\frac{132}{235} > \frac{260}{463}$

WORKSHOP 12

3 ASSESS

Students may make errors in comparing fractions without common denominators. Review the process of finding a common denominator and changing the fractions to their equivalent forms. Emphasize that the whole number 1 can be expressed as a fraction in various ways, such as $\frac{12}{12}$ or $\frac{27}{27}$. How it is expressed depends on the value of the denominators in the fractions being compared.

With the shortcut method, review students' work to see that they are correctly multiplying the right pairs of numbers according to the formula given.

4 CLOSE

The Practice problems can be assigned for class work and the answers checked in class to help students master the objective of the lesson.

WRAP-UP

Go over any problem for which a wrong answer is given.

Assignment Guide
  Basic: 13–28
Average: 29–33

 20 min.

1 FOCUS

Objectives

1. To rename a fraction as a decimal.
2. To write a decimal as a percent.

2 TEACH

Remind students that fractions and decimals are names for numbers. For example, the fraction $\frac{1}{2}$ and the decimal 0.5 are just two different ways to name the number one-half.

Point out that $\frac{2}{4}$, $\frac{3}{6}$, $\frac{4}{8}$, and $\frac{5}{10}$ are also names for $\frac{1}{2}$. Names for numbers are called numerals.

The objectives of this workshop are (1) concerned with ways to convert from one numeral form (fraction) to another numeral form (decimal) and (2) to review the meaning of percent. For the second objective, use this example: if there are 100 people in a movie theater and 47 of them are females, then you can say that 47 percent are females. Ask students what percent are males. **53%**

Fraction to Decimal, Decimal to Percent

Need Help? Go to...
▶ Skill 14: Changing Fractions/Decimals, page 741

FRACTION AS DECIMAL Any fraction can be renamed as a decimal and any decimal can be renamed as a fraction. To rename a fraction as a decimal, use division. Think of the fraction bar in the fraction as meaning "divide by." For example, $\frac{5}{8}$ means "5 divided by 8." After the 5, you'll write a decimal point and as many zeros as are needed. Then divide by 8. If a fraction does not divide out evenly, divide to one more decimal place than you are rounding to.

Example 1

Change $\frac{5}{6}$ to a decimal rounded to the nearest thousandth. (Divide to the ten thousandths place.)

STEP: Change the fraction to a decimal and then round the decimal to the nearest thousandths place.

$$\frac{5}{6} \longrightarrow 6\overline{)5.0000} \qquad 0.8333 = 0.833 \text{ (rounded)}$$

CONCEPT CHECK

SELF-CHECK ✔

Complete the problems, then check your answers at the end of the book on page 802. Change the fractions to decimals. Round to the nearest thousandth. (Divide to the ten thousandths place.)

1. $\frac{3}{7}$ 0.4286 = 0.429

2. $\frac{7}{8}$ 0.875

RENAMING A DECIMAL AS A FRACTION To rename a decimal as a fraction, name the place value of the digit at the far right. This is the denominator of the fraction. Note that the number of zeros in the denominator is the same as the number of places to the right of the decimal point. The fraction should always be written in lowest terms.

Example 2

a. 0.79   b. 0.003   c. 4.625

STEP: Change each decimal to a fraction.

a. $0.79 = \frac{79}{100}$ (9 is in the hundredths place, so the denominator is 100.)

b. $0.003 = \frac{3}{1,000}$ (3 is in the thousandths place, so the denominator is 1,000.)

c. $4.625 = \frac{4,625}{1,000} = 4\frac{5}{8}$

CONCEPT CHECK

Complete the problems, then check your answers at the end of the book on page 802. Change the decimals to fractions reduced to lowest terms.

3. 0.4 $0.4 = \frac{4}{10} = \frac{2}{5}$

4. 7.82 $7\frac{82}{100} = 7\frac{41}{50}$

WORKSHOP NOTES

WRITING A PERCENT AS A DECIMAL **Percent** is an abbreviation of the Latin words *per centum,* meaning "by the hundred." So percent means "divide by 100." A percent can be written as a decimal. To change a percent to a decimal, first write the percent as a fraction with a denominator of 100, then divide by 100.

When dividing by 100, you can just move the decimal point two places to the left. So when you write a percent as a decimal, you are moving the decimal point two places to the left and dropping the percent sign (%). If necessary, use zero as a placeholder.

(Example 3)

Change each percent to a decimal.   **a. 42%**   **b. 19.4%**

STEP: Change each percent to a decimal.

   a. $42\% = \frac{42}{100} = \mathbf{0.42}$ **b.** $19.4\% = \frac{19.4}{100} = \mathbf{0.194}$

CONCEPT CHECK

Complete the problems, then check your answers at the end of the book on page 802. Change the percents to decimals.

5. 37.5% **0.375**   **6.** 9% **0.09**

WRITING A DECIMAL AS A PERCENT To write a decimal as a percent, move the decimal point two places to the right and add a percent sign (%).

(Example 4)

a. 0.42   **b. 0.005**

STEP: Change the decimals to percents.   **a.** 0.42 = 0.42 = **42%**
       Move decimal 2 places. Add % sign.   **b.** 0.005 = 0.005 = **0.5%**

CONCEPT CHECK

Complete the problems, then check your answers at the end of the book on page 802. Change the decimals to percents.

7. 0.85 **85%**   **8.** 0.07 **7%**   **9.** 0.3 **30%**   **10.** 1.55 **155%**

PRACTICE

Change the fractions to decimals. Round to the nearest thousandth.

11. $\frac{13}{50}$ **0.260**   **12.** $\frac{1}{2}$ **0.500**   **13.** $\frac{8}{9}$ **0.889**

Change the fractions to decimals. Round to the nearest hundredth.

14. $\frac{4}{5}$ **0.8**   **15.** $\frac{5}{9}$ **0.56**   **16.** $\frac{1}{3}$ **0.33**

Change the decimals to fractions reduced to lowest terms.

17. 0.375 $\frac{3}{8}$ **18.** 0.05 $\frac{1}{20}$ **19.** 14.35 $\frac{287}{20}$ **or** $14\frac{7}{20}$

Write as decimals.   **20.** 34% **0.34**   **21.** 817% **8.17** **22.** 1.1% **0.011**

Write as percents.   **23.** 0.35 **35%**   **24.** 0.016 **1.6% 25.** 4.125 **412.5%**

Workshop 13 Fraction to Decimal, Decimal to Percent ▶ **29**

WORKSHOP

3 ASSESS

When renaming a decimal as a fraction, students make errors by not using the correct denominator. Students make errors with percent because they do not understand the concept itself. After students work the Self-Check, ask them to explain how they got their answers. If a response is based only on a mechanical procedure of moving a decimal point or adding a percent sign, then ask why the answer is correct.

4 CLOSE

The Practice problems can be assigned for class work and the answers checked in class to help students master the objective of the lesson.

WRAP-UP

Ask a student to explain the meaning of a percent. Ask a few others to give some examples of changing a percent to a decimal.

Assignment Guide
   Basic: 11–19
   Average: 20–25

20 min.

1 FOCUS

Objectives

To find the percentage of a number.

2 TEACH

The words *percent* and *percentage* are often used by students interchangeably, but they do have different meanings. A percent is a ratio of two numbers while a percentage is a single number. A percentage is the result of finding a percent of a number.

Using Example 1, point out to students that since:

20% of 95 = **19**

19 has the same relationship to 95 that 20 has to 100; that is: $\frac{19}{95} = \frac{20}{100}$. This equation can be checked by cross multiplying:

$$19 \times 100 = 1,900$$
$$\text{or}$$
$$95 \times 20 = 1,900$$

Stress also that 20 percent means 20/100 and that 19 **(20% of 95)** is called the percentage.

WORKSHOP ▼ ▲ ▲ ▲ ▲

Finding a Percentage

Need Help? Go to...
➤ Skill 30: **Finding the Percentage,** page 757

FINDING A PERCENTAGE Finding a percentage means finding a percent of a number. To find a percent of a number, change the percent to a decimal and then multiply it by the number.

Example 1

What number is 20 percent of 95?

STEP: Write it out as an equation.

Let n stand for the unknown number.

$n = 20\% \times 95$ (In mathematics, *of* means "times" and *is* means "equals.")

$n = 0.20 \times 95$ (Change the percent to a decimal. Multiply.)

$n = 19$

Write the answer. 20% of 95 is **19**.

CONCEPT CHECK

SELF-CHECK ✔

Complete the problems, then check your answers at the end of the book on page 802. Find the percentage in Problems 1–4.

1. 40 percent of 70 **28**　　　　**2.** 25 percent of 120 **30**

3. 5 percent of 30 **1.5**　　　　**4.** 145 percent of 200 **290**

Example 2

The delivery charge is 7 percent of the selling price of $140.00. Find the delivery charge.

STEP: Write it out as an equation.

Let n stand for the unknown number.

$n = 7\% \times \$140$

$n = 0.07 \times \$140$

$n = \$9.80$

The delivery charge is $9.80.

WORKSHOP NOTES

_____

_____

_____

_____

_____

_____

_____

Example 3

A student had 85 percent correct out of 60 questions. How many answers were correct?

STEP: Write it out as an equation.

Let n stand for the unknown number.

$n = 85\% \times 60$

$n = 0.85 \times 60$

$n = 51$

There were 51 correct answers.

CONCEPT CHECK

Complete the problems, then check your answers at the end of the book on page 802.

5. The discount is 35 percent of the selling price of $70. Find the discount.
$24.50 discount
6. Your share of the crop of beans is 60 percent of the total. Find your share if the total is 95 tons. **57 tons**

PRACTICE

Find the percentage.

7. 20% of 54 **10.8**   8. 40% of 216 **86.4**

9. 42% of 335 **140.7**   10. 75% of 815 **611.25**

11. 32% of 315 **100.8**   12. 8% of 50 **4**

13. 4% of 95 **3.8**   14. 6% of 48 **2.88**

Round answers to the nearest cent.

15. 5.5% of $60 **$3.30**   16. 6% of $70 **$4.20**

17. 7.75% of $30 **$2.33**   18. 6.5% of $420 **$27.30**

19. 7.5% of $160 **$12.00**   20. 4.25% of $470 **$19.98**

21. 8.25% of $76 **$6.27**   22. 4.5% of $36 **$1.62**

23. When installing a sub-floor using 1-inch by 8-inch boards laid diagonally, 18 percent is allowed for waste. How many board feet will be wasted out of 1,350 board feet? **243 feet**

24. An electrical repair shop charges 37 percent of the cost of a new motor for rewinding the motor. If the motor costs $375 new, how much would the rewinding cost be? **$138.75**

Workshop 14 Finding a Percentage ▶ **31**

WORKSHOP 14

3 ASSESS

The types of errors students make when finding the percent of a number are either computational, that is they multiply incorrectly, or are errors resulting from putting the decimal point in the answer. Both types of errors are easy to identify and correct.

4 CLOSE

The Practice problems can be assigned for class work and the answers checked in class to help students master the objective of the lesson.

WRAP-UP

Ask students to find 15 percent of 250 and have a student show the solution at the board. Ask another student to name the percentage. **37.5**

Assignment Guide
  Basic: 7–22
  Average: 23–24

20 min.

WORKSHOP 15

① FOCUS

Objectives

1. To add numbers with the same sign.
2. To add numbers with different signs.
3. To find the absolute value of a number.
4. To find the opposite of a signed number.
5. To subtract signed numbers.

② TEACH

Draw a number line on the board. Write numbers from -5 to $+5$ on the number line. Explain that negative numbers have a value less than 0. They are located to the left of 0 on the number line. Positive numbers have a value greater than 0 and are located to the right of 0. Have students locate a few positive and negative numbers on the number line. Explain that positive and negative numbers are also called *signed numbers*.

Work through Example 1 in the text. Emphasize that to add two numbers with the same sign, just add the numbers. The sum will have the same sign as the numbers you added: $-8 + (-4) = -12$

Use the number line to demonstrate absolute value. For example, both -3 and $+3$ have the same absolute value. Ask students to explain why. Point out that absolute value is important when you add two numbers with different signs.

Work through Example 3. Point out that because the numbers you want to add have different signs, you must first find the absolute value of each number. Next, subtract the smaller number from the larger. Then give the answer the same sign as the number with the larger absolute value.

WORKSHOP

Negative Numbers— Adding and Subtracting

SIGNED NUMBERS Positive and negative numbers are often referred to as *signed numbers*. When adding signed numbers that have the same sign, add the two numbers and attach the same sign as the numbers being added.

Example 1

a. $4 + 2$ **b.** $-5 + (-3)$ **c.** $(-7.2) + (-4.5)$ **d.** $-\frac{1}{2} + (-\frac{3}{2})$

STEP: Add the numbers.

     a. $4 + 2 = 6$ **b.** $-5 + (-3) = -8$

     c. $(-7.2) + (-4.5) = -11.7$ **d.** $-\frac{1}{2} + (-\frac{3}{2}) = -\frac{4}{2} = -2$

CONCEPT CHECK

SELF-CHECK ✔

Complete the problems, then check your answers at the end of the book on page 803.

1. $6 + 10$ **2.** $-8 + (-4)$ **3.** $-12 + (-5.5)$ **4.** $-\frac{4}{5} + (-\frac{3}{5})$

          16   -12 -17.5 $-1\frac{2}{5}$

ABSOLUTE VALUE When adding signed numbers with different signs, you need to know the *absolute value* of the numbers. The absolute value of a number is its distance from zero on the number line. The symbol for absolute value is: $|\ \ |$

Example 2

What is the absolute value of -2?

STEP: Find the absolute value.

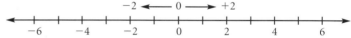

$$-2 \longleftarrow 0 \longrightarrow +2$$

$$-6 \quad -4 \quad -2 \quad 0 \quad 2 \quad 4 \quad 6$$

(Note: -2 is 2 units from zero on the number line.) Thus, $|-2|$ is **2**.

CONCEPT CHECK

SELF-CHECK ✔

Complete the problems, then check your answers at the end of the book on page 803. What is the absolute value of the following?

5. -4 **6.** -15 **7.** $+4$

    4   15   4

FINDING THE DIFFERENCE BETWEEN ABSOLUTE VALUES When you're adding two signed numbers with different signs, find the difference between the absolute values of the numbers. Give the answer the same sign as the number with the larger absolute value.

WORKSHOP NOTES

_____

_____

_____

_____

_____

_____

_____

Example 3

Add.

a. $-12 + 6$ **b.** $-7 + 15$

STEP: Add.

a. $-12 + 6$ ◄——The signs are different.——► **b.** $-7 + 15$
    $|-12| = 12$ ◄——Find the absolute value.——► $|-7| = 7$
    $12 - 6 = 6$ ◄——Subtract the smaller——► $15 - 7 = 8$
    number from the larger number.
    $-12 + 6 = -6$ ◄——Attach the sign of the——► $-7 + 15 = 8$
    number with the larger
    absolute value.

CONCEPT CHECK

Complete the problems, then check your answers at the end of the book on page 803.   **SELF-CHECK ✓**

8. $-21 + 8$ **−13**   **9.** $-23.5 + 21.2$ **−2.3** **10.** $\$15 + (-\$45)$ **−$30**

OPPOSITE OF A SIGNED NUMBER Subtracting signed numbers is based on knowing the opposite of a signed number. The opposite of -3 is $+3$ and the opposite of $+8$ is -8. To subtract signed numbers change the subtraction symbol to addition and add the opposite of the number being subtracted.

Example 4

Subtract.

a. $-5 - 7$ **b.** $-3 - (-9)$

STEP: Subtract.

a. $-5 - (+7)$ Change the subtraction   **b.** $-3 - (-9)$
            sign to addition and find
    $-5 + (-7)$ the opposite of $+7$ (it is -7) $-3 + 9$
            and -9 (it is $+9$).
    $-5 + (-7) = -12$ ◄——Follow the rules——► $-3 + 9 = 6$
            of addition.

CONCEPT CHECK

Complete the problems, then check your answers at the end of the book on page 803.   **SELF-CHECK ✓**

11. $10 - 12$ **−2**   **12.** $8 - 15$ **−7**   **13.** $-12 - (-3)$ **−9**   **14.** $9 - (-3)$ **12**

PRACTICE

15. $-3 + (-8)$ **−11**   **16.** $-8 + 3$ **−5**   **17.** $-3 + (-4)$ **−7**   **18.** $-12 + (-4)$ **−16**
19. $-15 + (-15)$ **−30**   **20.** $18 + (-18)$ **0**   **21.** $6 + (-4)$ **2**   **22.** $8 + (-5)$ **3**
23. $4 + (-8)$ **−4**   **24.** $-7 + (-5)$ **−12**   **25.** $16 + (-9)$ **7**   **26.** $-12 + 8$ **−4**

27. The record high temperature of $134°F$ was recorded in Death Valley, California, in 1913. The record low was $-80°F$ at Prospect Creek, Alaska, in 1971. What is the difference between the highest and lowest temperatures? **214° F**

28. At 2:00 A.M., a plant worker found that a dial was reading 12.0. At 3:00 A.M., she found that the reading had changed to -3.0. Find the difference between these two readings. **15**

Workshop 15 Negative Numbers—Adding and Subtracting ▶ **33**

Work through Example 4:
  $-5 - 7$
  $-5 - (+7)$ Identify the sign of the number being subtracted. **(7 is positive.)**
  Change subtraction symbol to addition.
  $-5 + (-7)$ Find the opposite of the number being subtracted. The opposite of $(+7)$ is (-7).
  $-5 + (-7) = -12$

③ ASSESS

When subtracting numbers with different signs, as in $-6 - 2$, students may confuse the subtraction symbol and think it means that the number 2 is negative, when in fact, 2 is positive. To avoid confusion, first rewrite the problem showing the sign of the number being subtracted: $-6 - (+2)$. Then change the subtraction symbol to an addition symbol: $-6 + (+2)$, and change the sign of the number being subtracted to its opposite: $-6 + (-2)$. **$-6 + (-2) = -8$**

④ CLOSE

The Practice problems can be assigned for class work and the answers checked in class to help students master the objective of the lesson.

WRAP-UP

Go over any problem for which a wrong answer is given.

Assignment Guide
  Basic: 15–26
  Average: 27–28

20 min.

WORKSHOP 16

1 FOCUS

Objectives

To find the average or mean of a group of numbers.

2 TEACH

Work through the four examples with students so that they understand how to find the average of a group of numbers. Then ask students to think about what an average represents. In other words, for Example 1, what meaning can be given to the statement that the average of: 7, 9, 4, 6, and 4 is **6**.

Arrange the numbers in numerical order as 4, 4, 6, 7, 9, and point out that 7 and 9 are greater than 6, and 4 is less than 6, thus, 6 is somewhere in the middle of the group. Tell students that the average, or mean, is a number that represents the middle, or center, of a group of numbers. Use Examples 2, 3, and 4 to show that the average may not always be one of the numbers in the group, as it is in Example 1.

WORKSHOP

Need Help? Go to...
► **Application Q:**
Mean, page 770

Average (Mean)

FINDING THE AVERAGE The average, or mean, is a single number used to represent a group of numbers. The average of two or more numbers is the sum of the numbers divided by the number of items added.

Example 1

Find the average of 7, 9, 4, 6, and 4.

STEP 1: Find the average.

$$\frac{7 + 9 + 4 + 6 + 4}{5} = \frac{30}{5} = 6$$

(Add to find the total. Divide by the number of items.)

Example 2

Find the average of 693, 367, 528, and 626.

STEP: Find the average.

$$\frac{693 + 367 + 528 + 626}{4} = \frac{2,214}{4} = 553.5$$

Example 3

Find the average of 5.7, 6.3, 4.2, 5.8, and 3.4.

STEP: Find the average. Round to the nearest tenth.

$$\frac{5.7 + 6.3 + 4.2 + 5.8 + 3.4}{5} = \frac{25.4}{5} = 5.08 \text{ or } 5.1$$

Example 4

Find the average of $17, $24, $38, $23, $19, and $26.

STEP: Find the average. Round to the nearest dollar.

$$\frac{\$17 + \$24 + \$38 + \$23 + \$19 + \$26}{6} = \frac{\$147}{6} = \$24.5 \text{ or } \$25$$

CONCEPT CHECK

SELF-CHECK ✓

Complete the problems, then check your answers at the end of book on page 803. Find the average for each set of numbers. Round to the nearest cent.

1. 3, 6, 2, 5, 8, 6 **5**

2. 3.2, 1.8, 6.5, 8.1, 5.9 **5.1**

3. 134, 126, 130 **130**

4. $25, $37, $49, $53, $42, $42 **$41.33**

WORKSHOP NOTES

PRACTICE

Find the average for each group.

5. 7, 8, 9, 12, 14 **10**

6. 4, 6, 10, 12, 8 **8**

7. 70, 85, 90, 75 **80**

8. 44, 86, 35, 95 **65**

9. 197, 108, 115 **140**

10. 225, 432, 321 **326**

11. 776, 709, 754, 733 **743**

12. 526, 387, 431, 388 **433**

13. 2.4, 3.5, 4.7, 2.9, 8.4 **4.38**

14. 6.8, 5.6, 3.4, 2.5, 4.7 **4.6**

15. 1.4, 2.5, 4.8, 3.7, 2.0, 3.9 **3.05**

16. 8.1, 5.3, 3.6, 7.9, 4.6, 3.2 **5.45**

17. $14, $12, $16, $14, $15 **$14.20**

18. $64, $38, $92, $51, $65 **$62**

Find the average for each group. Round to the amount indicated.

19. 7.8, 6.3, 8.3, 4.9, 7.7, 6.9, 5.1 (nearest tenth) **6.7**

20. 9.2, 7.6, 8.2, 5.9, 9.5, 7.8 (nearest tenth) **8.0**

21. 31.7, 33.9, 36.1, 33.8 (nearest tenth) **33.9**

22. 4.37, 3.74, 4.90, 5.74 (nearest hundredth) **4.69**

23. 34.87, 42.90, 46.21, 36.34, 39.89 (nearest hundredth) **40.04**

24. $37.50, $44.50, $39.65, $34.25, $15.61, $11.22 (nearest cent) **$30.46**

25. Ben Agars had bowling scores of 175, 132, and 142. What was his average? **150**

26. Latoya Miller recorded her pulse rate on four occasions as follows: 68, 85, 77, and 82. What was her average pulse rate? **78**

27. Rachel Kelley's tips from being a bellhop were $4.00, $2.00, $3.50, $1.00, $4.00, $2.00, $1.00, and $3.00. What was her average tip? **$2.56**

28. During a 6-day period in June, you earned an average of $25 a day for mowing lawns. What were your total earnings? **$150.00**

29. Last year, Andre Barsotti's telephone bills averaged $35.45 a month. What was his total bill for the year? **$425.40**

30. Hung Lee had an average grade of 92 on his first 4 business math tests. He had a 95 and a 98 on the next two tests. What was his average grade for the 6 tests? **93.5**

31. Carlita Cruz recorded her math test scores this quarter. What was her average? **85**

Test Number	1	2	3	4	5	6	7	8
Score	87	75	98	95	82	77	78	88

32. What does she need on the next test to have an average of 86? **94**

33. If there are a total of ten 100-point tests for the quarter, is it possible for her to raise her average to 90? **No**

③ ASSESS

Few students should make errors with computing average after working through the examples. Any errors that are made can usually be traced to carelessness. For example, students may miscount the number of numbers in the group and thus divide by the wrong number, or they make careless errors in addition. Emphasize the importance of being organized and orderly when doing mathematics.

④ CLOSE

The Practice problems can be assigned for class work and the answers checked in class to help students master the objective of the lesson.

WRAP-UP

Use Problem 21 to summarize the concept of an average and how it is computed.

Assignment Guide
  Basic: 5–24
  Average: 25–30

20 min.

WORKSHOP 17

Elapsed Time

CALCULATING ELAPSED TIME To find elapsed time, subtract the earlier time from the later time.

Need Help? Go to...
▸ **Application F: Elapsed Time (Hours)**, page 764

WORKSHOP

1 FOCUS

Objectives

To find elapsed time.

2 TEACH

Use a clock face to review the hours shown in 1 complete revolution of the hour hand from 12 to 12. Then discuss the 24-hour clock by using these examples: 1 P.M. is 12 + 1 **(or 13)** and is called 1,300 hours.

The 24-hour clock will help students understand how to find elapsed time when the time period spans 1 o'clock. Ask students to give the 24-hour clock time for 2 A.M., 5 A.M., 7 P.M., and 11 A.M.

Example 1

Find the elapsed time for someone who worked from:

a. 2:15 P.M. to 10:30 P.M.   **b.** 6:45 A.M. to 12:56 P.M.

STEP: Subtract.

a.	10:30	b.	12:56
	− 2:15		− 6:45
	8:15 or 8 hours, 15 minutes; written as **8 h:15 min**		6:11 or 6 hours, 11 minutes; written as **6 h:11 min**

CONCEPT CHECK

SELF-CHECK ✔

Complete the problems, then check your answers at the end of the book on page 803. Find the elapsed time for a person who worked from:

1. 9:15 A.M. to 11:15 A.M. **2 h:0 min**   **2.** 8:30 A.M. to 11:50 A.M. **3 h:20 min**

3. 1:45 P.M. to 8:50 P.M. **7 h:5 min**   **4.** 3:10 P.M. to 11:15 P.M. **8 h:5 min**

You cannot subtract 45 minutes from 30 minutes unless you borrow an hour and add it to the 30 minutes. Remember that 1 hour = 60 minutes.

Example 2

Find the elapsed time from 1:45 P.M. to 8:30 P.M.

STEP: Subtract and add.

$$8:30 = 7:30 + :60 = 7:90 \text{ borrowed 1 hour}$$
$$- 1:45 = -1:45 = -1:45$$
$$6:45 \text{ or } \mathbf{6 \text{ h:45 min}}$$

CONCEPT CHECK

SELF-CHECK ✔

Complete the problems, then check your answers at the end of the book on page 803. Find the elapsed time for a person who worked from:

5. 8:45 A.M. to 12:30 P.M. **3 h:45 min**   **6.** 2:50 P.M. to 10:20 P.M. **7 h:30 min**

7. 9:25 A.M. to 11:10 A.M. **1 h:45 min**   **8.** 1:25 P.M. to 11:15 P.M. **9 h:50 min**

WORKSHOP NOTES

To find elapsed time when the time period spans 1:00 o'clock, add 12 hours to the later time before subtracting.

Example 3

Find the elapsed time from 10:20 A.M. to 3:30 P.M.

STEP: Subtract and add.

$$
\begin{array}{rcl}
3:30 = & (12 + 3) + :30 = & 15:30 \\
-10:20 = & -10:20 & = -10:20 \\
\hline
& & 5:10 \text{ or } \textbf{5 h:10 min}
\end{array}
$$

CONCEPT CHECK

Complete the problems, then check your answers at the end of this book on page 803. Find the elapsed time for a person who worked from:

SELF-CHECK ✓

9. 8:30 A.M. to 4:30 P.M. **8 h:0 min**   10. 9:15 A.M. to 5:30 P.M. **8 h:15 min**

11. 7:45 A.M. to 4:00 P.M. **8 h:15 min**   12. 9:25 P.M. to 6:15 A.M. **8 h:50 min**

PRACTICE

Find the elapsed time for a person who worked from:

13. 4:30 P.M. to 11:45 P.M. **7 h:15 min**   14. 6:30 A.M. to 11:45 A.M. **5 h:15 min**

15. 4:15 P.M. to 10:10 P.M. **5 h:55 min**   16. 7:43 A.M. to 10:40 A.M. **2 h:57 min**

17. 8:00 A.M. to 4:30 P.M. **8 h:30 min**   18. 9:15 A.M. to 6:25 P.M. **9 h:10 min**

Find the elapsed time.

19. From 7:35 A.M. to 11:28 A.M.   20. From 2:50 A.M. to 11:05 A.M. **8 h:15 min**
    3 h:53 min

21. From 6:20 P.M. to 11:05 P.M.   22. From 1:37 A.M. to 9:28 A.M. **7 h:51 min**
    4 h:45 min

23. Samaki Watson worked from 9:45 A.M. to 6:12 P.M. How long did he work? **8 h:27 min**

24. Helene Angell took a bus that left Detroit at 9:25 A.M. and arrived in Chicago at 3:20 P.M. How long was the trip? (Disregard time zones.) **5 h:55 min**

25. Tom Henry started mowing his lawn at 10:45 A.M. and finished at 3:15 P.M. If he took one hour off for lunch, how much time did he spend mowing his lawn? **3 h:30 min**

26. Boyson's opened at 7:00 A.M. on Sunday, December 23 and did not close until 6:00 P.M. on Monday, December 24. How many hours straight did Boyson's stay open? **35 h:0 min**

27. Ashilla Grant started her actuarial exam at 9:45 A.M. and worked on it for $6\frac{1}{2}$ hours. What time did she finish? **4:15 P.M.**

Workshop 17 Elapsed Time ▶ **37**

③ **ASSESS**

The computations in this lesson are straightforward. Students will make the usual errors in subtraction, but the major problems with finding elapsed time are conceptual. Students may not understand the need to borrow 1 hour (60 minutes) in certain problems, or they may not use the 24-hour clock correctly. Both problems can be overcome with practice.

④ **CLOSE**

The Practice problems can be assigned for class work and the answers checked in class to help students master the objective of the lesson.

WRAP-UP

Work Problems 13 and 23 to summarize the objective of this workshop.

Assignment Guide
Basic: 13–22
Average: 23–25

20 min.

1 FOCUS

Objectives

1. To read a table or chart.
2. To classify an item in a table or chart.

2 TEACH

Discuss the meanings of the terms *column* and *row*. Stress that a column goes down a page and a row goes across a page. **You might want to tell students that a column runs "north to south" on a page and a row runs "east to west." These directional ideas can help students remember the difference between a column and a row.**

WORKSHOP

Reading Tables and Charts

> Need Help? Go to...
> ► Application C: Tables and Charts, page 762

READING A TABLE To read a table or chart, find the column containing one of the pieces of information you have. Look across the row containing the other piece of information. Read down the column and across the row. You'll find the information you need where the column and row cross.

Example 1

Any fraction of a pound over the weight shown takes the next higher rate. What is the cost to ship a 10-lb package to Rate Group D? (Use Figure W18.1.)

Figure W18.1

Table 1b: Postal Rates

Weight Not Over (lb)	Rate Groups							
	A	B	C	D	E	F	G	H
1.0	$36	$38	$ 44	$ 48	$ 59	$ 52	$ 55	$ 82
2.0	41	45	51	55	72	60	58	96
3.0	44	51	58	64	86	67	63	109
4.0	47	55	65	71	100	73	70	120
5.0	50	60	72	78	113	80	77	134
6.0	52	63	77	85	126	85	84	146
7.0	55	66	81	91	138	91	91	158
8.0	57	71	86	98	150	96	98	170
9.0	59	74	91	105	163	101	105	182
10.0	62	77	95	111	177	107	112	190
11.0	64	80	100	116	187	112	118	206
12.0	66	83	104	122	197	116	123	218
13.0	69	86	107	127	207	120	129	230
14.0	71	88	111	132	217	124	134	241
15.0	73	91	114	137	229	131	139	253

Source: USPS International Postal Rates and Fees Publication 51

STEP 1: Find the Rate Group D column.

STEP 2: Find the 10-lb row.

STEP 3: Read across the 10-lb row to the Rate Group D column. **The cost is $111.**

CONCEPT CHECK

SELF-CHECK✓

Complete the problems, then check your answers at the end of the book on page 803. Find the cost to ship each package to the indicated Rate Group in Figure W18.1.

1. 1 lb, Rate Group A **$36**   **2.** 1 lb, Rate Group G **$55**

3. 10 lb, Rate Group F **$107**   **4.** 13.2 lb, Rate Group C **$111**

CLASSIFYING AN ITEM To classify an item, find the row that contains the known data. Then read the classification from the head of the column.

WORKSHOP NOTES

Size Chart—Men's Sizes

Figure W18.2

Suits and Sport Coats Sizes 36 to 46 Order by chest size. Be sure waist will fit comfortably.	Order Size	36	37	38	39	40	42	44	46
	If chest is (inches)	35–36	36–37	37–38	38–39	39–40	41–42	43–44	45–46
	And waist is (inches)	28–31	29–32	30–33	31–34	32–35	34–37	36–39	38–41
Jackets Sizes 36 to 46 Order by chest size.	Order Size	36		38		40	42	44	46
	If chest is (inches)	$34\frac{1}{2}$–36		$36\frac{1}{2}$–38		$38\frac{1}{2}$–40	$40\frac{1}{2}$–42	$42\frac{1}{2}$–44	$44\frac{1}{2}$–46

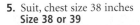
Example 2

What size suit should a man with a 41-inch chest order?

STEP 1: Find the Suits and Sport Coats section.

STEP 2: Find the row "if chest is (inches)."

STEP 3: Read across the row to 41–42.

STEP 4: Read the number at the head of the column (42).

   A man with a 41-inch chest should order a size 42 suit.

CONCEPT CHECK

Complete the problems, then check your answers at the end of the book on page 803. Determine what size garment should be ordered.

SELF-CHECK ✔

5. Suit, chest size 38 inches
   Size 38 or 39

6. Jacket, chest size 41 inches
   Size 42

PRACTICE

Use Figure W18.1 to find the cost to ship each package to the indicated Rate Group.

7. 6 lb, Rate Group E
   $126
8. 2 lb, Rate Group B
   $45
9. 11 lb, Rate Group E
   $187
10. 9 lb, Rate Group H
   $182
11. 12 lb, Rate Group C
   $104
12. 9 lb, Rate Group A
   $59
13. 6.5 lb, Rate Group D
   $91
14. 9.75 lb, Rate Group F
   $107
15. 11.2 lb, Rate Group G
   $123
16. 2.6 lb, Rate Group B
   $51
17. 1.35 lb, Rate Group D
   $55
18. 0.75 lb, Rate Group H
   $82

Use Figure W18.1 to determine the maximum weight a package can weigh.

	Shipping to Rate Group	Shipping Cost	Maximum Weight
19. a.	A	$ 66	**12.0 lb**
b.	B	51	**3.0 lb**
c.	C	100	**11.0 lb**
d.	D	85	**6.0 lb**
e.	F	207	**13.0 lb**
f.	F	52	**1.0 lb**

Use Figure W18.2 to determine what size garment should be ordered.

	Chest Size (inches)	Waist Size (inches)	Suit Order Size	Jacket Order Size
20. a.	37	30	**37 or 38**	**38**
b.	42	35	**42**	**42**
c.	45	39	**46**	**46**
d.	36	32	**37**	**36**
e.	40	35	**40**	**40**
f.	38	34	**39**	**38**

21. What size of suit should a man with a 36-inch chest and a 31-inch waist order? **Size 36 or 37**

22. What size of suit should a man with a 39-inch chest and a 33-inch waist order? **Size 39 or 40**

Workshop 18 Reading Tables and Charts ▶ **39**

3 **ASSESS**

Typical problems involve reading information from the wrong column or row or reading the wrong crossing point. Emphasize the need to be careful when reading data in a table or chart. Have students use a ruler or straight edge when reading across or down a row.

4 **CLOSE**

The Practice problems can be assigned for class work and the answers checked in class to help students master the objective of the lesson.

WRAP-UP

Use Problem 7 to illustrate and review the objective of the workshop.

Assignment Guide
   Basic: 7–18
   Average: 19–20

20 min.

WORKSHOP 19

① FOCUS

Objectives

1. To identify the parts of a graph.
2. To read data contained on a bar graph, pie chart, and a line graph.
3. To interpret data from a graph.

② TEACH

Work through Example 1 with students. Point out that a graph can present a great deal of information in a concise way. Emphasize that in addition to presenting information, graphs also allow for a quick comparison of data. Furthermore, graphs can help you draw conclusions from the data presented.

Ask students what general conclusion can be made about the number of robberies in California from Years A–K. **(The number of robberies declined.)** Graphs, however, have some limitations. Point out that it is unlikely that exactly 60,000 robberies occurred in each of the last 3 years represented on the graph. Ask students why they think the graph depicts the statistics for these years as if they were exactly the same. **(The large scale of the bar graph makes it hard to distinguish small differences in number of robberies.)**

Ask students to identify the type of each of the three remaining graphs. Explain that IPO stands for Initial Public Offering, the date a stock first becomes available for purchase by the public. Point out that a pie chart differs from a bar graph and a line graph in that it is a circle. A pie chart is particularly useful when representing a part of a whole, in this case, the percent of the top IPO stock for a specific year. The key indicates what each slice of the pie represents. The percent indicates how large each slice is.

40

Reading Graphs

Need Help? Go to...
▶ Application M: Reading Bar Graphs, page 767
▶ Application N: Reading Line Graphs, page 768

VISUAL READING Many mathematical applications are related to graphs. There are many different types of graphs including bar graphs, pie charts, and line graphs. Being able to analyze the information contained within a graph helps to make deductions and to interpret data. Because there are many different parts to a graph, identifying each part can help to answer questions related to the graph.

Example 1

Answer the questions about the graph.

a. What type of graph is shown?
b. What is the title of the graph?
c. What does the vertical axis represent?
d. In what year did the most robberies occur?
e. In which year did more robberies occur: Year J or Year K?

Figure W19.1

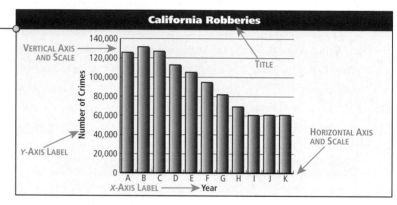

STEP: Read and follow the directions.

a. A bar graph is shown. (It displays data and compares facts in a vertical or horizontal format.)
b. The title of the graph is California Robberies.
c. The vertical axis represents the number of crimes committed.
d. Most of the robberies occurred in Year B. (This is determined by looking at the bar that is the tallest.)
e. Just by looking at the graph, it is difficult to determine in which year more robberies occurred. (The scale is so large that a small difference in numbers is difficult to distinguish.)

WORKSHOP NOTES

CONCEPT CHECK

Complete the problems, then check your answers at the end of the book on page 803. Answer the questions about Figure W19.1. SELF-CHECK ✓

1. What year had the fewest robberies? **Year I. Look at the bars for the shortest bar.**

2. Did twice as many robberies occur in Year I as in Year A? **No.**

3. About how many robberies occurred in Year K? **Just over 60,000. Look at the height of the bar and then look at the vertical scale.**

PRACTICE

Use Figure W19.2 to answer Problems 4–6.

4. What was the top Initial Public Offering (IPO) stock? **Kraft**

5. What two IPOs had about the same performance? **Statoil ASA and Prudential**

6. If the total revenue generated by the IPOs was $20 million, how much was generated by Kraft Foods? **$8.6 million**

Figure W19.2

Top IPOs
- 43% KPMG Consulting
- 18% Statoil ASA
- 15% Prudential Financial
- 14% Agere Systems
- 10% Kraft Foods

Use Figure W19.3 for Problems 7–10.

7. Which industry employed the most people? **service**

8. In which industry were there about 20 million people employed? **government**

9. Which industry had about 18 million people employed? **manufacturing**

10. Estimate the number of Retail Trade employees. **about 23 million**

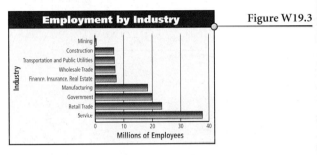
Figure W19.3

Employment by Industry

Industry: Mining, Construction, Transportation and Public Utilities, Wholesale Trade, Finance, Insurance, Real Estate, Manufacturing, Government, Retail Trade, Service — Millions of Employees (0, 10, 20, 30, 40)

Use Figure W19-4 for Problems 11–16.

11. Which year had the lowest stock price? **J**

12. Estimate the lowest stock price. **$40**

13. What year showed the highest stock price? **H**

14. Estimate the highest stock price. **$140**

15. Estimate how much the stock declined from Year H to Year J. **$100**

16. Estimate the stock price in Year A. **$110**

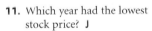
Figure W19.4

Year-End Closing Stock Price
(Adjusted for stock splits)

Stock Price (0, 20, 40, 60, 80, 100, 120, 140, 160) — Year (A, B, C, D, E, F, G, H, I, J, K)

Workshop 19 Reading Graphs ▶ **41**

WRAP-UP

Go over any problem for which a wrong answer is given.

Assignment Guide
   Basic: 4–10
   Average: 11–16

20 min.

WORKSHOP 19

Have students look at the bar graph on Employment by Industry. Ask how it differs from the bar graph on California robberies. **(The numbers—millions of employees—are represented horizontally on the x-axis, not vertically.)**

As students look at the line graph on the Year-End Closing Stock Price, point out its similarity to a bar graph in that both graphs have x- and y-axes. The line graph is particularly good at illustrating the fluctuating price of one stock. A bar graph would be better if you wanted to compare the price of several stocks in the same year.

③ ASSESS

If students have difficulty reading the graphs, review the parts of a graph. Explain that the main title reveals the general subject. In bar graphs and line graphs, the titles of the x- and y-axes tell what kind of information is being presented. One axis represents numbers as an amount of something—number of robberies, number of employees in millions, number of dollars per share of stock. The other axis represents things being compared—such as specific years or specific industries. When a bar graph represents a number between two line indicators, remind students to find the halfway point between indicators and estimate numbers from that point.

④ CLOSE

The Practice problems can be assigned for class work and the answers checked in class to help students master the objective of the lesson.

1 FOCUS

Objectives

1. To construct a vertical bar graph.
2. To construct a line graph.

2 TEACH

Use the example to review the procedure for constructing a vertical bar graph. Then have students work the Self-Check Problem 1 independently.

Ask a few students to reproduce their graphs on the board. Discuss what the graphs show and their value in comparing data. **(It's easy to see the comparisons in the data when the information is presented in graph form.)** Repeat the above procedure for constructing a line graph.

WORKSHOP ▲ ▲ ▲

Constructing Graphs

Need Help? Go to...
▶ **Application M:** Reading Bar Graphs, page 767
▶ **Application N:** Reading Line Graphs, page 768

BAR GRAPH A **bar graph** is a picture that displays and compares numerical facts in the form of vertical or horizontal bars. To construct a vertical bar graph, follow these steps:
• Draw the vertical y-axis and the horizontal x-axis.
• Scale the vertical axis to correspond to the given data. Draw one bar to represent each quantity.
• Label each bar and the vertical and horizontal axes and title the graph.

Example 1

Construct a vertical bar graph of the given data.

Metropolitan Statistical Areas

City	Population (in millions)
Chicago, Illinois	9.1
San Francisco, California	7.0
Detroit, Michigan	5.5
Washington, D.C.	5.0

STEP: Construct a vertical bar graph.
a. Draw vertical and horizontal axes.
b. Scale the vertical axis.

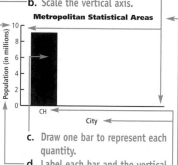

c. Draw one bar to represent each quantity.
d. Label each bar and the vertical and horizontal axes.
e. Title the graph.

1.

Metropolitan Statistical Areas

CONCEPT CHECK

SELF-CHECK✔

Complete the problem, then check your answer at the end of the book on page 803.

1. Complete construction of the vertical bar graph started in Example 1.

LINE GRAPH A **line graph** is a picture used to compare data over a period of time. It is an excellent way to show trends (increases or decreases). To construct a line graph, follow these steps:
• Draw the vertical and horizontal axes.
• Scale the vertical axis to correspond to the given data.
• Label the axes.
• Place a point on the graph to correspond to each item of data.
• Connect the points from left to right.
• Title the graph.

WORKSHOP NOTES

_____

_____

_____

_____

_____

_____

_____

(Example 2)

Construct a line graph of the given data.

Computer Classes	
Year	**Enrollment**
A	30
B	38
C	60
D	90
E	100

2.

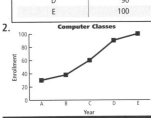
Computer Classes

STEP: Construct a line graph.
a. Draw vertical and horizontal axes.
b. Scale the vertical axis.

Computer Classes

c. Label the axes.
d. Place a point to correspond to each item of data.
e. Connect the points from left to right.
f. Title the line graph.

CONCEPT CHECK

Complete the problem, then check your answer at the end of the book on page 803.

(SELF-CHECK ✔)

2. Complete construction of the line graph started in Example 2.

PRACTICE

Construct vertical bar graphs of the given data.

3.

World Population	
Country	**Millions of People**
Brazil	173
China	1,262
India	1,014
Indonesia	225
Russia	146
United States	276

4.

Department Store	
Department	**Total Sales by Department**
Children's clothing	$145
Housewares	82
Women's clothing	120
Men's clothing	112
Appliances	75
Dishes	130

Construct line graphs for the given data.

5.

Trade with Advanced Technology	
Month	**Millions of Dollars**
January	18.4
February	18.1
March	20.6
April	16.6
May	17.2
June	17.7
July	15.0
August	15.7
September	14.8
October	15.7
November	14.9

6.

Coffee Beans	
Month	**Closing Stock Price**
January	$24.97
February	23.81
March	21.22
April	19.35
May	19.52
June	23.00
July	18.04
August	16.87
September	14.94
October	17.12
November	17.72
December	19.05

Workshop 20 Constructing Graphs ▶ **43**

5. **Trade with Advanced Technology**

6. **Coffee Beans Closing Stock Prices**

WRAP-UP

Discuss the steps involved in constructing bar graphs and line graphs.

Assignment Guide
 Basic: 3–4
 Average: 5–6

20 min.

(3) **ASSESS**

Students enjoy drawing graphs, but they tend to have difficulty deciding upon an appropriate scale to use. The choice of a scale depends upon the given data. Point out that the scale chosen must allow all the data to be represented on the graph and that it should be convenient to use. By having students draw their graphs on the board, you can analyze the scales used and guide students in understanding how to select a scale that works well.

Remind students to title their graphs. Titles should be short but accurate in describing the data graphed.

(4) **CLOSE**

The Practice problems can be assigned for class work and the answers checked in class to help students master the objectives of the lesson.

3.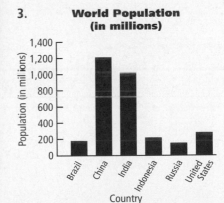
World Population (in millions)

4.
Department Store Total Sales By Department

1 FOCUS

Objectives

To convert from one unit of measure to another.

2 TEACH

Discuss the units of measure in both the U.S. Customary System and the metric system. Be sure to point out that none of the symbols for the units of measure use periods. However, the symbol for inch can use a period (*in.*) to avoid confusion in certain situations. After working through the examples, ask students why it is necessary to multiply when converting to a smaller unit. **(The number of smaller units is greater than the given larger unit.)** Ask why it is necessary to divide when converting to a larger unit. **The number of larger units is less than the given smaller unit.**

Units of Measurement

DIMENSIONAL ANALYSIS Below are the abbreviations and conversions for units of measure in the U.S. Customary System.

Length	Volume	Weight
12 inches (in) = 1 foot (ft)	2 cups (c) = 1 pint (pt)	16 ounces (oz) =
3 feet (ft) = 1 yard (yd)	2 pt = 1 quart (qt)	1 pound (lb)
5,280 ft = 1 mile (mi)	4 qt = 1 gallon (gal)	2,000 lb = 1 ton (t)

Below are the symbols and conversions for units of measure in the metric system.

Length	Volume
1,000 millimeters (mm) = 1 meter (m)	1,000 milliliters (mL) = 1 liter (L)
100 centimeters (cm) = 1 m	**Mass**
1,000 m = 1 kilometer (km)	1,000 grams (g) = 1 kilogram (kg)

To convert from one unit of measure to another, use the conversion lists above. When converting to a smaller unit, multiply.

Example 1

Convert 6 feet to inches.

STEP: Convert. (Note: Use 12 in = 1 ft) $6 \times 12 = 72$ **6 ft = 72 in**

Example 2

Convert 2 meters to centimeters.

STEP: Convert. (Note: Use 100 cm = 1 m) $2 \times 100 = 200$ **2 m = 200 cm**

Example 3

Convert 12 pints to quarts. (When converting to a larger unit, divide.)

STEP: Convert. (Note: Use 2 pt = 1 qt) $12 \div 2 = 6$ **12 pt = 6 qt**

Example 4

Convert 8,400 grams to kilograms.

STEP: Convert. (Note: Use 1,000 g = 1 kg) $8,400 \div 1,000 = 8.4$

8,400 g = 8.4 kg

CONCEPT CHECK

SELF-CHECK✔

Complete the problems, then check your answers at the end of the book on page 803. Convert.

1. 9 ft to inches **108 in**
2. 0.15 L to milliliters **150 ml**
3. 24 ft to yards **8 yd**
4. 350 cm to meters **3.5 m**

WORKSHOP NOTES

PRACTICE

Do the following conversions.

5. 9 yd to feet	**6.** 14 gal to quarts	**7.** 7 lb to ounces
8. 3 ft to inches	**9.** 6 lb to ounces	**10.** 4 L to milliliters
11. 3.8 km to meters	**12.** 16 pt to cups	**13.** 3.2 kg to grams
14. 96 in to yards	**15.** 9 qt to gallons	**16.** 42 oz to pounds
17. 14 qt to gallons	**18.** 33 oz to pounds	**19.** 2,000 g to kilograms
20. 90 cm to meters	**21.** 3,300 mL to liters	**22.** 450 cm to meters
23. 72.1 kg to grams	**24.** 3.4 L to milliliters	**25.** 723 g to kilograms
26. 11.316 mL to liters	**27.** 18 cm to millimeters	**28.** 383.2 cm to meters
29. 1 yd 4 in to inches	**30.** 4 ft 2 in to inches	**31.** 5 qt 1 pt to pints
32. 3 lb 7 oz to ounces	**33.** 2 gal 2 qt to quarts	**34.** 2 yd 2 ft 2 in to inches

35. How many quarts will a 5-gallon plastic bag hold? **20 qt**

36. How many milliliters will a 1-liter bottle hold? **1,000 mL**

37. How many cups of coffee does a 2-quart coffee pot hold? **8 c**

38. How many cups of hot chocolate will a 2-gallon thermos jug hold? **32 c**

39. How many inches long is a $6\frac{2}{3}$-yard roll of aluminium foil? **240 in**

40. Cottage cheese is sold in 1-pint containers. How many pints must be bought to have enough for a recipe that calls for 5 cups? **3**

41. James Hartman knows that his jogging stride is about 1 meter long. The jogging track he uses is 3.9 kilometers long. How many strides does it take him to go around the track once? **3,900**

42. The cafeteria receives 32 cases of milk each day. Each case contains 24 half-pint cartons. How many gallons of milk are received each day? **48 gal**

43. A soft drink is sold in 355 milliliter cans. How many liters are in a six-pack? **2.13 L**

44. Enrique Diaz, a pastry chef, baked a walnut cake weighing 2.4 kilograms. How many 75-gram servings can be cut from the cake? **32 servings**

45. Lakita Moore ordered baseboard moulding for the rooms of a new house. Moore needs to complete this chart to determine the total number of feet of moulding needed. How much moulding is needed?

	Length	Width	2 Lengths	+	2 Widths	=	Perimeter
	12 ft	9 ft	24 ft	+	18 ft	=	42 ft
a.	10 ft	8 ft	20 ft	+	16 ft	=	36 ft
b.	18 ft	24 ft	36 ft	+	48 ft	=	84 ft
c.	10 ft 6 in	9 ft 4 in	21 ft	+	18 ft 8 in	=	39 ft 8 in
d.	11 ft 3 in	7 ft 8 in	22 ft 6 in	+	15 ft 4 in	=	37 ft 10 in
e.	11 ft 4 in	13 ft 2 in	22 ft 8 in	+	26 ft 4 in	=	49 ft
f.	17 ft 8 in	12 ft 9 in	35 ft 4 in	+	25 ft 6 in	=	60 ft 10 in
g.	8 ft 5 in	7 ft 9 in	16 ft 10 in	+	15 ft 6 in	=	32 ft 4 in
						Total	381 ft 8 in

Workshop 21 Units of Measurement ▶ **45**

Answers (right column)

5. 27 ft
6. 56 qt
7. 112 oz
8. 36 in
9. 96 oz
10. 4,000 mL
11. 3,800 m
12. 32 c
13. 3,200 g
14. 2.7 yd
15. 2.25 gal
16. 2.625 lb
17. 3.5 gal
18. 2.0625 lb
19. 2 kg
20. 0.9 m
21. 3.3 L
22. 4.5 m
23. 72,100 g
24. 3,400 mL
25. 0.723 kg
26. 0.011316 L
27. 180 mm
28. 3.832 m
29. 40 in
30. 50 in
31. 11 pt
32. 55 oz
33. 10 qt
34. 98 in

③ ASSESS

Typical errors are made by using the wrong units of measure for conversions, for example: 2 cups = 1 quart.

Allow students to use the textbook for reference until they have memorized the conversions. Students also multiply when they should have divided and vice versa. If they understand why it's necessary to multiply or divide, these kinds of errors can be avoided.

④ CLOSE

The Practice problems can be assigned for class work and the answers checked in class to help students master the objective of the lesson.

WRAP-UP

Use Problems 5 and 35 to illustrate the objective of the workshop.

Assignment Guide
Basic: 5–34
Average: 35–43

20 min.

Metric System

① FOCUS

Objectives

1. To convert meters, liters, and grams from one metric unit to another.
2. To use the abbreviations used in the metric system.

② TEACH

Write the prefixes *kilo, hecto, deka, deci, centi,* and *milli* on the board. Combine *kilo* with the base word *meter* to get the word *kilometer.* Have students combine each of the remaining prefixes with the base word *meter* and write the new words.

Explain that the *meter* is the basic unit of measuring length in the metric system. **Figure W22.1** illustrates how each of these units of measurement is related to the meter. For example, a decimeter is 0.1 meter and a centimeter is 0.01 meter. Use **Figure W22.2** to describe the three steps for converting units within the metric system.

Use **Figure W22.3** as you work through Example 1 with students. You may wish to illustrate that moving the decimal point two places to the *right* is the same as multiplying the number you are converting by 10 × 10. For example:

2.5 meters = 2.5 × 100 or 250 centimeters; 2.50 meters = 250 centimeters

Explain that all metric systems use the same prefixes. If needed for clarity, repeat the prefix exercise with the base words *liter* and *gram.*

Use **Figure W22.4** as you work through Example 2 with students. You may wish to explain that moving the decimal point three places to the *left* is the same as dividing the number you are converting by 1,000. For example: 2,000 milliliters = 2,000 ÷ 1,000 or 2 liters

BASIC UNIT OF MEASURING The basic unit for measuring length in the metric system is the *meter* (m). The basic unit of capacity is the *liter* (L) and the basic unit of mass is the *gram* (g).

All metric measurements use the same prefix(es). Look at Figure W22.1 for the length. The prefix of each unit of length tells you how that unit is related to the meter.

Figure W22.1

Units of Measurement		
1 **kilo**meter	=	1,000 meters
1 **hecto**meter	=	100 meters
1 **deka**meter	=	10 meters
1 **deci**meter	=	0.1 meter
1 **centi**meter	=	0.01 meter
1 **milli**meter	=	0.001 meter

CONVERTING UNITS The procedure for converting from one metric unit to another can be accomplished by moving the decimal point of the original unit to the right or left. It is the same as multiplying or dividing by a power of 10. Here are some steps to take when converting units:

STEP 1: Locate the original metric unit on the chart below.

STEP 2: Count the number of jumps to the new desired unit.

STEP 3: Move the decimal point of the original unit as many places as jumps in the same left or right direction.

Figure W22.2

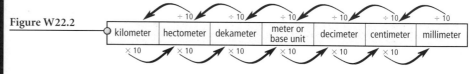

Example 1

A shipping crate is 2.5 meters long. How many centimeters is this?

STEP: Convert units.   Locate the original unit. [It is 2 jumps to the right to go from meters (base unit) to centimeters.]

Figure W22.3

kilo	hecto	deka	base unit	deci	centi	milli

Move the decimal point right 2 places.   2.5 m = 250 cm

CONCEPT CHECK

SELF-CHECK✓

Complete the problems, then check your answers at the end of the book on page 803.

1. 2.8 m = __280 cm__ cm
2. 0.15 m = __1.5 dm__ dm
3. 261 cm = __2.61 m__ m
4. 3,260 m = __3.26 km__ km

WORKSHOP NOTES

WORKSHOP

Example 2

How many liters are in a 2,000 mL plastic bottle?

STEP: Convert units. Locate the original unit, which is milliliters. (It is three jumps to the left to go from milliliters to liters—base unit.)

Figure W22.4

kilo	hecto	deka	base unit	deci	centi	milli

Move the decimal point left three places.
2,000 mL = 2.000 L = 2 L

CONCEPT CHECK

Complete the problems, then check your answers at the end of the book on page 803.

SELF-CHECK ✓

5. 2,500 mL = ____ L **2.5 m**

6. 980 cm = ____ hm **0.098 hm**

7. 3.87 L = ____ mL **3,870 mL**

8. 2.0 kg = ____ g **2,000 g**

PRACTICE

Complete the table. Each row should contain equivalent measures.

	Kilo	Hecto	Deka	Base Unit	Deci	Centi	Milli
9.	9	a. 90	b. 900	c. 9,000	d. 90,000	e.	f.
10.	a. 0.4	4	b. 40	c. 400	d. 4,000	e. 40,000	f. 400,000
11.	a. 0.02	b. 0.20	20	c. 200	d. 2,000	e. 20,000	f. 200,000
12.	a. 0.05	b. 0.50	c. 50	d. 500	5,000	e. 50,000	f. 500,000
13.	a. 0.033	b. 0.33	c. 3.3	d. 33	e. 330	3,300	f. 33,000
14.	a. 1.2	b. 12	c. 120	d. 1,200	e. 12,000	f.120,000	1,200,000

9. e. 900,000
　f. 9,000,000

15. 2 m = ____ cm

16. 400 cm = ____ mm

17. 200 cm = ____ dm

18. 80 mm = ____ m

19. 4,000 m = ____ km

20. 3 L = ____ mL

21. 250 mL = ____ L

22. 0.6 L = ____ mL

23. 0.5 L = ____ mL

24. 5 kg = ____ g

25. 10,000 g = ____ kg

26. 8.27 kg = ____ g

27. 0.038 kg = ____ mg

28. 18.2 g = ____ mg

29. 736 g = ____ kg

30. 6 dm = ____ mm

31. 50 cm = ____ dm

32. 2,500 mm = ____ cm

33. 800 m = ____ hm

34. 400 cm = ____ km

35. 32 km = ____ m

36. 8 m = ____ dm

37. 3.21 g = ____ hg

38. 2.854 g = ____ cg

39. A package of cereal weighs 3.17 kilograms. How many grams does it weigh?
3,170 g

40. A can of chili weighs 425 grams. How many kilograms does it weigh?
0.425 kg

41. A roll of aluminum foil measures 76.2 meters long by 304 millimeters wide. What is the length in millimeters? What is the width in meters? **76,200 mm, 0.304 m**

42. Sandwich bags measure 16.51 centimeters by 14.92 centimeters. What are the dimensions in millimeters? **165.1 mm by 149.2 mm**

43. A bag of flour weighs 2,270 grams. How many kilograms does it weigh?
2.27 kg

15. 200
16. 4,000
17. 20
18. 0.08
19. 4
20. 3,000
21. 0.25
22. 600
23. 500
24. 5,000
25. 10
26. 8,270
27. 38,000
28. 18,200
29. 0.736
30. 600
31. 5
32. 250
33. 8
34. 0.004
35. 32,000
36. 0.8
37. 0.0321
38. 285.4

WORKSHOP 22

2,000.0 milliliters = 2 liters Or, as illustrated in **Figure W22.2**:
$\frac{2,000 \text{ ml}}{10} = 200$ cl; $\frac{200 \text{ cl}}{10} = 20$ dl;
$\frac{20 \text{ dl}}{10} = 2$ L

Before students complete the problems, review the abbreviations used in the metric system.

3 ASSESS

If students are making errors, ask them to explain how they arrived at their answer. They may be moving the decimal point in the wrong direction or an incorrect number of places. They may also be misreading the abbreviations given in the problems.

4 CLOSE

The Practice problems can be assigned for class work and the answers checked in class to help students master the objective of the lesson.

WRAP-UP

Go over any problem for which a wrong answer is given.

Assignment Guide
　Basic: 9–14
　Average: 15–38

20 min.

47

1 FOCUS

Objectives

1. To exchange U.S. dollars to foreign currency.
2. To exchange foreign currency to U.S. dollars.
3. To change one foreign currency to another by first converting it to U.S. dollars.

2 TEACH

Review **Figure W23.1** with students. Explain that the first column lists the country and its monetary unit. The second column is used to convert foreign currency to U.S. dollars. It tells how much a particular foreign currency is worth in relation to one U.S. dollar. For instance, the British pound is worth 1.4371 U.S. dollars, or about $1.44. The third column is used to convert U.S. dollars to foreign currency. It states how many units a particular foreign currency is worth per U.S. dollar. For example, one U.S. dollar is worth 9.1875 Mexican pesos.

Conversion of International Currency—Rates of Exchange

CURRENCY EXCHANGE RATE An *exchange rate* is established between the national currencies to facilitate international travel and international trade. This exchange rate, as published daily in *The Wall Street Journal*, is based on the U.S. dollar. A partial table is given below.

Figure W23.1

Currency Exchange Rates		
Country	U.S. Dollar Equivalent	Currency per U.S. Dollar
Australia (dollar)	0.5153	1.9408
Bahrain (dinar)	2.6525	0.3770
Brazil (real)	0.4230	2.3540
Britain (pound)	1.4371	0.6958
Canada (dollar)	0.6253	1.5992
China (renminbi)	0.1208	8.2767
Denmark (krone)	0.1189	8.4138
European Union (euro)	0.8830	1.1325
India (rupee)	0.02073	48.250
Israel (shekel)	0.2202	4.5410
Japan (yen)	0.007586	131.83
Mexico (peso)	0.1088	9.1875
Russia (ruble)	0.03277	30.520
Sweden (krona)	0.0955	10.4715
Venezuela (bolivar)	0.001313	761.50

U.S. DOLLARS TO FOREIGN CURRENCY To exchange U.S. dollars to foreign currency, you need to multiply the number of U.S. dollars by the currency per U.S. dollars from **Figure W23.1.** Or it looks like:

U.S. Dollar to Foreign Currency = U.S. Dollar × Currency per U.S. Dollar

Example 1

A businessperson is traveling to the Far East and needs to exchange U.S. dollars to Japanese yen and Chinese renminbi. Exchange: $5,000 to Japanese yen.

STEP: Exchange.

U.S. Dollar	×	Currency per U.S. Dollar	
$5,000	×	131.83 yen per U.S. dollar	= **659,150 yen**
$5,000	×	8.2767 renminbi per U.S. dollar	= **24,830.1 renminbi**

WORKSHOP NOTES

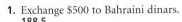

CONCEPT CHECK

Complete the problems, then check your answers at the end of the book on page 803. **SELF-CHECK✔**

1. Exchange $500 to Bahraini dinars.
188.5

2. Exchange $4,500 to Mexican pesos.
41,343.75

FOREIGN CURRENCY TO FOREIGN CURRENCY To exchange from one foreign currency to another foreign currency, exchange to U.S. dollars and then exchange the U.S. dollars to the other foreign currency. It looks like . . .

U.S. Dollars to Foreign Currency = Foreign Currency × U.S. Dollar Equivalent

 Example 2

Exchange 500 Swedish krona to euros.

STEP 1: Exchange Swedish krona to U.S. dollars.
Foreign Currency × U.S. Dollar Equivalent
500 × 0.0955 U.S. dollars per krona = $47.75

STEP 2: Exchange U.S. dollars to euros.
$47.75 × 1.1325 euros per U.S. dollars = 54.076875 euros,
therefore, **500 Swedish krona = 54.08 euros**

CONCEPT CHECK

Complete the problems, then check your answers at the end of the book on page 803. **SELF-CHECK✔**

3. Exchange 560 Canadian dollars to Australian dollars. **679.61**

4. Exchange 6,000 Israeli shekels to Indian rupees. **63,747.9**

PRACTICE

5. Exchange $12,750 to Brazilian real. **30,013.5**

6. Exchange $375 to Danish kroner. **3,155.18**

7. Exchange 15,800 euros to U.S. dollars. **$13,951.40**

8. Exchange 498 Australian dollars to U.S. dollars. **$256.6194 = $256.62**

9. Exchange 500 Swedish krona to Venezuelan bolivares.**36,361.625 = 36,361.63**

10. Exchange 45,750 Chinese renminbi to Japanese yen. **728,571.678 = 728,571.68**

11. At an auction held in London, an antique box sold for 1,150 British pounds. How much is that in U.S. dollars? **$1,652.665 = $1,652.67**

12. A sandwich in Cleveland, Ohio, sold for $1.95. The same sandwich, at the same price, would sell for how many rubles in Russia? **59.514 = 59.51**

13. A large bar of orange/olive oil soap sold for 4 euros. How much is that in U.S. dollars? **$3.532 = $3.53**

14. The *International Herald Tribune* sold for 1.5 euros in Frankfort, Germany. At the given rate of exchange, how much would it sell for in British pounds? **0.92**

WORKSHOP

 **③ ASSESS**

Write this problem on the board: Change the following foreign currency to U.S. dollars: (1) 7,000 Israeli shekels (**7,000 × 0.2202 = $1,541.40**) and (b) 7,000 Japanese yen (**7,000 × 0.007586 = $53.102 or $53.10**).

Write this problem on the board and ask students to explain the steps to solve it: Exchange 10,000 Japanese yen to Australian dollars.

Step 1: Change the first foreign currency to U.S. dollars by multiplying the first foreign currency times the U.S. dollar equivalent:
10,000 × 0.007586 = $75.86
Step 2: Change the U.S. dollars to the second foreign currency by multiplying the U.S. dollars times the currency per U.S. dollar:
75.86 × 1.9408 = 147.229088 or 147.23 Australian dollars

If students are making errors, review their work to be certain they are using the correct column of **Figure W23.1** to compute currency exchanges.

 ④ CLOSE

The Practice problems can be assigned for class work and the answers checked in class to help students master the objective of the lesson.

WRAP-UP

Go over any problem for which a wrong answer is given.

Assignment Guide
Basic: 5–9
Average: 10–12

 20 min.

① FOCUS

Objectives

To estimate an answer by rounding.

② TEACH

Using the numbers 76.761 and 39.302, ask students to name the highest place value **(tens place).** Then have them round the numbers to 80 and 40 respectively.

1. Ask students to round 75.761 to the highest place value. **(80)**

2. Then have them round 74.761 to the highest place value. **(70)**

3. Using the numbers 23.79 and 6.1 in Example 2, ask students why 23.79 was rounded to 24 rather than 20. **(The highest place value of 6.1 is the ones place so 23.79 is also rounded to the ones place.)**

Ask similar types of questions for the other examples given in the text.

Estimation: Rounding

ESTIMATING AN ANSWER Estimation is one method to determine the reasonableness of an answer. Rounding is often used to estimate an answer. First, round the numbers to the highest place value. Then perform the indicated computation. If all the numbers do not have the same place value, round the numbers to the highest place value of the smaller number and estimate the answer.

Example 1

Estimate 76.761 − 39.302.

STEP: Estimate.

$$\begin{array}{r} 76.761 \quad \text{(round to)} \quad 80 \\ -39.302 \quad \text{(round to)} \quad -40 \\ \hline 40 \end{array}$$

(By computation it is 37.459.)

Example 2

Estimate 23.79 ÷ 6.1.

STEP: Estimate.

$6.1\overline{)23.79}$ (round to) $6\overline{)24}^{\,4}$ (By computation it is 3.9.)

CONCEPT CHECK

SELF-CHECK ✓

Complete the problems, then check your answers at the end of the book on page 803. First round the numbers to the highest place value, estimate the answer, then perform the computation.

1. 43.986 − 27.491
   40 − 30 = 10; 16.495

2. 41.8474 ÷ 7.1
   42 ÷ 7 = 6; 5.894

Example 3

Estimate $2\frac{3}{4} \times 8\frac{1}{4}$.

STEP: Round, estimate the answer, then perform the computation.
    Round $2\frac{3}{4}$ to 3 and $8\frac{1}{4}$ to 8. Then 3 × 8 = 24, so the answer is **about 24.**
    (By computation it is $22\frac{11}{16}$.)

WORKSHOP NOTES

Example 4

Estimate 33 percent of $62.

STEP: Round, estimate the answer, then perform the computation.

Round 33% to $\frac{1}{3}$ and $62 to $60.

Then $\frac{1}{3} \times \$60 = \$20$, so the answer is **about $20.**

(By computation it is $20.46.)

CONCEPT CHECK

Complete the problems, then check your answers at the end of the book on page 803. First round the numbers to the highest place value, estimate the answer, then perform the computation.

3. $5\frac{1}{8} \times 4\frac{2}{3}$ **5 × 5 = 25; $23\frac{11}{12}$**

4. 63.91×9.83 **64 × 10 = 640; 628.2353**

PRACTICE

Round and estimate, then perform the indicated computation.

5. $5,965 + 1,824$

6. $7.791 + 2.151$ **8 + 2 = 10; 9.942**

7. $15.86 - 13.72$ **16 − 14 = 2; 2.14**

5. 6,000 + 2,000 = 8,000; 7,789

8. $73 − $6 = $67; $66.28

8. $\$72.75 - \$6.47$

9. 9.34×7.92 **9 × 8 = 72; 73.9728**

10. $\$28.40 \times 5.20$ **30 × 5 = 150; $147.68**

11. $48.518 \div 6.8$ **49 ÷ 7 = 7; 7.135**

12. $57.723 \div 21.3$ **60 ÷ 20 = 3; 2.71**

13. $2\frac{3}{4} \times 1\frac{1}{2}$ **3 × 2 = 6; $4\frac{1}{8}$**

14. $12\frac{1}{2} \times 2\frac{3}{5}$ **13 × 3 = 39; $32\frac{1}{2}$**

15. $\frac{1}{4} \times 12\frac{1}{2}$ **$\frac{1}{4}$ × 12 = 3; $3\frac{1}{8}$**

16. 31% of 18 **$\frac{1}{3}$ × 18 = 6; 5.58**

17. 70% of $49.95 **$\frac{7}{10}$ × $50 = $35; $34.97**

18. 27% of $12 **$\frac{1}{4}$ × 12 = 3; $3\frac{1}{8}$**

19. 52% of 160 **$\frac{1}{2}$ × 160 = 80; $83.20**

20. You purchase items for $39.45, $17.55, and $32.53. Estimate the total, then calculate. **$40 + $20 + $30 = $90; $89.53**

21. Forty-two people charter a bus for $788. Estimate the amount each person pays, then calculate. **800 ÷ 40 = 20; $18.76**

22. A living room measures $16\frac{1}{4}$ feet by $12\frac{1}{2}$ feet. Estimate the area in square feet, then calculate. **20 × 10 = 200; $203\frac{1}{8}$**

23. Blue jeans are on sale for 33 percent off the regular price of $35.95. Estimate the savings, then calculate. **$\frac{1}{3}$ × 36 = 12; $11.86**

WORKSHOP

③ ASSESS

Students do not really make errors in rounding in the same sense that errors are made in computations. If different students round the same numbers differently, then different estimates may be given. The result is that some estimates will be closer to the actual computational answers than others, and in that sense, they are better estimates. The key to making a good estimate is to follow the rule of rounding the numbers to the highest place value of the smaller number. This is why an understanding of place value is important when making estimates by rounding.

④ CLOSE

The Practice problems can be assigned for class work and the answers checked in class to help students master the objective of the lesson.

WRAP-UP

Use Practice Problems 5–7 to make sure that students understand how to make estimates by rounding numbers.

Assignment Guide
Basic: 5–19
Average: 20–23

20 min.

1 FOCUS

Objectives

1. To estimate an answer by adding the front-end digits.
2. To estimate an answer by adjusting the sum of the front-end digits.

2 TEACH

Point out to students that the front-end digits are the digits having the highest place value. Tell students that estimates made by adding the front-end digits are rough estimates that can be improved by considering the other digits in each number. Then work the other examples to illustrate how to do this.

WORKSHOP

Estimation: Front End

ADDING FRONT-END DIGITS Estimation is a very valuable tool in business mathematics. It can be used as a quick method of checking the reasonableness of a calculation or when an exact answer is not needed. It is important to know how to estimate. One way to estimate a sum is to add the front-end digits.

Example 1

```
  6,477
  2,142
+ 1,321
```

STEP: Estimate.

$$
\begin{array}{rcl}
6,477 & \longrightarrow & 6 \\
2,142 & \longrightarrow & 2 \\
+\,1,321 & \longrightarrow & +1 \\
\hline
& & 9 \text{ or about } 9,000
\end{array}
$$

Example 2

```
  $8.60
   3.19
+  0.65
```

STEP: Estimate.

$$
\begin{array}{rcl}
\$8.60 & \longrightarrow & 8 \\
3.19 & \longrightarrow & 3 \\
+\,0.65 & \longrightarrow & +\,0 \\
\hline
& & 11
\end{array}
$$

(By computation it is $12.44.)

CONCEPT CHECK

SELF-CHECK ✓

Complete the problems, then check your answers at the end of the book on page 803. Estimate by adding the front-end digits. Perform the computations.

1.	2.	3.	4.
389	475	$1,215	101.25
467	810	876	217.65
15	36	4,932	341.50
+ 240	+ 310	+ 315	+ 211.35
900; 1,100	**15,000; 1,631**	**6,000; 7,338**	**800; 871.75**

FINDING A CLOSER ESTIMATE Each estimate in the examples above is less than the correct sum. A closer estimate can be found by adjusting the sum of the front-end digits.

WORKSHOP NOTES

Example 3

567
335
124
+ 84

STEP 1: Seek a closer estimation. Look at a cluster of numbers. Decide if the two together add up to about 100.

5|67
3|35 } Cluster adds up to about 100.
1|24 } So, 100 + 100 = 200.
+ |84

STEP 2: Round and add up the front-end numbers.

5|67
3|35
1|24
+ 84
___
900

STEP 3: Add up the estimations in steps above.
900 + 200 = **1,100**

CONCEPT CHECK

Complete the problems, then check your answers at the end of the book on page 803. Estimate by first adding the front-end digits and then by adjusting the sum of the front-end digits. Perform the computations.

(SELF-CHECK✔)

5.	6.	7.	8.
335	127	359	825.19
660	259	286	367.42
74	85	924	598.15
+126	+535	+331	+791.85
600 + 200 =	700 + 200 =	1,700 + 200 =	2,200 + 300 =
800; 1,195	900; 1,006	1,900; 1,900	2,500; 2,582.61

PRACTICE

Estimate by adding the front-end digits. Perform the computations.

9.	10.	11.	12.
5,623	$3.45	4,427	7,178
221	1.49	3,274	4,298
9,879	9.72	+ 1,245	+ 5,370
+ 1,061	+ 0.35	8,000; 8,946	16,000; 16,846
15,000; 16,784	$13.00; $15.01		

Estimate by adjusting the sum of the front-end digits. Perform the computations.

13.	14.	15.	16.
285	$39.37	$15.95	$340.05
315	7.49	54.20	21.65
544	23.75	12.57	47.32
+361	+ 4.35	+ 21.54	+ 53.79
1,500; 1,505	$73; $74.96	$102; $104.26	$400; $462.81

17. Estimate first, then calculate the total attendance for six home soccer games: 3187, 2234, 2108, 3421, 6790, and 3907. **21,000; 21,647**

18. Estimate first, then calculate the cost of these grocery items: tissues $1.29, coffee $6.99, orange juice $1.45, T-bone steak $6.79, oatmeal $1.99, cocoa mix $2.89, and a jar of salad dressing $1.99. **$23.00; $23.39**

If the estimates of some students are not close to the answers given in the text, ask them to explain what they are doing. Then review the examples in the text and work some of the problems with them. When adjusting the sum of the front-end digits, some students may make errors in mental arithmetic. They may also have some trouble in seeing how to pair the non-front-end digits to refine the front-end estimate. Continue working closely with these students until they understand the process and can give good estimates.

4 CLOSE

The Practice problems can be assigned for class work and the answers checked in class to help students master the objective of the lesson.

WRAP-UP

Use Practice Problem 15 as a means of reviewing the objectives of the workshop.

Assignment Guide
Basic: 9–12
Average: 13–16

20 min.

1 FOCUS

Objectives

To make an estimate by using compatible numbers.

2 TEACH

Discuss the idea of compatible numbers by using examples in the text. Point out that compatible numbers are found by rounding the original numbers. Generally, numbers can be rounded to the nearest 10, 100, or 1,000 to make them compatible. In Example 1 36,414 is rounded to the nearest thousand. **(36,000)** When working with percents or fractions, compatible numbers are found by rounding to fractions such as $\frac{1}{2}$, $\frac{1}{4}$, $\frac{1}{3}$, $\frac{1}{5}$, and so on. However, remind students that there are no hard and fast rules for finding compatible numbers. The idea is simply to use rounded numbers that can be easily computed to arrive at an estimate.

WORKSHOP

Estimation: Compatible Numbers

ARRIVING AT A REASONABLE ESTIMATE By changing the numbers in a problem to numbers that can be computed easily, you can arrive at a reasonable estimate. These are called *compatible numbers*.

Example 1

$36{,}414 \div 9$

STEP: Estimate.

$$36{,}414 \div 9 \longrightarrow \frac{4{,}000}{9\overline{)36{,}000}}$$

The estimate is easy since 36,000 is close to 36,414 and is compatible with 9. The answer is **about 4,000.** (By computation it is 4,046.)

Example 2

$798 \div 42$

STEP: Estimate.

$$798 \div 42 \longrightarrow \frac{20}{40\overline{)800}}$$

The estimate is easy since 800 is close to 798 and 40 is close to 42. Eight hundred and 40 are compatible. The answer is **about 20.** (By computation it is 19.)

CONCEPT CHECK

SELF-CHECK ✔

Complete the problems, then check your answers at the end of the book on page 803. Estimate and then divide.

1. $661.74 \div 82$
   $640 \div 80 = 8;$
   8.07

2. $8{,}763.3 \div 321$
   $9{,}000 \div 300 =$
   $30; 27.3$

3. $47.6 \div 5.1$
   $50 \div 5 = 10;$
   9.33

4. $329.95 \div 6$
   $300 \div 6 = 5;$
   54.99

Example 3

$\frac{1}{3} \times 8\frac{3}{4}$

STEP: Estimate. $\quad \frac{1}{3} \times 8\frac{3}{4} \longrightarrow \frac{1}{3} \times 9 = 3$

The estimate is easy since 9 is close to $8\frac{3}{4}$ and is compatible with $\frac{1}{3}$. The answer is **about 3.** (By computation it is $2\frac{11}{12}$.)

Example 4

25.5% of $\$420$

STEP: Estimate. $\quad 25.5\%$ of $\$420 \longrightarrow \frac{1}{4} \times 400 = 100$

The estimate is easy since 25.5 percent is about $\frac{1}{4}$, $\$420$ is about 400, and 400 and $\frac{1}{4}$ are compatible. The answer is **about $100.** (By computation it is $107.10.)

54 ◀ Basic Math Skills: Workshops

WORKSHOP NOTES

CONCEPT CHECK

Complete the problems, then check your answers at the end of the book on page 803. Estimate using compatible numbers, then perform the computations.

(SELF-CHECK ✓)

5. $\frac{1}{4}$ of $12\frac{1}{8}$ **6.** $\frac{5}{8} \times 30.6$ **7.** $35\% \times \$926$ **8.** $27\% \times \$820$

$\frac{1}{4} \times 12 = 3;\ 3\frac{1}{32}$ $\frac{1}{2} \times 30 = 15;\ 19\frac{1}{8}$

7. $\frac{1}{3} \times \$900 = \$300;$ $\$324.10$

8. $\frac{1}{4} \times \$800 = \$200;$ $\$221.40$

PRACTICE

Estimate using compatible numbers, then perform the computations.

9. $8,824 \div 8$ **1,000; 1,103**

10. $4,879 \div 7$ **700; 697**

11. $6,095 \div 5$ **1,200; 1,219**

12. $642 \div 6$ **110; 107**

13. $896 \div 32$ **30; 28**

14. $24,564 \div 575$ **40; 42.72**

15. $8,766.63 \div 81$ **100; 108.23**

16. $\$6,447.6 \div 7.2$ **\$900; \$895.50**

17. $\frac{1}{3} \times 8\frac{1}{2}$ **3; $2\frac{5}{6}$**

18. $\frac{5}{7} \times 44\frac{1}{2}$ **30; $31\frac{11}{14}$**

19. 50% of $430 **\$215; \$215**

20. 65% of $75 **\$50; \$48.75**

21. Delbert Rowell drove his tractor-trailer rig 84,572.5 miles in 6 months. Estimate how many miles he drove each month. **14,000; 14,095.42**

22. Anna Nethery earned $47,500 this year as a stock analyst. Estimate how much she earns each month. **\$4,000; \$3,958.33**

23. A walking path is $20\frac{1}{2}$ miles long. You walk $\frac{1}{3}$ of the path by noon. Estimate the distance walked. **7; $6\frac{5}{6}$**

24. Harriet Murdock saves 33 percent of her paycheck each week. Last week, her check was for $247.95. Estimate the amount saved. **\$80; \$81.82**

25. During the high school state basketball finals, 75 percent of the 22,000 tickets were sold. Estimate how many tickets were not sold. **5,000; 5,500**

26. The hotel-motel tax in Pittsburgh is 9.5 percent of the price of a room. If a room costs $112.50 per night, estimate the tax for 3 nights. **\$33.00; \$32.06**

27. Fred Eskelsejah was hired as the bookkeeper at an annual salary of $36,300. Estimate his monthly salary. **\$3,000; \$3,025**

28. Cassius Russell learned at the job interview that he would be paid an annual salary of $24,600 as account executive. Estimate his monthly salary. **\$2,000; \$2,050**

29. Anitra Gatling took a job as a bookkeeper at an annual salary of $25,200. Estimate her weekly salary. **\$500; \$484.62**

30. Linda Jackson took a job at a manufacturing outlet. She earns $350 a week. Estimate her daily income if she works 5 days a week. Calculate her annual salary. **\$70; \$18,200**

31. Jianguo Wang is hired for a data entry position earning $8.50 per hour. Estimate his annual salary if he works 40 hours a week. **\$20,000; \$17,680**

32. Suppose you take a job as an office clerk earning $13.85 per hour. Estimate your weekly salary if you work 40 hours a week. **\$600; \$554**

33. Gonzalo Carlos purchased a cordless telephone that had a regular price of $71.50. If he received 25 percent off, estimate how much he saved. **\$18; \$17.88**

Workshop 26 Estimation: Compatible Numbers ▶ **55**

③ ASSESS

In using compatible numbers, there is a chance that an estimate may be too far off from the actual answer and thus be misleading. In the example $\frac{36,414}{9}$, if a student rounded the numbers to $\frac{36,000}{10}$, than the estimate would be 3,600 rather than 4,000. The number 3,600 is not a wrong estimate; it is just not as good an estimate as 4,000.

Caution students to try to use one of the original numbers, if possible, or to find two numbers as close to the original numbers as possible.

④ CLOSE

The Practice problems can be assigned for class work and the answers checked in class to help students master the objective of the lesson.

WORKSHOP

WRAP-UP

To demonstrate the use of compatible numbers to make estimates use Practice Problems 9–11.

Assignment Guide
Basic: 9–20
Average: 21–30

20 min.

1 FOCUS

Objectives

To make an estimate by clustering.

2 TEACH

Use clustering when the numbers fall within a narrow range of one another. Do not cluster when numbers are dispersed over a broad range of values. However, it may be possible, in the latter case to cluster some of the numbers in the group. See Example 2. In this workshop, students use their rounding skills to find estimates by clustering.

Estimation: Clustering

Estimation by clustering is another way of projecting what an answer will be. When the numbers to be added are close to the same quantity, the sum can be found by clustering.

Example 1

$4.85 + 5.15 + 4.89 + 5.17

STEP 1: Estimate.
$4.85
5.15   All cluster
4.89   around $5.00
+ 5.17

STEP 2: Add.
$5.00 × 4 = $20
(Approximately)

Example 2

$15.95 + 16.50 + 15.75 + 7.95

STEP 1: Estimate.
$15.95
16.50   Cluster around
15.75 $16.00
+   7.95 ← Clusters around $8.00

STEP 2: Add.
$16 × 3 = $48
$48 + 8 = $56
(Approximately)

CONCEPT CHECK

SELF-CHECK✔

Complete the problems, then check your answers at the end of the book on page 803. Estimate the sums by clustering, then compute the sums.

1. 563 **600 × 4 =**
    598 **2,400; 2,332**
    559
    +612

2. $27.95 **$30 × 4 =**
    31.42 **$120;**
    30.25 **$119.09**
    + 29.47

3. $1.59 **(3 × $2) + $1**
    1.79 **= $6 + $1**
    2.21 **= 7; $6.34**
    + 0.75

PRACTICE

Estimate the sums by clustering. Compute the actual amount.

4. 763 **800 × 4 =**
    781 **3,200; 3,127**
    773
    +810

5. 525 **500 × 4 =**
    496 **2,000; 2,063**
    512
    +530

6. $53.39 **$50 × 4 =**
    55.24 **$200;**
    49.26 **$207.86**
    + 49.97

7. $36.20 **$40 × 4 =**
    39.67 **$160;**
    41.78 **$161.24**
    + 43.59

8. 88,026 **90,000 × 4**
    91,521 **= 360,000;**
    87,842 **362,208**
    +94,819

9. 7.95 **(8 × 4) + 4 =**
    7.87 **32 + 4 = 36;**
    8.13 **35.87**
    8.25
    +3.67

WORKSHOP NOTES

10.
```
16.05   (16 × 4) + 6
15.95   = 64 + 6 =
15.50   70; 68.5
15.50
+ 5.50
```
11.
```
$2.29   (2 × 4) + 9
2.39    = 8 + 9 =
2.25    17; 18.28
2.40
+ 8.95
```
12.
```
$25.95   ($26 × 3) + ($38 × 2) =
26.30    $78 + $76 = $154;
25.70    $154.40
37.95
+ 38.50
```

13. School supplies costing $6.95, $7.25, $7.45, $6.65, and $6.79. **$7 × 5 = $35; $35.09**

14. Groceries costing $2.89, $3.15, $3.29, $2.67, $3.25, and $3.35. **$3 × 6 = $18; $18.60**

15. Work clothes costing $25.95, $23.95, $26.50, $39.95, and $41.25.
   ($26 × 3) + ($40 × 2) = $78 + $80 = $158; $157.60

16. School supplies costing $1.09, $0.99, $0.89, $2.29, $1.99, and $2.15.
   ($1 × 3) + ($2 × 3) = $3 + $6 = $9.00; $9.40

17. Clothes costing: shirt $17.95, shoes $39.95, six pairs of socks $18.25, tie
   $16.95, and belt $16.95. **($18 × 4) + $40 = $72 + $40 = $112; $110.05**

18. Cordell Brown drove the miles indicated: Monday 367, Tuesday 390,
   Wednesday 405, Thursday 386, Friday 402, and Saturday 396. Estimate first,
   then calculate the total miles for the week. **400 × 6 = 2,400; 2,346**

19. Jane Flanagan had the following sales: first quarter $52,900, second quarter
   $88,900, third quarter $91,980, and fourth quarter $89,830. Estimate first,
   then calculate the total sales for the year. **$50,000 + ($90,000 × 3) = $50,000 + $270,000 =
   $320,000; $323,610**

20. Juan Perez had the following long-distance phone charges: $6.15, $2.15,
   $5.98, $1.81, $5.87, $1.89, and $11.71. Estimate first, then calculate the total
   long-distance charges. **($6 × 3) + ($2 × 3) + $12 = $18 + $6 + $12 = $36; $35.56**

21. During an extended stay at the Union Square Hotel, Stacy Anderson had
   these dry cleaning charges: $29.90, $15.90, $7.95, $24.75, $15.90, $15.90, and
   $12.50. Estimate and then calculate the total. **$125; $122.80**

22. Shandel Williams used a calculator to solve the following problems. If she
   entered each number properly into the calculator, her answers should be
   correct. Estimate each answer and decide if Williams's answers are correct.

	Problem	Her Answer on Calculator	Your Estimate	Is She Right? Yes/No
a.	672 + 703 + 725 + 130	2,230.00	2,200	Yes
b.	$9.80 + $9.95 + $10.35 + $10.01	40.11	$40	Yes
c.	1.23 + 1.95 + 7.8 + 7.6 + 8.4	24.98	27	No (26.98)
d.	82 + 75 + 79 + 34 + 29 + 32	299.00	330	No (331)
e.	44.20 + 44.51 + 30.07 + 29.35	148.13	150	Yes
f.	625.1 + 615.2 + 12.35 + 10.75	1,263.40	1,260	Yes
g.	9.89 + 2.9 + 9.49 + 3.1 + 2.75	24.73	29	No (28.13)
h.	12,341 + 25,452 + 13,021 + 12,981	61,231.00	63,000	No (63,795)

WORKSHOP 27

3 ASSESS

If a group of numbers has one or
more numbers that do not cluster, then students should treat the
number or numbers separately.

Poor estimates can result if
students do not cluster the given
numbers in the right way.

4 CLOSE

The Practice problems can be
assigned for class work and the
answers checked in class to help
students master the objective of
the lesson.

WRAP-UP

Ask three students to work Practice
Problems 10–12 and to explain how
they arrive at their estimates.

Assignment Guide
   Basic: 4–12
   Average: 13–17

20 min.

1 FOCUS

Objectives

1. To write numbers that appear in scientific notation, in standard notation, and in word form.

2. To write numbers that appear in standard notation or word form in scientific notation.

2 TEACH

Write *7,265,000* on the board in standard form and in word form. Explain that another way to write this number is in a form called *scientific notation*. It looks like this: 7.265×10^6. Scientific notation is a shortcut for writing very large or very small numbers.

Explain that when you write a number in scientific notation, you are actually writing a multiplication problem. (**(7.265×10^6) means $7.265 \times 10 \times 10 \times 10 \times 10 \times 10 \times 10$**) Point out that scientific notation is the product of two parts:

1. a number > or = 1 but < 10 (**here 7.265**), and

2. a power of 10 (**here, 10^6**).

Next, write these two examples on the board: 2.543×10^3 and 6.481×10^{-3}. Explain that to change 2.543×10^3 to standard form, move the decimal point 3 places to the right. (**2,543**) To change 6.481×10^{-3} to standard form, move the decimal point 3 places to the left. Add zeros if needed. (**0.006481**) Work through Example 1a–e.

Example 2 shows how to change numbers written in standard form to scientific notation. Emphasize that the key idea here is to move the decimal point enough places to get a number > or = 1 but < 10.

Scientific Notation

THE POWER OF NUMBERS On most calculators, when you multiply 123,456 times 987,654, the product is displayed as 1.219318122 11. The number displayed is written in *scientific notation* and is interpreted as 1.219318122 times 10^{11} and is equal to 121,931,181,220 or one hundred twenty-one billion nine hundred thirty-one million one hundred eighty-one thousand two hundred twenty. Extremely large or extremely small numbers are often written in scientific notation and are examples of the elegance of concise mathematical notation.

Numbers written in scientific notation will be expressed as the product of a number equal to or greater than one and less than ten (1.219 . . .) and a power of ten (10^{11}). Changing a number written in scientific notation to standard form requires moving the decimal point. If the exponent on ten is positive, move the decimal point that many places to the right; if the exponent on ten is negative, move the decimal point that many places to the left.

Example 1

Write these numbers in standard notation and using words.

a. 1.1234×10^7 b. 4.56789×10^{10} c. $8.123456789 \times 10^{12}$

d. 1.8765×10^{-5} e. 2.987×10^{-10}

STEP: Write the numbers in standard notation and using words.

a. 11,234,000 or eleven million two hundred thirty-four thousand

b. 45,678,900,000 or forty-five billion six hundred seventy-eight million nine hundred thousand

c. 8,123,456,789,000 or eight trillion one hundred twenty-three billion four hundred fifty-six million seven hundred eighty-nine thousand

d. 0.000018765 or eighteen thousand seven hundred sixty-five billionths

e. 0.0000000002987 or two thousand nine hundred eighty-seven ten trillionths

1. 1,375,000 or One million three hundred seventy-five thousand

2. 386,420,000 or Three hundred eighty-six million four hundred twenty thousand

3. 712.3 or Seven hundred twelve and three tenths

4. 0.00000047945 or Forty-seven thousand nine hundred forty-five hundred billionths

CONCEPT CHECK

Complete the problems, then check your answers at the end of the book on page 804. Write these numbers in standard notation and using words.

1. 1.375×10^6 **2.** 3.8642×10^8 **3.** 7.123×10^2 **4.** 4.7945×10^{-7}

COUNTING THE PLACEMENT OF THE DECIMAL POINT To write numbers that appear in standard notation in scientific notation, count how many places the decimal point must be moved to get a number larger than one but less than ten, that is the exponent on ten. If the decimal point is moved to the left, the exponent is positive. If the decimal point is moved to the right, the exponent is negative.

WORKSHOP NOTES

Example 2

Write these numbers in scientific notation.

a. 12,632

b. $12.6 million

c. 0.000000571

d. Two hundred forty-one million five hundred six thousand three hundred seventy-nine

e. Ninety-three millionths

STEP: Write the numbers in scientific notation.

a. 1.2632×10^4

b. $\$12,600,000 = \$1.26 \times 10^7$

c. 5.71×10^{-7}

d. $241,506,379 = 2.41506379 \times 10^8$

e. $0.000093 = 9.3 \times 10^{-5}$

CONCEPT CHECK

Complete the problems, then check your answers at the end of the book on page 804. Write these numbers in scientific notation.

SELF-CHECK ✓

5. 93,000,000 9.3×10^7

6. 0.0000000386 3.86×10^{-8}

7. Seven million two hundred sixteen 7.000216×10^6

8. Four thousand twenty-one ten thousandths 4.021×10^{-1}

PRACTICE

In Problems 9–14, write the numbers in standard notation and using words.

9. 7.391×10^5

10. 3.51096×10^8

11. 8.71×10^{-4}

12. 6.200841×10^7

13. 2.92651×10^{11}

14. 1.82×10^{-6}

In Problems 15–20, write the numbers in scientific notation.

15. 12,620,380

16. 4,390,487,285,302

17. 0.0000286

18. 0.00000000000182

19. 4.75 million

20. 4.75 millionths

21. Beneath the tundra of Alaska's North Slope is a vast reservoir of natural gas, estimated at 2.6×10^{12} cubic feet. Write this number in standard notation and using words. **2,600,000,000 or Two billion six hundred million**

22. A health care company announced a need to increase the present monthly premium of some 2.47×10^5 senior citizens. Write this number in standard notation and using words. **247,000 or Two hundred forty-seven thousand**

23. During a recent water shortage, residents of Marin County, California, reduced their daily consumption of water to 1.04×10^7 gallons. Write this number in standard notation and using words. **10,400,000 or Ten million four hundred thousand**

24. Edward's Food Warehouse had baby food in the 220 gram size for $0.32. That is a unit price of 1.45×10^{-3} per gram. Write this number in standard notation and using words. **$0.00145 or One hundred forty-five hundred thousandths of a dollar**

25. Early in January, the currency exchange rate for one Indonesian rupiah was equivalent to 9.6×10^{-5} U. S. dollars. Write this number in standard notation and using words. **0.000096 or Ninety-six millionths**

26. A finance company had earnings of $53,091,000 before income taxes for the third quarter. Write this number in scientific notation. **5.3091×10^7**

27. Many life insurance companies set an annual level of sales for each of their underwriters. The goal set for Anne Lopez was $2 million. Write this number in scientific notation. **2.0×10^6**

9. 739,100 or Seven hundred thirty-nine thousand one hundred

10. 351,096,000 or Three hundred fifty-one million ninety-six thousand

11. 0.000871 or Eight hundred seventy-one millionths

12. 62,008,410 or Sixty-two million eight thousand four hundred ten

13. 292,651,000,000 or Two hundred ninety-two billion six hundred fifty-one million

14. 0.00000182 or One hundred eighty-two hun dred millionths

15. 1.262038×10^7

16. $4.390487285302 \times 10^{12}$

17. 2.86×10^{-5}

18. 1.82×10^{-12}

19. 4.75×10^6

20. 4.75×10^{-4}

WORKSHOP

WORKSHOP 28

Write 47,382 on the board. Ask students to locate the decimal point. **(After the 2)** To change 47,382 to scientific notation, which direction would they need to move the decimal point in order to get a number > or = 1 but < 10? **(left)** By how many places? **(4)** Emphasize that when you move the decimal point to the left to change a number to scientific notation, the exponent is positive. 4.7382×10^4

③ ASSESS

To avoid errors in converting numbers written in word form to scientific notation, suggest that students first write the number in standard form and then convert it to scientific notation.

To change scientific notation to standard form, a positive exponent tells you to move the decimal point to the right as many spaces as the exponent. A negative exponent means move the decimal point to the left.

To change standard form to scientific notation, move the decimal point as many spaces as needed to get a number > or = 1 but < 10. The number of spaces that you must move the decimal point tells you what the exponent is. Here, moving left will result in a positive exponent; moving right will result in a negative exponent.

④ CLOSE

The Practice problems can be assigned for class work and the answers checked in class to help students master the objective of the lesson.

WRAP-UP

Go over any problem for which a wrong answer is given.

Assignment Guide
Basic: 9–20
Average: 21–25

20 min.

59

Objectives

To solve problems using the four-step method.

Write the problem given in the example on the board. Then lead students in a discussion of the four steps of the problem-solving method, writing the key words on the board: Understand, Plan, Work, and Answer.

Discuss each step thoroughly. Then illustrate each step using the problem, as shown in the textbook. In order to answer the question in Step 4 ("Is your answer reasonable?") an estimate can be made.

Problem-Solving Strategy: Using the Four-Step Method

A STEP-BY-STEP PROCEDURE The problem-solving process consists of several interrelated actions. The steps to some problems are obvious and require very little effort. Others require a step-by-step procedure. Using a procedure such as the four-step method should help you to solve word problems.

THE FOUR-STEP METHOD

STEP 1: Understand	What is the problem? What is given? What are you asked to do?
STEP 2: Plan	What do you need to do to solve the problem? Choose a problem-solving strategy.
STEP 3: Work	Carry out the plan. Do any necessary calculations.
STEP 4: Answer	Is your answer reasonable? Did you answer the question?

Example 1

A small office building is being remodeled. It will take 3 plumbers 7 days to install all the pipes. Each plumber works 8 hours a day at $35 per hour. How much will it cost to hire the plumbers?

STEP 1: Given	3 plumbers, 7 days, 8 hours, $35 per hour
Find	The cost per day for 1 plumber.
	The cost per day for 3 plumbers.
	The cost of 3 plumbers for 7 days.
STEP 2: Plan	Find the cost per day for 1 plumber, then multiply by the number of plumbers, and then multiply by the number of days.
STEP 3: Work	8 hrs per day $\times$ $35 per hr = $280 per day for 1 plumber
	3 plumbers $\times$ $280 per day for 1 plumber = $840 per day for 3 plumbers
	7 days $\times$ $840 per day for 3 plumbers = $5880 for 3 plumbers for 7 days
STEP 4: Answer	**It will cost $5,880 for 3 plumbers for 7 days.**

Example 2

One hundred twenty-eight players entered the U. S. Open Men's Singles Tennis Tournament in Flushing Meadows, New York, held over the Labor Day weekend. How many tennis matches must be played in order to determine a winner if it's a single elimination tournament? (Single elimination means that if you lose one match you are eliminated from the tournament.)

STEP 1: Given	One hundred twenty-eight players entered in the tournament. Every player but the winner must lose one match.
Find	How many matches must be played to determine a winner.
STEP 2: Plan	Find out how many matches must be played for every player but one (the winner) to lose a match.

WORKSHOP NOTES

STEP 3: Work If there are 128 players and every player but one must lose a match, then 128 − 1 would be the answer.

STEP 4: Answer **There must be 127 matches played.**

WORKSHOP 29

CONCEPT CHECK

Complete the problem, then check your answer at the end of the book on page 804.

SELF-CHECK ✓

1. It takes 2 finish carpenters 8 days to do the work. Each finish carpenter earns $37.50 per hour and works 7 hours per day. How much will it cost to hire the finish carpenters? **$4,200**

PRACTICE

Identify the plan, work, and answer for each problem.

2. Calvina Miller makes a car payment of $214.50 every month. Her car loan is for 5 years. How much will she pay in 5 years? **$12,870**

3. Teresa Gonzalez and Alan Carillo spent a total of $215.75 on their prom date. Dinner cost $75.87. How much did everything else cost the couple? **$139.88**

4. Elaine Wong purchased 2 sweaters at $24.99 each, a belt for $14.49, slacks for $19.79, shoes for $54.49, and 5 pairs of socks at $3.99 a pair. How much did Wong spend? **$158.70**

5. A builder is building 5 new homes. It will take 4 electricians 2 days to wire each home. The electricians work 8 hours per day and earn $37.45 per hour. How much will it cost to pay the electricians? **$11,984**

6. A builder is building 5 new homes. Each home has a foyer measuring 9 feet by 18 feet. Laminate flooring for each foyer costs $26.91 per square yard. What is the cost of the laminate floors for the foyers in all 5 homes? **$2,421.90**

7. Chantel Monroe charges $3.75 per page for typing rough drafts and an additional $0.50 per page for changes and deletions. A manuscript had 212 pages, of which 147 pages had changes and deletions. What was the total cost of typing the manuscript? **$868.50**

8. Max Schulmann is paying $13.35 per week for a DVD player. The total cost of the DVD player was $694.20. How long will it take Schulmann to pay for the DVD player? **52 weeks**

9. Karen Johnson rode her 27″ bicycle to the store and back. The store is 1 mile from Johnson's home. Approximately how many rotations did Johnson's bicycle wheels make in going to the store and back? (Hint: The circumference of a circle is approximately 3.14 times the diameter.) **Approximately 1,495 rotations**

10. Ben Cornell and Tom Ingulli drove to Chicago—a distance of 510 miles. Their car gets 23 miles per gallon of gasoline. Gasoline costs them $1.29 per gallon. How much did they spend for gasoline on their trip? **$28.60**

11. Sita Rahim drove due north for 3 hours at 46 miles per hour. From the same spot, Yasmina Young drove due south for 2 hours at 43 miles per hour. How far apart were they after their trip? **224 miles**

12. Lincoln Norris bought 3 boxes of cereal at $3.79 each, a roll of paper towels for $1.78, and 2 pounds of margarine at $1.28 a pound. How much change would Norris get back from $20.00 if there was no sales tax? **$2.37**

---

③ ASSESS

Many students have a great deal of difficulty solving word problems. The four-step method will help students overcome their difficulty by giving them specific questions to answer by trying to understand the problem. Once a problem is understood, a plan can be formulated to solve it. Of course students can make errors in choosing a plan or in carrying out the plan.

Very often the choice of a plan rests upon an understanding of *when* numbers needed to be added or subtracted, or multiplied or divided. These are conceptual errors. Only by working closely with students and observing their work, or by asking questions and analyzing students' answers, will you be able to isolate the kinds of errors students make and thus be able to help them correct the errors.

④ CLOSE

The Practice problems can be assigned for class work and the answers checked in class to help students master the objective of the lesson.

WRAP-UP

Go over any problem for which a wrong answer is given.

Assignment Guide
  Basic: 2–5
  Average: 6–8

20 min.

WORKSHOP

Problem-Solving Strategy: Identifying Information

READING THE PROBLEM CAREFULLY Before you begin to solve an application problem, a word problem, or a story problem, first read the problem carefully and answer these questions:

- What are you asked to find?
- What facts are given?
- Are enough facts given? Do you need more information than the problem provides?

Some problems provide more information than is needed to solve the problem. Others cannot be solved without additional information. Identifying what is wanted, what is given, and what is needed allows you to organize the information and plan your solution.

(Example 1)

Laneshia James earns $27.25 per hour. She is married and claims 2 withholding allowances. Last week she worked 40 hours at the regular rate and 4 hours at the weekend rate. She is 28 years old. Find her gross pay last week.

STEP: Identify information.

1. What you are asked to find: Laneshia James's gross pay last week.

2. Facts given: She earns $27.25 per hour.
   - 40 hours worked at regular rate.
   - 4 hours worked at weekend rate.

3. Facts needed: Weekend rate.

This problem cannot be solved.

(Example 2)

John Skaggs runs 6 miles every day. How many miles does Skaggs run in a week?

STEP: Identify information.

1. What you are asked to find: Number of miles ran in 1 week.

2. Facts given: Runs 6 miles every day.

3. Facts needed: None.

This problem can be solved. Multiply the miles ran per day (6) by the number of days in a week (7). **The answer is 42 miles.**

CONCEPT CHECK

SELF-CHECK ✓

Complete the problem, then check your answer at the end of the book on page 804.

1. Tonia Walsh bought a new car with a $2,000 down payment and monthly payments of $274.50. How much did Walsh pay, in total, for her new car? **Problem cannot be solved. Need number of payments.**

▼ ▲ ▲ ▲

FOCUS 1

Objectives

1. To solve word problems that may provide more information than is needed to solve the problem.

2. To identify word problems for which additional information is needed and thus cannot be solved.

TEACH 2

Go over the information given in the textbook prior to Example 1. Then work through the examples with students.

Point out that in the real world, people encounter many problems that often have too much or too little information. Thus, they first have to identify pertinent information before attempting to solve the problem.

WORKSHOP NOTES

WORKSHOP

PRACTICE

Identify the wanted, given, and needed information. If enough information is given, solve the problem.

2. The Camp Store is having a sale on camping equipment. It has two-person tents for $79.49, cookstoves for $27.45, and cooking sets for $24.79. How much does a lantern and a tent cost? **Cannot be solved. Need cost of a lantern.**

3. The D & J Fruit Farm pays pickers $0.50 per pound to pick blueberries. The berries are packed in pint baskets and sold to grocery stores for $1.15 per pint. How many pint baskets are needed for 300 pounds of berries? **Cannot be solved. Need relationship between pints and pounds.**

4. Manuel Munoz paid $84 each way to fly round-trip from Detroit to Pittsburgh. Bob Tucker paid $139 for the round-trip fare. Who paid more? How much more? **Manuel paid $29 more for the round-trip.**

5. Edith Fairmont paid $226 for 3 tickets to a stage play. She paid for the tickets with three $100 bills. How much change did she receive? **$74**

6. Find the cost of 3 tablecloths, each 68 inches long and 52 inches wide. Each tablecloth costs $21.95. **$65.85**

7. Adam Larson paid for 2 watermelons with a $10 bill. He received $2.10 in change. What did the watermelons cost per pound? **Cannot be solved. Need weight of watermelons.**

8. Food for the party cost $44.95. Party supplies cost $17.48. Jayla Drake and her friends have agreed to share the total cost of food and supplies equally. How much will each pay? **Cannot be solved. Need to know how many friends.**

9. Ajou Hart is 6 feet 2 inches tall and weighs 195 pounds. He grew 3 inches in the past year. How tall was Hart one year ago? **5′ 11″**

10. Tamara Williams has finished 25 of the 30 mathematics problems on her test. It is now 11:50 A.M. The 1-hour test started at 11:00 A.M. What is the average number of minutes she can spend on each of the remaining problems? **2 minutes**

11. A tennis racket and a can of balls cost a total of $159.89. What is the cost of the tennis racket? **Cannot be solved. Need the cost of the tennis balls.**

12. A bottle of cider costs $1.95. The cider costs $0.95 more than the bottle. How much does the cider cost? **$1.45**

13. Richard Anderson sells magazine subscriptions and receives a weekly salary of $145. He also receives a $3 bonus for each subscription that he sells. Last week his gross pay was $202. How many subscriptions did Anderson sell last week? **19**

14. In shopping for the latest recording of her favorite artist, Alejandra Ramos found that the cost of the DVD was $19.20 more than the cost of the cassette tape, and the cost of the cassette tape was $4.84 less than the cost of the compact disc. How much less was the cost of the compact disc than the DVD? **$14.36**

15. Bob Jackson swims every Monday, Wednesday, and Friday morning at the senior center. He swims 18 lengths in 15 minutes. Each length is 75 feet long. To the nearest mile per hour, how fast is he swimming? **One mile per hour**

16. Assume you are driving on a two-mile circular racetrack. For the first half of the track, you average 30 miles per hour. What speed must you maintain for the second half of the racetrack to average 60 miles per hour? **It is impossible to average 60 miles per hour.**

Workshop 30 Problem-Solving Strategy: Identifying Information ▶ **63**

3 ASSESS

Sometimes students will say that a problem cannot be solved when, in fact, it can be solved. This is simply a situation in which the student cannot identify *how* to solve the problem.

Have these students list the four problem-solving steps from Workshop 29 as an aid in organizing their work when attempting to solve problems. This should help them to identify the given information and make a plan to solve the problem.

4 CLOSE

The Practice problems can be assigned for class work and the answers checked in class to help students master the objective of the lesson.

WRAP-UP

Work Practice Problems 3 and 4 to wrap up the workshop.

Assignment Guide
 Basic: 2–5
Average: 6–12

20 min.

WORKSHOP 31

1 FOCUS

Objectives
To solve problems that requires using several operations.

2 TEACH

It is important to work through both examples very carefully with students. Ask students *why questions* as you do the examples. In Example 1 ask: Why do you multiply 60 × $325 to get the total of payments? Why is $2,750 added to $19,500? Why is $18,750 subtracted from $22,250?

These types of questions will force students to think about the operations involved and the order in which they are used.

Problem-Solving Strategy: Multiple Operations

PRIORITIZING OPERATIONS Some problems require several operations to solve. After deciding which operations to use, you must decide the correct order in which to perform them.

Example 1

The cash price of a new sedan is $18,750. Arthur Dennis cannot pay cash, so he is making a down payment of $2,750 and 60 monthly payments of $325 each. How much more does it cost to buy the vehicle this way?

STEP
- **Given:** Cash price of $18,750
  $2,750 down + 60 payments of $325 each
- **Multiply:** To get total of payments
  60 × $325 = $19,500
- **Add:** $2,750 to total of payments
  $2,750 + $19,500 = $22,250
- **Subtract:** Total payments from cash price of car
  $22,250 − $18,750 = $3,500

It costs $3,500 more to buy the car this way. (In this example, the order of operations is very important; that is, to first multiply, then add, then subtract.)

CONCEPT CHECK

SELF-CHECK ✔

Complete the problems, then check your answers at the end of the book on page 804.

1. Sami Kemal spent $7.95, $15.20, and $12.47 on entertainment. His entertainment budget is $50.00. How much is left in his entertainment budget?
   $50.00 − ($7.95 + $15.20 + $12.47) = $14.38
2. Donna Preski works 8 hours a day, 5 days a week. So far this year she has worked 680 hours. How many weeks has she worked? **17**

Example 2

Nancy Paris bought 3 notebooks costing $3.98 each. She gave the cashier a $20 bill. How much change did she receive if there was no sales tax?

STEP
- **Given:** Bought 3 notebooks at $3.98 each.
  No sales tax. Gave cashier $20.00
- **Multiply:** To get total cost
  3 × $3.98 = $11.94
- **Subtract:** To find change
  $20.00 − $11.94 = $8.06

Paris received $8.06 in change.

WORKSHOP NOTES

CONCEPT CHECK

Complete the problems, then check your answers at the end of the book on page 804.

3. The band boosters sell cider and doughnuts at home football games. Last week they sold 318 cups of cider at $0.50 per cup and 12 dozen doughnuts at $0.50 per doughnut. What were the total sales? **$231.00**

4. Maria Fernandez paid monthly electric bills of $51.72, $47.75, and $53.21. Her electric budget is $150.00 for 3 months. Is she over or under her budget? By how much is she over or under? **$2.68**

PRACTICE

Complete the problems.

5. Victor Haddad sold 8 pumpkins for $2.75 each, 9 for $2.00 each, 24 for $1.50 each, and 15 for $1.00 each. He receives $0.35 for each pumpkin sold plus a $10.00 bonus if his sales total $75.00 or more. How much did he receive? **$29.60**

6. Xavier Zermeno worked through 174 pages of a 408-page computer training manual. It took him 2 days to work through the remaining pages. If he worked through the same number of pages each day, how many pages did he work through each day? **117**

7. Hoshi Sato worked 40 hours at $6.75 per hour. He worked 5 hours at $8.00 an hour. How much money did Sato earn? **$310.00**

8. The Parkers spent $42.78, $45.91, and $41.15 in 3 visits to the grocery store. Their food budget is $150.00. How much money do they have left to spend for food? **$20.16**

9. The temperature in the production department is 21° C at 12 noon. If the temperature increases 1.5° C every hour, what will the temperature be at 5 P.M.? **28.5 degrees C**

10. Flora Sturgeon walks 4 miles round-trip 3 times a week to work. How far will she walk in 1 year? **624**

11. John Piotrowski assembled a total of 642 circuit boards in 3 days of work. During the first 2 days, he assembled 211 and 208 circuit boards, respectively. How many did he assemble the last day? **223**

12. In a one-month sales contest, Ernie Johnkovich earned 4 two-point certificates, 2 three-point certificates, and 6 one-point certificates. How many points did he earn for the month? **20**

13. Seventeen hundred tickets costing $5 each were sold for a scholarship fund-raiser. One prize of $2,000, 3 prizes of $1,000, and 5 prizes of $250 were given away. How much money did the scholarship fund-raiser make? **$2,250**

14. Pepe Garza, sales leader for the past month, earned 47 one-point certificates. If he earned a total of 68 points, how many three-point certificates did he earn? **7**

15. DeBorah Miles bought 3 t-shirts for $7.50 each and a sweatshirt for $22.95. How much change did she receive from a $50 bill? **$4.55**

16. Adahy Catolst saved $212. After he earned an additional $124, he spent $149 for a small color TV, $35 for a rugby shirt, and $79 for a pair of sneakers. How much money did Catolst have left? **$73**

3 ASSESS

Some students try to formalize rules for solving problems. For example, they will think along these lines: Most problems require addition to solve. So, when in doubt add; or they think that when two numbers are given, one very large and the other very small, then divide the numbers. Of course, these types of approaches are often incorrect and demonstrate that the student doesn't understand the arithmetic operations and when they should be used.

Asking students what and why they are doing something can reveal the kinds of errors students are making. Then the correct reteaching methods can be used.

4 CLOSE

The Practice problems can be assigned for class work and the answers checked in class to help students master the objective of the lesson.

WRAP-UP

Use these problems below to wrap-up the workshop.

Assignment Guide
Basic: 5–7
Average: 8–11

20 min.

WORKSHOP 32

① FOCUS

Objectives
1. To estimate an answer.
2. To use estimation to check the reasonableness of an answer.

② TEACH

Before working through the examples with students, review the various ways of finding an estimate: rounding, front-end, compatible numbers, and clustering. Ask students which of these methods has been used in Example 1. **(Compatible numbers)** In discussing Example 2, point out that $198.50 is about $200 and $\frac{1}{4}$ of $200 is $50.

An estimate does not show that the answer, in fact, is correct. This can only be done by recalculating the answer.

Problem-Solving Strategy: Using Estimation

CHECKING THE REASONABLENESS OF AN ANSWER An important part of problem solving is determining the reasonableness of an answer. Checking an answer doesn't mean that you must recalculate it. Quite often, it is sufficient simply to determine if your answer makes sense. Estimation can be used to check the reasonableness of an answer. Some problems may ask for just an estimate.

Example 1

Three cans of juice cost $2.37, six cans of soda cost $2.40, and six peaches cost $1.98. About how much will it cost for one of each item?

STEP: Use estimation.

$2.37 ÷ 3 is about	$0.80
$2.40 ÷ 6 is about	$0.40
$1.98 ÷ 6 is about	$0.33
Total is about	**$1.53**

CONCEPT CHECK

SELF-CHECK ✓

Complete the problems, then check your answers at the end of the book on page 804.

1. Tom Lucas estimated the cost of 10 gallons of gas at $0.93 a gallon to be $930. Is his estimate reasonable? What error did he make?
No, he used 93 instead of $0.93. Answer is $9.30.

Example 2

Sandra Kaselman used her calculator to find 25 percent of $198.50 for a total of $4,962.50. Is her answer reasonable? Why or why not?

STEP: Check the reasonableness of the answer.

Her answer is not reasonable.

Twenty-five percent is equal to $\frac{1}{4}$, and $\frac{1}{4}$ of $198.50 is about $50.

It looks as if she multiplied by 25, not 25 percent.

CONCEPT CHECK

SELF-CHECK ✓

Complete the problems, then check your answers at the end of the book on page 804.

2. A picture frame requires 36 inches of frame moulding at $5.99 a foot. About how much will the moulding cost?
About $18.00; 36″ = 3 ft and 3 × $6 = $18

WORKSHOP NOTES

PRACTICE

Determine the reasonableness of the estimate. If it is not reasonable, state what error was made.

	Problem	Estimate	Reasonable	Error (if any)
3.	20% of $496.98	$ 100	a.	b.
4.	5 gallons of gas at $1.29 per gallon	650	a.	b.
5.	$14,203.00 ÷ 200	700	a.	b.
6.	98.7 × 516	50,000	a.	b.
7.	Tip of 15% on $19.47	3	a.	b.
8.	Sales tax of 5% on $1014.74	5	a.	b.
9.	$15.00 per sq yd carpeting for 2′ × 5′ area	150	a.	b.
10.	$49.79 − $19.49	70	a.	b.

3. a. Yes
b. No error

4. a. No
b. Used $130 instead of $1.29

5. a. No
b. Decimal point; estimate: $70

6. a. Yes
b. No error

7. a. Yes
b. No error

8. a. No
b. Decimal point; estimate: $50

9. a. No
b. Used 10 sq ft instead of 1 sq yd; estimate: $15

10. a. No
b. Added instead of subtracted; estimate: $30

11. Ursula VanMeer bought 100 shares of stock at $18 per share. One year later, she sold all her shares at $23 per share. About how much did she make on her stock? **about $500**

12. A new minivan costs $24,897. About how much would 4 minivans cost? **about $100,000**

13. If the sales tax rate is 6.5 percent, about how much sales tax will be due on a $24,897 minivan? **about $1,600**

14. If a 10 percent down payment is required to finance the purchase of a $24,897 minivan, about how much money would you need for a down payment? **about $2,500**

15. Emil Wauseka is buying a used car with a total purchase price including interest of $14,987. He plans to make a $3,000 down payment and to finance the rest for 5 years. About how much will his monthly payments be? **about $200**

16. Cheng Siau Yian purchased 6 dozen cupcakes for the 25 children attending a birthday party. All the cupcakes were eaten. About how many cupcakes did each child eat? **about 3**

17. Clayton Burrington purchased the following school supplies on sale: a $2.79 notebook for $1.99, a $1.49 ballpoint pen for $0.99, a $1.99 pack of notebook paper for $0.99, and a $3.49 automatic pencil for $2.79. Estimate the total savings. **about $3**

18. It is about 1,300 feet around the bicycle test track. How many times must you ride around the track to ride about 1 mile? **4 times**

19. Fruit baskets containing 6 apples, 4 oranges, and 2 grapefruits are on sale for $10.98. If you have 148 apples, 121 oranges, and 64 grapefruits, about how many fruit baskets can be made? **about 25**

 **3 ASSESS**

When using estimates to check the reasonableness of an answer, students may make a poor estimate and conclude the answer is not reasonable. However, this is not very likely to happen as most estimates can readily establish the degree of magnitude of the answer (that is to say, the correct answer is in the hundreds, or ten thousands, or millions).

Example 2 illustrates well the fact that the answer of $4,962.50 cannot possibly be correct because Kaselman is taking 25 percent of a number much smaller than $4,962.50, namely $198.50, and therefore, the answer must be less than $198.50. Finding the estimate shows the answer to be about $50.

4 CLOSE

The Practice problems can be assigned for class work and the answers checked in class to help students master the objective of the lesson.

WRAP-UP

In Example 2, change the percent to 125 percent and ask students to explain why the answer of $4,962.50 is much too large. **Using estimation, 125 percent of $198.50 is about $250.00. By mental math, 100 percent of a number is the number itself, and 25 percent of $198.50 is about $50.00. Therefore, $198.50 + 50.00 is about $250.00.**

Assignment Guide
Basic: 3–10
Average: 11–16

20 min.

1 FOCUS

Objectives

To solve problems by constructing a table.

2 TEACH

Use Example 1 to reteach solving problems by constructing a table. A table lists possible solutions. In the solution to Example 1, 16 new cars and no used cars are used to start the list because a total of 16 cars were sold. After three possibilities are listed, it is clear that 14 and 2 make a combination that is too high. Instead of continuing to list all combinations, have students choose a lower combination. In the example, 9 and 7 is the correct combination. The power of using a table is that the solution will eventually be found as the possibilities are listed. So the method of constructing a table provides a somewhat mechanical way to solve problems.

Problem-Solving Strategy: Constructing a Table

Constructing a table can be a good way of solving some problems. By organizing the data into a table, it is easier to identify the information that you need. A table is useful in classifying information.

Example 1

Meredith McCall is a car salesperson. For each new car she sells, she earns 10 bonus points; for each used car she sells, she earns 5 bonus points. She earned 125 bonus points by selling 16 cars last week. How many of each type of car did she sell?

STEP: Construct a table in order to evaluate the possibilities.

Figure W33.1

	New Cars	Used Cars	Total Points	
Start at 16 and 0 →	16	0	160 ←	$(16 \times 10) + (0) = 160 + 0$
	15	1	155 ←	$(15 \times 10) + (1 \times 5) = 150 + 5$
Too high; try a lower combination	14	2	150 ←	$(14 \times 10) + (2 \times 5) = 140 + 10$
	9	7	125 ←	$(9 \times 10) + (7 \times 5) = 90 + 35$

McCall sold 9 new cars and 7 used cars.

CONCEPT CHECK

SELF-CHECK ✓

Complete the problems, then check your answers at the end of the book on page 804.

1. A total of 11 vehicles consisting of unicycles (1 wheel) and bicycles (2 wheels) went by. Eighteen wheels were counted. How many of each were there?

   7 bicycles; 4 unicycles

Number of Bikes		Number of Wheels		Total Number of Wheels
Unicycles	Bicycles	Unicycles	Bicycles	
1	10	1	20	21
2	9	2	18	20
3	8	3	16	19
4	7	4	14	18

Example 2

Tomas Flores has a total of 20 coins consisting of dimes and quarters. The total value of the coins is $4.70. How many of each coin does he have?

WORKSHOP NOTES

_____

_____

_____

_____

_____

_____

_____

STEP: Construct a table in order to evaluate the possibilities.

Number of		Value of		Total Value
Quarters	Dimes	Quarters	Dimes	
20	0	$5.00	$0.00	$5.00
19	1	4.75	0.10	4.85
18	2	4.50	0.20	4.70

Flores has 18 quarters and 2 dimes.

Figure W33.2

WORKSHOP

CONCEPT CHECK

Complete the problems, then check your answers at the end of the book on page 804.

SELF-CHECK ✓

2. Lieutenant Sampson is a recruitment officer for the Marines. For each high school graduate he recruits, he gets 5 points; for each college graduate, 11 points. He earned 100 points last week by recruiting 14 high school and college graduates. How many of each did he recruit? **9 high school; 5 college**

PRACTICE

3. Nine cycles were produced using 21 wheels. How many bicycles and tricycles were produced? **6 bicycles; 3 tricycles**

4. Third National Bank charges a monthly service fee of $5.00 plus $0.25 per check. The bank is changing its policy to a $6 service charge and $0.15 per check. A bank officer said you would save money with the new system. How many checks must you write each month in order to save money? **11**

5. Wanda Cross has a total of 40 coins consisting of nickels and quarters with a total value of $6. How many of each coin does she have? **20 nickels; 20 quarters**

6. The Theatre Club sold a total of 415 tickets. The adult tickets cost $5 and the children's tickets cost $3. If $1,615 was collected, how many adult tickets were sold? **185**

7. There are 56 stools in the storeroom. Some stools have 3 legs and some have 4 legs. If there are 193 legs, how many 4-legged stools are in the storeroom? **25**

8. Steve Swartz has 4 dimes and 3 nickels. List the amounts of all the exact-change telephone calls Swartz could make using 1 or more of these coins. **11**

9. How many different ways can you make change for a quarter? **12**

10. Cambria Davis has exactly 20 dimes, 20 nickels, and 20 pennies. Find all the ways Davis can choose 22 coins whose total value is $1 if she must use at least 1 coin of each type. **2 (5 pennies, 15 nickels, 2 dimes or 10 pennies, 6 nickels, 6 dimes)**

11. Frank DeGeorge has $0.69 in coins. Bob White asked DeGeorge for change for a half-dollar. DeGeorge tried to make change but found that he didn't have the coins to do so. What coins did DeGeorge have if each coin was less than a half-dollar? **4 pennies; 4 dimes; 1 quarter**

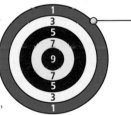

Figure W33.3

12. Christina Carranza was playing darts. She threw six darts, all of which hit the target shown in Figure W33.3. Which of the following scores could be hers: 2, 19, 58, 28, 33, or 37? **28**

Workshop 33 Problem-Solving Strategy: Constructing a Table ▶ **69**

③ ASSESS

The key to avoiding errors in constructing a table is to label the heading correctly. Then the data will fall into place naturally. Stress the importance of reading the problem carefully and identifying the information given.

Also, the question asked in the problem must be understood. Then a start can be made on constructing the table. Encourage students to check their first few entries in the table to see that they meet the conditions of the problem.

④ CLOSE

The Practice problems can be assigned for class work and the answers checked in class to help students master the objective of the lesson.

WRAP-UP

The following problem can be used to summarize the objective of this workshop. Solve by constructing a table.

Chuck, Amy, Jim, and Sue each subscribes to one of the following magazines: *Sports Today*, *Teen Times*, *Car Care*, and *Newsworld*. Use the following clues to determine which person subscribes to which magazine.
• Chuck's magazine has a one-word title.
• Amy hates sports.
• Jim changed the type of car wax he uses after reading an article in this magazine.
(Chuck, *Newsworld*; Jim, *Car Care*; Amy, *Teen Times*; Sue, *Sports Today*)

Assignment Guide
   Basic: 3–7   Average: 8–9

20 min.

69

 FOCUS

Objectives

To solve a problem by using a pattern.

2 TEACH

Discuss Example 1. Ask students what purpose the list or table serves (**it helps to organize the data so that a pattern can be identified**). Finding a pattern is the difficult part of solving a problem.

Ask students why $1.50 is subtracted from $2.55. **To get the total difference between the starting point in the pattern, $1.50, and the end point, $2.55. Dividing this difference, $1.05, by each increase in the pattern, $0.15, yields the number of quarters in the pattern, 7. Therefore, there are 8 dimes, since the total number of coins is 15.**

Problem-Solving Strategy: Looking for a Pattern

ORGANIZING THE INFORMATION Some problems can be solved more easily if the information is first organized into a list or table. Then the list or table can be examined to see if a pattern exists. A pattern may not "jump out" at you, but you may be able to discover a pattern after manipulating the information.

Example 1

Marie Arteshaw has 15 coins consisting of dimes and quarters. The total value of the coins is $2.55. How many of each coin does she have?

STEP: Calculate the number of coins given.

Given: Fifteen coins consisting of dimes and quarters.
The table displays different combinations of dimes and quarters with the total number of coins equaling 15.

Number of Dimes	15	14	13	12	11	
Number of Quarters	0	1	2	3	4	Look for
Total Value	$1.50	$1.65	$1.80	$1.95	$2.10	a pattern

You could continue the table, but it is easier if you see the pattern. Each time you take away a dime and add a quarter, the total value increases by $0.15. The difference between $2.55 and $1.50 is $1.05 and $1.05 ÷ $0.15 = 7. Therefore, subtract 7 from 15 and conclude that **there are 8 dimes and 7 quarters.** The total value of 7 quarters and 8 dimes is

$$(7 \times \$0.25) + (8 \times \$0.10) = \$1.75 + \$0.80 = \$2.55$$

CONCEPT CHECK

SELF-CHECK✔

Complete the problems, then check your answers at the end of the book on page 804. Write the next three numbers for the established pattern.

1. 1, 3, 9, 27, . . . **81, 243, 729**   **2.** 2, 4, 7, 11, . . . **16, 22, 29**

PRACTICE

In Problems 3–10, look for a pattern and then write the next three numbers.

3. 10, 16, 22, 28, . . . **34, 40, 46**   **4.** 2, 4, 8, 16, . . . **32, 64, 128**

5. 30, 27, 24, 21, . . . **18, 15, 12**   **6.** 8, 4, 2, 1, . . . $\frac{1}{2}, \frac{1}{4}, \frac{1}{8}$

7. 1, 4, 9, 16, . . . **25, 36, 49**   **8.** 2, 3, 5, 9, 17, 33, . . . **65, 129, 257**

9. 1, 4, 13, 40, 121, 364, . . . **1,093, 3,280, 9,841**   **10.** 1, 1, 2, 3, 5, 8, 13, . . . **21, 34, 55**

WORKSHOP NOTES

11. Sy Mah has 20 coins consisting of dimes and quarters. Their total value is $3.80. How many of each coin does Mah have? **8 dimes; 12 quarters**

12. Alicia Sanchez had 185 tickets to the school play. Adult tickets sold for $4 each and children's tickets sold for $2 each. The total value was $594. How many of each ticket did she sell? **112 adult; 73 children**

13. (Refer to Figure W34.1.) Three-sided numbers, such as 3, are so named because dots can be used to form a triangle with an equal number of dots on each side. What three-sided number has 12 dots on a side? **33**

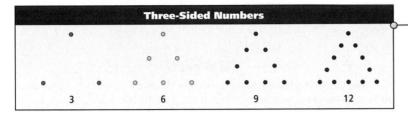

Three-Sided Numbers

3   6   9   12

Figure W34.1

14. On the first day of school, your teacher agrees to allow 1 minute of "fun" at the end of the first day, 2 minutes on the second day, 4 minutes on the third day, 8 minutes on the fourth day, and so on. How much time will you have for "fun" at the end of 10 days? **1,024 minutes**

15. At 9 A.M. there were 7 students in the computer room. At 9:30 A.M. 2 students left and at 10 A.M. 1 student arrived. At 10:30 A.M. 2 students left and at 11 A.M. 1 student arrived. This pattern continued with 2 students leaving at half past the hour and 1 student arriving on each hour. At what time did the computer room first become empty? **2:30 P.M.**

16. Keshawn and Derrick Kinsman were responsible for total lawn care of the factory grounds. The first week Keshawn mowed half the lawn. The next week, he mowed two-thirds as much as he had the first week. The third week, he mowed three-fourths as much as he had the second week, and so on. The tenth week, he mowed ten-elevenths as much as he mowed the ninth week. How much of the lawn did Keshawn mow the tenth week? $\frac{1}{11}$

17. There are 2 rectangular storage rooms whose sides are whole numbers and whose area and perimeter are the same number. What are their dimensions?
4 × 4; 6 × 3

18. A 5-pound bag of lawn food sells for $3.25 and a 3-pound bag sells for $2.29. You need 17 pounds of lawn food. What is the least amount you can pay and buy at least 17 pounds? **$12.04**

19. When it is 12 o'clock, the hands on the face of the clock overlap. How many more times will the hands overlap as the clock runs until it is again 12 o'clock? (Count the second time it is 12 o'clock but not the first.) **11**

20. Before the U.S. Supreme Court opens each year all 9 justices shakes hands with each other. How many handshakes are involved in this ceremony? **36**

3 ASSESS

When working with patterns, students may construct a pattern that does not solve the problem. A check of the result will show that the pattern did not work. Thus they need to start over.

In the example, if students have difficulty understanding the solution, point out that a continuation of the table from 11 dimes to 10, 9, and 8 dimes reveals the final result: **8 dimes, 7 quarters, totaling $2.55.**

Point out however, that if this problem required 50, or 100, or 1,000 steps to extend the table, then finding the pattern would be a much more practical way to solve the problem.

4 CLOSE

The Practice problems can be assigned for class work and the answers checked in class to help students master the objective of the lesson.

WRAP-UP

Work Practice Problem 11 with the students as a cooperative activity to illustrate the objective of this workshop.

Assignment Guide
  Basic: 3–10
  Average: 11–15

20 min.

1 FOCUS

Objectives

To solve problems using the guess-and-check method, or trial-and-error method.

2 TEACH

Work through Example 1 with the students showing all the information in the table. Then have the students look at the total cost figures and ask them if they see a pattern. **(Pairs of values are increasing: $18.13 and $17.63 to $19.22 and $18.72. With this observation, there is no need to continue the table; $18.13 is the lowest cost.)** Thus, emphasize the fact that problem-solving strategies can be combined to solve problems. Point out also that the guess-and-check method employs a good deal of common sense.

Problem-Solving Strategy: Using Guess and Check

One way to solve a problem is by using guess and check, or trial and error. Guessing at a solution doesn't mean making a blind guess in the hopes that it is correct. It means making an informed guess and then checking it against the conditions stated in the problem to determine if it is correct or how to make a better guess. The process is repeated until the correct answer is found.

Example 1

You need 80 sandwich buns. You can buy 8 for $2.09 or 12 for $2.59. What do you buy to obtain at least 80 sandwich buns at the lowest cost?

STEP: Guess and check until you find the lowest cost. Keep your information organized by using a table.

Figure W35.1

Number			Cost		
12/pkg	8/pkg	Total Buns	12/pkg	8/pkg	Total Cost
7	0	84	$(7 \times \$2.59) +$	$(0 \times \$2.09)$	$18.13
6	1	80	$(6 \times 2.59) +$	(1×2.09)	17.63
5	3	84	$(5 \times 2.59) +$	(3×2.09)	19.22
4	4	80	$(4 \times 2.59) +$	(4×2.09)	18.72
3	6	84	$(3 \times 2.59) +$	(6×2.09)	20.31
2	7	80	$(2 \times 2.59) +$	(7×2.09)	19.81
1	9	84	$(1 \times 2.59) +$	(9×2.09)	21.40
0	10	80	$(0 \times 2.59) +$	(10×2.09)	20.90

Six packages of 12 sandwich buns and one package of 8 sandwich buns cost $17.63, the least amount, and result in 80 sandwich buns.

Example 2

The factory building is 4 times as old as the equipment in the factory. Three years from now, the factory building will be 3 times as old as the equipment in the factory. How old is the equipment?

STEP: Guess and check to find the answer. Keep your information organized by using a table.

Figure W35.2

Current Age		Three Years from Now		
Guess Equipment Age	Building (4 × Equipment Age)	Equipment	Building (Current Age + 3)	Check
7	28	10	28 + 3 = 31	Does 10 × 3 = 31? (No)
8	32	11	32 + 3 = 35	Does 11 × 3 = 35? (No)
6	24	9	24 + 3 = 27	Does 9 × 3 = 27? (Yes)

The equipment is now 6 years old.

WORKSHOP NOTES

CONCEPT CHECK

Complete the problem, then check your answer at the end of the book on page 804.

(SELF-CHECK ✓)

1. The product of 3 consecutive whole numbers is 504. What are the numbers?
7, 8, and 9

PRACTICE

2. The hypothetical planet Tetriad only has creatures with 3 legs (triads) or 4 legs (tetrads). Astronauts Peter North and Sally Clark could not bear to look at these ugly creatures, so they kept their eyes on the ground. On their first day on Tetriad, they counted 81 legs as 22 creatures walked by. How many Triads and Tetrads did they meet? **7 Triads and 15 Tetrads.**

3. It costs $0.50 to mail a postcard to Canada and $0.60 to mail a one ounce letter to Canada. Ahmad Checkers wrote to 21 friends and spent $12.00 for postage. How many letters and how many postcards did he write? **15 letters and 6 postcards.**

4. Chantel McDale earns $12 per hour Monday through Friday and $18 per hour on weekends. One week, she worked 49 hours and earned $654. How many hours did she work on the weekend? **11 hours worked on the weekend.**

5. Arrange the 4 dominoes to the right into a domino donut so that all sides equal the same sum (not necessarily the same sum as that of the example at the right). **All sums are 12.**

Figure W35.3

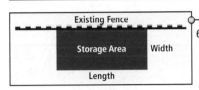

6. Ti Sun wants to fence off a storage area for surplus lumber. She has 96 meters of new fencing to put along an existing fence. What are the dimensions that will give Sun the largest storage area?

Figure W35.4

Existing Fence

Storage Area   Width

Length

6. **Length of 48 m along the existing fence and width of 24 m.**

7. In the square at the right, a rule applies from top to bottom and from left to right. Find the rule and figure out the missing number. **2**

Figure W35.5

6	2	4
2	?	0
4	0	4

8. Batteries come in packs of 3 or 4. If your class needs 30 batteries, how many different ways are there of buying exactly 30 batteries? Which combination do you think would be the cheapest?

8. **Three ways: 10 3-packs, 0 4-packs; 6 3-packs, 3 4-packs; 2 3-packs, 6 4-packs. 2 3-packs and 6 4-packs would probably be the cheapest.**

9. The ages of three delivery vans total 22 years. The green van is the oldest and is 10 years old. The blue van is 6 years younger than the green van. The third delivery van is white. What are the ages of the vans?

9. **Green van: 10 years old; white van: 8 years old; blue van: 4 years old.**

10. The product of 3 consecutive whole numbers is 120. What are the numbers? **4, 5, and 6**

11. Make a sum of 1,000 using some eights and some plus signs.

11. **Many different ways. Here are two: 888 + 8 + 8 + 8 + 8 + 8 + 8 + 8 + 8 + 8 + 8 + 8 + 8 + 8 + 8 + 8 or 888 + 88 + 8 + 8 + 8.**

12. Allison McCardle gave the counter person at Pizza Town a $20 bill for her large one-topping pizza. If the change she received was one-third the cost of the pizza, what did the pizza cost? **$15**

13. At the MetroPark Annual Bike Ride there were 486 participants. Most rode bicycles but there were some that rode tricycles. If there were 1,080 wheels in all, how many bicycles were there? How many tricycles?
378 bicycles and 108 tricycles.

WORKSHOP 35

③ ASSESS

Encourage students not to make wild guesses. The successful use of this strategy rests upon understanding the problem first and then making a fairly accurate guess. The result of the guess should be examined and then a second, improved guess made. This procedure is followed until the answer is found.

When using the guess-and-check method, students need to think about the possibility of there being more than one answer. In Example 1, using a pattern eliminates the possibility of more than one answer.

④ CLOSE

The Practice problems can be assigned for class work and the answer checked in class to help students master the objective of the lesson.

WRAP-UP

Use the following problem to summarize the discussion of the guess and check method.

Roy O'Neal gave the clerk a twenty-dollar bill. His change was $1.00 more than he paid for R&B CD. How much did he pay for the CD? **$9.50**

Assignment Guide
Basic: 2–4
Average: 5–7

20 min.

WORKSHOP 36

Problem-Solving Strategy: Using Simple Algebraic Operations

Previously you practiced writing and solving some basic equations. In this Workshop you'll apply the same technique to additional applications. Remember that equations are solved by applying simple algebraic operations, which are the inverse—or opposite—of the operations indicated, to both sides of the equation.

Example 1

Solve these equations:

a. $x - 3 = 18$ b. $y + 6 = 27$ c. $12z = 48$

d. $\frac{a}{7} = 5$ e. $3b - 5 = 13$ f. $\frac{c}{5} + 3 = 7$

STEPS: Use simple algebraic operations.

a. Since subtraction is indicated, do the inverse of the operation by adding 3 to both sides:

$x - 3 = 18$

$x - 3 + 3 = 18 + 3$, therefore $x = 21$

b. Since addition is indicated, do the inverse of the operation by subtracting 6 from both sides:

$y + 6 = 27$

$y + 6 - 6 = 27 - 6$, therefore $y = 21$

c. Since multiplication is indicated, do the inverse of the operation by dividing both sides by 12:

$12z = 48$

$\frac{12z}{12} = \frac{48}{12}$, therefore $z = 4$

d. Since division is indicated, do the inverse of the operation by multiplying both sides by 7:

$\frac{a}{7} = 5$

$\left(\frac{a}{7}\right) \times 7 = 5 \times 7$, therefore $a = 35$

e. Since both subtraction and multiplication are indicated, do the inverse in the reverse order of operations.

$3b - 5 = 13$

Add 5 to both sides: $3b - 5 + 5 = 13 + 5$, therefore $3b = 18$

Divide both sides by 3: $\frac{3b}{3} = \frac{18}{3}$, therefore $b = 6$

f. Since both addition and division are indicated, do the inverse in the reverse order of operations.

$\frac{c}{5} + 3 = 7$

Subtract 3 from both sides: $\frac{c}{5} + 3 - 3 = 7 - 3$, therefore $\frac{c}{5} = 4$

Multiply both sides by 5: $\frac{c}{5} \times 5 = 4 \times 5$, therefore $c = 20$

WORKSHOP 36

WORKSHOP

① FOCUS

Objectives

1. To solve equations using simple algebraic operations.
2. To solve word problems using algebraic operations.

② TEACH

Write Example 1a on the board: $x - 3 = 18$

First, ask students to explain what this equation means before you ask them to solve it. (**Explain that you're looking for a number; you'll call that number *x* and when you subtract 3 from it, you end up with 18.**)

Explain that to solve an equation, remember these key steps:

1. Get the variable on one side of the equation by performing the opposite arithmetic operation indicated in the equation.
2. Perform the same operation on the other side of the equation.
3. Simplify the equation, which means to perform the arithmetic.

Since the equation says to subtract 3 from *x*, do the opposite and add 3. (**$x - 3 + 3$**)

Perform the same operation on the other side of the equation. (**$x - 3 + 3 = 18 + 3$**)

Now simplify, which means to perform the arithmetic: $x - 0 = 21$; therefore $x = 21$. **Check your answer. Is $21 - 3 = 18$? Yes.**

WORKSHOP NOTES

CONCEPT CHECK

Complete the problems, then check your answers at the end of the book on page 804.

(SELF-CHECK ✓)

1. Solve these equations:
   a. $6m - 4 = 26$ b. $\frac{n}{3} + 12 = 15$ c. $\frac{2p}{5} - 9 = 3$

1. a. **Add 4, divide by 6: $m = 5$**
   b. **Subtract 12, multiply by 3: $n = 9$**
   c. **Add 3, multiply by 5, divide by 2: $p = 30$**

PRACTICE

Solve the equations in Problems 2–7.

2. $5r - 6 = 29$ **$r = 7$**   3. $\frac{s}{5} + 3 = 6$ **$s = 15$**

4. $\frac{2t}{7} - 4 = 6$ **$t = 35$**   5. $7u + 12 = 75$ **$u = 9$**

6. $\frac{v}{11} - 4 = 3$ **$v = 77$**   7. $\frac{5w}{8} + 31 = 36$ **$w = 8$**

8. You're thinking of a number, such that, if you add 9 to the product of that number and 5, then the sum will be 49. What number are you thinking of? **8**

9. Julio Montoya earns $16.80 per hour for a 40-hour work week. How much more per week would Montoya earn if he received a 10 percent increase in his hourly rate? **$67.20**

10. Alicia McKey has a plot of land that has a perimeter of 1,490 feet. If the length is 5 feet more than the width:
    a. What is the width of the plot of land? **370′**
    b. What is the length of the plot of land? **375′**
    c. What is the area of the plot of land? **138,750 square feet**

11. The Drama Club sold $1,345 worth of tickets for their production of *Oliver*. Adult tickets sold for $6.75 per ticket, while children's tickets sold for $3.50. If there were 245 tickets sold in all, how many adult tickets were sold? **150**

12. Krio Packaging Corporation averaged 158 units per day for Monday through Thursday. How many units would have to be produced on Friday for Krio to average 165 units per day for Monday through Friday? **193**

13. Malcolm Freddy starts out on a 100-mile bicycle ride at 9:00 A.M., averaging 12 miles per hour. At 11:00 A.M., Justin Garret starts out on the same route, averaging 18 miles per hour. At what time would Garret catch up with Freddy? **3:00 P.M.**

14. You're thinking of a number, such that, if you subtract 3 from the product of that number and 7, and then divide that difference by 13, and then double that quotient and add 30, you'll end up with 50. What number are you thinking of? **19**

15. Robert is thinking that his father is 7 years more than twice his own age, and his grandfather is 4 years less than twice his father's age. If Robert's grandfather is 70 years of age, how old is Robert? **15**

Workshop 36 Problem-Solving Strategy: Using Simple Algebraic Operations ▶ **75**

3 ASSESS

Students may require help setting up the equations for the word problems. Help them sort out what they already know in the problem and what they need to know.

4 CLOSE

The Practice problems can be assigned for class work and the answers checked in class to help students master the objective of the lesson.

WRAP-UP

Call upon individual students to read their answer to Practice Problems 2–4. Go over any problem for which a wrong answer is given.

Assignment Guide
   Basic: 2–7
Average: 8–12

20 min.

1 FOCUS

Objectives

To solve problems working backwards.

2 TEACH

After working the examples with students, emphasize that the following conditions necessitate working backward to find a solution: (1) a *series* of actions or events is described and the end result is given and (2) the task is to determine the conditions at a previous action.

Now go back over the examples and point out that the series of actions in Example 1 is the year-by-year value of the van. Ask students what the end result is? **($9,000)** What is the previous event? **(Value last year)** Ask similar questions about Example 2.

Problem-Solving Strategy: Working Backward

Problems that involve a sequence of events or actions can sometimes be solved by working backward. If the final result of the problem is given, start your solution with that result and work backward to arrive at the beginning conditions of the problem.

Example 1

Each year a delivery van is worth $\frac{3}{4}$ of its value from the previous year. A van is now worth $9,000. What was its value last year?

STEP 1: Work backward. What is the van worth now?

$9,000

STEP 2: How does last year's value relate to this year's value?

$\frac{3}{4}$ of last year's value = this year's value

$$\frac{3}{4}x = \$9,000$$

STEP 3: Solve.

$x = \$9,000 \div \frac{3}{4}$

$x = \$12,000$

The van was worth $12,000 last year.

Example 2

Central Bakery baked some cookies and put $\frac{1}{2}$ of them away for the next day. Then Central Bakery divided the remaining cookies evenly among its 3 sales outlets so that each outlet received 40 dozen. How many cookies did Central Bakery bake?

STEP: Work backward.

Each of the 3 sales outlets received 40 dozen cookies. Thus, Central Bakery divided a total of 120 dozen cookies. The 120 dozen cookies represent one half of what was baked; therefore, **they baked 240 dozen cookies.**

CONCEPT CHECK

Complete the problem, then check your answer at the end of the book on page 804.

1. A water lily doubles itself in size each day. It takes 30 days from the time the original plant is placed in a pond until the surface of the pond is completely covered with lilies. How long does it take for the pond to be half covered? **29 days**

PRACTICE

2. Cab Company charges a flat fee of $3.75 plus $0.30 for every $\frac{1}{4}$ mile driven. Dick Lewis paid a driver a total of $7.95 for a trip from the airport to his office. How many miles did he travel? **$3\frac{1}{2}$ miles**

WORKSHOP NOTES

3. A recipe for 24 medium-sized pancakes requires 2 eggs. Eggs are sold in cartons of 12 eggs. The Central High School band boosters plan to serve 240 people an average of 3 pancakes each. How many cartons of eggs are needed? **5 cartons**

4. Two barrels—A and B—contain unspecified amounts of cider, with A containing more than B. From A, pour into B as much cider as B already contains. Then from B, pour into A as much cider as A now contains. Finally, pour from A into B as much cider as B presently has. Both barrels now contain 80 litres of cider. How many liters of cider were in each barrel at the start of the process? **A: 110 L, B: 50 L**

5. Your company issued you a car that is now worth $12,000. An article states that each year this car is worth 80 percent of its previous year's value. What was the value of this car last year when you go it? **$15,000**

6. Tiffany Cole starts at point A and enters a fun house. She pays $2 to get in and loses half of the money in her possession while she is in the fun house. She then pays $1 when she exits at B. She goes to the next entrance (C), pays $2 to get in, loses half of her money, and pays $1 to exit at D. This is repeated until she exits at H and gives her last $1 to get out. How much money did she start with? **$60**

Figure W37.1

7. Wixey Bakery baked some cookies in their new solar powered oven. Stores No. 1, No. 2, No. 3, and No. 4 sold a total of 4 dozen cookies each. The remainder were put in storage. Later, another dozen cookies were sold and $\frac{1}{3}$ of what was left was sent to stores No. 5 and No. 6. Those two stores sold 2 dozen cookies each and had 9 dozen left between them. How many cookies did Wixey Bakery bake? **56 dozen**

8. Sixty-four players are entered in the company single elimination horseshoe competition. How many matches must be played to determine the winner? **63 matches**

9. In Figure W37.2, if you were to continue the number pattern until you got to the star, what number would you put in the star's square? **62**

Figure W37.2

10. Three girls played a game in which 2 of them won and 1 lost on each play. The girl who lost had to double the points that each winner had at that time by subtracting from her own points. The girls played the game 3 times, each winning twice and losing once. At the end of the 3 plays, each girl had 40 points. How many points did each girl have to start? **20, 35, and 65**

11. There were 8 women and 16 men at the last board of directors meeting. Every few minutes, 1 man and 1 woman (a couple) left the meeting together. How many couples must leave before there are exactly 5 times as many men as women left at the meeting? **6 couples**

12. Sixty-five teams are selected for the NCAA basketball tournament held in March. It is sometimes called "March Madness," and is a single elimination tournament. How many games must be played to determine a champion? **64 games**

13. In Problem 12, if the tournament was changed to a double elimination tournament, how many games would have to be played to determine a champion? **128 games if the champion is undefeated; 129 games if the champion has one loss.**

Workshop 37 Problem-Solving Strategy: Working Backward ▶ **77**

3 ASSESS

When starting with the final result, students must then link it to the previous event. This connection is crucial if previous actions or events are to be determined. Errors in working backwards generally occur at this step. In Example 1, the equation $\frac{3}{4}x = \$9,000$ provides the key connection between the last event (**$9,000**) and the previous event that is worth $\frac{3}{4}$ of its value the previous year.

4 CLOSE

The Practice problems can be assigned for class work and the answers checked in class to help students master the objective of the lesson.

WRAP-UP

Use Practice Problem 3 to illustrate the objective of this workshop.

Assignment Guide
  Basic: 2–5
  Average: 6–10

20 min.

FOCUS

Objectives
To solve problems by writing an equation.

TEACH

Review the meaning of an equation by using some examples. Write N + 7 = 10 on the board. Point out that in an equation the quantities on both sides of the equals sign must be equal. Therefore, N must be equal to 3. Ask students to solve the following equations:

$R - 20 = 50$ **R = 70**
$A + 4 = 13$ **A = 9**
$2W = 10$ **W = 5**
$100 \div B = 20$ **B = 5**

Remind students that writing an equation to solve a word problem involves translating words into mathematical symbols. Go over the words, symbols, and operations in the textbook before working through the examples.

WORKSHOP

Problem-Solving Strategy: Writing an Equation

A word problem can be translated into an equation that is solved by performing the same mathematical operation (adding, subtracting, multiplying, or dividing) to both sides. Solving the equation then leads to the solution of the problem. To set up the equation, look for words in the problem that suggest which of the four mathematical operations to use.

Words	Symbol	Mathematical Operation
The total, how many in all, the sum, plus	+	Addition
The difference, how much more, how much smaller, minus	−	Subtraction
The total for a number of equal items, the product	×	Multiplication
The number left over, the quotient	÷	Division

Example 1

In 40 hours at your regular rate of pay plus 5 hours of double time (twice your regular rate of pay), you earn $425. What is your regular rate of pay?

STEP: Write an equation. (Use the letter x to stand for your regular rate of pay.)

$$40x + 5(2x) = \$425.00$$
$$40x + 10x = \$425.00$$
$$50x = \$425.00$$
$$x = \$\ \ 8.50 \text{ (Divide each side by 50.)}$$

Regular rate of pay is $8.50

Example 2

A rectangle with a perimeter of 48 mm is 20 mm long. What is the width of the rectangle?

STEP: Write an equation. (Let w equal the width of the rectangle.)

$$w + 20 + w + 20 = 48$$
$$2w + 40 = 48 \text{ (Subtract 40 from both sides.)}$$
$$2w = \ \ 8 \text{ (Divide both sides by 2.)}$$
$$w = \ \ 4 \text{ mm wide}$$

The width of the rectangle is 4 mm

WORKSHOP NOTES

Complete the problems, then check your answers at the end of the book on page 804.

 SELF-CHECK ✔

1. The sum of 2 consecutive numbers is 23. What is the smaller number? **11**

2. One brand of computer scanner can read 74 documents per hour while a second scanner can read 92 documents per hour. How many hours will it take for both scanners together to read 747 documents? **4.5 hours**

3. A bottle and a cork cost $1.10. The bottle costs $1.00 more than the cork. How much does each cost? **Cork: $0.05; bottle: $1.05**

4. A robotic delivery unit travels 54 meters in traveling completely around the edge of a rectangular mailroom. If the rectangle is twice as long as it is wide, how long is each side? **18 m × 9 m**

5. A football field is 100 yards long and has a distance around of 308 yards. How wide is it? **54 yards**

6. Kotori and Lenmana Tewamina make monthly payments of $727.20 on their $80,000.00 mortgage. They will have paid $138,160.00 in interest when their mortgage is paid off. For how many years is their mortgage? **25 years**

7. Edith Harris had gross pay of $464.86 last week. She earns $8.85 per hour plus a 3 percent commission on all sales. She knows she worked 40 hours last week, but can't remember her total sales. What were her total sales? **$3,695.33**

8. Regina Herrera earns $7.60 per hour plus double time for all hours over 40 per week. How much did Herrera earn for working 46 hours last week? **$395.20**

9. Wilson Davis has 3 Guernsey cows and 2 Holstein cows that give as much milk in 4 days as 2 Guernsey and 4 Holstein cows give in 3 days. Which kind of cow is the better milk producer: the Guernsey or the Holstein? **Holstein**

10. The Karis Tool & Die Company building is 5 times as old as the equipment. The building was 24 years old when the equipment was purchased. How old is the equipment? **6 years**

11. The sum of 3 consecutive odd numbers is 27. What are the 3 numbers? **7, 9, 11**

12. Universal stock sells for $17 a share. ABC Stock Brokers charges a flat fee of $40 for every transaction. How many shares could you buy for $730? **40**

13. (Refer to Figure W38.1.) Write an equation expressing the relationship between A and B given in Figure W38.1. What would B equal when A is 40? **B = 3A − 2; 118**

A	1	2	3	4	5	. . .
B	1	4	7	10	13	. . .

Figure W38.1

14. In Problem 13, write an equation for A in terms of B. What would A equal when B is 253? **A = (B + 2) ÷ 3; 85**

15. Harry, Jerry, and Darrel have a combined weight of 599 pounds. Jerry weighs 13 pounds more than Harry, while Harry weighs 5 pounds more than Darrel. How much does each man weigh? **Harry = 197; Jerry = 210; Darrel = 192**

Workshop 38 Problem-Solving Strategy: Writing an Equation ▶ **79**

③ ASSESS

There are many opportunities for students to make errors when solving problems by writing an equation. If some students continue to get wrong answers, you'll need to examine their written work to see what errors they may be making. Errors occur when students use the incorrect operation in the translation process, or they may not use the correct coefficient with the variable. In other words, they don't write the correct equation as a model to solve the problem.

Other types of errors involve not knowing how to solve the equation. Students often forget the fundamental rule that an equation is solved by performing the *same* mathematical operations to both sides of the equation. Emphasize this point when working the examples and going over the solutions to the problems.

④ CLOSE

The Practice problems can be assigned for class work and the answers checked in class to help students master the objective of the lesson

---

WRAP-UP

Write the following sentences on the board. Have students write an equation for each sentence and then solve it.

1. Fifty dollars minus the cost of a sweater equals $22.
   $50 − C = $22; C = $28
2. Thirty-five hours multiplied by an hourly rate equals a gross weekly pay of $287.
   35 × R = $287; R = $8.20
3. The distance from Cobbs Landing to Green Hills is 520 miles. That equals twice the distance from Cobbs Landing to Glenview minus 20 miles. **520 = 2D − 20; D = 270**

Assignment Guide
   Basic: 2–5
Average: 6–12

 20 min.

WORKSHOP 39

Problem-Solving Strategy: Linear Combinations

1 FOCUS

Objectives

1. To solve linear combinations algebraically.
2. To add and subtract two equations.
3. To express one unknown in terms of the other.

2 TEACH

This lesson focuses on solving linear combinations, which may be a difficult concept for some students to grasp. Explain that linear combinations are equations with two unknowns. Build student confidence by writing this problem on the board: $A - 10 = 15$. Tell students that they already know how to solve this type of equation with 1 unknown.

Read Example 1 with students. Point out that the two unknowns are the number of nickels (N) and the number of dimes (D). Using information in the problem, they can set up two equations:

Equation 1: $0.05N + \$0.10D = \$3.05$ because the value of the nickels plus the value of the dimes is $3.05.

Equation 2: $D = N + 5$ because there are 5 more dimes than nickels.

As students look at these equations ask them to think about how they eliminate one of the variables.

Point out that they can substitute ($N + 5$) for D in the first equation. Thus they would have:

$\$0.05N + \$0.10D = \$3.05$
$\$0.05N + \$0.10(N + 5) = \$3.05$

Show that $\$0.10(N + 5) =$ ($\$0.10 \times N$) + ($\$0.10 \times 5$)

Thus the equation becomes:

$\$0.05N + \$0.10(N + 5) = \$3.05$
$\$0.05N + \$0.10N + \$0.50 = \$3.05$

There are many applications which result in two equations with two unknowns that need to be solved. Such systems are identified as linear combinations and are solved, algebraically, in this method:

Eliminate one of the variables by adding or subtracting the two equations. Then solve the resulting equation in one unknown. Substitute the solution into one of the original equations to find the value of the other variable.

Example 1

At the starting point of the 30 k Cycle Run there were a total of 50 cycles. Some were tricycles (3 wheels) whiles most were bicycles (2 wheels). The equipment counted just the wheels and found a total of 107 wheels. How many bicycles were there? How many tricycles were there?

STEP 1: Identify the unknowns.

Let B = the number of Bicycles ($2B$ wheels)

Let T = the number of Tricycles ($3T$ wheels)

STEP 2: Write the equations.

$B + T = 50$
$2B + 3T = 107$

Multiply the first equation by 3 $\qquad$ $3B + 3T = 150$
Subtract the second equation from the first $\qquad \underline{2B + 3T = 107}$
$\qquad\qquad\qquad\qquad\qquad\qquad\qquad\qquad B = 43$

Now substitute 43 for B in the first equation: $\qquad 43 + T = 50$

Therefore $T = 7$

There were 43 bicycles and 7 tricycles.

CONCEPT CHECK

Complete the problem, then check your answers at the end of the book on page 804.

1. The length of a rectangle is twice the width and the perimeter of the rectangle is 42 feet. After finding the width and the length, find the area of the rectangle. **Width = 7 feet; Length = 14 feet; Area = 98 square feet**

WORKSHOP NOTES

_____

_____

_____

_____

_____

_____

_____

_____

_____

Solve the system of equations in Problems 2–7.

2. $4c + 3d = 43$ **c = 7, d = 5**
$5c - 2d = 25$

3. $2g + 7f = 23$ **g = 8, f = 1**
$2g - f = 15$

4. $3m + 2n = 66$ **m = 20, n = 3**
$2m - 3n = 31$

5. $12p + 5q = 63$ **p = 4, q = 3**
$9p + 7q = 57$

6. $2r - 3s = 4$ **r = 11, s = 6**
$3r - 2s = 21$

7. $5v - 4w = 189$ **v = 53, w = 19**
$2v + 5w = 201$

8. When astronauts Antoine Weber and Rachel Sun landed on the hypothetical planet Trifour they found the inhabitants had either 3 or 4 extremities. Weber could not look at the inhabitants' faces so he just counted their extremities. He counted 173 extremities. Sun, on the other hand, could not look at their extremities so she just counted faces. She counted 51 faces. How many inhabitants had 3 extremities? How many were there that had 4 extremities? **31 inhabitants had 3 extremities and 20 inhabitants had 4 extremities**

9. On Friday the corner newsstand sold 5 more copies of *The New York Times* than it did copies of *The Washington Post*. If the newsstand sold 59 copies of *The New York Times* and *The Washington Post* combined, how many of each was sold? **32 copies of the *New York Times* and 27 copies of the *Washington Post***

10. If there are twice as many girls as boys in fourth period English and there are 33 students in all, how many girls are in fourth period English? How many boys? **22 girls and 11 boys**

11. General Auto Sales had sales totaling $1,900,500 during the first quarter compared to sales totaling $2,446,500 during the second quarter. During the second quarter, General Auto sold half as many of their $21,500 model and twice the number of their $28,500 model in the second quarter compared to the first quarter. How many of each model did General Auto sell in the first quarter? How many of each model in the second quarter?

11. Forty-two $21,500 model and thirty-five $28,500 model in the first quarter; Twenty-one $21,500 model and seventy $28,500 model in the second quarter.

12. John North has a paper route of 73 daily customers and 46 Sunday customers. North earns $0.25 more for each Sunday paper he delivers compared to the Monday through Saturday deliveries. If he earns $84.10 per week, how much does he earn from each daily delivery, and how much does he earn from the Sunday delivery? **$0.61 and $0.86**

WRAP-UP

Call upon individual students to read their answer to Practice Problems 2–4. Go over any problem for which a wrong answer is given.

Assignment Guide
    Basic: 2–7
Average: 8–10

20 min.

WORKSHOP 39

Next they need to combine like terms and subtract $0.50 from both sides. The would show:

$0.15N + $0.50 - $0.50 = $3.05 - $0.50
$0.15N = $2.55

Then divide both sides by $0.15
($0.15N ÷ $0.15) = ($2.55 ÷ $0.15)
$N = 17$

If $N = 17$, then $(N + 5) = (17 + 5) = 22$

Conclude that there are 17 nickels and 22 dimes.
Check: ($0.05 × 17) + ($0.05 × 22) = $0.85 + $2.20 = $3.05.

Instead of assigning the Self-Check, you may need to work through it together in class for additional reinforcement in mastering this skill.

 **ASSESS**

Tell students that an important part of solving equations with two unknowns is to check their answers when they are finished. Remind them to substitute the values of the two unknowns in both equations to see if they work. If their values for the variables don't work in the equations, review their work to see if they have set up both equations correctly. If the equations are set up correctly, have students check that they have solved them correctly.

 **CLOSE**

The Practice problems can be assigned for class work and the answers checked in class to help students master the objective of the lesson.

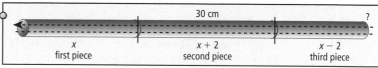
WORKSHOP 40

1 FOCUS

Objectives

To draw a sketch as a means to solving a word problem.

2 TEACH

Example 1 illustrates nicely that drawing a sketch helps to organize the conditions of the problem. The sketch writes the equation, which yields the solution to the problem.

In Example 2 the use of a sketch helps students to avoid the common error made with this problem of having the worm travel through the entire two books. You might suggest that students use graph paper to work the problems.

WORKSHOP

Problem-Solving Strategy: Drawing a Sketch

Some word problems, particularly those that involve lengths, widths, and dimensions, can be simplified if you draw a sketch. Sketches and diagrams can also help you keep track of information in multi-step problems.

Example 1

A 30-cm piece of pipe is cut into 3 pieces. The second piece is 2 cm longer than the first piece, and the third piece is 2 cm shorter than the first piece. How long is each piece?

STEP: Draw a sketch.

Figure W40.1

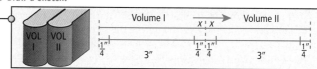

$$x + (x + 2) + (x - 2) = 30$$
$$3x = 30$$
$$x = 10 \text{ cm} \quad \text{(Length of first piece is 10 cm.)}$$
$$x + 2 = 12 \text{ cm} \quad \text{(Length of second piece is 12 cm.)}$$
$$x - 2 = 8 \text{ cm} \quad \text{(Length of third piece is 8 cm.)}$$

Example 2

A 2-volume set of classics is bound in $\frac{1}{4}$-inch covers. The text in each volume is 3 inches thick. The 2 volumes are side by side on the shelf. A bookworm travels from inside the front cover of Volume I to the inside back cover of Volume II. How far does the bookworm travel?

STEP: Draw a sketch.

Figure W40.2

Bookworm travels: $\frac{1}{4}'' + \frac{1}{4}'' = \frac{1}{2}''$

The bookworm travels $\frac{1}{2}$ inch from inside the front cover of Volume I to inside the back cover of Volume II.

CONCEPT CHECK

SELF-CHECK ✓

Complete the problems, then check your answers at the end of the book on page 804.

1. Suppose the bookworm in Example 2 travels from the inside back cover of Volume I to exit out on the front cover of Volume II. How far does the bookworm travel? $3'' + \frac{1}{4}'' + \frac{1}{4}'' + 3'' + \frac{1}{4}'' = 6\frac{3}{4}''$

WORKSHOP NOTES

2. Use an 18-inch, 10-inch, and 7-inch length of board to mark off a length of 15 inches. **(18 in + 7 in) − 10 in**

PRACTICE

3. Tom Khoury leaves his house and jogs 8 blocks west, 5 blocks south, 3 blocks east, 9 blocks north, 6 blocks east, 12 blocks south, 3 blocks west, and then stops to rest. Where is he in relation to his house? **2 blocks west and 8 blocks south**

4. Mariko Fujiwara bicycles to work. She travels 3 miles north of her house, turns right and bikes 2 miles, turns left and bikes 3 miles, and turns left and bikes 5 miles. At this point, where is she in relation to her home? **3 miles west and 6 miles north**

5. The rectangular area allotted to the shoe department of a store has a perimeter of 96 feet. The length of the rectangle is 8 feet longer than the width. What is the width of the rectangle? **20 ft**

6. A barn has dimensions of 50 feet by 60 feet. A cow is tethered to 1 corner of the barn with a 60-foot rope. The cow always stays outside the barn. How many square feet of grazing land can the cow reach? **8,556.5 sq ft**

7. A 60-foot piece of fencing is cut into 3 pieces. The second piece is 3 feet longer than the first piece, and the third piece is 9 feet longer than the first piece. Find the lengths of the pieces. **16 feet; 19 feet; 25 feet**

8. Assuming that each corner must be tacked, what is the least number of tacks that you need to display eight 8-inch by 10-inch photographs? **15**

9. Making identical cuts, a lumberjack can saw a log into 4 pieces in 12 minutes. How long would it take to cut a log of the same size and shape into 8 pieces? **28 minutes**

10. Master Chemical Company has containers with capacities of 4 liters, 7 liters, and 10 liters. How could you use these containers to measure exactly 1 liter? **(4L + 7L) − 10L**

11. Three book volumes are arranged as shown. The thickness of each cover is 0.2 cm. The text in each volume is 3 cm thick. What is the distance from the first page of Volume I to the last page of Volume III? **3.8 cm**

Figure W40.3

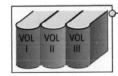

12. A dog is on a 12-foot leash that is tied to the corner of a 10-foot by 15-foot shed. The dog always stays outside the shed. How many square feet of ground can the dog reach? **342.26 sq ft**

13. Ohio Airlines is to provide service between cities as shown on the map. The airline employed 5 new people to sit in the control tower at each of the 5 cities. The people are Carol, Connie, Clare, Charles, and Cedric. The 2 people in the cities with connecting routes will be talking to each other a great deal, so it would be helpful if these people were friends. The pairs of friends are: Charles Connie, Carol Cedric, Charles Carol, Clare Cedric, and Carol Clare. Place the 5 people in the 5 cities so that the ones in connecting cities are friends.

Figure W40.4

Cedric or Clare in Canton or Cincinnati; Connie–Cleveland; Charles–Toledo; Carol–Columbus

③ ASSESS

Drawing a sketch helps avoid making errors in a problem. In Example 2 the correct sketch shows the solution immediately. Of course, an inaccurate sketch can lead to an incorrect answer. Point out to students that a sketch is a visual model of the problem and that it must satisfy the data given in the problem. Otherwise it is worthless. Check students' sketches to see that they are drawn carefully and accurately.

④ CLOSE

The Practice problems can be assigned for class work and the answers checked in class to help student's master the objective of the lesson.

WRAP-UP

Have students use graph paper to draw sketches of the following:
1. A square with an area of 4 square units.
2. A rectangle with a width of 3 units and a length that is 2 times the width.
3. A path that starts at 0, goes up 3 units, left 2 units, down 4 units, and right 5 units.
4. A path that starts at 0, goes south 2 units, east 3 units, north 4 units, west 5 units, and south 5 units

Assignment Guide
  Basic: 3–7
Average: 8–12

20 min.

WORKSHOP 41

1 FOCUS

Objectives
To solve problems by using a Venn diagram.

2 TEACH

Use the examples to reteach the objective of this workshop. A few key points to emphasize are the following: (1) The size of the circles is not relevant to the problem; (2) intersections of circles contain data from more than one group; and (3) work out from intersecting circles first.

Remind students that a Venn diagram is a visual model of a problem that can clarify the relationships among the various elements of the problem.

WORKSHOP

Problem-Solving Strategy: Making a Venn Diagram

Some problems can be solved with a diagram. Making a diagram can be an effective way of showing the information in a problem. In this workshop, you'll use diagrams called Venn diagrams. They can be used to show the relationship among several groups of people, animals, or objects.

Example 1

Figure W41.1

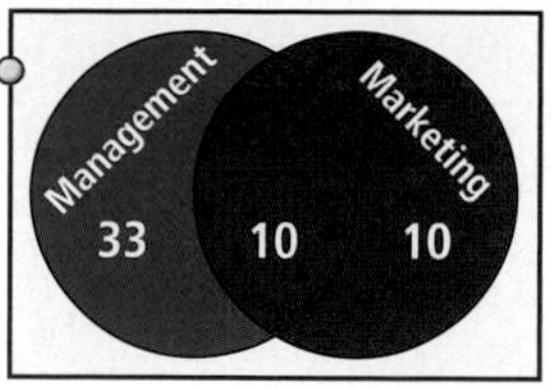

Of 53 employees surveyed, 43 have degrees in management, 20 have degrees in marketing, and 10 in both. How many have degrees in marketing but not management? Make a Venn diagram. Draw two intersecting circles—one for management and one for marketing. Work out from the middle region.

STEP 1: Fill in the number in both classes.   10

STEP 2: Fill in the remaining number in management. $43 - 10 = 33$

STEP 3: Fill in the remaining number in marketing. $20 - 10 = 10$

STEP 4: Add the numbers. $33 + 10 + 10 = 53$

Ten employees have degrees in marketing but not management.

Example 2

Two hundred people returning from a trip to Europe were asked which countries they had visited. One hundred forty-eight had been to England, 116 had been to France, and 96 had been to Spain. Eighty-two had been to England and France, 71 had been to France and Spain, 56 had been to England and Spain, and 44 had visited all 3 countries.

a. How many had visited France but not England or Spain?

b. How many had not visited any of these 3 countries?

STEP: Make a Venn diagram.

Figure W41.2

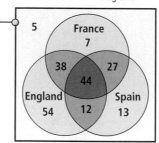

a. Follow the procedures:

- Draw a Venn diagram as shown.
- Forty-four visited all 3 countries.
- Twelve visited England and Spain only. $(56 - 44)$
- Twenty-seven visited France and Spain only. $(71 - 44)$
- Thirty-eight visited England and France only. $(82 - 44)$

WORKSHOP NOTES

- Thirteen visited Spain only. [96 − (12 + 44 + 27)]
- Seven visited France only. [116 − (38 + 44 + 27)]
- Fifty-four visited England only. [148 − (38 + 44 + 12)]

Seven people visited France only.

b. [200 − (54 + 7 + 13 + 38 + 27 + 12 + 44)] = 200 − 195 = 5

Five people did not visit any of the 3 countries.

CONCEPT CHECK

Complete the problems, then check your answers at the end of the book on page 804.

1. Of 12 classmates, 6 went to the game, 7 went to the dance, and 4 went to both. How many went to neither? **3**

PRACTICE

2. There are 197 delegates in the International Trade Association. Eighty-five of them speak Spanish, 74 speak French, and 15 speak both French and Spanish.
   a. How many speak Spanish but not French? **70**
   b. How many speak French but not Spanish? **59**
   c. How many speak neither French nor Spanish? **53**

3. A survey of 150 people revealed that 121 people watch the early evening TV news, 64 watch the noon news, and 47 watch both. How many do not watch either one? **12**

4. A survey of 120 college junior business students produced these results: 40 read a national newspaper, 48 read the local paper, 70 read the campus paper, 25 read a national newspaper and the local paper, 28 read the local paper and the campus paper, 21 read the campus paper and a national newspaper, and 18 read all three papers.
   a. How many do not read any of the papers? **18**
   b. How many read a national newspaper and the local paper but not the campus paper? **7**

5. Of 20 students eating at a local deli, 14 ordered salad, 10 ordered soup, and 4 ordered both salad and soup. How many did not order either? **none**

6. One hundred employees were asked which sports they play. Fifty play football, 48 play basketball, 54 play baseball, 24 play both football and basketball, 22 play both basketball and baseball, 25 play both football and baseball, and 14 play all 3 sports.
   a. How many play basketball only? **16**
   b. How many play football and baseball but not basketball? **11**
   c. How many play none of the 3 sports? **5**

7. In a marketing survey, 500 people were asked their 2 favorite colors. Red was chosen by 380, blue by 292, and 10 chose neither red nor blue.
   a. How many like both colors? **182**
   b. How many like red but not blue? **198**

WORKSHOP

3 ASSESS

Most students probably will not have any difficulty with Example 1. Example 2, however, is another matter. The relationships in this example are more complex, and you will need to help students not only draw the diagram correctly, but you will also need to help them find the correct number in each group. Again, stress that the place to begin is with those people who had visited all three countries. This group of 44 is represented by the intersection of all three circles. Secondly, the groups represented by the intersections of two circles should be determined. Thirdly, those people who have visited only one country are found. Knowing all of the above groups allows students to find the number of people who had not visited any of the three countries.

If students can understand and solve Example 2 successfully, they should not have any difficulty with the problems. Generally, students make errors in finding the numbers in the intersection group because they tend to get overwhelmed by all the data. The way to avoid the problem is to break down the original problem into a series of simple problems and to solve the simple problems one at a time.

4 CLOSE

The Practice problems can be assigned for class work and the answers checked in class to help students master the objective of the lesson.

WRAP-UP

Have students draw a Venn diagram to represent the following.
A survey of 100 teenagers found that
- 59 have seen the movie *Blue Crush*
- 51 have seen *Lord of the Rings*
- 48 have seen *Crossroads*
- 32 have seen *Lord of the Rings* and *Crossroads*
- 27 have seen *Blue Crush* and *Crossroads*
- 6 have seen *Blue Crush* and *Lord of the Rings*
- 20 have seen all three movies

Assignment Guide
Basic: 2–3 **Average:** 4–5

20 min.

Objectives

To solve a problem by restating it as a simple problem or as a series of simple problems.

Very often restating a problem as a series of simpler problems is the key to solving a difficult problem. Work through both examples with students to illustrate the point. In Example 1 the problem becomes easier by asking the right questions: How many matches does a player have to lose to be out of the tournament? **(1)** Then who is left? **The winner**

Problem-Solving Strategy: Using Simpler Numbers

To solve a problem, you may find it helpful to restate the problem in a different way. A difficult problem can be restated as a simpler problem and become easier to solve. Or a problem may involve a series of simpler problems that will lead to the solution of the original problem. Sometimes solving a similar problem with smaller or easier numbers will help.

Example 1

The National Football League playoffs start with twelve teams. The playoffs are a single elimination tournament. Single elimination means that you are eliminated from the playoffs if you lose a game. How many games will have to be played to determine the Super Bowl Champion? (Hint: A similar problem was encountered in the "Working Backward" workshop.)

STEP: Restate the problem.

Given that it is a single elimination tournament, every team (but the champion) will have to lose one game. Since 11 teams will have to lose 1 game, 11 games will have to be played. **Eleven games will have to be played to determine the Super Bowl Champion.**

Example 2

A 27-inch bicycle wheel makes 100 revolutions per minute. A stone stuck in the treads will travel how many feet in 1 hour?

STEP: Restate the problem to follow a series of simpler problems.

a. How many inches will the stone travel in 1 revolution?
$C = 3.14d$ or 3.14×27 inches $= 84.78$ inches

b. How many inches will the stone travel in 1 minute?
100 rpm $\times$ 84.78 inches per revolution $= 8,478$ inches

c. How many inches will the stone travel in 1 hour?
8,478 inches per minute $\times$ 60 minutes per hour $= 508,680$ inches

d. How many feet will the stone travel in 1 hour?
508,680 inches $\div$ 12 inches per foot $= 42,390$ feet
The stone will travel 42,390 feet in one hour.

CONCEPT CHECK

SELF-CHECK ✓

Complete the problem, then check your answer at the end of the book on page 804.

1. A 27-inch bicycle wheel makes 100 revolutions per minute. A stone stuck in the treads will travel how many *miles* in 1 hour? (Round the answer to the nearest mile.) **42,390 ÷ 5,280 = 8.028 miles**

WORKSHOP NOTES

2. Your automobile's gas mileage is 27.5 miles per gallon. Last month your automobile was driven 1,595 miles and a gallon of gasoline cost $1.19. What did it cost to buy gasoline for your automobile last month? **(1,595 ÷ 27.5) × $1.19 = $69.02**

3. (Note that $1 + 3 = 4$, $1 + 3 + 5 = 9$, and $1 + 3 + 5 + 7 = 16$)
   What is the sum of the first 25 odd numbers? **$25^2 = 625$**

4. Vanna Burzinski works in the stockroom at Keynote Auto Supply. Burzinski always stacks crates using the triangular pattern shown. The top row always has 1 crate. Each row always has 2 fewer crates than the row before it.

   Figure W42.1

   a. How many crates are in a stack that has 20 rows? **$20^2 = 400$**
   b. How many crates are in a stack if the bottom row has 29 crates? **$15^2 = 225$**

5. Tabathia Russell is having a party. The first time the doorbell rings, 3 guests arrive. Each time the doorbell rings after that, a group arrives with 2 more guests than the preceding group.
   a. How many guests arrive on the seventh ring? **15**
   b. If the doorbell rings ten times, how many guests came to the party? **99**

6. The Baron Collier High School Shootout is a 48 team double elimination basketball tournament. Double elimination means that a team is out of the tournament if it loses two games.
   a. How many games will have to be played to determine a winner?
   b. Why are there two possible answers?

6. a. **94 games if champion is undefeated; 95 games if champion has one loss.**
   b. **The champion may have one loss or may be undefeated.**

7. A train traveling at 60 miles per hour takes 4 seconds to enter a tunnel and another 50 seconds to pass completely through the tunnel.
   a. What is the length of the train in feet? **60 mph × 4 sec × $\left(\dfrac{1 \text{ hr}}{3,600 \text{ sec}}\right)$ × $\left(\dfrac{5,280 \text{ ft}}{1 \text{ mile}}\right)$ = 352 feet**
   b. What is the length of the tunnel in feet?

7. b. **60 mph × 50 sec × $\left(\dfrac{1 \text{ hr}}{3,600 \text{ sec}}\right)$ × $\left(\dfrac{5,280 \text{ ft}}{1 \text{ mile}}\right)$ = 4,400 feet**

8. There are 31 teams in the National Football League. To conduct their annual draft, teams in each city must have a direct telephone line to each of the other teams.
   a. How many direct telephone lines must be installed to accomplish this?
   b. How many direct telephone lines must be installed if the league expands to 36 teams? **(35 × 36) ÷ 2 = 630**

8. a. **30 + 29 + 28 + … + 1 = (30 × 31) ÷ 2 = 465**

9. Grandpa Moyer wanted to leave his 17 horses to his 3 grandsons. Rick was to get $\frac{1}{2}$ of the horses, Mike was to get $\frac{1}{3}$, and Peter was to get $\frac{1}{9}$. How could he accomplish this?

9. **Borrow one horse from neighbor, then 18 × $\frac{1}{2}$ = 9 for Rick, 18 × $\frac{1}{3}$ = 6 for Mike, and 18 × $\frac{1}{9}$ = 2 for Peter, and then return horse to neighbor.**

10. Two cyclists start toward each other from points 25 miles apart. Cyclist No. 1 travels 15 mph, while Cyclist No. 2 travels 10 mph. A trained bird leaves the shoulder of Cyclist No. 1 and travels to the shoulder of Cyclist No. 2 and back and forth until the cyclists meet. If the bird flies at 40 mph, how far will the bird fly? **Cyclists will meet in one hour [25 ÷ (15 + 10)], therefore, the bird will fly 40 miles.**

11. Chairs ready for shipment at the Northern Chair factory come down a ramp in single file. Inspector Edgerran Will checks every third chair, beginning with the third. Inspector Julio Lopez checks every fifth chair, beginning with the fifth. If 98 chairs came down the ramp while both inspectors were working on Monday, how many of these chairs were not checked by either of these two inspectors? **53**

WORKSHOP

WORKSHOP 42

③ ASSESS

Finding the simple problem(s) imbedded in a more complicated problem isn't an easy task. Some insight into the problem may be required in order to do this. Also, some approaches may lead into a "blind alley." These approaches shouldn't be considered errors. Rather, students can learn from them by finding out what doesn't work and then try a different approach. As students work the problems, ask questions and provide assistance as needed.

④ CLOSE

The Practice problems can be assigned for class work and the answers checked in class to help students master the objective of the lesson.

WRAP-UP

Write the following problems on the board. Have students solve each problem.

1. Carol earns $8.00 an hour as a word processor. She earns time and a half for any hours over a 35-hour work week. How much does she earn if she works a 55-hour work week? **$520**

2. A rotating sprinkler waters a lawn 40 feet in any direction. How many square feet of lawn can the sprinkler water? **Use $\pi \approx 3.14$; 5,024 ft²**

3. A bicyclist travels at an average rate of 15 mph. If she rides for 6 hours a day, 6 days a week, how many weeks will it take her to travel 21,060 miles? **39 weeks**

Assignment Guide
   Basic: 2–3
Average: 4–8

20 min.

87

PART ② Personal Finance

Part Overview

In Part 2, Personal Finance, students will explore life's most important math skills from how to understand a paycheck stub to keeping a checkbook in balance to buying that first car or home. These are skills, which just happen to involve mathematical applications that everyone needs to know to get by in life.

Key to Descriptive Icons

The following designations will help you decide which activities are appropriate for your students.

L1 **Level 1** activities should be within the ability range of all students.

L2 **Level 2** activities should be within the ability range of the average to above-average students.

L3 **Level 3** activities are designed for the ability range of above-average students.

ELL Activities should be within the ability range of the **English Language Learner.**

LS **Learning Styles** designation represents activities designed to address different learning styles.

CL **Cooperative Learning** activities are designed for small group work.

P **Portfolio** designation represents student products that can be placed into a best-work portfolio.

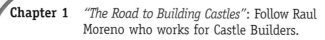

Living in the Real World

In Part 2 students will read the following stories about applying math in life:

Chapter 1 *"The Road to Building Castles"*: Follow Raul Moreno who works for Castle Builders.

Chapter 2 *"Jack's Jackpot"*: A young man finds out that financial freedom isn't everything he had expected.

Chapter 3 *"A Rock Star's Lyrical Leverage"*: A singer/accountant teaches her band a thing or two about life and money on the road.

Chapter 4 *"Fleet Footed Finances"*: A manager explains how this business operates the same way as your personal finances.

Chapter 5 *"Understanding the Williams Sisters"*: Two sisters take a trip to the bank.

Chapter 6 *"Sifting through the Gently Used"*: Take a look inside a business owner's junk, or treasures.

Chapter 7 *"A Financial Gem?"*: A jewelry artist takes a hold of the buying power (and disempowerment) of credit cards.

Chapter 8 *"A Picture-Perfect Loan"*: A little money is needed before a photographer can ride off into the sunset.

Chapter 9 *"A Hard One to Pick"*: An organic farmer does a little vehicle shopping.

Chapter 10 *"The Hunt to Find a Home"*: A family scouts out the Texas landscape for a house.

Chapter 11 *"Insuring Your Life"*: An artist with a healing leg looks for another health insurance plan.

Chapter 12 *"Life after Working Shifts"*: A waitress searches for ways to invest her money.

Teacher Resources

Incorporating Technology

Do you need a little extra help in the classroom? Take a look at the program resources that might make your life easier. These program resources are correlated to technology standards, with your time and efficiency in mind.

Teacher Program Resources

Technology Standard	Technology Resources				
	Mathematics Online	Interactive Lesson Planner	Exam*View*® Pro Test Generator	Student Activity Workbook, TAE CD-ROM	PowerPoint® Presentations
Proficiency in operating equipment	✓			✓	✓
Using technology for research	✓	✓	✓	✓	
Problem solving and collaboration	✓	✓	✓	✓	
Using computers and software to support lessons	✓	✓	✓	✓	✓

Part 2 Intervention and Assessment

Type	Student Edition	Teacher Program Resources
Continuing Needs	pp. 90, 114, 144, 164, 194, 230, 256, 282, 312, 342, 370, 392	Student Activity Workbook, TAE w/ CD-ROM Mathematics Online www.busmath.glencoe.com Teacher Resource Binder, Blackline Masters Teacher Resource Binder, Lesson Plans Teacher Resource Binder, Internet Resources
Cumulative Test Prep	pp. 254–255, 310–311	**Exam**View® Pro Test Generator Assessment Binder, Reproducible Tests Mathematics Online www.busmath.glencoe.com, Quizzes
Open-Ended Assessment	pp. 140–143, 228–229, 280–281, 390–391, 418–419	Assessment Binder, Alternative Assessment Strategies
Chapter Study Guide and Assessment	pp. 109–113, 133–138, 157–162, 189–193, 221–227, 249–253, 273–279, 305–309, 337–341, 365–369, 385–388, 413–417	Student Activity Workbook School-to-Home Activity Workbook
Alternative Assessment	pp. 139, 163, 389	Assessment Binder, Alternative Assessment Strategies Teacher Resource Binder, Internet Resources

Introduction

Take a moment and ask students what life skills they're gaining from their high school experience. **This could be anything— how to work with others, how to write and read for coherence and understanding, how to be on time, how to balance school and personal time, etc.** These are wonderful skills to have and dispense throughout life. Most of these have some element of transaction involved. They're completing something; they're involved in a communicative action involving two or more things. So, what does this have to do with math? Everything.

In Part 2 students will be asked to think and solve many different kinds of transactions that take place in daily life. Tell them this course is applied business math 101 to the nth degree. So, let's get started . . . .

Assessment Options

Part 2 Diagnostic Test
See diagnostic tests in the *Assessment Binder.* Select from the following diagnostic tests on workshops, skills, and applications. Gauge the students' skills on the fundamentals.

PART 2
Personal Finance

Chapter

How do you make a budget?

All in the same weekend, you graduated from high school and you landed a job. Now you can afford to find a place of your own. But wait . . . how much rent can you afford every month? Making a budget can help you live and spend within your means.

88 ◀ Personal Finance

Practicing Life Skills LAB

Procedure

1. The Dream Pad   Look through a local newspaper or an online classified section to find an apartment in an area where you'd like to live. Do you have a new city in mind? Have you always wanted to live in the trendy neighborhood above a coffee shop? Or what about a loft overlooking the city? How many rooms would your ideal apartment have?

2. You've Got Expenses   Make a list of other expenses such as food, utilities, transportation, laundry, and entertainment. Ask family and friends about the average costs of these expenses.

3. Track Your Spending   Complete a spreadsheet or a chart (like the one below) to show how you might spend your net monthly income.

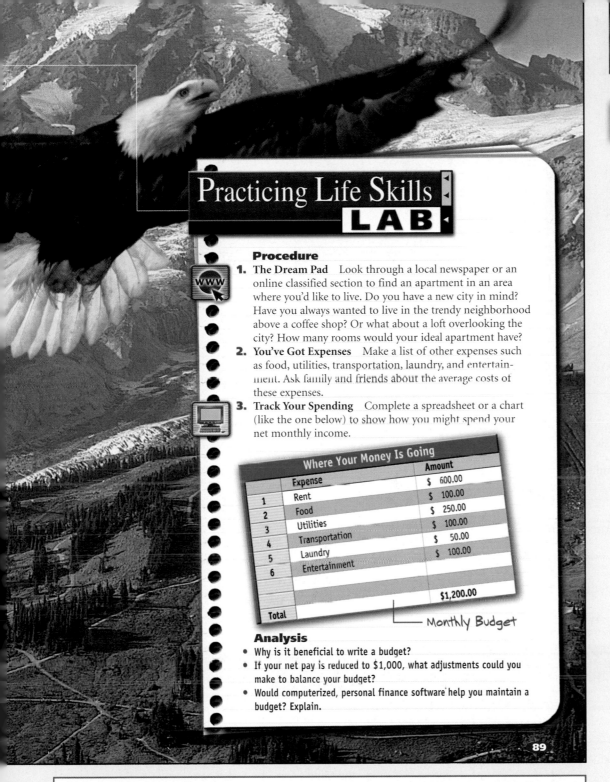

	Where Your Money Is Going	Amount
1	Rent	$ 600.00
2	Food	$ 100.00
3	Utilities	$ 250.00
4	Transportation	$ 100.00
5	Laundry	$ 50.00
6	Entertainment	$ 100.00
Total		$1,200.00

Monthly Budget

Analysis

- Why is it beneficial to write a budget?
- If your net pay is reduced to $1,000, what adjustments could you make to balance your budget?
- Would computerized, personal finance software help you maintain a budget? Explain.

89

Practicing Life Skills LAB

Teaching Suggestion
Have students complete the "How to make a budget?" on page 89. Ask them if they are surprised at the number of expenses involved once they are independent. **Also mention that these items on the chart are examples and not totally inclusive. They would still need to consider the cost of health insurance, vehicle insurance, and miscellaneous items.**

Analysis Answers
- Why is it beneficial to write a budget? **Alleviates debt (if you have credit cards), stops overspending, demonstrates financial discipline, organizes your spending habits, teaches prioritizing, etc.**
- If your net pay is reduced to $1,000, what adjustments could you make to balance your budget? **Rent—move to a cheaper place; food—start comparison shopping, use coupons, don't dine out; transportation—car pool, take the bus, ride a bike, walk; entertainment—cut these expenses to the bare minimum.**
- Would computerized, personal finance software help you maintain a budget? Explain. **Answers may vary, but might include it's helpful to input, track, and chart your expenses in relation to previous years of spending vs. expenses.**

▢▢ VOCABULARY BUILDER ▢▢

Ask students to read the chapter titles on pages vii–ix in their book. For each title, ask them to free associate. **(For example, chapter 6 Cash Purchases might stir up sales tax, money back, coupons, sales, markdown, etc.)** Encourage them to write down their first impressions of these words and then compare them later to the actual definition. You might suggest that they add this assignment to their study notebooks for future reference when they're conceptualizing the content.

National Standards for Business Education

Section Objectives	1. Mathematical Foundations	2. Number Relationships and Operations	3. Patterns, Functions, and Algebra	4. Measurements	5. Statistics and Probability	6. Problem-Solving Applications	
1-1 Hourly Pay (pp. 92–93) Calculate straight-time pay.	X	X					
1-2 Overtime Pay (pp. 94–95) Figure out straight-time, overtime, and total pay.	X	X				X	
1-3 Weekly Time Card (pp. 96–98) Calculate the total hours on a weekly time card.	X	X				X	
1-4 Piecework (pp. 99–100) Compute the total pay on a piecework basis.	X	X				X	
1-5 Salary (pp. 101–102) Determine the salary per pay period.	X	X					
1-6 Commission (pp. 103–105) Calculate the straight commission and determine the gross pay.	X	X				X	
1-7 Graduated Commission (pp. 106–107) Compute the total graduated commission.	X	X				X	

(Source: Reprinted with permission from the National Standards for Business Education, copyright © 2001 by National Business Education Association, 1914 Association Drive, Reston, Virginia 21901-1596)

SCANS Correlation

Foundation Skills

Basic Skills	Reading	Writing	Math	Listening	Speaking	
Thinking Skills	Creative Thinking	Decision Making	Problem Solving	Seeing Things in the Mind's Eye	Knowing How to Learn	Reasoning
Personal Qualities	Responsibility	Self-Esteem	Sociability	Self-Management	Integrity/Honesty	

This chapter's highlighted blocks indicate the chapter's content coverage in the Student Edition and the Teacher Wraparound Edition.

1. Numbers & Operations	2. Algebra	3. Geometry	4. Measurement	5. Data Analysis & Probability	6. Problem Solving	7. Reasoning & Proof	8. Communication	9. Connections	10. Representations
X					X				
X	X							X	
X	X							X	
X					X			X	
X					X			X	
X					X			X	
X					X			X	

SCANS Correlation

Workplace Competencies

Resources	Allocating Time	Allocating Money	Allocating Material and Facility Resources	Allocating Human Resources		
Information	Acquiring and Evaluating Information	Organizing and Maintaining Information	Interpreting and Communicating Information	Using Computers to Process Information		
Interpersonal Skills	Participating as a Member of a Team	Teaching Others	Serving Clients/Customers	Exercising Leadership	Negotiating to Arrive at a Decision	Working with Cultural Diversity
Systems	Understanding Systems	Monitoring and Correcting Performance	Improving and Designing Systems			
Technology	Selecting Technology	Applying Technology to Task	Maintaining and Troubleshooting Technology			

What You'll Learn

Ask students who have part-time jobs to tell how many hours a week they work. Ask if they get paid on a piecework basis and if they get paid overtime or paid on commission. In this chapter they'll calculate different types of pay and the total (or gross) pay.

Why It's Important

Knowing how your pay is determined is important. You're able to calculate whether you're being paid correctly. Knowing your income enables you to set a budget in order to reach financial goals. Different methods of payment allow comparison of gross pay for different jobs in the event a change of employment is being sought.

Key Word Review
Definitions

First ask students to look up the key terms in the Glossary. Then instruct the students to write the meanings of the key words in their journal.

CHAPTER (1)

Gross Income

What You'll Learn

Section 1-1 Calculate straight-time pay.

Section 1-2 Figure out straight-time, overtime, and total pay.

Section 1-3 Calculate the total hours on a weekly time card.

Section 1-4 Compute the total pay on a piecework basis.

Section 1-5 Determine the salary per pay period.

Section 1-6 Calculate the straight commission and determine the gross pay.

Section 1-7 Compute the total graduated commission.

When Will You Ever Use This?

People rarely work for free, unless it's a volunteer opportunity or an internship. So when you do work and get paid, it's important to know how to compute your gross income. You'll want to receive all the money you've earned.

Key Words to Know

- hourly rate
- straight-time pay
- overtime pay
- time and a half
- double time
- weekly time card
- piecework
- salary
- commission
- commission rate
- straight commission
- graduated commission

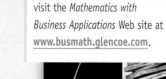

Mathematics Online

To learn more about gross income, visit the *Mathematics with Business Applications* Web site at www.busmath.glencoe.com.

CLASSROOM RESOURCES

Application and Enrichment
- *Teacher Wraparound Edition*
- *Teacher Resource Binder, Blackline Masters*
- *Interactive Lesson Planner* CD-ROM
- *PowerPoint® Presentations* CD-ROM

Review and Enforcement
- Mathematics Online
  www.busmath.glencoe.com
- *Teacher Resource Binder, Internet Resources*

- *Student Activity Workbook*
- *Student Activity Workbook, Teacher Annotated Edition*
- *School-to-Home Activity Workbook*

Assessment and Evaluation
- *Assessment Binder, Reproducible Tests*
- *Assessment Binder, Alternative Assessment Strategies*
- **Exam*View*® Pro Test Generator** CD-ROM

For the Teacher
- *Student Activity Workbook, Teacher Annotated Edition*
- *Assessment Binder*
- *Interactive Lesson Planner* CD-ROM
- *Teacher Resource Binder*
- Mathematics Online
  www.busmath.glencoe.com

For the Student
- *Student Activity Workbook*
- *School-to-Home Activity Workbook*

90

Living in the
Real World

Story's Summary

Raul Moreno is about to graduate from high school. He has worked at his uncle's general contracting firm during his summer breaks. His uncle has given him an opportunity to learn about different areas of the company, and now Raul is interested in the accounting side of the business, rather than working with a hammer and nails every day.

Living in the Real World

The Road to Building Castles

Working outside and being physically fit are two things that Raul Moreno enjoys. Oh, yeah, and also making good money while doing it in order to save and spend as he likes. Follow Raul in this chapter as he works for Castle Builders.

Read on. Go to . . .

91

Did You Know...

According to the U.S. Bureau of Labor Statistics, the average national wage for a full-time worker over 25 years old, with a high school diploma, was $26,000, while the average wage for a full-time worker over 25 years old, with a four-year degree, was $40,100 (which is 54 percent more).

Think about This

When might a person be able to successfully transition straight from high school to a satisfying, well-paying job? What types of jobs are most readily available to high school graduates? What do these jobs pay?

LOCAL STANDARDS

National Standards for Business Education

Standard 1	Mathematical Foundations
Standard 2	Number Relationships and Operations

National Council of Teachers of Mathematics Standards

Standard 1	Numbers and Operations
Standard 6	Problem Solving

FOCUS

You can motivate the discussion of straight-time pay by asking those students who have part-time jobs to raise their hands. Ask a few of these students to explain how they are paid and how many hours per week each works. Then compute the straight-time pay for each student at the board.

In-Class Examples

Use these exercises to help students review prerequisite skills for this lesson and to ascertain any arithmetic deficiencies that students may have. Work through these exercises with students before having them do the Self-Check.
Change each fraction to a decimal.

1. $36\frac{1}{2}$ **36.5**
2. $14\frac{1}{4}$ **14.25**
3. $10\frac{37}{40}$ **10.925**
4. $38\frac{23}{40}$ **38.575**

Multiply
5. $\$8.00 \times 16$ **$128.00**
6. $\$11.50 \times 22$ **$253.00**
7. $\$6.95 \times 36.775$ **$255.58625**

SECTION 1-1 Hourly Pay

Section Objective

Calculate straight-time pay.

Some jobs pay you a fixed amount of money for each hour you work. For example, the local cinema might pay you $7.50 an hour to sweep up popcorn and tear ticket stubs. The $7.50 is the **hourly rate** the cinema pays you per hour. Now, the manager has penciled you in to work 15 hours a week. These 15 hours are important for you to calculate your **straight-time pay**, or the total amount of money you earn for a pay period at the hourly rate. The important formula to remember is:

$$\text{Straight-Time Pay} = \text{Hourly Rate} \times \text{Hours Worked}$$

Living in the Real World

The Road to Building Castles

Wanted: A Cool Summer Job that Pays Well   When Raul Moreno graduated from high school, he knew he wanted to join his uncle's construction firm. During his high school summers, Raul already had worked for Castle Builders, his uncle's large general contracting firm that specialized in building expensive, custom homes.

Draw Conclusions   Why is it important to understand all facets of a business?

Continued on page 94

Need Help? Go to...
- Workshop 2: Rounding Numbers, page 6
- Workshop 6: Multiplying Decimals, page 14
- Skill 2: Rounding Numbers, page 729
- Skill 8: Multiplying Decimals, page 735
- Skill 14: Changing Fractions/Decimals, page 741
- Application A: Formulas, page 760

Example 1

Shawna Jackson is a mail clerk. She earns $8.40 per hour. Last week she worked 40 hours, and this week she worked $39\frac{1}{2}$ hours. What is her straight-time pay for each week?

STEP: Find the straight-time pay.

	Hourly Rate	×	Hours Worked	=	Straight-Time Pay
Last week	$8.40	×	40	=	$336.00
This week	8.40	×	$39\frac{1}{2}$	=	331.80

CONCEPT CHECK

SELF-CHECK

Complete the problems, then check your answers at the end of the chapter. Find the straight-time pay.

1. $7.60 per hour × 40 hours **$304.00**   2. $7.90 per hour × 37 hours **$292.30**

Living in the Real World

Answers will vary, but might include understanding how a business stays afloat, how decisions are often monetary based, and so on.

COOPERATIVE LEARNING

Piecework Pays
At Safelite Glass Corporation workers install automobile glass. Safelite used to pay workers about $11 an hour. When Safelite offered workers $20 per unit installed, productivity rose 20 percent. Workers' earnings increased 10 percent. Ask groups of students to find other examples of piecework and how it affects the company or the worker. **CL** , **LS**

FYI

Teenage Research Unlimited has interviewed more than half a million teenagers about their spending habits and lifestyles. Its data shows that teens react to economic downturns and political upheaval by spending less and saving more.

▶▶▶

SECTION 1-1 PRACTICE

	Employee	Regular Hourly Rate	×	Hours Worked	=	Straight-Time Pay
3.	Wright, S.	$ 8.00	×	36	=	$288.00
4.	Reardon, E.	7.50	×	18	=	$135.00
5.	Levitt, R.	16.20	×	30	=	$486.00
6.	Maguire, M.	10.25	×	24½	=	
7.	Reyes, A.	14.525	×	31.125	=	
8.	Vadola, G.	26.675	×	25.625	=	

6. $251.125 = $251.13

7. $452.090625 = $452.09

8. $683.546875 = $683.55

9. You earn $6.50 per hour and work 30 hours this week. What is your straight-time pay? **$195.00**

10. A local car wash pays you $8.00 per hour. Last summer you worked 35.25 hours a week. What was your total straight-time pay for the entire week? **$282.00**

11. Renaldo Scanlon is a financial consultant. He earns $25.00 per hour and works 32.5 hours a week. What is his straight-time pay? **$812.50**

12. Marian Abelt likes being a mail clerk. She earns $8.125 per hour and her boss allows her to work flexible hours. Last week she worked 35.525 hours. What was her straight-time pay? **$288.640625 = $288.64**

13. Sylvia O'Keefe is a teacher's aide. She earns $12.80 per hour. Last week she worked 34 hours. What was her straight-time pay for last week? **$435.20**

14. Tanaka Madison has a part-time job. She earns $7.75 per hour. She works 20 hours each week. What is her straight-time pay for a week? **$155.00**

15. Don Moline, a construction worker, earns $18.25 per hour. He worked his regular 36 hours last week. What was his straight-time pay? **$657.00**

16. Dominic Marzetti is a machine operator at the Donovan Manufacturing Corporation. He works 37.875 hours per week and earns $9.755 per hour. What is his straight-time pay each week? **$369.470625 = $369.47**

17. A banjo player earns $8.50 per hour for playing at the local coffee shop 10 hours a week. What is the musician's straight-time pay? **$85.00**

MAINTAINING YOUR SKILLS

Need Help? Go to...
- Skill 14: Changing Fractions/Decimals, page 741
- Skill 8: Multiplying Decimals, page 735
- Skill 2: Rounding Numbers, page 729

Write the fractions as decimals.

18. $\frac{1}{4}$ **0.25** 19. $\frac{1}{2}$ **0.5** 20. $\frac{3}{4}$ **0.75**

Multiply the numbers. Round the answers to the nearest cent.

21. $4.50 × 30.25 **$136.125 = $136.13** 22. $8.30 × 3.25 **$26.975 = $26.98** 23. $14.50 × 32.5 **$471.25**

Round to the place value that is indicated. Round to the nearest ten.

24. 22 **20** 25. 138 **140** 26. 8 **10**

Round to the nearest hundred.

27. 91 **100** 28. 3,092 **3,100** 29. 14,431 **14,400**

Round to the nearest thousand.

30. 15,374 **15,000** 31. 722 **1,000** 32. 158,481 **158,000**

Section 1-1 Hourly Pay ▶ **93**

PROBLEM SOLVING

Problem-Solving Tip
Students benefit by being reminded of important problem-solving skills, such as being sure to carefully read each problem, identify the key question in the problem, and then note the given facts. Applying the appropriate formula can then usually solve the problem.

WRAP-UP

Go over any problem for which a wrong answer is given.

Assignment Guide
Basic: 3–9 (odd)
Average: 10–17

20 min.

SECTION 1-1

2 TEACH

The key terms *hourly rate* and *straight-time pay* need to be explained. Relate these terms to the examples worked above with the students' data. Then work through the example in the text. Use additional examples by reading some want ads from your local newspaper and have students do the computations. Ask volunteers to give their answers.

Motivating the Lesson
You earn $8.50 per hour. How many hours will it take you to earn $1,088.00? **128 hours**

In-Class Examples
1. Tia earns $19.25 per hour. She works 36 hours. What is her straight-time pay? **$693.00**
2. Samantha earns $6.75 per hour. She works 17 hours. What is her straight-time pay? **$114.75**

3 ASSESS

Error Analysis
Some students may need help in converting fractions to decimals. Explain that to convert a fraction to a decimal, divide the numerator (top number) by the denominator (bottom number). For example, to convert $\frac{1}{8}$ to a decimal, divide 1 by 8.

4 CLOSE

Closing Activity
1. Hourly rate: $16.00
   Hours worked: 37.75
   Compute the straight-time pay: **$604**
2. Hourly rate: $7.685
   Hours worked: 18.367
   Compute the straight-time pay: **$141.150395 = $141.05**
3. Round 433 to the nearest hundred **400**
4. Round 125,691 to the nearest thousand **126,000**

93

National Standards for Business Education

Standard 1	Mathematical Foundations
Standard 2	Number Relationships and Operations
Standard 6	Problem-Solving Applications

National Council of Teachers of Mathematics Standards

Standard 1	Numbers and Operations
Standard 6	Problem Solving
Standard 9	Connections

① FOCUS

To compute the straight-time, overtime, and total pay, students must first understand the idea of *regular hours.* Ask students how many hours they think most adults work each week on their jobs. Point out that overtime pay isn't usually given to a person who works less than 35 or 40 hours a week or less than 8 hours a day.

In-Class Examples

Use these exercises to help students review prerequisite skills for this lesson and to ascertain any arithmetic deficiencies that students may have. Work through these exercises with students before having them do the Self-Check. Change each fraction to a decimal.

1. $46\frac{3}{4}$ **46.75**
2. $50\frac{1}{2}$ **50.5**
3. $49\frac{1}{4}$ **49.25**

Multiply

4. $\$10.00 \times 40$ **\$400.00**
5. $\$15.00 \times 6\frac{3}{4}$ **\$101.25**
6. $\$8.67 \times 40$ **\$346.80**
7. $(1\frac{1}{2} \times \$14.00) \times 9$ **\$189.00**
8. $(1\frac{1}{2} \times \$9.00) \times 4\frac{1}{2}$ **\$60.75**
9. $(1\frac{1}{2} \times \$13.42) \times 12$ **\$241.56**

● **Section Objective**
Figure out straight-time, overtime, and total pay.

SECTION 1-2 Overtime Pay

When you work more than your regular hours, you might receive **overtime pay**. The overtime rate might be $1\frac{1}{2}$ times your hourly rate. This is called **time and a half**. You may receive **double time**, or two times your regular hourly rate. Often times employers pay this overtime for Sundays and for holidays. To figure out your overtime pay, remember this:

$$\text{Overtime Pay} = \text{Overtime Rate} \times \text{Overtime Hours Worked}$$

$$\text{Total Pay} = \text{Straight-Time Pay} + \text{Overtime Pay}$$

(Note: The total pay is often called gross pay.)

Living in the Real World

The Road to Building Castles

Working on a Holiday Part of the reason Raul was able to buy a truck and customize his audio system was because he spent some of his summers working overtime shifts. "It was great," he says, "because it was regular work, but I got paid one-and-a-half times as much for it. Of course, sometimes I didn't like working on weekends when my friends were going to movies or to the beach. But then, that's why I got paid extra."

Draw Conclusions What are the benefits of working time and a half?

Continued on page 96

Need Help? Go to...
➤ **Workshop 4: Adding Decimals,** page 10
➤ **Skill 5: Adding Decimals,** page 732
➤ **Application A: Formulas,** page 760

Example 1

Alonso Perez is paid \$8.20 an hour for a regular 40-hour week. His overtime rate is $1\frac{1}{2}$ times his regular hourly rate. This week Perez worked his regular 40 hours plus 10 hours of overtime. What is his total pay?

STEP 1: Find the straight-time pay.
Hourly Rate × Regular Hours Worked
$\$8.20 \quad\times\quad 40 \quad = \$328.00$ straight-time pay

STEP 2: Find the overtime pay.
Overtime Rate × Overtime Hours Worked
$(1.5 \times \$8.20) \times \quad 10 \quad = \$123.00$ overtime pay

STEP 3: Find the total pay.
Straight-Time Pay + Overtime Pay
$\$328.00 \quad + \quad \$123.00 \quad = \textbf{\$451.00 total pay}$

8.20 ☒ 40 ☲

328 M+ 1.5 ☒ 8.20 ☒ 10 ☲ 123 M+ RM 451

Living in the Real World

More money, more on-the-job experiences to possibly move you ahead of the others.

ALTERNATIVE ASSESSMENT

Self-Management

Apply a simple two-question technique to find out how well students understand something they have just learned: (1) What is the most important thing I learned; and (2) what question(s) do I still have? For practice, have students use this technique after reading the chapter key words, a paragraph, and a section. Have students write down this simple learning self-evaluation tool in their journals. LS , CL , P

CONCEPT CHECK

SELF-CHECK ✓

Complete the problems, then check your answers at the end of the chapter. Find the total pay.

1. Josie Spelling earns $9.00 per hour and works 40 hours per week. Because she had to work on Thanksgiving, her employer paid her time and a half for the additional 6 hours she put in. ($9.00 × 40) + ($9.00 × 1.5 × 6) = ($360.00 × $81.00) = $441.00

2. Eddie Lange earns $11.50 per hour. He worked 40 hours, plus time and a half for 7 hours. ($11.50 × 40) + ($11.50 × 1.5 × 7) = ($460.00 + $120.75) = $580.75

SECTION 1-2 PRACTICE

	Hourly Pay (40 hours)	Straight-Time Pay	Overtime Rate	Overtime Hours	Overtime Pay	Total Pay
3.	$ 6.00	a. $240	$1\frac{1}{2}$	8	b. $72	c. $312
4.	10.60	a. $424.00	$1\frac{1}{2}$	5	b. $79.50	c. $503.50
5.	6.80	a. $272.00	$1\frac{1}{2}$	4	b. $40.80	c. $312.80
6.	5.55	a. $222.00	2	8	b. $88.80	c. $310.80
7.	17.00	a. $680	2	13	b. $442	c. $1,122
8.	19.125	a. $765.00	$1\frac{1}{2}$	6.25	b. $179.30	c. $944.30

9. Steven Kellogg, a machine operator, works at an hourly rate of $10.60 and earns time and a half if he works any overtime. Given this, last week he worked 37 hours plus 8 hours overtime. What is his straight-time pay? What is his overtime pay? What is his total pay? **$392.20; $127.20; $519.40**

10. Dorothy Kaatz, a computer programmer, earns a regular hourly rate of $15.25 and earns double that when she works overtime. Kaatz usually works 40 regular hours and 12 hours overtime while she's trying to update the company's systems before the month's end. What is her straight-time pay? What is her overtime pay? What is her total pay? **$610.00; $366.00; $976.00**

11. Cindy Haskins is paid $8.00 an hour for a regular 35-hour week. Her overtime rate is $1\frac{1}{2}$ times her regular hourly rate. This week Haskins worked her regular 35 hours plus 8 hours of overtime. What is her total pay? **$280 + $96 = $376**

12. As a case manager, Bonnie Zoltowski earns $13.47 an hour plus time and a half for weekend work. Last week she worked her regular 40 hours plus 8 hours of overtime on the weekend. What was her total pay for the week? **$538.80 + $161.64 = $700.44**

MAINTAINING YOUR SKILLS

Need Help? Go to...
- ▶ Skill 5: Adding Decimals, page 732
- ▶ Skill 8: Multiplying Fractions, page 735
- ▶ Skill 14: Changing Fractions/Decimals, page 741

Add.

13. $42.50
+ 24.76
$67.26

14. $160.45
+ 86.90
$247.35

15. $10.62
9.34
+ 0.45
$20.41

16. $56.7
0.007
121.33
+ 1,568.125
$1,746.162

Use multiplication to solve Problems 17–20.

17. $(1\frac{1}{2} × $8.40) × 7$ **$88.20**

18. $(2 × $18.40) × 12$ **$441.60**

19. $(1\frac{1}{4} × $6.00) × 9$ **$67.50**

20. $(1.5 × $12.50) × 8$ **$150.00**

Section 1-2 Overtime Pay ▶ **95**

COMMUNICATION SKILLS

What Do People Earn?
Students choose three fields of work they are interested in and contact a person in each field. The contact can be by phone or by e-mail. Students ask if the yearly earnings include commission. Students may gather photos, pictures, or props to illustrate a short oral report of their findings. **LS , CL , P**

WRAP-UP

Go over any problem for which a wrong answer is given.

Assignment Guide
Basic: 3–7 (odd)
Average: 9–12

20 min.

SECTION 1-2

② TEACH

Explain that *time and a half* means the regular hourly rate of pay plus one-half of the regular hourly rate. For example, if the regular rate is $8.00 per hour, then the time-and-a-half rate is $8.00 + $4.00, or $12.00. Now show students that this problem can be worked by multiplying $8.00 by 1.5 or $8.00 × 1.5 = $12.00.

Motivating the Lesson
You earn $10.00 per hour. Although you have already worked 40 hours this week, your manager asks you to work 8 hours on Saturday. She will pay you $1\frac{1}{2}$ times your hourly rate to work on Saturday. How much money will you earn on Saturday? $(1\frac{1}{2} × $10.00) × 8 = 120.00

In-Class Example
Maria Kolinski is a dental hygienist. Her regular hourly rate is $27.00 per hour, and she receives time and a half for overtime. This week she worked 38 hours, and 5 hours overtime. What is her straight-time pay? **($1,026.00)** What is her overtime pay? **($202.50)** What is her total pay? **$1,228.50**

③ ASSESS

Error Analysis
If students make mistakes in computing total pay, check to see that they have first correctly computed the straight-time pay and the overtime pay. Then, check that they have correctly aligned the decimal points before adding the straight-time pay plus the overtime pay.

④ CLOSE

Closing Activity
1. $(1.5 × 13.88) × 4$ **83.28**
2. $(1.5 × 10.90) × 7$ **114.45**
3. $(2 × 8.86) × 11$ **194.92**

National Standards for Business Education

Standard 1	Mathematical Foundations
Standard 2	Number Relationships and Operations
Standard 6	Problem-Solving Applications

National Council of Teachers of Mathematics Standards

Standard 1	Numbers and Operations
Standard 6	Problem Solving
Standard 9	Connections

1 FOCUS

Ask those students who have part-time jobs how they keep track of the number of hours they work each week. Use their answers to lead into a discussion of the example, showing how to compute the total hours on a weekly time card.

In-Class Examples

Use these exercises to help students review prerequisite skills for this lesson and to ascertain any arithmetic deficiencies that students may have. Work through these exercises with students before having them do the Self-Check. Find the total time.
1. 8:10 to 12:25 **4 h: 15 min.**
2. 7:45 to 11:30 **3 h: 45 min.**
Round to the nearest quarter hour.
3. 5 hours 26 mins. **$5\frac{1}{2}$ hrs.**
4. 10 hours 13 mins. **$10\frac{1}{4}$ hrs.**
Convert the following times to military time.
5. 4:00 P.M. **16:00**
6. 6:30 P.M. **18:30**

SECTION 1-3 Weekly Time Card

○ **Section Objective**

Calculate the total hours on a weekly time card.

At your job at the cinema, you're required to keep track of your hours on a **weekly time card .** This shows the time you reported for work and the time you departed each day of the week. Each day you compute the hours worked. The daily hours are added to give you the total number of hours worked that week. Round to the nearest quarter hour if you don't work an entire hour. Remember that:

Total Hours = Sum of Daily Hours

Living in the Real World

The Road to Building Castles

You're Getting Paid for Sore Muscles Raul laughs about his first week on the job with Castle Builders.

He often forgot to turn in his time sheet. Fortunately for Raul, Castle Builders's bookkeeper Mrs. Jenkins was looking out for the company's youngest employee. After two weeks, she noticed that Raul had not turned in a weekly time card. Mrs. Jenkins took him aside and explained how to record his time at work.

Draw Conclusions Why is it important to accurately record your time?

Continued on page 99

Example 1

Gail Stough is required to keep a weekly time card. What are her daily hours for September 18? What are her total hours for the week?

Figure 1.1

Employee Time Card

Employee Name: __Gail Stough__   Department: __Credit__

	DATE	IN	OUT	IN	OUT	HOURS
Sun.						
Mon.	9/15	8:15	12:15	1:00	5:00	8
Tue.	9/16	8:30	12:00	12:35	5:20	$8\frac{1}{4}$
Wed.	9/17	8:28	12:05	12:30	4:30	$7\frac{1}{2}$
Thur.	9/18	8:15	1:45	2:15	4:59	
Fri.	9/19	8:30	12:20	12:50	5:00	8
Sat.						

Employee Signature: __Gail Stough__   **TOTAL HOURS** | **40**

Living in the Real World

So you get paid for the time you've worked.

RETEACH / ENRICHMENT

Real-World Experience
Make this lesson a real-world experience by having students look at the newspaper's opportunities section. Students list the salaries of six different jobs offered. Have them calculate the hourly, weekly, monthly, and annual salaries of the jobs. **LS** , **CL**

STEP 1: Find the hours worked on September 18.

   A. Time between 8:15 A.M. and 1:45 P.M. (This is before lunch.)
     When the start time is prior to 1:00 and the end time is 1:00
     or later, add 12:00 to the end time.

     (1:45 + 12:00)   –   8:15
         13:45   –   8:15   5h:30min

   B. Time between 2:15 P.M. and 4:59 P.M. (After lunch.)
        4:59   –   2:15   2h:44min
     5h:30min   +   2h:44min   7h:74min

     (Round to the nearest quarter hour) = $8\frac{1}{4}$ **hours**

STEP 2: Find the total hours for the week.
   Sum of daily hours

   $8 + 8\frac{1}{4} + 7\frac{1}{2} + 8\frac{1}{4} + 8$

   $8 + 8\frac{1}{4} + 7\frac{1}{2} + 8\frac{1}{4} + 8 = 39 + \frac{4}{4} =$ **40 total hours**

CONCEPT CHECK

Complete the problems, then check your answers at the end of the chapter.
Find the total number of hours for each person.

  1. Regina Blanco worked from 8:00 to 10:45 and from 12:30 to 4:15. $2\frac{3}{4} + 3\frac{3}{4} = 6\frac{1}{2}$

  2. Ruth Abet worked from 7:30 to 11:55 and from 1:00 to 4:50. $4\frac{1}{2} + 3\frac{3}{4} = 8\frac{1}{4}$

SECTION 1-3 PRACTICE

Eddie Irwin works as a computer operator in the data processing department
at Needham Medical Center. He is required to keep a weekly time card. What
are his hours for each day? What are his total hours for the week?

Figure 1.2

Employee Time Card					Needham Medical Center
Employee Name: **Eddie Irwin**			Department: **Data Processing**		
	DATE	IN	OUT	IN	OUT	TOTAL
Sun.						
Mon.	12/13	8:15 A.M.	12:00 PM	12:30 PM	4:30 P.M.	$3\frac{3}{4} + 4 = 7\frac{3}{4}$
Tue.	12/14	8:30 A.M.	12:30 P.M.	1:10 P.M.	5:10 P.M.	
Wed.	12/15	8:35 A.M.	12:50 P.M.	1:30 P.M.	5:00 P.M.	$4\frac{1}{4} + 3\frac{1}{2} = 7\frac{3}{4}$
Thur.	12/16	8:15 A.M.	12:10 P.M.	12:45 P.M.	4:25 P.M.	
Fri.	12/17	8:25 A.M.	1:15 P.M.	1:50 P.M.	5:30 P.M.	$4\frac{3}{4} + 3\frac{3}{4} = 8\frac{1}{2}$
Sat.						
Employee Signature: *Eddie Irwin*					TOTAL HOURS	$39\frac{3}{4}$

3.
4. $4 + 4 = 8$
5.
6. $4 + 3\frac{1}{2} = 7\frac{1}{2}$
7
8.

Continued on next page

GLOBAL PERSPECTIVE

Tipping

Service workers, such as food servers,
taxi drivers, and haircutters, often earn
low wages and rely on tips. In France,
Holland, and Germany a tip of 10 percent
is considered the absolute maximum.

   Have students research the standards
for tipping in various countries. Is tipping
a custom in the country? Is there a service
fee? Are service workers paid a reasonable
wage, or a low wage? Students summarize
their findings in a paragraph, or chart.

SECTION 1-3

② TEACH

After discussing the example, ask
students to suggest some examples of businesses that use time
cards. **(Most department stores,
restaurants, banks, and manufacturers, for example, require hourly
employees to keep a weekly time
card.)** A time clock automatically
records the time employees come
to work, when they break for
lunch and return and when they
leave for the day. Total daily and
weekly hours are determined
either by a computer or by hand.
Many businesses round to the
nearest quarter hour; however,
computerized timekeeping has
made it possible for some businesses to pay employees to the
nearest minute.

   Some students may need help
in computing elapsed time when
the minutes of the minuend are
less that the minutes of the subtrahend. For example, when subtracting time 1:45 from 6:34, tell
students to rewrite 6:34 as 5:94.

Motivating the Lesson
You work part time at an
electronics store on Mondays,
Thursdays, and Fridays from 3:30
to 8:00. How many hours do you
work each week? **13$\frac{1}{2}$ hours**

In-Class Examples
1. On Monday, Christy Vasquez
   worked from 8:30 to 12:00 and
   from 12:55 to 5:10. Find the
   hours worked on October 1.
   7$\frac{3}{4}$ hrs.
2. On Tuesday, Christy Vasquez
   worked from 7:20 to 11:35 and
   from 12:15 to 4:00. Find the
   hours worked on October 2.
   8 hrs.

ASSESS

Error Analysis

If students need help with military time, tell them to add 12:00 to the P.M. time they are converting. For example, 3:00 P.M. can be changed to military time like this: $12:00 + 3:00 = 15:00$. Students might also find it helpful to make a chart converting every hour from 1:00 P.M. through midnight to military time and use it as a reference.

Some students might need help adding fractions when they total the number of hours worked per week. For example, to add $\frac{1}{4} + \frac{1}{2} + \frac{3}{4}$, have students first find the least common denominator among the fractions, which is 4. Then change $\frac{1}{2}$ to $\frac{2}{4}$ and add the numerators. $\frac{1}{4} + \frac{2}{4} + \frac{3}{4} = \frac{6}{4} = 1\frac{1}{2}$. Change $\frac{5}{4}$ to a mixed number, that is, $1\frac{1}{4}$.

CLOSE

Closing Activity

1. James Geisler works from 7:45 to 11:15 and from 12:05 until 3:50. Find the total hours he works. **$7\frac{1}{4}$ hrs.**
2. $7\frac{1}{8} + 6\frac{1}{2} + 7\frac{1}{4} =$ **$20\frac{7}{8}$**
3. Change 10:29 P.M. to military time. **22:29**

---

9. Gail Stough earns $8.40 per hour. Use her time card (see **Figure 1.1** on page 96) to find her total pay for the week. **$336.00**

10. Eddie Irwin is paid $7.25 for a regular 37-hour week. His overtime rate is $1\frac{1}{2}$ times his regular hourly rate. Use his time card (see **Figure 1.2** on page 97) to find his total pay for the week. **$296.34**

11. You are scheduled to work from 7:00 A.M. to 11:00 A.M. and from 12:00 noon to 4:00 P.M. You are not allowed to work overtime. Your hourly rate is $7.50. Use **Figure 1.3** to find the hours worked and the total pay for the week.

Figure 1.3

	DATE	IN	OUT	IN	OUT	HOURS
Sun.						
Mon.	—	7:00 A.M.	11:00 A.M.	12:00 P.M.	4:04 P.M.	a. 8
Tue.	—	7:05 A.M.	11:10 A.M.	11:55 P.M.	3:59 P.M.	b. 8
Wed.	—	7:01 A.M.	10:59 A.M.	12:05 P.M.	3:57 P.M.	c. 8
Thur.	—	6:59 A.M.	10:55 A.M.	12:01 P.M.	4:03 P.M.	d. 8
Fri.	—	6:55 A.M.	12:01 P.M.	12:02 P.M.	3:49 P.M.	e. $7\frac{3}{4}$
Sat.						
					TOTAL HOURS	f. $39\frac{3}{4}$

Employee Time Card

MAINTAINING YOUR SKILLS

Need Help? Go to...

➤ Skill 16: Adding Fractions, Unlike Denominators, page 743

➤ Application E: Rounding Time: Nearest Quarter Hour, page 764

➤ Skill 2: Rounding Numbers, page 729

Add.

12. $\frac{1}{4} + \frac{1}{4} + \frac{1}{2}$ **1**

13. $\frac{3}{4} + \frac{1}{8}$ **$\frac{7}{8}$**

14. $\frac{3}{8} + \frac{1}{4} + \frac{1}{4}$ **$\frac{7}{8}$**

15. $\frac{5}{8} + \frac{1}{3}$ **$\frac{23}{24}$**

Round to the nearest quarter hour.

16. 8:09 **8:00**

17. 7:47 **7:45**

18. 11:55 **12:00**

Round to the place value indicated. Round to the nearest thousand.

19. 39,972 **40,000**

20. 21,944 **22,000**

21. 68,498 **68,000**

Round to the nearest hundred.

22. 842 **800**

23. 257 **300**

24. 3,580 **3,600**

WRAP-UP

Go over any problem for which a wrong answer is given.

Assignment Guide
Basic: 3–8 (odd)
Average: 9–11

20 min.

SECTION (1-4) Piecework

Section Objective

Compute the total pay on a piecework basis.

Some jobs pay you on a **piecework** basis. This is when you receive a specified amount of money for each item of work that you complete. To calculate this, remember that:

Total Pay = Rate per Item × Number of Items Produced

For example, pretend that the cinema paid you this way. The manager pays you for each theater you clean. On Wednesday night you cleaned 10 theaters at $10.00 a piece. So you would have made

$100.00 = $10.00 (rate per theater) × 10 (number of theaters cleaned)

Living in the Real World

The Road to Building Castles

Hooking up Your Buddies Cabinetmaker subcontractor Jim Sweeney stopped Raul as he was leaving the job site. Sweeney wanted to know if Raul would be interested in painting primer on shelves for one of Castle Builders's new homes. He explained that he would pay Raul by the piece—that is, he would get paid a certain amount for each shelf he painted.

Draw Conclusions Is it better to be paid on an hourly rate or by piecework?

Continued on page 101

Example 1

Need Help? Go to...
- ▶ Workshop 6: Multiplying Decimals, page 14
- ▶ Skill 8: Multiplying Decimals, page 735
- ▶ Application A: Formulas, page 760

Ramon Hernandez works for National Cabinet Company. He is paid $8.00 for each cabinet he assembles. Last week he assembled 45 cabinets. This week he assembled 42. What is his pay for each week?

STEP: Find the total pay.

	Rate per Item	×	Number of Items Produced	=	Total Pay
Last week	$8.00	×	45	=	$360.00
This week	8.00	×	42	=	336.00

CONCEPT CHECK

Complete the problems, then check your answers at the end of the chapter. Find the total pay.

1. $3.20 per item × 140 items produced **$3.20 × 140 = $448.00**

2. $0.15 per item × 1,494 items produced **$0.15 × 1,494 = $224.10**

Section 1-4 Piecework ▶ **99**

Living in the Real World

Depends on how much piecework you're given in relation to how long it takes you to complete it. Evaluate piecework versus hourly rate work case by case.

THINKING CRITICALLY

Wages by Education
A recent U.S. Bureau of the Census Current Population Survey shows the hourly wages for workers with different levels of education: less than high school: $8.03; high school $10.60; some college $11.92; college $17.49; and advanced degree $23.33.

Have students calculate the annual salary for all five levels, assuming a 40-hour week, 50 weeks in the year.

National Standards for Business Education

Standard 1	Mathematical Foundations
Standard 2	Number Relationships and Operations
Standard 6	Problem-Solving Applications

National Council of Teachers of Mathematics Standards

Standard 1	Numbers and Operations
Standard 6	Problem Solving
Standard 9	Connections

(1) FOCUS

Ask those students how they would be paid to wash a car, deliver newspapers, paint a house, or cut a lawn. Discuss why some jobs pay on a piecework basis rather than an hourly rate basis. Ask students to calculate the total amount of money raised at a school fundraising activity if 74 cars were washed at $5.00 per car. **$370**

In-Class Examples
These exercises can be used to review prerequisite skills for this lesson and to ascertain any arithmetic deficiencies that students may have. Work through these exercises with students before having them do the Self-Check.
1. 2.50 × 100 **250**
2. 0.18 × 297 **53.46**
3. (0.89 × 134) + (0.45 × 279) + (0.18 × 758) = **381.25**
4. ($79.95) + ($36.95 × 12) + ($68.95 × 9) = **$1,143.90**

Point out that for some manu-facturing jobs, employers use a piecework method of payment to encourage employees to produce more. However, as the United States has moved from a manu-facturing economy to a more service-oriented economy during the latter half of the twentieth century, piecework jobs have declined substantially. Ask students if they know any adults who are paid on a piecework basis and what these people actually do.

Motivating the Lesson

Your neighbor asks you to wash the 18 windows in her house. She will pay you $3.75 per window. How much will you earn if you accept the job? **$67.50**

In-Class Example

Elizabeth Capella, a silk floral arranger, makes 57 wreaths at $45.00 per wreath. **$2,565.00**

Error Analysis

If students need help multiplying decimals, remind them that mul-tiplication of decimals is similar to multiplying whole numbers. Emphasize the need for setting up the problems neatly and properly aligning the numbers in columns. Discuss the rule for finding the number of decimal places in the answer.

Closing Activity

Multiply.
1. $0.08 × 477 **$38.16**
2. $4.61 × 159 **$732.99**
3. 27 × $736.99 **$19,898.73**

SECTION 1-4 PRACTICE

3. Federico Santos operates a salon. He charges $12 per haircut. Often by Saturday he has given 60 haircuts. What is his total pay? **$720.00**

4. Ellen Kolazinski picks strawberries every Wednesday morning. The farm pays her $0.25 per quart and she normally picks 1,053 quarts. Find her total pay. **$263.25**

5. Paul Aymes is a chrome plater at a local plant. If he plates 300 items or more, he is paid $1.25 each. For less than 300 items, he is paid $0.75 each. What is his total pay if he plates 321 items on Wednesday and 154 items on Thursday? **$516.75**

6. Antonio Rubio is a shirt silk screener. The owner will pay him $0.45 per shirt and $0.75 per sweatshirt. On Tuesday Rubio completed 288 shirts and 72 sweatshirts. What is his total pay? **$183.60**

7. Carol Ying is paid $0.45 for each calculator she assembles. What is her pay for a day in which she assembles 134 calculators? **$60.30**

8. Leah Elliot runs a cleaning service. She charges $21.95 per room. On Monday she cleaned 3 rooms in one house, 2 in another, and 4 in a third. Find her total cleaning charges. **$197.55**

9. Jeremy Sullivan delivers newspapers for the *Dispatch*. He receives 14.2¢ per paper, 6 days a week (for the daily paper), and 50¢ for the Sunday paper. He delivers 124 daily papers each day and 151 Sunday papers each week. What is his total pay for the week? **$93.11**

10. Charelle Cleaves operates an oil change and tune-up service. She charges $33.95 per oil change, $72.50 to tune a four-cylinder engine, $82.50 to tune a six-cylinder engine, and $92.50 to tune an eight-cylinder engine. What are the charges for a week in which she did 35 oil changes, tuned 5 four-cylinder engines, 7 six-cylinder engines, and 2 eight-cylinder engines? **$2,313.25**

MAINTAINING YOUR SKILLS

Need Help? Go to...
► **Skill 8: Multiplying Decimals,** page 735

Multiply the numbers. Round the answers to the nearest cent.

11. $0.23 × 89 **$20.47**   12. $1.10 × 240 **$264.00**

13. $0.06 × 4,192 **$251.52**   14. $0.06 × 906 **$54.36**

15. $5.20 × 23 **$119.60**   16. $0.04 × 3,200 **$128.00**

17. $0.66 × 350 **$231.00**   18. $0.047 × 731 **$34.36**

Multiply the numbers.

19.
$$\begin{array}{r} 1.17 \\ \times\,100 \\ \hline 117 \end{array}$$

20.
$$\begin{array}{r} 15.876 \\ \times\,100 \\ \hline 1,587.6 \end{array}$$

21.
$$\begin{array}{r} 242 \\ \times\quad 0.04 \\ \hline 9.68 \end{array}$$

22.
$$\begin{array}{r} 456 \\ \times\,1000 \\ \hline 456,000 \end{array}$$

23.
$$\begin{array}{r} 693.25 \\ \times\,482 \\ \hline 334,146.5 \end{array}$$

Great Ideas from the Classroom Of...

Elaine A. Peeters
North Rose-Wolcott High School, Wolcott, NY

Real-Life Income

Ask your students to take three things out of their wallet or bag that they value. Why are these items valuable to them? What do these items say about their value system? Give each student a chance to say some-thing about how they are connected to the items they displayed.

WRAP-UP

Go over any problem for which a wrong answer is given.

Assignment Guide
  Basic: 3–5 (odd)
Average: 6–9

20 min.

SECTION 1-5 Salary

○ **Section Objective**
Determine the salary per pay period.

You have worked at the cinema for six years and make your way up to assistant manager and finally manager. Because you're at this status, the company pays you a **salary** . This is a fixed amount of money that you earn on a regular basis. Your salary may be paid weekly, biweekly, semimonthly, or monthly. Your annual salary is the total salary you earn during a year. There are 52 weekly, 26 biweekly, 24 semimonthly, and 12 monthly pay periods per year.

$$\text{Salary per Pay Period} = \frac{\text{Annual Salary}}{\text{Number of Pay Periods per Year}}$$

Living in the Real World

The Road to Building Castles

A Change of Scenery Now that Raul has graduated from high school and has worked for Castle Builders for several summers, he's considering his options. After talking with Mrs. Jenkins, he is interested in the accounting side of running a business. Uncle Rafael has decided to let Raul work as an assistant bookkeeper for a few months. He'll become a salaried employee and be paid biweekly.

Draw Conclusions Does your boss expect less from you when you become a salaried employee? Explain your answer.

Continued on page 103

Example 1

Beth Huggins is a computer programmer. Her annual salary is $42,648. What is her monthly salary? What is her weekly salary?

STEP: Find the salary per pay period.

	Annual Salary	÷	Number of Pay Periods per Year	=	Salary per Pay Period
Monthly	$42,648.00	:	12	=	$3,554.00 monthly salary
Weekly	42,648.00	÷	52	=	820.15 weekly salary

42648 ÷ 52 = 820.1538

Need Help? Go to...
➤ Workshop 7: Dividing Decimals, page 16
➤ Skill 11: Dividing Decimals, page 738
➤ Application K: Chronological Expressions, page 766

Living in the Real World

Absolutely not. In fact as a salaried employee, the company might make more demands on your time and increase your workload. The benefit is that you're locked into a regular paycheck as well as receiving the company's benefits (e.g., health and dental insurance, and retirement package).

TECHNOLOGY POWER

Since the early 1980's, companies have been using personal computers in a quest for a "paperless office." This objective is now closer than ever with the use of direct deposit for employee paychecks. Payments are wired directly to the employee's bank account. While direct deposit has been around for quite a few years, employees still receive a paper pay stub to provide the details of the check. Now, pay stubs are available on company Intranet sites.

National Standards for Business Education

Standard 1	Mathematics Foundations
Standard 2	Number Relationship and Operations

National Council of Teachers of Mathematics Standards

Standard 1	Numbers and Operations
Standard 6	Problem Solving

1 FOCUS

Read a few newspaper ads for jobs that are paid on a salary basis, and discuss the meaning of *salary*. Ask students to suggest some jobs that would earn a salary. Have students find the monthly salary for a person earning $30,000 a year. **$2,500**

In-Class Examples
These exercises can be used to review prerequisite skills for this lesson and to ascertain any arithmetic deficiencies that students may have. Work through these exercises with students before having them do the Self-Check.

1. $\frac{\$24,000}{12}$ **$2,000**
2. $\frac{\$60,000}{24}$ **$2,500**
3. $\frac{\$49,400}{26}$ **$1,900**
4. $\frac{\$16,068}{52}$ **$309**

2 TEACH

Discuss the different meanings of the terms weekly, biweekly, semimonthly, and monthly. Point out that in a biweekly schedule, typically there is a payday every other Friday, but twice during the year there will be three biweekly paydays in a month.

101

② TEACH (cont'd)

Typically, a semimonthly pay period means that the employee is paid on the 1st and 15th of each month.

Point out also that a salary, like an hourly rate, is also based upon time, but the unit of time is a week, a month, or a year. Ask students if they think a salaried employee is paid for overtime work.

In-Class Examples

1. A hospital advertised for a radiology technician at a monthly salary of $4,680. What is the annual salary? **($56,160)** What is the weekly salary? **$1,080**
2. Find the annual salary when the weekly salary is $735. **$38,220**
3. Find the semimonthly salary when the weekly salary is $600. **$1,300**

③ ASSESS

Error Analysis

Some students may confuse the terms *biweekly* and *semimonthly*. Remind them that a person who is paid *biweekly* will be paid every 2 weeks or 26 times per year. A person who is paid *semimonthly* will be paid twice a month or 24 times a year.

④ CLOSE

Closing Activity

Divide. Round to the nearest hundredth.
1. Sang Vong is a Web photo editor. He earns $984 per week. What is his annual salary? **$51,168**
2. Find the number of pay periods. Semimonthly for 15 years. **360**

CONCEPT CHECK

SELF-CHECK✓

Complete the problems, then check your answers at the end of the chapter.

1. Find the biweekly salary. $42,900 ÷ 26 = **$1,650**
2. Find the semimonthly salary. $18,200 ÷ 24 = **$758.33**

Need Help? Go to...
▶ Skill 11: **Dividing Decimals**, page 738
▶ Application K: **Chronological Expressions**, page 766

The city of Carson advertised for a redevelopment project manager at a monthly salary of $5,480. What is the annual salary? What is the weekly salary?

STEP: Find the salary per pay period.

    Annual Salary = Monthly Salary × 12
            $5,480   × 12   = **$65,760 annual salary**
    Weekly Salary = Annual Salary ÷ 52
            $65,760   ÷ 52   = **$1,264.615 or $1,264.62 weekly salary**

CONCEPT CHECK

SELF-CHECK✓

Complete the problems, then check your answers at the end of the chapter.

3. Find the annual salary when the monthly salary is $4,725.
                       $4,725 × 12 = $56,700
4. Find the semimonthly salary when the weekly salary is $1,200.
                       $62,400 ÷ 24 = $2,600

SECTION 1-5 PRACTICE

5. Your annual salary is $22,500. What is your weekly salary? **$432.69**
6. Your annual salary is $28,320. What is your semimonthly salary? **$1,180**
7. A weekly salary is $810. What is the annual and semimonthly salary?
          Annual = $42,120; Semimonthly = $1,755
8. Turell Grant is a claims adjustor. His biweekly salary is $1,075. What is his annual and monthly salary? **Annual = $27,950; Monthly = 2,329.17**
9. An electrical engineer earns $58,400 per year. What is her monthly salary? What is her weekly salary? **$4,866.67; $1,123.08**
10. Louis Rahn is currently earning an annual salary of $25,090 at Budgett Electronics. He has been offered a job at Delta Tech at an annual salary of $26,660. How much more would Rahn earn per week at Delta Tech than at Budgett Electronics? **$30.19**
11. Paul Sellers was paid a biweekly salary of $1,230. Now he's paid on a semimonthly basis. What will Sellers' semimonthly salary be? **$1,332.50**
12. Assume that your present job pays a monthly gross salary of $1,560. You are offered a new position that pays $8.60 per hour with $1\frac{1}{2}$ times more per hour for all hours over 40 per week. How many hours of overtime per week would you need to work to earn the same amount per week as your present job?
                               1.24 hours of overtime

Need Help? Go to...
▶ Skill 11: **Dividing Decimals**, page 738
▶ Application K: **Chronological Expressions**, page 766

MAINTAINING YOUR SKILLS

Divide the numbers and then round the answers to the nearest hundredth.

13. $14,290 ÷ 50 **285.80**   **14.** 41.62 ÷ 8.6 **4.84**   **15.** 191.3 ÷ 14.7 **13.01**

Find the number of pay periods.

16. Weekly for 2 years **104**   **17.** Semimonthly for 3 years **72**

COOPERATIVE LEARNING

Share
Pairs of students work together on problems. After completing the problems on paper, have pairs of students volunteer to write their process and solution on the board for one of the problems.

WRAP-UP

Go over any problem for which a wrong answer is given.

Assignment Guide
Basic: 5–7 (odd)
Average: 8–12

20 min.

SECTION 1-6 Commission

Section Objective

Calculate the straight commission and determine the gross pay.

Although you've worked your way up the corporate ladder and became the cinema manager, you've always wanted to be a salesperson. You're outgoing and friendly. Someone suggests you start working in retail, like selling furniture or cars. Often times retail positions pay you based on **commission** . This is an amount of money that you are paid for selling a product or service.

Commission works in two ways. First, you might work on a **commission rate**. This might be a specified amount of money for each sale or it might be a percent of the *total value* of your sales. If the commission is the only pay you receive, you work on **straight commission** . The important formula to remember for commission is:

Commission = Total Sales × Commission Rate

Living in the Real World

The Road to Building Castles

A Hook behind the Hustle One afternoon, Mrs. Jenkins sends Raul to Lumberland to pay a bill for a load of two-by-fours that were to be delivered the next day.

"Man, that was one huge lumberyard," Raul tells Mrs. Jenkins. "They had salespeople all over the place. And the one who talked to me was sure eager to sell us more lumber."

"That's because he works on commission," Mrs. Jenkins says. "The salespeople at that lumberyard get paid according to how much they sell. The more you sell, the more you're paid."

Draw Conclusions What are the risks involved in working on commission?

Continued on page 106

Need Help? Go to...

- ▶ Workshop 2: Rounding Numbers, page 6
- ▶ Workshop 14: Finding a Percentage, page 30
- ▶ Skill 2: Rounding Numbers, page 729
- ▶ Skill 30: Finding the Percentage, page 757
- ▶ Application A: Formulas, page 760

Example 1

Milton Arps sells real estate at a $7\frac{1}{2}$ percent straight commission. Last week his sales totaled $290,000. What was his commission?

STEP: Find the commission.

Total Sales × Commission Rate

$290,000 × $7\frac{1}{2}$%

$290,000 × 0.075 = **$21,750 straight commission**

290000 ⊠ 0.075 ⊟ 21750 or 290000 ⊠ 7.5 % ⊟ 21750

Section 1-6 Commission ▶ **103**

Living in the Real World

You're paid on how much you sell. In the case of retail sales (e.g., clothing and furniture stores), employees are paid a small hourly rate to offset the possibility of not selling products during a workday.

COMMUNICATION SKILLS

Commission

Have groups of students discuss how working on commission affects the employee, the employer, and the customer. Ask each group to create a poster listing the main points of the discussion such as: incentive for employee to be more productive, more profit for employer, and pressure to get the customer to buy more.

National Standards for Business Education

Standard 1	Mathematical Foundations
Standard 2	Number Relationships and Operations
Standard 6	Problem-Solving Applications

National Council of Teachers of Mathematics Standards

Standard 1	Numbers and Operations
Standard 6	Problem Solving
Standard 9	Connections

1 FOCUS

The focus of this lesson is on computing straight commission and gross pay. Engage students in a brief discussion of why many businesses pay sales employees on a commission basis.

In-Class Examples

These exercises can be used to review prerequisite skills for this lesson and to ascertain any arithmetic deficiencies that students may have. Work through these exercises with students before having them do the Self-Check.

1. Write $8\frac{1}{2}$ percent as a decimal. **0.085**
2. Write $5\frac{3}{4}$ percent as a decimal. **0.0575**
3. $4\frac{1}{2}$ percent of $500 **$22.50**
4. 3 percent of $1,545 **$46.35**
5. $11\frac{1}{2}$ percent of $1,250 **$143.75**
6. 8 percent of $590.42 **$47.23**

SECTION 1-6

② TEACH

After working through the example with students, point out that the concept of a commission is similar to that of piecework. Commission pay is based upon the number of items sold while piecework pay depends on the number of items produced.

A commission is a way to provide an employee with an incentive to sell more items while piecework provides an incentive to make more items.

Motivating the Lesson
You sell sports equipment at your local sporting goods store. You receive 10 percent commission on everything you sell. What is your commission on sales of $2,480 for the week? **$248**

In-Class Examples
1. Tanya Woods. $5\frac{1}{2}$ percent commission on sales. $5,600 in sales for a week. What is her commission? **$308**
2. Jessica Drake. 4.75 percent commission on sales. $15,240 in sales for a week. What is her commission? **$723.90**

CONCEPT CHECK

 SELF-CHECK✓

Complete the problems, then check your answers at the end of the chapter. Find the commission.

1. $9,400 × 8 percent commission rate **$9,400 × 8% = $752.00**
2. $143,400 × $5\frac{1}{2}$ percent commission rate **$143,400 × $5\frac{1}{2}$% = $7,887.00**

Instead of only working on commission, you might be guaranteed a minimum weekly or monthly salary. The commission you earn during a week or month is compared with your minimum salary. Your gross pay is the *greater* of the two amounts. Remember this formula for gross pay:

Gross Pay = Salary or Commission

Example 2

Need Help? Go to...
▶ Skill 30: **Finding the Percentage,** page 757
▶ **Application A: Formulas,** page 760

Owen Theil is guaranteed a minimum salary of $250 a week, or 7 percent of his total sales, depending on whichever is greater. What is his gross pay for a week in which his total sales were $3,614?

STEP 1: Find the commission.
Total Sales × Commission Rate
$3,614 × 7% = $252.98 commission

STEP 2: Find the gross pay.
Salary or Commission
$250 or $252.98 **Gross pay is $252.98 (the greater amount).**

CONCEPT CHECK

 SELF-CHECK✓

Complete the problems, then check your answers at the end of the chapter.

3. Minimum salary: $160. Commission: $5\frac{1}{2}$ percent on $2,900. Which is greater? **$5\frac{1}{2}$% × $2,900 = $159.50, $160.00 is greater**
4. Minimum salary: $2,000. Commission: 6 percent on $34,000. Which is greater? **6% × $34,000 = $2,040, $2,040 is greater**

SECTION 1-6 PRACTICE

5. Roger Tussing earns 3 percent on sales of $9,500 in sales for a week. What is his commission? **$285.00**

	Sales Position	Total Sales	×	Commission Rate	=	Commission
6.	Real estate	$98,000	×	8%	=	$7,840.00
7.	Computers	18,100	×	2%	=	$362.00
8.	Major appliances	9,598	×	6%	=	$575.88
9.	Clothing	1,311	×	9%	=	$117.99
10.	Computer supplies	929	×	15%	=	$139.35
11.	Siding contract	5,754	×	12%	=	$690.48
12.	Auto	68,417	×	3%	=	$2,052.51

USING CALCULATORS

Using Calculators
There are several ways to use a calculator when solving percentage problems such as 30 percent of 2000. If your calculator has a percent key, the keystroke would be 2000 [×] 30 [%]. If you do not use the percent key, remember to rewrite the percent as its decimal equivalent. The keystroke would be 2000 [×] [.] 30 [=].

Salesperson	Minimum Monthly Salary	Total Monthly Sales	×	Commission Rate	=	Monthly Commission	Gross Pay
13. Anne Moser	$2,100	$28,000	×	8.0%	=	a.	b.
14. Peter Zinn	1,600	23,000	×	6.5%	=	a.	b.
15. Vern Yoder	3,140	31,000	×	9.25%	=	a.	b.
16. Yevette Vershum	850	10,400	×	3.5%	=	a.	b.
17. Rashad Ulrich	1,200	45,000	×	5.5%	=	a.	b.
18. DeWanda Coy	3,410	29,100	×	12.1%	=	a.	b.

13. a. $2,240.00
 b. $2,240.00
14. a. $1,495.00
 b. $1,600.00
15. a. $2,867.50
 b. $3,140.00
16. a. $364.00
 b. $850.00
17. a. $2,475.00
 b. $2,475.00
18. a. $3,521.10
 b. $3,521.10

19. Sam Taylor earns $6\frac{1}{2}$ percent commission on sales of $4,226. What is his commission? **$274.69**

20. John Navarro is a salesperson in the appliance department at Morris Appliance, Inc. He is guaranteed a minimum salary of $185 per week, or 5.5 percent of his total sales—whichever is greater. What is his gross pay for a week in which his total sales were $3,422? **$188.21 is greater**

21. Maude Eggert sells cosmetics for Soft Touch, Inc. She is guaranteed a salary of $790 a month, or 7 percent of her total sales—whichever is greater. What is her gross pay for a month in which her total sales were $10,984?
$790 is greater

22. Some jobs pay a commission plus a bonus at the end of the year. The bonus may be a percent of the salesperson's total commission for the year.
 a. Madelyn Carr is a sales representative. She receives 7 percent commission on all sales. At the end of the year, she receives a bonus of 5 percent of her commission. What is her total pay for a year in which she had sales totaling $412,454? **$28,871.78 + $1,443.59 = $30,315.37**
 b. What would Carr's total pay be if her sales were $316,250?
 $22,137.50 + $1,106.88 = $23,244.38

MAINTAINING YOUR SKILLS

Need Help? Go to...
▶ Skill 14: **Changing Fractions/Decimals,** page 741
▶ Skill 30: **Finding the Percentage,** page 757
▶ Skill 2: **Rounding Numbers,** page 729

Write each as a decimal.

23. $5\frac{1}{2}$ **5.50**

24. $6\frac{3}{4}$ **6.75**

25. $9\frac{1}{4}$ **9.25**

Find the percentage for each, then round to the nearest cent or hundredth.

26. 4% of $1,250 **$50**

27. $8\frac{1}{2}$% of $4,300 **$365.50**

28. $7\frac{1}{4}$% of $8,200 **$594.50**

29. 9.2% of $3,600 **$331.20**

30. 7.3% of $120 **$8.76**

31. 8.92% of 1,380 **123.1**

Round the answers to the nearest tenth.

32. 0.081 **0.1**

33. 0.60 **0.6**

34. 0.92 **0.9**

Error Analysis
If students need help in computing gross pay, remind them to compare the amount of the commission with the guaranteed minimum salary. The gross pay is the higher of the two amounts.

You may also wish to check that students are correctly converting percent to decimals. For instance, $14\frac{1}{2}\% = 0.1450$.

CLOSE

Closing Activity
1. Write $3\frac{1}{4}$ percent as a decimal.
 0.0325
2. Find $8\frac{1}{2}$ percent of $7,488
 $636.48
3. Alex Creighton.
 Receives 18 percent straight commission.
 Weekly sales of $5,425.
 What is his commission?
 $976.50
4. Enrique Martinez.
 Minimum monthly salary $1,575.
 Rate of commission: $6\frac{3}{4}$ percent.
 Monthly sales $24,600.
 Find the monthly commission.
 $1,660.50
 Find the gross pay. **$1,660.50**

ALTERNATIVE ASSESSMENT

English Language Learners
Large numbers, such as total monthly sales or gross pay, are a special challenge to students who are learning English. Fluent English speakers have a tendency to blur the sounds and say the numbers quickly. To help students understand the meaning to the numbers, say them slowly, write them on the board, and consider having students read the numbers back to you. **ELL**

WRAP-UP

Go over any problem for which a wrong answer is given.

Assignment Guide
 Basic: 13–18 (odd)
 Average: 19–21

20 min.

National Standards for Business Education

Standard 1	Mathematical Foundations
Standard 2	Number Relationships and Operations
Standard 6	Problem-Solving Applications

National Council of Teachers of Mathematics Standards

Standard 1	Numbers and Operations
Standard 6	Problem Solving
Standard 9	Connections

1 FOCUS

Point out to students that sometimes a business may set different commission rates for different levels of sales to motivate employees to sell more. Thus, as sales increase, so do the rates of commission. In this lesson, students compute the total graduated commission.

In-Class Examples

Work through these exercises with students before having them do the Self-Check.
1. 8% of $800 **$64**
2. $12\frac{1}{2}$% of $920 **$115**
3. (8% of $1000) + (12% of $2,000) **$320**
4. (12% of $5000) + (15% of $3000) + (18% of $1200) **$1,266**

2 TEACH

Explain the meaning of the term *graduated* to students. Suggest that they think of things that involve height, weight, depth, or difficulty.

SECTION 1-7 Graduated Commission

○ **Section Objective**

Compute the total graduated commission.

Your commission rate may increase as your sales increase. A **graduated commission** offers a different rate of commission for each of several levels of sales. It provides an extra incentive to sell more. The general formula to remember is:

Total Graduated Commission = Sum of Commissions for All Levels of Sales

Living in the Real World

The Road to Building Castles

Commission and Its Caviar Club Raul thinks about what Mrs. Jenkins told him about commissions and then remembers that his cousin, Benita, also works on commission. She sells gourmet-cooking equipment at people's homes. Benita sold so much she was promoted to the "Caviar Club," which means she sold so much that her commission rate kept increasing.

Draw Conclusions Describe the kind of personality a salesperson might have. How does this influence his or her sales?

Continued on page 109

Example 1

Irene Gomaz sells appliances at Twin City Sales. She receives a graduated commission as shown:

Gomaz's sales for the past month totaled $9,840. What is her commission for the month?

Commission Percent	Level of Sales
4%	First $1,000
6%	Next $2,000
8%	Over $3,000

Need Help? Go to...
► Skill 5: Adding Decimals, page 732
► Skill 28: Writing Percents as Decimals, page 755
► Skill 30: Finding the Percentage, page 757
► Application A: Formulas, page 760

STEP: Find the sum of commissions for all levels of sales.

	Sales	×	Commission Rate	
First $1,000:	$1,000	×	4%	= $ 40.00
Next $2,000:	$2,000	×	6%	= 120.00
Over $3,000: ($9,840 − $3,000)	×		8%	
	$6,840	×	8%	= 547.20
Total Graduated Commission				**$707.20**

1000 ✕ 4 % 40 M+ 2000 ✕ 6 % 120 M+

9840 − 3000 = 6840 ✕ 8 % 547.2 M+ RM 707.2

THINKING CRITICALLY

Substituting in a Formula

You're traveling from Houston to London on the "red-eye" flight. You packed your flight plan in the overhead storage bin, and you can't be bothered to find it. You want to know what time you'll arrive in London. You know that London is 6 hours ahead of Houston. The plane took off from Houston at 6 P.M. The pilot announced that the airplane is traveling at a rate of 956 kilometers per hour. It's 11,000 km from Houston to London.

Formula: Distance = Rate × Time
Time = Distance ÷ Rate.
Solve: Time = 11,000 ÷ 956 = $11\frac{1}{2}$ hours traveling time;
6:00 P.M. + $11\frac{1}{2}$ hours = 5:30 A.M. Houston time;
5:30 A.M. + 6 hours time difference = 11:30 A.M. in London

CONCEPT CHECK

SELF-CHECK ✓

Complete the problems, then check your answers at the end of the chapter.

1. Commission: 10 percent on first $5,000; 15 percent over $5,000. Find the total graduated commission on $22,000.

2. Commission: 5 percent first $2,000; 8 percent over $2,000. Find the total graduated commission on $7,740.

SECTION 1-7 PRACTICE

3. Manuel Romo sells tires at the local shopping mall. Romo earns 20 percent commission on the first $500, 25 percent on the next $1,000, and 30 percent on sales over $1,500. Last weekend he sold $1,940 worth of tires. What is his total commission? **$482**

4. Tunisia Buehrer sells sporting goods equipment. Buehrer earns 5 percent commission on the first $6,000, $7\frac{1}{2}$ percent on the next $6,000, and 10 percent on sales over $12,000. Her total sales for the month are $14,640. What is her total commission? **$1,014**

5. Jean Gray sells office supplies. She receives a graduated commission of 4 percent on her first $2,000 of sales and $8\frac{1}{2}$ percent on all sales over $2,000. Gray's sales for the past week totaled $3,925. What is her commission for the week? **$243.63**

$1,444 6. Charles Beaudry sells computer hardware for a computer firm. He is paid 4 percent commission on the first $8,000 of sales, 6 percent on the next $10,000, and 8 percent on sales over $18,000. What is his commission on $24,550 in sales?

7. Booker Bond demonstrates cookware at the National Food Fair. He is paid $6.00 each for the first 10 demonstrations in one day and $7.50 for each demonstration over 10. What is Bond's commission for a day in which he makes 21 demonstrations? **$142.50**

8. Odessa Dilulo demonstrates home fire alarm systems. She is paid $10.00 per demonstration for the first 10 demonstrations given during a week and $15.50 for each demonstration over 10. Also, for every sale, she gets a bonus of $15.00. What is her commission for a week in which she gives 18 demonstrations and makes 6 sales? **$314.00**

9. Some sales positions pay a commission only if sales exceed a sales quota. The salesperson is rewarded only for having sales beyond an expected amount. Joyce Doyle is a sales trainee. She is paid $1,550 per month plus a commission of 7.5 percent on all sales over a quota of $20,000 per month. What is her total pay for a month in which she has sales totaling $22,650? **$1,748.75**

MAINTAINING YOUR SKILLS

Need Help? Go to...
- Skill 5: **Adding Decimals,** page 732
- Skill 28: **Writing Percents as Decimals,** page 755
- Skill 30: **Finding the Percentage,** page 757

Add.

10.	11.	12.
$123.72	$567.89	$1,350.23
112.69	34.69	946.00
+ 45.23	+ 431.73	+ 18.11
$281.64	**$1,034.31**	**$2,314.34**

Write each as a decimal.

13. $5\frac{1}{2}$% **0.055**   14. $10\frac{1}{4}$% **0.1025**   15. 15% **0.15**

Find the percentage of each.

16. $5\frac{1}{4}$% of $2,000 **$105**   17. 7% of $4,560 **$319.20**   18. $15\frac{1}{2}$% of $3,500 **$542.50**

Section 1-7 Graduated Commission ▶ **107**

Living in the Real World

Answers will vary, but might include outgoing, charismatic, friendly, sociable, and so on.

WRAP-UP

Go over any problem for which a wrong answer is given.

Assignment Guide
- **Basic:** 3–5 (odd)
- **Average:** 6–8

20 min.

---

1. **First $5,000:**
   $5,000 × 10% = $ 500.00
   Over $5,000:
   ($22,000 − $5,000) × 15%
   $17,000 × 15% = 2,550.00
   Total Graduated Commission: $3,050.00

2. **First $2,000:**
   $2,000 × 5% = $ 100.00
   Over $2,000:
   ($7,740 − $2,000) × 8%
   $5,740 × 8% = 459.20
   Total Graduated Commission: $ 559.20

In-Class Examples

1. Six percent commission on first $10,000. Eight percent commission over $10,000. Find the total graduated commission on $13,200. **$856**

2. Four percent commission on first $8,000. Six percent commission over $8,000. Find the total graduated commission on $8962. **$377.72**

3 ASSESS

Error Analysis

If students experience difficulty in computing the total graduated commission, check to see that they are accurately computing each level of commission separately before totaling the amounts. In sales with three levels of graduated commission, students must subtract the third level of sales from the total amount sold. The remainder will be the amount on which they compute the third level of commission.

4 CLOSE

Closing Activity

1. Find $2\frac{1}{2}$ percent of $368,700. **$9,217.50**

2. Commission: 10 percent on first $20,000. Receive 15 percent over $20,000. Find the total graduated commission on $43,085. **$5,462.75**

107

Quick Quiz

1. Michael Lopez is a postal worker. He earns $14.86 per hour plus time and a half for overtime. He works 40 hours per week. What is his straight time pay for the week? **($594.40)** What is his total pay in a week in which he works $44\frac{3}{4}$ hours? Round to the nearest cent. **$700.28**

2. On one day last week, Erica Benson worked from 7:52 A.M. to 11:30 A.M. and from 12:25 P.M. until 4:46 P.M. Find the hours worked. Round to the nearest quarter hour. **8**

3. Marshall Hayes is a driver for a trucking company. He earns $0.34 per mile. What is his total pay for a week in which he drives 2,482 miles? **$843.88**

4. Julia Johnson is a floor installer for a tile company. Her biweekly pay is $1,705.58. Next month her company is switching from a biweekly pay period to a semimonthly pay period. What will her semimonthly pay be? Round to the nearest cent. **$1,847.71**

5. Chi Chu Lin sells televisions and DVD players. She receives a weekly commission of 9 percent of her first $1,000 of sales, 10 percent of her next $2,000, and 14 percent of sales over $3,000. What is her total pay in a week where she sells $4,978? **$566.92**

SECTION 1-1 **CONCEPT CHECK** (p. 92)

1. $304.00
2. $292.30

SECTION 1-2 **CONCEPT CHECK** (p. 95)

1. ($9.00 × 40) + ($9.00 × 1.5 × 6) = ($360.00 × $81.00) = **$441.00**
2. ($11.50 × 40) + ($11.50 × 1.5 × 7) = ($460.00 + $120.75) = **$580.75**

SECTION 1-3 **CONCEPT CHECK** (p. 97)

1. $2\frac{3}{4} + 3\frac{3}{4} = 6\frac{1}{2}$
2. $4\frac{1}{2} + 3\frac{3}{4} = 8\frac{1}{4}$

SECTION 1-4 **CONCEPT CHECK** (p. 99)

1. $3.20 × 140 = **$448.00**
2. $0.15 × 1,494 = **$224.10**

SECTION 1-5 **CONCEPT CHECK** (p. 102)

1. **$1,650**
2. **$758.33**
3. $4,725 × 12 = **$56,700**
4. $62,400 ÷ 24 = **$2,600**

SECTION 1-6 **CONCEPT CHECK** (p. 104)

1. $9,400 × 8% = **$752.00**
2. $143,400 × $5\frac{1}{2}$% = **$7,887.00**
3. $5\frac{1}{2}$% × $2,900 = **$159.50, $160.00 is greater**
4. 6% × $34,000 = **$2,040, $2,040 is greater**

SECTION 1-7 **CONCEPT CHECK** (p. 107)

1. First $5,000: $5,000   × 10% = $ 500.00
   Over $5,000:   ($22,000 − $5,000) × 15%
                       $17,000   × 15% =   2,550.00
   Total Graduated Commission $3,050.00

2. First $2,000: $2,000   × 5% = $ 100.00
   Over $2,000:   ($7,740 − $2,000) × 8%
                       $5,740   × 8% =   459.20
   Total Graduated Commission $ 559.20

Living in the
Real World

Direct deposit speeds up the process of getting money in your banking account.

Living in the Real World

The Road to Building Castles

Preparing Paychecks As a newly salaried employee of Castle Builders, Raul doesn't have to worry about time cards. Mrs. Jenkins encouraged him to enroll in the company's *direct deposit* system. This is when an employee's net pay is deposited automatically in an employee's designated bank account.

Analysis Why might employers like the direct deposit function for preparing paychecks?

REVIEW OF KEY WORDS

hourly rate (p. 92)
straight-time pay (p. 92)
overtime pay (p. 94)
time and a half (p. 94)

double time (p. 94)
weekly time card (p. 96)
piecework (p. 99)
salary (p. 101)

commission (p. 103)
commission rate (p. 103)
straight commission (p. 103)
graduated commission (p. 106)

Determine if the following statements are true or false.

1. Your **hourly rate** is the amount of money you earn per hour. **True**

2. The formula for figuring **straight-time pay** is your hourly rate divided by the number of hours worked in a week. **False**

3. If you work more than your regular hours, you may be eligible for **overtime** pay. **True**

4. Overtime is always **time and a half**. **False**

5. **Double time** is figured by multiplying your hourly rate by your overtime pay. **False**

6. Employees keep **weekly time cards** in order to show how many hours were worked each pay period. **True**

7. Employees who are paid on a **piecework** basis receive cash every day that they work. **False**

8. The fixed amount of money you earn on a regular basis is your **salary**. **True**

9. When you receive **commission**, you are earning money based on the number of hours you work per day. **False**

10. In order to determine your **straight commission**, you need to multiply your total sales by the commission rate. **True**

11. Your **commission rate** is your hourly rate multiplied by the number of hours you work each week. **False**

12. If you earn **graduated commission**, it means that you have received a recent promotion. **False**

Skills and Concepts

SECTION OBJECTIVE 1-1 AND EXAMPLES

Compute the straight-time pay.

Rita Carlson works at a coffee shop. She earns $6.75 per hour. Last week she worked 28 hours. What is her straight-time pay?

STEP: Find the straight-time pay.

Hourly Rate × Hours Worked

$6.75 × 28 hours = **$189 straight-time pay**

REVIEW EXERCISES

For the month of June, Marla May worked the following. Her hourly rate is $9.45 per hour. What is her straight-time pay for each week?

13. Week 1   40 hours   40 × $9.45 = $378
14. Week 2   36.25 hours   36.25 × $9.45 = $342.56
15. Week 3   17.50 hours   17.50 × $9.45 = $165.38
16. Week 4   39.75 hours   39.75 × $9.45 = $375.64

Find the straight-time pay.

17. $6.55 per hour, 40 hours worked. **$262**
18. $8.96 per hour, 36 hours worked. **$322.56**
19. $12.85 per hour, 19.5 hours worked. **$250.58**
20. $8.755 per hour, 38.925 hours worked. **$340.79**

SECTION OBJECTIVE 1-2 AND EXAMPLES

Figure out straight-time, overtime, and total pay.

Dori Newman earns $9.50 per hour for 40 hours and time and a half for overtime. If she worked 5 hours overtime, what is her total pay?

STEP 1: Find the straight-time pay.

Hourly Rate × Regular Hours Worked

$9.50 × 40 = $380.00 straight-time pay

STEP 2: Find the overtime pay.

Overtime Rate × Overtime Hours Worked

(1.5 × $9.50) × 5 = $71.25 overtime pay

STEP 3: Find the total pay.

Straight-Time Pay + Overtime Pay

$380.00 + $71.25 = **$451.25 total pay**

21. $9.17 × 40 = $366.80 straight-time pay
(1.5 × $9.17) × 7 = $96.29 overtime pay
$366.80 + $96.29 = $463.09

22. $12.35 × 40 = $494.00 straight-time pay
(1.5 × 12.35) × 16 = $296.40 overtime pay
$494.00 + $296.40 = $790.40

REVIEW EXERCISES

21. Tony Sperazza is a school bus driver. He earns $9.17 per hour and time and a half for overtime. Last week he worked his regular 40 hours plus 7 hours of overtime. What was his total pay for the week?

22. As a zookeeper, Chi Ho earns $12.35 an hour plus time and a half for weekend work. Last week Ho worked his regular 40 hours plus 16 hours of overtime on the weekend. What was his total pay for the week?

Find the total pay.

23. $8.20 per hour for 40 hours. Time and a half for 7 hours. **$414.10**

24. $9.65 per hour for 40 hours. Time and a half for 5 hours. **$458.38**

25. $9.25 per hour for 40 hours. Time and a half for 8 hours. **$481.00**

26. $6.50 per hour for 37.5 hours. Time and a half for 3 hours. **$273.00**

REINFORCEMENT

Section 1-1

1. Bill earns $12.00 per hour. He works 40 hours. What is his straight-time pay? **$480.00**
2. Izumi is a musician. She earns $35.00 per hour. She works $32\frac{1}{2}$ hours. What is her straight-time pay? **$1,137.50**
3. Steve is a plumber. He earns $28.75 per hour. He works $39\frac{3}{4}$ hours. What is his straight-time pay? **$1,142.81**

Section 1-2

1. Jiwon Chang earns $11.70 per hour plus time and a half. He worked his regular 40 hours plus 6 hours on the weekend. What is his total pay for the week? **$573.30**
2. Nadia Campana earns a regular hourly rate of $23.60. She earns double time for work on Sundays. She worked her regular 36 hours plus $7\frac{1}{2}$ hours on Sunday. What is her total pay for the week? **$1,203.60**

SECTION OBJECTIVE 1-3 AND EXAMPLES

Compute the total hours on a weekly time card.

Terry Bartlett worked from 7:00 A.M. to 10:45 A.M. and from 12:30 P.M. to 3:15 P.M. Find the total hours.

STEP: Calculate the total hours.

Total Hours = Sum of Daily Hours

10:45	−	7:00	= 3h:45min
3:15	−	12:30	= 2h:45min
3h:45min	+ 2h:45min		= 5h:90min = $6\frac{1}{2}$ hours

REVIEW EXERCISES

John Kim works in a hospital. Use his time card to find his total hours worked each day and his total hours for the week. Round off the total hours each day to the nearest quarter hour.

Employee Time Card — Central Arkansas Hospital

Employee Name: John Kim Department: Radiology

	DATE	IN	OUT	IN	OUT	TOTAL
Sun.						
27. Mon.	9/1	6:45 A.M.	11:30 A.M.	12:00 P.M.	3:45 P.M.	8.50
28. Tue.	9/2	7:00 A.M.	11:30 A.M.	12:00 P.M.	3:45 P.M.	8.25
29. Wed.	9/3	6:56 A.M.	11:45 A.M.	12:30 P.M.	4:00 P.M.	8.25
30. Thur.	9/4	6:45 A.M.	12:50 P.M.	1:50 P.M.	3:00 P.M.	7.25
31. Fri.	9/5	7:10 A.M.	11:30 A.M.	12:30 P.M.	4:20 P.M.	8.25
Sat.						

32. Employee Signature: John Kim   TOTAL HOURS 40.50

SECTION OBJECTIVE 1-4 AND EXAMPLES

Compute the total pay on a piecework basis.

Vidia Roswell earns $2.57 per CD that she boxes for shipment. Yesterday, she boxed 85 CDs. What was her total pay?

STEP: Find the total pay. Rate per Item × Number of Items Produced

$2.57   ×   85   = $218.45 total pay

REVIEW EXERCISES

33. $125 × 11 = $1,375; $18 × 9 = $162. $1,375 + $162 = $1,537

33. Roger Levingold works in a motorcycle shop. He is paid to set up new motorcycles when they arrive from the factory. He is also responsible for test riding each one. His boss pays him $125 per motorcycle and another $18 per test ride. Last week he set up 11 motorcycles and test rode 9 of them. How much money did he earn?

34. Vicki Giddeon delivers flowers every Valentine's Day. She earns $3.50 to deliver a small arrangement, $4.50 to deliver a medium arrangement, and $6.05 to deliver a large arrangement. Last year, she delivered 68 small arrangements, 15 medium arrangements, and 23 large arrangements. What was her total pay for the day?

Compute the total pay on a piecework basis.

35. $3.05 per item, 136 items produced. $414.80

36. $2.38 per item, 85 items produced. $202.30

34. $3.50 × 68 = $238; $4.50 × 15 = $67.50; $6.05 × 23 = $139.15. $238 + $67.50 + $139.15 = $444.65

Study Guide and Assessment ▶ **111**

REINFORCEMENT

Section 1-3

1. Jamal Parker works at a company that uses military time to keep track of employees' work hours. Thus, 1:00 P.M. is shown as 13:00, 2:00 P.M. as 14:00, etc. On Monday, October 1, Parker worked from 8:02 to 11:47 and from 13:08 to 17:06. How many hours did he work on Monday? **(7 hours 43 minutes)** Rounded to the nearest quarter hour? $7\frac{3}{4}$

Section 1-4

1. Gabriella Santos is a Little League umpire. She is paid $20 per game on weekdays and $25 per game on weekends. She umpired 14 weekday games and 3 weekend games. What is her total pay? **$335.00**

SECTION OBJECTIVE 1-5 AND EXAMPLES

Compute the salary per pay period.

Richard Martin is a network administrator for a large law firm. His annual salary is $43,450. What is his monthly salary? What is his weekly salary?

STEP: Find the salary per pay period.

Annual Salary ÷ Number of Pay Periods per Year

$43,450	÷	12	= $3,620.83 monthly salary
$43,450	÷	52	= $835.58 weekly salary

REVIEW EXERCISES

Find the number of pay periods.

37. Weekly for 3 years. **156**
38. Biweekly for $1\frac{1}{2}$ years. **39**
39. Semimonthly for 4 years. **96**
40. Monthly for $2\frac{1}{2}$ years. **30**

Determine the salary per pay period.

41. If your annual salary is $36,575, what is your weekly salary? **$703.37**
42. If your annual salary is $47,980, what is your biweekly salary? **$1,845.38**
43. If your annual salary is $64,710, what is your semimonthly salary? **$2,696.25**
44. If your annual salary is $24,700, what is your monthly salary? **$2,058.33**

SECTION OBJECTIVE 1-6 AND EXAMPLES

Calculate the straight commission and determine the gross pay.

Bonnie Heisey sells clothing. Her commission rate is 7.5 percent. Last month her sales were $10,875. What was her commission?

STEP: Find the commission.   Total Sales × Commission Rate

$10,875   ×   7.5%   = $815.63 commission

REVIEW EXERCISES

Compute the straight commission.

45. $7,600 total sales, 4 percent commission rate. **$304**
46. $122,360 total sales, $6\frac{1}{4}$ percent commission rate. **$7,647.50**
47. $34,996 total sales, 3.5 percent commission rate. **$1,224.86**
48. $1,600 total sales, 15.8 percent commission rate. **$252.80**

Compute the straight commission and gross pay.

49. Minimum weekly salary is $185. Rate of commission is 6.5 percent. Weekly sales are $3,790. What is the commission? What is the gross pay? **$246.35; $246.35**
50. Minimum weekly salary is $250. Rate of commission is 5.65 percent. Weekly sales are $1,515. What is the commission? What is the gross pay? **$85.60; $250.00**
51. Minimum weekly salary is $1,500. Rate of commission is $4\frac{1}{4}$ percent. Weekly sales are $4,500. What is the commission? What is the gross pay? **$191.25; $1,500.00**
52. Minimum weekly salary is $325. Rate of commission is $6\frac{3}{4}$ percent. Weekly sales are $22,300. What is the commission? What is the gross pay? **$1,505.25; $1,505.25**

REINFORCEMENT

Section 1-5

1. Michelle Giuseffi is a police officer. Her annual salary is $40,560. What is her biweekly salary? **$1,560**
2. Ted Sucharski works at Logan General Hospital as a nurse anesthetist. He is paid a semimonthly salary of $3,950. What is his annual salary? **$94,800**
3. Colin Evans is a hotel desk clerk who earns an annual salary of $21,216. What is his weekly salary? **$408**

Section 1-6

1. Jermaine Dixon sells electronic equipment. He receives a straight commission of $6\frac{1}{2}$ percent of his total sales. What commission will he receive in a week where his sales total $12,416? **$807.04**

SECTION OBJECTIVE 1-7 AND EXAMPLES

Compute the total graduated commission.

Carl earns a commission rate of 6 percent for the first $6,500 in sales and 9 percent on sales over $6,500. Find the total graduated commission on sales of $10,500.

STEP: Find the graduated commission. Multiply and add.

Total Graduated Commission = Sum of Commissions for All Levels of Sales

$6,500 × .06 = $390
$4,000 × .09 = $360
$390 + $360 = $750 **total graduated commission**

REVIEW EXERCISES

53. Vito Avido is a sales representative for a company that sells roofing material. He receives a graduated commission of 5 percent on the first $5,000 of sales, 6.5 percent on the next $15,000, and 7 percent on sales over $20,000. What is his commission on $23,458 in sales?

54. Connie Hamm demonstrates microwave ovens at a home décor center. She is paid $35.00 per demonstration for the first 10 demonstrations and $45.00 for each demonstration over 10. Also, for every microwave sold, she earns $20.55. What is Hamm's commission on a day in which she makes 12 demonstrations and 4 sales?

Compute the graduated commission.

55. Commission: 25 percent on the first $1,900; 27 percent on the next $1,000; 30 percent on sales over $2,900. Total sales equal $3,500. What is the total commission? **$925**

56. Commission: 5 percent on the first $4,000; $6\frac{1}{2}$ percent on the next $6,000; 11 percent on sales over $10,000. Total sales equal $12,360. What is the total commission? **$849.60**

57. Social Science In Indonesia, women often work 15 hours per day making blue jeans for companies in the United States to sell. If a young woman was paid $0.23 per pair of jeans she produces, what is her total piecework pay for the week if she produces 43 pairs? (See Section 1-4.) **$9.89**

58. Computer Technology OMY, Inc. is a computer chip factory located in Washington. The front line supervisor is paid $658 per week. She has been offered a position in a chip factory in Colorado. Her pay would be $1,190 biweekly. What is the annual salary for each job? Should she take the job in Colorado? (See Section 1-5.)
Washington—$34,216; Colorado—$30,940. Most students will say no.

53. $5,000 × .05 = $250; $15,000 × .065 = $975; $3,458 × 0.07 = $242.06; $250 + $975 + $242.06 = $1,467.06

54. $35.00 × 10 = $350; $45.00 × 2 = $90.00; $20.55 × 4 = $82.20. $350 + $90 + $82.20 = $522.20

REINFORCEMENT

Section 1-6 *(cont'd)*

2. Ryan O'Malley is paid either a commission or by the hour, whichever is greater. His hourly pay is $8.00 per hour with time and a half for all hours that exceed 40 hours per week. His commission is 7 percent of his sales. Find his gross pay in a week in which he worked 48 hours. His total sales for the week were $6,120. **$428.40**

Section 1-7

1. Pamela Miller sells musical instruments. She earns $6\frac{1}{2}$ percent commission on the first $2,000, 8 percent on the next $3,000, and 10 percent on sales over $5,000. Find the graduated commission on $7,368. **$606.80**

2. Bob Elliott sells lumber. He earns 9 percent commission on the first $25,000, 11 percent commission on the next $30,000, and 15 percent on sales over $55,000. Find the graduated commission on monthly sales of $56,575. **$5786.25**

National Standards for Business Education

Section Objectives	1. Mathematical Foundations	2. Number Relationships and Operations	3. Patterns, Functions, and Algebra	4. Measurements	5. Statistics and Probability	6. Problem-Solving Applications	
2-1 Federal Income Tax, (pp. 116–118) Read tables to find the amount withheld for federal income tax.	X	X					
2-2 State Income Tax, (pp. 119–121) Compute the state taxes on a straight percent basis.	X					X	
2-3 Graduated State Income Tax, (pp. 122–123) Determine the state taxes on a graduated income basis.	X	X					
2-4 Social Security and Medicare Taxes, (pp. 124–125) Work out the amount of income withheld for Social Security and Medicare taxes.	X	X					
2-5 Group Health Insurance, (pp. 126–127) Calculate the deduction for group insurance.	X	X					
2-6 Statement of Earnings, (pp. 128–131) Figure out net pay per pay period.	X				X		

(Source: Reprinted with permission from the National Standards for Business Education, copyright © 2001 by National Business Education Association, 1914 Association Drive, Reston, Virginia 21901-1596)

SCANS Correlation

Foundation Skills

Basic Skills	Reading	Writing	Math	Listening	Speaking	
Thinking Skills	Creative Thinking	Decision Making	Problem Solving	Seeing Things in the Mind's Eye	Knowing How to Learn	Reasoning
Personal Qualities	Responsibility	Self-Esteem	Sociability	Self-Management	Integrity/Honesty	

This chapter's highlighted blocks indicate the chapter's content coverage in the Student Edition and the Teacher Wraparound Edition.

National Council of Teachers of Mathematics Standards

1. Numbers & Operations	2. Algebra	3. Geometry	4. Measurement	5. Data Analysis & Probability	6. Problem Solving	7. Reasoning & Proof	8. Communication	9. Connections	10. Representations
X					X				
					X			X	
X					X				
X					X				
					X			X	
X					X				

SCANS Correlation

Workplace Competencies

Resources	Allocating Time	Allocating Money	Allocating Material and Facility Resources	Allocating Human Resources		
Information	Acquiring and Evaluating Information	Organizing and Maintaining Information	Interpreting and Communicating Information	Using Computers to Process Information		
Interpersonal Skills	Participating as a Member of a Team	Teaching Others	Serving Clients/Customers	Exercising Leadership	Negotiating to Arrive at a Decision	Working with Cultural Diversity
Systems	Understanding Systems	Monitoring and Correcting Performance	Improving and Designing Systems			
Technology	Selecting Technology	Applying Technology to Task	Maintaining and Troubleshooting Technology			

What You'll Learn
In this chapter students will focus on finding the deductions from a paycheck, so that they can figure out the take-home pay.

Why It's Important
Ask students if they agree with this statement: "Managing your life means managing your money." Ask students to think of reasons why you need to know how much money you'll bring in. Is it necessary to check that the withholdings and the deductions are correct? Why or why not?

Key Word Review
Beat the Clock
Set a timer for five minutes. Read aloud the definition of one of this chapter's key words. Ask a volunteer to repeat the meaning in his or her own words. Score how many key words the class completes in five minutes. Repeat the process and have the class try to beat the score.

CHAPTER 2

Net Income

What You'll Learn
Section 2-1 Read tables to find the amount withheld for federal income tax.
Section 2-2 Compute the state taxes on a straight percent basis.
Section 2-3 Determine the state taxes on a graduated income basis.
Section 2-4 Work out the amount of income withheld for Social Security and Medicare taxes.
Section 2-5 Calculate the deduction for group insurance.
Section 2-6 Figure out net pay per pay period.

When Will You Ever Use This?
If you earn money, you pay taxes . . . if you don't, you could end up in jail. Set a realistic budget when you know the amount of taxes and insurance withheld from your paycheck.

Key Words to Know
- federal income tax
- personal exemptions
- graduated income tax
- Social Security
- Medicare
- group insurance
- net pay

Mathematics Online
To learn more about net income, visit the *Mathematics with Business Applications* Web site at www.busmath.glencoe.com.

CLASSROOM RESOURCES

Application and Enrichment
- Teacher Wraparound Edition
- Teacher Resource Binder, Blackline Masters
- Interactive Lesson Planner CD-ROM
- PowerPoint® Presentations CD-ROM

Review and Enforcement
- Mathematics Online
  www.busmath.glencoe.com
- Teacher Resource Binder, Internet Resources

- Student Activity Workbook
- Student Activity Workbook, Teacher Annotated Edition
- School-to-Home Activity Workbook

Assessment and Evaluation
- Assessment Binder, Reproducible Tests
- Assessment Binder, Alternative Assessment Strategies
- ExamView® Pro Test Generator CD-ROM

For the Teacher
- Student Activity Workbook, Teacher Annotated Edition
- Assessment Binder
- Interactive Lesson Planner CD-ROM
- Teacher Resource Binder
- Mathematics Online
  www.busmath.glencoe.com

For the Student
- Student Activity Workbook
- School-to-Home Activity Workbook

Living in the Real World

Jack's Jackpot

Money. Freedom. Independence. Oh, how you've wanted these for so long. So had Jack Myers, a twenty-something who just graduated from an apprenticeship program in Peoria, Illinois. In this chapter you'll read a story about a young man who's stepping out into the real world. He's finding out financial freedom isn't exactly working out as he had expected.

Read on. Go to . . .

115

Living in the Real World

Story's Summary

Jack Myers is learning the hard lessons of income tax. New to the working world, he's learning—with the help of his brother, Jon—about state and federal taxes, Social Security and Medicare deductions, as well as medical plan costs and pre-tax retirement savings. Jack and Jon think about money in very different ways: Jack wants to live for today, while Jon wants to retire comfortably.

Did You Know...

Several states, including Alaska, Florida, Washington and Texas, do not charge state income tax. Revenue in these states is made up in other ways, such as property and sales taxes.

Think about This

How would your community be affected if there were no state income tax?

LOCAL STANDARDS

National Standards for Business Education

Standard 1	Mathematical Foundations
Standard 2	Number Relationships and Operations

National Council of Teachers of Mathematics Standards

Standard 1	Numbers and Operations
Standard 6	Problem Solving

① FOCUS

To motivate the lesson and chapter, ask students if they've ever heard someone complaining about how much money is taken out of their paycheck for taxes. Did they ever wonder how these tax amounts are calculated? In this lesson, students will use tax tables to find the amount withheld for federal income tax.

In-Class Examples

Work through these exercises with students before having them do the Self-Check.

1. How much is withheld from the weekly wage of a married person earning $297 with 1 withholding allowance? **$11**

2. How much is withheld from the weekly wage of a married person earning $379 with 2 allowances? **$16**

3. How much is withheld from the weekly wage of a single person earning $238 with no allowances? **$22**

4. How much is withheld from the weekly wage of a single person earning $318 with 5 allowances? **$0**

SECTION 2-1 Federal Income Tax

Section Objective

Read tables to find the amount withheld for federal income tax.

Federal taxes are necessary to keep the government agencies and services afloat. Employers are required by law to withhold a certain amount of your pay for **federal income tax** (or FIT). The Internal Revenue Service (IRS) provides employers with tables that show how much money to withhold. The amount withheld depends on your income, marital status, and withholding allowances. You may claim 1 allowance for yourself and 1 allowance for your spouse if you are married. You may claim additional allowances for any others you support.

Living in the Real World

Jack's Jackpot

► **FYI**

Federal prosecutors convict those who fail to file a tax return. The average sentence is more than three years.

►►►

Where's All My Money? Jack Myers blinks, rubs his eyes, and blinks again. "Wait. Hey, there's no $1,200 in this paycheck." His brother Jon, a certified public accountant, has been trying to tell him that he needs to take into account withholdings from his paycheck. One large chunk of the money he thought he was going to get actually goes to paying FIT. "This is going to affect my truck payment," Jack said. "I thought there was going to be more."

Draw Conclusions What do you do when your bills are more than your paycheck amount?

Continued on page 119

Use table Married Persons Weekly Payroll on page 790 for Examples 1 and 2.

Need Help? Go to...
► Skill 1: Numbers, page 727
► Application C: Tables and Charts, page 762

Example 1

Carla Garza's gross pay for this week is $425.88. She is married and claims 2 allowances — herself and her husband. What amount will be withheld from Garza's pay for FIT?

STEPS:
1. Find the income range from the table. (It's 420–430.)
2. Find the column for 2 allowances.
3. The amount of income to be withheld is $19.

Example 2

Lance Han's gross pay for this week is $460.00. He is married and claims 1 allowance. What amount will be withheld from Han's pay for FIT?

STEPS:
1. Find the income range from the table. (It's at least 460, but less than 470.)
2. Find the column for 1 allowance.
3. The amount of income to be withheld is $31.

Living in the Real World

Answers may vary, but might include analyze budget, reduce spending, get another job, etc.

BUSINESS NOTES

Communication

Students talk with relatives and employers to find out what other deductions—besides taxes and medical insurance—are taken from wages. Pair students to combine their findings then share them with the class. **CL** , **LS**

SELF-CHECK ✔

CONCEPT CHECK

Complete Problems 1–7 using the Married Persons Weekly Payroll table (see page 790), then check your answers at the end of the chapter.

A Payroll Period

	Employee	Weekly Income	Allowances	Amount Withheld
1.	D. Caine	$390.50	1	$21
2.	A. Kim	435.95	2	$20
3.	D. Cadena	399.95	2	$16
4.	H. Nguyen	444.23	1	$28
5.	G. Ginn	382.23	1	$20
6.	K. Morris	421.98	0	$34
7.	C. Dukowski	371.09	2	$14

SECTION 2-1 PRACTICE

Use the **Single Persons Weekly Payroll** and **Married Persons Weekly Payroll** tables on pages 788–791 to find the amount withheld.

8. Carrie Burnside, single. Earns $350.15 weekly. Claims 1 allowance. What is the FIT withheld? **$31**

9. Raymond Barbee, single. Earns $300.74 weekly. Claims 2 allowances. What is the FIT withheld? **$15**

10. Stephen Cabellero, married. Earns $369.23 weekly. Claims 2 allowances. What is the FIT withheld? **$13**

11. Lisa Steamer, married. Earns $290.34 weekly. Claims no allowances. What is the FIT withheld? **$17**

12. Catherine Hanna earns $208.35 a week. She is single and claims 2 allowances. What amount is withheld weekly for federal income tax? **$4**

13. Ike Svenious earns $225.32 a week. He is single and claims 1 allowance. What amount is withheld weekly for federal income tax? **$12**

14. Doug Smalley is married and earns $304.30 a week. He claims 2 allowances. What amount is withheld weekly for federal income tax? **$7**

15. Kristen Martinez is married, earns $252.75 a week, and claims 1 allowance. What amount is withheld weekly for federal income tax? **$7**

Continued on next page

The crux of this lesson is learning to read income tax tables. To help students familiarize themselves with the tax table on pages 788–791, point out the format of the determining factors: marital status, wages, allowances, and payroll schedule. Regarding wages, be sure to emphasize the column headings "At least" and "But less than." Mention that there are also tax tables for other payroll schedules, such as monthly and biweekly.

Discuss the headings "At least" and "But less than" when finding the correct range of a person's income.

You might wish to explain that by law a person cannot claim more allowances than those to which he or she is entitled. However, a person can claim fewer allowances.

Motivating the Lesson

Ask students who have part-time jobs or have older siblings with part-time jobs to bring in a weekly pay stub. Discuss the amount withheld by the federal government each week. Compute the annual amount withheld in federal income taxes.

In-Class Examples

Use the Single Persons—Weekly Payroll Period table on pages 788 and 789 to find the amount withheld.

1. Joseph Napoli, single. Earns $524 per week. Claims 2 allowances. **$48**

2. Kazuo Miyazaki, single. Earns $428 per week. Claims 1 allowance. **$42**

THINKING CRITICALLY

Top Taxes

Do the rich pay more? Recent Tax Foundation data show that in one year the top one percent of all tax-payers combined paid $317,450,000,000 in income taxes; the top five percent paid $486,500,000,000; and the top ten percent paid $583,300,000,000. The bottom 50 percent paid $35,120,000,000. Rewrite these large numbers as decimals. **Skill 1 $317.45 billion, $486.5 billion, $583.3 billion, and $35.12 billion.**

PROBLEM SOLVING

Reading Tables

Pairs of students find a table about federal income tax in the "Tax Bites" section of the Tax Foundation Web site. They print two copies of the table. Student use their table to write five questions for their partner to answer.

2 TEACH (cont'd)

Use the Married Persons—Weekly Payroll Period table on pages 790 and 791 to find the amount withheld.

3. Damon Anderson is married, earns $507 week, and claims 2 allowances. **$28**

4. Peter Quinoz is married, earns $628 week, and claims 5 allowances. **$22**

3 ASSESS

Error Analysis

If students' answers are incorrect, have them check to see that they are using the correct tax table. Remind them to use the Single Persons—Weekly Payroll Period table when computing the federal income tax withheld for single persons and the Married Persons—Weekly Payroll Period table when finding the federal income tax for married individuals.

4 CLOSE

Closing Activity

1. Melissa Campbell is single and earns $284 a week. She claims no allowances. What amount is withheld weekly for federal income tax? **$29**

2. Elijah Evans is paid $427 a week. He is married and claimed 3 allowances last year. This year he lowered his allowances to 1 because he hopes to receive a refund on his next tax return. How much more in withholdings deducted from his weekly pay now that he claims just 1 allowance? **$25 − $13 = $12**

Some companies use a percentage method instead of the tax tables to compute the income tax withheld. Use Figure 2.1 to find the amount withheld for the single employees below. Each weekly allowance is $55.77.

STEP 1: Find the allowance amount.
Number of Allowances × $55.77

STEP 2: Find the taxable wages.
Weekly Wage − Allowance Amount

STEP 3: Find the amount withheld for the employees below.

Figure 2.1

A Payroll Period		
Weekly Wage (after Subtracting Withholdings)		Amount of Income Tax Withheld
Over	But not over	
$ 24.00	$ 415.00	15%
415.00	972.00	$ 58.65 + 28%
972.00	1,529.00	214.61 + 31%

	Amount Withheld				
Employee	Weekly Wage	Number of Allowances	Allowance Amount	Taxable Wages	Amount Withheld
D. Boon	$ 293.23	2	$111.54	$181.69	$27.25
16. M. Watt	587.94	4	223.08	364.86	a. **$54.73**
17. B. Mould	792.02	1	a. **$55.77**	b. **$736.25**	c.
18. C. Kirkwood	1,243.49	3	a.	b.	c.

**18. a. $167.31
b. $1,076.18**

17. c. ($736.25 − $415.00) × 28% + $58.65 = $148.60

18. c. ($1,076.18 − $972.00) × 31% + $214.61 = $246.91

MAINTAINING YOUR SKILLS

Need Help? Go to...
► Skill 1: Numbers, page 727
► Skill 30: Finding the Percentage, page 757

Give the place and value of the underlined digit.

19. 8,943 thousands **20.** 63.12 tens **21.** 543 hundreds

22. 92.32 tenths **23.** 231 ones **24.** 243.234 thousandths

Find the percentage.

25. 228% × $52.00 **$118.56** **26.** 26.50% × $656.00 **$173.84**

27. ¼% × $621.00 **$1.55** **28.** 22.50% × $120.00 **$27.00**

Subtract.

29. $6003.04 − $68.45 **$5,934.59** **30.** $920.03 − $803.76 **$116.27** **31.** $823.45 − $21.76 **$801.69**

ALTERNATIVE ASSESSMENT

Students with Learning Disabilities
Some students with learning disabilities have trouble following tasks involving numbers and step-by-step instructions. For example they may have trouble completing a worksheet or chart. Allow these students extra time to complete the assignment. Consider pairing all students. This gives the opportunity for a partner to help the student with a learning disability complete his or her assignment. **LS**

WRAP-UP

Go over any problem for which a wrong answer is given.

Assignment Guide
Basic: 8–11
Average: 12–18

20 min.

SECTION (2-2) State Income Tax

Most states require employers to withhold a certain amount of your pay for state income tax. In some states, the tax withheld is a percent of your taxable wages. Your taxable wages depend on **personal exemptions**, or withholding allowances, which allow for supporting yourself and others in your family.

○ **Section Objective**

Compute the state taxes on a straight percent basis.

Important Questions	What Formula Do I Use?
How do I calculate **taxable wages**?	Taxable Wages = Annual Gross Pay − Personal Exemptions
How do I calculate **annual tax withheld**?	Annual Tax Withheld = Taxable Wages × Tax Rate

Living in the Real World

Jack's Jackpot

Need Help? Go to...
▶ Skill 1: Numbers, page 727
▶ Application C: Tables and Charts, page 762

Who Else Is Taking My Money? "I mean," Jack said, "how can this really be fair? You mean I work from seven-thirty in the morning until five at night, forty hours a week . . . and the STATE also takes out money? Isn't it enough that the Fed takes out taxes?"

Draw Conclusions Why do most states charge taxes?

Continued on page 122

(Example 1)

PERSONAL EXEMPTIONS
Single—$1,500
Married—$3,000
Each Dependent—$700

Patricia Line's gross pay is $65,800 a year. The state income tax rate is 3 percent of taxable wages. Line takes a married exemption for herself and her husband. How much is withheld from her gross earnings for state income tax within the year?

STEP 1: Find the taxable wages.
Annual Gross Pay − Personal Exemptions
$65,800   − $3,000   = $62,800

STEP 2: Find the annual tax withheld.
Taxable Wages × Tax Rate
$62,800   ×   3%   = **$1,884 annual tax withheld**

65800 − 3000 = 62800 × 3 % 1884

Section 2-2 State Income Tax ▶ **119**

Living in the Real World

States charge taxes to pay for police and fire protection, public schools, roads, libraries, inspection of foods, drugs, and other products.

National Standards for Business Education

Standard 1	Mathematical Foundations
Standard 6	Problem-Solving Applications

National Council of Teachers of Mathematics Standards

Standard 6	Problem Solving
Standard 9	Connections

(1) FOCUS

In this section, students will compute a state tax on a straight percent basis, which is one method to generate money for a state's expenses. The method used and the tax rate vary from state to state. Ask students why the federal government needs to collect money from taxes (**examples: to pay for human services, national defense, government employees' salaries and expenses**). Ask why states need to collect taxes (**examples: education, highways, police protection**).

In-Class Examples
Work through these exercises with students before having them do the Self-Check. Write as decimals.
1. 9% **0.09**
2. $4\frac{1}{2}$% **0.045**
3. $2\frac{1}{4}$% **0.0225**
4. 7.24% **0.0724**

Multiply or divide.
5. 2.5% × $560 **$14**
6. $3\frac{1}{4}$% × $754.50 **$24.52**
7. $\frac{1}{4}$% of $800 **$2.00**
8. 0.9% of $600 **$5.40**
9. $\frac{$21,600}{12}$ **$1,800**
10. $\frac{$59,800}{26}$ **$2,300**

119

② TEACH

Before working the example with students, write the formulas for taxable wages and annual tax withheld on the board. Stress that the tax rate is used with taxable wages, not on gross pay. Therefore, students must first find the taxable wages.

Motivating the Lesson

You are single and earn an annual salary of $25,000. The personal exemption in your state is $1,500. What are your taxable wages? **($23,500)** The state tax rate is 3 percent of your taxable wages. What is the annual tax withheld from your salary for state income tax? **$705**

In-Class Examples

Use the personal exemptions table on page 119 for personal exemptions, and find the amount withheld.

1. Tomoko Nakazawa earns $38,657 annually and is married with no dependents. **$3,000**

2. Elizabeth Zwiebel earns $88,900 annually and is married with 4 dependents. The state tax is 3.8 percent. What is withheld for the state tax? **$3,157.80**

3. Reyna Torres earns $43,500 and is single with 2 dependents. The state tax is 4.2 percent. What are her personal exemptions? **($2,900)** What is withheld for state tax? **$1,705.20**

4. Saroj Chaturvedi earns $52,388 as a teacher. She is married and supports 2 children. The state tax rate in her state is 3.5 percent of taxable income. What amount is withheld yearly for state income tax? **$1,679.58**

CONCEPT CHECK

SELF-CHECK ✓

Check your answers at the end of the chapter. Find the taxable wages and the annual tax withheld. State income tax rate is 1.5 percent of taxable income. (Remember to refer to the Personal Exemptions table on page 119.)

1. Annual gross pay is $28,000. Married.
$28,000 − $3,000 =
$25,000 × 0.015 = $375

2. Annual gross pay is $34,300. Single.
$34,300 − $1,500 =
$32,800 × 0.015 = $492

Example 2

Tony Yamakoshi's gross pay is $44,750 a year. The state income tax rate is 3 percent of taxable wages. Yamakoshi takes a single exemption for himself and 1 personal exemption for a child. How much is withheld from his gross earnings for state income tax for the year? (Again, use the Personal Exemptions table on page 119 to complete this example.)

STEP 1: Find the taxable wages.
Annual Gross Pay − Personal Exemptions
$44,750 − ($1,500 + $700) =
$44,750 − $2,200 = $42,550

STEP 2: Find the annual tax withheld.
Taxable Wages × Tax Rate
$42,550 × 3% = **$1,276.50 annual tax withheld**

CONCEPT CHECK

SELF-CHECK ✓

Complete the problems, then check your answers at the end of the chapter. Find the amount withheld annually for state tax.

3. Gross pay: $23,760.
Married, 3 dependents.
State income tax rate: 4 percent.
$23,760 − ($3,000 + $700 + $700 + $700) = $18,660 × 0.04 = $746.40

4. Gross pay: $43,300.
Single, 1 dependent.
State income tax rate: 5 percent.
$43,300 − ($1,500 + $700) = $41,100 × 0.05 = $2,055

SECTION 2-2 PRACTICE

Complete the formula to find the tax withheld.

(Gross Pay	−	Personal Exemptions	=	Taxable Wages)	×	State Tax Rate	=	Tax Withheld
5. ($27,000	−	$2,200	=	$24,800)	×	2%	=	**$496**
6. ($32,000	−	$3,000	=	**$29,000**)	×	5%	=	**$1,450**
7. ($12,500	−	$1,500	=	**$11,000**)	×	3.5%	=	**$385**

Use the Personal Exemptions table on page 119 for personal exemptions, and find the amount withheld annually for state income taxes.

8. Farouc Jaffer.
Earns $57,900 annually.
Single, 3 dependents.
State tax rate is 3 percent.
What are his personal exemptions?

$1,629 withheld for state income tax; $3,600 annual exemption

---

COMMUNICATION SKILLS

Visualization

Tell students that successful people often picture themselves succeeding—winning an award, becoming a faster runner, making a new friend, or completing a math problem. Students can get on the path to greater success by setting small, realistic goals and then visualizing themselves achieving those goals. Have students write a paragraph in their journal about a time they felt successful at school. Ask volunteers to read their paragraphs to the class. Ask students how they can apply the technique of visualization to completing math problems. **LS** , **CL**

9. Monica Mooney.
   Earns $63,840 annually.
   Married, 2 dependents.
   State tax rate is 4 percent.   **$2,377.60 personal exemption;**
   What are her personal exemptions?   **$4,400 tax withheld**

10. Dean Delgado.
    Earns $43,500 annually.
    Married, no dependents.
    State tax rate is 4.6 percent.
    a. What are his personal exemptions?   **$3,000**
    b. What is withheld for state tax?   **$1,863**

11. Julie Bookwalter.
    Earns $32,300 annually.
    Single, 1 dependent.
    State tax rate is 2.5 percent.
    a. What are her personal exemptions?   **$2,200**
    b. What is withheld for state tax?   **$752.50**

12. Wayne Ko earns $36,200 annually as a college instructor. He is married and supports 2 children. The state tax rate in his state is 4 percent of taxable income. What amount is withheld yearly for state income tax?   **$1,272**

13. Erica Matthies earns $28,640 per year as a video editor. Her personal exemptions include herself and her husband. The state tax rate in her state is 3.5 percent of taxable income. What amount is withheld yearly for state income tax?   **$897.40**

14. Dale Yngvesson is a physical therapist. He earns $49,830 a year and is single. The state income tax rate is 5 percent of taxable income. What amount is withheld yearly for state income tax?   **$2,416.50**

Use the Married Persons Weekly Payroll table on pages 790–791 for federal withholding taxes.

15. David Chow earns $42,000 a year as a fine artist. He is paid on a weekly basis. He is married, with no dependents, and claims 2 withholding allowances for federal income tax purposes. The state tax rate is 2 percent of taxable income. How much is withheld annually from Chow's gross pay for state and federal income taxes?   **$3,796 FIT + $780 state = $4,576**

MAINTAINING YOUR SKILLS

Need Help? Go to...
▶ Skill 6: Subtracting Decimals, page 733
▶ Skill 30: Finding the Percentage, page 757

Subtract.

16. $83.17 - 56.19$ **26.98**   17. $43 - 16.02$ **26.98**   18. $65.2 - 34.309$ **30.891**

Find the percentage.

19. 220% of 79 **173.8**   20. 9% of 522 **46.98**   21. $\frac{1}{4}$% of 2,500 **6.25**

RETEACH / ENRICHMENT

State Income Tax
Have students pull the names of three states out of a hat. Students compare the state income tax rates and procedures in the three different states. Then for the three states, they compute the state income tax for a single person earning $24,000 annually and claiming 1 exemption. Also compute the state income tax for a married person earning $32,000 and claiming 4 exemptions.

WRAP-UP

Go over any problem for which a wrong answer is given.

Assignment Guide
   Basic: 5–7
   Average: 8–14

20 min.

3 ASSESS

Error Analysis
Review the concept that Taxable Wages = Annual Gross Pay − Personal Exemptions. Remind students that the personal exemption is $1,500 for an individual and $1,500 for a spouse, but only $700 per person for each dependent.

4 CLOSE

Closing Activity
1.   961.42
    − 187.56
      773.86

2. What is $43\frac{1}{2}$ percent of 900?
   $391.50

3. Katherine McHugh is an athletic trainer. She earns $52,650 a year and is single. The state income tax rate is $4\frac{1}{2}$ percent. What amount is withheld yearly for state income tax?   **$2,301.75**

4. Eric Wall earns $32,100 annually as a security guard. He is married with 1 child. The state tax rate is 5.3 percent. What amount is withheld yearly for state income tax?
   $1,505.20

5. Hector Bañuelos earns $67,000 a year as a geologist. He is paid on a weekly basis. He is married and has 2 dependents. The state tax rate is 3.6 percent of taxable income. How much is withheld each year from his gross pay?
   [$67,000 − (2 × $1,500) − (2 × $750)] × 3.6% = $2,250

National Standards for Business Education

Standard 1	Mathematical Foundations
Standard 2	Number Relationships and Operations
Standard 5	Statistics and Probability

National Council of Teachers of Mathematics Standards

Standard 1	Numbers and Operations
Standard 6	Problem Solving

① FOCUS

Ask students to give as many definitions of the word *graduate* as they can. Elicit the definitions "to change gradually," "to divide into grades," and "to mark with degrees of measurement." This lesson has students compute state taxes using the graduated income tax method.

In-Class Examples

Work through these exercises with students before having them do the Self-Check. Write as decimals.
1. 2.2% **0.022**
2. 16.5% **0.165**
3. 2% of $1,000 **$20**
4. 2.5% of 2,000 **$50**
5. $20 + $50 + $90 + $1,440 **$1,600**

② TEACH

Remind students that personal exemptions are first subtracted from gross pay to find the amount of income to be taxed.

Review with students the number of pay periods in a year for weekly, monthly, biweekly, and semimonthly pay periods.

SECTION 2-3 Graduated State Income Tax

○ **Section Objective**

Determine the state taxes on a graduated income basis.

Some states have a graduated income tax. **Graduated income tax** involves a different tax rate for each of several levels of income. The tax rate increases as income increases. The tax rate on low incomes is usually 1 percent to 3 percent. The tax rate on high incomes may be as much as 20 percent.

$$\text{Tax Withheld per Pay Period} = \frac{\text{Annual Tax Withheld}}{\text{Number of Pay Periods per Year}}$$

Living in the Real World

Jack's Jackpot

Can You Live without Paying Taxes? "You can't escape taxes being deducted. But you can be smart about how you calculate state tax, since the percentage differs state to state. If you understand the proper taxation, then you'll pay the proper amount and you're not overtaxed or penalized," Jon says to Jack.

Draw Conclusions Each year the Tax Foundation determines how much of the year the average person works to pay taxes. How many months do you think the average person works just to pay taxes?

Continued on page 124

Need Help? Go to...
➤ Workshop 4: **Adding Decimals,** page 10
➤ Workshop 7: **Dividing Decimals,** page 16
➤ Skill 5: **Adding Decimals,** page 732
➤ Skill 11: **Dividing Decimals,** page 738
➤ Application K: **Chronological Expressions,** page 766

Example 1

Louise Maffeo's annual salary is $34,500. She is paid semimonthly. Her personal exemptions total $1,500. How much does her employer deduct from each of Maffeo's semimonthly paychecks for state income tax?

Figure 2.2

State Tax	
Annual Gross Pay	**Tax Rate**
First $1,000	1.5%
Next $2,000	3.0%
Next $2,000	4.5%
Over $5,000	5.0%

STEP 1: Find the taxable wages.

$$\begin{array}{ccc} \text{Annual} & - & \text{Personal} \\ \text{Gross Pay} & & \text{Exemptions} \end{array}$$

$34,500.00 − $1,500.00 = $33,000.00

STEP 2: Find the annual tax withheld.
(1) First $1,000:
  1.5% of $1,000.00 $ 15.00
(2) Next $2,000:
  3.0% of $2,000.00   60.00
(3) Next $2,000: 4.5% of $2,000.00   90.00
(4) Over $5,000: 5.0% of ($33,000.00 − $5,000.00) =
  5.0% of $28,000.00   =   1,400.00
                                    Total $1,565.00

Living in the Real World

Five months out of the year.

GLOBAL PERSPECTIVE

Income Tax Comparison
The average per capita (per person) tax paid in the United States is $6,358. Around the world other per capita totals include: United Kingdom $6,232, Germany $8,882, Sweden $15,154, Canada $8,042, Luxembourg $11,516, and Japan $7,432. Ask students to find data on the tax rate of various countries for discussion in class.

STEP 3: Find the tax withheld per pay period.

$$\underset{\text{Withheld}}{\text{Annual Tax}} \div \underset{\text{Periods per Year}}{\text{Number of Pay}}$$

$$\$1,565.00 \div 24 = \$65.208 \text{ or } \$65.21 \text{ tax withheld semimonthly}$$

CONCEPT CHECK

Complete the problem, then check your answer at the end of the chapter. Using the graduated income tax rates in Figure 2.2 on page 122, find the tax withheld per pay period.

1. Annual salary: $21,350. Personal exemptions: $3,000. 26 pay periods.

SECTION 2-3 PRACTICE

Find the taxable wages for Problems 2 and 3.

2. Toby Vail.
   Annual gross pay of $18,200.
   Personal exemptions of $1,500.
   State tax on first $3,000: 1.5 percent.
   Tax on amount over $3,000:
   3 percent. **$456**

3. Carl Brownstein.
   Annual gross pay of $45,500.
   Personal exemptions of $3,000.
   State tax on first $2,500: 1.5 percent.
   Tax on amount over $2,500:
   3 percent. **$1,238**

Use Figure 2.3 to compute the state tax for Problems 4–5.

Figure 2.3

Personal Exemptions	
Single	$1,500
Married	3,000
Each Dependent	750

State Tax	
Annual Gross Pay	Tax Rate
First $3,500	3.0%
Next $3,500	4.5%
Over $7,000	7.0%

4. Leslie Channings's annual gross pay is $54,400. He is single and is paid on a monthly basis. How much is withheld monthly for state tax? **$289.63**

5. Anita Muzquiz's annual gross pay is $45,520. She is married with 2 dependents. How much is withheld from her biweekly paycheck for state income tax? **$101.69**

MAINTAINING YOUR SKILLS

Need Help? Go to...
➤ Skill 5: Adding Decimals, page 732
➤ Skill 11: Dividing Decimals, page 738
➤ Application K: Chronological Expressions, page 766

6.
$$\begin{array}{r} 0.014 \\ 0.937 \\ + 0.341 \\ \hline \mathbf{1.292} \end{array}$$

7.
$$\begin{array}{r} 2.342 \\ 223.670 \\ + 15.131 \\ \hline \mathbf{241.143} \end{array}$$

Divide. Round answers to the nearest hundredth.

8. $327 \div 73$ **4.48**

9. $67.632 \div 3.3$ **20.49**

Find the number of occurrences.

10. Weekly for 3 years **156**

11. Quarterly for 4 years **16**

12. Monthly for 11 years **132**

13. Daily for 4 years **365 × 4 = 1,460; (365 × 4) + 1 = 1,461 for the leap year**

Self-Check Answer

1. Taxable wage = $21,350 − $3,000 = $18.350

First $1,000	1.5%		$15
Next $2,000	3.0%		$60
Next $2,000	4.5%		$90
Over $5,000	5.0%	$13,350	$668
Total Annual Tax			$833

Tax per pay period = $833 ÷ 26 = **$32.02**

WRAP-UP

Go over any problem for which a wrong answer is given.

Assignment Guide
  Basic: 2–3
  Average: 4–5

20 min.

Motivating the Lesson
Ask students whether they think it is fair for someone who earns $10,000 annually to be taxed at the same rate as someone who earns $90,000 annually. **(Explain that this is why some states have implemented a graduated income tax.)**

3 ASSESS

Error Analysis
Remind students that with a graduated state income tax, the dollar amount of income tax is constant for all but highest level of tax rates. Say, for instance, that the state tax is 1 percent of $2,000, 2 percent of the next $2,000, and 5 percent of the amount over $4,000. All taxpayers earning over $4,000 of taxable income will pay $20 on the first $2,000 and $40 on the next $2,000, or $60 on the first $4,000 of their taxable income. Only the taxes on the amount *over* $4,000 will vary from taxpayer to taxpayer.

4 CLOSE

Closing Activity
1. Ellen Furasawa grosses $49,700 annually, with personal exemptions of $4,400. The state taxes 1 percent on the first $3,000, 3 percent on an amount over $3,000. What is her taxable income? **$45,300**

2. Andrew Sheehy earns $51,472 annually. He has personal exemptions of $5,800. The state sales tax is 1.5 percent of the first $3,500, 2.5 percent of the next $6,500, and 3 percent on amounts over $10,000. How much is withheld from his biweekly paycheck for state income tax? **$49.43**

National Standards for Business Education

Standard 1	Mathematical Foundations
Standard 2	Number Relationships and Operations

National Council of Teachers of Mathematics Standards

Standard 1	Numbers and Operations
Standard 6	Problem Solving

1 FOCUS

The discussion of Social Security and Medicare tax can be motivated by asking how students think older adults pay for living expenses when they are no longer working.

2 TEACH

Stress that you and your employer pay taxes for Social Security and Medicare. You each paid 7.65 percent of your gross salary, up to a limit of $84,900. A self-employed person paid 15.3 percent. The limit normally rises yearly based on increases in average wages. You pay Medicare on all your earnings. This portion of the tax is 1.45 percent for both employers and employees and 2.9 percent for self-employed persons.

In-Class Example
Tom Mendoza earns $4,800 a month (or $52,800 earned to date). How much is deducted this pay period for Social Security and for Medicare? **$297.60; $69.60**

○ **Section Objective**

Work out the amount of income withheld for Social Security and Medicare taxes.

2. $350 × 0.062 = $21.70 Social Security; $350 × 0.0145 = $5.08 Medicare; $21.70 + $5.08 = $26.78 total deductions

SECTION 2-4 Social Security and Medicare Taxes

The Federal Insurance Contributions Act (FICA) requires employers to deduct 7.65 percent of your income for **Social Security** and **Medicare** taxes. **Social Security** (6.2 percent) is deducted on the first $84,900 of income, but Medicare (1.45 percent) is paid on all your earnings. The employer must contribute an amount that equals your contribution. The federal government uses Social Security to pay for retirement and disability benefits and Medicare to provide health insurance for those 65 and older.

$$\text{Tax Withheld} = \text{Gross Pay} \times \text{Tax Rate}$$

Living in the Real World

Jack's Jackpot

What Else Aren't You Telling Me? Jack is starting to accept that he doesn't get to take home all the money he actually earns. Jon tells him not to forget the Social Security and Medicare taxes withheld from his paycheck.

Draw Conclusions Why is Social Security important?

Continued on page 126

(**Need Help? Go to...**)

▶ Skill 2: **Rounding Numbers**, page 729
▶ Skill 30: **Finding the Percentage**, page 757
▶ Application A: **Formulas**, page 760

Example 1

Otis Hassan's gross biweekly pay is $648.00. His earnings to date for the year total $15,228. What amount is deducted from his pay this week for Social Security taxes? For Medicare taxes? What is the total deduction? His earnings to date are less than $84,900.

STEP 1: Find the Social Security tax withheld.
Gross Pay × Tax Rate
$648.00 × 6.2% = $40.176 = **$40.18 Social Security tax**

STEP 2: Find the Medicare tax withheld.
Gross Pay × Tax Rate
$648.00 × 1.45% = $9.396 = **$9.40 Medicare tax**

STEP 3: Find the total deduction.
Social Security Tax + Medicare Tax
$40.18 + $9.40 = **$49.58 total deduction**

CONCEPT CHECK

(SELF-CHECK ✓)

Complete the problems, then check your answers at the end of the chapter. Find the amount withheld for Social Security, Medicare, and total deductions.

1. Monthly salary: $3,100.
Earnings to date: $15,500.

2. Weekly salary: $350.
Earnings to date: $16,800.

1. $532 × 0.062 = $192.20 Social Security; $532 × 0.0145 = $44.95 Medicare; $192.20 + $44.95 = $237.15 total deductions

Living in the Real World

Funds collected finance the retirement, disability, and life insurance of the federal government's Social Security program.

SECTION 2-4 PRACTICE

For problems 3–7 use the Social Security tax rate of 6.2 percent and Medicare tax rate of 1.45 percent to determine each tax and the total deduction.

	Gross Pay	Soc. Sec. Tax Withheld	Medicare Tax Withheld	Total Deduction
3.	$ 125.00	a. $7.75	b. $1.81	c. $9.56
4.	432.00	a. $26.78	b. $6.26	c. $33.04
5.	241.00	a. $14.94	b. $3.49	c. $18.43
6.	1,562.00	a. $96.84	b. $22.65	c. $119.49
7.	2,521.00	a. $156.30	b. $36.55	c. $192.85

Use the Social Security tax rate of 6.2 percent of the first $84,900 and Medicare tax rate of 1.45 percent on all income when solving Problems 8 and 9.

8. Shelly Kugo is paid monthly. Her gross pay this month is $6,223. Her earnings to date for this year are $23,631. How much is deducted from her paycheck this month for Social Security? For Medicare? **$385.83; $90.23**

9. Oliver Gelfand earns $45,440 a year, paid on a semimonthly basis. How much is deducted per pay period for Social Security tax? For Medicare tax? What is the total? **$117.39; $27.45; $144.84**

Use the Married Persons Weekly Payroll table on pages 790–791 for federal withholding taxes.

10. Thomas Schmitt is a designer for Stix Toys. He is married, earns $526 weekly, and claims no allowances. His gross pay to date this year is $9,912. How much is deducted from his paycheck this week for federal income, Social Security, and Medicare taxes? What is the total? **Fed: $49.00; S.S.: $32.61; Med: $7.63; Total: $89.24**

11. Jorge Powell is married and claims 2 allowances. How much is withheld from his weekly paycheck of $550 for the last week of December for federal income, Social Security, and Medicare taxes? What is the total? **Fed: $36.00; S.S.: $34.10; Med: $7.98; Total: $78.08**

12. Stacey Peralta was hired on January 2 for the supervisory position. She earns a salary of $88,000 and is paid monthly. How much is withheld in December for Social Security and Medicare? What is the total? **S.S.: $262.47; Med: $106.33; Total: $368.80**

MAINTAINING YOUR SKILLS

Need Help? Go to...
► Skill 30: **Finding the Percentage,** page 757
► Skill 2: **Rounding Numbers,** page 729

Find the percentage. Round to the nearest hundredth.

13. 8.9% of 543 **48.33**   14. 5.43% of 4 **0.22**   15. 723.6% of 62 **448.63**

Round to the place value indicated.

Nearest ten.

16. 216 **220**   17. 624.83 **620**   18. 8,990.97 **8,990**

Nearest hundred.

19. 8,231 **8,200**   20. 9,851 **9,900**   21. 623,201 **623,200**

Section 2-4 Social Security and Medicare Taxes ► **125**

Great Ideas from the Classroom Of...

Eddie Davidson, East Union High School, Manteca, Calif.

Groups create a single person's income and expenses statement for one month. Each group picks from a box the gross pay for the job. Calculate the net income by taking into account the deductions. Each student is responsible for his or her own report and taking part in group discussions.

WRAP-UP

Go over any problem for which a wrong answer is given.

Assignment Guide
   Basic: 3–7
   Average: 8–11

20 min.

SECTION 2-4

Error Analysis

When students compute Social Security tax on income over $84,900, remind them to first determine the amount of salary earned per pay period. In the pay period where the salary exceeds $84,900, they must subtract $84,900 from the year-to-date earnings for that pay period. The remainder is *not* subject to Social Security tax. To compute the amount earned in that pay period that *is* subject to Social Security tax, subtract the remainder from the amount earned in that pay period. For example, an annual salary of $93,000 would equal a monthly salary of $7,750. A portion of November's income would not be subject to Social Security tax since the year-to-date earnings for November would exceed $84,900. $85,250 − $84,900 = $350. $350 of November's income is not subject to Social Security. $7,750 − 350 = $7,400. This amount ($7,400) is subject to Social Security tax. $7,400 × 0.062 = $458.80.

Closing Activity

Use the tables on pages 788–791 for federal withholding taxes. Find the federal income tax, the Social Security tax, and the Medicare tax withheld weekly. Round to the nearest cent.

1. Diana Cisneros is single and claims 1 allowance. She earns $21,372 a year. What taxes are withheld weekly? **$40 federal; $25.48 Social Security; $5.96 Medicare**

National Standards for Business Education

Standard 1	Mathematical Foundations
Standard 2	Number Relationships and Operations

National Council of Teachers of Mathematics Standards

Standard 6	Problem Solving
Standard 9	Connections

① FOCUS

List the following items and approximate costs on the board: emergency room, $200; X-rays, $125; surgery, $5,000; and medication and supplies, $220.

Explain that these costs are what could be incurred should you break an arm or a leg. A portion of those costs will be paid for by your medical insurance if you are enrolled in a group medical plan through your company. Your cost for the plan is deducted from your paycheck.

In-Class Examples

Work through these exercises with students before having them do the Self-Check. Write as decimals.

1. 80% **0.80**
2. $2,500 × 70% **$1,750**
3. $\frac{\$984}{12}$ **$82**

② TEACH

Point out that group insurance is an employee benefit that many companies offer. Usually, dependents also are covered under a family medical plan. If the amount an employee pays appears to be too high, the error could be caused by not subtracting the percent the employer pays. Is $1,000 about 20 percent of $5,000?

126

SECTION 2-5 Group Health Insurance

● Section Objective

Calculate the deduction for group insurance.

Many businesses offer group insurance plans to their employees. You can purchase **group insurance** for a lower cost than individual insurance. Businesses often pay part of the cost of the insurance and the employee pays the remaining amount.

$$\text{Employee's Share} = \text{Annual Amount} \times \text{Employee's Percent}$$

The employee's amount is usually deducted each pay period. Remember that:

$$\text{Deduction per Pay Period} = \frac{\text{Total Annual Amount Paid by Employee}}{\text{Number of Pay Periods per Year}}$$

Living in the Real World

Jack's Jackpot

I Thought Mom and Dad Paid for That "You have to remember not only are your deductions for federal and state taxes, but you also have to take into account deductions for your medical plan."

"Wait, I thought mom and dad took care of this?"

"Not anymore. Not when you're dependent on yourself."

"Jack, everyone needs health insurance. If you ever broke your leg or got into a car accident, you'd be paying for your medical bills for the rest of your life."

Draw Conclusions Describe at least two scenarios when a young, healthy person would need health insurance.

Continued on page 128

Need Help? Go to...

▶ **Workshop 5:** Subtracting Decimals, page 12
▶ **Workshop 7:** Dividing Decimals, page 16
▶ **Workshop 14:** Finding the Percentage, page 30
▶ **Skill 6:** Subtracting Decimals, page 733
▶ **Skill 11:** Dividing Decimals, page 738
▶ **Skill 30:** Finding the Percentage, page 757
▶ **Application A:** Formulas, page 760

Example 1

Lawrence Butler is a manager for Sound Pharmaceuticals. He has family medical coverage through the group medical plan that Sound provides for its employees. The annual cost of Butler's family membership is $4,500. The company pays 80 percent of the cost. How much does he pay annually for medical insurance?

STEP 1: Find the percent paid by employee.
100% − Percent Company Pays
100% − 80% = 20%

STEP 2: Find the total amount paid by employee.
Annual Amount × Employee's Percent
$4,500.00 × 20% = **$900.00 total paid by employee**

CONCEPT CHECK

SELF-CHECK✓

Complete the problems, then check your answers at the end of the chapter. Find the total amount paid by the employee.

1. Annual cost of insurance: $4,400. Employer pays 80 percent.
$4,400 × (100% − 80%) =
$4,400 × 0.2 = $880

2. Annual cost of insurance: $6,700. Employer pays 60 percent.
$6,700 × (100% − 60%) =
$6,700 × 0.4 = $2,680

Living in the Real World

Answers will vary but might include unexpected illnesses or injuries.

COMMUNICATION SKILLS

Explain on the Board

In Example 1, Section 2-5, Sound Pharmaceuticals pays 80 percent of Lawrence Butler's medical insurance. The cost of the family membership is $4,500. What is the dollar value the employer pays for the employee's insurance? **($3,360)** How much would the employer pay if there were 1,000 employees in the medical insurance program? **($3,360,000)** Have volunteers come to the board to explain their answer. **LS**

Example 2

Nicholette McClure is a carpenter for Olympia Construction Company. She has family medical coverage through the group medical plan that Olympia provides for its employees. The annual cost of McClure's family membership is $5,000. The company pays 75 percent of the cost. How much is deducted from her biweekly paycheck for medical insurance?

STEP 1: Find the percent paid by employee.
100% − Percent Company Pays
100% −   75%   = 25%

STEP 2: Find the total amount paid by employee.
Annual Amount × Employee's Percent
  $5,000   ×   25%   = $1,250

STEP 3: Find the deduction per pay period.
$$\frac{\text{Total Annual Amount Paid by Employee}}{\text{Number of Pay Periods per Year}}$$
$$\frac{\$1,250}{26} = \$48.076 \text{ or } \$48.08 \text{ deducted per pay period}$$

CONCEPT CHECK

SELF-CHECK ✓

Complete the problems, then check your answers at the end of the chapter. Find the deduction per pay period.

3. Annual cost of insurance: $3,570. Employer pays 70 percent. 12 pay periods.
100% − 70% = 30%; $3,570 × 30% = $1,071; $1,071 ÷ 12 = **$89.25**

4. Annual cost of insurance: $6,000. Employer pays 80 percent. 26 pay periods.
100% − 80% = 20%; $6,000 × 20% = $1,200; $1,200 ÷ 26 = **$46.15**

SECTION 2-5 PRACTICE

5. Margie Yang, pilot. Annual group insurance costs $3,800. Company pays 50 percent of the cost. How much does Yang pay monthly? **$158.33**

6. Maxwell Fischer, beekeeper. Annual group insurance costs $5,400. Employer pays 70 percent of the cost. How much does Fischer pay semimonthly? **$67.50**

7. Bill Bernstein's group medical insurance coverage costs $5,480 a year. The company pays 65 percent of the cost. How much is deducted each month from his paycheck for medical insurance? **$159.83**

8. Catherine Parker, a clerk at La Mirage Motel, earns $342.22 weekly. Her group medical insurance costs $2,650 a year, of which the company pays 70 percent of the costs. How much is deducted weekly from her paycheck for medical insurance? **$15.29**

MAINTAINING YOUR SKILLS

Need Help? Go to...
➤ Skill 11: Dividing Decimals, page 738
➤ Skill 30: Finding the Percentage, page 757

Divide. Round answers to the nearest hundredth.

9. 4.48 ÷ 4 **1.12**   **10.** 8.123 ÷ 2.2 **3.69**   **11.** 0.00532 ÷ 0.31 **0.02**

Find the percentage.

12. 5% of 340 **17**   **13.** 98% of 742 **727.16**   **14.** $5\frac{1}{4}$% of 56 **2.94**

Section 2-5 Group Health Insurance ▶ **127**

SECTION 2-5

Motivating the Lesson

Group medical insurance costs $3,200 per year. Would this insurance cost you more if you worked for a company that pays 90 percent of this cost or a company that pays 75 percent of this cost?
100% − 90% = 10%
10% × $3,200 = $320 (your cost) or
100% − 75% = 25%
25% × $3,200 = $800
You would pay more for medical insurance working for a company that pays 75 percent of the cost.

In-Class Example

Carole Vanderlan is a veterinary assistant. Her employer pays 75 percent of her medical insurance and 40 percent of her dental insurance. Medical insurance costs $3,900 per year and dental insurance costs $750. How much is deducted weekly for medical insurance? for dental? **$18.75; $8.65**

 **ASSESS**

Error Analysis

If students are making errors, check to see that they have correctly computed the employee's cost of insurance by first subtracting the percent of the employer's contribution from 100 percent. The remainder is the percent of the insurance cost that the employee is responsible for paying. You may also wish to review the number of pay periods in biweekly (26) and semimonthly (24) payroll systems.

4 CLOSE

Closing Activity

Ruby Carsello is a botanist. Annual group insurance costs $4,320. The employer pays 50 percent. How much does Carsello pay monthly? **$180**

WRAP-UP

Go over any problem for which a wrong answer is given.

Assignment Guide
   Basic: 5–6
   Average: 7–8

 20 min.

Standard 1	Mathematics Foundations
Standard 5	Statistics and Probability

National Council of Teachers of Mathematics Standards

Standard 1	Numbers and Operations
Standard 6	Problem Solving

1 FOCUS

Write the gross salary of $270.00 on the board, and have students calculate the deductions, subtracting the following amounts from the $270.00: federal tax: $28.00; state tax: $5.40; Social Security: $16.74; Medicare: $3.92; and medical insurance: $18.00. Point out that the remaining $197.94 is about three-fourths of the gross salary this person earned.

In-Class Examples

Work through these exercises with students before having them do the Self-Check. Add.

1. $38.91
   18.79
   + 12.76
   $70.46

2. $69.00
   40.31
   18.20
   25.00
   + 8.50
   $161.01

3. 74.36 + 20.19 + 15.98 + 6.25
   116.78

4. $891.14 − $275.58 **$615.56**

5. $1,228.50 − $491.29 **$737.21**

SECTION 2·6 Statement of Earnings

Section Objective

Figure out net pay per pay period.

You may have additional deductions taken from your gross pay for union dues, contributions to community funds, savings plans, and so on. The earnings statement attached to your paycheck lists all your deductions, your gross pay, and your **net pay** for the pay period. Net pay is the amount you have left after all tax withholdings and personal deductions have been subtracted.

$$\text{Net Pay} = \text{Gross Pay} - \text{Total Deductions}$$

Living in the Real World

Jack's Jackpot

Live in the Now ... or Not   Oh, brotherly love. The competition never stops, especially when their philosophies on money aren't shared. Jon encourages investing in a retirement account. Jack prefers to live in the now and worry about life at 65 later.

Draw Conclusions   Describe your philosophy on money.

Continued on page 133

Need Help? Go to...
- ► Skill 5: Adding Decimals, page 732
- ► Skill 6: Subtracting Decimals, page 733
- ► Application A: Formulas, page 760

Example 1

Alyasha Moore's gross weekly salary is $600. She is married and claims 3 allowances. The Social Security tax is 6.2 percent of the first $84,900. On a paycheck stub, it shows up as Federal Insurance Corporation Act (FICA). The Medicare tax is 1.45 percent of gross pay. The state tax is 1.5 percent of gross pay. Each week she pays $12.40 for medical insurance and $2.50 for charity. Is Moore's earnings statement correct?

Figure 2.4

Dept	Employee	Check Number	Gross Pay	Net Pay
15	Alyasha Moore	1501	$600.00	$495.20

Tax Deductions					Other Deductions		
FIT	FICA	Medicare	State	Local	Medical	Union Dues	Others
35	37.20	8.70	9.00	—	12.40	—	2.50

STEP 1: Find the total deductions.

a.	Federal withholding: (from table on page 790)	$ 35.00
b.	Social Security: 6.2% of $600.00 =	37.20
c.	Medicare: 1.45% of $600.00 =	8.70
d.	State tax: 1.5% of $600.00 =	9.00
e.	Medical insurance	12.40
f.	Charity	+ 2.50
	Total	$104.80

Living in the Real World

Emotions are attached to the concept of money. The average household with one credit card carries $8,523 in debt. For some they like to live debt-free. When it comes to spending and living in debt, it's a matter of lifestyle choices you're willing to make.

COOPERATIVE LEARNING

e-Activity

Have students work in pairs or small groups to use a paycheck withholding calculator, such as the one available at www.TurboTax.com. Instruct students to launch the Turbo Tax Web site, then click on "Free Tax Tools" in the navigation bar. Then choose "Paycheck Withholding Calculator." Suggest the groups use realistic values for the entries and have them record or print the values and resulting paycheck amount. LS , CL

STEP 2: Find the net pay.

Gross Pay — Total Deductions

$600.00 — $104.80 = **$495.20 net pay**

Her statement is correct.

CONCEPT CHECK

SELF-CHECK ✓

Complete the problem, then check your answer at the end of the chapter.

1. Ron Regent is single and claims 1 allowance. His gross weekly salary is $320. Each week he pays federal, Social Security, and Medicare taxes, $16.20 for medical insurance, and $25 for the credit union. What is his net pay?

   $320 − ($27.00 + $19.84 + $4.64 + $16.20 + $25.00) = **$277.32**

Example 2

Mandy Jenkins's gross weekly salary is $450. She is single and claims 2 allowances. The Social Security tax is 6.2 percent of the first $84,900. The Medicare tax is 1.45 percent of gross pay. The state tax is 2.5 percent of gross pay. Each week she pays $10.40 for medical insurance and $2.50 for charity. Is Jenkins's earnings statement correct?

Figure 2.5

Dept	Employee	Check Number	Gross Pay	Net Pay
2	Mandy Jenkins	14	$450.00	$353.42

Tax Deductions					Other Deductions		
FIT	FICA	Medicare	State	Local	Medical	Union Dues	Others
38	27.90	6.53	11.25	—	10.40	—	2.50

STEP 1: Find the total deductions.

a. Federal withholding: (from table on page 788)	$38.00
b. Social Security: 6.2% of $450.00	27.90
c. Medicare: 1.45% of $450.00	6.53
d. State tax: 2.5% of $450.00	11.25
e. Medical insurance	10.40
f. Charity	+ 2.50
Total	$96.58

STEP 2: Find the net pay.

Gross Pay — Total Deductions

$450.00 — $96.58 = **$353.42 net pay**

Her statement is correct.

CONCEPT CHECK

SELF-CHECK ✓

Complete the problem, then check your answer at the end of the chapter.

2. Briana Ralph is married and claims 2 allowances. Her gross weekly salary is $450. Each week she pays federal, Social Security, and Medicare taxes, $11.20 for medical insurance, and $5.00 for the credit union. What is her net pay?

   $450 − ($22.00 + $27.90 + $6.53 + $11.20 + $5.00) = **$377.38**

Section 2-6 Statement of Earnings ▶ **129**

USING CALCULATORS

Memory Keys

When adding or subtracting large quantities of numbers, the memory key(s) on a calculator can be helpful. If your calculator has an [M+] or [M−] key, this allows you to enter many numbers and add or subtract those numbers. Be sure to consult the instruction book that came with your calculator for the proper use of the memory key as they may function differently on different calculators.

Allow students time to familiarize themselves with the earnings statement. Direct students to where each piece of information in the example is shown on the statement.

Encourage students to check their addition of deductions since errors occur when adding lists of numbers. Have students find subtotals for taxes for personal deductions and then add the subtotals to check the final answer.

Motivating the Lesson

Ask students to estimate how much of the gross pay they think a single person with no allowances will take home if that person earns $500 per week. Now, from the gross pay of $500, have students subtract $62 for federal income tax; $31 for Social Security; $7.25 for Medicare; and $15 for state income tax. The net pay or "take home pay" equals $384.75. How close was their estimate? **(Point out that other deductions, such as medical, dental, or life insurance as well as union dues, savings, and charitable contributions will also affect the amount of net pay.)**

In-Class Examples

Find the deductions and the net pay. Social Security is 6.2 percent of the first $84,900. Medicare is 1.45 percent of all income. Use the tax tables on pages 788–791 for federal tax. Round to the nearest cent.

1. Pierre Lamont is married and claims 4 allowances. His gross weekly salary is $628. Each week he pays federal, Social Security, and Medicare taxes, as well as $28 for medical insurance and $12 for union dues. What are his deductions and his net pay? **$29 federal; $38.94 Social Security; $9.11 Medicare; net pay: $510.95**

SECTION 2-6

2 TEACH (cont'd)

2. Elena Cordova is single and claims no allowances. Her gross weekly salary is $390. Each week she pays federal, Social Security, Medicare, and state taxes of 2.5 percent of her gross pay. She also has $14.50 deducted for medical insurance and saves $25 in the credit union. What are her deductions and her net pay? **$46 federal; $24.18 Social Security; $5.66 Medicare; $9.75 state; net pay: $264.91**

3. James Ellis earns $520 per week. He is single and claims 2 allowances. His state personal exemptions are $55.77 per week. The state tax rate is 4 percent of taxable wages. He pays Social Security and Medicare taxes. His deductions for medical and dental insurance together total $24.88 per week. He also donates $5 per week to charity. What are his deductions and his net pay? **$48 federal; $18.57 state; $32.24 Social Security; $7.54 Medicare; net pay: $383.77**

4. Javier Martinez earns $31,564 a year as a branch manager trainee for a bank. He is married and claims 1 allowance. Deductions include federal income tax, Social Security, Medicare, state taxes of $4\frac{1}{4}$ percent of gross income, and local taxes of 1 percent of gross income. His employer pays 75 percent of the cost of medical insurance, which is $4,600 a year. What are the weekly deductions and net pay? **$53 federal; $37.64 Social Security; $8.80 Medicare; $25.80 state tax; $6.07 local tax; $22.12 medical insurance; net pay: $453.57**

Find the deductions and the net pay. Social Security is 6.2 percent of the first $84,900. Medicare is 1.45 percent of all income. Use the tax tables on pages 788–791 for federal tax. For Problems 3–7, the state tax is 2 percent of gross pay and the local tax is 1.5 percent of gross pay.

3. Terence Hall is single and claims 1 allowance.

Figure 2.6

Dept	Employee	Check Number	Gross Pay	Net Pay
23	Terence Hall	463	$598.00	$428.82

Tax Deductions					Other Deductions		
FIT	FICA	Medicare	State	Local	Medical	Union Dues	Others
67.00	37.08	8.67	11.96	8.97	15.50	14.00	6.00

4. Jeri Dammers is married and claims 3 allowances.

Figure 2.7

Dept	Employee	Check Number	Gross Pay	Net Pay
44B	Jeri Dammers	3205	$735.00	$567.04

Tax Deductions					Other Deductions		
FIT	FICA	Medicare	State	Local	Medical	Union Dues	Others
54.00	45.57	10.66	14.70	11.03	32.00	—	—

5. Rhonda Dakar, an interior decorator for Special Design, is married and claims 1 allowance. Each week she pays $18 for medical insurance, $10 union dues, and $20 for a stock option plan.

Figure 2.8

Dept	Employee	Check Number	Gross Pay	Net Pay
SPDI	Rhonda Dakar	1574	$425.00	$304.61

Tax Deductions					Other Deductions		
FIT	FICA	Medicare	State	Local	Medical	Union Dues	Others
25.00	26.35	6.16	8.50	6.38	18.00	10.00	20.00

TECHNOLOGY POWER

Electronic Filing

With the widespread use of the Internet, many online electronic filing income tax services are available. Online income tax filing allows you to quickly prepare and file your tax return so that you receive your refund sooner than traditional filing. Some Internet companies advertise that you will receive your refund in as little as 8–16 days. Most of the time, your refund will be directly deposited in your bank account. A few companies say that they will prepare and print your tax return for free but charge for the electronic filing. The typical cost is between $10 and $30.

6. Orville Staples is a painter who earns $30,000 a year. He is single and claims 3 allowances. Weekly deductions include $14.50 for medical insurance and union dues of $15.

Figure 2.9

Dept	Employee	Check Number	Gross Pay	Net Pay
	Orville Staples	235	$576.92	$436.09

Tax Deductions					Other Deductions		
FIT	FICA	Medicare	State	Local	Medical	Union Dues	Others
47.00	35.77	8.37	11.54	8.65	14.50	15.00	0.00

7. Lynn Golding is employed as a payroll supervisor and earns $18.00 per hour. She is married and claims 6 allowances. The state tax is 3.0 percent of gross earnings and the local tax is 1.5 percent of gross earnings. She pays $35.00 for medical insurance and $17.00 in union dues. She worked 40 hours.

Figure 2.10

Dept	Employee	Check Number	Gross Pay	Net Pay
PAYR	Lynn Golding	355-5887-01	$720.00	$553.52

Tax Deductions					Other Deductions		
FIT	FICA	Medicare	State	Local	Medical	Union Dues	Others
27.00	44.64	10.44	21.60	10.80	35.00	17.00	0.00

MAINTAINING YOUR SKILLS

Need Help? Go to...
- Skill 1: **Numbers,** page 727
- Skill 2: **Rounding Numbers,** page 729
- Skill 5: **Adding Decimals,** page 732
- Skill 6: **Subtracting Decimals,** page 733
- Skill 11: **Dividing Decimals,** page 738
- Skill 30: **Finding the Percentage,** page 757

Add.

8.
```
  125.231
    1.008
+  42.112
  168.351
```

9.
```
  16.3
   2
+43.432
  61.732
```

10.
```
  231.9
    6.157
+  33.45
  271.507
```

Subtract.

11.
```
  432.21
−  32.96
  399.25
```

12.
```
  75.1
−  5.26
  69.84
```

13.
```
  43.98
 −46.19
  −2.21
```

Write the number that is greater.

14. $439.00 or $430.98 **$439.00**

15. $94.45 or $100.45 **$100.45**

Round to the nearest cent.

16. $432.801 **$432.80**

17. $5.308 **$5.31**

18. $40.0947 **$40.10**

Solve. Round answers to the nearest cent.

19. $65.72 + $63.59 **$129.31**

20. $84.71 − $80.72 **$3.99**

21. $432.75 ÷ 12 **$36.06**

22. 4.5% of $105.45 **$4.75**

Section 2-6 Statement of Earnings ▶ **131**

WRAP-UP

Go over any problem for which a wrong answer is given.

Assignment Guide
Basic: 3–4
Average: 5–7

20 min.

---

③ ASSESS

Error Analysis
Personal exemptions when given are deducted from gross income before computing state tax. Also, have students carefully check their addition and subtraction when they total deductions to be subtracted from gross pay.

④ CLOSE

Closing Activity
Find the deductions and the net pay. Social Security is 6.2 percent of the first $84,900. Medicare is 1.45 percent of all income. Use the tax tables on pages 788–792 for federal tax. Round to the nearest cent.

1. Nicholas Evans earns $575 per week. He is married and claims 6 allowances. Each week he pays federal, Social Security, Medicare, and 2.5 percent state tax on gross income. He also pays $52 per week for medical insurance and contributes $3 to charity. What are his deductions and his net pay? **$10 federal; $35.65 Social Security; $8.34 Medicare; $14.38 state tax; $451.63 net pay**

2. Frank Swanson earns $23,000 per year. He is single and claims no allowances. Each week he pays federal, Social Security, and Medicare taxes. State taxes are 1.9 percent of gross income. His employer pays 65 percent of medical insurance, which is $4,700 per year. He also has $17 deducted weekly for union dues, and he contributes $10 to charity. Find his weekly deductions and net pay. **$53 federal; $27.42 Social Security; $6.41 Medicare; $8.40 state tax; $31.63 medical insurance; net pay: $288.45**

Quick Quiz

Use the tax charts on pages 788–791 whenever you need to find the federal withholding tax. Social Security tax is paid on the first $84,900 of income.

1. Eileen Zurek earns $257 per week. She is married and claims 3 allowances. How much is withheld weekly for federal income tax? **$0**

2. LaTroy Miller earns $62,420 a year. He is married and has 2 dependents. The state income tax is 3.9 percent of taxable income. His personal exemptions are $3,000 for married persons and $700 for each dependent. How much is deducted from his annual salary for state income tax? **$2,262.78**

3. Jennifer Min is single and earns gross pay of $48,962 a year. Her personal exemption is $1,500. Her state has a graduated income tax of 2 percent of the first $5,000; 3 percent of the next $5,000; and 6 percent of income over $10,000. How much is withheld weekly for state income tax? Round to the nearest cent. **$48.03**

4. Mariah Rubinstein earns $86,270 per year and is paid monthly. How much will be deducted from her December check for Social Security? For Medicare? **$84.94 Social Security; $104.24 Medicare.**

SECTION 2-1 CONCEPT CHECK (p. 117)

1. $21
2. $20
3. $16
4. $28
5. $20
6. $34
7. $14

SECTION 2-2 CONCEPT CHECK (p. 120)

1. $28,000 − $3,000 = **$25,000** × 0.015 = **$375**
2. $34,300 − $1,500 = **$32,800** × 0.015 = **$492**
3. $23,760 − ($3,000 + $700 + $700 + $700) = $18,660 × 0.04 = **$746.40**
4. $43,300 − ($1,500 + $700) = $41,100 × 0.05 = **$2,055**

SECTION 2-3 CONCEPT CHECK (p. 123)

1. Taxable wage = $21,350 − $3,000 = $18,350

First $1,000	1.5%	$15
Next $2,000	3.0%	$60
Next $2,000	4.5%	$90
Over $5,000	5.0% $13,350	$668
Total Annual Tax		$833
Tax per pay period = $833 ÷ 26 =		**$32.02**

SECTION 2-4 CONCEPT CHECK (p. 124)

1. $532 × 0.062 = **$192.20 Social Security**; $532 × 0.0145 = **$44.95 Medicare**; $192.20 + $44.95 = **$237.15 total deductions**
2. $350 × 0.062 = **$21.70 Social Security**; $350 × 0.0145 = **$5.08 Medicare**; $21.70 + $5.08 = **$26.78 total deductions**

SECTION 2-5 CONCEPT CHECK (p. 126, 127)

1. $4,400 × (100% − 80%) = $4,400 × 0.2 = **$880**
2. $6,700 × (100% − 60%) = $6,700 × 0.4 = **$2,680**
3. 100% − 70% = 30%; $3,570 × 30% = $1,071; $1,071 ÷ 12 = **$89.25**
4. 100% − 80% = 20%; $6,000 × 20% = $1,200; $1,200 ÷ 26 = **$46.15**

SECTION 2-6 CONCEPT CHECK (p. 129)

1. $320 − ($27.00 + $19.84 + $4.64 + $16.20 + $25.00) = **$227.32**
2. $450 − ($22.00 + $27.90 + $6.53 + $11.20 + $5.00) = **$377.37**

Study Guide and Assessment

Living in the Real World

Jack's Jackpot

Analyze the Story As Jack has found out from his paycheck stub and Jon's advice, money is docked from each paycheck. He can start to pre-plan his expenses by putting together a budget.

1 Reasoning. In small groups discuss and explain why such a deduction system has been established. How does it affect the national and state economies? Create a master list of these influences.

2 Writing and Analyzing. Create a table that shows the strengths and weaknesses of Jon's and Jack's philosophies on money. How do their financial philosophies differ? Which one do you side with more? Go back to all the sections to review their conversation if you don't recall their positions.

3 Debating Your Position. Decide whose position you're going to defend: Jon's or Jack's. Create a mini-mock trial and defend Jon's or Jack's position in front of the class. Make sure your position addresses:
  A. Why is it important to know how much is being deducted from your paycheck?
  B. Why is or why isn't a budget important?
  C. How does your spending reflect your outlook on money?

REVIEW OF KEY WORDS

federal income tax (p. 116) Social Security (p. 124) group insurance (p. 126)
personal exemptions (p. 119) Medicare (p. 124) net pay (p. 128)
graduated income tax (p. 122)

Determine if the following statements are true or false.

1. **Federal income tax** is handled by the Federal Bureau of Investigation. **False**

2. Employers are not required by law to withhold a certain amount of pay for **federal income tax**. **False**

3. It is not possible to have zero **withholding allowances** when calculating income tax. **False**

4. **Withholding allowances** are also known as personal exemptions. **True**

5. The **graduated income tax** for high incomes may be as much as 20 percent. **True**

6. **Personal exemptions** are deducted on the first $84,000 of income annually. **False**

7. The **Social Security** tax is 0.062 percent. **False**

8. **Medicare** taxes are paid on all earnings. **True**

9. **Group insurance** allows employees to gain medical coverage for less than the individual rate. **True**

10. **Net pay** plus total deductions equals gross pay. **True**

Study Guide and Assessment ▶ **133**

Living in the Real World

Draw Conclusions

3A. The amount of tax deducted from a paycheck is a large determining factor in how much a person will pay in taxes or be refunded.

3B. Answers will vary depending on if the student thinks a budget is or is not important. A budget is important to help reach long-term goals and keep expenses under control. Someone who is not interested in keeping his or her finances under control probably wouldn't consider a budget important.

3C. Answers will vary, depending on the student's attitude about money.

P

Section Objective and Examples Answers

1. False
2. False
3. False
4. True
5. True
6. False
7. False
8. True
9. True
10. True

Skills and Concepts

SECTION OBJECTIVE 2-1 AND EXAMPLES

Read the Married Persons Weekly Payroll and Single Persons Weekly Payroll tables on pages 788–791 to find the amount withheld for federal income taxes.

William Stevenson, who is married and claims 2 allowances, earns $600.50 a week. How much is withheld from his weekly paycheck for federal income tax?

STEP 1: Find the income range from the table.

STEP 2: Find the column for 2 allowances.

STEP 3: Amount to be withheld is $43.

REVIEW EXERCISES

Use these exercises to review and prepare for the chapter test.

		Marital Status	Weekly Gross Income	Allowances	FIT Withheld
	A Payroll Period				
11.	B. Brown	Single	$450.00	2	$38
12.	M. Shah	Married	500.00	2	$28
13.	S. Sheeks	Single	330.00	3	$11
14.	J. Williams	Married	590.00	2	$42

SECTION OBJECTIVE 2-2 AND EXAMPLES

Compute the state taxes on a straight percent basis.

Mila Aukerman earns $38,000 a year as a professor. The state income tax rate is 2.6 percent of taxable income. Her personal exemptions total $3,700. How much is withheld from Aukerman's gross pay for state income tax for the year?

STEP 1: Find the taxable wages.

Annual Gross Pay   −   Personal Exemptions
$38,000   − $3,700   = $34,300

STEP 2: Find the annual tax withheld.

Taxable Wages   ×   Tax Rate
$34,300   ×   0.026   = **$891.80 annual tax withheld**

REINFORCEMENT

Section 2-1

Use the Married Persons—Weekly Payroll Period table on pages 790 and 791 to find the amount withheld.

Amanda Hagel earns $476 a week. She is married and claims 2 allowances. Beginning next year, she will have a child and will claim an additional allowance. How much less will be withheld for federal income tax for the year? **$312**

Section 2-2

Use the Personal Exemptions table on page 119 for personal exemptions, and find the amount withheld.

Elizabeth Zwiebel. Earns $88,900. Married, 4 dependents. State tax rate is 3.8 percent. What are her personal exemptions? **$5,800** What is withheld for state tax? **$3,157.80**

REVIEW EXERCISES

Find the state tax withheld following this:

Personal Exemptions

Single	$1,500
Married	$3,000
Family	$ 700

15. Chris Butcher earns $21,423 per year. His personal exemptions include himself, his wife, and their son. The state tax rate in his state is 4.5 percent of taxable income. What amount is withheld yearly for state income tax? **$797.54**

16. Queena Kimbrell earns $32,000 per year as a journalist. She is single. The state tax rate in her state is 2 percent of taxable income.

16. $50.83

What amount is withheld from each of her monthly paychecks for state income tax?

17. Rita Yucatan earns $42,000 as a TV producer. She is married with two dependents. The state tax in her state is 3 percent of taxable income. What amount is withheld from each of her biweekly paychecks for state income tax? **$43.38**

18. Al Masters earns $22,500 as a lab technician. He is single with 1 dependent. The state tax in his state is 5 percent of taxable income. What amount is withheld from each of his monthly paychecks for state income tax? **$84.58**

Section Objective and Examples Answers (cont'd)

27. $35.00
28. $23.08
29. $36.35
30. $47.50

SECTION OBJECTIVE 2-3 AND EXAMPLES

Determine the state taxes on a graduated income basis.

Raymond Cooper, an oceanographer, earns an annual salary of $32,540. He is paid monthly. His personal exemptions total $2,400. How much is deducted each pay period from his paycheck for state income tax?

STEP 1: Find the taxable wages.

Annual Gross Pay	−	Personal Exemptions	
$32,540	−	$2,200	= $30,340

STEP 2: Find the annual tax withheld. Base your calculations on the state's graduated income tax rate.

(1) First $1,000:	1.5% of $1,000	$ 15
(2) Next $2,000:	3.0% of $2,000	60
(3) Next $2,000:	4.5% of $2,000	80
(4) Over $5,000:	5.0% of ($30,340 − $5,000) =	
	5.0% of $25,340 =	1,267
	Total	$ 1,422

STEP 3: Find how much is deducted per pay period.

$1,422 ÷ 12 = **$118.50 deducted per pay period**

Continued on next page

REINFORCEMENT

Section 2-3

Use the tax table to the right to find the amount of state tax withheld in Problem 1.

First $3,500	3%
Next $3,500	4.5%
Over $7,000	7%

1. Maria Munoz earns gross pay of $75,644. She has personal exemptions of $3,000 and is paid on a weekly basis. How much is withheld weekly for state income tax? Round to the nearest cent. **$93.42**

REVIEW EXERCISES

Find the state tax withheld per pay period using the exemptions on page 123 and the graduated tax rates below:

State Tax	
Taxable Wages	**Tax Rate**
First $1,000	1.5%
Next $2,000	3.0%
Next $2,000	4.5%
Over $5,000	5.0%

19. Annual salary: $18,750
Married
26 pay periods **$27.02**

20. Annual salary: $24,400
Single
24 pay periods **$44.17**

21. Annual salary: $30,000
Married, one dependent
Weekly **$23.61**

22. Annual salary: $21,500
Married, two dependents
Biweekly **$29.62**

SECTION OBJECTIVE 2-4 AND EXAMPLES

Work out the amount of income withheld for Social Security and Medicare taxes.

Douglas Carrion, a musician, is paid $255.20 a week. His earnings to date this year total $10,718.40. The Social Security tax rate is 6.2 percent of the first $80,400 earned. How much is deducted from his paycheck this week for Social Security tax and Medicare tax?

STEP 1: Find the Social Security tax withheld.

Gross Pay	×	Tax Rate	
$255.20	×	6.2%	= $15.82 Social Security tax

STEP 2: Find the Medicare tax withheld.

Gross Pay	×	Tax Rate	
$255.20	×	1.45%	= $3.70 Medicare tax

REVIEW EXERCISES

Find the Social Security (6.2 percent up to $80,400) and Medicare (1.45 percent) taxes withheld per pay period in the following chart.

		Gross Annual Pay			
		Annual Gross Pay	Pay Periods per Year	Soc. Sec. Tax Withheld per Paycheck	Medicare Tax Withheld per Paycheck
23.	J. Otto	$76,432	12	a. $394.90	b. $92.36
24.	G. Hernandez	43,902	26	a. $104.69	b. $24.48
25.	A. Tomine	20,235	24	a. $52.27	b. $12.23
26.	R. Greenblat	32,231	52	a. $38.43	b. $8.99

REINFORCEMENT

Section 2-4

Stephanie Metcalf earns $91,992 a year as a computer analyst. Her salary is paid monthly. What are her year-to-date earnings for November? How much is deducted from her check in November for Social Security tax ? For Medicare? How much is deducted from her check in December for Social Security tax? For Medicare? **$84,326; $475.29; $111.16; $35.59; $111.16**

Section 2-5

Carole Vanderlan is a veterinary assistant. Her employer pays 75 percent of her medical insurance and 40 percent of her dental insurance. Medical insurance costs $3,900 per year and dental insurance costs $750. How much is deducted weekly for medical insurance? For dental? **$18.75; $8.65**

SECTION OBJECTIVE 2-5 AND EXAMPLES

Calculate the deduction for group insurance.

Karla Alvarez, a technical writer for All Electronics, earns $550 a week. Her medical insurance costs $3,500 a year, of which her company pays 65 percent of the costs. How much is deducted each week from her paycheck for medical insurance?

STEP 1: Find the percent paid by employee.
100% — Percent Company Pays
100% — 65% = 35%

STEP 2: Find the total amount paid by the employee.
Annual Amount × Employee's Percent
$3,500 × 0.35 = $1,225

STEP 3: Find the deduction per pay period.
Total Amount Paid ÷ Number of Pay Periods
$1,225 ÷ 52 = $23.56 deducted

REVIEW EXERCISES
Find the deduction per pay period.

27. Annual cost of insurance: $2,800
Employer pays 75%
24 pay periods **$29.17**

28. Annual cost of insurance: $3,000
Employer pays 60%
52 pay periods **$23.08**

29. J. McDonald is a jeweler. She earns an annual salary of $40,000. Her annual medical insurance costs $2,300. Her employer pays 70 percent of the costs. How much is deducted each week from her paycheck? **$13.27**

30. S. McDonald is a tailor. He earns an annual salary of $23,000. His annual medical insurance costs $1,800. His employer pays 85 percent of the costs. How much is deducted each month from his paycheck? **$22.50**

SECTION OBJECTIVE 2-6 AND EXAMPLES

Figure out the net pay per pay period.

Toni Lombardo is married and claims 2 allowances. She earns $432.75 a week. The Social Security tax rate is 6.2 percent of the first $80,400 earned. The Medicare tax rate is 1.45 percent of gross. The state tax is $10.82 a week. She has weekly deductions of $21.00 for medical insurance and $30.00 for payroll savings. Use the table on page 790 to find Lombardo's federal tax withheld. What is her net pay for a week?

Continued on next page

REINFORCEMENT

Section 2-6
Find the deductions and the net pay. Social Security is 6.2 percent of the first $84,900. Medicare is 1.45 percent of all income. Use the tax tables on pages 788-791 for federal tax. The state tax is 2 percent of gross pay and the local tax is 1.5 percent of gross pay.

1. Jim Dunn is single and claims 1 allowance.

Dept	Employee	Check Number	Gross Pay	Net Pay
23	Jim Dunn	468	$595.00	426.15

Tax Deductions					Other Deductions		
FIT	FICA	MEDICARE	STATE	LOCAL	MEDICAL	UNION DUES	OTHERS
67.00	36.89	8.63	11.90	8.93	15.50	14.00	6.00

STEP 1: Find the total deductions.

Federal withholding (from table)	$ 20.00
Social Security: 6.2% of $432.75	26.83
Medicare: 1.45% of $432.75	6.27
State tax	10.82
Medical insurance	21.00
Payroll savings	+ 30.00
Total Deductions	**$ 114.92**

STEP 2: Find the net pay.

Weekly Income − Deductions

$432.75 − $114.92 = **$317.83 net pay**

REVIEW EXERCISES

Find the deductions and the net pay. Social Security is 6.2 percent of the first $80,400. Medicare is 1.45 percent of all income. Use the tax tables on pages 788–791 for federal tax. The state tax is 2 percent of gross pay and the local tax is 1.5 percent of gross pay.

31. Don Chapman, single, 1 allowance

General Check Information					
Dept.	Employee	Check #	Week Ending	Gross pay	Net pay
23	Chapman, D.	432	3/5/--	$640.00	$481.64

Tax and Personal Deductions							
FIT	FICA	Medicare	State	Local	Medical	Union Dues	Others
77.00	39.68	9.28	12.80	9.60	10.00	—	—

32. Jen Weiss, married, 2 allowances

General Check Information					
Dept.	Employee	Check #	Week Ending	Gross pay	Net pay
3	Weiss, J.	352	11/4/--	$324.00	$246.87

Tax and Personal Deductions							
FIT	FICA	Medicare	State	Local	Medical	Union Dues	Others
9.00	20.09	4.70	6.48	4.86	12.00	20.00	—

REINFORCEMENT

Section 2-6 (cont'd)

2. Linda Wo is employed by Go Associates and works in the marketing department. She has an annual salary of $36,000. She is single and claims 2 allowances. Weekly deductions include FIT, Social Security, Medicare, state tax of 1.5 percent on gross earnings, local tax of 1.25 percent on gross earnings, and medical insurance. The company pays 75 percent of the $4,200 annual medical cost.

Dept	Employee	Check Number		Gross Pay	Net Pay
Mkt	Linda Wo	65-587-22		$692.31	$525.13

Tax Deductions					Other Deductions		
FIT	FICA	MEDICARE	STATE	LOCAL	MEDICAL	UNION DUES	OTHERS
75.00	42.92	10.04	10.38	8.65	20.19	0.00	0.00

Alternative Assessment

Count Me In: *How You'll Use Math*

 Sweet Rewards Locals flock to Frozen Custard, a legendary stand where the servers hand to you its special custard "concrete" upside down. (And it doesn't fall flat on the ground. Now that's a thick, sweet treat.)

Behind the counter are plenty of high school students dressed in bright yellow uniforms. It pays an hourly wage of $6.25. Deductions are taken out of each paycheck for federal withholding, Social Security, Medicare, and city income tax (CIT) of 1.5 percent. Input the information in the following problems to determine the net income.

Count Me In: *How You'll Use Math*

36. Before taxes, Dan Cole takes home $412.50; Ann Drake $443.75; Marie Lusetti $325.00; Mike Pappas $375.00; Luellen Smith $325.00. Net income will vary depending on marital status, number of dependents, state income tax, and so on. For an expanded answer, see page 141.

Employee	Hours Worked June 15	Hours Worked June 22	Income Tax Information
Cole, Dan	32	34	Single, 1 allowance
Drake, Ann	36	35	Single, 0 allowance
Lusetti, Marie	25	27	Single, 1 allowance
Pappas, Mike	30	30	Single, 0 allowance
Smith, Luellen	32	20	Single, 1 allowance

Snapshot of June's Work Schedule

33. Explain how you find net pay. **Gross Pay − Total Deductions = Net Pay**
34. Name examples of total deductions. **FIT, FICA, state, Medicare, local, medical**
35. What additional information do you need to know in order to calculate each employee's standard deductions?

Filing status, allowances, any other deductions, such as state or medical

36. Calculate how much each employee takes home every two weeks by working at Frozen Custard.

 Thinking Critically
- Before you figure out your deductions, is it wise to overestimate your take-home pay? Give an example when it is better to give a conservative estimate.
- Explain why you think city income tax is different than federal income tax.
- What is the city income tax in your hometown?

 Portfolio
Select one of the assignments from this chapter that you found especially challenging and place it in your portfolio.

 THINKING CRITICALLY

Before you figure out your deductions, is it wise to overestimate your take-home pay? Give an example when it is better to give a conservative estimate. **Overestimating take-home pay can result in an excess of tax withheld. Some sees this as a positive, as it can mean a tax refund; others see it as an interest-free loan to the government. It is better to give a conservative estimate to avoid being hit with a potentially large tax bill.** Explain why you think state income tax is different than federal income tax. **State income taxes go to fund state projects, such as education. Not all states have a state income tax, (for example Florida and Alaska don't). Everybody who is eligible pays federal income taxes. Federal income taxes go to the federal government to fund national projects, such as defense.**

What is the city income tax in your hometown? **Answers will vary depending on location.**

① FOCUS

Math Studio Overview

What's the old adage? Nothing is certain except death and taxes. In this Math Studio, students are asked to fill out a 1040EZ federal income tax form. Using detailed information provided in the text, students practice how to file their taxes.

Bell Ringer Activity

Bring to class several examples of tax forms (all I.R.S. forms are available on its Web site.) For example, how does the 1040EZ vary from the 1040? What rules dictate which form a person fills out? Have students examine the forms and list some of the differences between them.

② TEACH

Cooperative Learning

Ask groups of students to gather information about taxes. How long have people paid them? What happens if a person chooses to ignore the law and not file a tax return? How do other countries handle taxes? Have each group write a short report about the history of taxes, then ask them to develop a presentation about a recent news item detailing a case of tax evasion. The presentation should give a clear background on the story, explaining how the individual or business evaded tax payment, how they were caught, and how they were punished. LS , CL , P

Getting Ready for Tax Day

A part-time job means money in your bank account and perhaps spoiling yourself on a little shopping spree. On the job you're already learning important communication skills that you can take on to bigger and brighter endeavors. What you're also learning is how to become an independent adult. This requires anyone receiving money for a job to file a tax return.

Purpose

The law requires anyone who has a job to prepare an income tax return. Every year it is due by April 15. You send it to the Internal Revenue Service (IRS).

Supplies Needed

- Pencil
- 1040EZ (see pages 792–793)
- Eraser
- W-2 forms (see page 141)
- Tax computer software (optional)

Your Activity

You'll be preparing a 1040EZ income tax return, because you'll have to do this sooner than later in life. When you file your tax return you must report your adjusted gross income (the total of your wages, salaries, tips, interest, and other income). Based on your adjusted gross income, use tax tables to figure out your tax liability (or the amount of income tax you must pay). Keep in mind that:

- if your tax liability is *greater than* your withholdings, you must pay the IRS an amount called the "amount you owe."

- if your tax liability is *less than* your withholdings, the IRS will return the extra money to you as a tax refund.

Don't blow your tax return. Instead be smart and plan for the unexpected in life. Financial advisors suggest having three to six months of "rainy day" savings. If you bring home $1,200 a month, how much should you have in savings?

Each year your employer must send you a Wage and Tax Statement form called a W-2 form. This form tells how much money you earned, and how much was withheld for federal, state, and local income taxes.

It's very important to remember that you'll receive copies of your W-2 form to send with your federal, state, and local income tax returns, as well as a copy to keep for your records. (So it's not a mistake that you get so many copies. Don't dispose of any of them!)

BUSINESS NOTES

Online Tax Filing

Online tax filing has become big business. While millions of taxpayers continue to sort through page after page of paper forms, increasing numbers are turning to electronic filing. Electronic tax filing is a process by which a tax return is sent via modem to the Internal Revenue Service (IRS). When a person uses electronic filing, their refund can be received by direct deposit to an account designated by the taxpayer much faster than traditional methods.

There are several benefits to online tax preparation. As mentioned, refunds are received much quicker—in many cases, within half the time of traditional paper filing. Mathematical errors are less likely to occur when filing electronically, due in part to extensive checking and validation performed by e-file software before the final information is sent to the I.R.S.

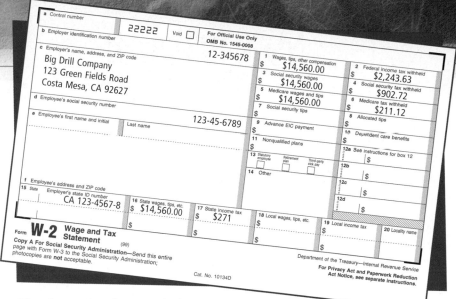

Form W-2 Wage and Tax Statement (99)

Copy A For Social Security Administration—Send this entire page with Form W-3 to the Social Security Administration; photocopies are **not** acceptable.

Cat. No. 10134D

Department of the Treasury—Internal Revenue Service
For Privacy Act and Paperwork Reduction Act Notice, see separate instructions.

Step 1: Use the information in the W-2 form to fill out a photocopy of the 1040EZ on pages 792–793. Assume that you received $10.66 in interest on your savings account and no unemployment compensation.

A. What amount would you write on line 1?

B. What amount would you write on line 2?

C. What amount would you write on line 3?

D. Add the amounts on lines 1, 2, and 3 to find your adjusted gross income. Write this sum on line 4.

Step 2: For this Math Studio, assume you'll be claimed as a dependent on another person's return. Then check "Yes" on line 5 and complete the following. Turn to page 793 and find the section titled "Worksheet for Dependents Who Checked 'Yes' on Line 5." (Directly below, letters A–E correspond to letters A–E on page 793.)

A. Enter the amount from line 1.

B. Minimum standard deduction.

C. Compare the amounts on lines A and B. Enter the larger of the two amounts here.

D. Enter the maximum standard deduction.

E. Compare the amounts on lines C and D. Enter the smaller of the two amounts here and on line 5.

Step 3: Subtract line 5 from line 4 and write the difference on line 6. This is your taxable income.

Step 4: Refer to the federal income tax withheld from box 2 of your W-2 form. What amount will go on line 7? Assume that you did not receive the earned income credit on line 8; add lines 7 and 8 and then write the answer on line 9.

Step 5: For line 10 of a 1040EZ return, you need to find your tax liability. To do this, you use tax tables like the one on page 143. Your tax liability depends on your filing status, the number of exemptions you claim, and your taxable income. (See line 6 on the 1040EZ).

Continued on next page

Math Studio *Getting Ready for Tax Day* ▶ **141**

Independent Practice

L1 Have students interview a parent or another tax-paying adult. Does this person do his or her own taxes each year? Which forms are used? How much time does it take to complete the task? The student must then write a short essay detailing what he or she learned during the interview.

L2 Many people choose to pay an accountant or other professional to do their taxes. Have students research tax preparation businesses in their area. How much does each tax preparer charge? What must the taxpayer provide the preparer for the job to be done? Have the students create charts that detail differences in each tax preparation business, whether it is the size of the company, a charge for tax filing, and so on.

L3 Arrange to have an accountant visit your class and explain how he or she runs a tax preparation business. Have students prepare questions ahead of time, especially questions focusing on the impact of technology in accounting and tax preparation. After the lecture, have students write a one-page report. Encourage students to include specific details in their report.

From page 139.

36.

Name	Rate	15-Jun	22-Jun	Total Hrs	Gross Pay	FIT	SS	Med	City 1.5%	Total Deductions	Ded Tot Round	Net Pay
Cole	6.25	32	34	66	412.5	40	25.575	5.98125	6.1875	77.74375	77.74	334.76
Drake	6.25	36	35	71	443.75	53	27.5125	6.434375	6.65625	93.603125	93.6	350.15
Lusetti	6.26	25	27	52	325	27	20.15	4.7125	4.875	56.7375	56.74	268.26
Pappas	6.25	30	30	60	375	43	23.25	5.4375	5.625	77.3125	77.31	297.69
Smith	6.25	32	20	52	325	27	20.15	4.7125	4.875	56.7375	56.74	268.26

Math STUDIO
A Creative Lab

Enrichment

Changes are made to tax laws every year. This is one of the reasons people choose to have their taxes prepared by a professional, who can keep up with the changing rules. Ask students to identify several recent changes in tax law, describing why they think these changes are positive or negative.

Example

So, how do you read a tax table?

1. Say, Debra Lopez is single. Her taxable income is $20,650.

2. On line 6 of the 1040EZ, she must find the range in which her taxable income falls. (Remember, her taxable income is $20,650.) Find $20,650 on the table.

3. Note that Lopez made *at least* $20,650 (but not less than $20,650). She finds 20,650 to 20,700 on the income line.

If Form 1040EZ line 6 is—		And you are—	
At least	But less than	Single	Married filing jointly
20,600	20,650	3,094	3,094
20,650	20,700	3,101	3,101
20,700	20,750	3,109	3,109
20,750	20,800	3,116	3,116

4. Next she finds the "And you are—" heading. Under the "Single" column, she reads down the column. The amount shown where the income line and filing status column meet is $3,101. This is the tax amount she should enter on line 10 of Form 1040EZ.

Step 6: Refer to the tax table on page 143. What amount would you write as your tax on line 10?

Step 7: Is line 9 larger than line 10? If yes, subtract line 10 from line 9 and this is your refund.

Step 8: Is line 10 larger than line 9? If yes, subtract line 9 from line 10. This is the amount you owe.

Step 9: To complete the tax return, sign your name, write the date, and attach a copy of your W-2 form. If you owe a balance due, you attach a check or money order for the amount you owe. If you owe less than $1, you do not have to pay.

Step 10: Make a copy of your completed return for your records.

Step 11: Then you would send the tax return to the address listed in the instruction booklet that came with the return.

Critique It

Define What computational skills did you use to complete the tax return?

- Why is it necessary to correctly file your return?

- Discuss what happens when someone incorrectly calculates the amount due or amount withheld.

RETEACH / ENRICHMENT

Can You Explain?

Be prepared to time for 30 seconds in a team game called "Can you explain _____?" Ask students to collect their notes on all the important phrases, key words, and formulas used in this chapter and the Math Studio. Have two volunteers write the key words and phrases on the board as students call them out. After the list is complete, split the class into two teams. Ask for two new volunteers. Have the first volunteer randomly choose a key word or phrase on the board, circle it, say "Can you explain [the word]," and call on a member of Team A to give a definition or explanation. An answer earns a point if it's correct and given within 30 seconds. In rapid succession, the second volunteer does the same, choosing from words that have not been circled, and this time calling on a member of Team B. Teams accumulate points until all key words and phrases are circled.

LS , CL , P

1040EZ Tax Table

9,000

If Form 1040EZ, line 6, is—		And you are—	
At least	But less than	Single	Married filing jointly
		Your tax is—	
9,000	9,050	1,354	1,354
9,050	9,100	1,361	1,361
9,100	9,150	1,369	1,369
9,150	9,200	1,376	1,376
9,200	9,250	1,384	1,384
9,250	9,300	1,391	1,391
9,300	9,350	1,399	1,399
9,350	9,400	1,406	1,406
9,400	9,450	1,414	1,414
9,450	9,500	1,421	1,421
9,500	9,550	1,429	1,429
9,550	9,600	1,436	1,436
9,600	9,650	1,444	1,444
9,650	9,700	1,451	1,451
9,700	9,750	1,459	1,459
9,750	9,800	1,466	1,466
9,800	9,850	1,474	1,474
9,850	9,900	1,481	1,481
9,900	9,950	1,489	1,489
9,950	10,000	1,496	1,496

10,000

At least	But less than	Single	Married filing jointly
10,000	10,050	1,504	1,504
10,050	10,100	1,511	1,511
10,100	10,150	1,519	1,519
10,150	10,200	1,526	1,526
10,200	10,250	1,534	1,534
10,250	10,300	1,541	1,541
10,300	10,350	1,549	1,549
10,350	10,400	1,556	1,556
10,400	10,450	1,564	1,564
10,450	10,500	1,571	1,571
10,500	10,550	1,579	1,579
10,550	10,600	1,586	1,586
10,600	10,650	1,594	1,594
10,650	10,700	1,601	1,601
10,700	10,750	1,609	1,609
10,750	10,800	1,616	1,616
10,800	10,850	1,624	1,624
10,850	10,900	1,631	1,631
10,900	10,950	1,639	1,639
10,950	11,000	1,646	1,646

11,000

At least	But less than	Single	Married filing jointly
11,000	11,050	1,654	1,654
11,050	11,100	1,661	1,661
11,100	11,150	1,669	1,669
11,150	11,200	1,676	1,676
11,200	11,250	1,684	1,684
11,250	11,300	1,691	1,691
11,300	11,350	1,699	1,699
11,350	11,400	1,706	1,706
11,400	11,450	1,714	1,714
11,450	11,500	1,721	1,721
11,500	11,550	1,729	1,729
11,550	11,600	1,736	1,736
11,600	11,650	1,744	1,744
11,650	11,700	1,751	1,751
11,700	11,750	1,759	1,759
11,750	11,800	1,766	1,766
11,800	11,850	1,774	1,774
11,850	11,900	1,781	1,781
11,900	11,950	1,789	1,789
11,950	12,000	1,796	1,796

12,000

At least	But less than	Single	Married filing jointly
12,000	12,050	1,804	1,804
12,050	12,100	1,811	1,811
12,100	12,150	1,819	1,819
12,150	12,200	1,826	1,826
12,200	12,250	1,834	1,834
12,250	12,300	1,841	1,841
12,300	12,350	1,849	1,849
12,350	12,400	1,856	1,856
12,400	12,450	1,864	1,864
12,450	12,500	1,871	1,871
12,500	12,550	1,879	1,879
12,550	12,600	1,886	1,886
12,600	12,650	1,894	1,894
12,650	12,700	1,901	1,901
12,700	12,750	1,909	1,909
12,750	12,800	1,916	1,916
12,800	12,850	1,924	1,924
12,850	12,900	1,931	1,931
12,900	12,950	1,939	1,939
12,950	13,000	1,946	1,946

13,000

At least	But less than	Single	Married filing jointly
13,000	13,050	1,954	1,954
13,050	13,100	1,961	1,961
13,100	13,150	1,969	1,969
13,150	13,200	1,976	1,976
13,200	13,250	1,984	1,984
13,250	13,300	1,991	1,991
13,300	13,350	1,999	1,999
13,350	13,400	2,006	2,006
13,400	13,450	2,014	2,014
13,450	13,500	2,021	2,021
13,500	13,550	2,029	2,029
13,550	13,600	2,036	2,036
13,600	13,650	2,044	2,044
13,650	13,700	2,051	2,051
13,700	13,750	2,059	2,059
13,750	13,800	2,066	2,066
13,800	13,850	2,074	2,074
13,850	13,900	2,081	2,081
13,900	13,950	2,089	2,089
13,950	14,000	2,096	2,096

14,000

At least	But less than	Single	Married filing jointly
14,000	14,050	2,104	2,104
14,050	14,100	2,111	2,111
14,100	14,150	2,119	2,119
14,150	14,200	2,126	2,126
14,200	14,250	2,134	2,134
14,250	14,300	2,141	2,141
14,300	14,350	2,149	2,149
14,350	14,400	2,156	2,156
14,400	14,450	2,164	2,164
14,450	14,500	2,171	2,171
14,500	14,550	2,179	2,179
14,550	14,600	2,186	2,186
14,600	14,650	2,194	2,194
14,650	14,700	2,201	2,201
14,700	14,750	2,209	2,209
14,750	14,800	2,216	2,216
14,800	14,850	2,224	2,224
14,850	14,900	2,231	2,231
14,900	14,950	2,239	2,239
14,950	15,000	2,246	2,246

15,000

At least	But less than	Single	Married filing jointly
15,000	15,050	2,254	2,254
15,050	15,100	2,261	2,261
15,100	15,150	2,269	2,269
15,150	15,200	2,276	2,276
15,200	15,250	2,284	2,284
15,250	15,300	2,291	2,291
15,300	15,350	2,299	2,299
15,350	15,400	2,306	2,306
15,400	15,450	2,314	2,314
15,450	15,500	2,321	2,321
15,500	15,550	2,329	2,329
15,550	15,600	2,336	2,336
15,600	15,650	2,344	2,344
15,650	15,700	2,351	2,351
15,700	15,750	2,359	2,359
15,750	15,800	2,366	2,366
15,800	15,850	2,374	2,374
15,850	15,900	2,381	2,381
15,900	15,950	2,389	2,389
15,950	16,000	2,396	2,396

16,000

At least	But less than	Single	Married filing jointly
16,000	16,050	2,404	2,404
16,050	16,100	2,411	2,411
16,100	16,150	2,419	2,419
16,150	16,200	2,426	2,426
16,200	16,250	2,434	2,434
16,250	16,300	2,441	2,441
16,300	16,350	2,449	2,449
16,350	16,400	2,456	2,456
16,400	16,450	2,464	2,464
16,450	16,500	2,471	2,471
16,500	16,550	2,479	2,479
16,550	16,600	2,486	2,486
16,600	16,650	2,494	2,494
16,650	16,700	2,501	2,501
16,700	16,750	2,509	2,509
16,750	16,800	2,516	2,516
16,800	16,850	2,524	2,524
16,850	16,900	2,531	2,531
16,900	16,950	2,539	2,539
16,950	17,000	2,546	2,546

17,000

At least	But less than	Single	Married filing jointly
17,000	17,050	2,554	2,554
17,050	17,100	2,561	2,561
17,100	17,150	2,569	2,569
17,150	17,200	2,576	2,576
17,200	17,250	2,584	2,584
17,250	17,300	2,591	2,591
17,300	17,350	2,599	2,599
17,350	17,400	2,606	2,606
17,400	17,450	2,614	2,614
17,450	17,500	2,621	2,621
17,500	17,550	2,629	2,629
17,550	17,600	2,636	2,636
17,600	17,650	2,644	2,644
17,650	17,700	2,651	2,651
17,700	17,750	2,659	2,659
17,750	17,800	2,666	2,666
17,800	17,850	2,674	2,674
17,850	17,900	2,681	2,681
17,900	17,950	2,689	2,689
17,950	18,000	2,696	2,696

18,000

At least	But less than	Single	Married filing jointly
18,000	18,050	2,704	2,704
18,050	18,100	2,711	2,711
18,100	18,150	2,719	2,719
18,150	18,200	2,726	2,726
18,200	18,250	2,734	2,734
18,250	18,300	2,741	2,741
18,300	18,350	2,749	2,749
18,350	18,400	2,756	2,756
18,400	18,450	2,764	2,764
18,450	18,500	2,771	2,771
18,500	18,550	2,779	2,779
18,550	18,600	2,786	2,786
18,600	18,650	2,794	2,794
18,650	18,700	2,801	2,801
18,700	18,750	2,809	2,809
18,750	18,800	2,816	2,816
18,800	18,850	2,824	2,824
18,850	18,900	2,831	2,831
18,900	18,950	2,839	2,839
18,950	19,000	2,846	2,846

19,000

At least	But less than	Single	Married filing jointly
19,000	19,050	2,854	2,854
19,050	19,100	2,861	2,861
19,100	19,150	2,869	2,869
19,150	19,200	2,876	2,876
19,200	19,250	2,884	2,884
19,250	19,300	2,891	2,891
19,300	19,350	2,899	2,899
19,350	19,400	2,906	2,906
19,400	19,450	2,914	2,914
19,450	19,500	2,921	2,921
19,500	19,550	2,929	2,929
19,550	19,600	2,936	2,936
19,600	19,650	2,944	2,944
19,650	19,700	2,951	2,951
19,700	19,750	2,959	2,959
19,750	19,800	2,966	2,966
19,800	19,850	2,974	2,974
19,850	19,900	2,981	2,981
19,900	19,950	2,989	2,989
19,950	20,000	2,996	2,996

20,000

At least	But less than	Single	Married filing jointly
20,000	20,050	3,004	3,004
20,050	20,100	3,011	3,011
20,100	20,150	3,019	3,019
20,150	20,200	3,026	3,026
20,200	20,250	3,034	3,034
20,250	20,300	3,041	3,041
20,300	20,350	3,049	3,049
20,350	20,400	3,056	3,056
20,400	20,450	3,064	3,064
20,450	20,500	3,071	3,071
20,500	20,550	3,079	3,079
20,550	20,600	3,086	3,086
20,600	20,650	3,094	3,094
20,650	20,700	3,101	3,101
20,700	20,750	3,109	3,109
20,750	20,800	3,116	3,116
20,800	20,850	3,124	3,124
20,850	20,900	3,131	3,131
20,900	20,950	3,139	3,139
20,950	21,000	3,146	3,146

4 CLOSE

Critique It

Filling out a tax form involves simple addition, subtraction, multiplication, and division math skills. It's always important to file a tax return correctly to avoid costly mistakes. An incorrectly calculated tax form can be discovered and adjusted by the Internal Revenue Service. In some cases, a monetary penalty will apply.

National Standards for Business Education

Section Objectives	1. Mathematical Foundations	2. Number Relationships and Operations	3. Patterns, Functions, and Algebra	4. Measurements	5. Statistics and Probability	6. Problem-Solving Applications	
3-1 Average Monthly Expernditures (pp. 146–148) Compute the average monthly expenditure.	X	X					
3-2 Preparing a Budget Sheet (pp. 149–152) Use records of past expenditures to prepare a monthly budget sheet.	X	X					
3-3 Using a Budget (pp. 153–155) Compare amount budgeted to actual expenditures.	X	X					

(Source: Reprinted with permission from the National Standards for Business Education, copyright © 2001 by National Business Education Association, 1914 Association Drive, Reston, Virginia 21901-1596)

SCANS Correlation

Foundation Skills

Basic Skills	Reading	Writing	Math	Listening	Speaking	
Thinking Skills	Creative Thinking	Decision Making	Problem Solving	Seeing Things in the Mind's Eye	Knowing How to Learn	Reasoning
Personal Qualities	Responsibility	Self-Esteem	Sociability	Self-Management	Integrity/Honesty	

This chapter's highlighted blocks indicate the chapter's content coverage in the Student Edition and the Teacher Wraparound Edition.

1. Numbers & Operations	2. Algebra	3. Geometry	4. Measurement	5. Data Analysis & Probability	6. Problem Solving	7. Reasoning & Proof	8. Communication	9. Connections	10. Representations
X					X				
X					X				
X					X				

SCANS Correlation

Workplace Competencies

Resources	Allocating Time	Allocating Money	Allocating Material and Facility Resources	Allocating Human Resources		
Information	Acquiring and Evaluating Information	Organizing and Maintaining Information	Interpreting and Communicating Information	Using Computers to Process Information		
Interpersonal Skills	Participating as a Member of a Team	Teaching Others	Serving Clients/Customers	Exercising Leadership	Negotiating to Arrive at a Decision	Working with Cultural Diversity
Systems	Understanding Systems	Monitoring and Correcting Performance	Improving and Designing Systems			
Technology	Selecting Technology	Applying Technology to Task	Maintaining and Troubleshooting Technology			

CHAPTER 3

Recordkeeping

What You'll Learn

In this chapter you'll examine how people manage their money, so that you can figure out how much money you need to live on and where you spend your money.

Why It Is Important

Keeping track of the money that you spend is wise money management. Budgeting allows you to pay all of your bills and helps to implement a plan so that you can afford higher priced items through long-term savings. Seeing your expenditures written down on a budget sheet may help you decide where you may need to cut back spending and where you can increase monetary allocations.

Key Word Review

Unscramble the Words

Students unscramble the words then look up the meaning of each word in the Glossary or the chapter. Write these scrambled terms on the board:

1. NAALNU SEEENPXS **annual expenses**
2. TEGUDB HTEES **budget sheet**
3. EXFID XSEESNEP **fixed expenses**
4. CENGMYEER DNUF **emergency fund**
5. DENTPERIXEUS **expenditures**
6. VINIGL NEPXEESS **living expenses**
7. XNEEPES MURAYMS **expense summary**
8. PORCNREGIDEKE **recordkeeping**

What You'll Learn

Section 3-1 Compute the average monthly expenditure.

Section 3-2 Use records of past expenditures to prepare a monthly budget sheet.

Section 3-3 Compare amount budgeted to actual expenditures.

When Will You Ever Use This?

The purpose of a budget is to allow you to compare how much money you are spending with how much money you are earning. Stay out of debt by keeping your expenses less than your earnings.

Key Words to Know
- recordkeeping
- expenditures
- budget sheet
- living expenses
- fixed expenses
- annual expenses
- expense summary
- emergency fund

Mathematics Online

To learn more about recordkeeping, visit the *Mathematics with Business Applications* Web site at www.busmath.glencoe.com.

CLASSROOM RESOURCES

Application and Enrichment
- *Teacher Wraparound Edition*
- *Teacher Resource Binder, Blackline Masters*
- *Interactive Lesson Planner* CD-ROM
- *PowerPoint® Presentations* CD-ROM

Review and Enforcement
- Mathematics Online
  www.busmath.glencoe.com
- *Teacher Resource Binder, Internet Resources*

- *Student Activity Workbook*
- *Student Activity Workbook, Teacher Annotated Edition*
- *School-to-Home Activity Workbook*

Assessment and Evaluation
- *Assessment Binder, Reproducible Tests*
- *Assessment Binder, Alternative Assessment Strategies*
- **Exam***View*® *Pro Test Generator* CD-ROM

For the Teacher
- *Student Activity Workbook, Teacher Annotated Edition*
- *Assessment Binder*
- *Interactive Lesson Planner* CD-ROM
- *Teacher Resource Binder*
- Mathematics Online
  www.busmath.glencoe.com

For the Student
- *Student Activity Workbook*
- *School-to-Home Activity Workbook*

Living in the Real World

A Rock Star's Lyrical Leverage

Tonya Foster is the lead singer for a new rock band, Classified. Foster's day job as an accountant helps the group by keeping track of the records.

She's careful and hardworking, and she makes sure to print off the monthly statements, which show everything the band has earned and spent. That information also is essential for completing the band's tax statements.

Read on. Go to . . .

145

Living in the Real World

Story's Summary

Keeping a rock band rolling involves more than tuned instruments and a good sound system. Tonya Foster is lead singer and "bean counter" for Classified, a rock band, who tastes enough success to realize the importance of keeping track of expenses and earnings. With her careful recordkeeping, Classified will continue to make music—and money—for a long time to come.

Did You Know...

There are nearly 12 million self-employed workers in the United States. Many expenses for a musician—or any other self-employed person—can be tracked and deducted as business expenses come tax time.

Think about This

Why is it important for a self-employed person—or anyone, really—to keep track of expenses?

LOCAL STANDARDS

National Standards for Business Education

Standard 1	Mathematical Foundations
Standard 2	Number Relationships and Operations

National Council of Teachers of Mathematics Standards

Standard 1	Numbers and Operations
Standard 6	Problem Solving
Standard 8	Communication

FOCUS

Ask students how many either earn money from a job or work for an allowance. Ask these students if they are expected to help meet their own needs from this money. Make a list of ways students spend the money they receive.

In-Class Examples

Work through these exercises with students before having them do the Self-Check.

1. $\frac{(\$48 + \$51 + \$42)}{3}$ **$47**

2. $\frac{(\$17.89 + \$21.11 + \$25.95)}{3}$ **$21.65**

3. $\frac{(\$212.50 + \$241.75 + \$227.80)}{3}$ **$227.35**

4. $\frac{(\$151.60 + \$49.80 + \$232.30 + \$96.42)}{4}$ **$132.53**

5. $\frac{92.27 + \$107.51 + \$97.54 + \$103.92}{4}$ **$100.31**

Section Objective
Compute the average monthly expenditure.

SECTION 3-1 Average Monthly Expenditures

You might write things down to remember them tomorrow morning or next week. Think of utilizing this same memory device and applying it to your money. **Recordkeeping** is a way for you to manage your money. Record your monthly **expenditures**, or the items you spend your money on. By keeping track of your monthly expenditures, you can find out how you have spent your money and how much money you need for living expenses.

Start recording your expenses on a **budget sheet**. Use a notepad to record expenditures on the day you make them. Don't procrastinate because you won't remember where you spent money. So, at the end of the day, record what you've spent. Then at the end of the month, group them and total them. By keeping a record of your expenditures, you'll be able to examine your spending habits. Remember this:

$$\text{Average Monthly Expenditure} = \frac{\text{Sum of Monthly Expenditures}}{\text{Number of Months}}$$

Living in the Real World

A Rock Star's Lyrical Leverage

Budget by a Beach Even though the rock group Classified just formed 11 months ago, it is already making a name for itself. The band has gotten gigs in nearby towns just about every weekend this summer.

Foster keeps track of the expenses, such as new guitar strings, venue rental, better instruments, and advertising. All these expenditures are part of the cost of doing business.

Draw Conclusions What's the importance of Classified's keeping a budget?

Continued on page 149

▶FYI

The Bureau of Engraving and Printing produces about 37 million pieces of paper money per day. Ninety-five percent of the money printed each year replaces worn-out bills already in circulation.
▶▶▶

Example 1

Sue and Bob Miller keep records of their expenditures. They want to know how much they spend each month (on the average). Here are their records for three months. What is their average monthly expenditure?

STEP: Compute the average monthly expenditure.

A. Find the sum of monthly expenditures.
$1,368.22 + $1,365.00 + $1,337.21 = $4,070.43

B. Take the sum of monthly expenditures and divide by the number of months.

Sum of Monthly Expenditures ÷ Number of Months
$4,070.43 ÷ 3

= **$1,356.81 average monthly expenditure**

Living in the Real World

It keeps them from running out of money before the next gig, helps them plan for future purchases, and lets them track the financial growth of the band.

PROBLEM SOLVING

Finding an Average
Finding an average is the critical mathematical skill required in this lesson. Review with your students finding the average of these expenditures:

1. $470, $486, $490, $450 **$474**
2. $1,450, $1,470, $1,498, $1,500, $1480, $1410 **$1,468**
3. $75.60, $81.45, $78.90, $76.75, $80.65 **$78.67**
4. $21,468.90, $19,785.86, $20,653.09 **$20,635.95**

Figure 3.1

	July		August		September	
Mortgage payment	$ 675.00	Mortgage payment	$ 675.00	Mortgage payment	$ 675.00
Grocery bill	51.35	Beth's allowance	32.00	Electric bill	51.42
Beth's allowance	32.00	Electric bill	73.56	Doctor bill	35.00
Electric bill	71.47	Restaurant	27.80	Cleaners	17.65
Dentist	43.50	Movies	13.50	Telephone bill	32.75
Telephone bill	27.85	Telephone bill	26.45	Gasoline	16.75
Gasoline	15.60	Donation	25.00	Grocery bill	59.74
Water/sewer bill	31.45	Grocery bill	62.35	Football game	15.00
Credit card payment	41.74	Personal expenses	75.00	Credit card payment	71.46
Baseball game	19.50	Credit card payment	54.92	Gasoline	16.45
Gift	45.00	Gasoline	17.94	Beth's allowance	32.00
Clothing	71.56	Magazine subscription	31.50	Grocery bill	56.74
Car payment	178.50	Car payment	178.50	Car payment	178.50
Grocery bill	63.70	Grocery bill	71.48	Fuel oil	78.75
TOTAL	**$ 1,368.22**	**TOTAL**	**$ 1,365.00**	**TOTAL**	**$ 1,337.21**

Need Help? Go to...

➤ Workshop 4:
Adding Decimals,
page 10

➤ Workshop 7:
Dividing Decimals,
page 16

➤ Skill 5: Adding
Decimals, page 732

➤ Skill 11: Dividing
Decimals, page 738

➤ Application A:
Formulas, page 760

➤ Application Q:
Mean, page 770

1368.22 ➕ 1365 ➕ 1337.21 🟰 4070.43 ➗ 3 🟰 1356.81

CONCEPT CHECK

SELF-CHECK✓

Complete the problems, then check your answers at the end of the chapter.
Find the average monthly expenditure.

1. January, $795; February, $776; March, $751 **($795 + $776 + $751) = $2,322;**
$2,322 ÷ 3 = $774

2. May, $1,571.83; June, $1,491.75; July, $1,543.85; August, $1,526.77
$1,571.83 + $1,491.75 + $1,543.85 + $1,526.77 = $6,134.20;
$6,134.20 ÷ 4 = $1,533.55

Example 2

Use the Millers' records of monthly expenditures in Figure 3.1 above to find the
average monthly amount spent for the electric bill.

STEP: Compute the average monthly expenditure.

A. Find the sum of monthly expenditures.
$71.47 + $73.56 + $51.42 = $196.45

B. Take the sum of monthly expenditures and divide by the number
of months.

Sum of Monthly Expenditures ÷ Number of Months
$196.45 ÷ 3
= **$65.48 average monthly expenditure**

Section 3-1 Average Monthly Expenditures ▶ **147**

② TEACH

Part of money management is
seeing how much money is being
spent and where. Point out that
each monthly record has been
written in the order in which the
money was spent. This avoids
missing any spending that was
done. A simple notation will help
keep track of how the money was
spent. Point out that an average
monthly expenditure is better
than just looking at one month
since many bills are seasonal or
are not reoccurring.

Motivating the Lesson

On Friday evening you go to
dinner and a movie with your
friends. You pay $9 for the movie,
$6 for popcorn and a drink, and
$10 for dinner at a local restau-
rant. On Saturday night, you go
to a concert. The ticket costs $40.
You evenly divide the cost of
parking, which is $12, with two
of your friends. At the concert,
you spend $12 for food and buy
a t-shirt for $25. What is the
cost of entertainment for these
two nights? **$106**

In-Class Examples

1. Amy and Todd Irvings'
monthly expenses for June,
July, and August are as follows:
June, $3260; July, $3537; and
August, $3430. Find the aver-
age monthly expenditure for
the Irvings. **$3,409**

2. The Benson family has weekly
grocery bills in April for the
amounts of $90.85, $106.24,
$79.87, and $101.16. What is
their average weekly expense
for groceries? **$94.53**

BUSINESS NOTES

Personal Finance Software
Students look on the Internet, in magazines, or in electronics stores for different types of personal finance software.
Students compare prices, features, and
so on. Students create a poster collage
or computer presentation to share the
results of their comparison with their
classmates. **LS** , **CL**

COOPERATIVE LEARNING

Monthly Expenses
Groups of students estimate the monthly
expenses for a single person living in an
apartment. To come up with real-world
figures—students use the textbook, the
local newspaper, and their general
knowledge. Groups use a computer
spreadsheet program to calculate the
total expenses. Groups keep these figures to use them in the Communication
Skills activity on page 150.
LS , **CL** , **P**

Error Analysis

Caution students that when computing average monthly expenditure, the number of months may vary. Remind them to divide the sum of the monthly expenses by the number of months in order to find the average monthly expenditure.

4 **CLOSE**

Closing Activity

Find the average.

1. $3084 + $2964 + $3117
   $3,055
2. $2837 + $2963 + $2849 + $2795 + $2906 **$2,870**
3. $4236, $4549, $4418 **$4,401**

CONCEPT CHECK

SELF-CHECK ✓

Complete the problems, then check your answers at the end of the chapter. Use the Millers' records of monthly expenditures in Figure 3.1 on page 147 to find the average monthly amount spent for the item indicated.

3. Credit card payment
   ($41.74 + $54.92 + $71.46) = $168.12; $168.12 ÷ 3 = $56.04

4. Telephone bill
   ($27.85 + $26.45 + $32.75) = $87.05; $87.05 ÷ 3 = $29.02

SECTION 3-1 PRACTICE

Find the average monthly expenditure.

	May	June	July	Aug.	Sept.	Total	Average
5.	$ 640.00	$ 710.00	$ 700.00	$ 685.00	$ 705.00	a. $3,440.00	b. $688.00
6.	1,178.50	1,091.80	1,207.70	1,197.80	1,245.90	a. $5,921.70	b. $1,184.34
7.	1,789.75	1,741.36	1,707.85	1,751.63	1,811.75	a. $8,802.34	b. $1,760.47
8.	2,311.75	2,210.91	2,371.85	2,353.67	2,412.91	a. $11,661.09	b. $2,332.22
9.	112.11	97.13	106.45	121.85	107.91	a. $545.45	b. $109.09

Use the Millers' records of monthly expenditures in Figure 3.1 on page 147 to answer the following questions.

10. What is the Millers' average monthly expenditure for groceries? **$121.79**

11. Household costs include amounts for electric bills, telephone bills, water and sewer bills, home fuel oil bills, and so on. What is their average monthly expenditure for household expenses? **$131.23**

12. Entertainment expenses include amounts for restaurants, movies, and recreation. What is their average monthly expenditure for entertainment? **$25.27**

13. What do the Millers pay each month to repay their mortgage loan? **$675.00**

14. Transportation costs include car payments and amounts for gasoline, oil, repairs, and so on. What is their average monthly expenditure for transportation costs? **$200.75**

15. Can you determine how much the Millers save each month? Why or why not? **No; do not know their monthly net income.**

MAINTAINING YOUR SKILLS

Need Help? Go to...
→ Skill 5: Adding Decimals, page 732
→ Application Q: Mean, page 770

Add.

16. $716.45 + $820.97 **$1,537.42**

17. $21.63 + $22.71 + $24.95 **$69.29**

Find the average.

18. $1,170, $1,241, $1,193, $1,250 **$1,213.50**

19. $17.91, $18.43, $16.25 **$17.53**

WRAP-UP

Go over any problem for which a wrong answer is given.

Assignment Guide
   Basic: 5–9
Average: 10–12

20 min.

SECTION **3-2** Preparing a Budget Sheet

○ **Section Objective**

Use records of past expenditures to prepare a monthly budget sheet.

If you have records of your past expenditures, you can use them to prepare a budget sheet outlining your total monthly expenses. You'll want to calculate your **living expenses**. These include amounts for food, utility bills, pocket money, and so on and vary from month to month. Then there are those expenses, which are more fixed, such as rent. These are called **fixed expenses**, and they *don't* vary from one month to the next. Also remember to take into account your **annual expenses** (that is, insurance premiums and real estate taxes), which occur once a year.

$$\begin{array}{ccccc} \text{Total} & & \text{Monthly} & \text{Monthly} & \text{Monthly Share} \\ \text{Monthly} = & \text{Living} + & \text{Fixed} + & \text{of Annual} \\ \text{Expenses} & \text{Expenses} & \text{Expenses} & \text{Expenses} \end{array}$$

Living in the Real World

. . . .

A Rock Star's Lyrical Leverage

Forecast: Looks Like a Scorcher "OK, now let's take a look at this," Foster says after each band member has a copy of her budget sheet. "Notice that I used last summer's expenditures to predict what this summer's will look like. Our living expenses were highest last summer when we were on the road the most. But, of course, we also made more money then. We also have certain annual expenses, including insurance on the van. And you'll notice that as a small business, we're paying our taxes every three months."

Draw Conclusions Why do you think their expenses were highest last summer?

Continued on page 153

Need Help? Go to...

▶ Workshop 4:
  Adding Decimals,
  page 10
▶ Workshop 7:
  Dividing Decimals,
  page 16
▶ Skill 5: Adding
  Decimals, page 732
▶ Skill 11: Dividing
  Decimals, page 738
▶ Application A:
  Formulas, page 760

Example 1

The Millers use records of their past expenditures to complete the budget sheet on page 150. What is the total of their monthly expenses?

STEP: Find the total monthly expenses.

$$\begin{array}{ccc} \text{Monthly} & \text{Monthly} & \text{Monthly Share} \\ \text{Living} + & \text{Fixed} + & \text{of Annual} \\ \text{Expenses} & \text{Expenses} & \text{Expenses} \\ \$505.00 + & \$978.50 + & \$219.29 \end{array} = \$1,702.79 \text{ total monthly expenses}$$

505 `+` 978.5 `+` 219.29 `=` 1702.79

Continued on next page

Section 3-2 Preparing a Budget Sheet ▶ **149**

ALTERNATIVE ASSESSMENT STRATEGIES

English Language Learners

One of the most difficult parts of learning a second language can be navigating cultural differences. In some cultures, asking personal questions related to income, preferences, and so on could be considered an invasion of privacy.

Some activities in this course require students to conduct surveys. If they're recently arrived in this country, students may need examples of research questionnaires to get a sense of the types of questions asked. **ELL**

SECTION 3-2

National Standards for Business Education

Standard 1	Mathematical Foundations
Standard 2	Number Relationships and Operations
Standard 5	Statistics and Probability

National Council of Teachers of Mathematics Standards

Standard 1	Numbers and Operations
Standard 6	Problem Solving

1 FOCUS

The focus of this lesson is to use records of past expenditures to prepare a monthly budget. Ask students if they have ever heard anyone talk about having to live on a budget. Ask students where else they have heard the term *budget*. **Some may suggest a school budget, the federal budget, and so on.**

In-Class Examples

Work through these exercises with students before having them do the Self-Check.

1. $17.80
   19.30
   24.70
   + 20.50
   $82.30

2. $74.60
   81.90
   71.60
   + 78.70
   $306.80

3. $1590.72 ÷ 12 **$132.56**

4. $167.34 ÷ 6 **$27.89**

2 TEACH

Go over the main categories on the budget sheet. Point out that the fixed expenses are those which cannot be changed from month to month. Any adjustments in a budget are usually made in the living expenses. Have students discuss which living expenses would be easiest to change and which would be the most difficult to change. Point out that for items such as movies, the money can be carried from month to month, or used elsewhere, if it is not used in a particular month. Some annual expenses, such as real estate taxes or auto insurance, can sometimes be paid more often than annually. This would not change the monthly budgeted amount, however.

Motivating the Lesson

Matt Gibson kept track of the money he spent last month. He spent $36 for lunch, $20 for a new hat, $15 for a CD, $35 for a pair of jeans, $3 on candy for a school fund raiser, $7 to rent two videos, and $60 for a new video game. What were his total monthly expenses? **$176**

In-Class Examples

Find the total monthly expenses.
1. Living, $846; fixed, $1,560; monthly share of annual expenses, $387. **$2,793**
2. Living, $638; fixed, $972; monthly share of annual expenses, $415. **$2,025**

Figure 3.2

| A Money Manager for | Sue and Bob Miller | Date | 10/1/20-- |

MONTHLY LIVING EXPENSES		MONTHLY FIXED EXPENSES	
Food/Grocery Bill	$ 125.00	Rent/Mortgage Payment	$ 675.00
Household Expenses		Car Payment	$ 178.50
Electricity	$ 70.00	Other Installments	
Heating Fuel	$ 45.00	Appliances	$
Telephone	$ 30.00	Furniture	$
Water	$ 11.00	Regular Savings	$ 75.00
Garbage/Sewer Fee	$	Emergency Fund	$ 50.00
Other _____	$	**TOTAL**	$ 978.50
_____	$	**ANNUAL EXPENSES**	
Transportation		Life Insurance	$ 575.00
Gasoline/Oil	$ 25.00	Home Insurance	$ 240.00
Parking	$	Car Insurance	$ 475.00
Tolls	$	Real Estate Taxes	$ 1,215.00
Commuting	$	Car Registration	$ 26.50
Other	$	Pledges/Contributions	$ 100.00
Personal Spending		Other _____	$
Clothing	$ 30.00	**TOTAL**	$2,631.50
Credit Payments	$ 60.00	**MONTHLY SHARE** (Divide by 12)	$ 219.29
Newspaper, Gifts, Etc.	$ 25.00	**MONTHLY BALANCE SHEET**	
Pocket Money	$ 57.00	Net Income	
Entertainment		(Total Budget)	$
Movie/Theater	$ 5.00	Living Expenses:	$ 505.00
Sporting Events	$ 12.00	Fixed Expenses:	$ 978.50
Recreation	$	Annual Expenses:	$ 219.29
Dining Out	$ 10.00	**TOTAL MONTHLY EXPENSES**	$
TOTAL	$ 505.00	BALANCE	$

CONCEPT CHECK

SELF-CHECK ✓

Complete the problems, then check your answers at the end of the chapter. Find the total monthly expenses.

1. Living, $670; fixed, $800; share of annual, $350.
$$\$670 + \$800 + \$350 = \$1,820$$

2. Living, $475.75; fixed, $679.65; share of annual, $291.17.
$$\$475.75 + \$679.65 + \$291.17 = \$1,446.57$$

Example 2

Tanishia and Jabari Brown have monthly living expenses of $875.00, monthly fixed expenses of $1,025.80, and annual expenses of $4,974.00. After calculating the Browns' monthly share of annual expenses, find their total monthly expenses.

STEP 1: Find the monthly share of annual expenses.

$$\frac{\text{Annual Expenses}}{12}$$

$$\frac{\$4,974}{12} = \$414.50$$

STEP 2: Add up the expenses.

Monthly Living Expenses	+	Monthly Fixed Expenses	+	Monthly Share of Annual Expenses	
$875.00	+	$1,025.80	+	$414.50	= $2,315.30 total monthly expenses

COMMUNICATION SKILLS

Presentation and Discussion

Student groups use the figures they collected in the Cooperative Learning activity on page 147 to prepare a budget for a single person.

Groups estimate the yearly take-home income of a single person. Each group presents its budget to the class using a pie chart, table, spreadsheet, or budget sheet. After each presentation the class discusses any items that the group may have over or under budgeted. For example, students might not have considered costs, such as pet care, haircuts, and parking fees. LS , CL , P

CONCEPT CHECK

SELF-CHECK✓

Complete the problems, then check your answers at the end of the chapter.
Find the monthly share of annual expenses and the total monthly expenses.

	Monthly Living Expenses	Monthly Fixed Expenses	Annual Expenses	Monthly Share of Annual Expenses	Total
3.	$ 1,200.00	$ 1,600.00	$ 4,800.00	a. $400.00	b. $3,200.00
4.	885.40	1,458.90	3,658.20	a. $304.85	b. $2,649.15

SECTION 3-2 PRACTICE

Betty Kujawa is a landscaper. Her husband, Walter, is a used car salesman. They complete the budget sheet shown using records of their past expenditures. Use the budget sheet to answer the following questions.

Figure 3.3

A Money Manager for ___Walter and Betty Kujawa___ **Date** __4/10/20--__

MONTHLY LIVING EXPENSES		MONTHLY FIXED EXPENSES	
Food/Grocery Bill	$ 160.00	Rent/Mortgage Payment	$ 625.00
Household Expenses		Car Payment	$ ____
Electricity	$ 45.00	Other Installments	
Heating Fuel	$ 50.00	Appliances	$ ____
Telephone	$ 35.00	Furniture	$ 125.00
Water	$ 24.50	Regular Savings	$ 100.00
Garbage/Sewer Fee	$ ____	Emergency Fund	$ 50.00
Other Cable TV	$ 25.00	TOTAL	$ ____
	$ ____	ANNUAL EXPENSES	
Transportation		Life Insurance	$ 840.00
Gasoline/Oil	$ 85.00	Home Insurance	$ ____
Parking	$ 5.00	Car Insurance	$ 750.00
Tolls	$ 10.00	Real Estate Taxes	$ ____
Commuting	$ ____	Car Registration	$ 52.00
Other ____	$ ____	Pledges/Contributions	$ 100.00
Personal Spending		Other ____	$ ____
Clothing	$ 40.00	TOTAL	$ ____
Credit Payments	$ 50.00	MONTHLY SHARE (Divide by 12)	$ ____
Newspaper, Gifts, Etc.	$ 20.00	MONTHLY BALANCE SHEET	
Pocket Money	$ 60.00	Net Income	
Entertainment		(Total Budget)	$ 1,800.00
Movie/Theater	$ 10.00	Living Expenses:	$ ____
Sporting Events	$ 20.00	Fixed Expenses:	$ ____
Recreation	$ 12.00	Annual Expenses:	$ ____
Dining Out	$ 100.00	TOTAL MONTHLY EXPENSES	$ ____
TOTAL	$ ____	BALANCE	$ ____

5. What are the Kujawas' total monthly living expenses? **$751.50**

6. What is the total of their monthly fixed expenses? **$900.00**

7. What is the total of their annual expenses? **$1,742**

8. What must be set aside each month for annual expenses? **$145.17**

9. What are their total monthly expenses? **$1,796.67**

10. Do the Kujawas live within their monthly net income? **Yes**

11. What individual expenses would be difficult for the Kujawas to cut back on?
Rent, life insurance, car insurance, car registration (i.e., fixed expenses, annual expenses) *Continued on next page*

Continued on next page

---

3 **ASSESS**

Error Analysis

When calculating monthly living expenses, fixed expenses, and annual expenses, remind students to write the expenses neatly in columns and make sure they vertically line up the decimal points. Have them add the monthly living expenses, fixed expenses and the monthly share of annual expenses to calculate the total monthly expenditure. If total monthly expenses seem too high, have students check that they have first divided the annual expenses by 12 to arrive at the monthly share.

THINKING CRITICALLY

Pie Graph
The Fisher household nets $30,000 a year. The Fisher's expenses last year were: clothing, $1,800; food, $4,500; housing, $9,300; insurance, $2,700; transportation, $5,700; other, $6,000. Show in a pie graph each expense as a portion of the Fisher's income.

④ CLOSE

Closing Activity

1. $29.86 + $8.47 + $11.62 + $18.75 **$68.70**
2. $71.83 + $56.68 + $47.33 + $106.81 + $211.53 **$494.18**

Find the total monthly expenses.

3. Living, $812; fixed, $1,075; share of annual expenses, $429. **$2,316**

4. Lourdes and Arturo Martinez have monthly living expenses of $915, monthly fixed expenses of $2,100, and annual expenses of $6,732. Calculate their monthly share of annual expenses, and find their total monthly expenditure. **$561; $3,576**

Nancy and Joe Thomas completed the budget sheet shown using records of their past expenditures. Use the budget sheet to answer the following questions.

Figure 3.4

A Money Manager for Nancy and Joe Thomas	Date 7/20/20--
MONTHLY LIVING EXPENSES	**MONTHLY FIXED EXPENSES**
Food/Grocery Bill .... $ 210.00	Rent/Mortgage Payment .... $ 715.20
Household Expenses	Car Payment .... $ ____
Electricity .... $ 55.65	Other Installments
Heating Fuel .... $ 63.75	Appliances .... $ 57.75
Telephone .... $ 21.47	Furniture .... $ 110.80
Water .... $ 31.80	Regular Savings .... $ 75.00
Garbage/Sewer Fee .... $ 17.21	Emergency Fund .... $ 50.00
Other Security .... $ 25.00	TOTAL .... $ ____
_____ .... $ ____	**ANNUAL EXPENSES**
Transportation	Life Insurance .... $ 480.00
Gasoline/Oil .... $ 60.00	Home Insurance .... $ 180.00
Parking .... $ 35.00	Car Insurance .... $ 475.00
Tolls .... $ 12.00	Real Estate Taxes $1,200.00
Commuting .... $ 20.00	Car Registration .... $ 26.50
Other _____ .... $ 35.00	Pledges/Contributions .... $ 360.00
Personal Spending	Other _____ .... $ ____
Clothing .... $ 100.00	TOTAL .... $ ____
Credit Payments .... $ 25.00	MONTHLY SHARE (Divide by 12) .. $ ____
Newspaper, Gifts, Etc. .... $ 16.75	**MONTHLY BALANCE SHEET**
Pocket Money .... $ 32.00	Net Income
Entertainment	(Total Budget) $1,800.00
Movie/Theater .... $ 20.00	Living Expenses: .... $ ____
Sporting Events .... $ 20.00	Fixed Expenses: .... $ ____
Recreation .... $ 15.00	Annual Expenses: .... $ ____
Dining Out .... $ 32.00	TOTAL MONTHLY EXPENSES ...... $ ____
TOTAL .... $ ____	BALANCE .... $ ____

12. What is the total of their monthly living expenses? **$847.63**

13. What is the total of their monthly fixed expenses? **$1,008.75**

14. What is the total of their annual expenses? **$2,721.50**

15. What must be set aside each month for annual expenses? **$226.79**

16. What is their total monthly expenditure? **$2,083.17**

17. Do the Thomases live within their monthly net income? **No**

18. What individual expenses would be difficult for the Thomases to cut back on? **Mortgage, utilities, transportation, fixed expenses, taxes, insurance**

MAINTAINING YOUR SKILLS

Need Help? Go to...
▶ Skill 5: **Adding Decimals**, page 732
▶ Skill 11: **Dividing Decimals**, page 738

Add.

19. $75 + $45 + $53 + $68 **$241**

20. $475.80 + $519.20 + $647.80 **$1,642.80**

21. $6.18 + $7.23 + $4.37 + $7.96 **$25.74**

22. $71.14 + $86.23 + $64.91 **$222.28**

23. $619.76 + $723.39 + $671.46 **$2,014.61**

24. $1,178.21 + $1,371.89 + $1,475.84 **$4,025.94**

Divide. Round to the nearest cent.

25. $241 ÷ 4 **$60.25**

26. $1,642.80 ÷ 3 **$547.60**

27. $25.74 ÷ 4 **$6.44**

28. $222.28 ÷ 3 **$74.09**

WRAP-UP

Call upon individual students to read their answer to Practice Problems 5 and 6 to the class. Go over any problem for which a wrong answer is given.

Assignment Guide
  Basic: 5–10, 12–17
Average: 11, 18

20 min.

SECTION 3-3 Using a Budget

Section Objective

Compare the amount budgeted to actual expenditures.

Once you have completed a budget sheet outlining your past expenditures, you can use it to plan for future spending. You may want to prepare a monthly **expense summary**. This compares the amounts that you spend to the amounts that you have budgeted. When you draft a budget, you should include an **emergency fund**. This is extra monies set aside to be used for unpredictable expenses, such as medical bills and vehicle repairs.

Living in the Real World

A Rock Star's Lyrical Leverage

Expect the Unexpected Phillipe says, "OK, Tonya, so we've seen what you've budgeted, but how much are we actually spending?"

Foster smiles and hands out another set of papers on which she has compared the amount the band has actually spent with the amount she budgeted for each of the last six months.

Draw Conclusions List a few "surprise" expenses that you might incur in a year.

Continued on page 157

National Standards for Business Education

Standard 1	Mathematical Foundations
Standard 2	Number Relationships and Operations
Standard 5	Statistics and Probability

National Council of Teachers of Mathematics Standards

Standard 1	Numbers and Operations
Standard 6	Problem Solving

1 FOCUS

The focus of this lesson is to compare the amount budgeted to actual expenditure and personal spending to typical spending. The overall purpose of a budget is for a person or family to check on how money is being spent and to make adjustments where necessary. Point out that any budget must be somewhat flexible since unbudgeted expenses are usually encountered at some time.

Example 1

Need Help? Go to...

▶ Workshop 3: Comparing Numbers, page 8

▶ Workshop 5: Subtracting Decimals, page 12

▶ Skill 1: Numbers, page 727

▶ Skill 6: Subtracting Decimals, page 733

The Zornows have always kept accurate records of their expenditures. At the end of March, they prepared an expense summary. They had planned to spend $220 on groceries. They actually spent $231.85. How much more or less did they spend on groceries than they had budgeted for?

STEP 1: Compare.
Is the amount spent more or less than the amount budgeted?
Is $231.85 more or less than $220.00? (More.)

STEP 2: Find the difference.
$231.85 − $220.00 = **$11.85 more than the amount budgeted**

CONCEPT CHECK

SELF-CHECK ✓

Complete the problems, then check your answers at the end of the chapter.
Find how much more or less the amount spent is than the amount budgeted.

1. Budgeted $167.80, spent $158.90. **$167.80 − $158.90 = $8.90 less**

2. Budgeted $647.50, spent $671.92. **$671.92 − $647.50 = $24.42 more**

In-Class Examples
Work through these exercises with students before having them do the Self-Check.
1. $245 − $240 **$5**
2. $79 − $67 **$12**
3. $1475 − $1279 **$196**
4. $71.74 − $65 **$6.74**
5. $247.86 − $225 **$22.86**
6. $75 − $68.71 **$6.29**
7. $1425 − $1397.63 **$27.37**
8. $2131.78 − $2125 **$6.78**
9. $3137.63 − 3078.74 **$58.89**

Living in the Real World

Answers will vary, but could include a birthday gift for a friend, replacing a broken bicycle or skateboard, an unexpected automotive repair bill, etc.

RETEACH / ENRICHMENT

Compare Expenditures
Students maintain an actual list of expenditures and compare them to their budgeted expenditures. Students could estimate their expenditures over the next week or next month.

② TEACH

Discuss the importance of the expense summary. Emphasize that it is not necessarily careless spending that causes someone to spend more money than was budgeted originally. Rising costs of items (such as food) may require periodic adjustments to budgets. This may mean allowing less to be spent for entertainment, clothes, etc. Stress that it is not wise to spend more than you earn.

Motivating the Lesson

Last month you budgeted $75.00 for clothing, but you actually spent $62.70. Is the amount you spent more or less than the amount you budgeted? **(Less)** By how much? **$12.30**

In-Class Examples

1. The Murrays' electricity bill for July. Budgeted $88. Actually spent $124. How much more or less did the Murrays spend than they budgeted? **$36 more**

2. The Zieglers' entertainment expenses for August. Budgeted $110. Actually spent $104.62. How much more or less did the Zieglers spend than they budgeted? **$5.38 less**

Example 2

Ignacia and Duardo Escobar kept accurate records of their expenditures. At the end of September, they prepared an expense summary. They had planned to spend $210 on transportation. They actually spent $197.80. How much more or less did they spend on transportation than they had budgeted for?

STEP 1: Is the amount spent more or less than the amount budgeted? Is $197.80 more or less than $210? (Less.)

STEP 2: Find the difference.
$210.00 − $197.80 = **$12.20 less than the amount budgeted**

CONCEPT CHECK

SELF-CHECK ✔

Complete the problems, then check your answers at the end of the chapter. Find how much more or less the amount spent is than the amount budgeted.

3. For May's grocery bills, Maki Hakola budgeted $176.80. She actually spent $161.75. **$176.80 − $161.75 = $15.05 less**

4. Rishi Maharan's telephone bill for June was $53.78, but he budgeted only $45. **$53.78 − $45 = $8.78 more**

SECTION 3-3 PRACTICE

Figure 3.5 on page 155 is the Kujawas' expense summary for the month of July. They want to compare what they had budgeted to what they actually spent. Use the Kujawas' expense summary to answer the following questions.

5. Which household expenses for the month were more than the amount budgeted? **Food, telephone, water, gasoline, pocket money**

6. Did they spend more or less than the amount budgeted for household expenses for the month? By how much? **Less; $22.25**

7. How much did they budget for transportation costs? Were the amounts spent for transportation during the month more or less than the amount budgeted? By how much? **$100.00; More; $16.70**

8. Which personal expenses did they spend more on than they had budgeted? **Pocket money**

9. Were their total personal expenditures for the month more or less than the amount budgeted? By how much? **Less; $12.86**

10. Were their total entertainment expenditures for the month more or less than the amount budgeted? By how much? **Less; $41.20**

11. Were there any monthly fixed expenses for which the Kujawas spent more than the amount budgeted? **No**

12. What annual expenses occurred during the month? Was the amount budgeted for annual expenses more or less than the amount actually spent? **Life and car insurance; More**

13. What was the Kujawas' total expenditure for the month of July? Was this amount more or less than the amount they had originally budgeted? By how much? **$1,796.66 budgeted; $1,740.09 expenses; $56.57 less**

Great Ideas from the Classroom Of...

**Naomi Harwood
Rutherfordton Spindle
High School
Rutherfordton, NC**

Real-LIfe Discounts

Have students calculate discounts by giving them a grocery list, a pricing list, and coupons. Find the total grocery bill. Then final the total grocery bill using the coupons. Explore savings in terms of percent by finding the discount on the final grocery bill.

GLOBAL PERSPECTIVE

A Day in the City

You meet a friend in the city for lunch and then for a movie. Use the figures in the chart below to find which city will cost you the least. All prices are converted to U.S. dollars. **Sydney, Australia**

	Tokyo, Japan	Sydney, Australia	Rio De Janeiro, Brazil	Berlin, Germany
Subway fare (one way)	$1.60	$1.79	$0.28	$2.60
Lunch (per person)	$20.16	$9.88	$13.58	$11.76
Movie ticket	$20.00	$8.23	$8.11	$6.35

Figure 3.5

Expenditures for the Month of July		
Expenses	Amount Budgeted	Actual Amount Spent
Food	$160.00	$175.70
Household		
Electric Bill	45.00	44.35
Telephone Bill	35.00	41.20
Heating Fuel	50.00	15.00
Water Bill	24.50	31.70
Cable TV Bill	25.00	25.00
Transportation		
Gasoline Purchases	85.00	101.70
Parking/Tolls	15.00	15.00
Personal		
Clothing	40.00	31.75
Credit Payments	50.00	41.74
Newspapers, Gifts	20.00	11.65
Pocket Money	60.00	72.00
Entertainment		
Movies	10.00	5.00
Sporting Events/Recreation	32.00	32.00
Dining Out	100.00	63.80
Fixed		
Rent	625.00	625.00
Furniture	125.00	125.00
Savings	100.00	100.00
Emergency Fund	50.00	50.00
Life/Car Insurance Premiums	132.50	132.50
Car Registration	4.33	0.00
Pledges, Contributions	8.33	0.00

14. Your total monthly expenditure will vary from month to month. During the winter months, your home heating bills may push your total monthly expenditure over the amount budgeted. In some months, spending will be less. Name some factors that might affect your spending for specific months.
The electricity bill may be higher in the summer because of air conditioning or a pool filter.

MAINTAINING YOUR SKILLS

Need Help? Go to...
➤ Skill 1: **Numbers,** page 727
➤ Skill 6: **Subtracting Decimals,** page 733

Identify which number is greater.

15. $174.85 or $159.94 **$174.85**   **16.** $35 or $37.19 **$37.19**

17. $2,215.73 or $2,231.61 **$2,231.61**   **18.** $302.01 or $301.99 **$302.01**

Subtract.

19. $47.50 − $43.86 **$3.64**   **20.** $171.84 − $165.00 **$6.84**

21. $19.47 − $15.50 **$3.97**   **22.** $1,712.50 − $1,697.43 **$15.07**

23. $2,179.84 − $2,050.00 **$129.84**   **24.** $3,500.00 − $3,147.81 **$352.19**

Section 3-3 Using a Budget ▶ **155**

SECTION 3-3

③ ASSESS

Error Analysis
Have students check their work for computational errors when subtracting dollars and cents. Remind them to line up the decimal points vertically before subtracting.

④ CLOSE

Closing Activity
Which number is greater?
1. $48.67 or $47.68? **$48.67**
2. $375.49 or $351.93? **$375.49**
Find how much more or less the amount spent is than the amount budgeted.
3. Budgeted $654.75; spent $657.39 **$2.64 more**
4. Budgeted $2753.45; spent $2719.95 **$33.50 less**

ALTERNATIVE ASSESSMENT

Students with Hearing Impairments
When you talk to a student with a hearing impairment, look directly at the student. It also helps to enunciate clearly. When you are writing on the board, turn toward the class before you speak. When you are referring to a textbook, look up before you talk. When other students speak, students with hearing impairments will probably not hear them. When other students ask questions or give input, repeat the information while looking toward the class.

WRAP-UP

Go over any problem for which a wrong answer is given.

Assignment Guide
   Basic: 5–11
   Average: 12–14

20 min.

Quick Quiz

1. The Duroshenko family spent $328.15 for groceries in January, $317.60 in February, $307.91 in March, and $324.58 in April. What is their average monthly expenditure for groceries? **$319.56**

2. The Petersons have monthly expenditures for April, May, and June that totaled $1,967.44, 2,079.58, and $2,041.27, respectively. What is their average monthly expenditure for these months? **$2,029.43**

3. Find the total monthly expenses: Living, $1,235.36; fixed $1972.11; share of annual $637.40. **$3,844.87**

4. Eliza and Anthony Romano have monthly living expenses of $1,163.94, monthly fixed expenses of $1,755.28, and annual expenses of $5,342.76. What is their monthly share of annual expenses? **($445.23)** What is their total monthly expenditure? **$3,364.45**

5. The Kunihiro family budgeted $2,690 for total expenditures in April. They actually spent $2,586.34. How much more or less did they actually spend than they budgeted? **$103.66 less**

CHAPTER 3 Self-Check Answers

 CONCEPT CHECK (p. 147, 148)

1. ($795 + $776 + $751) = $2,322
   $2,322 ÷ 3 = **$774**

2. $1,571.83 + $1,491.75 + $1,543.85 + $1,526.77 = $6,134.20
   $6,134.20 ÷ 4 = **$1,533.55**

3. ($41.74 + $54.92 + $71.46) = $168.12
   $168.12 ÷ 3 = **$56.04**

4. ($27.85 + $26.45 + $32.75) = $87.05
   $87.05 ÷ 3 = **$29.02**

 CONCEPT CHECK (p. 150, 151)

1. $670 + $800 + $350 = **$1,820**

2. $475.75 + $679.65 + $291.17 = **$1,446.57**

	Monthly Living Expenses	Monthly Fixed Expenses	Annual Expenses	Monthly Share of Annual Expenses		Total	
3.	$1,200.00	$1,600.00	$4,800.00	a.	$400.00	b.	$3,200.00
4.	885.40	1,458.90	3,658.20	a.	304.85	b.	2,649.15

 CONCEPT CHECK (p. 153, 154)

1. $167.80 − $158.90 = **$8.90 less**

2. $671.92 − $647.50 = **$24.42 more**

3. $176.80 − $161.75 = **$15.05 less**

4. $53.78 − $45 = **$8.78 more**

Living in the Real World

A Rock Star's Lyrical Leverage

Review Money shouldn't get in the way of making art, right? Wrong. While artists and musicians like the idea of practicing their craft, they also have to remember that without money to buy the necessities in life, they're not going to get very far. That's why everyone—no matter what your profession is—must be able to keep records of expenses and stick to a smart budget.

Now that you've read about the band Classified's take on budgeting, answer these questions based on your own life.

1 Recording. Estimate what you think your family will spend for each of these budgeted items during the next month. Now keep track of actual family expenditures for one month. Compare your family's actual expenditures with your estimates.

2 Itemizing. List all the types of items your family pays for during a three-month period. Include necessities such as rent or mortgage payments, food, clothing, and transportation. Also list luxuries such as entertainment and vacation travel. Show the list to a family member and see if he or she has other items to add to your budget list. Did you include items that your family member didn't? Were things added that you hadn't thought about?

Living in the Real World

1. Answers will vary. Ask your family to show you receipts for purchases (this includes all check, cash, and credit card purchases). Each student will realize how much money it takes to "run" a household.
2. Answers will vary, but it's important that students honestly estimate household expenses. Then it's important to compare the estimate versus the actual.

REVIEW OF KEY WORDS

recordkeeping (p. 146)
expenditures (p. 146)
budget sheet (p. 146)

living expenses (p. 149)
fixed expenses (p. 149)
annual expenses (p. 149)

expense summary (p. 153)
emergency fund (p. 153)

Determine if the following statements are true or false.

1. Good **recordkeeping** requires that you keep an accurate record of how you spend your money. **True**

2. Your monthly **expenditures** include the money you earn plus the money you spend each month. **False**

3. When you're preparing a budget, you'll want to calculate your **living expenses**. **True**

4. **Fixed expenses** change from month to month. **False**

5. To complete a **budget sheet**, you can use past records to know what you have spent in the past. **True**

6. **Living expenses** do not vary from month to month. **False**

7. **Fixed expenses** include amounts spent on food, utility bills, and spending money. **False**

8. Car insurance premiums and real estate taxes are examples of **annual expenses**. **True**

9. To determine your **expense summary**, you must have at least three years of history to review. **False**

10. To budget for the unexpected, you should include an **emergency fund**. **True**

Study Guide and Assessment ▶ **157**

Skills and Concepts

SECTION OBJECTIVE 3-1 AND EXAMPLES

Compute the average monthly expenditure.

Kewan Johnson keeps records of his living expenses. Total monthly expenses for January, February, and March were $1,341.29, $1,438.77, and $1,399.11, respectively. What was his average monthly expenditure?

STEP: Compute the average monthly expenditure.

$$\frac{\text{Sum of Monthly Expenditures}}{\text{Number of Months}}$$

$1,341.29 + $1,438.77 + $1,399.11 = $4,179.17

$$\frac{\$4,179.17}{3} = \$1,393.06 \text{ average monthly expenditure}$$

REVIEW EXERCISES

11. $2,334.09 + $2,567.33 + $3,451.96 + $1,988.78 = $10,342.16; $10,342.16 ÷ 4 = $2,585.54

Find the average monthly expenditure.

11. Sabrina West has been keeping track of her parent's living expenses. The total monthly expenses for June, July, August, and September were $2,334.09, $2,567.33, $3,451.96, and $1,988.78, respectively.

12. January, $867; February $763; March, $671. **$767**

13. September electric bill, $87.55; October electric bill, $97.34; November electric bill, $100.44; December electric bill, $156.88. **$110.55**

14. November gasoline bill, $51.34; December gasoline bill, $78.09; January gasoline bill, $61.29; February gasoline bill, $56.89. **$61.90**

SECTION OBJECTIVE 3-2 AND EXAMPLES

Use records of past expenditures to prepare a monthly budget sheet.

Use the budget sheet on page 159 to answer the questions below.

STEP: Find the total monthly expenses.

$$\frac{\text{Monthly Living}}{\text{Expenses}} + \frac{\text{Monthly Fixed}}{\text{Expenses}} + \frac{\text{Monthly Share of}}{\text{Annual Expenses}}$$

A. What is the total of Kevin Berstein's monthly living expenses?

STEP: Add all items in first column under Monthly Living Expenses.
   Total = **$1,033.00**

B. What is the total of his monthly fixed expenses?

STEP: Add.
   $1,160.00 + $235.00 + $200.00 + $150.00 = **$1,745.00 monthly fixed expenses**

C. What is the total of his annual expenses?

STEP: Add.
   $875.00 + $960.00 + $995.00 + $674.00 + $76.75 + $120.00 = **$3,700.75 total annual expenses**

REINFORCEMENT

Section 3-1

1. The Callahan family had the following transportation costs, including train fare, car payments, gasoline, oil changes, and repairs for the months of July through December: $947, $895, $923, $851, $816, and $908. What is their average monthly expenditure for transportation costs? **$890**

2. The Livingstons had monthly expenses of $2,183, $2,247, $2,459, and $2,225. What is their average monthly expenditure for these four months? **$2,278.50**

D. What must he set aside each month for his annual expenses?

STEP: Divide.

$3,700.75 ÷ 12 = **$308.40 set aside monthly**

E. What is the total of his monthly expenses?

STEP: Add.

$1,033.00 + $1,745.00 + $308.40 = **$3,086.40 total monthly expenses**

F. Does Berstein live within his monthly net income?

STEP: Subtract.

$3,750.00 − $3,086.40 = $663.60; **Yes**

G. What individual expenses would be difficult for Berstein to cut?

STEP: Analyze.

All annual expenses, mortgage, car payment, electricity, and heating fuel.

A Money Manager for	Kevin Bernstein	Date	October

MONTHLY LIVING EXPENSES		MONTHLY FIXED EXPENSES	
Food/Grocery Bill	$ 150.61	Mortgage Payment	$ 1,160.00
Household Expenses		Car Payment	$ 235.00
Electricity	$ 89.68	Regular Savings	$ 200.00
Heating Fuel	$ 67.82	Emergency Fund	$ 150.00
Telephone	$ 45.72	**TOTAL**	$1,745.00
Water	$ 11.00	**ANNUAL EXPENSES**	
Cable TV	$ 39.95	Life Insurance	$ 875.00
Transportation		Home Insurance	$ 960.00
Gasoline/Oil	$ 45.80	Car Insurance	$ 995.00
Parking	$ 70.50	Real Estate Taxes	$ 674.00
Tolls	$ 8.00	Car Registration	$ 76.75
Commuting	$ 60.00	Contributions	$ 120.00
Misc.	$ 24.88	**TOTAL**	$3,700.75
Personal Spending		MONTHLY SHARE (Divide by 12)	$ 308.40
Clothing	$ 98.24	**MONTHLY BALANCE SHEET**	
Credit Payments	$ 55.00	Net Income	
Newspaper, Gifts, Etc.	$ 20.12	(Total Budget)	$3,750.00
Pocket Money	$ 115.00	Living Expenses	$1,033.00
Entertainment		Fixed Expenses	$1,745.00
Movie/Theater	$ 55.00	Annual Expenses	$ 308.40
Dining Out	$ 75.68	**TOTAL MONTHLY EXPENSES**	$3,086.40
TOTAL	$1,033.00	BALANCE	$ 663.60

Continued on next page

Study Guide and Assessment ▶ **159**

REVIEW EXERCISES

Use the budget sheet to answer the following questions.

15. What are Whang's total monthly living expenses? **$847.01**

16. What are Whang's total monthly fixed expenses? **$995.00**

17. What must be set aside each month for annual expenses? **$173.90**

18. What is Whang's total monthly expenditure? **$2,015.91**

19. Is Whang able to live within her monthly net income? **Yes**

A Money Manager for	Leslie Whang	Date	February

MONTHLY LIVING EXPENSES		MONTHLY FIXED EXPENSES	
Food/Grocery Bill	$ 130.65	Rent Payment	$ 660.00
Household Expenses		Car Payment	$ 185.00
Electricity	$ 75.66	Regular Savings	$ 100.00
Heating Fuel	$ 34.55	Emergency Fund	$ 50.00
Telephone	$ 38.76	TOTAL	$ _____
Water	$ 12.30	**ANNUAL EXPENSES**	
Cable TV	$ 56.00	Life Insurance	$ 675.00
Transportation		Renter's Insurance	$ 360.00
Gasoline/Oil	$ 102.33	Car Insurance	$ 895.00
Parking	$ 60.00	Car Registration	$ 56.75
Personal Spending		Contributions	$ 100.00
Clothing	$ 57.74	TOTAL	$ _____
Credit Payments	$ 98.00	MONTHLY SHARE (Divide by 12) $ _____	
Newspaper, Gifts, Etc.	$ 45.34	**MONTHLY BALANCE SHEET**	
Pocket Money	$ 85.00	Net Income	
Entertainment		(Total Budget)	$ _____
Movie/Theater	$ 15.00	Living Expenses	$ _____
Dining Out	$ 35.68	Fixed Expenses	$ _____
TOTAL	$ _____	Annual Expenses	$ _____
		TOTAL MONTHLY EXPENSES	$ _____
		BALANCE	$ _____

REINFORCEMENT

Section 3-2

1. Add the following monthly fixed expenses of Keri and Michael Kojima to find their total monthly fixed expenses.

Monthly Fixed Expenses

Rent/mortgage payment	$ 900.00
Car payment/lease	448.00
Other Installments	
Furniture	147.00
Computer	86.00
Regular savings	25.00
Emergency fund	50.00
Total	**$1,656.00**

SECTION OBJECTIVE 3-3 AND EXAMPLES

Compare amount budgeted to actual expenditures.

Oscar and Maria Vasquez kept accurate records of their expenditures. Compare the amount budgeted to the amount spent. (You'll find the rest of the example and accompanying problems on page 162.)

Expenditures		
Expenses	**Amount Budgeted**	**Actual Amount Spent**
Food	$235.00	$261.38
Household		
Electric	48.48	51.29
Telephone	65.90	59.88
Heating Fuel	46.77	60.10
Water Bill	12.30	12.30
Garbage/Sewer Fee	21.90	19.85
Security	19.95	21.95
Transportation		
Gasoline	68.00	87.00
Parking/Misc.	75.00	60.80
Personal		
Clothing	125.00	73.89
Credit Payments	50.00	50.00
Newspapers/Gifts	45.00	39.85
Pocket Money	60.00	75.12
Entertainment		
Movies	30.00	22.50
Sports Events	35.00	38.00
Dining Out	75.00	82.35
Fixed		
Mortgage Payments	859.00	859.00
Loan Payments	185.23	185.23
Savings	125.00	125.00
Life/Home/Car Insurance	186.50	186.50
Property Taxes	93.45	93.45
Car Registration	5.41	0.00
Pledges/Contributions	40.00	40.00

Continued on next page

REINFORCEMENT

Section 3-3

1. In the month of August, Eduardo and Maria Chavez budgeted $250 for groceries. They actually spent $236.53. How much more or less did they spend than they budgeted? **$13.47 less**

2. Here is the August expense summary for the Chavez family: electricity, budgeted $110; spent $113.81. Telephone, budgeted $40; spent $35.66. Heating fuel: budgeted $50; spent $18.45. Water: budgeted $35; spent $42.76. Cable TV, budgeted $39.95; spent $39.95. Which household expenses for August were more than budgeted? Which were less? **More: electricity and water; Less: telephone and heating fuel.**

3. Did the Chavez family spend more or less than the amount budgeted for August? By how much? **Less; $24.32**

24. Expenditure: $261.38 + $51.29 + $59.88 + $60.10 + $12.30 + $19.85 + $21.95 + $87.00 + $60.80 + $73.89 + $50.00 + $39.85 + $75.12 + $22.50 + $38.00 + $82.35 + $859.00 + $185.23 + $125.00 + $186.50 + $93.45 + $40.00 = $2,505.44.
Amount budgeted: $235.00 + $48.48 + $65.90 + $46.77 + $12.30 + $21.90 + $19.95 + $68.00 + $75.00 + $125.00 + $50.00 + $45.00 + $60.00 + $30.00 + $35.00 + $75.00 + $859.00 + $185.23 + $125.00 + $186.50 + $93.45 + $5.41 + $40.00 = $2,507.89. $2,507.89 − $2,505.44 = $2.45.
Expenditures were $2.45 less than the amount budgeted.

A. Which household expenses for the month were more than the amount budgeted?

  STEP: Critically think. Compare and contrast.

  Household expenses: food, electric, heating fuel, security, gas/oil, pocket money, sports events, dining out.

B. Did Oscar and Maria spend more or less than the amount budgeted for household expenses for the month? By how much?

  STEP 1: Find the amounts. Compare.
  Household expenses budgeted = **$215.30**
  Actual household expenses = **$225.37**

  STEP 2: Find the difference.
  $225.37 − $215.30 = $10.07
  They spent more than budgeted by $10.07.

REVIEW EXERCISES

20. Which transportation expenses were more than the amount budgeted? **Gasoline.**

21. How much did they budget for personal costs? Were the amounts spent for personal more or less than the amount budgeted? By how much?

22. Were their total entertainment expenditures for the month more or less than the amount budgeted?

23. Were there any monthly fixed expenses for which the Vasquezes spent less than the amount budgeted? **Yes; car registration.**

24. What was the Vasquez's total expenditures for the month of September? Was this amount more or less than the amount they had originally budgeted? By how much?

21. $125.00 + $50.00 + $45.00 + $60.00 = $280.00 budgeted for personal expenses. Actual personal expenses: $73.89 + $50.00 + $39.85 + $75.12 = $238.86. $280.00 − $238.86 = $41.14. They spent less than the amount budgeted by $41.14.

22. Amount budgeted: $30.00 + $35.00 + $75.00 = $140.00. Expenditure: $22.50 + $38.00 + $82.35 = $142.85. Expenditures were more than amount budgeted.

 25. Language Arts Patricia Oakley is a motivational speaker. She travels all over the country speaking to high school students about the importance of staying in school. Her total monthly expenses for February, March, and April were $6,512.30, $8,397.25, and $926.58 respectively. What was her average monthly expenditure? (Section 3-1.) **$5,278.71**

 26. Computer Technology Adil Najam has applied for a position with a computer manufacturing company. Najam has been reviewing his monthly expenses so he can negotiate a salary. His monthly living expenses are $879, his monthly fixed expenses are $1,207.28, and his annual expenses total $1,965 per year. What is Najam's total monthly expenditure? (Section 3-2.) **$2,250.03**

REINFORCEMENT

Section 3-3 *(cont'd)*

4. Here is the August expense summary for the Chavez family's transportation costs: Gasoline: budgeted $130; spent $127. Parking: budgeted $60; spent $54. Were the amounts spent for transportation in August more or less than the amount budgeted? By how much? **Less; $9**

5. The Goldsteins budgeted $2,165 for their total monthly expenditures in July. They actually spent $2074.98. Is this amount spent more or less than the amount they had originally budgeted? By how much? **Less; $90.02**

Alternative Assessment

Count Me In: *How You'll Use Math*

Budgeting Your Way to Luxury Does a budget make you shudder? After all, doesn't it mean to cut back, sacrifice, and do without? Actually "to budget" means "to plan or schedule." So instead of cringing when someone tells you to budget your finances, think of it this way: If you plan well today, you will be able to enjoy some of your important financial goals in the future.

So what are your future financial goals? They might include big-ticket items such as a ski trip, a new stereo, a car, or even a college education. Along the way to achieving those goals, you will be able to afford other smaller prizes, such as that new coat you've wanted or a special gift for someone.

27. **a.** What kinds of expenses do you have? **Answers will vary for answers a–d.**
    b. Which of your family's expenses are the same (or fixed) expenses each month?
    c. Which expenses change (or are variable)?
    d. Where do you think you can trim expenses most easily?

28. Record each of your family's expenses for a month. Re-create these tables, and use them to record the expenses. Identify your personal financial goals and create an action plan. Based on your personal and household needs and values, identify specific goals that require action. **Answers will vary.**

Monetary Goals				
Description	Amount Needed	Months to Achieve	Action to Be Taken	Priority
Example: Mortgage	$900	1	Always pay on time so penalties and extra interest won't be assessed.	High

Nonmonetary Goals		
Description	Time Frame	Actions to Be Taken
Example: Set up personal financial records and documents.	Next 2 to 3 months	Locate all personal finance records; set up files for receipts, savings, and checking

29. Make a list of ways you can save money, but still enjoy yourself (i.e., go to the matinee, rather than an evening show; walk instead of drive to school; eat out less often). **Answers will vary.**

Thinking Critically

Compare the list to your monthly expense record and figure out how much money you would save each month if you trimmed each of these expenses.

Portfolio

Select one of the assignments in this chapter that you found especially challenging, and place it in your portfolio.

Study Guide and Assessment ▶ **163**

27. Answers will vary, but could include the following:
    a. Clothing, entertainment (movies, CDs, books), eating out, car insurance, gasoline, bus pass, gifts for family, etc.
    b. Mortgage, car payment, insurance.
    c. Utilities, groceries, car maintenance.
    d. Entertainment, clothing, eating out.
28. Answers will vary.
29. Answers will vary, but might include shopping at clothing sales, renting books, CDs, or movies (instead of buying), take lunch to school (instead of eating out), and so on.

Section Objectives	National Standards for Business Education						
	1. Mathematical Foundations	2. Number Relationships and Operations	3. Patterns, Functions, and Algebra	4. Measurements	5. Statistics and Probability	6. Problem-Solving Applications	
4-1 Deposits (pp. 166–168) Compute the total checking account deposit.	X	X					
4-2 Writing Checks (pp. 169–171) Write a check.	X	X					
4-3 Check Registers (pp. 172–174) Figure out the balance in a check register.	X	X					
4-4 Bank Statements (pp. 175–177) Calculate the present balance on a checking account bank statement.	X	X					
4-5 Reconciling the Bank Statement (pp. 178–181) Reconcile a check register with a bank account statement.	X	X					
4-6 Online Banking (pp. 182–187) Compute online banking charges and update the check register.	X	X					

(Source: Reprinted with permission from the National Standards for Business Education, copyright © 2001 by National Business Education Association, 1914 Association Drive, Reston, Virginia 21901-1596)

SCANS Correlation

Foundation Skills

Basic Skills	Reading	Writing	Math	Listening	Speaking	
Thinking Skills	Creative Thinking	Decision Making	Problem Solving	Seeing Things in the Mind's Eye	Knowing How to Learn	Reasoning
Personal Qualities	Responsibility	Self-Esteem	Sociability	Self-Management	Integrity/Honesty	

This chapter's highlighted blocks indicate the chapter's content coverage in the Student Edition and the Teacher Wraparound Edition.

National Council of Teachers of Mathematics Standards

1. Numbers & Operations	2. Algebra	3. Geometry	4. Measurement	5. Data Analysis & Probability	6. Problem Solving	7. Reasoning & Proof	8. Communication	9. Connections	10. Representations
X			X		X		X		
X			X				X		
X			X		X		X		
X			X		X		X		
X			X		X		X		
X			X		X		X		

SCANS Correlation

Workplace Competencies

Resources	Allocating Time	Allocating Money	Allocating Material and Facility Resources	Allocating Human Resources		
Information	Acquiring and Evaluating Information	Organizing and Maintaining Information	Interpreting and Communicating Information	Using Computers to Process Information		
Interpersonal Skills	Participating as a Member of a Team	Teaching Others	Serving Clients/Customers	Exercising Leadership	Negotiating to Arrive at a Decision	Working with Cultural Diversity
Systems	Understanding Systems	Monitoring and Correcting Performance	Improving and Designing Systems			
Technology	Selecting Technology	Applying Technology to Task	Maintaining and Troubleshooting Technology			

What You'll Learn

In this chapter you'll study checking accounts and how to use them.

Why It's Important

A checking account enables you to spend money with several advantages. You may eliminate the need to carry large amounts of cash and it serves as a record-keeping document in the event that an error occurs in making a purchase. Keeping accurate records of the amount in a checking account is crucial to your financial situation. Reconciling your account will make sure that the bank balance in your checking account matches your register balance.

Key Word Review

Explain

Write the key words on the board. Ask for volunteers to explain where they have heard or have seen the words used.

CHAPTER ④

Checking Accounts

What You'll Learn

Work, spend, and play—all in a week's time. You'll work for money so it can pay for the basics in life, as well as recreation on the weekend. More than likely you'll use a checking account to hold and track your money coming and going.

Section 4-1 Compute the total checking account deposit.

Section 4-2 Write a check.

Section 4-3 Figure out the balance in a check register.

Section 4-4 Calculate the present balance on a checking account bank statement.

Section 4-5 Reconcile a check register with a bank account statement.

Section 4-6 Compute online banking charges and update the check register.

When Will You Ever Use This?

You need a place to store your money (and under your bed isn't the best place). With the bank safekeeping your money in a checking account, you have the security and the convenience of a business tracking your transactions.

Key Words to Know

- deposit
- automatic teller machine (ATM)
- personal identification number (PIN)
- checking account
- check
- check register
- balance
- bank statement
- service charge
- reconcile
- online banking

Mathematics Online

To learn more about checking accounts, visit the *Mathematics with Business Applications* Web site at www.busmath.glencoe.com.

CLASSROOM RESOURCES

Application and Enrichment

- 📖 *Teacher Wraparound Edition*
- 📖 *Teacher Resource Binder, Blackline Masters*
- 💿 *Interactive Lesson Planner* CD-ROM
- 💿 *PowerPoint® Presentations* CD-ROM

Review and Enforcement

Mathematics Online
www.busmath.glencoe.com

- 📖 *Teacher Resource Binder, Internet Resources*

- 📖 *Student Activity Workbook*
- 📖 *Student Activity Workbook, Teacher Annotated Edition*
- 📖 *School-to-Home Activity Workbook*

Assessment and Evaluation

- 📖 *Assessment Binder, Reproducible Tests*
- 📖 *Assessment Binder, Alternative Assessment Strategies*
- 💿 **Exam***View®* Pro Test Generator CD-ROM

For the Teacher

- 📖 *Student Activity Workbook, Teacher Annotated Edition*
- 📖 *Assessment Binder*
- 💿 *Interactive Lesson Planner* CD-ROM
- 📖 *Teacher Resource Binder*
- 🖥 Mathematics Online
www.busmath.glencoe.com

For the Student

- 📖 *Student Activity Workbook*
- 📖 *School-to-Home Activity Workbook*

Living in the Real World

Fleet Footed Finances

Zach Pinsky works as the manager of Fleet Footed, a shoe store that specializes in athletic shoes. He's training a new manager, Wendy Yang, who has worked in sales for three years but has no managerial experience. As the newest manager, Yang will work the evening and weekend shifts. Read how this business operates its checking account.

Read on. Go to . . .

165

Living in the Real World

Story's Summary

Follow in the footsteps of store manager Zach Pinsky as he coaches management trainee Wendy Yang. He reveals the similarities of managing money between a small business and personal finance.

Did You Know...

According to the International Data Corporation, the number of banks and credit unions offering online services jumped 69 percent in 5 years.

Think about This

Why might it be beneficial to use direct deposit on payday rather than making a deposit in person at the bank? Why might it be beneficial to have certain bills automatically paid each month?

LOCAL STANDARDS

National Standards for Business Education

Standard 1	Mathematical Foundations
Standard 2	Number Relationships and Operations

National Council of Teachers of Mathematics Standards

Standard 1	Numbers and Operations
Standard 4	Measurement
Standard 6	Problem Solving
Standard 8	Communication

1 FOCUS

Ask students if any of them have a checking account. Ask these students if they deposit their checks themselves, or if their employer arranges for the check to be sent to the student's account.

In-Class Examples

Work through these exercises with students before having them do the Self-Check.

1. $6.82 + $18 + $14.79 + $212.50 **$252.11**
2. $41.92 + $171.80 − $75.95 **$137.77**
3. $347.26 + $98.51 + $520.07 − $225.00 **$740.84**
4. $25.00 + $165.89 + $428.33 + $573.84 − $600 **$593.06**
5. Find the total deposit: Currency: 7 one-dollar bills, 3 five-dollar bills, and 6 ten-dollar bills. Coins: 22 dimes, 41 quarters, and 5 half-dollars. Checks of $17.89 and $31.16. **$146**

SECTION 4-1 Deposits

Section Objective

Compute the total checking account deposit.

You've got a check in your hand from your employer, but what good is that when you need cash to fill up the car? You'll need to **deposit** that check in your bank account. A deposit is an amount of money that you put into a bank account.

If you want to make an electronic deposit, then use the **automatic teller machine (ATM)**. To use an ATM machine you'll need an ATM card (it looks like a credit card) and a **personal identification number (PIN)**. The card allows you to access your bank account and deposit your check into the machine. Remember that:

Total Deposit = (Currency + Coins + Checks) − Cash Received

Living in the Real World

Fleet Footed Finances

What's in the Bag? "We make deposits twice a day," Pinsky explains to Yang. "When you take money to deposit in the bank, you should know how much of each kind of sales income—bills, coins, and checks—you are depositing."

Draw Conclusions What's the purpose of a deposit slip?

Continued on page 169

Need Help? Go to...
- Workshop 4: Adding Decimals, page 10
- Workshop 5: Subtracting Decimals, page 12
- Skill 5: Adding Decimals, page 732
- Skill 6: Subtracting Decimals, page 733

Example 1

Margaret Miller makes a deposit at an ATM. She has a check for $235.42 and a check for $55.47. She would like to receive $40 in cash and deposit the rest of the money in her checking account. What is her total deposit?

STEP: Compute the total checking account deposit.

(Currency + Coins + Checks) − Cash Received

Figure 4.1

CHECKING DEPOSIT				DOLLARS	CENTS
Margaret C. Miller		First City Bank	CURRENCY		
Date March 11, 20--			COINS		
		LIST SEPARATELY	7639	235	42
		CHECKS	11752	55	47
Currency + Coins + Checks			SUBTOTAL	290	89
SIGN HERE IF CASH RECEIVED FROM DEPOSIT			LESS CASH RECEIVED	40	00
Miller's Account Number			TOTAL DEPOSIT	250	89
753 243 3332 8765 213					

166 ◄ Chapter 4 Checking Accounts

Living in the Real World

To record the amount of each type of currency being deposited.

BUSINESS NOTES

Crime Stoppers

The banking industry loses about $85 million a year through consumer fraud and forgeries. This may translate into higher fees for regular customers. Students interview local bank officials to find out how often the bank receives notice of forged checks and what procedure it follows when dealing with forgery. Have students work in pairs to present their findings as a two-minute "Crime Stoppers" feature, as if it's for an evening TV broadcast. LS , CL

CONCEPT CHECK

Complete the problems, then check your answers at the end of the chapter. Find the total deposit.

1. ($60.00 + $0.90 + $14.00) − $0.00 = ($60.00 + $0.90 + $14.00) = $74.90

2. ($45.00 + $80.00) − $20.00 = ($45.00 + $80.00) − $20.00 = $105.00

3. Checks: $231.09 + $987.67 = $1,218.76
Cash: $9.00 + (9 × $5 = $45) + (8 × $10 = $80) = $134.00
Coins: (14 × 0.25 = $3.50) + (25 × $0.10 = $2.50) + (18 × $0.05 = $0.90) + ($0.64) = $7.54
Total: $1,218.76 + $134.00 + $7.54 = $1,360.30 − $40.00 = $1,320.30

Figure 4.2

4. Checks: $341.79 + $17.96 = $359.75
Cash: $35.00 I (17 × $5 = $85) + (44 × $10 = $440) = $560.00
Coins: (54 × 0.25 = $13.50) + (36 × $0.10 = $3.60) + (32 × $0.05 = $1.60) + ($0.21) = $18.91
Total: $359.75 + $560.00 + $18.91 = $938.66

Example 2

Manuel Romeo is making a deposit in his checking account. He has checks for $435.20, $271.19, and $327.96. He has cash consisting of 15 one-dollar bills, 7 five-dollar bills, 3 ten-dollar bills, 24 quarters, 5 dimes, 15 nickels, and 14 pennies. He would like to keep $75 in cash. What is his total deposit?

STEP: Compute the total deposit.

$$\text{The currency deposit} = \$15 + (7 \times \$5) + (3 \times \$10)$$
$$= \$15 + \$35 + \$30$$
$$= \$80$$

$$\text{The coins deposit} = (24 \times \$0.25) + (5 \times \$0.10) + (15 \times \$0.05) + \$0.14$$
$$= \$6.00 + \$0.50 + \$0.75 + \$0.14$$
$$= \$7.39$$

CHECKING DEPOSIT

Manuel Romeo

DATE

9/27/20--

First City Bank

Currency + Coins + Checks

SIGN HERE IF CASH RECEIVED FROM DEPOSIT

485 392 5612 3512 476

		DOLLARS	CENTS
CASH	CURRENCY	80	00
	COINS	7	39
CHECKS	LIST SEPARATELY 85-40	435	20
	116-25	271	19
	897-32	327	96
	SUBTOTAL	1121	74
	⟳ LESS CASH RECEIVED	75	00
	TOTAL DEPOSIT	1046	74

CONCEPT CHECK

Complete the problems, then check your answers at the end of the chapter. Find the total deposit.

3. Checks: $231.09 and $987.67.
Cash: 9 one-dollar bills, 9 five-dollar bills, 8 ten-dollar bills, 14 quarters, 25 dimes, 18 nickels, and 64 pennies. Less $40.00 cash received.

4. Checks: $341.79 and $17.96.
Cash: 35 one-dollar bills, 17 five-dollar bills, 44 ten-dollar bills, 54 quarters, 36 dimes, 32 nickels, and 21 pennies.

Section 4-1 Deposits ▶ **167**

2 TEACH

Have students discuss the benefits of having a checking account. You may also wish to discuss services offered with a checking account. Discuss the steps in opening a checking account. Point out that many checking accounts are interest-bearing accounts.

Motivating the Lesson

You receive several gifts for your birthday in the form of checks for the amounts of $25.00, $25.00, $35.00, $40.00, and $50.00. In addition, you have been saving loose change in a jar. You have 88 quarters, 173 dimes, and 224 nickels. You want to cash your checks and deposit them in the bank along with the coins you have been saving. What is the total amount of money you have to deposit? **$225.50**

In-Class Examples

Find the total deposit.

1. $82.63 + $14.28 + $155 **$251.91**

2. $113.47 + $65 − $35 **$143.47**

3. Checks $426.19 and $827.43. Cash: 24 one-dollar bills, 8 five-dollar bills, and 11 ten-dollar bills. Coins: 18 quarters, 52 dimes, 57 nickels, and 15 pennies. **$1,440.32**

COOPERATIVE LEARNING

Communication

Have teams participate in "Trade-a-Question." First, teams write problems based on problems from this chapter on 3" by 5" cards. Second, teams trade their problems with another team and write the answers on the reverse side of the cards. Third, teams trade again for the teams to get exposure to more problems and attempt the answers before looking at the answers written on the cards. Finally, teams should continue trading problems to gain more practice, until all teams have attempted all problems on the cards. **LS** , **CL**

 **ASSESS**

Error Analysis

Remind students that when they convert a number of coins to dollars and cents, they should be sure to use a decimal point. For instance, they would multiply the number of quarters by 0.25, dimes by 0.10, nickels by 0.05, and pennies by 0.01.

If students are making errors in finding the total deposit, have them check to see that they have carefully organized their work before beginning any computation. Remind them to vertically align decimal points for the amount of cash, coins, and checks they are adding. When they have added the total amount, remind them to subtract any cash received to figure out the total deposit.

4 **CLOSE**

Closing Activity

1. $467.94 + $249.51 + $38.37 + $18.29 **$774.11**
2. $1435.62 − $481.47 **$954.15**
3. Emily Cheung stops at an ATM location to make a deposit in her checking account. She has checks for $256.34, $77.28, and $29.50. She wants to receive $85.00 in cash. What is her total deposit? **$278.12**
4. Leah Campbell stops at her bank on her way home from work. She wants to deposit her payroll check of $748.59, a $25.00 rebate check, and insurance check for $62.25. She would like to receive $250.00 in cash. What is her total deposit? **$585.84**

Find the subtotal and total deposit.

	Currency	Coins	Checks	Subtotal	Less Cash Received	Total Deposit
5.	$ 30.00	$11.80	—	a. $41.80	—	b. $41.80
6.	74.00	9.65	—	a. $83.65	—	b. $83.65
7.	—	—	$ 84.50 93.70	a. $178.20	$10.00	b. $168.20
8.	—	—	124.26 48.79	a. $173.05	20.00	b. $153.05
9.	400.00	—	734.00 141.55	a. $1,275.55	35.00	b. $1,240.55
10.	975.00	40.00	986.53 91.11	a. $2,092.64	80.00	b. $2,012.64

 ▶**FYI**

More than 500 million checks are forged every year, according to the accounting firm Ernst & Young. Some experts estimate that check fraud costs American banks and businesses about $50 billion per year.

▶▶▶

11. Olive Baker stops at an ATM location in the lobby of her office building. She has a paycheck for $173.45 and a refund check for $3. She would like to receive $25 in cash and deposit the remaining amount. What is her total deposit? **$151.45**

12. Jess Norton stopped at an ATM location to deposit a check for $474.85 and a check for $321.15. He received $50 in cash. What was his total deposit? **$746.00**

13. Jocelyn & Donnell Schelling made a deposit at an ATM location. Their paychecks were $611.33 and $701.45 and a check from their insurance company was $75.25. They received $150 in cash. What was their total deposit? **$1,238.03**

14. Morgan Meers stopped at his bank to deposit his paycheck for $201.20, a refund check from a store for $19.78, and deposit $34.23 in cash. What was his total deposit? **$255.21**

15. Carole Winer deposits checks for $425.22, $883.99, and $57.05. She has cash consisting of 45 one-dollar bills, 15 five-dollar bills, 12 ten-dollar bills, 28 quarters, 16 dimes, 19 nickels, and 65 pennies. She would like to receive $60 in cash. What is her total deposit? **$1,556.46**

16. Ignazio Rubio deposits checks for $598.20, $2,274.26, and $3,248.79. He has cash consisting of 75 one-dollar bills, 78 five-dollar bills, 33 ten-dollar bills, 80 quarters, 32 dimes, 95 nickels, and 5 pennies. He would like to receive $40 in cash. What is his total deposit? **$6,904.25**

MAINTAINING YOUR SKILLS

(Need Help? Go to...)
▶ Skill 6: Subtracting Decimals, page 733

Subtract.

17. $734.40 − $75.00 **$659.40** 18. $619.20 − $40.00 **$579.20**

19. $718.32 − $65.00 **$653.32** 20. $316.37 − $55.00 **$261.37**

THINKING CRITICALLY

Event Trip
You're planning a trip with a friend to an event. You record your own costs: tickets, $24.50; lunch, $8.24; snacks $14.75; and taxi $19.50. Calculate your total costs. **$66.99**

WRAP-UP

Call upon individual students to read their answer to Practice Problems 5–7 to the class. Go over any problem for which a wrong answer is given.

Assignment Guide
Basic: 5–10
Average: 11–14

20 min.

SECTION (4-2) Writing Checks

Section Objective

Write a check.

First you need to open a **checking account**. This monetary account allows the holder to write checks against money that has been deposited into it. After you open a checking account and make a deposit, you can write checks. A **check** directs a bank to deduct money from your checking account to make a payment. Your account must contain as much money as the amount of the check you are writing so that you do not overdraw your account. To write checks you need to be able to write dollar amounts in *word form*, with the decimal portion expressed as a fraction.

Living in the Real World

Fleet Footed Finances

How to Avoid the Bounce   Pinsky opens the book of business account checks to show Yang how the store's finances operate. He explains that managers write checks to pay for shoe shipments, employee sales bonuses, and advertising.

Draw Conclusions   What does it mean if you bounce a check?

Continued on page 172

Need Help? Go to...

➤ Workshop 1: Writing and Reading Numbers, page 4
➤ Skill 1: Numbers, page 727

Example 1

Write the following in word form.

a. $65.29   b. $235.58

   STEP: Write the amounts in word form.

   a. $65.29 in word form is **sixty-five and $\frac{29}{100}$ dollars**

   b. $235.58 in word form is **two hundred thirty-five and $\frac{58}{100}$ dollars**

CONCEPT CHECK

Complete the problems, then check your answers at the end of the chapter. Write each of the following in word form.

1. $26.55 **Twenty-six and $\frac{55}{100}$ dollars**   2. $156.92 **One hundred fifty-six and $\frac{92}{100}$ dollars**

Example 2

Margaret Miller is buying a gift at the Department Store on March 23. The cost of the gift is $45.78. Miller is paying by check. How should she write the check?

   STEP 1: Write the date. (All writing should be in *pen*.)

   STEP 2: Write the name of the person or organization to whom payment will be made.

   STEP 3: Write the amount of the check as a numeral.

Continued on next page

Section 4-2 Writing Checks ▶ **169**

Living in the Real World

Your account has insufficient funds to cover a check that you wrote.

ALTERNATIVE ASSESSMENT

Students with Behavior Disorders Students with behavior disorders have a hard time focusing their attention. To assist these students and encourage them to persist, you may wish to speak with them on an individual basis about their strengths and weaknesses. It might also be helpful at this time to outline chapter objectives with an eye toward helping them feel successful. This may require a flexible assessment program and enrichment material that capitalizes on their interests.

National Standards for Business Education

Standard 1	Mathematical Foundations
Standard 2	Number Relationships and Operations

National Council of Teachers of Mathematics Standards

Standard 1	Numbers and Operations
Standard 4	Measurement
Standard 8	Communication

(1) FOCUS

Ask students if any of them have ever written a check or if they have ever watched someone write a check. Ask students the reason the checks were written.

In-Class Examples
Work through these exercises with students before having them do the Self-Check.
Write in words:

1. $12.32 **twelve and $\frac{32}{100}$**
2. $105.08 **one hundred five and $\frac{09}{100}$**
3. $24.75 **twenty-four and $\frac{75}{100}$**
4. $550.63 **five hundred fifty and $\frac{63}{100}$**
5. $1658.99 **one thousand six hundred fifty-eight and $\frac{99}{100}$**

② TEACH

When filling out the date on a check, emphasize the importance of using the correct date. Checks cannot be postdated or cashed after many months have passed.

Point out that others can fill in the line *Pay to the Order of,* but only the person whose name is on the account can sign the check. The signature can be compared to the one on the signature card if forgery is suspected.

Motivating the Lesson

Tony Navarro recently opened a checking account. On April 16, he wrote his first check for a baseball cap that he bought at Sporting Goods. The hat costs $21.68. How would he write the dollar-and-cents amount with words as it would appear on the check? **(twenty-one and $\frac{68}{100}$)** What should he write on the line that reads *"Pay to the Order of"*? **(Sporting Goods)** What other information would he write on the check? **The date; the amount of the check written in numerals: $21.68; his signature: *Tim Navarro*; and a notation on the check indicating its purpose: *baseball cap***

In-Class Examples

Write each amount in word form with cents expressed as a fraction of a dollar.

1. $88.37 **eighty-eight and $\frac{37}{100}$**
2. $546.52 **five hundred forty six and $\frac{52}{100}$**
3. $1,183.75 **one thousand one hundred eighty-three and $\frac{75}{100}$**

Write each amount in numerals as it would appear on a check.

4. four hundred sixty-four and $\frac{11}{100}$ **$464.11**
5. thirty-seven and $\frac{78}{100}$ **$37.78**

STEP 4: Write the amount of the check in words with cents expressed as a fraction of a dollar.

STEP 5: Make a notation on the check to indicate its purpose.

STEP 6: Sign the check.

Figure 4.3

> Margaret C. Miller Date **March 23, 20--** 202 6-32/1
>
> Pay to the order of _**Department Store**_ $ **45.78**
>
> Forty-five and $\frac{78}{100}$ _____ Dollars
>
> **First City Bank**
>
> Memo **Kendra's Birthday** *Margaret C. Miller*
>
> 531 876 5220 2795 202

CONCEPT CHECK

SELF-CHECK ✓

Complete the problems, then check your answers at the end of the chapter. Write each of the following as a numeral.

3. thirty and $\frac{20}{100}$ dollars **$30.20**

4. three thousand two hundred fifty-six and $\frac{23}{100}$ dollars **$3,256.23**

Manuel Romeo is buying a drill press at Harry's Hardware Store. The cost is $165.52. He is going to write a check. Answer the following questions about the check:

Figure 4.4

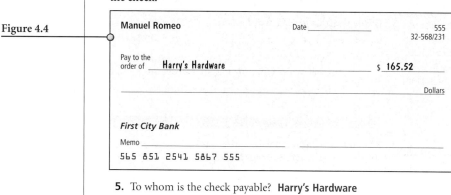

> Manuel Romeo Date _____ 555 32-568/231
>
> Pay to the order of _**Harry's Hardware**_ $ **165.52**
>
> _____ Dollars
>
> **First City Bank**
>
> Memo _____
>
> 565 851 2541 5867 555

5. To whom is the check payable? **Harry's Hardware**

6. How do you write the amount in word form? **One hundred sixty-five and $\frac{52}{100}$ dollars**

7. What should be put in the memo portion? **Drill press**

8. Who signs the check? **Manuel Romeo**

SECTION 4-2 PRACTICE

Write each amount in word form as it would appear on a check.

9. $40.40 **Forty and $\frac{40}{100}$ dollars**

10. $703.00 **Seven hundred three and $\frac{00}{100}$ dollars**

11. $63.74 **Sixty-three and $\frac{74}{100}$ dollars**

COMMUNICATION SKILLS

Upcoming Checking Accounts
Checking accounts might look very different in just a few years. Students use the Internet to research one of the following topics: digital checks, digital coupons, digital cashier's checks, e-money, or smart cards. Students write a one-page paper with their findings.

LS , CL

12. $7.94 $\frac{94}{100}$ dollars — Seven and

13. $34.06 $\frac{06}{100}$ dollars — Thirty-four and

14. $66.00 $\frac{00}{100}$ dollars — Sixty-six and

15. $1,917.00

16. $17,200.00

17. $201.09

18. $172.61

19. $5,327.17

20. $47,983.39

For Problems 21 and 22, use Figure 4.5a.

Figure 4.5a

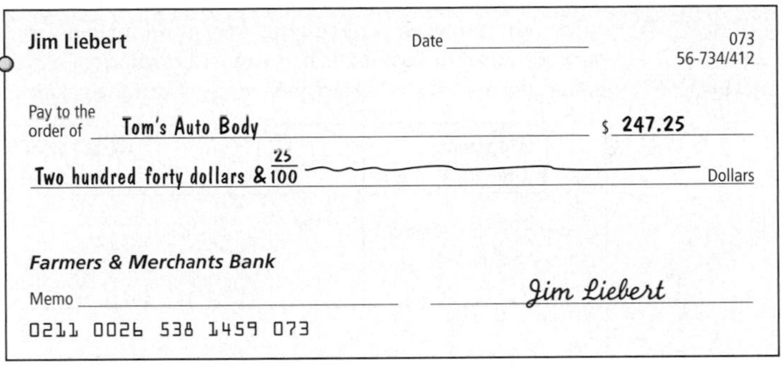

17. Two hundred one and $\frac{09}{100}$ dollars

18. One hundred seventy-two and $\frac{61}{100}$ dollars

19. Five thousand two hundred twenty-seven and $\frac{17}{100}$ dollars

20. Forty-seven thousand nine hundred eighty-three and $\frac{39}{100}$ dollars

Jim Liebert   Date _____   073
                                           56-734/412

Pay to the
order of ___Tom's Auto Body_____ $ 247.25 ___

Two hundred forty dollars & $\frac{25}{100}$ _____ Dollars

Farmers & Merchants Bank

Memo _____   *Jim Liebert*

0211 0026 538 1459 073

21. Jim Liebert is paying by check for an auto repair bill in the amount of $247.25. Did Liebert write the amount of the check correctly, both as a numeral and in words? **No, two hundred forty-seven and $\frac{25}{100}$ dollars**

22. What is the check number Liebert used to pay for his auto repair bill? **073**

For Problems 23 and 24, use Figure 4.5b.

Figure 4.5b

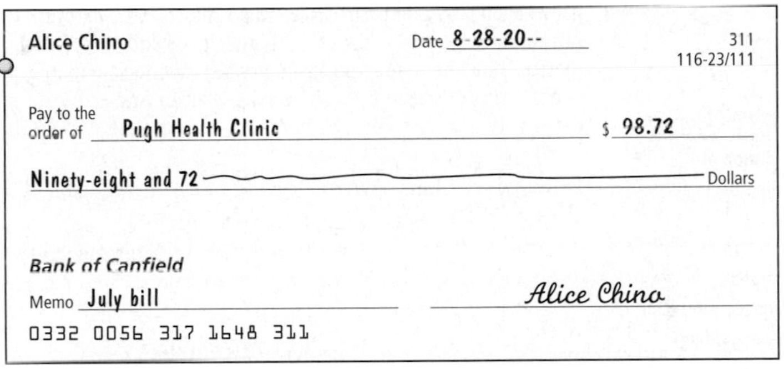

23. No, should be written ninety-eight and $\frac{72}{100}$ dollars

27. Nineteen and $\frac{25}{100}$ dollars

29. Four hundred thirty-five and $\frac{00}{100}$ dollars

30. Three hundred forty-five and $\frac{42}{100}$ dollars

Alice Chino   Date 8-28-20--___   311
                                           116-23/111

Pay to the
order of ___Pugh Health Clinic_____ $ 98.72 ___

Ninety-eight and 72 _____ Dollars

Bank of Canfield

Memo **July bill** _____   *Alice Chino*

0332 0056 317 1648 311

23. Alice Chino wrote check No. 311 to Pugh Health Clinic for $98.72. Did she write the amount in words correctly? If not, write the amount in words correctly.

24. For what purpose did Alice Chino write the check to the Pugh Health Clinic?
July bill

MAINTAINING YOUR SKILLS

Need Help? Go to...
▶ Skill 1: Numbers, page 727

31. Five thousand two hundred seventy-four and $\frac{19}{100}$ dollars

Write the numeral.

25. Thirty-five and $\frac{15}{100}$ dollars **$35.15**   **26.** Seventy-four and $\frac{00}{100}$ dollars **$74.00**

Write in word form with cents expressed as a fraction of a dollar.

27. $19.25   **28.** $50.32 Fifty and $\frac{32}{100}$ dollars   **29.** $435.00

30. $345.42   **31.** $5,274.19   **32.** $11,871.63

32. Eleven thousand eight hundred seventy-one and $\frac{63}{100}$ dollars

---

3 ASSESS

Error Analysis

A typical error that students make when writing numbers as words is to use the word *and* in the wrong place. For example, they may write 743 as "seven hundred and forty-three" instead of "seven hundred forty-three." Stress that *and* is used only to replace the decimal point.

Stress also that all numbers between twenty-one and ninety-nine (other than multiples of ten) should be hyphenated.

4 CLOSE

Closing Activity

Write the number.

1. twenty-two and $\frac{44}{100}$ dollars **$22.44**

2. four hundred seventy-nine and $\frac{55}{100}$ dollars **$479.55**

Write in word form with cents expressed as a fraction of a dollar.

3. $14.95 **fourteen and $\frac{95}{100}$**

4. $237.81 **two hundred thirty-seven and $\frac{81}{100}$**

5. 6,415.13 **six thousand four hundred fifteen and $\frac{13}{100}$**

15. One thousand nine hundred seventeen and $\frac{00}{100}$ dollars

16. Seventeen thousand two hundred and $\frac{00}{100}$ dollars

---

WRAP-UP

Call upon individual students to read their answer to Practice Problems 3 and 5 to the class. Go over any problem for which a wrong answer is given.

Assignment Guide
  Basic: 9–20
  Average: 21–22

20 min.

National Standards for Business Education

Standard 1	Mathematical Foundations
Standard 2	Number Relationships and Operations

National Council of Teachers of Mathematics Standards

Standard 1	Numbers and Operations
Standard 4	Measurement
Standard 6	Problem Solving
Standard 8	Communication

 FOCUS

Ask students if they have ever seen a sign by a cash register stating that there will be a certain dollar charge if a check is returned for insufficient funds. Point out that one way to make sure a checking account has enough money to cover a check written is by means of a written record.

In-Class Examples

Work through these exercises with students before having them do the Self-Check.
1. $719.63 − $124.91 **$594.72**
2. $112.61 + $75.49 **$188.10**
Find the new balance after each check or deposit. In Problems 4 and 5, explain that a check indicates an amount to be subtracted from the balance and a deposit indicates an addition to the balance.
3. Balance: $96.25
   Deposit: $71.93
   New balance? **$168.18**
4. Balance: $271.80
   Check: $54.92
   New balance? **$216.88**

○ **Section Objective**

Figure out the balance in a check register.

SECTION 4-3 Check Registers

You use a **check register** to keep a record of your deposits, electronic transfers (or automatic transfers, AT), and the checks you have written. The **balance** is the amount of money in your account. When you make a deposit, add the amount of the deposit to the balance. When you write a check or electronically transfer funds out of your account, subtract the amount from the balance.

Important Question	What Formulas Do I Use?
How do I calculate the **new balance**?	Step 1: New Balance = Previous Balance − Check Amount − Automatic Transfers
	Step 2: New Balance = Previous Balance + Deposit Amount

Living in the Real World

Fleet Footed Finances

A Safe Habit Yang notices that the Fleet Footed checkbook, which is the size of a large photo album, contains many checks printed on a single page. Each check has a "self-carbon," which produces a copy identical to the check. In addition, Pinsky insists that the managers keep a separate check register, which is a continuous record of all checks written and deposits made. After each transaction, the manager must figure out the balance in the account.

Draw Conclusions Why is it good to get in the habit of tracking the money in your checking account?

Continued on page 175

Need Help? Go to...
➤ **Workshop 4:** Adding Decimals, page 10
➤ **Workshop 5:** Subtracting Decimals, page 12
➤ **Skill 5:** Adding Decimals, page 732
➤ **Skill 6:** Subtracting Decimals, page 733
➤ **Application A:** Formulas, page 760

Example 1

The previous balance in your check register is $345.98. You make a deposit of $75.00. You write a check for $45.00. What is your new balance?

STEP: Figure out the balance.
$345.98 + $75.00 − $45.00 = **$375.98 new balance**

CONCEPT CHECK

SELF-CHECK ✓

Complete the problems, then check your answers at the end of the chapter.

1. Balance	$1,236.29	2. Balance	$992.71
Deposit	+ 235.50	AT	− 45.20
Balance	**$1,471.79**	**Balance**	**$947.51**
Amount of Check	− 35.28	Deposit	+ 138.84
Balance	**$1,436.51**	**Balance**	**$1,086.35**

Living in the Real World

It ensures that you're always aware of how much money you have and lessens the danger of bouncing a check.

RETEACH / ENRICHMENT

Stop Payment

A stop payment is an order for a bank not to cash a particular check. Ask students: Why might you want to stop payment on a check? **(The check might be lost, be for a wrong amount, or be sent to the wrong address.)** If the check hasn't yet been processed, the bank will not cash the check. The bank charges a fee for the stop payment service.

Example 2

Margaret Miller's checking account had a balance of $313.54. She wrote a check for $45.78 on March 2. On March 5 the bank made an automatic transfer (AT) of $52.55 to pay her phone bill. She made a deposit of $240.32 on March 10. What is the new balance in Miller's account?

STEP: Figure out the balance.

Figure 4.6

Trans. Type or Check No.	Date	Description of Transaction	Payment/ Debit (−)	✔	Deposit/ Credit (+)	Balance
Previous Balance	Check Amount − Automatic Transfer		Balance Brought Forward →			313 54
202	3/2	Department Store	45 78			267 76
AT	3/5	Phone Bill	52 55			215 21
	3/10	Deposit			240 32	455 53
				Previous Balance + Deposit Amount		

CONCEPT CHECK

SELF-CHECK ✔

Complete the problems, then check your answers at the end of the chapter.

3.
Balance	$625.39
Deposit	+ 875.80
Deposit	+ 14.27
Balance	**$1,515.46**
Amount of Check	− 953.24
Amount of Check	− 74.96
Balance	**$487.26**

4.
Balance	$7,357.87
Amount of Check	− 132.75
AT	− 6,544.55
Balance	**$680.57**
Deposit	+ 138.84
Balance	**$819.41**

SECTION 4-3 PRACTICE

Find the new balance after each check or deposit.

Check Register

	Payment/ Debit (−)	✔	Deposit/ Credit (+)	Balance
	Balance Brought Forward →			448 35
5.	46 92			401 43
6.			216 84	618 27
7.	251 55			366 72

8. Your balance is $89.75 on May 23. Deposit $156.90 on May 30. Write a $34.79 check on June 1. ATM withdrawal of $50.00 on June 1. What is your new balance? **$161.86**

9. Your balance is $131.02 on April 4. Write a $31.28 check on April 9. Write a $45.92 check on April 14. AT deposit of paycheck for $215.48 on April 15. What is your new balance? **$269.30**

Continued on next page

GLOBAL PERSPECTIVE

Traveler's Checks

When you travel in another country, it's usually not possible to cash a personal check. Before their trip most travelers purchase traveler's checks. Traveler's checks are widely accepted. Why? **A traveler's check is guaranteed by the issuing bank to be good, while a personal check is not guaranteed.**

---

5. Balance: $423.67
Check: $45.24
Deposit: $68.09
Check: $13.54
Deposit: $11.90
New balance? **$444.88**

② TEACH

Point out that the balance in a check register changes with every transaction. It is possible to both make a deposit and write a check on the same day. It is also possible to write several checks on the same day as long as enough money exists in the account to cover each check.

Emphasize the use of two columns in the check register—one for checks and one for deposits.

Motivating the Lesson

Your employer electronically deposits your paycheck in your checking account. You have a balance in your check register of $156.41. You write a check for $39.00 to pay for a new track team sweatshirt and pants. What is your new balance? **$117.41**

In-Class Examples

Find the new balance after each check or deposit.

1. Balance: $542.62
Deposit: $125.00
Balance? **$667.62**
Amount of Check: $74.38
Balance? **$593.24**

2. Balance $197.23
Amount of Check: $48.72
Balance? **$148.51**
Amount of Check: $17.49
Balance? **$131.02**

3 ASSESS

Error Analysis

Be sure that students know when to subtract an amount from the balance and when to add an amount. Remind them that when they write a check or have an automatic electronic transfer to pay a bill, they must subtract the amount from the balance. If they have an automatic deposit, they add the amount to the balance.

4 CLOSE

Closing Activity

1. $634.27 + $271.93 **$906.20**
2. $408.56 − $139.48 **$269.08**
3. Cindy Napier's balance in her check register is $212.84. Deposit $612.20. Write a check for $348.25. Write a check for $80.92. What is her new balance? **$395.87**
4. Teretha Kane has a balance of $73.78 in her check register. One June 1, her payroll check for $741.80 is automatically deposited in her account. One June 2, she writes a check for $291.49. One June 4, she writes a check for $52.46. What is her new balance? **$471.63**

---

10. Mac Valent opened a new checking account and deposited his paycheck for $209.81. The check register shows his transactions since opening his account. What is his balance after each transaction?

Figure 4.7

Trans. Type or Check No.	Date	Description of Transaction	Payment/ Debit (−)	✔	Deposit/ Credit (+)	Balance
					Balance Brought Forward →	209 81
101	8/12	Electric Energy	47 15			a. 162.66
102	8/18	Grocery Store	53 03			b. 109.63
103	8/20	Department Store	107 30			c. 2.33

11. Magdala Santos's checkbook balance was $149.21 on October 5. Her check register shows her transactions since then. What is her balance after each transaction?

Figure 4.8

Trans. Type or Check No.	Date	Description of Transaction	Payment/ Debit (−)	✔	Deposit/ Credit (+)	Balance
					Balance Brought Forward →	149 21
571	10/6	Pettisville Flower	45 79			a. 103.42
	10/9	Deposit			213 80	b. 317.22
572	10/10	Bookstore	16 94			c. 300.28
AT	10/19	Phone Co.	75 25			d. 225.03

12. Leah Ahren's latest transactions are shown on the check register. Find her balance after each transaction.

Trans. Type or Check No.	Date	Description of Transaction	Payment/ Debit (−)	✔	Deposit/ Credit (+)	Balance
					Balance Brought Forward →	397 16
916	9/20	Baggett Auto Store	83 28			a. 313.88
	9/22	Deposit			45 10	b. 358.98
917	10/3	Rolland Buchele	134 67			c. 224.31
918	10/4	First Federal S&L	201 99			d. 22.32
	10/5	Deposit			139 40	e. 161.72
919	10/19	Vollmars Ceramics	111 15			f. 50.57
920	10/20	Cash	30 00			g. 20.57
921	10/22	Rapids Pharmacy	48 92			h. −28.35

MAINTAINING YOUR SKILLS

Need Help? Go to...
- Skill 5: Adding Decimals, page 732
- Skill 6: Subtracting Decimals, page 733

Add.

13. $414.85 + $265.50 **$680.35**
14. $845.96 + $400.00 **$1,245.96**
15. $192.78 + $112.50 **$305.28**
16. $72.85 + $393.36 **$466.21**
17. $2,371.81 + $491.48 **$2,863.29**
18. $371.80 + $444.75 **$816.55**

Subtract.

19. $579.23 − $212.60 **$366.63**
20. $347.89 − $99.92 **$247.97**
21. $261.85 − $8.47 **$253.38**
22. $141.82 − $64.73 **$77.09**
23. $3,427.80 − $635.60 **$2,792.20**
24. $671.82 − $314.91 **$356.91**

WRAP-UP

Call upon individual students to read their answer to Practice Problems 5–7 to the class. Go over any problem for which a wrong answer is given.

Assignment Guide
- **Basic:** 5–7
- **Average:** 8–11

20 min.

SECTION 4-4 Bank Statements

Section Objective

Calculate the present balance on a checking account bank statement.

When you have a checking account, you receive a **bank statement** from the bank each month. It lists all your checks that the bank has cleared, including any automatic transfers, ATM transactions, and deposits that the bank has recorded since your last statement. A bank might tack on a **service charge** to your statement. This is a fee charged for services rendered. Here's a sample of what's explained on your account balance:

$$\text{Present Balance} = \text{Previous Balance} + \text{Deposits} - \text{Withdrawals} - \text{Service Charges} + \text{Interest}$$

Living in the Real World

Fleet Footed Finances

Timing Is Everything   Yang flips through the monthly statements and notices the information they provide. Each month's statement lists the number and amount of each check that has been cashed. Photocopies of the cancelled checks are attached. In addition, the statement indicates the deposits made and a few withdrawals of cash.

Draw Conclusions   What are the penalties for being overdrawn?

Continued on page 178

(Example 1)

Need Help? Go to...
- ► Workshop 4: Adding Decimals, page 10
- ► Workshop 5: Subtracting Decimals, page 12
- ► Skill 5: Adding Decimals, page 732
- ► Skill 6: Subtracting Decimals, page 733
- ► Application A: Formulas, page 760

Your bank statement shows a previous balance of $944.50. You make deposits of $755.50 and $210.40, and write checks for $355.50 and $125.50. You have a $3.00 service charge and earn $0.25 in interest. What is your present balance?

STEP: Calculate the balance in the account.

$$\begin{array}{ccccccc}
\text{Previous Balance} & + & \text{Deposits} & - & \text{Withdrawals} & - & \text{Service Charges} & + & \text{Interest} \\
\end{array}$$

$$= \$944.50 + \left(\begin{array}{c}\$755.50 \\ +\$210.40\end{array}\right) - \left(\begin{array}{c}\$355.50 \\ +\$125.50\end{array}\right) - \$3.00 + \$0.25$$

$$= \$944.50 + \$965.90 - \$481.00 - \$3.00 + \$0.25$$

$$= \$1,426.65 \text{ present balance}$$

1 FOCUS

Just as anyone with a checking account must keep a written record of deposits made and checks written, so must a bank. The bank periodically sends each person, with an account, a record of the transactions as the bank has recorded them.

In-Class Examples
Work through these exercises with students before having them do the Self-Check.

1. $387.22 + $171.56 − $67.45 **$491.33**
2. $114.96 − $12.84 − $37.48 + $293.97 **$358.61**
3. $558.71 + $83.46 − $45.22 − $2.50 **$594.45**
4. $712.90 − $275.64 + $18.30 − $195.24 − $58.17 **$202.15**
5. $1148.27 − $266.41 − $85.19 − $29.61 **$767.06**

National Standards for Business Education

Standard 1	Mathematical Foundations
Standard 2	Number Relationships and Operations

National Council of Teachers of Mathematics Standards

Standard 1	Numbers and Operations
Standard 4	Measurement
Standard 6	Problem Solving
Standard 8	Communication

Living in the Real World

Penalties will vary depending on the merchant and financial institution, but fees levied by both can be steep.

Great Ideas from the Classroom Of...

Tracy Plesek
Lincoln-Way East High School, Frankfort, Ill.

Real-Life Income

Give your students a checkbook register with a balance of $742, 10 blank checks, 4 deposit slips, and a list of names that the check should be drafted to and for what amount. The students have one class period to fill in the checks, deposit slips, and check register to get a final accurate balance.

2 TEACH

Students may not be familiar with a service charge. You may wish to mention that the service charge helps to defray the bank's cost of handling a checking account. Some banks may charge per check written; some use a flat rate; and some may charge based on a combination of the two.

Banks that charge a service fee may also offer interest on some accounts that maintain a minimum balance.

Motivating the Lesson

You receive a bank statement for your checking account. The bank statement indicates you had a previous balance of $185.13. You write three checks for $24.95, $52.73, and $11.20. What is your present balance? **$96.25**

In-Class Examples

1. Vince Murray's bank statement for May lists deposits of $14.75, $99.22, and $531.18. What are his total deposits for May? **$645.15**

2. Gina Valerio's bank statement for April lists withdrawals of $58.17, $19.95, $756.60, $93.28, and $106.41. What are her total withdrawals for the month? **$1,034.41**

CONCEPT CHECK

SELF-CHECK ✓ Complete the problems, then check your answers at the end of the chapter.

	Previous Balance	+	Deposits	−	Withdrawals	−	Service Charges	+	Interest	=	Present Balance
1.	$280.00	+	$120.00	−	$140.00	−	$2.50	+	$0.30	=	$257.80
2.	275.00	+	105.00	−	312.60	−	4.00	+	0.00	=	$63.40

Example 2

Margaret Miller received her bank statement and cancelled checks for March. She checks the statement. Verify her present balance.

Figure 4.9

First City Bank			Monthly Statement	

Margaret Miller
175 LaPlas Court
San Diego, California

	Statement Period	Account Number
	3/2 through 3/31	87652

3/1	Previous Balance	313.54
	2 Deposits	913.40
	5 Withdrawals	554.54
	Service Charge/Fee	
	Interest Earned	
4/1	Present Balance	672.40

CHECKS

Check	Date	Amount	Check	Date	Amount	Check	Date	Amount
202	3/2	45.78	203	3/12	137.42	204	3/19	275.81

DEPOSITS/CREDITS			PAYMENTS/DEBITS		
Date	Amount	Description	Date	Amount	Description
3/10	240.32	Deposit	3/5	52.55	Phone Bill 11564
3/15	673.08	Appliance Corp. Payroll 25760	3/28	42.98	Elec Pwr 11020

DAILY BALANCE

Daily Balance		Daily Balance		Daily Balance		Daily Balance	
3/1	313.54	3/5	215.21	3/12	318.11	3/19	715.38
3/2	267.76	3/10	455.53	3/15	991.19	3/28	672.40

STEP: Calculate the balance in the account.

Total Deposits = $240.32 + $673.08 = $913.40

Total Withdrawals =
$45.78 + $137.42 + $275.81 + $52.55 + $42.98 = $554.54

Previous Balance	+	Deposits	−	Withdrawals	−	Service Charges	+	Interest
$313.54	+	$913.40	−	$554.54				

= **$672.40 balance**

TECHNOLOGY POWER

Two online banks are making a name for themselves through effective leadership. NetBank and Wells Fargo are two examples of online banks that have survived. NetBank is an online bank. Most of the customers have simple checking or money-market accounts and have very few borrowers. Wells Fargo is a traditional bank that has branched into an online service as well. Nearly half of the transactions for Wells Fargo customers take place online.

CONCEPT CHECK

SELF-CHECK ✓

Complete the problems, then check your answers at the end of the chapter.

	Previous Balance	+	Deposits	−	Withdrawals	−	Service Charges	+	Interest	=	Present Balance
3.	$290.00	+	$120.00 +150.00	−	$140.00 +110.00	−	$2.70	+	$0.25	=	$307.55
4.	965.15	+	125.54 +175.98	−	265.32 +210.03 + 30.20	−	2.30	+	0.00	=	$758.82

SECTION 4-4 PRACTICE

	Previous Balance	Deposits	Withdrawals	Service Charge	Interest	Present Balance
5.	$ 40.10	$ 200.00	$ 190.10	$2.34	$ 0.00	$47.66
6.	487.67	430.75	598.17	0.00	1.38	$321.63
7.	1,949.07	4,201.00 + 750.90	319.80 + 289.34	4.15	0.00	$6,287.68
8.	9,421.99	7,509.23 +1,412.46 + 256.40	1,397.86 +1,209.32	5.60	12.47	$15,999.77

9. A portion of Takeisha Hallett's bank statement is shown. Her previous balance was $271.31. What is her present balance? **$684.66**

Figure 4.10

CHECKS								
Check	Date	Amount	Check	Date	Amount	Check	Date	Amount
304	6/11	19.45	305	6/15	21.02	307	6/30	95.98

DEPOSITS/CREDITS			PAYMENTS/DEBITS		
Date	Amount	Description	Date	Amount	Description
6/12	115.90	Deli Payroll 11002	6/26	25.85	Gas Bill 11564
6/19	115.90	Deli Payroll 11012	6/28	2.00	Service Charge
6/26	345.85	Deposit			

MAINTAINING YOUR SKILLS

Need Help? Go to...
➤ Skill 5: Adding Decimals, page 732
➤ Skill 6: Subtracting Decimals, page 733

Add.

10. $346.50 + $215.50 + $35.97
$597.97

11. $543.07 + $172.40 + $351.23
$1,066.70

12. $917.35 + $448.55 + $627.25
$1,993.15

13. $43,906.54 + $3,172 + $4.20
$47,082.74

Subtract.

14. $915.87
− 748.42
$167.45

15. $684.31
− 83.49
$600.82

16. $342.18
− 191.84
$150.34

17. $2,346.39
− 983.42
$1,362.97

Section 4-4 Bank Statements ▶ **177**

COMMUNICATION SKILLS

Reporting about Financial Institutions
Students call or visit several financial institutions in the local area to find out how to open a checking account. Students ask questions about the minimum age to open an account, the initial deposit, any service charges, and whether or not interest-bearing accounts are available. Students share their findings with the class. **LS** , **CL** , **P**

WRAP-UP

Go over any problem for which a wrong answer is given.

Assignment Guide
Basic: 5–8
Average: 9

20 min.

③ ASSESS

Error Analysis
If students are making errors, be sure they are breaking down the process of finding the current balance into smaller steps. Remind them to first total the deposits and the withdrawals. Then, have them add the total deposits to the previous month's balance. Then, they can subtract the total withdrawals. If the bank charges a service fee, remind them to subtract that amount. If the bank pays interest on the account, remind them to add the monthly interest to find the current balance.

④ CLOSE

Closing Activity
1. $528.42 + $174.39 +$18.07 **$720.88**
2. $1533.70 − $895.49 **$638.21**
3. Giovanni Marzano received his bank statement for June. His previous balance was $1351.60. He wrote checks for $652.18, $24.26, $70.12, and $218.65. He made deposits of $93.88 and $250.14. What is his current balance? **$730.41**
4. Jacinta Alvarro's bank statement for May shows a previous balance of $592.15. Her total deposits for the month were $841.77. Her total withdrawals were $1,030.74. She received $1.24 in interest. What is her current balance **$404.42**
5. Ashanti Knight received her bank statement for June. Her previous balance was $728.93. She made deposits of $488.16, $152.90, and $340.55. She wrote checks for $29.41, $145.23, $62.54, and $850.10. She paid a monthly service fee of $3.25. What is her current balance? **$620.01**

177

National Standards for Business Education

Standard 1	Mathematical Foundations
Standard 2	Number Relationships and Operations

National Council of Teachers of Mathematics Standards

Standard 1	Numbers and Operations
Standard 4	Measurement
Standard 6	Problem Solving
Standard 8	Communication

1 FOCUS

Ask students to give a definition of *reconcile* (**to agree; to make consistent**). Explain that in this lesson they'll learn how to make sure that the bank's records agree with the records of a person with a checking account.

In-Class Examples

Work through these exercises with students before having them do the Self-Check.

1. $241.50 − $121.60 + $375.42 **$495.32**
2. $34.80 − $19.32 + $172.90 + $45.81 **$234.19**
3. $420.18 + $225.60 − $25.26 + $3.20 **$623.72**
4. $278.45 + $567.31 − $13.29 − $56.32 + $181.32 **$957.47**
5. $1398.65 − $234.11 + $56.85 − $11.00 − $93.68 **$1,116.71**

SECTION 4-5 Reconciling the Bank Statement

○ Section Objective

Reconcile a check register with a bank account statement.

When you receive your bank statement, compare the bank statement and your check register to be sure they agree. You **reconcile** the statement to make sure it agrees with your check register. You may find some outstanding deposits (or outstanding checks) that didn't post or that didn't clear. These appear on your register but didn't reach the bank in time to list them on your statement. When comparing the two, remember that:

$$\text{Adjusted Balance} = \text{Statement Balance} − \text{Outstanding Checks/Payments or Debits} + \text{Outstanding Deposits}$$

Living in the Real World

Fleet Footed Finances

Tracking Your Money "One of the most important jobs you will have as a manager," Pinsky says, "is reconciling the store's monthly bank statement with the information on the account's check register."

"That can be tricky," Yang says, "especially when you have a lot of outstanding checks that haven't been cashed yet."

Draw Conclusions What documents are needed to reconcile your monthly bank statement?

Continued on page 182

Need Help? Go to...

► **Workshop 4:** Adding Decimals, page 10
► **Workshop 5:** Subtracting Decimals, page 12
► **Skill 5:** Adding Decimals, page 732
► **Skill 6:** Subtracting Decimals, page 733
► **Application A:** Formulas, page 760

Example 1

Your statement balance is $598.67. You have an outstanding check for $125.44 and an outstanding debit of $235.42 that didn't post yet. You also have an outstanding deposit of $231.98. What is your adjusted balance?

STEP: Calculate the adjusted balance.

$$\text{Statement Balance} − \text{Outstanding Checks/Payments or Debits} + \text{Outstanding Deposits}$$

$$\$598.67 − (\$125.44 + \$235.42) + \$231.98$$
$$= \$598.67 − \$360.86 + \$231.98$$
$$= \$469.79 \text{ adjusted balance}$$

Living in the Real World

A check register that carefully records account activity.

PROBLEM SOLVING

Reconciliation

If Margaret Miller's check register balance and adjusted bank statement don't agree, there's a problem. **(Example 2)** Ask students what they would tell Miller to look for to find the problem. **Answers will include making sure numbers were entered correctly, and checking that the addition and subtraction were computed correctly.**

CONCEPT CHECK

Complete the problems, then check your answers at the end of the chapter.

1.

Statement balance	$374.47
Outstanding checks	− 238.98
Outstanding deposits	+ 140.00
Adjusted balance	**$275.49**

2.

Statement balance	$772.33
Outstanding checks	− 283.75
Outstanding deposits	+ 427.75
Adjusted balance	**$916.33**

Example 2

Margaret Miller's check register balance is $2,261.50. She compares her statement and check register. For each check and deposit listed on her statement, she places a check mark next to the information in her register. She notes that the bank paid her $0.86 in interest. Miller finds these outstanding checks and deposits:

Check #525 $341.50   Check #527 $266.25   Deposit $709.75

How does Miller reconcile her statement?

STEP: Reconcile the balance.

Miller uses the reconciliation form on the back of her bank statement to reconcile her account.

Figure 4.11

Reconciliation Statement				
Check Register Balance	$2,261.50	Statement Balance		$2,160.36
Service Charges/ Fees		Outstanding Checks/ Payments/Debits		
		Check #525	$341.50	
Interest	+0.86	Check #527	266.25	
		(Total outstanding checks/payments/debits)		−607.75
		Outstanding Deposits/ Credits		
		Deposit	709.75	+709.75
New Balance	$2,262.36	Adjusted Balance		$2,262.36

2261.50 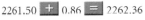 + 0.86 = 2262.36

341.50 + 266.25 M+ 2160.36 − RM = 607.75 =

1552.61 + 709.75 = 2262.36

CONCEPT CHECK

Complete the problems, then check your answers at the end of the chapter.

3. Asuko Naito's check register balance is $8,754.33. He compares his statement with his check register. He notes that the bank paid him $2.86 in interest and charged him $1.20 for bill payment fees. He finds these outstanding checks and deposits:

Check #845 $751.75   Check #847 $2,455.89   Deposit $805.14

Continued on next page

USING CALCULATORS

Reconciling your checking account is a process that contains a large amount of adding and subtracting. Using a calculator to perform these operations is of definite advantage in that it saves time. However, an error in entering numbers may cause an incorrect result. It is a good idea to go through the process of reconciling several times to ensure that the correct figures are used.

② TEACH

Make sure students understand the meaning of an *outstanding check* and an *outstanding deposit*. (Review that an outstanding check or deposit is one that hasn't yet been processed at the bank in time to appear on a person's bank statement.)

Many people don't subtract their monthly service charge until the bank statement arrives. Interest, also, may not be known until this time. Both need to be entered into the register to complete the records.

Point out that services are usually available at a bank to help someone having difficulty in reconciling his or her statement.

Motivating the Lesson

Your check register states that you have a balance of $286.46. Your bank statement arrives and indicates your balance is $315.46. What is the difference between the balance you have recorded in your check register and the balance indicated on the bank statement? **$29**

Your bank statement lists that you have cashed the following checks:

5/14	Check # 301	$61.32
5/17	Check # 302	$72.98
5/24	Check # 304	$81.55

You place a checkmark after each check in your check register that is listed as having been cashed on your bank statement. The last check you have written according to your check register is Check # 304. Which check number has not been cashed? **Check # 303**

2 TEACH (cont'd)

In-Class Examples
Find the adjusted balance.
1. Statement balance: $1708.43
   Outstanding checks: $185.29
   Outstanding deposits: $263.04
   Adjusted balance? **$1,786.18**
2. Statement balance: $841.92
   Outstanding checks: $338.60
   Outstanding deposits: $561.42
   Adjusted balance? **$1,064.74**
   Fill in the missing amounts.
   Then determine whether the register and statement balances agree.
3. Check register balance: $717.16
   Interest: $1.20
   Service charge/fees: 0
   New balance: **$718.36**
   Statement balance: $854.07
   Outstanding checks: $197.46
   Outstanding deposits: $61.75
   Adjusted balance: **$718.36**
   Do the register and statement balances agree? **Yes**

3 ASSESS

Error Analysis
If students are having difficulty reconciling a bank statement, break down the process into three major steps: finding the new check register balance, finding the adjusted balance, and comparing the new check register balance to the adjusted balance.

To find the new check register balance, have students add any interest earned to the balance in their check register. If there are any services charges or fees, have students subtract the amount from the check register balance. If the bank doesn't pay interest or charge fees, then the new check register balance will be the same as the old check register balance.

Reconcile the statement by filling in the blanks.

Figure 4.12

Reconciliation Statement			
Check Register Balance	$8,754.33	Statement Balance	$11,158.49
Service Charges/Fees	a. $1.20	Oustanding Checks/Payments/Debits	
		Check #845	$ 751.75
Interest	b. $2.86	Check #847	2,455.89
		(Total outstanding checks/payments/debits)	d. $3,207.64
		Outstanding Deposits/Credits	
		Deposit	805.14 e. $805.14
New Balance	c. $8,755.99	Adjusted Balance	f. $8,755.99

SECTION 4-5 PRACTICE

Complete the table. Do the register and statement balances agree?

4. $142.90; $142.90
5. $496.05; $496.05
6. $1,446.89; $1,446.89
7. $4,604.53; $4,604.53

	Check Register Balance	Interest	Service Charge/Fees	New Balance	Statement Balance	Outstanding Checks	Outstanding Deposits	Adjusted Balance
4.	$ 147.60	$ 0.00	$4.70	a.	$ 388.29	$345.39	$ 100.00	b.
5.	505.85	0.00	9.80	a.	507.21	132.90	121.74	b.
6.	1,439.76	7.13	0.00	a.	1,360.44	432.81	519.26	b.
7.	4,581.62	22.91	0.00	a.	1,328.66	421.99	3,697.86	b.

8. David Cassadore received his bank statement and cancelled checks for the period ending November 20. He compared the check register (**Figure 4.13a**) with the cancelled checks and deposits listed on the statement (**Figure 4.13b**), then placed a check mark next to the items processed. He reconciles the bank statement (**Figure 4.13c**).
   a. What total amount does he have in outstanding checks? **$44.89**
   b. What total amount does he have in outstanding deposits? **$191.37**
   c. What is his adjusted balance? **$794.83**
   d. What is his new check register balance? **$794.83**
   e. Do the register and adjusted balances agree? **Yes**

Figure 4.13a

Trans. Type or Check No.	Date	Description of Transaction	Payment/Debit (−)	✔	Deposit/Credit (+)	Balance
		Balance Brought Forward →				389 49
047	11/03	Country Pride	47 29	✓		342 20
	11/04	Deposit		✓	400 00	742 20
048	11/09	General Telephone Co.	37 35	✓		704 85
	11/15	Cash	50 00	✓		654 85
	11/20	Deposit			191 37	846 22
049	11/20	Consumer Power Co.	44 89			801 33

Figure 4.13b

Sky Bank						Monthly Statement		

David Cassadore

	Statement Period	Account Number
	10/20 through 11/20	83-30283

Date	Description	Amount
10/20	Previous Balance	389.49
	1 Deposit	400.00
	3 Withdrawals	134.64
	Service Charge/Fee	6.50
	Interest Earned	
11/20	Present Balance	648.35

CHECKS

Check	Date	Amount	Check	Date	Amount	Check	Date	Amount
047	11/03	47.29	048	11/09	37.35			

DEPOSITS/CREDITS			PAYMENTS/DEBITS		
Date	Amount	Description	Date	Amount	Description
11/04	400.00	Deposit	11/15	50.00	ATM Cash

DAILY BALANCE

Daily Balance		Daily Balance		Daily Balance		Daily Balance
10/20	389.49	11/04	742.20	11/15	654.85	
11/03	342.20	11/09	704.85	11/20	648.35	

Figure 4.13c

Reconciliation Statement				
Check Register Balance	$801.33	Statement Balance		$648.35
Service Charges/Fees	6.50	Oustanding Checks/Payments/Debits		
		Check #049	$ 44.89	
Interest	0.00			
		(Total outstanding checks/payments/debits)		a. $44.89
		Outstanding Deposits/Credits		
		Deposit	191.37	b. $191.37
New Balance	d.	Adjusted Balance		c. $794.83

d. $794.83

MAINTAINING YOUR SKILLS

Need Help? Go to...
► Skill 6: Subtracting Decimals, page 733

Subtract.

9. $412.30 − $1.25
$411.05

10. $219.63 − $2.50
$217.13

11. $96.78 − $3.00
$93.78

12. $349.82 − $116.78
$233.04

13. $491.60 − $247.83
$243.77

14. $127.80 − $64.92
$62.88

Section 4-5 Reconciling the Bank Statement ► **181**

WRAP-UP

Go over any problem for which a wrong answer is given.

Assignment Guide
Basic: 4–7
Average: 8

20 min.

SECTION 4-5

To find the adjusted balance, have students mark each check and deposit in the check register that appears on the bank statement. Then have them list and add up the amounts of all the checks in the check register that do not appear on the bank statement. This amount is the total of their outstanding checks. They also need to list and add up the amount of any deposits that do not appear on the bank statement. This amount is the total of their outstanding deposits. Subtract the outstanding checks from the statement balance. Then add the outstanding deposits. The answer is the adjusted balance.

Now have students compare the new check register balance to the adjusted balance. These amounts should agree. If they do, the checkbook is balanced. If not, students can review their addition and subtraction in the check register to find and correct any errors. Point out that an error in entering numbers may cause an incorrect result.

4 CLOSE

Closing Activity
1. $496.54 − $75.04 **$421.50**
2. $2316.19 $546.75 **$1,769.44**

Find the adjusted balance.
3. Statement balance: $1,088.66
   Outstanding checks: $227.21
   Outstanding deposits: $158.37
   Adjusted balance: **$1,019.82**

Find the adjusted balance. Then decide whether the register and statement balances agree.
4. Check register balance $315.93
   Interest: 0
   Service charge/fees: $1.50
   New balance: **$314.43**
   Statement balance: $395.85
   Outstanding checks: $121.13
   Outstanding deposits: $39.71
   Adjusted balance: **$314.43**
   Do the register and statement balances agree? **Yes**

181

National Standards for Business Education

Standard 1	Mathematical Foundations
Standard 2	Number Relationships and Operations

National Council of Teachers of Mathematics Standards

Standard 1	Numbers and Operations
Standard 4	Measurement
Standard 6	Problem Solving
Standard 8	Communication

1 FOCUS

Ask students what advantages online banking can provide for them. Point out that online banking allows an account holder the convenience of accessing their account information 24 hours a day, 7 days a week. They can transfer money between two or more accounts and pay bills without leaving their home. Online banking is made possible through an Internet connection.

In-Class Examples

Work through these exercises with students before having them do the Self-Check.

1. $4.95 + $0.50 + $6.00 + $25.00 **$36.45**
2. $8.95 + $.50 (10 − 3) + $2.00 + $1.00 **$15.45**
3. $10.00 + $0.75 (16 − 10) + $5.00 + $20.00 **$39.50**
4. $7.45 + $1.25 (14 − 5) + $15.00 + $4.50 + $30.00 **$68.20**
5. $2508.41 − $300.00 − $0.50 − $62.34 **$2,145.57**

SECTION 4·6 Online Banking

Section Objective

Compute online banking charges and update the check register.

Figure 4.14

It's 1 A.M. and you're dying to know your account balance. Or perhaps it's snowing out and you need to transfer some funds. **Online banking**, or Internet banking, allows you to bank from anywhere. All you need is a connection to the Internet, and you can access your account(s) round-the-clock, even on weekends.

Once you've logged onto your account at the online bank, you can:

- transfer funds from checking to savings or savings to checking,
- make loan payments from checking to loan accounts,
- make payments to third parties (such as utility companies),
- get information about account balances, previous deposits, previous withdrawals, and loan balances.

Online Banking Charges	
Service	**Fee**
Basic Monthly Charge	$ 6.95
Bill Payment—first 5 N/C	0.50
Printed Statement	4.00
Replace Lost Card	5.00
Overdraft	25.00
International Wire Transfer	20.00
ATM Transaction Charges	
Local Network	N/C
Regional Network Surcharge	1.00
National Network Surcharge	2.00
Out-of-Network Surcharge	3.00
Cash Advance—2.00% of Amt. $10.00 Max	

You may be charged a fee for these services. **Figure 4.14** shows some online banking charges.

Remember that:

$$\text{Total Fees} = \text{Basic Charge} + \text{Bill Payments} + \text{Statement} + \text{ATM Surcharge} + \text{Cash Advance Fee}$$

Living in the Real World

Fleet Footed Finances

Shopping Around Pinsky's boss has asked him to look into how Fleet Footed might pay less in bank service fees. Pinsky is a big fan of online banking—your account is available and live 24 hours a day, 7 days a week. He starts shopping around for rates and packages presented by online banks, and then presents his findings to his manager.

Draw Conclusions How might online banking affect Pinsky's knowledge of the money in Fleet Footed's bank account?

Continued on page 189

Living in the Real World

It provides Pinsky up-to-the-minute details on account activity and allows him to keep track of cleared checks and deposits.

COOPERATIVE LEARNING

Online Banking

Pairs of students research online banking and find two different banks. Students evaluate the banking services using criteria such as: Is this service designed for the individual or for business use? Are there cost savings compared with regular banking? What type of security is in place to protect the consumer? Pairs present a comparison of the online banks to the class.

Need Help? Go to...

► Workshop 18:
Reading Tables and
Charts, page 38
► Workshop 36:
Problem Solving
Strategy: Using
Simple Algebraic
Operations, page 74
► Workshop 30:
Problem Solving
Strategy: Identify-
ing Information,
page 62
► Application A:
Formulas, page 760
► Application B:
More Formulas,
page 761
► Application C:
Tables and Charts,
page 762

Example 1

Tiwana Gombash uses online banking. She pays the basic charge, 7 bills, plus she requests a printed statement. She also has ATM transactions, including 1 out-of-network, and a cash advance of $400.00. What are her total fees for the month?

STEP: Add the fees.

Basic Charge	+	Bill Payments	+	Statement	+	ATM Surcharge	+	Cash Advance Fee
$6.95	+	$0.50(7 − 5) +		$4.00	+	$3.00	+	(2% × $400)
$6.95	+	$1.00	+	$4.00	+	$3.00	+	$8.00

= $22.95 total fees

6.95 [M+] 0.50 [×] 2.00 [M+] 4.00 [M+] 3.00 [M+]

400.00 [×] 0.02 [M+] [MR] 22.95

1. Total Fees: $6.95 + $0.50(8 − 5) + $5.00 + (2 × $2.00) + (2 × $3.00) = $6.95 + $1.50 + $5.00 + $4.00 + $6.00 = $23.45

CONCEPT CHECK

SELF-CHECK✓

Complete the problems, then check your answers at the end of the chapter. Use Figure 4.14 on page 182 to compute the total fees.

1. Service: Basic charge, 8 bills paid, lost card replacement.
   ATM: 2 National, 2 Out-of-Network.

2. Service: Basic charge, 6 bills paid, 1 overdraft.
   ATM: 3 Regional, $500 advance.
   Total Fees: $6.95 + $0.50(6 − 5) + $25.00 + (3 × $1.00) + (2% × $500) = $6.95 + $0.50 + $25.00 + $3.00 + $10.00 = $45.45

When you bank online, you need to maintain a check register to keep a record of your finances. One feature of online banking is that you can download your current online transactions and put the information into a computer program (such as an Excel spreadsheet, Microsoft Money, or Quicken) that will contain a check register.

Example 2

On March 15, Tiwana Gombash uses online banking and downloads these transactions so she can put them on her spreadsheet where she keeps a check register. Note that the transactions since her last log on are shown.

Continued on next page

Section 4-6 Online Banking ► **183**

---

② TEACH

Point out that online banking services have various rates for specific services, such as withdrawing money from an ATM or automatically transferring money to pay monthly bills. Account holders can download their online transactions and record the information in an electronic check register, such as one found in a computer program spreadsheet.

Remind students that the balance changes in an electronic check register just as it does in a traditional checking account when a transaction is made. Account holders must periodically update their electronic register by recording electronic transactions. They add deposits and subtract payments just as they would in a traditional check register. Each month they'll also need to reconcile their electronic check register with their online statement or with a printed statement of transactions if one is requested.

THINKING CRITICALLY

Online Banking Survey

Students survey adults in their family to find out their feelings on online banking. Students should prepare a chart of their survey questions allowing space to record responses. Students may ask these questions and questions of their own: Do you feel that online banking is safe? **(Online banking is safer than sending a check in the mail. Most banks guarantee online bill payment.)** Do you like the idea of online banking? What do you like about online banking? What don't you like? Are you aware that credit unions and some banks often offer free online bill payments? Do you bank online? If so, does your bank charge for online banking?

2 TEACH (cont'd)

Motivating the Lesson
Your employer already automatically deposits your payroll check in your checking account, so you decide to try online banking. You begin with a balance of $275.00 in your account. Your bank is closed in the evenings, so you withdraw $100 from your account from an ATM and record it in your check register. Since you used an ATM in your local network, there is no fee. What is the balance in your checking account after you withdraw the money? **$175**

Figure 4.15

Date	Amount	Check Number	Description
03/06/20--	400.00		ATM Withdrawal
03/06/20--	2.00		ATM National Network Fee
03/15/20--	1661.57	+	Payee/Description: AT DEPOSIT Memo: COMPUTER INC. EDIPAYMENT 0555
03/15/20--	0.50		Memo: BILL PAYMENT FEE
03/15/20--	0.50		Memo: BILL PAYMENT FEE
03/15/20--	3341.29		CREDIT CARD PYMT TO 004:555-555 Online Payment
03/15/20--	100.00		FINDLAY YOUTH PYMT TO 009:W555 Online Payment
03/15/20--	30.55	1289	CHECK Memo: Food Town
03/15/20--	153.39		AT WITHDRAWAL Memo: INSURANCE 031202

Update the check register.

STEP: Compute the new balance.

Gombash had check number 1288 entered and started with a balance of $2,895.90 − $59.46 = $2,836.44. She subtracted the $400.00 ATM withdrawal and the $2.00 ATM fee. Then she added the payroll check and subtracted the other items. **The new balance is $469.78.**

Figure 4.16

			Check Register				
Trans. Type or Check No.	Date	Description of Transaction	Payment/ Debit (−)	✔	Deposit/ Credit (+)	Balance	
		Balance Brought Forward →				2,895	90
1288	12-Mar	Fabric Store	59 46			2,836	44
ATM	06-Mar	ATM withdrawal	400 00			2,436	44
ATM	06-Mar	ATM fee	2 00			2,434	44
AT	15-Mar	Computer Inc. Payroll			1,661 57	4,096	01
Online	15-Mar	Bill Payment Fee	0 50			4,095	51
Online	15-Mar	Bill Payment Fee	0 50			4,095	01
Online	15-Mar	Credit Card Pmt	3,341 29			753	72
Online	15-Mar	Findlay Youth Pmt	100 00			653	72
1289	15-Mar	Food Town	30 55			623	17
AT	15-Mar	Insurance Company	153 39			469	78

COMMUNICATION SKILLS

Internet Resources
There are many informative Internet resources on online banking. Have students try out online banking by going to the American Express site and choosing "Test Drive." Ask students to make a payment or make a transfer, use help, and print out a help screen. If the American Express site is not available, have students search using the search words: online banking advice. Students then choose one of the sites to investigate. Facilitate a discussion of students' findings.

CONCEPT CHECK

SELF-CHECK ✓

Complete the problems, then check your answers at the end of the chapter.

3. Tiwana Gombash (from Example 2) had these online transactions on April 1. Note that the balance is $871.78.

Figure 4.17

Date	Amount		Check Number	Description
04/01/20--	1661.57	+		Payee/Description: AT DEPOSIT Memo: COMPUTER INC. EDIPAYMENT 0555
04/01/20--	0.50			Memo: BILL PAYMENT FEE
04/01/20--	38.49			WIRELESS STORE TO 003:4555-555 ONLINE PAYMENT
04/01/20--	14.07		1290	CHECK Memo: Office Supply
04/01/20--	86.95			Payee/Description: AT WITHDRAWAL Memo: GAS OH SERV PYMT 031202

Complete the check register for these transactions.

Figure 4.18

Trans. Type or Check No.	Date	Description of Transaction	Payment/ Debit (−)	✔	Deposit/ Credit (+)	Balance
		Balance Brought Forward ➤				871 78
AT	01-Apr	Payroll			a. $1,661.57	b. $2,533.35
Online	01-Apr	Bill Payment Fee	c. $0.50			d. $2,532.85
Online	01-Apr	Wireless Service	e. $38.49			f. $2,494.36
1290	01-Apr	Office Equip.	g. $14.07			h. $2,480.29
AT	01-Apr	Gas Comp.	i. $86.95			j. $2,393.34

SECTION 4-6 PRACTICE

Use Figure 4.14 on page 182 to determine the total fees.

4. Service: Basic charge, 9 bills paid, lost card replacement.
   ATM: 3 National, 3 Out-of-Network. **$28.95**

5. Service: Basic charge, 8 bills paid, 1 overdraft.
   ATM: 3 Regional, $450 cash advance. **$45.45**

Continued on next page

Section 4-6 Online Banking ▶ **185**

In-Class Examples

Use **Figure 4.14** on page 182 to calculate the fees.

1. Service: basic charge, 18 bills, 1 overdraft.
   ATM: 4 national, 2 out of network, cash advance of $200. **$56.45**

2. Service: basic charge, 11 bills paid, printed statement, international wire transfer.
   ATM: 2 regional, 1 national, $700 cash advance online banking fee. **$51.95**

ASSESS

Error Analysis

Some of the problems in this section require students to use **Figure 4.14** to find and compute online banking charges. Be sure they're referring to the correct chart as they work through the problems. Remind them that in **Figure 4.14,** online account holders are only charged bill payment fees when they exceed five per month.

Many students may be unfamiliar with online banking. It may be helpful to review all items listed in the downloaded transactions contained in **Figure 4.15, 4.17, 4.19a,** and **4.20** before students work through the corresponding problems. Be certain they know which amounts must be added to the check register balance and which must be subtracted before they begin computing.

Remind students that a transfer from a savings account and an automatic payroll transfer are credits. Have students look for the *plus* sign which appears after the amount. This sign indicates that the amount should be added to the balance as the student updates the check register. Items such as ATM withdrawals and credit card payments are withdrawals and should be subtracted from the balance.

6. On June 15 Benton Andrews uses First USA online banking and downloads these transactions so he can put them on his spreadsheet where he keeps a check register. Use **Figure 4.19a** to complete the check register for the transactions on **Figure 4.19b.**

Figure 4.19a

Date	Amount		Check Number	Description
06/01/20--	6.95			Online Banking Basic Charge
06/05/20--	250.00			ATM Withdrawal
06/12/20--	5,850.00	+		AT DEPOSIT Memo: Transfer from Savings Act. 066555
06/15/20--	0.50			Memo: BILL PAYMENT FEE No. 6
06/15/20--	0.50			Memo: BILL PAYMENT FEE No. 7
06/15/20--	557.86			Credit Card PYMT TO 008-555-555 Online Payment
06/15/20--	35.00			Fair Board Trophy PYMT TO 002:W6555 Online Payment
06/15/20--	85.55		789	CHECK Memo: Food
06/15/20--	853.39			AT WITHDRAWAL Memo: Real Estate Taxes

Figure 4.19b

a. $6.95
b. $1,568.04
c. $250.00
d. $1,318.04
e. $5,850.00
f. $7,168.04
g. $0.50
h. $7,167.54
i. $0.50
j. $7,167.04
k. $557.86
l. $6,609.18
m. $35.00
n. $6,574.18
o. $85.55
p. $6,488.63
q. $853.39
r. $5,635.24

Check Register						
Trans. Type or Check No.	Date	Description of Transaction	Payment/ Debit (−)	✔	Deposit/ Credit (+)	Balance
				Balance Brought Forward ➤		1,574 99
Bank Charge	01-June	Online Basic Charge	a.			b.
ATM	05-June	ATM Withdrawal	c.			d.
AT	15-June	Transfer from Savings			e.	f.
Online	15-June	Bill Payment Fee	g.			h.
Online	15-June	Bill Payment Fee	i.			j.
Online	15-June	Credit Card Payment	k.			l.
Online	15-June	Fair Board Trophy	m.			n.
789	15-June	Food	o.			p.
AT	15-June	Real Estate Taxes	q.			r.

7. **Figure 4.20** shows George Kaquatosh's end-of-month bank statement. Notice the last activity is at the top of the list. *Start at the bottom of the list* and calculate the balance for each date shown.

Figure 4.20

	National City—Online Banking			
	Account: Checking 555-561-663			**ACTIVITY**
	Date	**Amount**	**Check**	**Description**
$800.92 **d.**	01-Apr	?		Balance
	01-Apr	$ 6.95		Online Banking Fee
	31-Mar	78.94	5174	
	31-Mar	25.00	5172	
	31-Mar	321.20		Debit Card, Dept. Store—Point-of-Sale Purchase
	31-Mar	172.73	5167	
	31-Mar	24.95	5170	
	31-Mar	252.70	5161	
	31-Mar	147.80		AT—American Electric Power
$1,831.19 **c.**	31-Mar	?		Balance
	20-Mar	150.00		ATM Withdrawal
	20-Mar	2.00		ATM National Network Chg.
	20-Mar	0.50		Bill Payment Fee No. 8
	20-Mar	1,095.73		Household Credit Online Pmt. 200-55-5555
	20-Mar	65.32	5165	
	20-Mar	495.72	5166	
$3,640.46 **b.**	20-Mar	?		Balance
	19-Mar	2,458.50	"+"	AT—Payroll MSNBC Inc.
	19-Mar	45.62		Debit Card, Joe's Pizza—Point-of-Sale Purchase
	19-Mar	0.50		Bill Payment Fee No. 7
	19-Mar	365.89		Commercial Truck Plate—Online Pmt.
$1,593.97 **a.**	19-Mar	?		Balance
	10-Mar	0.50		Bill Payment Fee No. 6
	10-Mar	468.52		Credit Card Pmt.
	10-Mar	300.00		ATM Withdrawal
	10-Mar	3.00		ATM Out of Network Charge
	01-Mar	2,365.99		Balance

MAINTAINING YOUR SKILLS

Need Help? Go to...
➤ Skill 6: Subtracting Decimals, page 733
➤ Skill 5: Adding Decimals, page 732

Subtract.

8. $9,887.89 − $23.61 **$9,864.28**

9. $16,246.64 − $887.35 **$15,359.29**

10. $564,648.50 − $1,568.39
       $563,080.11

11. $942.35 − $58.28 **$884.07**

Add.

12. $568.35 + $98.23 **$666.58**

13. $89,564.89 + $85.21 **$89,650.10**

14. $791.29 + $54.68 **$845.97**

15. $231.31 + $50.00 **$281.31**

④ CLOSE

Closing Activity
1. $8.95 + $5.00 + $35.00 + $9.68 **$58.63**
2. $7,641.88 − $4,360.55 **$3,281.33**
   Use **Figure 4.14** for online banking fees.
3. Service: basic charge, 6 bills, printed statement
   ATM: 3 regional, 1 national, 1 out of network, cash advance of $1,500. **$29.45**

WRAP-UP

Go over any problem for which a wrong answer is given.

Assignment Guide
  Basic: 4–5
Average: 6

20 min.

Quick Quiz

Find the total deposit.

1. Checks: $382.21 and $170.49
   Cash: 6 one-dollar bills, 4 five-dollar bills, 8 ten-dollar bills, 12 quarters, 38 dimes, and 54 nickels.
   $668.20

2. Christine Abernathy had a balance of $526.30 in her checking account on April 30. On May 1, her payroll check of $994.06 was electronically deposited in her account. On May 2, she withdrew $420.00 in cash and wrote a check for $71.75. What is her new balance after these three transactions? **$1,028.61**

3. Statement balance: $808.47
   Outstanding checks: $171.62
   Outstanding deposits: $453.14
   Adjusted balance: **$1,089.99**

4. Check register balance: $3,290.71
   Interest: $6.86
   Service charge/fee: 0
   New balance: **$3,297.57**
   Statement balance: $3,485.28
   Outstanding checks: $294.05
   Outstanding deposits: $106.34
   Adjusted balance: **$3,297.57**
   Do the register balance and statement balance agree? **Yes**

Use **Figure 4.14** on page 182 to find the total of the online banking fees.

5. Service: basic charge, 12 bills, 1 printed statement, 1 overdraft.
   ATM: 1 out of network, 1 cash advance of $700.
   $52.45

SECTION (4-1) CONCEPT CHECK (p. 167)

1. ($60.00 + $0.90 + $14.00) = **$74.90**

2. ($45.00 + $80.00) − $20.00 = **$105.00**

3. Checks: $231.09 + $987.67 = $1,218.76
   Cash: $9.00 + (9 × $5 = $45) + (8 × $10 = $80) = $134.00
   Coins: (14 × 0.25 = $3.50) + (25 × $0.10 = $2.50) + (18 × $0.05 = $0.90) + ($0.64) = $7.54
   Total: $1,218.76 + $134.00 + $7.54 = $1,360.30 − $40.00 = **$1,320.30**

4. Checks: $341.79 + $17.96 = $359.75
   Cash: $35.00 + (17 × $5 = $85) + (44 × $10 = $440) = $560.00
   Coins: (54 × 0.25 = $13.50) + (36 × $0.10 = $3.60) + (32 × $0.05 = $1.60) + ($0.21) = $18.91
   Total: $359.75 + $560.00 + $18.91 = **$938.66**

SECTION (4-2) CONCEPT CHECK (p. 169, 170)

1. Twenty-six and $\frac{55}{100}$ dollars
2. One hundred fifty-six and $\frac{92}{100}$ dollars
3. $30.20
4. $3,256.23
5. Harry's Hardware
6. One hundred sixty-five and $\frac{52}{100}$ dollars
7. Drill press
8. Manuel Romeo

SECTION (4-3) CONCEPT CHECK (p. 172, 173)

1. $1,471.79; $1,436.51
2. $947.51; $1,086.35
3. $1,515.46; $487.26
4. $680.57; $819.41

SECTION (4-4) CONCEPT CHECK (p. 176, 177)

1. $257.80
2. $63.40
3. $307.55
4. $758.82

SECTION (4-5) CONCEPT CHECK (p. 179, 180)

1. $275.49
2. $916.33
3. a. $1.20   b. $2.86
   c. $8,755.99   d. $3,207.64
   e. $805.14   f. $8,755.99

SECTION (4-6) CONCEPT CHECK (p. 183, 185)

1. Total Fees: $6.95 + $0.50(8 − 5) + $5.00 + (2 × $2.00) + (2 × $3.00)
   = $6.95 + $1.50 + $5.00 + $4.00 + $6.00 = **$23.45**

2. Total Fees: $6.95 + $0.50(6 − 5) + $25.00 + (3 × $1.00) + (2% × $500)
   = $6.95 + $0.50 + $25.00 + $3.00 + $10.00 = **$45.45**

3. a. $1,661.57   b. $2,533.35   c. $0.50   d. $2,532.85
   e. $38.49   f. $2,494.36   g. $14.07   h. $2,480.29
   i. $86.95   j. $2,393.34

Living in the Real World

Fleet Footed Finances

Review Keeping a close eye on your checking account balance keeps you "in check," and it makes you a smart consumer. When you're aware of how much you've got to spend, you'll start to spend more wisely and choose things you need and can afford, as opposed to what you want.

Now that you've read about Fleet Footed's situation, answer these questions as they pertain to your life.

1 Calculating. Ask your family if you can be in charge of calculating and reconciling the family checking account for two months. Each day, record in the check register checks, transferred funds, and deposits. Then calculate the balance. When the monthly statement arrives, reconcile it with the balance in the check register. If there is a discrepancy, try to figure out why.

2 Researching. Call your local bank and find out what happens when a bank customer bounces a check. Must a deposit be posted by mid-afternoon to be recorded as deposited on that day? What about a withdrawal? Has the speed of electronic banking affected the number of overdrawn accounts? What happens if someone chronically overdraws his or her account? Does the bank take some kind of action? Does it affect the customer's credit rating?

Living in the Real World

1. Answers will vary.
2. Answers will vary, but make sure students thoroughly interview a bank employee regarding these questions. It's important to know how a bank penalizes you if you bounce a check. This is important for good personal financial literacy.

REVIEW OF KEY WORDS

automatic teller machine (ATM) (p. 166)
personal identification number (PIN) (p. 166)
deposit (p. 166)

check register (p. 172)
balance (p. 172)
reconcile (p. 178)
online banking (p. 182)

checking account (p. 169)
check (p. 169)
bank statement (p. 175)
service charge (p. 175)

Match one of the key words above with a definition below.

1. to obtain agreement between two financial records by accounting for outstanding items. **reconcile**
2. the amount of money that you put into an account. **deposit**
3. the amount of money in your account. **balance**
4. a written order directing the bank to deduct money from your checking account to make a payment. **check**
5. a record prepared by the bank listing all transactions the bank has recorded. **bank statement**

6. a type of account that allows you to pay for goods and services with a written order instead of cash. **checking account**
7. the ledger where you record the deposits you made and the checks you've written.
8. a fee charged by the bank for handling your account. **service charge**
9. an electronic process of paying bills while connected to the Internet. **online banking**
7. **check register**

Skills and Concepts

SECTION OBJECTIVE 4-1 AND EXAMPLES

Compute the total checking account deposit.

Robin Jenkins deposited currency totaling $119.00 and coins totaling $12.36. She also deposited a check for $532.19. What was her total deposit?

STEP: Compute the total checking account deposit.

(Currency + Coins + Checks) − Cash Received

$119.00 + $12.36 + $532.19   = **$663.55 total deposit**

REVIEW EXERCISES

10. Christopher Cummings deposited a check for $86.55 and a check for $387.44. He received $75.00 in cash. What was his total deposit? **$86.55 + $387.44 − $75.00 = $398.99**

11. Achak Akule has a check for $256.00 and a check for $194.55. He would like to deposit the checks and receive 3 ten-dollar bills, 7 one-dollar bills, 8 quarters, and 3 dimes. What is his total deposit? **$256.00 + $194.55 − $39.30 = $411.25**

12. You deposit the following in your checking account: 13 one-dollar bills, 8 five-dollar bills, 11 half-dollars, 18 quarters, 109 dimes, 63 nickels, 12 pennies, and a check for $25.66. What is your total deposit? **$102.83**

13. You deposit a check for $287.66 and one for $873.55 in your checking account. You would like to receive 3 ten-dollar bills, 4 one-dollar bills, 16 quarters, and 13 dimes. What is your total deposit? **$1,121.91**

SECTION OBJECTIVE 4-2 AND EXAMPLES

Write a check.

STEP: Write $403.98 in words as it would appear on a check.

Four hundred three and $\frac{98}{100}$ dollars

REVIEW EXERCISES

14. Carla Caputo wrote a check to Archer's Grocery Store in the amount of $57.02. Write the amount of the check in words with cents expressed as a fraction of a dollar. **Fifty-seven and $\frac{02}{100}$ dollars**

15. Keisha Jackson wrote a check to Greenstone Electric in the amount of $123.45. Write the amount of the check in words with cents expressed as a fraction of a dollar. **One hundred twenty-three and $\frac{45}{100}$ dollars**

Write each amount in word form as it would appear on a check. Some amounts might require that the cents be expressed as a fraction of a dollar.

16. $845.00 **Eight hundred forty-five and $\frac{00}{100}$ dollars**

17. $54.33 **Fifty-four and $\frac{33}{100}$ dollars**

18. $13,586.16 **Thirteen thousand five hundred eighty-six and $\frac{16}{100}$ dollars**

19. $387.21 **Three hundred eighty-seven and $\frac{21}{100}$ dollars**

REINFORCEMENT

Section 4–1

1. Emmett and Kaye Foster deposit their paychecks at an ATM location. They have checks of $687.34 and $591.82. They receive $350.00 in cash. What is their total deposit? **$929.16**

Section 4-2

On December 1, Rachel Collins bought a digital camera at Bob's Electronics. The cost was $359.21. She wrote a check to pay for the camera. Answer the following questions about the check.

1. What should be written in the date portion of the check? **12-01**

2. Who is the check payable to? **Bob's Electronics**

3. How do you write the amount in word form? **three hundred fifty-nine and $\frac{21}{100}$**

SECTION OBJECTIVE 4-3 AND EXAMPLES

Figure out the balance in a check register.

Harrison Rohen's checkbook balance was $376.22 on May 25. His check register shows the transactions since. What is his balance after each transaction?

STEP: Figure out the balance.

New Balance = Previous Balance − Check Amount

New Balance = Previous Balance + Deposit Amount

Check Register						
Trans. Type or Check No.	Date	Description of Transaction	Payment/ Debit (−)	✔	Deposit/ Credit (+)	Balance
		Balance Brought Forward ➤				376 22
234	6/27	ABC Cable TV	34 12			a.
235	6/28	Water Company	15 77			b.
	6/28	Deposit			776 50	c.
236	6/29	Carolina Apt.	540 00			d.

a. $342.10   b. $326.33   c. $1,102.83   d. $562.83

REVIEW EXERCISES

Find the new balance after each check or deposit.

Check Register			
Payment/ Debit (−)	✔	Deposit/ Credit (+)	Balance
Balance Brought Forward ➤			398 12
20. 112 21			$285.91
21.		186 34	$472.25
22. 28 27			$443.98
23. 129 11			$314.87

SECTION OBJECTIVE 4-4 AND EXAMPLES

Calculate the present balance on a checking account bank statement.

Kippen Carter received his checking account statement and cancelled checks for July. His previous balance was $966.51. What is his present balance?

STEP: Calculate the new balance.

$$\frac{\text{Previous}}{\text{Balance}} + \frac{\text{Deposits}}{\text{Recorded}} - \frac{\text{Checks}}{\text{Paid}} - \frac{\text{Service}}{\text{Charge}} + \text{Interest}$$

Continued on next page

REINFORCEMENT

Section 4-3

1. Your balance is $225.36 on June 9. AT deposit of $164.55 on June 11. Write a check for $73.96 on June 13. ATM withdrawal of $100.00 on June 16. What is your new balance? **$215.95**

2. Your balance is $189.47 on June 23. Write a check for $41.95 on June 24. Write a check for $64.82 on June 26. AT deposit of paycheck for $228.34 on June 29. What is your new balance? **$311.04**

3. Tyler Hayman's checking account had a balance of $1,486.43. On May 28 he wrote a check for $127.58. On June 1, the bank made an automatic transfer (AT) of $925 to pay his rent. What is the new balance in Hayman's account after these two transactions? **$433.85**

Checks and Other Charges			Deposits and Credits		Balance
Date	Number	Amount	Date	Amount	
7/06	213	$712.90	7/08	$112.54	
7/14	214	34.29	7/15	459.96	
			Interest	1.29	
Service Charge		5.60	Deposit	572.50	

$966.51 + \$572.50 - \$747.19 - \$5.60 + \$1.29 = $ **$787.51 present balance**

REVIEW EXERCISES

24. Berta Varblow received her checking account statement and cancelled checks for November. Her previous balance was $851.97. What is her present balance? **$891.53**

Checks and Other Charges			Deposits and Credits		Balance
Date	Number	Amount	Date	Amount	
3/17	333	$ 34.55	3/18	$259.00	
3/18	334	123.44	3/20	102.00	
3/22	335	210.00	3/21	50.00	
Service Charge		3.45			

	Previous Balance	Total Deposits	Total Checks	Service Charge	Interest	Present Balance
25.	$405.80	$ 76.13	$ 300.00	$5.00	$0.00	**$176.93**
26.	187.90	1,200.99	456.66	0.00	2.23	**$934.46**
27.	73.66	1,395.44	123.99	2.45	1.96	**$1,344.62**
28.	755.32	231.33	878.66	2.50	2.88	**$108.37**

SECTION OBJECTIVE 4-5 AND EXAMPLES

Reconcile a check register with a bank account statement.

STEP: Calculate the adjusted balance.

Statement Balance − Outstanding Checks + Outstanding Deposits

---

REINFORCEMENT

Section 4-4

1. Steve Cabrera received his bank statement for April. His previous balance was $740.16. His total deposits for the month were $655.37. His total withdrawals were $1,108.29. What is his present balance? **$287.24**

2. Marcella Dorgan received her bank statement for March. Her previous balance was $216.40. Her total deposits were $1,541.58. Her total withdrawals are $1,365.31. Her bank charges a monthly service fee of $3.50. What is her present balance? **$389.17**

3. Hallie Hunter looks over her April bank statement. Her previous balance was $674.26. Her total deposits for the month were $850.54. Her total withdrawals were $1,042.33. Her interest for the month is $1.68. What is her present balance? **$484.15**

Check Register Balance	$4,561.20	$357.99
Interest	6.59	2.33
Service Charge	5.05	2.15
New Balance	a.	c.
Statement Balance	3,987.00	476.35
Outstanding Checks	75.74	435.18
Outstanding Deposits	651.48	317.00
Adjusted Balance	b.	d.

a. $4,561.20 + $6.59 − $5.05 = **$4,562.74**

b. $3,987.00 − $75.74 + $651.48 = **$4,562.74**

c. $357.99 + $2.33 − $2.15 = **$358.17**

d. $476.35 − $435.18 + $317.00 = **$358.17**

REVIEW EXERCISES

Complete the table.

	Check Register Balance	Interest	Service Charge	New Balance	Statement Balance	Outstanding Checks	Outstanding Deposits	Adjusted Balance
29.	$176.55	$0.00	$4.34	**$172.21**	—	—	—	—
30.	525.79	0.00	5.05	**$520.74**	—	—	—	—
31.	—	—	—	—	$477.09	$404.93	$100.05	**$172.21**
32.	—	—	—	—	306.55	129.65	343.84	**$520.74**

SECTION OBJECTIVE 4-6 AND EXAMPLES

Compute online banking charges and update the check register.

Hasheem Warren uses online banking. Last month, Hasheem had these charges: basic charge of $7.50, 8 service charges at $0.50 each, and $4.00 for a printed statement. Hasheem also had ATM fees of $3.00 for out-of-network use and a cash advance fee of 2 percent of $300. What are the total fees?

STEP: Add the fees.

Basic Charge + Bill Payments + Statement + ATM Surcharge + Cash Advance Fee

$7.50 + (8 × $0.50) + $4.00 + $3.00 + (0.02 × $300)

= $7.50 + $4.00 + $4.00 + $3.00 + $6.00

= **$24.50 total fees**

REVIEW EXERCISES

33. Tula Woods uses online banking. Last month Woods had these charges: basic charge of $6.95, 7 service charges at $0.50 each, and $5.00 to replace a lost card. Woods also had ATM fees of $4.00 for out-of-network use and a cash advance fee of 2 percent of $200. What are the total fees? **$23.45**

34. Rufus Collier uses Savings and Loan online banking. Last month Collier had these charges: basic charge of $7.95, 6 service charges at $0.70 each, and $25.00 for an overdraft charge. He also had ATM fees of $2.00 for using the regional network and a cash advance fee of 2.5 percent of $400. What are the total fees? **$49.15**

REINFORCEMENT

Section 4-5

Fill in the missing amounts. Then determine whether the register and statement balances agree.

1. Check register balance: $2,358.14
   Interest: 0
   Service charge/fees: $7.30
   New balance: **$2,350.84**
   Statement balance: $2,781.09
   Outstanding checks: $680.22
   Outstanding deposits: $249.97
   Adjusted balance: **$2,350.84**
   Do the register and statement balances agree? **Yes**

Section 4-6

1. Use **Figure 4.14** to determine the online banking fee.
   Service: basic charge, 10 bills paid, lost card replacement.
   ATM: 4 regional, 1 out of network, 2 cash advances for $350 and $275.
   Online banking fee? **$33.95**

Section Objectives	National Standards for Business Education					
	1. Mathematical Foundations	2. Number Relationships and Operations	3. Patterns, Functions, and Algebra	4. Measurements	5. Statistics and Probability	6. Problem-Solving Applications
5-1 Deposits (pp. 196–198) Complete a savings account deposit slip, and compute the total deposit.	X	X				
5-2 Withdrawals (pp. 199–201) Fill out a savings account withdrawal slip.	X	X				
5-3 Account Statements (pp. 202–204) Compute the new balance on a savings account statement.	X	X				
5-4 Simple Interest (pp. 205–207) Calculate simple interest.	X	X				
5-5 Compound Interest (pp. 208–210) Figure out the compound interest and the amount.	X	X				
5-6 Compund Interest Tables (pp. 211–213) Find compound interest using tables.	X	X				
5-7 Daily Compunding (pp. 214–216) Find interest for daily compounding.	X	X				
5-8 Annuities (pp. 217–219) Compute the future value of an ordinary annuity and an annuity due.	X	X				

(Source: Reprinted with permission from the National Standards for Business Education, copyright © 2001 by National Business Education Association, 1914 Association Drive, Reston, Virginia 21901-1596)

SCANS Correlation

Foundation Skills

Basic Skills	Reading	Writing	Math	Listening	Speaking	
Thinking Skills	Creative Thinking	Decision Making	Problem Solving	Seeing Things in the Mind's Eye	Knowing How to Learn	Reasoning
Personal Qualities	Responsibility	Self-Esteem	Sociability	Self-Management	Integrity/Honesty	

This chapter's highlighted blocks indicate the chapter's content coverage in the Student Edition and the Teacher Wraparound Edition.

National Council of Teachers of Mathematics Standards

1. Numbers & Operations	2. Algebra	3. Geometry	4. Measurement	5. Data Analysis & Probability	6. Problem Solving	7. Reasoning & Proof	8. Communication	9. Connections	10. Representations
X			X		X		X		X
X			X				X	X	
X			X		X		X	X	
X			X		X		X	X	
X			X		X		X	X	
X			X		X		X	X	
X			X		X		X	X	
X			X		X		X	X	

SCANS Correlation

Workplace Competencies

Resources	Allocating Time	Allocating Money	Allocating Material and Facility Resources	Allocating Human Resources		
Information	Acquiring and Evaluating Information	Organizing and Maintaining Information	Interpreting and Communicating Information	Using Computers to Process Information		
Interpersonal Skills	Participating as a Member of a Team	Teaching Others	Serving Clients/Customers	Exercising Leadership	Negotiating to Arrive at a Decision	Working with Cultural Diversity
Systems	Understanding Systems	Monitoring and Correcting Performance	Improving and Designing Systems			
Technology	Selecting Technology	Applying Technology to Task	Maintaining and Troubleshooting Technology			

What You'll Learn

In this chapter you'll focus on savings accounts—how to manage deposits and withdrawals and how savings accounts earn you money by earning interest.

Why It's Important

Having a savings account in a federally insured institution provides you with the opportunity to save money, earn interest, and the security of knowing that your money will be there when you need it. An important factor in choosing the type of savings account is how often the interest is calculated. Knowing which type of interest calculation provides the optimal interest can assist you in deciding what institution will suit your financial needs.

Key Word Review
Ask Questions

Studies show that one of the best ways to learn is to ask questions. Give fourteen 3″ by 5″ cards to each student. For each key word, have students write a question using the key word on one side of a card. Instruct students to use the Glossary or the text to write the answer on the back of the card.

CHAPTER 5
Savings Accounts

What You'll Learn

Section 5-1 Complete a savings account deposit slip, and compute the total deposit.

Section 5-2 Fill out a savings account withdrawal slip.

Section 5-3 Compute the new balance on a savings account statement.

Section 5-4 Calculate simple interest.

Section 5-5 Figure out the compound interest and the amount.

Section 5-6 Find compound interest using tables.

Section 5-7 Find interest for daily compounding.

Section 5-8 Compute the future value of an ordinary annuity and an annuity due.

When Will You Ever Use This?

Want a better life than the one you're living? Achieving your dreams will take hard work and money. Although the hard work takes dedication, so does saving money. To accomplish your future goals, you've got to have money. Saving money is a crucial step to living a financially free life.

Key Words to Know

- savings account
- deposit
- withdrawal
- account statement
- interest
- simple interest
- principal
- annual interest rate
- compound interest
- daily compounding
- annuity
- ordinary annuity
- annuity due

Mathematics Online

To learn more about savings accounts, visit the *Mathematics with Business Applications* Web site at www.busmath.glencoe.com.

CLASSROOM RESOURCES

Application and Enrichment
- *Teacher Wraparound Edition*
- *Teacher Resource Binder, Blackline Masters*
- *Interactive Lesson Planner CD-ROM*
- *PowerPoint® Presentations CD-ROM*

Review and Enforcement
- Mathematics Online
  www.busmath.glencoe.com
- *Teacher Resource Binder, Internet Resources*

- *Student Activity Workbook*
- *Student Activity Workbook, Teacher Annotated Edition*
- *School-to-Home Activity Workbook*

Assessment and Evaluation
- *Assessment Binder, Reproducible Tests*
- *Assessment Binder, Alternative Assessment Strategies*
- **ExamView® Pro Test Generator** CD-ROM

For the Teacher
- *Student Activity Workbook, Teacher Annotated Edition*
- *Assessment Binder*
- *Interactive Lesson Planner CD-ROM*
- *Teacher Resource Binder*
- Mathematics Online
  www.busmath.glencoe.com

For the Student
- *Student Activity Workbook*
- *School-to-Home Activity Workbook*

Living in the Real World

Understanding the Williams Sisters

Jaydene Williams has offered to drive her 10-year-old sister, Aisha, to their State Bank. Aisha is going to open her first savings account today. To earn money, she has been doing extra work around the house—raking leaves and washing windows. Read how this sibling twosome tackles the process of starting a savings account.

Read on. Go to . . .

195

Living in the Real World

Story's Summary

Ten-year-old Aisha Williams is ready to open her first savings account. Her older sister Jaydene drives her to the bank. She teaches Aisha about withdrawal and deposit slips, statements, and simple interest. After reaching the teller window of Mr. Gleason, he further educates Aisha, showing her an account statement and explaining compound interest. Jaydene does a bit of banking herself during their visit, adding an annuity to her savings account.

Did You Know...

The United States opened its first bank in 1871, established in Philadelphia, Pennsylvania, and named the Bank of North America.

Think about This

What are the benefits to keeping your money in a savings account, rather than hidden in a safe or somewhere in your home?

LOCAL STANDARDS

National Standards for Business Education

Standard 1	Mathematical Foundations
Standard 2	Number Relationships and Operations

National Council of Teachers of Mathematics Standards

Standard 1	Numbers and Operations
Standard 4	Measurement
Standard 6	Problem Solving
Standard 8	Communication
Standard 10	Representations

① FOCUS

Ask students if any of them have a savings account. For those who do, ask them if they have a plan for saving—say 10 percent of any money received, $5 every time money is received, and so on. This lesson deals with how to make a deposit to a savings account.

In-Class Examples

Work through these exercises with students before having them do the Self-Check.

1. $97.40 + $22.35 **$119.75**
2. $71.50 + $142.93 **$214.43**
3. $356.90 + $146.20 − $50 **$453.10**
4. $161.81 + $39.47 − $40 **$161.28**
5. $1,520.61 + $149.93 + $99.02 − $50 **$1,719.56**

○ **Section Objective**

Complete a savings account deposit slip, and compute the total deposit.

SECTION 5-1 Deposits

To open a **savings account**, which is a special bank account that earns interest, you must make a **deposit**. A deposit is the money you give the bank to hold in your savings account. Each time you make a deposit, it is added to your account's balance. To do this you fill out a savings account deposit slip to record currency, coins, and checks that you are depositing. If you want to receive cash back, subtract the amount from the subtotal to find the total deposit amount.

Total Deposit = (Currency + Coins + Checks) − Cash Received

Living in the Real World

Understanding the Williams Sisters

Earning Money for Your Account Jaydene has explained to her sister that a savings account actually earns money for the account owner. "The bank takes all the money people put into it and invests it by making mortgage loans, car loans, buying government securities, and loaning it to other banks. It earns money for the bank, and the bank shares some of that extra money with its customers."

Draw Conclusions If you deposited $100 into a savings account with 2.3 percent interest, what would be your total balance at the end of the year?

Continued on page 199

Need Help? Go to...

➤ Workshop 4: Adding Decimals, page 10

➤ Workshop 5: Subtracting Decimals, page 12

Example 1

Gustavo Barrera has a check for $145.58 and a check for $47.51. He also has 14 one-dollar bills. He would like to receive $20 in cash and deposit the rest of the money in his savings account. What is the total deposit?

STEP: Compute the total deposit.

(Currency + Coins + Checks) − Cash Received
($14.00 + $145.58 + $47.51) − $20.00 =
$207.09 − $20.00 = **$187.09 total deposit**

CONCEPT CHECK

SELF-CHECK✓

Complete the problems, then check your answers at the end of the chapter. Find the total deposit.

1. ($160.00 + $10.95 + $114.35) − $25.00 = **$285.30 − $25.00 = $260.30**

2. ($125.60 + $180.00 + $22.21) − $20.00 = **$327.81 − $20.00 = $307.81**

Living in the Real World

$102.30

Example 2

Robert Cassidy wants to deposit the following into his savings account: 28 one-dollar bills, 8 five-dollar bills, 24 quarters, 35 dimes, 90 pennies, a check for $29.34, and a check for $124.19. He wants to receive a fifty-dollar bill in cash. How much will he deposit?

Figure 5.1

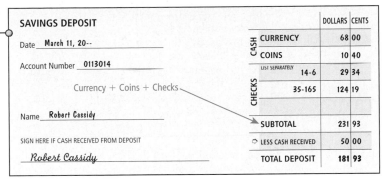

SAVINGS DEPOSIT		DOLLARS	CENTS
Date __March 11, 20--__	CASH CURRENCY	68	00
	COINS	10	40
Account Number __0113014__	CHECKS LIST SEPARATELY 14-6	29	34
	35-165	124	19
Currency + Coins + Checks →			
Name __Robert Cassidy__			
	→ SUBTOTAL	231	93
SIGN HERE IF CASH RECEIVED FROM DEPOSIT	↻ LESS CASH RECEIVED	50	00
Robert Cassidy	TOTAL DEPOSIT	181	93

STEP: Compute the total deposit.

The currency deposit: $28 + (8 \times \$5) =$
$$\$28 + \quad \$40 \quad = \$68$$

The coins deposit: $(24 \times \$0.25) + (35 \times \$0.10) + \$0.90 =$
$$\$6.00 \quad + \quad \$3.50 \quad + \ 0.90 \ = \$10.40$$

$$\$68.00 + \$10.40 + \$29.34 + \$124.19 - \$50.00 = \$181.93 \text{ total deposit}$$

CONCEPT CHECK

SELF-CHECK ✓

Complete the problem, then check your answer at the end of the chapter. Find the total deposit.

3. Checks: $152.54 and $147.46.
   Cash: 54 one-dollar bills, 12 five-dollars, 6 ten-dollar bills, 35 quarters, 18 dimes, 40 nickels, and 75 pennies. Less a fifty-dollar bill as cash received.

$152.54 + $147.46 = $300.00; $54.00 + (12 \times \$5) + (6 \times \$10) = \$54 + \$60 + \$60 - \$174$;
$(35 \times \$0.25) + (18 \times \$0.10) + (40 \times \$0.05) + \$0.75 = \$8.75 + \$1.80 + \$2.00 + \$0.75 = \$13.30$;
$0.75 + $300 + $174 + $13.30 = $487.30 - $50 = $437.30

SECTION 5-1 PRACTICE

Find the subtotal and total deposit.

4. Guadalupe Garcia wants to deposit $74.00 in cash and a check for $124.17. **$198.17**

5. Ernest McMahon deposits $73.23 in cash and $3.95 in coins. **$77.18**

6. Kenneth Hal deposits a check for $335.28, another check for $61.88, and $90 in cash. **$487.16**

7. Zina Templeton deposits a check for $823.40, a check for $29.50, and $50 in cash. **$902.90**

Continued on next page

SECTION 5-1

② TEACH

Many banks require a minimum initial deposit in order to open a savings account. After that any amount may be deposited. There is usually a minimum balance that is required in order to earn interest. Mention that if cash is to be received at the time of making the deposit, most banks require the depositor to sign the deposit slip.

Motivating the Lesson

You've been saving your money to buy a guitar. You have 3 ten-dollar bills, 8 five-dollar bills, and 26 one-dollar bills. You also have 47 quarters, 105 dimes, 62 nickels, and 149 pennies. In addition, you have a check for $25.00, which is a gift from a relative. You decide to deposit this money in your savings account. How much is your total deposit? **$147.84**

In-Class Examples

Find the total deposit.

1. $286.04 + $518.91 + $1730.80 - $250.00 **$2285.75**

2. Checks: $59.13 + $81.29 + $241.72 Cash: 43 one-dollar bills, 19 five-dollar bills, 13 ten-dollar bills; 54 quarters, 94 dimes, and 79 nickels. Less two $50 bills as cash received. **$576.99**

PROBLEM SOLVING

Deposits

Students complete a deposit slip for savings accounts for the following deposits:

1. Deposit a check for $68.50 and currency of $80.25. **$148.75**

2. Deposit a check for $310.75, a check for $82.76, currency of $50.25, and coins of $4.75. **$448.51**

3. Deposit a check for $1,327.68 and withdraw $150.00 in cash. **Total deposit: $1,177.68**

 **ASSESS**

Error Analysis

Have students who are making mistakes review their work for computational errors. Also, remind them to line up decimal points vertically before they add or subtract numerals.

4 CLOSE

Closing Activity

1. $2,359.41 + $917.53 + $71.44 **$3,348.38**
   Find the total deposit.
2. $1290.53 − $168.84 **$1,121.69**
3. Checks: $576.24 and $88.16
   Cash: $115.36
   Currency: 256 quarters, 377 dimes, 181 nickels, and 407 pennies **$894.58**
4. Angela Drexler filled out a savings account deposit slip on which she recorded checks for $428.97 and $261.56. She received $300 in cash. What was her total deposit? **$390.53**

	Deposits	Subtotal	Less Cash Received	Total Deposit
8.	$ 44.00 8.35 26.80	a. $79.15	$ 0.00	b. $79.15
9.	76.00 9.27 44.38	a. $129.65	0.00	b. $129.65
10.	52.96 39.75	a. $92.71	30.00	b. $62.71
11.	180.81 115.35	a. $296.16	150.00	b. $146.16
12.	64.89 39.57 928.12	a. $1,032.58	20.00	b. $1,012.58

13. Joe Gryster deposited a check for $475.77 and another check for $94.26 in his savings account. He received $70.00 in cash. What was his total deposit? **$500.03**

14. Ande Corbin completed a savings account deposit slip on which he recorded checks for $327.19 and $52.88 for deposit. He received $38.00 in cash. What was his total deposit? **$342.07**

15. Laura Martinez deposited 4 twenty-dollar bills, 9 ten-dollar bills, 35 quarters, 8 dimes, 97 pennies, and a check for $75.96 in her savings account. What was her total deposit? **$256.48**

16. David Rodero operates a booth during special concert events. Following each event he makes a deposit in his savings account. He has checks for $40, $50, and $35. He has cash and coins consisting of 8 fifty-dollar bills, 12 twenty-dollar bills, 12 ten-dollar bills, 8 five-dollar bills, 22 one-dollar bills, 48 quarters, 19 dimes, 22 nickels, and 52 pennies. He would like to receive a hundred-dollar bill in cash. What is his total deposit? **$862.52**

17. Winona Gendron is a street vendor selling souvenirs in front of Comerica Baseball Park. She deposits her sales income directly into a savings account. Her deposit today consists of 5 one-hundred-dollar bills, 8 fifty-dollar bills, 25 twenty-dollar bills, 22 five-dollar bills, 8 two-dollar bills, 19 one-dollar bills, 18 half-dollars, 42 quarters, 36 dimes, 28 nickels, and one check for $40.00. What is the total deposit? **$1,609.50**

MAINTAINING YOUR SKILLS

Need Help? Go to...
- Skill 5: **Adding Decimals**, page 732
- Skill 6: **Subtracting Decimals**, page 733

Add.

| 18. | $31.50 + 42.45 **$73.95** | 19. | $40.46 + 18.32 **$58.78** | 20. | $173.79 + 45.93 **$219.72** | 21. | $551.16 + 146.81 **$697.97** |

Subtract.

| 22. | $98.93 − 20.00 **$78.93** | 23. | $692.57 − 35.40 **$657.17** | 24. | $103.33 − 60.00 **$43.33** | 25. | $687.28 − 75.00 **$612.28** |

WRAP-UP

Go over any problem for which a wrong answer is given.

Assignment Guide
Basic: 4–7
Average: 8–15

 20 min.

SECTION 5-2 Withdrawals

Section Objective

Fill out a savings account withdrawal slip.

To withdraw is to take away. So when you fill out a **withdrawal** slip, you're taking money out of your bank account. Your withdrawal is subtracted from the account's balance. When making a withdrawal from a savings account, you need to be able to write dollar amounts in *word form*, with the decimal portion expressed as a fraction. (You learned the same process in Chapter 4 Checking Accounts.)

Living in the Real World

Understanding the Williams Sisters

Carrying Your Worth in a Shoebox Pennies rattle in the shoe box Aisha is carrying. "OK, so how do I deposit all my money?" Aisha asks as she and her sister enter the bank.

"Well, first," Jaydene says, "we'll have to open a savings account for you and deposit your money into it. Then you can take money out when you need it. That's called making a withdrawal."

"Do I just go up to the window and ask for my money when I want it back?"

"Well sort of," Jaydene says, "but first you have to fill out a piece of paper called a withdrawal slip."

Draw Conclusions Where else can you find a withdrawal slip other than at the lobby of the bank?

Continued on page 202

Example 1

Need Help? Go to...
> Workshop 1: Writing and Reading Numbers, page 4

a. Write $45.00 in word form.

b. Write $355 in word form.

c. Write *twenty-five and $\frac{50}{100}$ dollars* as a numeral.

STEP: Write the amounts in word form or as numerals.

    a. $45.00 in word form is **forty-five and $\frac{00}{100}$ dollars.**

    b. $355.00 in word form is **three hundred fifty-five and $\frac{00}{100}$ dollars.**

    c. Twenty-five and $\frac{50}{100}$ dollars as a numeral is **$25.50.**

CONCEPT CHECK

SELF-CHECK ✓

Complete the problems, then check your answers at the end of the chapter Write each of the following in word form or as a numeral.

1. $60.00 **Sixty and $\frac{00}{100}$ dollars**

2. $280.50 **Two hundred eighty and $\frac{50}{100}$ dollars**

3. Ninety-eight and $\frac{75}{100}$ dollars **$98.75**

4. Six thousand five hundred eighty-six and $\frac{95}{100}$ dollars **$6,586.95**

Section 5-2 Withdrawals ▶ **199**

Living in the Real World

Deposit/withdrawal slips are found at the back of every book of checks.

---

① FOCUS

The focus of this lesson is on completing a savings account withdrawal slip. Point out that this form must be used when no money is being deposited, only being taken out of a savings account.

In-Class Examples
Work through these exercises with students before having them do the Self-Check.
Write in words.
1. $47.83 **forty-seven and $\frac{83}{100}$ dollars**
2. $261.87 **two hundred sixty-one and $\frac{87}{100}$ dollars**
3. $1,391.46 **one thousand three hundred ninety-one and $\frac{46}{100}$ dollars**
Write as numerals.
4. Fifty-six and $\frac{71}{100}$ dollars **$56.71**
5. Five hundred seventeen and $\frac{00}{100}$ dollars **$517.00**

National Standards for Business Education

Standard 1	Mathematical Foundations
Standard 2	Number Relationships and Operations

National Council of Teachers of Mathematics Standards

Standard 1	Numbers and Operations
Standard 4	Measurement
Standard 8	Communication
Standard 9	Connections

2 TEACH

Point out the similarities between filling out the withdrawal slip and writing a check. If there is a discrepancy between the numeral amount and the amount in words of the withdrawal, the amount in words takes precedence.

Motivating the Lesson

Roberto Escobar wanted to withdraw $275.34 from his savings account to buy a new video game system. How would he write the dollar-and-cents amount with words as it would appear on a savings account withdrawal slip? **Two hundred seventy-five and $\frac{34}{100}$ dollars**

In-Class Examples

Write the numerals in word form, as they would appear on a savings account withdrawal slip.
1. $44.95 **forty-four and $\frac{95}{100}$ dollars**
2. $381.60 **three hundred eighty-one and $\frac{60}{100}$ dollars**

Write each of the following word forms as a numeral.
3. Four hundred eleven and $\frac{01}{100}$
   $411.01
4. Five thousand six hundred fifty-nine and $\frac{17}{100}$ dollars
   $5,659.17

3 ASSESS

Error Analysis

You may wish to review the idea that when writing numerals as words, people sometimes use the word *and* in the wrong place. For example, they may write 427 *as four hundred and twenty-seven* instead of *four hundred twenty-seven*. Stress that *and* is used only to replace the decimal point.

Also, remind students that all numbers between twenty-one and ninety-nine are hyphenated, with the exception of multiples of ten.

Example 2

Dalton Rhodes would like to withdraw $45 from his savings account. His account number is 0113014. How should he fill out the withdrawal slip? (Note: In order to prevent someone from altering your check, you always start writing out the amount to the left.)

Figure 5.2

State Bank		Savings Withdrawal

DATE November 14, 20--	ACCOUNT NUMBER 0113014	AMOUNT $45.00

NOT NEGOTIABLE—TO BE USED ONLY AT COUNTER OF THIS BANK BY DEPOSITOR PERSONALLY

Forty-five and $\frac{00}{100}$ ———————————————— DOLLARS

NAME (SIGNATURE)
Dalton Rhodes

ADDRESS
18 Laurel Lane, Bridgetown, CT 05120

STEP 1: Write the date of withdrawal.
STEP 2: Write the savings account number.
STEP 3: Write the amount withdrawn in words with cents expressed as a fraction of a dollar. (Note that you start at the far left.)
STEP 4: Write the amount withdrawn as a numeral.
STEP 5: Did he sign the withdrawal slip?

CONCEPT CHECK

SELF-CHECK ✓   Complete the problem, then check your answer at the end of the chapter.

5. Tyrone Shumpert would like to withdraw $150 from his savings account. Use the withdrawal slip to answer the following:

Figure 5.3

University Bank		Savings Withdrawal

DATE January 10, 20--	ACCOUNT NUMBER 559821	AMOUNT $150.00

NOT NEGOTIABLE—TO BE USED ONLY AT COUNTER OF THIS BANK BY DEPOSITOR PERSONALLY

One hundred fifty and $\frac{00}{100}$ ———————————————— DOLLARS

NAME (SIGNATURE)
Tyrone Shumpert

ADDRESS
5532 Hilltop Court, Lake Havasu City, AZ 86403

a. What is the date of withdrawal? **January 10, 20--**
b. What is the savings account number? **559821**
c. Is the amount withdrawn correctly written in word form? **yes**
d. Who signed the withdrawal slip? **Tyrone Shumpert**

ALTERNATIVE ASSESSMENT STRATEGIES

English Language Learners

If your class includes second language learners, provide outlines of lecture notes in advance. Perhaps provide a copy of the relevant PowerPoint presentation. Written materials help reinforce what you say. They also make it possible for the student to review materials later at a slower pace or to look up unfamiliar vocabulary. Keep in mind how you would feel if you suddenly found yourself as a student in another country where the language was only marginally familiar to you. Even though you are educated in your own language, you would appreciate outlines of lecture notes to help you comprehend the discussions in class. ELL , LS

FYI

Make sure you ask how many free withdrawals the bank allows each month. If you withdraw more than the limit, you may be charged $5.00 or more per withdrawal.

SECTION 5-2 PRACTICE

Write each amount in word form, as it would appear on a withdrawal slip.

6. $25.00

7. $150.00

8. $44.93

9. $68.74

10. $406.00

11. $137.51

Write each as a numeral.

12. Thirty-five and $\frac{00}{100}$ dollars **$35.00**

13. Nine hundred thirty-two and $\frac{25}{100}$ dollars **$932.25**

14. Seventy-four and $\frac{10}{100}$ dollars **$74.10**

15. Seven thousand five hundred eighty-five and $\frac{00}{100}$ dollars **$7,585.00**

For Problems 16 to 20 write (a) the account number, (b) the amount as a numeral, and (c) the amount in words.

16. Avis Bogart's savings account number is 81-0-174927. He fills out a savings withdrawal slip for $318.29 to purchase a gift.

17. Nina Cantu has been saving for a trip abroad. Her travel agent has arranged a trip to Europe that will cost $2,460. Cantu withdraws the amount from her savings account. Her account number is 13-122-541.

18. Damone Bashier has been saving to buy a commemorative stamp for his stamp collection. He fills out the savings withdrawal slip shown for $76.70. His account number is 06-029-175.

Answers

6. Twenty-five and $\frac{00}{100}$ dollars

7. One hundred fifty and $\frac{00}{100}$ dollars

8. Forty-four and $\frac{93}{100}$ dollars

9. Sixty-eight and $\frac{74}{100}$ dollars

10. Four hundred six and $\frac{00}{100}$ dollars

11. One hundred thirty-seven and $\frac{51}{100}$ dollars

16. a. 81-0-174927; b. $318.29; c. Three hundred eighteen and $\frac{29}{100}$ dollars

17. a. 13-122-541; b. $2,460.00; c. Two thousand four hundred sixty and $\frac{00}{100}$ dollars

18. a. 06-029-175; b. $76.70; c. Seventy-six and $\frac{70}{100}$ dollars

19. a. 17594179; b. $831.95; c. Eight hundred thirty-one and $\frac{95}{100}$ dollars

20. a. 16010368; b. $374.28; c. Three hundred seventy-four and $\frac{28}{100}$ dollars

Need Help? Go to...
▶ Skill 1: Numbers, page 727

19.

Farmer's Mercantile		
Date	Savings Acct. No.	
5/19/20--	17594179	$831.95
Pay to Myself or to	Home Finance Co.	
		Dollars
And Charge to the above Numbered Account		
Sign Here *Calvin Gordon*		
Withdrawal		

20.

Farmer's Mercantile		
Date	Savings Acct. No.	
1/12/20--	16010368	$374.28
Pay to Myself or to	Odessa French	
		Dollars
And Charge to the above Numbered Account		
Sign Here *Odessa French*		
Withdrawal		

MAINTAINING YOUR SKILLS

Write in words with cents expressed as a fraction of a dollar.

21. $94.78 **Ninety-four and $\frac{78}{100}$**

22. $219.34 **Two hundred nineteen and $\frac{34}{100}$**

23. $162.05 **One hundred sixty-two and $\frac{05}{100}$**

24. $15.71 **Fifteen and $\frac{71}{100}$**

Write as a numeral.

25. Thirty-nine and $\frac{41}{100}$ dollars **$39.41**

26. Two hundred fifty-one and $\frac{27}{100}$ dollars **$251.27**

27. Six thousand three hundred forty and $\frac{22}{100}$ dollars **$6,340.22**

28. Twenty-five thousand six hundred ninety-six and $\frac{29}{100}$ dollars **$25,696.29**

④ CLOSE

Closing Activity

Write each of the following numerals in word form, as they would appear on a savings account withdrawal slip.

1. $827.39 **eight hundred twenty-seven and $\frac{39}{100}$ dollars**

2. $5,392.85 **five thousand three hundred ninety-two and $\frac{85}{100}$ dollars**

Write each of the following word forms as a numeral.

3. Seven hundred fourteen and $\frac{83}{100}$ dollars **$714.83**

4. Sixty-two thousand five hundred thirty one and $\frac{12}{100}$ dollars **$62,531.12**

COMMUNICATION SKILLS

Take a Turn

Prepare small slips of paper with problems such as: (1) Today's date, savings account number 4538903, the amount of $425.00 and (2) Today's date, savings account number 7396815, the amount of three hundred fifty-two dollars and thirty-five cents. Give students blank savings account withdrawal slips. Have volunteers take turns picking a slip of paper and then slowly reading the problem to the class. **LS** , **CL**

WRAP-UP

Go over any problem for which a wrong answer is given.

Assignment Guide
  Basic: 6–11
  Average: 12–18

20 min.

National Standards for Business Education

Standard 1	Mathematical Foundations
Standard 2	Number Relationships and Operations

National Council of Teachers of Mathematics Standards

Standard 1	Numbers and Operations
Standard 4	Measurement
Standard 6	Problem Solving
Standard 8	Communication
Standard 9	Connections

① FOCUS

A written record of all deposits, withdrawals, and interest is kept on a monthly or quarterly account statement. It is important to make sure your teller window and/or ATM receipts for deposits and withdrawals match your account statement information. The focus of this lesson is to compute the new balance on an account statement after a transaction has been made and/or interest has been credited.

In-Class Examples

Work through these exercises with students before having them do the Self-Check.

1. $691.75 − $124.90 + $215.16 + $12.35 **$794.36**
2. $41.50 + $116.71 + $90.73 + $8.42 **$257.36**
3. $539.10 + $295.84 − $125.00 + $3.27 **$713.21**
4. $6,472 − $207.50 − $935.02 + $36.17 **$5,365.65**
5. $838.15 + $2.49 + $75 − $33.42 **$882.22**

SECTION 5-3 Account Statements

○ **Section Objective**

Compute the new balance on a savings account statement.

When you have a savings account, your bank may mail you a monthly or quarterly **account statement.** The account statement shows all deposits, withdrawals, and interest credited to your account.

New Balance = Previous Balance + Interest + Deposits − Withdrawals

Living in the Real World

Understanding the Williams Sisters

It Happens Four Times a Year "How do I know the bank is really putting my money into my account?" Aisha asks, narrowing her eyes.

"They will give you a copy of the deposit slip," Jaydene says, "and then every three months, they'll send you an account statement. You check it against the records you've been keeping to see if they are the same. The statement will show everything that's happened in your account since the last statement— deposits, withdrawals, and your interest."

Draw Conclusions Why is it important to reconcile your savings account?

Continued on page 205

Example 1

▶ **Need Help? Go to...**

▶ Workshop 4: Adding Decimals, page 10

▶ Workshop 5: Subtracting Decimals, page 12

Your savings account statement shows a previous balance of $1,258.22 and $2.10 in interest. You made deposits of $210.00, $50.00, and $40.00. You had withdrawals of $50.00 and $75.00. What is your new balance?

STEP: Compute the new balance.

Previous Balance + Interest + Deposits − Withdrawals
$1,258.22 + $2.10 + ($210 + $50 + $40) − ($50 + $75)
= $1,258.22 + $2.10 + $300 − $125
= **$1,435.32 new balance**

CONCEPT CHECK

✓ SELF-CHECK

Complete the problems, then check your answers at the end of the chapter.

	Previous Balance	+	Interest	+	Deposits	−	Withdrawals	=	New Balance
1.	$ 998.50	+	$1.25	+	$ 80	−	$100	=	$979.75
2.	1,589.33	+	2.67	+	750	−	440	=	$1,902.00

Living in the Real World

By doing so, a person can be certain no errors were made with their deposits or withdrawals.

RETEACH / ENRICHMENT

Account Status

Many customers use the Internet or automated teller machine (ATM) for financial transactions. Have students find out how the financial institutions notify their savings account customers of the status of their accounts.

Example 2

Christine Yamaguchi receives her savings account statement quarterly. After checking her passbook and transactions to be sure all items have been recorded correctly, she checks the calculations. What is the balance in her account on July 1?

Figure 5.4

Savings Account Statement				
Name Christine Yamaguchi			**Beginning Date**	4/01/20--
			Ending Date	7/01/20--
Account Number	5891235		**Interest Earned This Period**	4.11
Date	Withdrawal	Deposit	Interest	Balance
4/01				274.50
4/15		250.00		524.50
5/11		125.00		649.50
6/10	100.00			549.50
7/01			4.11	553.61
7/01		80.00		633.61

STEP: Find the new balance.

Previous Balance + Interest +   Deposits   − Withdrawals
   $274.50   + $4.11 + ($250 + $125 + $80) − $100.00
= **$633.61 new balance**

274.5 **+** 4.11 **+** 250 **+** 125 **+** 80 **−** 100 **=** 633.61

CONCEPT CHECK

Complete the problem, then check your answer at the end of the chapter.

3. Previous balance, $700; interest, $1.50; deposits of $100.00 and $250.00; withdrawals of $80.00 and $110.00. What is the new balance?
$700.00 + $1.50 + ($100.00 + $250.00) − ($80.00 + $110.00) =
$701.50 + $350.00 − $190.00 = $861.50

SECTION 5-3 PRACTICE

	Previous Balance	+	Interest	+	Deposits	− Withdrawals	=	New Balance
4.	$ 400.00	+	$1.90	+	$ 50.00	− $150.00	=	**$301.90**
5.	485.00	+	1.95	+	125.00	− 200.00	=	**$411.95**
6.	674.00	+	1.22	+	160.00	− 190.00	=	**$645.22**
7.	7,381.19	+	9.64	+	231.43	− 180.00	=	**$7,442.26**

8. Judi Imhoff's previous balance is $717.52. Imhoff receives $4.36 in interest, $125.00 and $276.95 in deposits, and $90.00 in withdrawals. What is her new balance? **$1,033.83**

Continued on next page

Go over the formula for computing the new balance from the old balance. Point out that interest is only entered on the account statement on a periodic basis, such as monthly or quarterly. The interest is given in this lesson; however, students will learn to compute the interest at a later time.

Point out that reconciliation is important for anyone who has automatic transfer of funds—that is, money from savings can automatically be transferred to checking if needed to cover a check.

Motivating the Lesson

Faye Donovan has $536.00 in a savings account at the bank. She has also been saving loose change and now deposits it into her savings account. The change totals $51.40. What is her new balance after her deposit? **$587.40**

In-Class Examples

1. Previous balance: $820.75
   Interest of $1.36
   Deposits of $35 and $105
   What is the new balance?
   $962.11

2. Previous balance: $8,914.51
   Interest of $14.85
   Deposits of $297.38 and $417.10
   Withdrawal of $1,500.00
   What is the new balance?
   $8,143.84

3. Lewis Belmonte's previous balance is $26,474.04. His account earns interest of $44.12. He deposits $550.43 and $197.16. What is his new balance? **$27,265.75**

4. Doug Fallon's previous balance was $520.94. He made four deposits of $50 each. His account earned $0.87 in interest. What is his new balance? **$721.81**

GLOBAL PERSPECTIVE

International Banks
Assign groups of students to find historical and current information about one of the following: The International Bank for Reconstruction and Development (World Bank), European Central Bank (ECB), or International Monetary Fund (IMF). Information might be about when the bank was established and the bank's main role. Groups present a short news segment. **LS** , **CL**

COMMUNICATION SKILLS

History of Banking
When the people of Egypt and Greece wanted to deposit their gold and silver for safekeeping, they went to the temples. The temples practiced a simple form of banking by then loaning gold and silver to others for a high rate of interest. Have students research the history of banking and create a timeline. Students choose between researching the history of banking in general or the history of banking in the United States.

 **ASSESS**

Error Analysis

If students are making errors, remind them that interest and deposits are added to the previous balance. Have them check their work to see that they have correctly added the interest and deposits. After all the additions have been made to the previous balance, then have them subtract any withdrawals. The amount left will be the new balance.

4 **CLOSE**

Closing Activity

1. $3,664.25 + $38.67 + $90.22
   $3,793.14

2. $86,255.36 − $35,400
   $50,855.36

3. Find the new balance if the previous balance is $2,314.53, deposits are $97.50 and $276.93, a withdrawal of $50.00 is made, and interest of $12.38 is earned. **$2,651.34**

4. Erin O'Malley looked over her savings account statement. Her previous balance was $981.93. She made deposits of $150.00, $80.00, and $120.00. In addition, her money earned $1.63 in interest. She withdrew $45.17. What is her new balance? **$1,288.39**

5. Sebastian Crane's savings account statement showed a previous balance of $5,291.70. His money earned $15.43 in interest on April 30. He made deposits of $230.31 on May 2, $875.28 on May 9, and $204.10 on May 18. What is his balance on each of the days in which a transaction occurred? **$5,307.13 on April 30; $5,537.44 on May 2; $6,412.72 on May 9; and $6,616.82 on May 18.**

9. Darrick Taylor's previous balance is $2,161.41. On his bank statement there is a record of $20.04 in interest, deposits of $345.00 and $575.80, and withdrawals of $210.00 and $945.00. What is his new balance? **$1,947.25**

10. Sara Averett's previous balance is $74,561.49, with $1,017.98 in interest, deposits of $918.37 and $944.56, and withdrawals of $959.40 and $14,391.47. What is her new balance? **$62,091.53**

11. Kevin Elliott received his savings account statement. Fill in the missing information on Elliott's statement.

Figure 5.5

Savings Account Statement				
Name Kevin Elliott			**Beginning Date**	1/15/20--
			Ending Date	7/15/20--
Account Number	12-36-5000		**Interest Earned This Period**	f. **$15.59**
Date	**Withdrawal**	**Deposit**	**Interest**	**Balance**
01/15				$503.27
01/28		$ 45.00		548.27
02/03		80.40		628.67
02/15			$2.85	631.52
03/15			2.86	634.38
04/10	$400.00			234.38
04/15			2.37	a. **$236.75**
05/01		335.60		b. **$572.35**
05/15			2.28	c. **$574.63**
06/15			2.61	d. **$577.24**
07/15			2.62	e. **$579.86**

MAINTAINING YOUR SKILLS

Need Help? Go to...
➤ Skill 5: **Adding Decimals**, page 732
➤ Skill 6: **Subtracting Decimals**, page 733

Add.

12. $450.00 + $9.50 + $40.00 **$499.50**   13. $385.00 + $7.52 + $875.00 **$1,267.52**

14. $793.60 + $2.38 + $5.00 **$800.98**   15. $426.30 + $278.41 + $342.91 **$1,047.62**

Subtract.

16. $7,942.70 − $3,453.80 **$4,488.90**   17. $16,865.95 − $14,991.39 **$1,874.56**

18. $338.49 − $299.39 **$39.10**   19. $41,215.24 − $11,645.91 **$29,569.33**

WRAP-UP

Go over any problem for which a wrong answer is given.

Assignment Guide
Basic: 4–7
Average: 8–10

20 min.

SECTION (5-4) Simple Interest

○ **Section Objective**

Calculate simple interest.

When you deposit money into a savings account, you are permitting the bank to use the money. The bank pays you **interest**, or a rental fee for letting them use your money. The most common method of calculating interest is the **simple interest** formula. This is the interest paid on the original **principal**, the amount of money earning interest. Simple interest is based on three factors: the principal, the interest rate, and the amount of time for which the principal is borrowed.

To figure out how much interest your money will earn in the first year, multiply the principal by the **annual interest rate**, the percent of the principal that you earn as interest based on one year.

To compute use this formula:

$$\text{Interest} = \text{Principal} \times \text{Rate} \times \text{Time}$$

(Important Note: In this formula, rate is expressed as a decimal, fraction, or percent; time is expressed in years or a fraction of a year.)

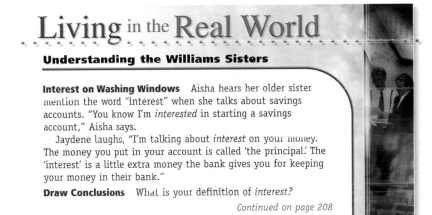

Living in the Real World

Understanding the Williams Sisters

Interest on Washing Windows Aisha hears her older sister mention the word "interest" when she talks about savings accounts. "You know I'm *interested* in starting a savings account," Aisha says.

Jaydene laughs, "I'm talking about *interest* on your money. The money you put in your account is called 'the principal.' The 'interest' is a little extra money the bank gives you for keeping your money in their bank."

Draw Conclusions What is your definition of *interest*?

Continued on page 208

Example 1

Need Help? Go to...
➤ Workshop 6: Multiplying Decimals, page 14
➤ Workshop 13: Fraction to Decimal, Decimal to Percent, page 28

Joyce Tyler deposits $900 in a savings account at Hamler State Bank. The account pays an annual interest rate of $5\frac{1}{2}$ percent. She makes no other deposits or withdrawals. After three months, the interest is calculated. How much simple interest does her money earn?

STEP: Find the interest at $5\frac{1}{2}$ percent.

Principal × Rate × Time
$900.00 × $5\frac{1}{2}$% × $\frac{3}{12}$
$900.00 × 0.055 × 0.25 — **$12.375 or $12.38 interest**

900 ⊠ 5.5 **%** 49.5 ⊠ 3 ÷ 12 ⊟ 12.375 or

900 ⊠ 0.055 ⊠ 0.25 ⊟ 12.375

Living in the Real World

Answers will vary depending on the student. Interest, Typically, is the amount of money paid for the use of money.

National Standards for Business Education

Standard 1	Mathematical Foundations
Standard 2	Number Relationships and Operations

National Council of Teachers of Mathematics Standards

Standard 1	Numbers and Operations
Standard 4	Measurement
Standard 6	Problem Solving
Standard 8	Communication
Standard 9	Connections

① FOCUS

Ask students if any of them have accounts that earn interest. Point out that they'll learn how to compute simple interest in this lesson.

In-Class Examples

Work through these exercises with students before having them do the Self-Check.

Write as a fraction of a year and then as a decimal. In Problems 3–5, calculate the decimals to seven place values. Do not round.

1. 6 months $\frac{1}{2}$, **0.5**
2. 9 months $\frac{3}{4}$, **0.75**
3. 15 days $\frac{15}{365}$, **0.0410958**
4. 21 days $\frac{21}{365}$, **0.0575342**
5. 87 days $\frac{87}{365}$, **0.2383561**

Write as a decimal.

6. $2\frac{1}{2}$% **0.025**
7. 6% **0.06**
8. 12% **0.12**
9. $250 × 0.12 × 0.75 **$22.50**
10. $5,000 × 0.03 × 0.25 **$37.50**

SECTION 5-4

② TEACH

Go over the terms *annual interest rate, interest, principal, rate,* and *time.* Emphasize that time must be expressed as a part of a year. For example, 3 months is written as $\frac{1}{4}$ year, and 7 months is written as $\frac{7}{12}$ year. Fifteen days is written as $\frac{15}{365}$ and twenty-six days as $\frac{26}{365}$. Point out that these fractions must be changed to decimals when computing interest.

Banks and savings and loan associations often use simple interest for loans of less than one year's duration and for home mortgages.

Motivating the Lesson

You open a savings account and deposit $1,000. Your bank will pay you an annual interest rate of 6 percent on the principal, which in this case is $1,000. If you make no deposits or withdrawals, how much interest will you earn in one year? **$60.00**

In-Class Examples

1. Principal: $700
   Annual interest rate: 3%
   What is the interest after 3 months? **$5.25**

2. Principal: $2,000
   Annual interest rate: $4\frac{3}{4}$%
   What is the interest after 9 months? **$71.25**

3. Colleen O'Rourke's savings account $4,900 on deposit $4\frac{1}{4}$ percent annual interest rate. Time is 6 months Find the interest. **$104.13**

4. Principal × Rate × Time
   $2500 × .025 + \frac{10}{365} = ?$ **$1.71**
   $2000 × .025 × \frac{5}{365} = ?$ **$0.68**
   $3000 × .025 × \frac{15}{365} = ?$ **$3.08**
   Total interest? **$5.47**
   Total amount in the account?
   $3,005.47

CONCEPT CHECK

SELF-CHECK ✓

Complete the problems, then check your answers at the end of the chapter.

1. Principal: $400
   Annual interest rate: 6 percent
   What is the interest after 3 months?
   $400 × 6% × \frac{3}{12}$;
   $400 × 0.06 × 0.25 = \$6.00$

2. Principal: $1,500
   Annual interest rate: 2.5 percent
   What is the interest after 6 months?
   $\$1,500 × 0.025 × \frac{6}{12} = \$18.75$

Example 2

Lena Green's bank computes 4 percent interest on a daily basis. She has $1,000 in the account for 10 days. She makes a deposit of $600 and it is in the account for 15 days. She withdraws $400 and the balance earns interest for 6 days. How much interest does she earn? What is the amount in the account at the end of the month?

STEP: Find the interest at 4 percent for each set of days.

Principal × Rate × Time

(Note: Remember that the time has to be a fraction of a year, so divide the number of days by 365.)

$\$1,000 × 4\% × \frac{10}{365} = \$1.0958$	= \$	1.10
$(\$1,000 + \$600) × 4\% × \frac{15}{365} = \$2.630$	=	2.63
$(\$1,600 - \$400) × 4\% × \frac{6}{365} = \$0.789$	=	0.79
Total interest for the month	\$	**4.52**

The amount in the account is ($1,200 + $4.52) = **$1,204.52**

CONCEPT CHECK

SELF-CHECK ✓

Complete the problems, then check your answers at the end of the chapter.

3. Some banks calculate the interest on a daily basis. The daily interest is added to the account at the end of the month. Complete the following interest calculations:

	Principal	×	Rate	×	Time	=	Interest
a.	$2,000	×	0.03	×	$\frac{12}{365}$	=	**$1.97**
b.	3,000	×	0.03	×	$\frac{8}{365}$	=	**$1.97**
c.	2,500	×	0.03	×	$\frac{5}{365}$	=	**$1.03**
d.	2,000	×	0.03	×	$\frac{6}{365}$	=	**$0.99**
e.	Total interest					=	**$5.96**
f.	Total amount in the account					=	**$2,005.96**

4. On May 1 Geraldo Saldana opened a savings account that paid 3.5 percent interest at Fulton Savings Bank with a deposit of $3,600. Ten days later he deposited $3,000. Fourteen days later he deposited $5,000. No other deposits or withdrawals were made. Six days later the bank calculated the daily interest.
   a. How much simple interest did his money earn? **$18.98**
   b. How much was in the account at the end of the 30 days? **$11,618.98**

TECHNOLOGY POWER

Wells Fargo is a prime example of how a 150-year-old institution can build a round-the-clock cyber bank running alongside an old-fashioned traditional bank. Internet customers do nearly half their banking transactions online. Customers interested in home equity loans can chat online with a service representative and often get a follow-up phone call from the bank. And customers who open a checking account will automatically be signed up for online service. With the Web service in place, branch employees spend less time filling out paperwork and answering basic questions and more time selling products.

SECTION 5-4 PRACTICE

	Principal	×	Rate	=	Annual Interest	×	Time	=	Interest
5.	$ 720.00	×	0.06	=	a. $43.20	×	$\frac{3}{12}$	=	b. $10.80
6.	960.00	×	0.02	=	a. $19.20	×	$\frac{1}{12}$	=	b. $1.60
7.	327.00	×	0.08	=	a. $26.16	×	$\frac{6}{12}$	=	b. $13.08
8.	4,842.00	×	0.10	=	a. $484.20	×	$\frac{12}{365}$	=	b. $15.92
9.	3,945.37	×	0.065	=	a. $256.45	×	$\frac{8}{365}$	=	b. $5.62

		Principal	×	Rate	×	Time	=	Interest
10.	a.	$5,000	×	0.02	×	$\frac{15}{365}$	=	$4.11
	b.	4,000	×	0.02	×	$\frac{5}{365}$	=	$1.10
	c.	1,000	×	0.02	×	$\frac{5}{365}$	=	$0.27
	d.	1,500	×	0.02	×	$\frac{5}{365}$	=	$0.41
	e.	Total interest					=	$5.89
	f.	Total amount in the account					=	$1,505.89

14. Mar 6 $9,364.85 × 0.04 × $\frac{5}{365}$ = 5.13;

Mar 18 $8,364.85 × 0.04 × $\frac{12}{365}$ = 11.00;

Mar 28 $6,364.85 × 0.04 × $\frac{10}{365}$ = 6.98;

Mar 31 $4,364.85 × 0.04 × $\frac{3}{365}$ = 1.44;

$24.55

11. Tyee LaFleure deposited $760. No other deposits or withdrawals were made. After 3 months the interest was computed at an annual interest rate of 5 percent. How much simple interest did his money earn? **$9.50**

12. Malicia Dukes-Miller deposited $2,430. She made no other deposits or withdrawals. After 1 month the interest was computed at an annual rate of 6 percent. How much simple interest did her money earn? **$12.15**

13. Vernon Taber deposited his $2,000 scholarship money in a savings account at State Home Savings Bank on June 1. At the end of 2 months, interest was computed at an annual interest rate of 6 percent. How much simple interest did his money earn? **$20.00**

14. On March 1 Tessa Obee deposited her IRS refund check for $9,364.85 in a savings account at State Bank. The account pays 4 percent interest calculated on a daily basis. Five days later on March 6 she withdrew $1,000.00. On March 18, 12 days later, she withdrew $2,000.00. On March 28, 10 days later, she withdrew another $2,000.00. Three days later on March 31 interest was computed. How much simple interest did her money earn?

MAINTAINING YOUR SKILLS

Need Help? Go to...
▶ Skill 14: Changing Fractions/Decimals, page 741
▶ Skill 28: Writing Percents as Decimals, page 755

Change the fractions and mixed numbers to decimals.

15. $\frac{1}{2}$ 0.5   16. $\frac{3}{4}$ 0.75   17. $\frac{1}{4}$ 0.25

18. $5\frac{1}{2}$ 5.5   19. $6\frac{1}{4}$ 6.25   20. $7\frac{3}{4}$ 7.75

Write the percents as decimals.

21. $5\frac{1}{2}$% 0.055   22. $6\frac{1}{4}$% 0.0625   23. $9\frac{1}{2}$% 0.095

24. $7\frac{3}{4}$% 0.0775   25. $10\frac{5}{8}$% 0.10625   26. $5\frac{3}{8}$% 0.05375

THINKING CRITICALLY

Parts of a Year
You have a two-month summer vacation. What fraction of a year is your vacation? ($\frac{2}{12} = \frac{1}{6}$) Write your answer as a decimal. $\frac{1}{6}$ = **0.16666 = 0.17**

WRAP-UP

Go over any problem for which a wrong answer is given.

Assignment Guide
  Basic: 5–9
  Average: 10–13

20 min.

③ ASSESS

Error Analysis
Have students review problems that refer to calculating interest on a daily basis, such as a problem that asks students to compute interest for 10 days. First, remind students to write 10 days as a fraction of a year, or $\frac{10}{365}$.

Next, students must divide 10 by 365 in order to get the decimal equivalent: $\frac{10}{365}$ = 0.0273972 Tell students to write the entire decimal with its 7 place values. Do not round.

Finally, have students multiply the principal ($2,500) × rate (0.025) × time (0.0273972) to calculate the simple interest ($1.71).

④ CLOSE

Closing Activity
Change the mixed numbers to decimals.
1. $6\frac{1}{2}$ **6.5**
2. $3\frac{1}{4}$ **3.25**
Write the percent as decimals.
3. $2\frac{3}{4}$% **0.0275**
4. $5\frac{1}{4}$% **0.0525**
5. Gabrielle Patterson deposited $3,600 in a new savings account. She made no other deposits or withdrawals. The bank pays an annual interest rate of 4.75 percent. How much simple interest did her money earn after 3 months? **$42.75**

National Standards for Business Education

Standard 1	Mathematical Foundations
Standard 2	Number Relationships and Operations

National Council of Teachers of Mathematics Standards

Standard 1	Numbers and Operations
Standard 4	Measurement
Standard 6	Problem Solving
Standard 8	Communication
Standard 9	Connections

1 FOCUS

The focus of this lesson is on computing the compound interest and the amount in a savings account. Locate some advertisements in newspapers that deal with compound interest. Ask students if any of them have accounts paying compound interest.

In-Class Examples

Work through these exercises with students before having them do the Self-Check.

1. $1,319.50 + $18.41 **$1,337.91**
2. $1,951.21 + $16.43 **$1,967.64**
3. $1,000 × 12% × $\frac{1}{4}$ **$30**
4. $6,000 × 6% × $\frac{1}{12}$ **$30**
5. $4,712 − $46.91 **$4,665.09**
6. $2,536 − $2,521.45 **$14.55**

SECTION 5·5 Compound Interest

○ Section Objective

Figure out the compound interest and the amount.

Interest that you earn in a savings account during an interest period is added to your account. Your new balance is used to calculate the interest for the next interest period and the next interest period and so on.

Compound interest is interest earned not only on the original principal, but also on the interest earned during previous interest periods. Think of compound interest as having a snowball effect—a little snowball starts at the top of a big hill and as it rolls down, it keeps picking up more snow, making it bigger and bigger. The first step to figure out compound interest is to use this formula:

$$\text{Amount} = \text{Principal} + \text{Interest}$$

The amount is the balance in the account at the end of an interest period. Once you have the amount, then you do a series of simple interest computations. To find the compound interest, you find the difference between the amount in the account and the original principal. The formula looks like this:

$$\text{Compound Interest} = \text{Amount} - \text{Original Principal}$$

Living in the Real World

Understanding the Williams Sisters

Compounding Is Good for You Mr. Gleason, a bank teller, smiles when Aisha tells him she wants to open a savings account. She requests a passbook, but he tells her that most banks no longer issue them. Instead most have gone to the monthly account statement. Deposits, withdrawals, and interest are tracked there.

Draw Conclusions Give an example of compound interest. How does it work for you?

Continued on page 211

Need Help? Go to...

▶ **Skill 14:** Changing Fractions/Decimals, page 741
▶ **Skill 28:** Writing Percents as Decimals, page 755
▶ **Skill 30:** Finding the Percentage, page 757
▶ **Application K:** Chronological Expressions, page 766

Example 1

Jamal Quillet deposited $1,800 in a savings account, which earns 6 percent interest that is compounded quarterly. He made no deposits or withdrawals. What was the amount in the account at the end of the second quarter?

STEP: Find the amount for each quarter.

First Quarter							
Principal	×	**Rate**	×	**Time**	=	**Interest**
$1,800.00	×	6%	×	$\frac{1}{4}$	=	$27.00
Principal	+	**Interest**			=	**Amount**
$1,800.00	+	$27.00			=	$1,827.00

Living in the Real World

Examples will vary. Compound interest is calculated not only on the amount an accountholder deposits into a savings account, but also on any interest that has accrued, or built up, at the time of the calculation.

<table>
<tr><th colspan="7">Second Quarter</th></tr>
<tr><th>Principal</th><th>×</th><th>Rate</th><th>×</th><th>Time</th><th>=</th><th>Interest</th></tr>
<tr><td>$1,827.00</td><td>×</td><td>6%</td><td>×</td><td>$\frac{1}{4}$</td><td>=</td><td>$27.41</td></tr>
<tr><th>Principal</th><th>+</th><th colspan="3">Interest</th><th>=</th><th>Amount</th></tr>
<tr><td>$1,827.00</td><td>+</td><td colspan="3">$27.41</td><td>=</td><td>$1,854.41</td></tr>
</table>

1800 M+ × 6 % 108 × .25 = 27 + RM

1800 = 1827 CM M+ × 6 % 109.62 × .25 =

27.405 + RM 1827 = 1854.405

CONCEPT CHECK

 SELF-CHECK✔

Complete the problem, then check your answer at the end of the chapter.

1. Two thousand dollars is deposited at 8 percent compounded semiannually. Find the amount in the account after 1 year.
$2,000 × 0.08 × $\frac{1}{2}$ = $80; $2,080 × 0.08 × $\frac{1}{2}$ = $83.20; $2,163.20

Example 2

In Example 1 Jamal Quillet deposited $1,800 in a savings account that earns 6 percent interest compounded quarterly. You determined that the amount in his account at the end of the second quarter was $1,854.41. What is the compound interest?

STEP: Figure out the compound interest.
Amount − Original Principal
$1,854.41 − $1,800.00 = $54.41 compound interest

CONCEPT CHECK

SELF-CHECK✔

Complete the problem, then check your answer at the end of the chapter.

2. How much did the account in Self-Check Problem 1 earn in compound interest? $2,163.20 − $2,000 − $163.20

SECTION 5-5 PRACTICE

	Principal	Annual Interest Rate	Interest Period	First Period Interest	Amount	Second Period Interest	Amount
3.	$ 900.00	6%	quarterly	$13.50	$913.50	a. $13.70	b. $927.20
4.	400.00	6%	monthly	2.00	402.00	a. $2.01	b. $404.01
5.	2,360.00	$4\frac{1}{3}$%	semiannually	53.10	a.	b.	c.
6.	18,260.00	$2\frac{1}{2}$%	quarterly	a.	b.	c.	d.
7.	27,721.00	9.513%	annually	a.	b.	c.	d.

5. a. $2,413.10; b. $54.29; c. $2,467.39
6. a. $114.13; b. $18,374.13; c. $114.84; d. $18,488.97 *Continued on next page*
7. a. $2,637.10; b. $30,358.10; c. $2,887.97; d. $33,246.07

COOPERATIVE LEARNING

The Power of Compound Interest

Emphasize the power of compound interest by using this example: The Alaska Bicentennial Commission had $1,000 left after the celebration in 1976. The money was not to be touched until the tricentennial celebration in 2076. At 6 percent interest compounded monthly the $1,000 will be worth $397,442.32 in 2076. At 6 percent simple interest the $1,000 will be worth $7,000 in 2076. A difference of $390,442.32! Have students work in groups to search the Internet to find other examples of the power of compound interest.

LS , CL , P

② TEACH

Emphasize the fact that the interest must be added to the principal at the end of each interest period. This figure becomes the principal for the new interest period.

Make sure students understand the difference between compounding interest annually, semi-annually, quarterly, and monthly. Write the following example on the board to illustrate how the same principal and interest rate can result in different amounts of money at the end of the year.

Original deposit: $10,000
Interest rate: 6 percent
Compounded annually:
$10,600.00
Compounded semiannually:
$10,609.00
Compounded quarterly:
$10,613.64
Compounded monthly:
$10,616.78

Motivating the Lesson

You deposit $800 in a new savings account. If the account pays an annual interest rate of 6 percent, your money will earn $12 of simple interest after 3 months. Remember that interest = principal ($500) × rate (6%) × time (3 months). In six months, your original principal of $800 will earn simple interest of $24.

Now imagine that you deposit $800 in an account that pays the same rate, 6 percent, but the interest is compounded quarterly. This means that every three months, your money would earn interest on the principal ($800) + interest earned in the last quarterly period ($12). ($800 + $12 = $812) How much interest would you earn on $812 at 6 percent in the next quarterly period ($812 × 0.06 × 0.25)? Would your money grow faster in an account that pays simple interest or in one that pays compound interest? $12.18 compound interest

3 ASSESS

Error Analysis

Have students carefully review their work for errors. Help them break down the process of computing compound interest into the following steps:

1. Find the amount at the end of the first interest period by multiplying the principal × annual interest rate × first interest period.

2. Add interest earned at the end of first interest period to the original principal to obtain a new principal.

3. Multiply the new principal × annual interest rate × second interest period.

4. Add interest earned at the end of the second interest period to the new principal.

5. If you are computing interest for more than two interest periods, repeat step 3. Then add the interest earned at the end of each interest period to the latest principal.

4 CLOSE

Closing Activity

Write as a decimal.
1. 4.9% **0.049**
2. $5\frac{3}{4}$% **0.0575**

Find the percentage.
3. $761 × 7% **$53.27**
4. $5,512 × $6\frac{1}{4}$% **$344.50**
5. Deborah Roth's savings account has a principal of $3,500. Her money earns $4\frac{3}{4}$ percent interest compounded semiannually. She makes no other deposits or withdrawals.
   a. What is the amount in her account at the end of the year? **$3,668.22**
   b. How much is compound interest? **$168.22**

8. Alicia Martin's savings account has a principal of $1,200. It earns 6 percent interest compounded quarterly.
   a. What is the amount in the account at the end of the second quarter? **$1,236.27**
   b. How much is the compound interest? **$36.27**

9. Angelo Larragu's savings account has a principal of $800. It earns 6 percent interest compounded quarterly.
   a. What is the amount in the account at the end of the third quarter? **$836.54**
   b. How much is the compound interest? **$36.54**

10. Manny Simpson deposited $860 in a new regular savings account that earns 5.5 percent interest compounded semiannually. He made no other deposits or withdrawals. What was the amount in the account at the end of 1 year? **$907.95**

11. Jana Dejute deposited $4,860 in a new credit union savings account on the first of the quarter. The principal earns 4 percent interest compounded quarterly. She made no other deposits or withdrawals. What was the amount in her account at the end of 6 months? **$4,957.69**

12. Betty and Sam Sim's savings account had a balance of $9,544 on May 1. The account earns interest at a rate of 5.25 percent compounded monthly.
    a. What is the amount in their account at the end of August if no deposits or withdrawals were made during the period? **$9,712.12**
    b. How much is the compound interest? **$168.13**

13. Ernie Boddy had $3,620 on deposit at Savings Bank on July 1. The money earns interest at a rate of 6.5 percent compounded quarterly.
    a. What is the amount in the account on April 1 of the following year if no deposits or withdrawals were made? **$3,799.36**
    b. How much is the compound interest? **$179.36**

14. The Vassillis opened a savings account with a deposit of $2,000 on January 1. The account pays interest at 6 percent compounded semiannually. On July 1 they deposited another $2,000.
    a. What amount will they have in their account on July 1? **$2,060.00**
    b. What will they have in the account on January first one year later? **$4,181.80**
    c. How much is the compound interest? **$181.80**

MAINTAINING YOUR SKILLS

Need Help? Go to...
➤ Skill 28: Writing Percents as Decimals, page 755
➤ Skill 30: Finding the Percentage, page 757
➤ Skill 14: Changing Fractions/Decimals, page 741

Write the percents as decimals.

15. $5\frac{1}{4}$% **0.0525**   16. $8\frac{1}{2}$% **0.085**   17. $5\frac{3}{4}$% **0.0575**

Find the percentage.

18. $950 × 8% **$76.00**   19. $760 × $6\frac{1}{2}$% **$49.40**   20. $3,620 × 9% **$325.80**

Write the fractions as decimals. Round answers to the nearest hundredth.

21. $\frac{3}{10}$ **0.30**   22. $\frac{4}{12}$ **0.33**   23. $\frac{5}{8}$ **0.63**

USING CALCULATORS

Compound interest can be a lengthy calculation. It is helpful to have a set of keystrokes that will accomplish the task effectively and efficiently. Use of the [M+] and [RM] key can assist in this process. Have students work the following on a calculator.

1500 [M+] 1500 [×] 5 [%] [×] 0.25 [=] [M+] [RM] [×] 5 [%] [×] 0.25 [=] [M+] [RM]

Have students explain what the sequence of keystrokes calculates.

WRAP-UP

Go over any problem for which a wrong answer is given.

Assignment Guide
Basic: 3–7
Average: 8–13

20 min.

SECTION (5·6) Compound Interest Tables

Section Objective

Find compound interest using tables.

To compute compound interest quickly, you can use a compound interest table, which shows the amount of $1.00 for many interest rates and interest periods. To use the table you must know the *total number of interest periods* and the *interest rate per period*. Throughout this chapter, you'll use these formulas:

Amount = Original Principal × Amount of $1.00

Compound Interest = Amount − Original Principal

Living in the Real World

Understanding the Williams Sisters

The Work's Done for You Figuring compound interest seems complicated to Aisha, but Mr. Gleason tells her that if you know the number of interest periods and the interest rate per period, you can use a table to figure out the amount of compound interest your money has earned.

Draw Conclusions In your own words, how do you read a chart in order to find the information you need?

Continued on page 214

Example 1

> Need Help? Go to...
> ▶ Workshop 7: Dividing Decimals, page 16
> ▶ Workshop 6: Multiplying Decimals, page 14
> ▶ Application C: Tables and Charts, page 762

State Bank pays 6 percent interest compounded quarterly on regular savings accounts. Marta Carmona deposited $3,000 for 2 years. She made no other deposits or withdrawals. How much interest did Carmona earn during the 2 years? (Note: Use the Compound Interest—Amount of $1.00 table on page 797 to solve this problem.)

STEP 1: Find the total interest periods.
Periods per Year × Number of Years
4 quarters per year × 2 years = 8

STEP 2: Find the interest rate per period.
$$\frac{\text{Annual Rate}}{\text{Number of Periods per Year}}$$
$$\frac{6\%}{4} = 1.5\%$$

STEP 3: Find the amount of $1.00 for 8 periods at 1.5 percent per period using the Compound Interest—Amount of $1.00 table on page 797.
= 1.12649

STEP 4: Find the amount.
Original Principal × Amount of $1.00
$3,000.00 × 1.12649 = $3,379.47

Continued on next page

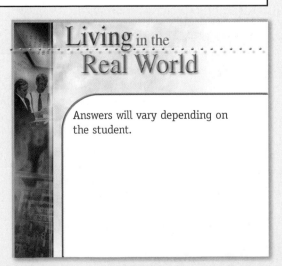

Living in the Real World

Answers will vary depending on the student.

---

(1) FOCUS

Ask students how many times they would have to compute the compound interest on an original amount if it is left in the account for two years and is compounded monthly. **(24)** The focus of this lesson is finding compound interest with tables. Tables can be useful in situations where many calculations would be necessary.

In-Class Examples

Work through these exercises with students before having them do the Self-Check.

1. $100 × 1.025 **$102.50**
2. $700 × 1.772 **$1,240.40**
3. $2,000 × 1.1154 **$2,230.80**
4. 5.75% divided by 4 **1.4375%**
5. 6.5% divided by 12 **0.5417%**
6. 12.5% divided by 4 **3.125%**
7. $754.68 − $700.00 **$54.68**
8. $9,215 − $373 **$8,842**

National Standards for Business Education

Standard 1	Mathematical Foundations
Standard 2	Number Relationships and Operations

National Council of Teachers of Mathematics Standards

Standard 1	Numbers and Operations
Standard 4	Measurement
Standard 6	Problem Solving
Standard 8	Communication
Standard 9	Connections

Point out that the table is based on $1 so that the entries in the table can be applied to any dollar amount.

Motivating the Lesson

You put $500 in a savings account where the interest is compounded quarterly. Your money has been in the account for 1 year. How many times during the year does your money earn interest? If you leave your money in the account for a total of 3 years, how many times will your money earn interest? **4 times; 12 times**

In-Class Examples

1. Five thousand dollars invested at 6 percent compounded quarterly for 2 years. No additional deposits or withdrawals. Find the amount. **$5,632.45**

2. Alyssa Birdwell deposited $3,357 in a savings account at McKinley Bank. The account pays 6 percent interest that is compounded quarterly. At the end of the first year, she deposited $2,000. What amount will be in the account at the end of two more years if she makes no additional deposits or withdrawals? What is the total interest earned? **$6,266.65; $909.65**

3 ASSESS

Error Analysis

In problems where money is earning interest in an account with no additional deposits or withdrawals, have students follow the steps in Example 1 on page 211 for computing interest. However, if additional money is put into the account, have students follow the steps in Example 2 on page 212. Remind students to determine how much money is in the account for the duration of each interest period

---

STEP 5: Find the compound interest.

Amount − Original Principal

$3,379.47 − $3,000   = $379.47 compound interest

CONCEPT CHECK

SELF-CHECK ✓

Complete the problems, then check your answers at the end of the chapter.

1. Two thousand dollars is invested at 5.5 percent interest compounded quarterly for 2 years. Find the amount. **1.11544 × $2,000 = $2,230.88**

2. Four thousand five hundred dollars is invested at 3 percent interest compounded semiannually for 2 years. Find the amount.
1.06136 × $4,500 = $4,776.12

Example 2

Juan Lopez opens an account and deposits $4,379.47. The account pays 6 percent annual interest and compounds quarterly. Six months later he deposits $2,000. How much will he have in the account $1\frac{1}{2}$ years later if it continues to pay 6 percent interest compounded quarterly?

STEP 1: Find the total interest periods for first 6 months.

Periods per Year × Number of Years

4 quarters per year × $\frac{1}{2}$ year   = 2 interest periods

STEP 2: Find the interest rate per period.

$$\frac{\text{Annual Rate}}{\text{Number of Periods per Year}}$$

$$\frac{6\%}{4} = 1.5\%$$

STEP 3: Find the amount of $1.00 for 2 periods at 1.5 percent per period using the Compound Interest—Amount of $1.00 table on page 797. = 1.03023

STEP 4: Find the amount for 6 months.

Original Principal × Amount of $1.00

$4,379.47   ×   1.03023   = $4,511.86 (new principal)

STEP 5: Find the amount for 1.5 years.

Periods per Year × Number of Years

4 quarters per year ×   1.5 years   = 6 interest periods

STEP 6: Find the amount of $1.00 for 6 periods at 1.5 percent per period using the Compound Interest—Amount of $1.00 table on page 797. = 1.09344

STEP 7: Find the amount for 1.5 years.

New Principal   × Amount of $1.00

($4,511.86 + $2,000.00) ×   1.09344   =

$6,511.86   ×   1.09344   = **$7,120.33 in the account**

CONCEPT CHECK

SELF-CHECK ✓

Complete the problem, then check your answer at the end of the chapter.

3. You invested $2,000 at 5.5 percent interest compounded quarterly for 1 year. You added $4,000 to the account at the end of 1 year. How much is in the account at the end of 2 more years?
1.05614 × $2,000 = $2,112.28; (2,112.28 + 4,000.00) × 1.11544 = $6,817.88

THINKING CRITICALLY

Using Tables and Charts

Use the Delivery Chart on page 762 to answer the following questions. Use the row and column headings to find the shipping charges.

1. An order weighing 10 lbs is to be delivered to Zone 1. What are the shipping charges? **$11.25**

2. An order weighing 3 lbs is to be delivered by Express custom delivery. How much are the shipping charges? **$11.00**

3. An order weighing 14 lbs is to be delivered by Express Plus delivery. What are the shipping charges? **$32.25**

SECTION 5-6 PRACTICE

Use Compound Interest—Amount of $1.00 table on page 797 to solve Problems 4 to 8. Round answers to the nearest cent.

	Principal	Annual Interest Rate	Interest Periods per Year	Total Time	Amount	Compound Interest
4.	$ 900.00	5.50%	4	2 years	a.$1,003.90	b. $103.90
5.	640.00	6.00%	2	1 year	a. $678.98	b. $38.98
6.	1,340.00	5.00%	4	3 years	a.$1,551.41	b. $215.41
7.	6,231.40	5.75%	2	5 years	a.$8,273.43	b.$2,042.03
8.	3,871.67	18.00%	12	6 months	a.$4,233.44	b. $361.77

9. State Bank pays 5.5 percent interest compounded semiannually on regular savings accounts. Iva Howe deposited $2,800 in a regular savings account for 2 years. She made no other deposits or withdrawals during the period. How much interest did her money earn? **$320.94**

10. Currito Zermeno deposited $900 in a savings plan with her credit union. The credit union savings plan pays 6 percent interest compounded quarterly. If she makes no other deposits or withdrawals, how much interest will her money earn in 1 year? **$55.22**

11. National Credit Union pays 6.25 percent interest compounded semiannually on special notice savings accounts. Jessie McKenzie deposits $3,438.70 in a special notice savings account for 2 years. At the end of 2 years, she deposits $5,000 in the account. How much is in the account at the end of 5 more years? **$12,092.02**

12. University Bank pays 5 percent interest compounded quarterly on regular savings accounts. Rose and Bob Yung had $4,000 on deposit for 1 year. At the end of the year, they withdrew all their money and deposited $4,000 at National Bank, which pays 5.75 percent compounded semiannually. How much more did the $4,000 earn at National Bank for 1 year? **$29.52**

13. Nathan Murphy opened a savings account at Savings and Loan on January 1 with a deposit of $800. Savings and Loan pays 11.5 percent interest compounded quarterly. What will the $800 be worth on January 1 of the following year? How much interest will the $800 have earned by January 1 of the following year? **$896.04; $96.04**

14. Wilma Bracken opened a savings account at Dallas Trust Bank on March 1. Dallas Trust pays 12 percent interest compounded quarterly. Bracken opened her account with an initial deposit of $10,000. She made $1,000 deposits at the end of each quarter. How much is in the account at the end of 6 quarters? **$17,408.93**

MAINTAINING YOUR SKILLS

Need Help? Go to...
➡ Skill 11: Dividing Decimals, page 738

Convert the percent to a decimal and then divide.

15. 8% ÷ 4 **0.02**   **16.** 4% ÷ 4 **0.01**   **17.** 6% ÷ 12 **0.005**

18. 7% ÷ 4 **0.0175**   **19.** 8.5% ÷ 2 **0.0425**   **20.** 3.5% ÷ 4 **0.00875**

GLOBAL PERSPECTIVE

Savings
Explain to students that on average individuals in the United States save about 5 percent of their income. In contrast, individuals in many other countries save a larger percent of their income. Direct students to discuss the economic problems the country faces because of the low level of savings. Then, have them write a letter or e-mail to a friend or family member, detailing the advantages of savings. LS , CL

WRAP-UP

Go over any problem for which a wrong answer is given.

Assignment Guide
   Basic: 4–8
   Average: 9–12

20 min.

SECTION 5-6

before they begin computing interest for that period.

One stumbling block may occur in computing the total number of interest periods. Remind students to carefully examine how often interest is compounded. Interest compounded semiannually is compounded twice a year, quarterly interest is compounded four times a year, and monthly interest is compounded twelve times a year. To find the total interest periods, multiply periods per year by the number of years (Step 1 in Example 1 on page 211). Then have students carefully follow Steps 2–5 to find the amount and the total interest, if required.

4 CLOSE

Closing Activity
Divide.

1. $\frac{10\%}{4}$ **2.5%**

2. $\frac{8.5\%}{2}$ **4.25%**

3. $\frac{7.2\%}{12}$ **0.6%**

4. Edmonton National Bank pays $5\frac{3}{4}$ percent interest compounded semiannually. Adrian Zechmcister deposits $20,000 in a savings account. He makes no additional deposits or withdrawals. What amount will be in the account in 12 years if the rate remains unchanged and he makes no additional deposits or withdrawals? **$39,488**

5. Arturo Mendez deposits $3,500 in a savings account that pays 5.5 percent interest compounded quarterly. He makes no additional deposits or withdrawals. What amount will be in the account 5 years later? **($4,599.21)** How much is interest? **$1,099.21**

6. Malcolm Edwards deposits $10,000 in an account that pays 12 percent interest compounded quarterly. If he has no further deposits or withdrawals, what amount will be in his account 4 years later? **$16,047**

National Standards for Business Education

Standard 1	Mathematical Foundations
Standard 2	Number Relationships and Operations

National Council of Teachers of Mathematics Standards

Standard 1	Numbers and Operations
Standard 4	Measurement
Standard 6	Problem Solving
Standard 8	Communication
Standard 9	Connections

1 FOCUS

Point out that students have learned that compounding semiannually earns more interest than compounding annually; compounding quarterly earns more than compounding semiannually; and monthly earns more than quarterly. The most competitive method of computing interest is compounding daily. That is the focus of this lesson.

In-Class Examples

Work through these exercises with students before having them do the Self-Check.

1. $500.00 × 1.01670 **$508.35**
2. $5,147.85 × 1.00452 **$5,171.12**
3. $7,435.89 × 1.00755 **$7,492.03**
4. $5,617.21 − $5,500 **$117.21**
5. $4,288.83 − $4,268.85 **$19.98**
6. $15,626.49 − $315.44 **$15,311.05**

Round to the nearest cent.

7. $5,417.205 **$5,417.21**
8. $6,429.4012 **$6,429.40**
9. $8,610.5591 **$8,610.56**
10. $44,238.4719 **$44,238.47**

○ Section Objective
Find interest for daily compounding.

Usually the more frequently interest is compounded, the more interest you will earn. Many banks offer savings accounts with **daily compounding.** When interest is compounded daily, it is computed each day and added to the account balance. The account will earn interest from the day of deposit to the day of withdrawal. A table can be used to calculate the amount and interest for daily compounding. Remember these formulas from previous sections:

$$\text{Amount} = \text{Original Principal} \times \text{Amount of \$1.00}$$

$$\text{Compound Interest} = \text{Amount} - \text{Original Principal}$$

Living in the Real World

Understanding the Williams Sisters

Growing Faster "The more often the bank adds interest to your account and recalculates the compound interest, the faster your account will grow," Mr. Gleason says. "If the bank compounds daily, you will earn interest on your interest almost immediately."

Draw Conclusions What are the benefits of compound interest over simple interest?

Continued on page 217

Need Help? Go to...

► Workshop 6: Multiplying Decimals, page 14
► Workshop 17: Elapsed Time, page 36
► Skill 8: Multiplying Decimals, page 735
► Application G: Elapsed Time (Days), page 765

Example 1

Suppose you deposit $8,000 in an account that pays 5.5 percent interest compounded daily. How much interest will you earn in 31 days?

STEP 1: Find the amount of $1.00 for 31 days using Figure 5.6.
= 1.00468

Figure 5.6

Amount of $1.00 at 5.5% Compounded Daily (365-Day Year)*			
Day	Amount	Day	Amount
21	1.00316	31	1.00468
22	1.00331	32	1.00483
23	1.00347	33	1.00498
24	1.00362	34	1.00513
25	1.00377	35	1.00528

*See the table on page 796 for more values.

Living in the Real World

Compound interest grows faster than simple interest. The more frequently interest compounds, the more money an accountholder will make.

USING CALCULATORS

The amount of compound interest can be determined using the following keystrokes: (original principal ×) amount of $1.00 from table) − original principal =.
Example: (500 × 1.00316) − 500 =
Have students explain what the above keystrokes represent.

STEP 2: Find the amount.

Original Principal × Amount of $1.00

$8,000.00   ×   1.00468   = $8,037.44

STEP 3: Find the compound interest.

Amount − Original Principal

$8,037.44 − $8,000.00   = **$37.44 compound interest**

CONCEPT CHECK

Complete the problems, then check your answers at the end of the chapter.

1. Six thousand dollars deposited at 5.5 percent interest compounded daily for 25 days.
   a. Find the amount. **1.00377 × $6,000 = $6,022.62**
   b. Find the compound interest. **$22.62**

2. Six thousand dollars deposited at 5.5 percent interest compounded daily for 31 days.
   a. Find the amount. **1.00468 × $6,000 = $6,028.08**
   b. Find the compound interest. **$28.08**

Example 2

Need Help? Go to...
▶ Workshop 17: Elapsed Time, page 36

On May 31 Deloris Zelms deposited $1,000 in a savings account that pays 5.5 percent interest compounded daily. On July 1 how much interest had been earned on the principal in her account?

STEP 1: Find the number of days from May 31 to July 1. Use the Elapsed Time table on page 796.

July 1 is day 182. May 31 is day 151.

182 − 151 = 31 days

STEP 2: Find the amount of $1.00 for 31 days using the Amount of $1.00 at 5.5 Percent, Compounded Daily (365-Day Year) table on page 796.

= 1.00468

STEP 3: Find the amount.

Original Principal × Amount of $1.00

$1,000.00   ×   1.00468   − $1,004.68

STEP 4: Find the compound interest.

Amount − Original Principal

$1,004.68 − $1,000.00   = **$4.68 compound interest**

CONCEPT CHECK

Complete the problem, then check your answer at the end of the chapter.

3. On February 1 (in a non-leap year) Raul Avila deposited $10,000 in a savings account that pays 5.5 percent interest compounded daily. On June 21 how much interest had been earned on the principal in the account?
   1.02131 × $10,000 = $10,213.10; $10,213.10 − $10,000 = $213.10

COOPERATIVE LEARNING

Creating a Visual Aid

As a group, choose one type of savings account. Conduct research and prepare a visual display describing the advantages and disadvantages of the selected savings account. Use local banks and the Internet as resources for your research. Share your visual display with the class.

CL , LS , P

---

② TEACH

In order to compound interest on a daily basis, students have to be able to figure out how many days the original principal was in the account. Have students practice using the Elapsed Time Table on page 796.

Point out that **Figure 5.6** on page 214 only computes an annual interest rate of 5.5 percent compounded daily. Separate tables would be needed to compute different annual interest rates. Daily compounding of interest relies on the use of computers.

Motivating the Lesson

In the last section you learned that the more frequently interest is compounded, the quicker money will grow. If you deposit $1,000 in an account that pays 5.5 percent interest compounded daily, you would have $1,021.31 at the end of 140 days. How much interest would your money earn? **$21.31**

In-Class Examples

1. Deposited $4,000 at 5.5 percent compounded for 35 days. Find the amount. **($4,021.12)** Find the compound interest. **$21.12**

2. Deposited $11,600 at 5.5 percent compounded for 130 days. Find the amount. **($11,829.33)** Find the compound interest. **$229.33**

3. Leon Evans deposited $6,325 in a savings account on June 27. The account pays 5.5 percent interest compounded daily. What amount will be in the account 39 days later? **($6,362.25)** How much will be compound interest? **$37.25**

4. On March 11 Nandakumar Shah deposited $800 in a savings account that pays 5.5 percent interest compounded daily. How much interest will be earned on the principal by July 19? **$15.82**

215

③ ASSESS

Error Analysis

Students may make errors when they compute the number of days an account is earning interest. Review how to use the Elapsed Time Table on page 796. Have students practice finding the day of the month in the first column and finding the month in the top row. Explain that the point where the column and row intersect is a number. Students will need to find the first day the money is in the account and the last day before any new deposits are made. Subtract the smaller number on the table from the larger number. The answer will tell them how many days to compute interest.

④ CLOSE

Closing Activity

Multiply. Round to the nearest cent.
1. $379 × 1.02131 **$387.08**
2. $7,324 × 1.00165 **$7,336.08**
3. Matt Li deposited $25,000 in a savings account. The account earns 5.5 percent interest compounded daily. What amount will he have in his account 28 days later? **$25,105.50** How much will be compound interest? **$105.50**
4. Lorena Quinones deposited $3,480 in a savings account on February 22. The account earns 5.5 percent interest compounded daily. What amount will be in the account on July 12? **$3,554.16** How much is compound interest? **$74.16**

Use the Amount of $1.00 at 5.5 Percent, Compounded Daily (365-Day Year) table on page 796 to solve. Round answers to the nearest cent. Interest is 5.5 percent compounded daily.

	Principal	Number of Days	Amount	Compound Interest
4.	$80,000	25	a. $80,301.60	b. $301.60
5.	900	31	a. $904.21	b. $4.21
6.	6,500	50	a. $6,549.08	b. $49.08
7.	3,800	90	a. $3,851.83	b. $51.83
8.	15,321	120	a. $15,600.30	b. $279.30

9. On June 10 Bertha Polanski deposited $8,241.78 in a savings account that pays 5.5 percent interest compounded daily. How much interest will the money earn in 31 days? **$38.57**

10. Oprah Egland has a savings account that earns 5.5 percent interest compounded daily. On May 5 the amount in the account was $28,214.35. How much interest will the money earn in 90 days? **$384.84**

11. On April 11 Ramona Jimerson had $6,521.37 in his savings account. The account pays 5.5 percent interest compounded daily. How much interest will the money earn by June 30? **$79.04**

12. On August 23 Diego Quiroz had $1,432.19 in his savings account at Camden Savings and Trust. The account earns 5.5 percent interest compounded daily. What will be the amount in his savings account when he closes it on October 1? **$1,440.63**

13. Debra Goforth's savings account shows a balance of $904.31 on March 1. The same day, she made a deposit of $375.00 to the account. She also made deposits of $500.00 on April 1 and May 1. The bank pays interest at a rate of 5.5 percent compounded daily. What will be the amount in her account on May 29? **$2,303.05**

Need Help? Go to...
➤ Skill 2: **Rounding Numbers,** page 729
➤ Skill 8: **Multiplying Decimals,** page 735

Multiply and round to the nearest hundredth.

14. $4,000 × 1.02131 **$4,085.24** 15. $9,000 × 1.00135 **$9,012.15**

16. $550 × 1.00907 **$554.99** 17. $1,437 × 1.00392 **$1,442.63**

18. $950 × 1.00392 **$953.72** 19. $1,416 × 1.01059 **$1,431.00**

20. $7,370 × 1.00347 **$7,395.57** 21. $41,520 × 1.00407 **$41,688.99**

22. $94 × 1.00196 **$94.18** 23. $389 × 1.00301 **$390.17**

24. $7,925.14 × 1.01670 **$8,057.49** 25. $327.78 × 1.00015 **$327.83**

WRAP-UP

Go over any problem for which a wrong answer is given.

Assignment Guide
  Basic: 4–8
Average: 9–12

20 min.

SECTION (5·8) Annuities

Section Objective

Compute the future value of an ordinary annuity and an annuity due.

Financial advisors recommend that their clients make regular deposits in a savings plan, such as an Individual Retirement Account (IRA). When an equal amount of money is deposited into an account at equal periods of time, this is called an **annuity**. There are two categories of annuities:

1. **Ordinary annuity** occurs when equal deposits are made at the *end* of each interest period (such as salaries).

2. **Annuity due** occurs when you have regular deposits at the *beginning* of the period (such as rent). The money immediately starts earning interest because it is deposited at the beginning of the interest period.

So how do you calculate the interest on a series of equal payments over regular intervals of time? Easy. Both annuity groups use the *future value*. This is the amount of money in the annuity account at the *end* of a specific period of time. To find the future value of an ordinary annuity, follow the steps in Example 1 below. (Throughout this section you might also refer to the expanded Future Value of an Ordinary Annuity for $1.00 per Period table on page 798.) For now familiarize yourself with the formula:

$$\text{Future Value} = \text{Amount of Deposit} \times \text{Future Value of } \$1.00$$

$$\begin{array}{c}\text{Future Value of} \\ \text{an Annuity Due}\end{array} = \begin{array}{c}\text{Future Value of an} \\ \text{Ordinary Annuity}\end{array} \times (\$1.00 + \text{Rate per Period})$$

Living in the Real World

Understanding the Williams Sisters

Get Proof "When you're done opening your account," Jaydene says to Aisha, "I'd like to start an annuity account. I received a raise at work. I want to make sure I make regular deposits into my annuity account."

Draw Conclusions How often can you add deposits to your annuity account?

Continued on page 221

Need Help? Go to...

▶ Workshop 18: **Reading Tables and Charts,** page 38
▶ Workshop 6: **Multiplying Decimals,** page 14
▶ Skill 8: **Multiplying Decimals,** page 735
▶ Application C: **Tables and Charts,** page 762

Example 1

Aiko Murakami deposits $500 in an ordinary annuity at the end of each quarter in an account earning 6 percent interest compounded quarterly. What is the future value of the account in 2 years?

STEP 1: Find the total number of periods.

Periods per Year × Number of Years

4 × 2 = 8

STEP 2: Find the interest rate per period.

$$\frac{\text{Annual Rate}}{\text{Number of Periods per Year}}$$

$$\frac{6\%}{4} = 1.5\%$$

Continued on next page

Section 5-8 Annuities ▶ **217**

Living in the Real World

Annuities are usually paid on a monthly, quarterly or annual basis. Even small additions to savings add up over time.

COMMUNICATION SKILLS

Special Report
Students prepare a special report on annuities for a three-minute financial news slot. Students find an article on annuities, perhaps using *BusinessWeek* magazine, *BusinessWeek* Online, or other financial sources. Students present the report to the class. CL , LS , P

National Standards for Business Education

Standard 1	Mathematical Foundations
Standard 2	Number Relationships and Operations

National Council of Teachers of Mathematics Standards

Standard 1	Numbers and Operations
Standard 4	Measurement
Standard 6	Problem Solving
Standard 8	Communication
Standard 9	Connections

① FOCUS

This lesson focuses on how money will grow in an account when equal deposits are made for regular periods of time. Students will learn to compute the future value of an *ordinary annuity*, (where a set amount of money is regularly deposited in the account at the *end* of each interest period) and the future value of an *annuity due* (where money is deposited at the *beginning* of the interest period).

In-Class Examples
Work through these exercises with students before having them do the Self-Check.

1. $300 × 4.03010 **$1,209.03**
2. $4,000 × 5.20404 **$20,816.16**
3. $6,000 × 10.70272 **$64,216.32**
4. $\frac{8\%}{4}$ **2%**
5. $\frac{4.5\%}{4}$ **1.125%**
6. $\frac{6.5\%}{2}$ **3.25%**

Write the percents as decimals.

7. 2.5% **0.025**
8. 6.75% **0.0675**

② TEACH

Make certain that students understand the difference between an ordinary annuity and an annuity due. As students work through each problem, help them determine whether they are asked to compute the future value of an ordinary annuity or the future value of an annuity due.

If students are computing the future value of an ordinary annuity, have them follow Steps 1–4 in Example 1 on page 217. Be sure they understand why it is necessary to find the total number of periods in Step 1 and the interest rate per period in Step 2 (This information is needed to find the future value of $1.00 in Step 3).

If students are computing the future value of an annuity due, have them follow Steps 1–3 in Example 2 on page 218. However, before they find the future value of an annuity due, they may first need to find the future value of an ordinary annuity if the value is not given.

Motivating the Lesson

Suppose you plan to invest $100 each quarter in a savings account that compounds interest quarterly. You plan to do this for 5 years. What amount (principal) would you have contributed to the account at the end of five years excluding any interest earned? **($2,000)** At the end of 10 years? **$4,000**

In-Class Examples

Refer to the Future Value of an Ordinary Annuity for $1.00 per Period on page 798 for the problems.

1. Suppose that Meredeith Young deposits $1,500 in an annuity due at the beginning of each year for 8 years. The account pays 7 percent interest compounded annually. What is the future value of the account in 8 years? **$16,466.98**

218

STEP 3: Find the future value of $1.00 for 8 periods at 1.5 percent per period using the Future Value of an Ordinary Annuity for $1.00 per Period table on page 798.
  = 8.43284

STEP 4: Find the future value.
  Amount of Deposit × Future Value of $1.00
  $500   ×   8.43284   = **$4,216.42 future value**

CONCEPT CHECK

SELF-CHECK✔

Complete the problems, then check your answers at the end of the chapter.

1. One thousand dollars is deposited into an ordinary annuity after each 6-month period for 2 years. The account pays 4 percent interest compounded semiannually. What is the future value of the account in 2 years?
  $1,000 × 4.12161 = $4,121.61

2. Five thousand dollars is deposited into an ordinary annuity after each quarter for 3 years. The account pays 6 percent interest compounded quarterly. What is the future value of the account in 3 years?
  $5,000 × 13.04121 = $65,206.05

ANNUITY DUE Now that you know how to calculate an ordinary annuity, it's time to learn how to calculate the other kind of annuity—the *annuity due*. An annuity due occurs when you have regular deposits at the *beginning* of the period. In an annuity due, the money starts earning interest immediately since it is deposited at the beginning of the interest period. The future value of an annuity due is found by multiplying the future value of an ordinary annuity by $1.00 plus the rate per period. It looks like this:

$$\text{Future Value of an Annuity Due} = \text{Future Value of an Ordinary Annuity} \times (\$1.00 + \text{Rate per Period})$$

Example 2

3. You know from Self-Check Problem 1 that the future value of the ordinary annuity is $4,121.61. You also know that the rate per period is 2 percent = 0.02. Therefore, $4,121.61 × ($1.00 + 0.02) = $4,121.61 × 1.02 = $4,204.04

Suppose that Aiko Murakami (from Example 1) had made $500 deposits in an annuity due at the beginning of each quarter in an account earning 6 percent interest compounded quarterly. What is the future value of the account in 2 years?

STEP 1: You know from Example 1 that the future value of the ordinary annuity is $4,216.42.

STEP 2: You also know that the rate per period is 1.5 percent.
  = 0.015

STEP 3: Use the calculation for future value of an annuity due.
  Future Value of an Ordinary Annuity × ($1.00 + Rate per Period)
  $4,216.42   × (1.00 +   0.015)
  = $4,216.42   ×   1.015
  = **$4,279.67 future value of an annuity due**

CONCEPT CHECK

SELF-CHECK✔

Complete the problems, then check your answers at the end of the chapter.

3. See Self-Check Problem 1. Suppose $1,000 is deposited into an annuity due at the beginning of each 6-month period for 2 years. The account pays 4 percent interest compounded semiannually. What is the future value of the account in 2 years?

BUSINESS NOTES

FDIC

Have you heard the phrase "FDIC insured"? The Federal Deposit Insurance Corporation (FDIC) was created in 1933. If you deposit money in a FDIC bank your money is protected up to $100,000 if the bank fails and can't return the money you deposited. Students brainstorm and then research the reasons why the FDIC was created.

CL

4. You know from Self-Check Problem 2 that the future value of the ordinary annuity is $65,206.05. You also know that the rate per period is 1.5 percent = 0.015. Therefore, $65,206.05 × ($1.00 + 0.015) = $65,206.05 × 1.015 = $66,184.14

4. See Self-Check Problem 2. Suppose $5,000 is deposited into an annuity due at the beginning of each quarter for 3 years. The account pays 6 percent interest compounded quarterly. What is the future value of the account in 3 years?

SECTION 5-8 PRACTICE

Use the Future Value of an Ordinary Annuity for $1.00 per Period table on page 798 to solve Problems 5–15.

	End of Period Deposit	Compounded	Rate	Years	Rate per Period	Number of Periods	Amount of $1.00	Future Value of Ordinary Annuity	$1.00 + Rate per Period	Future Value of Annuity Due
5.	$5,000	quarterly	6%	2	a.	b.	c.	d.	e.	f.
6.	800	semiannually	4%	6	a.	b.	c.	d.	e.	f.
7.	2,000	annually	4%	10	a.	b.	c.	d.	e.	f.
8.	1,000	monthly	6%	3	a.	b.	c.	d.	e.	f.
9.	525	quarterly	8%	10	a.	b.	c.	d.	e.	f.

5. a. 1.50
  b. 8
  c. 8.43284
  d. $42,164.20
  e. 1.0150
  f. $42,796.66

6. a. 2.00
  b. 12
  c. 13.41209
  d. $10,729.67
  e. 1.0200
  f. $10,944.27

7. a. 4.00
  b. 10
  c. 12.00611
  d. $24,012.22
  e. 1.0400
  f. $24,972.71

8. a. 0.50
  b. 36
  c. 39.33610
  d. $39,336.10
  e. 1.0050
  f. $39,532.78

9. a. 2.00
  b. 40
  c. 60.40198
  d. $31,711.04
  e. 1.0200
  f. $32,345.26

> **Need Help? Go to...**
> ➤ Skill 8: **Multiplying Decimals,** page 735

10. Regina Aguirre deposits $2,000 into an ordinary annuity after each 6-month period for 4 years. The account pays 6 percent interest compounded semiannually. What is the future value of the account in 4 years? **$17,784.68**

11. Vernon Taber deposits $600 into an ordinary annuity after each quarter for 4 years. The account pays 4 percent interest compounded quarterly. What is the future value of the account in 4 years? **$10,354.72**

12. Rob Walthall deposits $4,000 in an annuity due at the beginning of each 6-month period for 4 years. The account pays 6 percent interest compounded semiannually. What is the future value of the account in 4 years? **$36,636.44**

13. Suppose Kimi Matsumoto deposits $2,000 at the beginning of each year into an Individual Retirement Account at Boise Bank. The account pays 7 percent compounded annually. How much will be in the account in 25 years? **$135,352.95**

14. Jane Martin-Smith and her husband deposited $500 in an account on their wedding day and each subsequent anniversary. The money was deposited in an account that pays 7 percent compounded annually. How much will they have on their 25th anniversary? **$31,624.52**

15. Richard and Elaine McCormick would like to have $20,000 in 5 years to make a down payment on a home. They decide to save $350 at the beginning of each month for the next 4 years. The money is in an account that pays 6 percent compounded monthly. How much will they need to save the fifth year? **$971.09**

MAINTAINING YOUR SKILLS

Multiply.

16. $2,000 × 1.05000
  $2,100

17. $8,000 × 1.45210
  $11,616.80

18. $6,250 × 2.01500
  $12,593.75

19. $3,698 × 4.12161
  $15,241.71

20. $1,100 × 5.10101
  $5,611.11

21. $1,587 × 6.07550
  $9,641.82

22. $8,520 × 3.01502
  $25,687.97

23. $45,620 × 7.10588
  $324,170.24

24. $980 × 9.18212
  $8,998.48 (or $8,998.47 or $8,998.478)

Section 5-8 Annuities ▶ **219**

WRAP-UP

Go over any problem for which a wrong answer is given.

Assignment Guide
  Basic: 5–9
  Average: 10–14

20 min.

SECTION 5-8

2. Jasmine Reynolds deposits $3,200 in an annuity due at the beginning of each year. The account pays 5 percent interest compounded annually. What amount will be in the account in 15 years? **$72,503.96**

ASSESS

Error Analysis
Remind students that when computing the future value of an ordinary annuity, they must first find the total interest periods and the rate per period. Also, remind students to look over their work to see that they have used decimals correctly.

CLOSE

Closing Activity
Use Future Value of an Ordinary Annuity for $1.00 per period on page 798 for Problems 3 and 4.

1. $6,340 × 5.10101 **$32,340.40**

2. $24,700 × 2.01500 **$49,770.50**

3. Jamie LaRocca deposits $1,200 in an ordinary annuity at the end of each 6-month period. The account pays 6 percent interest compounded semiannually. What is the future value of the account in 25 years? **$135,356.24**

4. Noriko Matsunami deposits $900 in an annuity due at the beginning of each quarter for 3 years. The account pays 6 percent interest compounded quarterly. What is the future value of the account in 3 years? **$11,913.15**

Quick Quiz

1. Nancy Genova's savings account shows a previous balance of $2,360.54. She made deposits of $35.00, $125.00, and $200.00. She had withdrawals of $350.00 and $75.00. Her account earned interest of $5.23. What is her new balance? **$2,300.77**

2. Leander Paine deposits $1,600 in a savings account. The account pays an annual interest rate of 4 percent. He makes no other deposits or withdrawals. How much simple interest does his money earn in 6 months? **$32**

3. Hortencia Aurilla deposits $5,000 in a savings account. The account pays 7 percent annual interest compounded semiannually. Find the amount after 1 year. How much is compound interest? **$5,356.13; $356.13**

For Problem 4, use the Amount of $1.00 at 5.5 percent Compounded Daily (365-day year) table on page 796 and the Elapsed Time Table on page 796.

4. On May 7 Suzanne Dombrowski deposits $600 in a savings account that pays 5.5 percent interest compounded daily. What amount will be in her account on September 14 if she makes no deposits or withdrawals? **($611.86)** How much is compound interest? **$11.86**

SECTION 5·1 CONCEPT CHECK (p. 196, 197)

1. ($160.00 + $10.95 + $114.35) − $25.00 = $285.30 − $25.00 = **$260.30**
2. ($125.60 + $180.00 + $22.21) − $20.00 = $327.81 − $20.00 = **$307.81**
3. $152.54 + $147.46 = $300.00; $54.00 + (12 × $5) + (6 × $10) = $54 + $60 + $60 = $174; (35 × $0.25) + (18 × $0.10) + (40 × $0.05) + $0.75 = $8.75 + $1.80 + $2.00 + $0.75 = $13.30; $0.75 + $300 + $174 + $13.30 = $487.30 − $50 = **$437.30**

SECTION 5·2 CONCEPT CHECK (p. 199, 200)

1. Sixty and $\frac{00}{100}$ dollars
2. Two hundred eighty and $\frac{50}{100}$ dollars
3. $98.75
4. $6,586.95
5. a. January 10, 20-- b. 559821 c. yes d. Tyrone Shumpert

SECTION 5·3 CONCEPT CHECK (p. 202, 203)

1. $979.75
2. $1,902.00
3. $700.00 + $1.50 + ($100.00 + $250.00) − ($80.00 + $110.00) =
   $701.50 + $350.00 − $190.00 = **$861.50**

SECTION 5·4 CONCEPT CHECK (p. 206)

1. $400 × 6% × $\frac{3}{12}$; $400 × 0.06 × 0.25 = **$6.00**
2. $1,500 × 0.025 × $\frac{6}{12}$ = **$18.75**
3. a. $1.97 b. $1.97 c. $1.03 d. $0.99 e. $5.96 f. $2,005.96
4. a. $18.98 b. $11,618.98

SECTION 5·5 CONCEPT CHECK (p. 209)

1. $2,000 × 0.08 × $\frac{1}{2}$ = $80; $2,080 × 0.08 × $\frac{1}{2}$ = $83.20; **$2,163.20**
2. $2,163.20 − $2,000 = **$163.20**

SECTION 5·6 CONCEPT CHECK (p. 212)

1. 1.11544 × $2,000 = **$2,230.88**
2. 1.06136 × $4,500 = **$4,776.12**
3. 1.05614 × $2,000 = $2,112.28; (2,112.28 + 4,000.00) × 1.11544 = **$6,817.88**

SECTION 5·7 CONCEPT CHECK (p. 215)

1. a. 1.00377 × $6,000 = **$6,022.62** b. **$22.62**
2. a. 1.00468 × $6,000 = **$6,028.08** b. **$28.08**
3. 1.02131 × $10,000 = $10,213.10; $10,213.10 − $10,000 = **$213.10**

SECTION 5·8 CONCEPT CHECK (p. 218, 219)

1. $1,000 × 4.12161 = **$4,121.61**
2. $5,000 × 13.04121 = **$65,206.05**
3. You know from Self-Check Problem 1 that the future value of the ordinary annuity is $4,121.61. You also know that the rate per period is 2 percent = 0.02. Therefore, $4,121.61 × ($1.00 + 0.02) = $4,121.61 × 1.02 = **$4,204.04**
4. You know from Self-Check Problem 2 that the future value of the ordinary annuity is $65,206.05. You also know that the rate per period is 1.5 percent = 0.015. Therefore, $65,206.05 × ($1.00 + 0.015) = $65,206.05 × 1.015 = **$66,184.14**

Living in the Real World

Understanding the Williams Sisters

Assessment   A savings account is a good way to ease into financial independence. The golden rule is to put money aside each month for unexpected expenses (such as your car breaking down) and long-term goals, such as purchasing a car or taking a trip to Jamaica. As your savings account balance grows, you should consider other investments that can earn a potentially higher return. If inflation increases at a higher rate than your savings account return, you can lose purchasing power. Consider that a loaf of bread that cost $.50 twenty years ago now costs about $2.00, an increase of 400 percent. Money you set aside for long-term goals, such as retirement, will need to earn more than the rates usually paid on savings accounts to stay ahead of the inflation and taxes.

Now that you've read about Aisha and Jaydene, answer these questions as they pertain to your life.

① **Analyzing.** Looking at your family's financial situation, what unexpected expenses has your family had? Name them. How did your family react and deal with it?

② **Communicating.** Long-term financial security starts with saving. How does you family view saving, spending, and borrowing money?

③ **Predicting.** When you strike out on your own, what will be your personal financial strategy for saving money? Explain how your experiences have shaped your outlook.

REVIEW OF KEY WORDS

Write your own definition for each of the terms below.

1. savings account (p. 196)
2. deposit (p. 196)
3. withdrawal (p. 199)
4. account statement (p. 202)
5. interest (p. 205)
6. principal (p. 205)
7. annual interest rate (p. 205)
8. simple interest (p. 205)
9. compound interest (p. 208)
10. daily compounding (p. 214)
11. annuity (p. 217)
12. ordinary annuity (p. 217)
13. annuity due (p. 217)

1–13. Answers will vary. Evaluate based on the students' understanding of the term and their ability to put the definition into their own words.

For Problem 5 use the Future Value of an Ordinary Annuity for $1.00 per Period on page 798.

5. Ron Chao deposits $350 in an annuity due at the beginning of each quarter. The account pays 8 percent interest compounded quarterly. What is the future value of the account in 11 years? **$24,812.45**

Living in the Real World

1. Answers will vary depending on your situation.

2. Answers will vary depending on your situation.

3. Answers will vary depending on your situation. Ask them what personal finance strategies have they already taken away from this class that can be applied to their life.

CHAPTER 5 Study Guide and Assessment

Skills and Concepts

SECTION OBJECTIVE 5-1 AND EXAMPLES

Complete a savings account deposit slip, and compute the total deposit.

Fredie Enberg has 34 one-dollar bills in currency, $8.74 in coins, and a check for $102.35 to deposit into his savings account. He wants to receive a ten-dollar bill in cash. How much will he deposit?

STEP: Compute the total deposit.

(Currency + Coins + Checks) − Cash Received
($34.00 + $8.74 + $102.35) − $10.00 = **$135.09 total deposit**

REVIEW EXERCISES
Find the subtotal and total deposit.

	Deposits	Subtotal	Less Cash Received	Total Deposit
14.	$ 38.90 34.28 21.01	a. $94.19	$ 0.00	b. $94.19
15.	93.44 12.58 102.66	a. $208.68	35.50	b. $173.18
16.	184.66 54.76 96.44	a. $335.86	50.98	b. $284.88
17.	13.49 122.34 77.45	a. $213.28	115.00	b. $98.28
18.	33.28 45.98 67.98	a. $147.24	15.50	b. $131.74
19.	101.95 10.29 75.65	a. $187.89	75.00	b. $112.89

Complete the deposit slip on a separate sheet of paper.

20. Hazel Bruot fills out the savings deposit form shown. What is her total deposit? **$226.83**

DEPOSITED FOR ACCOUNT OF		DOLLARS	CENTS	
Hazel Bruot	CASH	31	17	
	LIST EACH SEPARATELY	92	12	
Address 412 E. Broadway	CHECKS 77	13	BE SURE EACH ITEM IS PROPERLY ENDORSED
Milton, NC 22020	26	41	
Date October 11 , 20			
FEDERAL SAVINGS TRENTON HEIGHTS	TOTAL		

All items are received by this Bank for purposes of collection and all credits for items are provisional. Use REGISTERED MAIL when mailing cash or coupons.

SAVINGS ACCOUNT DEPOSIT TICKET

REINFORCEMENT

Section 5-1

1. Naomi Greenberg fills out a deposit slip for her savings account. She deposits a check for $445.96. She also has $215.44 in cash and $23.17 in coins. What is her total deposit? **$684.57**

2. Jeff Nelson stops at the bank on his way home from work to deposit the following checks in his savings account: $33.61, $70.58, $225.60, and $391.90. What is his total deposit? **$721.69**

3. Rafael Valderez owns a carryout shrimp business. On Saturday, he deposits checks for $26.27 and $19.53 in his savings account. He also deposits 138 one-dollar bills, 62 five-dollar bills, 81 ten-dollar bills in currency, 60 quarters, 97 dimes, 59 nickels, and 42 pennies in coins. What is his total deposit for the week? **$1,331.87**

SECTION OBJECTIVE 5-2 AND EXAMPLES

Fill out a savings account withdrawal slip.

Serita Escobar would like to withdraw $85.34 from her savings account. Her account number is 00–170–14. Write (a) the account number, (b) the amount as a numeral, and (c) the amount in words.

a. 00–170–14   b. $85.34   c. *Eighty-five and $\frac{34}{100}$ dollars*

REVIEW EXERCISES

Write each amount in words as it would appear on a withdrawal slip.

21. $21.44   22. $396.00

For Problems 23–25, write (a) the account number, (b) the amount as a numeral, and (c) the amount in words.

23.

Farmer's Mercantile		
Date	Savings Acct. No.	
11/8/20--	06029175	$76.60
Pay to Myself or to	Damone Bashier	
Seventy-six and $\frac{60}{100}$		Dollars
And Charge to the above Numbered Account		
Sign Here	Damone Bashier	
Withdrawal		

24. a. 8642-00-908
    b. $2,359.04
    c. Two thousand three hundred fifty-nine and $\frac{04}{100}$ dollars

24. Murphie Wohler has been saving to buy a big-screen TV. The total purchase price is $2,359.04. She fills out a withdrawal slip for the amount. Her savings account number is 8642–00–908.

25. Ruben LaChorrera loves baseball. He has been saving to buy season tickets for the Atlanta Braves. The total purchase price is $985.40. He fills out a withdrawal slip for the amount. His savings account number is 045–8996.

25. a. 045-8996
    b. $985.40
    c. Nine hundred eighty-five and $\frac{40}{100}$ dollars

SECTION OBJECTIVE 5-3 AND EXAMPLES

Compute the new balance on a savings account statement.

Your savings account statement shows a previous balance of $543.92 and $1.23 in interest. You made deposits of $100, $50, and $300.86. You had withdrawals of $35.46 and $128.44. What is your new balance?

21. Twenty-one and $\frac{44}{100}$ dollars

22. Three hundred ninety-six and $\frac{00}{100}$ dollars

STEP: Compute the new balance.

Previous Balance + Interest + Deposits − Withdrawals
$543.92   + $1.23 + ($100 + $50 + $300.86) − ($35.46 + $128.44) = **$832.11**

REVIEW EXERCISES

26. Previous balance, $650.25; interest, $4.02; deposit, $125.44; withdrawal, $50. What is the new balance? **$729.71**

27. Previous balance, $2,349.95; interest, $21.34; deposit, $125.00; withdrawal, $409.86. What is the new balance? **$2,086.43**

28. Sergio Santiago's savings account statement showed a previous balance of $234.95 and interest of $1.06. The statement also showed deposits of $123.42 and $50.66 and withdrawals of $323.09. What is his new balance? **$234.95 + $1.06 + ($123.42 + $50.66) − $323.09 = $87.00**

29. Tasi Sun's savings account statement showed a previous balance of $21,395.65 and interest of $14.39. The statement also showed deposits of $498.88 and $98.10 and withdrawals of $8,498.23. What is her new balance?

29. $21,395.65 + $14.39 + ($498.88 + $98.10) − $8,498.23 = $13,508.79

REINFORCEMENT

Section 5-2

1. Mario Giovanelli makes the following deposit in his savings account: 4 one-hundred-dollar bills, 3 fifty-dollar bills, 17 twenty-dollar bills, 25 ten-dollar bills, 22 five-dollar bills, and 39 one-dollar bills. He also deposits his income tax refund check for $758.35. What is his total deposit? **$2,047.35**

Section 5-3

1. Teresa Estrada received her savings account statement. Her previous balance was $2,039.63. On May 31 her account earned $3.39 in interest. On June 5 she made a deposit of $708.00, and on June 14 she deposited $375.00. On June 28 she withdrew $1,412.56 to purchase new kitchen appliances. What is the balance in her account on each day in which a transaction occurred? **$2,043.02 on May 31; $2,751.02 on June 5; $3,126.02 on June 14; $1,713.46 on June 28**

SECTION OBJECTIVE 5-4 AND EXAMPLES

Calculate simple interest.

Your principal is $800. The annual rate of interest is $5\frac{1}{2}$ percent. What is the interest after 6 months?

STEP: Find the interest at $5\frac{1}{2}$ percent.

Principal × Rate × Time

$800.00 × $5\frac{1}{2}$% × $\frac{6}{12}$

$800.00 × 0.055 × 0.5 = **$22.00 in interest**

REVIEW EXERCISES

	Principal	Rate	Time	Interest
30.	$328.00	5%	3 months	**$4.10**
31.	635.85	7%	6 months	**$22.25**
32.	175.00	8%	9 months	**$10.50**

33. Craig Deloy's bank computes $4\frac{1}{4}$ percent interest on a daily basis. He had $1,250 in the account for 20 days. He makes a deposit of $450 and it is in the account for 10 days. He withdraws $300 and the balance earns interest for 8 days. How much interest does he earn? What is the amount in the account at the end of the month?

33. A. $1,250 × 0.0425 × $\frac{20}{365}$ = $2.9109 = **$2.91**

B. ($1,250 + $450) × 0.0425 × $\frac{10}{365}$ = $1.9789 = **$1.98**

C. ($1,700 − $300) × 0.0425 × $\frac{8}{365}$ = $1.3030 = **$1.30**

Total Interest for the Month = $6.19; Account at end of month: $1,406.19

SECTION OBJECTIVE 5-5 AND EXAMPLES

Figure out the compound interest and the amount.

Pat Villone deposited $3,000 into a savings account that earns 4 percent interest compounded quarterly. She made no deposits or withdrawals. What was the amount in the account at the end of the second quarter?

STEP: Find the amount for each quarter.

1ˢᵗ quarter   Principal × Rate × Time = Interest

$3,000.00 × 4% × $\frac{1}{4}$ = $30.00

Principal + Interest = Amount

$3,000.00 + $30.00 = $3,030.00

2ⁿᵈ quarter $3,030.00 × 4% × $\frac{1}{4}$ = $30.30

Principal + Interest = Amount

$3,030.00 + $30.30 = **$3,060.30 amount at end of second quarter**

REINFORCEMENT

Section 5-4

1. Victoria Wright deposited $1,500 in a savings account. No other deposits or withdrawals were made. The account paid an annual interest rate of 2 percent. How much simple interest did her money earn after 6 months? **$15.00**

2. Rodolfo Ortega deposited $4,200 in a new savings account. The bank pays $5\frac{1}{4}$ percent simple interest computed on a daily basis. He made no other deposits or withdrawals. How much simple interest will his money earn after 214 days? **$129.28**

Section 5-5

1. Alison Strauss deposited $2,500 in a savings account which pays $5\frac{1}{4}$ percent interest compounded quarterly. She made no deposits or withdrawals.

a. What was the amount in the account at the end of the second quarter? **$2,566.05**

b. How much is compound interest? **$66.05**

34. $350 × 6.5% × \frac{1}{2}$ = $11.38 (rounded from $11.375)

($350 + 11.38) × 6.5% × \frac{1}{2}$ = $11.74; $361.38 + $11.74 = $373.12

REVIEW EXERCISES

34. Dak Nardo deposited $350 into a new regular savings account that earns 6.5 percent interest compounded semiannually. He made no other deposits or withdrawals. What was his amount in the account at the end of 1 year?

	Principal	Annual Interest Rate	Interest Period	First Period Interest	Amount	Second Period Interest	Amount
35.	$1,200.00	6.0%	quarterly	a.	b.	c.	d.
36.	3,500.00	5.5%	monthly	a.	b.	c.	d.
37.	965.00	$3\frac{1}{4}$%	quarterly	a.	b.	c.	d.

35. a. $18.00
  b. $1,218.00
  c. $18.27
  d. $1,236.27

36. a. $16.04
  b. $3,516.04
  c. $16.11 (or rounded $16.12)
  d. $3,532.15 (or rounded $3,532.16)

37. a. $7.84
  b. $972.84
  c. $7.90
  d. $980.74

SECTION OBJECTIVE 5-6 AND EXAMPLES

Find compound interest using tables.

First Central Bank pays 6 percent interest compounded quarterly on a regular savings accounts. Shawn Green deposited $6,500 for 3 years. He made no other deposits or withdrawals. How much interest did he earn during the 3 years?

STEP 1: Find the total interest periods.

Periods per Year × Number of Years

4 quarters per year × 3 years = 12 total interest periods

STEP 2: Find the interest rate per period.

$$\frac{\text{Annual Rate}}{\text{Number of Periods per Year}}$$

$$\frac{6\%}{4} = 1.5\%$$

STEP 3: Find the amount of $1.00 for 8 periods at 1.5 percent per period using the Compound Interest—Amount of $1.00 table on page 797.
  = 1.12649

STEP 4: Find the amount.
  Original Principal × Amount of $1.00
        $6,500 × 1.19562 = $7,771.53

STEP 5: Find the compound interest.
  Amount − Original Principal
  $7,771.53 − $6,500 = **$1,271.53 compound interest**

Continued on next page

REINFORCEMENT

Section 5-5 *(cont'd)*

2. On July 1 Jeff Wagoner deposited $1,925 in a new savings account. The principal earns $3\frac{3}{4}$ percent compounded monthly. They had no deposits or withdrawals.
  a. What was the amount in the account at the end of September? **$1,943.10**
  b. How much is compound interest? **$18.10**

Section 5-6

1. You invested $8,240 at 5.75 percent compounded semiannually for 3 years. No additional deposits or withdrawals. Find the amount. **$9,767.53**

2. You invested $12,000 at 15 percent compounded monthly for 8 months. No additional deposits or withdrawals. Find the amount. **($13,253.76)** How much interest did the money earn in 8 months? **$1,253.76**

38. A. Find the total interest periods.
= Periods per Year × Number of Years
= 2 periods per year × 2 years
= 4 total interest periods

B. Find the interest rate per period.
$\frac{5.5\%}{2} = 2.75\%$

C. Find the amount of $1.00 for 4 periods at 2.75% per period.
It is 1.11462.

D. Find the amount.
= Original Principal × Amount of $1.00
= $875 × 1.11462 = $975.29

E. Find the compound interest.
= $975.29 − $875 = $100.29 compound interest

REVIEW EXERCISES

Use Compound Interest—Amount of $1.00 table on page 797 to solve. Round answers to the nearest cent.

38. Kathy Cole deposited $875 in a savings plan with her employer's credit union. The credit union savings plan pays $5\frac{1}{2}$ percent interest compounded semiannually. If she makes no other deposits or withdrawals, how much interest will her money earn in 2 years?

	Principal	Annual Interest Rate	Interest Periods per Year	Total Time	Amount	Compound Interest
39.	$1,200.00	6.0%	semiannually	1 year	a.$1,273.08	b. $73.08
40.	750.00	5.5%	quarterly	3 years	a. $883.55	b. $133.55
41.	1,230.00	5.0%	quarterly	2 years	a.	b.

41. a. $1,358.51 (or rounded $1,358.52)
b. $128.51 (or rounded $128.52)

SECTION OBJECTIVE 5-7 AND EXAMPLES

Find interest for daily compounding.

Imagine you deposit $4,500 into an account that pays 5.5 percent interest compounded daily. How much interest will you earn in 30 days? (Note: Use the Amount of $1.00 at 5.5 Percent Compounded Daily (365-Day Year) table on page 796.)

STEP 1: Find the amount of $1.00 using the Amount of $1.00 at 5.5 Percent Compounded Daily (365-Day Year) table on page 796 for 30 days.
= 1.00452

STEP 2: Find the amount.
Original Principal × Amount of $1.00
$4,500 × 1.00452 = $4,520.34

STEP 3: Find the compound interest.
Amount − Original Principal
$4,520.34 − $4,500 = $20.34

45. Find the number of days from June 30 to August 1. Use the Elapsed Time table on page 796. August 1 is day 213. June 30 is day 181.
213 − 181 = 32 days
Find the amount of $1.00 for 32 days. It is 1.00483.
$1,500 × 1.00483 = $1,507.25
$1,507.25 − $1,500 = $7.25

REVIEW EXERCISES

Use the Amount of $1.00 at 5.5 Percent Compounded Daily (365-Day Year) table on page 796 to solve. Round answers to the nearest cent.

	Principal	Number of Days	Amount	Compound Interest
42.	$120,000	30	a. $120,542.40	b. $542.40
43.	8,500	40	a. $8,551.34	b. $51.34
44.	1,730	60	a. $1,745.69	b. $15.69

45. On June 30 Ed Klempel deposited $1,500 into a savings account that pays 5.5 percent interest compounded daily. On August 1 how much interest had been earned on the principal in his account?

REINFORCEMENT

Section 5-6 (cont'd)

3. You invested $1,900 at 6.25 percent compounded semiannually for 5 years. No additional deposits or withdrawals. Find the amount. **$2,584.59** How much interest did the money earn in 5 years? **$684.59**

Section 5-7

1. On April 20 Veronica Osborne deposited $1,600 in a savings account. The account pays 5.5 percent interest compounded daily. How much interest will the money earn by May 26? **$8.69**

2. Benjamin Finestein's savings account has a balance of $2,404.53 on September 2. The account earns 5.5 percent interest compounded daily. What amount will be in the account on November 21? **$2,433.67**

SECTION OBJECTIVE 5-8 AND EXAMPLES

Compute the future value of an ordinary annuity and an annuity due.

Suppose you deposited $750 into an ordinary annuity at the end of each quarter in an account earning 6 percent interest compounded quarterly. What is the future value of the account in 3 years? Suppose it had been an annuity due instead. What would be the future value of the account in 3 years?

STEP 1: Find the total number of periods.

Periods per Year × Number of Years

$$4 \quad \times \quad 3 \quad = 12$$

STEP 2: Find the interest rate per period.

$$\frac{\text{Annual Rate}}{\text{Number of Periods per Year}}$$

$$\frac{6\%}{4} = 1.5\%$$

STEP 3: Find the future value of $1.00 for 12 periods at 1.5 percent from the Future Value of an Ordinary Annuity for $1.00 per Period table on page 798.

= $13.04121

STEP 4: Find the future value.

Amount of Deposit × Future Value of $1.00

$$\$750 \quad \times \quad \$13.04121 \quad = \$9,780.91$$

(Note: This is the rounded number of $9,780.908.)

STEP 5: Find the future value of an annuity due.

$9,780.91 × ($1.00 + 0.015)

$9,780.91 × 1.015 = **$9,927.62 future value of an annuity due**

(Note: This is the rounded number of $9,927.624.)

REVIEW EXERCISES

46. Walton Clark deposited $1,750 into an ordinary annuity at the end of each quarter in an account earning 8 percent interest compounded quarterly. What is the future value of the account in 3 years?

Use the Future Value of an Ordinary Annuity for $1.00 per Period table on page 798 to solve the following.

	End of Period Deposit	Compounded	Rate	Years	Rate per Period	Number of Periods	Amount of $1.00	Future Value of Ordinary Annuity	
47.	$3,000	quarterly	4%	2	a. 1%	b. 8	c.	d. $24,857.01	c. $8.28567
48.	900	semiannually	4%	4	a. 2%	b. 8	c.	d. $7,724.67	c. $8.58297
49.	2,500	quarterly	8%	3	a. 2%	b. 12	c.	d. $33,530.22	c. $13.41209

(or rounded $33,530.23)

50. Elmer Pasture deposits $2,000 at the end of each year into an Individual Retirement Account at Boise Bank. The account pays 7 percent compounded annually. How much will be in the account in 25 years? **$126,498.08**

46.

A. Find the total number of periods.
Periods per Year × Number of Years
4 × 3 = 12

B. Find the interest rate per period.
Rate per Period =
$$\frac{\text{Annual Rate}}{\text{Number of Periods per Year}} =$$
$$\frac{8\%}{4} = 2\%$$

C. Find the future value of $1.00 for 12 periods at 2% per period. It is $13.41209.

D. Find the future value.
Future Value = Amount of Deposit × Future Value of $1.00 = $1,750 × $13.41209 = **$23,471.16**

REINFORCEMENT

Section 5-8

Refer to the Future Value of an Ordinary Annuity for $1.00 per Period on page 798 for Problem 1.

1. Meredith Young deposits $1,500 in an ordinary annuity after each year for 8 years. The account pays 7 percent interest compounded annually. What is the future value of the account in 8 years? **$15,389.70**

2. Margarita Tejada deposits $1,000 in an IRA account each year at the beginning of the year. The account pays 8 percent interest compounded annually. What is the value of the account in 20 years? **$49,422.92** If she continued to deposit $1,000 at the beginning of each year for an additional 15 years, what is the value of the account at the end of 35 years? **$186,102.14**

① FOCUS

Math Studio Overview

Students are asked to prepare an advertising campaign for an Alaskan savings and loan that draws on the metaphor of the Mendenhall Glacier as it pertains to saving habits. Students are asked to come up with a logo and prepare a "pitch" for the savings and loan executives that will persuade them that the creative ad campaign will drive more clients to open savings accounts.

Bell Ringer Activity

Write the following on the board: "Another metaphor for money is _____." Ask students to think of as many words as possible to fill in the blank. Some likely answers
• time—"time is money"
• water—"drowning in money"
• idea—"putting in her two cents worth."

② TEACH

Cooperative Learning

Ask groups of students to find examples of advertisements for banks or other financial institutions in magazines or newspapers. Have them mount the advertisements for display or scan them for use in a PowerPoint presentation. Ask groups to give a short oral report detailing some of the ads.
• Who are some of the biggest competitors in your area for the average person's savings or investment dollars?
• Which ones were most persuasive or most memorable? Explain your answer.

Have students point out visual techniques used in the advertisements to make them persuasive or appealing.

A Cool Savings Strategy

You may not realize it, but glaciers have a lot in common with your approach to saving money. Both you and a glacier transport, erode, and deposit. Both try to move ahead. And both can dwindle if not enough is added to them.

The marketing director of a new savings and loan company in Alaska has asked your advertising firm to put together a marketing campaign to draw new customers. You have decided to use an advertising theme that draws on Alaska's natural beauty.

Purpose

Alaska is a land of many glaciers, including the renowned Mendenhall Glacier, a favorite tourist spot near the state's capital, Juneau. You will develop an ad campaign for Mendenhall Savings & Loan that uses the famous glacier as a metaphor for a typical savings account owner.

Supplies Needed

• Pen, paper
• Colored pencils, markers
• Poster board
• Computer

Your Activity

Step 1: You'll be preparing a "pitch" for the executives of Mendenhall Savings & Loan to persuade them that your ad campaign will encourage more customers to invest in savings accounts in their bank. The materials you prepare must persuade the savings and loan company (your client) that your ad theme and visual presentation will be successful in bringing them more business. In other words, your presentation needs to persuade your clients that you can persuade their customers!

Successful advertising executives know how to develop campaigns that are appropriate for their clients and attractive and convincing to consumers. You'll need to create a catchy, memorable slogan (for example, Nike's "Just Do It"; Chevrolet trucks' "Like a Rock").

Step 2: Even if you don't own a savings account, you probably understand how one works. Before you begin designing your ad campaign, however, you also will need to understand something about glaciers.

Think about areas of high elevation such as the tops of high mountains (or high latitude like the land near the Arctic Circle, where snow that falls during the winter never completely melts even in the summer). Eventually, a large *snowfield* develops, and as the years pass, this thick layer may turn into a *glacier*. Glaciers exhibit the following characteristics:

• They are large and permanent.
• They move.
• They consist of thick layers of ice with snow on top.

NEWSWORTHY TREND

Saving for College: Part 1

Saving money for a college education has become easier in recent years. As larger numbers of high school graduates move on to two- and four-year institutions, federal, state, and banking programs are being created to ease the burden of ever increasing higher learning costs.

Pre-paid tuition programs can lock in today's tuition rates, allowing parents, grandparents and other interested parties to purchase amounts of tuition (years or units) in a one-time lump sum or monthly installment payments. These funds can then be used at any of the state's eligible colleges or universities, or an equal payment to private and out-of-state schools. These programs pool money and make long-term investments so that earnings meet or surpass tuition increases.

Glaciers are powerful, natural forces. Like natural bulldozers, glaciers *erode* (or *withdraw*) tons of material from the land as they move. They later *deposit* this material—much of it huge boulders. When the glacier melts, these deposits remain behind as large hills, or *moraines*.

Now that you know something about glaciers, try to create an ad campaign using at least one of the features of glaciers as a metaphor (a symbol) for a savings account owner. You probably won't want to include all the features of glaciers, but, rather, focus on one. For instance, glaciers deposit boulders that grow into moraines; people deposit money into savings accounts that grow through interest.

Stretch your imagination and try to find interesting parallels between the actions of glaciers and the actions of savings account depositors.

Step 3: Create a description of how the theme will be used in words and graphics. This should require at least several paragraphs. The description should:

- explain why the glacier theme has been chosen,
- show why you think it will influence customers, and
- offer several examples of how it can be used verbally and visually.

Step 4: Use a visual aid to present how a magazine or television ad might convey your client's message. Consider developing a logo (such as the Nike "swoosh," which is one of the most widely recognized and effective logos ever created). In addition, prepare a mockup of a magazine ad that incorporates the slogan, the logo, photographs, and other graphics, as well as some words.

Step 5: Break into small groups and present your proposed ad campaign. Use the written material, a poster, and your oral powers of persuasion to convince Mendenhall Savings & Loan's clients that your ad campaign will be so eye-catching and memorable that it will bring in new customers.

Critique It

You've just compared math to glaciers. How did this Math Studio allow you to understand math in a different way other than working out problems and performing calculations?

MATH STUDIO

3 ASSESS

Enrichment

Have each student interview a person who works at a bank or credit union. Ask students to write a report detailing a typical work-day, the person's career path that led him or her to this position, and describe this person's personal fulfillment in the position. Would the student be interested in a similar sort of job? Why or why not?

4 CLOSE

Critique It

You've just compared math to science. How did this Math Studio allow you to understand math in a different way other than working out problems and performing calculations? **Answers will vary but might include seeing a connection between math equations on the page and math realities in real life. For example, if a student helps a parent build a deck, he or she will quickly learn how math applies to the real world. If a student opens himself or herself up to the idea, he or she will be able to look around and see math at work in nearly every aspect of life.**

NEWSWORTHY TREND

Saving for College: Part 2

Savings plans allow contributors to set aside money in special college savings accounts for a designated recipient's higher education expenses. Contributions vary, depending on individual savings goals. Most plans offer variable rates of return, although some programs guarantee a minimum rate of return.

States have fashioned a variety of college savings programs to meet the savings needs of the average family. State-sponsored savings plans promote planning for education expenses, dependence on family resources instead of reliance on government aid programs, and saving for education expenses, rather than relying on student loans. Many of these programs gained federal tax-exemption in 2001, while states offer additional tax advantages.

National Standards for Business Education

Section Objectives	1. Mathematical Foundations	2. Number Relationships and Operations	3. Patterns, Functions, and Algebra	4. Measurements	5. Statistics and Probability	6. Problem-Solving Applications
6-1 Sales Tax (pp. 232–233) Compute the sales tax.	X	X				
6-2 Total Purchase Price (pp. 234–236) Calculate the total purchase price.	X	X				
6-3 Unit Pricing (pp. 237–238) Figure out the unit price.	X	X				
6-4 Comparison Shopping (pp. 239–240) Find the better buy based on unit price.	X	X				
6-5 Coupons and Rebates (pp. 241–242) Work out the final price after using a coupon or rebate.	X	X				
6-6 Markdown (pp. 243–245) Solve for the dollar amount of the markdown.	X	X				
6-7 Sale Price (pp. 246–247) Compute the sale price when markdown rate is known.	X	X				

(Source: Reprinted with permission from the National Standards for Business Education, copyright © 2001 by National Business Education Association, 1914 Association Drive, Reston, Virginia 21901-1596)

SCANS Correlation

Foundation Skills

Basic Skills	Reading	Writing	Math	Listening	Speaking	
Thinking Skills	Creative Thinking	Decision Making	Problem Solving	Seeing Things in the Mind's Eye	Knowing How to Learn	Reasoning
Personal Qualities	Responsibility	Self-Esteem	Sociability	Self-Management	Integrity/Honesty	

This chapter's highlighted blocks indicate the chapter's content coverage in the Student Edition and the Teacher Wraparound Edition.

1. Numbers & Operations	2. Algebra	3. Geometry	4. Measurement	5. Data Analysis & Probability	6. Problem Solving	7. Reasoning & Proof	8. Communication	9. Connections	10. Representations
X			X		X		X	X	
X			X		X		X	X	
X			X		X		X	X	
X			X		X		X	X	
X			X		X		X	X	
X			X		X		X	X	
X			X		X		X	X	

SCANS Correlation

Workplace Competencies

Resources	Allocating Time	Allocating Money	Allocating Material and Facility Resources	Allocating Human Resources		
Information	Acquiring and Evaluating Information	Organizing and Maintaining Information	Interpreting and Communicating Information	Using Computers to Process Information		
Interpersonal Skills	Participating as a Member of a Team	Teaching Others	Serving Clients/Customers	Exercising Leadership	Negotiating to Arrive at a Decision	Working with Cultural Diversity
Systems	Understanding Systems	Monitoring and Correcting Performance	Improving and Designing Systems			
Technology	Selecting Technology	Applying Technology to Task	Maintaining and Troubleshooting Technology			

What You'll Learn

In this chapter you'll examine how stores set prices and offer coupons and rebates to encourage consumers to buy. You'll also look at how to comparison shop in order to find the best buys.

Why It's Important

Making a cash purchase is something that many people do almost everyday. Smart shoppers look for items that are on sale or discounted. Looking for the best buy is a way to save money. Knowing how to calculate the sale price enables you to determine the final selling price and decide if the purchase is wise.

Key Word Review

Poster

Students look up the meaning of the key words in the Glossary. Students work in pairs to create a "Do's and Don'ts" poster to advise students in the school about ways to become a smart shopper. Students select magazine or newspaper pictures and advertising to illustrate the topic.

CHAPTER 6

Cash Purchases

What You'll Learn

Section 6-1 Compute the sales tax.

Section 6-2 Calculate the total purchase price.

Section 6-3 Figure out the unit price.

Section 6-4 Find the better buy based on unit price.

Section 6-5 Work out the final price after using a coupon or rebate.

Section 6-6 Solve for the dollar amount of the markdown.

Section 6-7 Compute the sale price when the markdown rate is known.

When Will You Ever Use This?

While shopping you might have noticed a store's coupons, rebates, sale prices, or markdowns. You'll determine the exact price of an item (including calculating the sales tax on it) given whichever method a store uses to move its goods or services.

Key Words to Know

- sales tax
- sales receipt
- total purchase price
- unit pricing
- coupons
- rebates
- markdown
- markdown rate
- sale price

Mathematics Online

To learn more about cash purchases, visit the *Mathematics with Business Applications* Web site at www.busmath.glencoe.com.

CLASSROOM RESOURCES

Application and Enrichment

- *Teacher Wraparound Edition*
- *Teacher Resource Binder, Blackline Masters*
- *Interactive Lesson Planner* CD-ROM
- *PowerPoint® Presentations* CD-ROM

Review and Enforcement

Mathematics Online
www.busmath.glencoe.com
- *Teacher Resource Binder, Internet Resources*

- *Student Activity Workbook*
- *Student Activity Workbook, Teacher Annotated Edition*
- *School-to-Home Activity Workbook*

Assessment and Evaluation

- *Assessment Binder, Reproducible Tests*
- *Assessment Binder, Alternative Assessment Strategies*
- **Exam***View® Pro Test Generator* CD-ROM

For the Teacher

- *Student Activity Workbook, Teacher Annotated Edition*
- *Assessment Binder*
- *Interactive Lesson Planner* CD-ROM
- *Teacher Resource Binder*
- Mathematics Online
www.busmath.glencoe.com

For the Student

- *Student Activity Workbook*
- *School-to-Home Activity Workbook*

Living in the Real World

Story's Summary
Sue Reitz is the owner of Secondhand Rose, a store specializing in "gently used" household items. By reading about a typical day selling wares in her shop, students learn several insider tips about pricing, taxing, and moving merchandise.

Living in the Real World

Sifting through the Gently Used

Sue Reitz opens the door of her shop and turns on the light. Secondhand Rose has been in business for only seven months, but it's already turning a profit. The store sells "gently used" household items—everything from gold velvet sofas to ceramic frog paperweights. A thrift store is a world of hidden treasures. Take a look inside this chapter to discover the owner's treasures.

Read on. Go to . . .

231

Did You Know...
Although it might be difficult to believe, the automatic teller machine (ATM) that is so readily available today has only been around since the mid-1970s, and the popularity of the cash-dispensing apparatus didn't really catch on until a decade after that. Today you could find nearly 350,000 ATMs.

Think about This
Before the advent of the ATM, people could only receive cash from a banking institution. In what ways do you think this changed the way people use money compared to today?

LOCAL STANDARDS

National Standards for Business Education

Standard 1	Mathematical Foundations
Standard 2	Number Relationships and Operations

National Council of Teachers of Mathematics Standards

Standard 1	Numbers and Operations
Standard 4	Measurement
Standard 6	Problem Solving
Standard 8	Communication
Standard 9	Connections

1 FOCUS

The focus of this lesson is on computing the sales tax. If your state has a sales tax, ask students if they know what the rate is.

In-Class Examples

Work through these exercises with students before having them do the Self-Check.

1. $67.43 + $15.99 + $7.98 **$91.40**
2. $29.68 + $80.75 + $149.95 **$260.38**
3. 5% of $19.00 **$0.95**
4. 4.5% of $7.50 **$0.34**
5. $6\frac{3}{4}$% of $76.90 **$5.19**

2 TEACH

Ask students how they find the sales tax on the total selling price. Some stores use a table showing the tax, while others may have a sales tax key on the cash register that automatically calculates the tax. The tax may be found by doing the actual computation, as shown in the examples.

232

SECTION 6-1 Sales Tax

○ **Section Objective**

Compute the sales tax.

You just purchased a computer game at the electronics store. How much money did you just contribute to the state or local government for buying it? You'll find that most states charge a state **sales tax** on goods sold. This is a tax on the selling price of an item or service that you purchase. The sales tax rate is usually expressed as a percent and varies from state to state. Many states permit county and city governments to add an additional tax to the state sales tax as well.

To figure out how much the sales tax is, use this formula:

$$\text{Sales Tax} = \text{Total Selling Price} \times \text{Sales Tax Rate}$$

Living in the Real World

Sifting through the Gently Used

How Much Does Your State Charge? The first customer of the day walks into Secondhand Rose. The woman is looking for plastic pink flamingoes for her front yard.

It just so happens that the store does have two flamingoes that cost $3.50 a piece. Reitz rings up the total price of $7.00 and then calculates the sales tax.

Draw Conclusions How much is the sales tax in your state?

Continued on page 234

Need Help? Go to...

▶ Workshop 14: Finding a Percentage, page 30
▶ Workshop 2: Rounding Numbers, page 6
▶ Skill 30: Finding the Percentage, page 757
▶ Skill 2: Rounding Numbers, page 729

Example 1

Aleta Carbajal bought a cell phone for $199.95 and a phone case for $19.95. What is the total sales tax if Carbajal lives in Austin, Texas, where the state tax is 6.25 percent and the city tax is 2.00 percent?

STEP 1: Find the total selling price.
$199.95 + $19.95 = $219.90

STEP 2: Find the sales tax.

Total Selling Price	×	Sales Tax Rate	
$219.90	× (6.25% + 2.00%)		
$219.90	×	0.0825	= **$18.14 or $18.14 sales tax**

CONCEPT CHECK

SELF-CHECK ✓

Complete the problems, then check your answers at the end of the chapter.

1. Total selling price: $420.
   Maine sales tax rate: 5 percent.
   Find the sales tax.
   $420 × 0.05 = $21.00

2. Total selling price: $2,520.
   Florida sales tax rate: 6 percent.
   Gainesville sales tax rate: 1 percent.
   Find the state tax and city tax.
   $2,520.00 × (6.00% + 1.00%) =
   $2,520.00 × 0.07 = $176.40

232 ◀ Chapter 6 Cash Purchases

Living in the Real World

Answers will vary depending on the state.

BUSINESS NOTES

Sales Tax

Students can use the Internet, call a local government office, or talk to a local businessperson to find out about the state and local sales taxes. How much are they? What items are taxed, and what are not taxed? What is the revenue used for? If the state doesn't have a sales tax, why not? CL , LS , P

SECTION 6-1 PRACTICE

Find the sales tax.

	Item	Total Selling Price	×	State Tax Rate	City Tax Rate	=	Sales Tax
3.	Clothing	$ 81.39	×	3.00%	0.00%	=	$2.44
4.	Pillowcases	22.99	×	4.00%	0.00%	=	$0.92
5.	Calculator	21.75	×	5.00%	0.00%	=	$1.09
6.	Compact disc	16.95	×	4.00%	2.00%	=	$1.02
7.	Computer	1,995.00	×	4.90%	3.00%	=	$157.61
8.	Breakfast	9.95	×	4.75%	3.25%	=	$0.80

9. Purchases include a $39.95 blanket, a $24.95 mini blind, an adjustable screen for $15.95, and a 12-foot extension cord for $9.49. The purchases were made in Massachusetts, where the tax rate is 5 percent. What is the total selling price? What is the sales tax? **$90.34; $4.52**

10. Carlotta Martinez purchased a $399.99 electronic organizer for work. What is the total sales tax if Martinez lives in Toledo, Ohio, where the state tax is 5 percent and the county tax is 1.25 percent? **$24.99**

11. Alfredo Rodriguez purchases a DVD for $29.95, a dictionary for $31.50, a paperback book for $9.25, and a magazine for $5.00. What is the total sales tax if he lives in Acme, Washington, where the state tax is 6.5 percent and the city tax is 1.1 percent? **$5.75**

12. Jenny Zaragoza purchases a $1,599.99 treadmill, a $49.99 pair of walking shoes, and a $79.99 leather handbag at the Suffolk County Store in Bay Shore, New York. The state sales tax rate is 4 percent, the county rate is 4.25 percent, and the city rate is 0.25 percent. What is the sales tax on her purchases?
$1,729.97 × (0.04 + 0.425 + 0.0025) = $147.05

MAINTAINING YOUR SKILLS

Need Help? Go to...
▶ Skill 30: Finding the Percentage, page 757
▶ Skill 2: Rounding Numbers, page 729

Find the percentage.

13. 8% of $29.90 **$2.39**   14. 4% of $13,840 **$553.60**   15. 120% of $90 **$108**

Round to the place value indicated. Round to the nearest thousand.

16. 85,713 **86,000**   17. 4,139 **4,000**   18. 31,234 **31,000**

Round to the nearest ten.

19. 435 **440**   20. 35,229 **35,230**   21. 94 **90**

Round to the nearest hundredth (also known as cent).

22. $34.125 **$34.13**   23. $279.5429 **$279.54**   24. $357.346 **$357.35**

Round to the nearest tenth.

25. 37.614 **37.6**   26. 357.982 **358**   27. 131.025 **131.0**

Section 6-1 Sales Tax ▶ **233**

PROBLEM SOLVING

Pick Three Items
Give students cutout pictures of items from magazines or catalogs. Make sure each item is priced. Write the state sales tax rate (in percent) on the picture. Students pick three items and figure out the sales tax on each by first changing percent to decimal, then rounding if necessary. **CL** , **LS** , **P**

WRAP-UP

Go over any problem for which a wrong answer is given.

Assignment Guide
  Basic: 3–8
  Average: 9–11

20 min.

In-Class Examples

1. Brenda Sutherland purchases a vacuum cleaner for $299.99. She lives in Wisconsin, where the sales tax is 5 percent. Find the sales tax. **$15.00**

2. Mikiko Iwayama purchases a photo printer for $399.99 and a package of photo paper for $24.99. What is the total selling price? **($424.98)** What is the sales tax on her purchases in Hawaii where the sales tax is 4 percent? **$17.00**

3 ASSESS

Error Analysis

Before students multiply the sales tax rate times the total selling price, have them check to see that they have correctly converted the percent to a decimal. For instance, 6 percent would be written as 0.06 and 3 percent as 0.03.

4 CLOSE

Closing Activity

Find the percentage.
1. 6% of $93.52 **$5.61**
2. 8% of $730.49 **$58.44**
3. Derek Holmes lives in Virginia where the state sales tax is 3.5 percent. He buys 2 gallons of paint for $15.88 per gallon, a rag roller for $4.79, a plastic drop cloth for $3.99, and a paintbrush for $7.99. What is the total selling price? **($48.53)** What is the sales tax? **$1.70**
4. Christina Burke purchased 2 decorative pillows for $24.77 each, a set of queen size sheets for $39.99, matching curtains for $72.69, and a curtain rod for $27.88. The sales tax rate in her state is 4.75 percent and the local sales tax is 1 percent. What is the sales tax on her purchases? **$10.93**

National Standards for Business Education

Standard 1	Mathematical Foundations
Standard 2	Number Relationships and Operations

National Council of Teachers of Mathematics Standards

Standard 1	Numbers and Operations
Standard 4	Measurement
Standard 6	Problem Solving
Standard 8	Communication
Standard 9	Connections

1 FOCUS

Ask students if they ever check their total purchase price by adding the cost of each purchase, finding the sales tax, and then adding the two figures together.

In-Class Examples

Work through these exercises with students before having them do the Self-Check.

1. Add: $12.49, $3.16, $0.07, $10.40 **$26.12**
2. $129.55 + $37.50 + $1.22 + $0.67 **$168.94**
3. $539.21 + $97.86 + $38.07 + $7.15 **$682.29**
4. 6 × $3.99 **$23.94**
5. 15 × $2.79 **$41.85**

○ Section Objective

Calculate the total purchase price.

Most stores give you a **sales receipt** as proof of purchase. The sales receipt may be a handwritten sales slip or a cash register tape. The sales receipt shows the selling price of each item or service you purchased, the total selling price, any sales tax, and the total purchase price. Note that the tax is computed on the combined state, county, and city tax rates.

The **total purchase price** of an item is equal to the selling price plus the sales tax. Remember that:

$$\text{Sales Tax} = \text{Total Selling Price} \times \text{Sales Tax Rate}$$

$$\text{Total Purchase Price} = \text{Total Selling Price} + \text{Sales Tax}$$

1. a. Find the total selling price: $179.50 + $39.50 = $219.00
   b. Find the sales tax: $219.00 × 0.0825 = $18.0675 = $18.07
   c. Find the total purchase price: $219.00 + $18.07 = $237.07

Need Help? Go to...

- ► **Workshop 6:** Multiplying Decimals, page 14
- ► **Workshop 4:** Adding Decimals, page 10
- ► **Skill 8: Multiplying Decimals,** page 735
- ► **Skill 5: Adding Decimals,** page 732
- ► **Application A: Formulas,** page 760

Living in the Real World

Sifting through the Gently Used

The Flamingoes Will Cost You "So, those two gorgeous flamingoes cost $7.00 and $0.56 'for the governor,'" Reitz says to her first customer of the day. "That's a total price, tax included, of $7.56."

Draw Conclusions What does your state do with sales tax money that it collects?

Continued on page 237

Example 1

A store in Madison, Wisconsin, advertised a smoke alarm for $24.95 and a fire extinguisher for $39.95. What is the sales tax if the combined state and city rate is 6 percent? What is the total purchase price?

STEP 1: Find the total selling price.
$24.95 + $39.95 = $64.90

STEP 2: Find the sales tax.
Total Selling Price × Sales Tax Rate
$64.90 × 0.06 = $3.894 or $3.89

STEP 3: Find the total purchase price.
Total Selling Price + Sales Tax
$64.90 + $3.89 = **$68.79 total purchase price**

CONCEPT CHECK

SELF-CHECK ✓

Complete the problem, then check your answer at the end of the chapter.

1. Kate Farison bought a dome tent priced at $179.50 and a propane stove priced at $39.50 in Dallas, Texas. The combined city and state sales tax rate is 8.25 percent. Find the total purchase price.

Living in the Real World

Answers may vary depending on the state, but could include answers such as social programs, education, road construction projects, justice and corrections departments, etc.

ALTERNATIVE ASSESSMENT

Learning Techniques

Remind students that many people are visual learners. To aid their learning in this section, announce to students that they will draw a poster-size graphic organizer. Suggest students prepare a diagram or chart to use as a tool to organize the information they will come across in the section. **LS** , **CL** , **P**

Example 2

Mike Gustweller, a logger, purchases the items listed on the sales receipt from Verl's Saw Shop. He checks the information on the receipt. The sales tax rate is 5 percent. What is the total selling price?

Figure 6.1

Verl's Saw Shop			Harrison Lake, Ohio
Quantity	Description	Price	Amount
1	Chain saw	$459.95	$459.95
12	Chain saw bar oil PRICE PER ITEM	4.95	59.40
2	Safety chaps	59.95	119.90
2	Safety helmet TOTAL PRICE	39.95	79.90
	TOTAL SELLING PRICE →	Subtotal	$719.15
NUMBER PURCHASED		Sales Tax 5%	35.96
	TOTAL PURCHASE PRICE	→Total	$755.11

Note the following:
- "Quantity" is the number purchased.
- "Price" is the price per item.
- "Amount" is the quantity multiplied by price of item.
- "Total selling price" is the subtotal.
- "Total purchase price" is the total.

STEP 1: Find the total selling price.
$495.95 + $59.40 + $119.90 + $79.90 = $719.15

STEP 2: Find the sales tax.
Total Selling Price × Sales Tax Rate
$719.15   ×   0.05   = $35.96

STEP 3: Find the total purchase price.
Total Selling Price + Sales Tax
$719.95   + $35.96   = **$755.11 total purchase price**

  459.95 M+ 12 × 4.95 = 59.40 M+ 2 × 59.95 =
119.90 M+ 2 × 39.95 = 79.90 M+ RM 719.15
× 5 % = 35.9575 + RM 719.15 = 755.1075

2. a. Find the total selling price:
(2 × $59.99) + (2 × $19.99) = $119.98 + $39.98 = $159.96
b. Find the sales tax: $159.96 × 0.06 = $9.5976 = $9.60
c. Find the total purchase price: $159.96 + $9.60 = $169.56

SELF-CHECK✓

CONCEPT CHECK

Complete the problem, then check your answer at the end of the chapter.

2. William Eyawat bought 2 two-way radios for $59.99 each and 2 surge protectors at $19.99 each. What is the total purchase price if he lives in West Virginia, where the sales tax rate is 6 percent?

SECTION 6-2 PRACTICE

	Item	Total Selling Price	×	Sales Tax Rate	=	Sales Tax		Total Purchase Price
3.	Glue stick	$ 1.69	×	5.00%	=	$0.08	a.	$1.77
4.	Notepad	1.15	×	6.00%	=	0.07	a.	$1.22
5.	Sweatpants	21.75	×	4.00%	=	a. $0.87	b.	$22.62
6.	Minivan	22,450.00	×	8.75%	=	a.$1,964.38	b.	$24,414.38

Continued on next page

COOPERATIVE LEARNING

Sales Tax Savings
One advantage of shopping by mail or on the Internet is that out-of-state customers don't have to pay a state's sales tax. Students work in pairs to list what types of purchases they would buy by mail or on the Web. The sales tax savings on larger purchases often more than makes up for the cost of delivery.

COMMUNICATION SKILLS

Planning a Lesson
Have teams of students draw up a lesson plan for teaching a group of younger students how to calculate the total purchase price. Encourage teams to think of examples and visual aids they could use to help teach some of the concepts. If possible, have teams actually prepare lessons and arrange to present the lessons to students in a lower grade.

CL , LS

2 **TEACH**

Discuss the importance of the sales receipt as a record of purchase when manufacturers' rebates and special offers are involved. Review the important parts of a sales receipt, namely, (a) the quantity and selling price of each item or service purchased, (b) the total selling price of the items, (c) the sales tax, if any, and (d) the total purchase price. Emphasize the importance of checking the sales receipt.

Motivating the Lesson
You buy a portable CD player for $69.99 and a CD for $11.99. The sales tax on these items is $6.76. What is the total purchase price including tax? **$88.74**

In-Class Examples
1. Quincy Grant buys a snow-plowing machine for $389.00. The sales tax rate is 6.5 percent. What is the total purchase price? **$414.29**
2. Maggie Hanrahan purchases a down comforter for $149, 2 pillows for $24 each, and a wall clock for $38. The sales tax on these items is $11.75. What is the total purchase price? **$246.75**
3. Dawson Reed buys a bag of fertilizer for $26.99, a broadcast spreader for $28.96, a solar light kit for $48.00, and 2 terracotta planters for $9.97 each. The sales tax is $5.00. What is the total purchase price? **$128.89**
4. Whitney Roberts purchases a 36-inch color TV for $756 and a DVD player for $222. What is the sales tax if the combined state and city rate is 4.75 percent + 3.25 percent? **($78.24)** What is the total purchase price? **$1056.24**

235

3 ASSESS

Error Analysis

Review how to compute the amount of multiple items. (Amount = Quantity × Price) For instance, the amount of 5 pens at $1.49 per pen would be $7.45. Help students find the subtotal of multiple items. Remind students that they must add sales tax to the total selling price in order to find the *total purchase price*.

4 CLOSE

Closing Activity

1. (4 × $8.77) + (12 × $0.98) + $2.74 **$49.58**

2. $72.19 + $56.49 +$ 193.37 + $12.38 **$334.43**

3. Michelle Watson purchases a bottle of perfume for $35.00, a dress for $49.99, and a skirt for $24.99. The sales tax on these items is $6.60. What is the total purchase price? **$116.58**

4. Cory Fleming buys 3 packages of white inkjet paper for $7.99 each, a black inkjet printer cartridge for $27.99, 2 corrugated cardboard storage boxes for $6.49 each, and a box of 500 envelopes for $4.69. The combined state, county, and city sales tax is 8.25 percent. What is the total purchase price? **$75.37**

▶FYI

Sales taxes on necessities are called "regressive taxes" because they are more of a financial burden for the poor. To help ease this burden, many states do not tax food, clothing, or medicine.

▶▶▶

7. Anita Ewing buys a shirt for $29.99 and tie for $29.95. The sales tax is $4.20. What is the total purchase price? **$64.14**

8. Carl Gonzales has a sales slip that shows purchases of a briefcase for $59.99, 2 notepads at $0.59 each, and sales tax of $3.06. What is the total purchase price? **$64.23**

9. Aurelio Esparza buys a computer disk file for $14.95, a surge protector for $19.95, and 2 boxes of labels at $19.99 each. The sales tax rate is 4 percent. What is the total purchase price? **$77.88**

10. Norma Engel buys a microwave for $149.99, a microwave cart for $119.95, and microwave cookware for $19.95. The sales tax rate is 5.5 percent. What is the total purchase price? **$305.83**

11. Ralph McDounagh purchases a power saw for $85.85 and an extension cord for $25.95 at the Home Store in Los Angeles. The sales tax rate is 8.25 percent. What is the total purchase price? **$121.02**

12. Frank Norris purchases a digital camera for $799.99, a tripod for $59.97, and a camera accessory kit for $89.99 in Denver, Colorado. The sales tax rate is 6.4 percent. What is the total purchase price? **$1,010.75**

13. Tanya Burley purchases 6 quarts of motor oil at $1.19 per quart, 8 spark plugs at $2.29 per plug, and an oil filter for $5.99 in Boston, Massachusetts. The sales tax rate is 5 percent. What is the total purchase price? **$33.02**

14. At Corner Grocery store, Liz Doyle purchases a 22-pound turkey at $1.59 per pound, 6 oranges at 4 for $1.00, a $6.99 box of laundry detergent, a gallon of milk for $2.69, a $0.99 frozen pie, and 6 cans of condensed soup at 2 cans for $0.74. The sales tax rate is 4 percent. There is no sales tax charged on food items. What is the total purchase price? **$49.65**

15. Nancy Topok purchases a suit for $229.75, a blouse for $29.50, a pair of shoes for $66.25, and jewelry for $65.50. She pays a Nebraska state tax of 5 percent and a local tax of 0.75 percent. What is the total sales tax on her purchases? What is the total purchase price? **$22.48; $413.48**

MAINTAINING YOUR SKILLS

Need Help? Go to...
▶ Skill 8: **Multiplying Decimals**, page 735
▶ Skill 5: **Adding Decimals**, page 732

Multiply.

16. 7.4 × 9.2 **68.08**

17. 15.6 × 9.142 **142.6152**

18. 0.91 × 0.004 **0.00364**

Add.

19.
```
  322.29
  174.00
+   4.52
  500.81
```

20.
```
  19.38
   7.8
+ .007
 27.187
```

21.
```
   9.65
   0.0024
+342.1
 351.75
```

22.
```
  708.326
   57.942
+   9.888
  776.156
```

23.
```
  542.36
  400.50
+   0.724
  943.584
```

24.
```
  414.6
    8.05
+960
1,382.65
```

WRAP-UP

Go over any problem for which a wrong answer is given.

Assignment Guide
Basic: 3–6
Average: 7–13

20 min.

SECTION (6·3) Unit Pricing

Section Objective

Figure out the unit price.

There's a barbecue on Saturday, and you're in charge of bringing paper plates. At the grocery store you notice two different sizes. You're comparing the unit price. **Unit pricing** is a system that allows shoppers to compare the prices of various items quickly and easily. Retail stores often give unit price information for their products. You can use this information to determine which size of a product is the better buy based solely on price. The unit price of an item is the price of the item divided by its measure or count. It might be expressed as dollars per pound or cents per dozen. You'll need to know:

$$\text{Unit Price} = \frac{\text{Price per Item}}{\text{Measure or Count}}$$

Figure 6.2

Paper Plates	
55 plates ← COUNT PER PACKAGE	
PRICE PER UNIT → $0.014 per plate	$0.77 ← PRICE PER PACKAGE
Unit Price	Your Price
UNIT OF MEASURE	

Living in the Real World

Sifting through the Gently Used

Mismatched Tumblers Don't Cost Much   As the pink flamingoes disappear around the corner, another customer enters Secondhand Rose. The man heads for the glassware section where vintage cups and glasses are lined up like soldiers on the shelves. Reitz shows him a box of 48 large smoky blue tumblers. She'll sell them for $24.

Draw Conclusions   How did the customer calculate that each glass cost $0.50 a piece?

Continued on page 239

Need Help? Go to...

▶ Workshop 7: Dividing Decimals, page 16
▶ Workshop 2: Rounding Numbers, page 6
▶ Skill 11: Dividing Decimals, page 738
▶ Skill 2: Rounding Numbers, page 729
▶ Application A: Formulas, page 760

(**Example 1**)

Shane Burns purchased a 34.5 ounce can of coffee for $3.99, a 2-liter bottle of cleaner for $3.98, and a dozen oranges for $3.96. What is the unit price of the items to the nearest tenth of a cent?

STEP: Find the unit price.

	Price per Item	÷	Measure or Count	
Coffee:	$3.99	÷	34.5	= $0.1156 or $0.116 or $0.12 per ounce
Cleaner:	$3.98	÷	2	= $1.99 per liter
Oranges:	$3.96	÷	12	= $0.33 per orange

Section 6-3 Unit Pricing ▶ **237**

National Standards for Business Education

Standard 1	Mathematical Foundations
Standard 2	Number Relationships and Operations

National Council of Teachers of Mathematics Standards

Standard 1	Numbers and Operations
Standard 4	Measurement
Standard 6	Problem Solving
Standard 8	Communication
Standard 9	Connections

1 FOCUS

The use of some advertisements for a product based upon common units of measure can be used to motivate the topic of computing unit price.

In-Class Examples

Work through these exercises with students before having them do the Self-Check. Round to the nearest cent.

1. $\frac{\$9.96}{30}$ **$0.33**
2. $\frac{\$2.75}{25}$ **$0.11**
3. $\frac{\$5.64}{15}$ **$0.38**
4. $\frac{\$11.57}{85}$ **$0.14**
5. $\frac{\$4.50}{8}$ **$0.56**

Living in the Real World

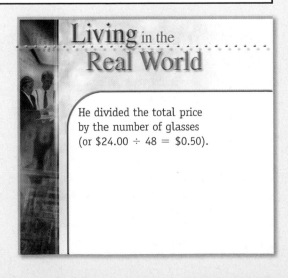

He divided the total price by the number of glasses (or $24.00 ÷ 48 = $0.50).

SECTION 6-3

2 TEACH

Discuss the idea of a unit of measure and a count, using the illustration in the textbook. Ask students to name some other units of measure (pound, gallon, yard, ounce, and so on). The computation in this lesson can be rather tedious unless calculators are used. Point out that the amount of $0.1369 can be written in another way as 13.7¢. This is the form required when the direction line states "to the nearest tenth of a cent."

In-Class Examples
Round to the nearest cent.
1. A 53-ounce container of powdered ice tea mix costs $4.39. Find the unit price per ounce rounded to the nearest cent. **$0.08 per ounce**
2. Trash bags sell for $5.39. The box contains 42 trash bags. What is the unit price per trash bag? **$0.13 per trash bag**

3 ASSESS

Error Analysis
When students compute unit price for special offers, such as "Buy One, Get One Free" offers, remind them to first total the number of units if they take advantage of the special offer. Then have them total the price based on the special offer. Finally, they should divide the price by the total units to arrive at the price per unit.

4 CLOSE

Closing Activity
Round to the nearest cent.
1. A package of 4 light bulbs costs $1.44. Find the unit price per light bulb. **$0.36**
2. A Polish delicatessen sells homemade cheese pierogis for $4.86 per dozen. What is the unit price? **$0.41 each**

238

CONCEPT CHECK

SELF-CHECK✓ Complete the problems, then check your answers at the end of the chapter.

1. A 64-ounce carton of orange juice costs $3.69. Find the unit price per ounce to the nearest tenth of a cent. **$3.69 ÷ 64 = $0.05765 = $0.0577 or $0.06 per ounce**
2. A 20-count package of plastic storage bags costs $2.29. Find the price per bag to the nearest tenth of a cent. **$2.29 ÷ 20 = $0.1145 = $0.115 or $0.12 per bag**

SECTION 6-3 PRACTICE

Round to the nearest tenth of a cent.

	Price per Item	÷	Measure or Count	=	Unit Price
3.	$ 0.99	÷	12 oz	=	$0.08
4.	7.99	÷	40 oz	=	$0.20
5.	10.54	÷	16 m	=	$0.66
6.	0.89	÷	2 L	=	$0.45

Round to the nearest cent.

7. Bernard Parks buys jam at 32 ounces for $3.89. What is the price per ounce? **$0.12**
8. Market Foods sells 24 cans of soda for $6.79. What is the price per can? **$0.28**
9. Batteries (2 per pack) sell for $2.99. What is the price per battery? **$1.50**
10. A 12-pack of markers sells for $5.54. What is the price per marker? **$0.46**
11. Laura Zeedy recently purchased 4 tires for her sport utility vehicle. The total purchase price was $339.16. What was the price per tire? **$84.79**
12. Alan Kinsman sees that salsa is on sale for 3 sixteen-ounce jars for $5.99. What is the price per ounce when he buys three jars? **$0.12**
13. Tania Ramirez purchases 25 hanging file folders for $6.99. What is the price per folder? **$0.28**
14. A 12-ounce box of cereal costs $2.29. What is the unit price to the nearest tenth of a cent? **$0.19**

MAINTAINING YOUR SKILLS

Need Help? Go to...
Skill 2: Rounding Numbers, page 729

Divide. Round answers to the nearest hundredth (also known as cent).

15. 190.50 ÷ 76 **2.51**   16. 13.4 ÷ 2.9 **4.62**   17. 27.218 ÷ 7.6 **3.58**

Round to the place value indicated. Round to the nearest ten.

18. 62.9 **60**   19. 19.8 **20**   20. 411.61 **410**

Round to the nearest tenth.

21. 21.78 **21.8**   22. 741.92 **741.9**   23. 2.348 **2.3**

Round to the nearest hundredth (also known as cent).

24. 3.218 **3.22**   25. 87.161 **87.16**   26. 430.144 **430.14**

Great Ideas from the Classroom Of...
Eric Matsuoka
University of Hawaii
Pearl City, Hawaii
Real-Life Discounts
Percent discounts are commutative but not additive. Consider a sale like "40 percent off plus an additional 20 percent" on a $100 camera. The total discount is not 60 percent. Even when you reverse the order of the percent off, it still doesn't change the final sale price of $48.

WRAP-UP

Go over any problem for which a wrong answer is given.

Assignment Guide
Basic: 3–6
Average: 7–12

20 min.

SECTION 6·4 Comparison Shopping

SECTION 6-4

○ **Section Objective**

Find the better buy based on unit price.

You compare the unit prices of products so you can decide which size to buy. If price is the only consideration, then the package with the lowest unit price is the better buy. If the larger size product is the better buy, consider whether or not you will use it all before it goes to waste.

Living in the Real World

Sifting through the Gently Used

It's a Deal Reitz's customer continues to look for glasses for his wife's birthday party. Reitz brings out four dozen glasses that she paid only $10 for at auction, so she can sell them for twice that.

Draw Conclusions What are the benefits of comparison shopping?

Continued on page 241

Example 1

Oatmeal is sold in three sizes. The price of an 18-ounce package is $1.86. The price of a 42-ounce package is $3.17. The price of a 112-ounce package is $6.29. Based on price alone, which package is the best buy?

STEP 1: Find the unit price for each item.

	Price per Item	÷	Measure or Count	
18-ounce package:	$1.86	÷	18	= $0.10333
	$0.10333	×	100	= **10.33¢**
				per ounce
42-ounce package:	$3.17	÷	42	= $0.07547
	$0.07547	×	100	= **7.55¢**
				per ounce
112-ounce package:	$6.29	÷	112	= $0.05616
	$0.05616	×	100	= **5.62¢**
				per ounce

STEP 2: Find the best buy.

Compare: 10.33¢, 7.55¢, and (5.62¢) ← **best buy**

Need Help? Go to...

▸ **Workshop 7: Dividing Decimals,** page 16
▸ **Workshop 1: Writing and Reading Numbers,** page 4
▸ **Skill 11: Dividing Decimals,** page 738
▸ **Skill 1: Numbers,** page 727
▸ **Application A: Formulas,** page 760

CONCEPT CHECK

SELF-CHECK✔

Complete the problems, then check your answers at the end of the chapter. Find the better buy.

1. Coffee creamer comes in two sizes: a 22-ounce jar costs $2.95 and a 16-ounce jar costs $2.19.

2. Granola cereal is offered in two sizes: a 14-ounce box costing $2.50 and a 20-ounce box costing $3.58.

Section 6-4 Comparison Shopping ▸ **239**

Living in the Real World

Reitz paid roughly $0.21 per glass and is selling them at nearly $0.42 each.

GLOBAL PERSPECTIVE

Shop Smart
Being a smart shopper means knowing how to comparison shop. Students choose a clothing, food, or electronics item that comes from another country. Students use catalogs or the Internet to find various prices for similar items, then calculate the unit price for each item and circle the best buy. `CL` , `LS`

National Standards for Business Education

Standard 1	Mathematical Foundations
Standard 2	Number Relationships and Operations

National Council of Teachers of Mathematics Standards

Standard 1	Numbers and Operations
Standard 4	Measurement
Standard 6	Problem Solving
Standard 8	Communication
Standard 9	Connections

① FOCUS

In choosing a product having different sizes, a decision can be made based upon the unit price. Ask students how they would do this. **Choose the size with the lower unit price.**

In-Class Examples
Work through these exercises with students before having them do the Self-Check. Which number is greater?

1. 0.0264 or 0.0239 **0.0264**
2. 23.621 or 23.692 **23.692**
3. 18.296 or 17.999 **18.296**
4. 1.9 or 9.1 **9.1**

Divide. Do not round.

5. $\frac{\$0.22}{8}$ **$0.0275**
6. $\frac{1.44}{12}$ **0.12**
7. $\frac{0.50}{3.2}$ **0.15625**
8. $\frac{19.20}{32}$ **0.6**

1. See answer on page 248.
2. See answer on page 248.

TEACH

You might discuss students' expectations when comparing the same brand packaged in different sizes. Ask them whether or not they expect the larger size to be the most economical purchase. As they work through the problems, have them check to see if their expectations were proven correct.

In-Class Example

1. A 5-quart container of motor oil sells for $6.97. Individual quarts sell for $1.28 per quart. Based on price alone, which is the better buy? $\frac{$6.97}{5} = 1.39 **per one quart container: $1.28 per quart; one quart container is the better buy.**

ASSESS

Error Analysis

Review the process of finding the best buy. Remind students to first find the unit price of all sizes being compared. Then, determine which price is the least expensive.

Be sure students understand that 3.7¢ is not the same as $3.07. Three point seven cents is an amount greater than 3¢ but less than 4¢. It can also be written as $0.037.

CLOSE

Closing Activity

Which number is greater?

1. Peanuts are sold in two sizes: a 978-gram jar for $3.78 and a 340 gram can for $2.38. Which is the better buy? $\frac{$3.78}{978} = $0.003865 = 0.37 per gram; $\frac{$2.38}{340} = $0.007 = 0.7 per gram; **978 gram jar is the better buy.**

Find the unit price to the nearest tenth of a cent and then determine the better buy based on price alone.

3. Note cards.
   a. Pack of 100 for $1.69. **$0.0169 or 1.7¢**
   b. Pack of 300 for $1.27. **$0.004 or 0.4¢**
   c. Which is the better buy? **300 for $1.27**

4. Paper clips.
   a. Box of 100 for $0.38.
   b. Five-pack of 100 each for $1.27.
   c. Which is the better buy?

   4. a. $0.0038 or 0.4¢
   b. $0.0025 or 0.3¢
   4. a.
   b.
   c.
   4. c. 0.0167 = 1.7¢; 0.0084 = 0.8¢; 5 pack for $1.27

5. Alicia Murphy has a choice of two sizes of stain and varnish. The 237-milliliter can sells for $3.96, while the 946-milliliter can sells for $7.96. Which size is the better buy? What must she consider other than price?

6. Jeff Evans wants to purchase some assorted chocolates. A 2-ounce box sells for $0.88, a 16-ounce box sells for $7.18, and a 32-ounce box sells for $14.38. Which size box is the best buy? **2-ounce box**

7. Kathy Kruse is shopping for spaghetti sauce in Columbus, Ohio. She sees the spaghetti sauces as follows: the 26-ounce jar for $1.50, the 45-ounce jar for $2.48, and the 66-ounce jar for $3.12. What size is the best buy? **66-ounce jar**

8. An 8-pack of 75 notes per pad sells for $4.97. A 12-pack of 75 notes per pad sells for $7.47. A 4-pack of 50 notes per pad sells for $1.97. Which size package is the best buy? **8-pack of 75 notes; when rounded to the tenth of cent then options are the same price.**

9. Guiseppe Gerken wants to purchase some batteries. A 6-pack costs $4.77. An 8-pack costs $5.67. A package of four 4-packs costs $7.95. Which is the best buy? **Four 4-packs for $7.95**

10. Kenny Chape's favorite microwave popcorn sells as follows: a 3-pack for $0.97, an 8-pack for $2.00, and a 28-pack for $5.99. Which size is the best buy? **28-pack for $5.99**

11. Wu Chong is buying potato chips. He notes that the following sizes are for sale: $1\frac{3}{4}$-ounce for $0.50, $5\frac{3}{4}$-ounce for $1.00, and a 2-pack of the $5\frac{3}{4}$-ounce size for $1.88. Which size is the best buy? **2-pack of $5\frac{3}{4}$ oz**

12. The Food Chain sells spearmint gum in packs containing five sticks of gum. A single pack costs $0.25, a ten-pack carton sells for $1.79, 2 ten-pack cartons sell for $3.00, and 2 twenty-pack cartons sell for $4.99. Which size is the best buy? **2 twenty-pack cartons**

5. 946 mL can is better buy. She must consider if the stain will go bad before it is all used up.

Need Help? Go to...
- Skill 11: Dividing Decimals, page 738
- Skill 1: Numbers, page 727

Divide. Round answers to the nearest hundredth (also known as cent).

13. $2.3 \div 49.16$ **0.05**
14. $0.250 \div 18.5$ **0.01**
15. $0.006 \div 0.8703$ **0.01**

Which number is greater?

16. $1.568 or $1.586 **$1.586**
17. $0.2326 or $0.2349 **$0.2349**
18. $0.51 or $0.501 **$0.51**

THINKING CRITICALLY

Discussion
Lead students in a discussion of the following statement: "Cheaper isn't always better." Use this statement when discussing quality of goods and services, convenience of location, quantity, and availability.

WRAP-UP

Go over any problem for which a wrong answer is given.

Assignment Guide
- **Basic:** 3–4
- **Average:** 5–11

20 min.

SECTION 6-5 Coupons and Rebates

SECTION 6-5

Section Objective
Work out the final price after using a coupon or rebate.

Many manufacturers, stores, and service establishments offer customers discounts through **coupons** and **rebates**, or refunds. These special discounts are an incentive for customers to purchase a particular item in order to save money (coupon) or to get money back (rebate). Manufacturer or store coupons are redeemed at the time of purchase. To obtain a manufacturer's rebate, the consumer must mail in a rebate coupon along with the sales slip and the Universal Product Code (UPC) label from the items.

You can remember to calculate the final price of an item by using:

Final Price = Total Selling Price − Total Savings

Living in the Real World

Sifting through the Gently Used

"Boostcoup" Savings Reitz is very active in the community where she lives. She has agreed to allow the local high school chess club booster organization to put a discount coupon for her store in their "Boostcoup" booklet. The club raises money by selling the booklets for $20, and the buyers use the coupons in local stores and restaurants. Today, a college student has come in to buy a bookcase. He hauls the furniture to the counter and presents the coupon.

"Twenty percent off," Reitz says. "The sale price is $32."

Draw Conclusions How much does the college student save on the bookcase? What is the college student's total bill (include $1.28 in tax for the sale)?

Continued on page 243

Need Help? Go to...
- ► **Workshop 5:** Subtracting Decimals, page 12
- ► **Skill 6:** Subtracting Decimals, page 733
- ► **Application A:** Formulas, page 760

Example 1

Gus Senton purchased a heavy-duty nailer for $249.00 and a compressor for $349.00. He had a coupon for $50 off. What is the final price of the items?

STEP: Find the final price.

Total Selling Price − Total Savings
($249 + $349)   − $50   =
$598   − $50   − $548 final price

CONCEPT CHECK

SELF-CHECK ✓

Complete the problems, then check your answers at the end of the chapter.

1. Forty-ounce pancake mix: $3.39
   Coupon for $0.55.
   What is the final price?
   $3.39 − $0.55 = $2.84 final price

2. Tea: $2.59
   Coupon for $0.35.
   What is the final price?
   $2.59 − $0.35 = $2.24 final price

Continued on next page

Living in the Real World

She saves $6.40 on the bookcase. Her bill comes to $25.60, plus $1.28 in tax, for a total of $26.88.

TECHNOLOGY POWER

Octopus Cards Ltd., a Hong Kong company, runs the world's most successful smart-card operation. These are the credit-card size pieces of plastic with computer chips embedded in them that allow people to store and spend cash. After paying about $6 for the card, a consumer can then put money into the card's electronic wallet by transferring funds from a bank account at an ATM.

SECTION 6-5

National Standards for Business Education

Standard 1	Mathematical Foundations
Standard 2	Number Relationships and Operations

National Council of Teachers of Mathematics Standards

Standard 1	Numbers and Operations
Standard 4	Measurement
Standard 6	Problem Solving
Standard 8	Communication
Standard 9	Connections

1 FOCUS

Ask students if they have ever received coupons in the mail at home. Where else have they seen coupons? **(newspapers, magazines)** Discuss the value of coupons to a consumer.

In-Class Examples
Work through these exercises with students before having them do the Self-Check.
1. $1.79 − $0.25 **$1.54**
2. $2.59 − $0.50 **$2.09**
3. $82.99 − $15.00 **$67.99**
4. $26,528 − $1,800 **$24,728**

2 TEACH

If you can bring some coupons to class, they would serve as good examples for this lesson. Use them to compute the final price by making up the selling price, if necessary. Then work through the examples.

2 TEACH (cont'd)

Motivating the Lesson

An air hockey table costs $349 at your local sporting goods store. You have a store coupon for $50 off any purchase over $200. What is the final price of the air hockey table? **$299**

In-Class Examples

1. A can of shaving cream costs $2.19. You have a coupon for $0.50 off. What is the final price? **$1.69**

2. Raisins sells for $3.99. You have a store coupon for $1.50 off. What is the final price? **$2.49**

3. A blank videocassette costs $1.99. What is the final price if you use a coupon for $1.00 off? **$0.99**

3 ASSESS

Error Analysis

Remind students to line up decimals vertically when they are subtracting the amount of the coupon or rebate from the selling price of an item.

4 CLOSE

Closing Activity

1. $4.37 − $0.75 **$3.62**
2. $56.88 − $10.00 **$46.88**
3. A set of luggage sells for $277.99. You have a store coupon for $55 off. What is the final price of the luggage? **$222.99**
4. A pair of pants sells for $38.00. A matching top costs $29.99. You have a store coupon for $25.00 off any pair of pants and top if both are purchased. What is the final cost of the pants and top? **$42.99**
5. An electronic dictionary costs $24.99. The manufacturer offers a $5.00 rebate. What is the final price? **$19.99**

---

3. Thirty-two-ounce jam costs $3.69. Twenty-eight-ounce peanut butter costs $3.79. Coupon for $0.35 if both items are bought. What is the final price?
($3.69 + $3.79) − $0.35 =
$7.48 − $0.35 = **$7.13 final price**

4. Oatmeal costs $4.19. Coupon for $1.00 off if two boxes are bought. What is the final price if you buy two?
($4.19 × 2) − $1.00 =
$8.38 − $1.00 = **$7.38 final price**

SECTION 6-5 PRACTICE

For Problems 5–10, find the final price of each item.

	Item	Total Selling Price	Coupon	Final Price
5.	Bleach	$3.95	$0.50	**$3.45**
6.	Floor cleaner	5.99	0.50	**$5.49**
7.	Toilet paper 24-pack	7.89	1.00	**$6.89**
8.	Pancake 60-oz	4.69	0.75	**$3.94**
9.	Yogurt	0.79	0.55 buy 6	**$4.19**
10.	Chocolate chunks	2.79	0.50 buy 2	**$5.08**

11. Audrey Bailey purchased a chicken combo sandwich for $4.59. She had a store coupon for $0.50. What is the final price of the sandwich? **$4.09**

12. Wilbur Clark purchased a computer hard drive for the regular price of $129.99. The store gave him a $30.00 manufacturer's rebate to mail in. What is the final price? **$99.99**

13. Michael Noll purchased the men's razor refill for the regular price of $6.29. He had a $2.00 manufacturer's rebate. What is the final price? **$4.29**

14. Jonnie Marker has a coupon for $1.00 off a jar of bean dip if he buys 2 bags of corn chips. He purchased 2 bags of chips for $3.99 per bag and a jar of salsa for $2.79. What is the final price? **$9.77**

15. Shawn Derricotte purchased a scanner for $129.99. What is the price after the $50.00 manufacturer's rebate? **$79.99**

16. Tammy Duffey purchased a digital phone for $179.99. She received an $80.00 mail-in rebate from the manufacturer and a $50.00 mail-in rebate from the telephone company. What is the price after the rebates? **$49.99**

17. Additional memory for your computer sells for $109.99 with a mail-in rebate of $10.00. What is the final price after the rebate if an envelope costs $0.25 and a postage stamp costs $0.37? **$100.61**

MAINTAINING YOUR SKILLS

Need Help? Go to...
► Skill 6: Subtracting Decimals, page 733

Subtract.

18.	$1.65	19.	$11.65	20.	$1.79
	− 0.35		− 3.00		− 0.25
	$1.30		**$8.65**		**$1.54**

COMMUNICATION SKILLS

E-Coupons

There are e-tickets, e-mail, e-tail, and e-coupons. E-coupons are coupons available online. Consumers can print out coupons from the Internet for the specific products they want to buy. Students discuss in groups how e-coupons benefit businesses. **Businesses save on the cost of printing and distribution. Businesses can identify and target the customers who actually use their coupons.** LS , CL

WRAP-UP

Go over any problem for which a wrong answer is given.

Assignment Guide
   Basic: 5–10
   Average: 11–14

20 min.

SECTION 6-6 Markdown

Stores often sell products at sale prices, which are lower than their regular selling prices. The **markdown,** or discount, is the amount of money that you save by purchasing a product at the sale price.

○ **Section Objective**

Solve for the dollar amount of the markdown.

Markdown = Regular Selling Price − Sale Price

Living in the Real World

Sifting through the Gently Used

Yellow Tags and Fuchsia Cats A customer likes a cat crocheted of fuchsia yarn. She notices the color of the price tag attached to the cat's ear; this signifies it's marked down 25 percent.

Draw Conclusions What are the benefits of a store marking down products? Are there any drawbacks?

Continued on page 246

【Need Help? Go to...】

▶ **Workshop 5:** Subtracting Decimals, page 12
▶ **Skill 6:** Subtracting Decimals, page 733
▶ **Application A:** Formulas, page 760

〖 Example 1 〗

Nora Maag purchased a camcorder at a sale price of $499.99. The regular selling price is $549.99. What was the markdown?

STEP: Find the markdown.

Regular Selling Price − Sale Price
$549.99 − $499.99 = **$50.00 markdown**

CONCEPT CHECK

【SELF-CHECK ✔】

Complete the problems, then check your answers at the end of the chapter.

1. Shirts Are Us has a clearance on overstocked merchandise. A long-sleeve V-neck top that usually sells for $36.00 is on sale for $23.00. What is the markdown? **$36.00 − $23.00 = $13.00**

2. The regular selling price of a HDTV monitor is $1,899.99. The sale price is $1,789.99. Find the markdown. **$1,899.99 − $1,789.99 = $110.00**

The **markdown rate,** or discount rate, of an item is its markdown expressed as a percent of its regular selling price. Businesses frequently advertise the markdown rate rather than the sale price. You'll need to know that:

Markdown = Regular Selling Price × Markdown Rate

Section 6-6 Markdown ▶ **243**

National Standards for Business Education

Standard 1	Mathematical Foundations
Standard 2	Number Relationships and Operations

National Council of Teachers of Mathematics Standards

Standard 1	Numbers and Operations
Standard 4	Measurement
Standard 6	Problem Solving
Standard 8	Communication
Standard 9	Connections

1 FOCUS

Ask students if they know the meaning of the term *discount.* Then ask them to give some examples of when discounts are used.

In-Class Examples
Work through these exercises with students before having them do the Self Check.
1. $8.99 − $4.50 **$4.49**
2. $16.00 − $12.88 **$3.12**
3. 20% of $85 **$17**
4. $12\frac{1}{2}$% of $96 **$12**
5. $39.95 × 40% **$15.98**
6. $1,390 × 15% **$208.50**

Living in the Real World

Markdowns can help sell products that have been slow to move off the shelves, making room for new merchandise. There are possible drawbacks, in that an item could potentially sell at a higher price. The sales price of the cat is $3.30. (0.025 × 4.40 is 1.10; $4.40 − $1.10 = $3.30)

2 TEACH

Use your students' examples from the Focus section on page 243 to introduce the other key words used in this lesson. Point out that markdowns on sale items are often advertised either by giving the dollar amount or the markdown rate. The rate could be a percent off, such as "30 percent off" or it could be a fraction off, such as "$\frac{1}{3}$ off."

Stress to students that to find the amount of savings on a sale item, it is necessary to know the regular selling price. The regular selling price serves as the base upon which the markdown is computed.

You may wish to bring to class advertisements for sales from such resources as newspapers, magazines, and advertisements. Depending on the information given in an advertisement, have students compute the markdown.

Motivating the Lesson

A steel frame folding backpack chair with canopy regularly sells for $45. This week the backpack chair is on sale for $30. What is the savings, or markdown? **$15**

In-Class Examples

1. The regular selling price of an electric ice cream maker is $34.99. The sale price is $29.99. Find the markdown. **$5.00**

2. Watches are on sale at a local jeweler for $55. They regularly sell for $80. What is the markdown? **$25**

3. A place setting of stainless steel flatware is on sale for $49.99. The flatware regularly sells for $75.00. What is the markdown? **$25.01**

Need Help? Go to...

- ▶ Workshop 14: Finding a Percentage, page 30
- ▶ Workshop 2: Rounding Numbers, page 6
- ▶ Skill 30: Finding the Percentage, page 757
- ▶ Skill 2: Rounding Numbers, page 729

SELF-CHECK ✓

Example 2

Furniture World has a special on oak furniture at 40 percent to 55 percent off the regular selling price. Chad Wolfrum purchased an oak table at 40 percent off the regular price of $799. How much is the markdown?

STEP: Find the markdown.

Regular Selling Price × Markdown Rate

$799.00 × 40% = **$319.60 markdown**

CONCEPT CHECK

Complete the problems, then check your answers at the end of the chapter.

3. Outerwear coats and jackets are on sale at the clearance sale. A leather jacket is on sale for 40 percent off the regular selling price of $219.99. Find the markdown. **$219.99 × 40% = $87.996 = $88.00**

4. Microfiber raincoats are on sale for 50 percent off the regular selling price of $239.99. What is the markdown? **$239.99 × 50% = $119.995 = $120.00**

SECTION 6-6 PRACTICE

	Item	Regular Selling Price	−	Sale Price	=	Markdown
5.	Table	$169.99	−	$ 99.99	=	**$70.00**
6.	Shirt	16.99	−	11.99	=	**$5.00**
7.	Purse	65.95	−	45.50	=	**$20.45**
8.	TV	499.00	−	399.00	=	**$100.00**

9. Tax software. Regularly sells for $74.95. Sale price is $59.95. What is the markdown? **$15.00**

10. Minivan. Regularly sells for $34,495. Sale price is $29,595. What is the markdown? **$4,900.00**

11. Jeans. Regularly sell for $36.99. Markdown rate is 25 percent. What is the markdown? **$9.25**

12. Plastic cups. Regularly sell for $2.29. Markdown rate is 30 percent. What is the markdown? **$0.69**

13. Bargains on video games usually occur in January. Angie Sigler purchases a game console set that regularly sells for $59.95. The set is on sale for $44.95. What is the markdown? **$15.00**

14. April is usually a good month to purchase home improvement supplies. A sheet of cedar paneling at the lumber company regularly sells for $58.50. Jud Stassi purchases the paneling on sale for $48.95 a sheet. What is the markdown? **$9.55**

THINKING CRITICALLY

Markdown Ads

Relate this lesson to the real world by using newspaper advertisements as a source of math problems. Point out different types of markdown ads.

A. Reg. price $229
   Sale price − 199
   Markdown $ 30

B. Reg. price: $44
   Markdown: 25 %
   Markdown = 25% of $44 = $11

15. A 24.9 cubic foot side-by-side refrigerator that regularly sells for $1,049.92 is marked down 10 percent during a May sale. What is the markdown? **$104.99**

16. Instant oatmeal sells for $3.67 a box. During a January sale the oatmeal has a special deal of 2 for $5.00. How much can be saved by purchasing the oatmeal during the sale? **$2.34**

17. Printer Paper Store sells laser paper for $9.99 per ream. A special offer states: Buy 2, get 1 free. If you buy 2 reams, and get 1 free, what is your cost per ream? What is your markdown per ream? **$6.66/ream; $3.33 per ream**

18. Office Products has a box of 500 envelopes on sale for as low as $12.99 (with a list price of $44.00). What is the total markdown? **$31.01**

19. Mattress & Furniture sells a queen 2-piece bedroom set for $1,100. The sale price is $559.95 with a bonus discount of $60 if purchased during a mid-winter clearance sale. What is the total markdown? **$600.05**

20. Men's waterproof safety toe boots are on sale for $89.99. The regular price is $150.00. What is the markdown? **$60.01**

21. Jeremy Berkowitz purchases a down jacket during an April coat sale at the Ski Shop. All coats are discounted 45 percent. The down jacket regularly sells for $154.50. What is the markdown? **$69.53**

22. Consider the Veterans Day sale on men's clothing. The ad says that the store will take an extra 50 percent off for a total savings of 60 to 65 percent on clearance dress shirts. Shirts that were originally $29.50 to $45.00 will have a final cost of $11.06 to $16.88. Is the total savings 60 percent to 65 percent?
Yes: ($29.50 − $11.06) ÷ $29.50 = 0.625 = 62.5% off
Yes: ($45.00 − $16.88) ÷ $45.00 = 0.625 = 62.5% off

MAINTAINING YOUR SKILLS

Need Help? Go to...
→ Skill 6: **Subtracting Decimals,** page 733
→ Skill 30: **Finding the Percentage,** page 757

Subtract.

23.
```
  401.44
−  98.25
  303.19
```

24.
```
   79.7
−  9.924
  69.776
```

25.
```
   5.6
− 4.6301
  0.9699
```

26.
```
  73.291
− 62.824
  10.467
```

Find the percentage.

27. 30% of $120 **$36.00**

28. 40% of $280 **$112.00**

29. $\frac{1}{4}$% of 850 **$2.13**

30. 230% of 550 **1,265**

Section 6-6 Markdown ▶ **245**

PROBLEM SOLVING

Did You Know?
Almost 90 percent of all American households use grocery coupons weekly. Manufacturers distribute over $380 billion worth of grocery store coupons each year, but less than 1 percent is actually used. About how many dollars worth of coupons are used each year?
Less than $3.8 billion

WRAP-UP

Go over any problem for which a wrong answer is given.

Assignment Guide
   Basic: 5–12
Average: 13–16

20 min.

3 ASSESS

Error Analysis
When students compute markdown, remind them to read each problem carefully to determine what information is given. If the regular price and the sale price are given, then the markdown is figured by subtracting the sale price from the regular selling price (for example, $99.99 − $79.99 = $20.00. The markdown is $20.00.).

When the markdown is given as a percent off the regular price (for example, 20 percent off the regular price of $500) the markdown is figured by multiplying the regular price × the markdown rate. **$500 × 0.20 = $100 markdown**

4 CLOSE

Closing Activity
1. 25% of $864 **$216**
2. 30% of $79.99 **$24.00**
3. An automotive store is running a special on oil filters that regularly sell for $2.89. They are on sale this week for $1.77. What is the markdown? **$1.12**
4. An office supplies store is having a sale on home office furniture. A leather swivel chair that regularly sells for $129.99 is advertised at 40 percent off. What is the markdown? **$52.00**
5. During a pre-season sale, a heating and air conditioning company is selling a central air conditioner at 10 percent off the regular price of $1,899. What is the markdown? **$189.99**

National Standards for Business Education

Standard 1	Mathematical Foundations
Standard 2	Number Relationships and Operations

National Council of Teachers of Mathematics Standards

Standard 1	Numbers and Operations
Standard 4	Measurement
Standard 6	Problem Solving
Standard 8	Communication
Standard 9	Connections

① FOCUS

In this lesson, students compute the sale price when the markdown rate is known. Ask students what they must multiply the markdown rate by in order to find the amount of the markdown.

In-Class Examples
Work through these exercises with students before having them do the Self-Check.
1. $235.00 − $23.50 **$211.50**
2. $7.88 − $1.56 **$6.32**
3. $494 − $74 **$420**
4. $899.95 × 25% **$224.99**
5. $565 × 50% **$282.50**
6. $219 × 40% **$87.60**
7. $62.75 × 80% **$50.20**
8. $1,240 × 75% **$930**

SECTION 6-7 Sale Price

○ **Section Objective**

Compute the sale price when markdown rate is known.

For items that are on sale, some stores advertise the amount of markdown and the regular selling price. Some stores indicate that the item is a stated percent off the regular price. If you know the markdown, you can calculate the **sale price** as follows:

Sale Price = Regular Selling Price − Markdown

What if you know the markdown percent? When you receive 25 percent off the selling price of an item, you pay 75 percent of the selling price of the item. The regular selling price of an item is 100 percent. The *percent paid*, then, is 100 percent minus the percent off. Here's what you'll need to remember:

Sale Price = Percent Paid × Regular Selling Price

Note: If you use the second formula, then you first need to calculate the percent paid:

Percent Paid = 100% − Percent Off

Living in the Real World

Sifting through the Gently Used

Come Again for More Cats   The woman holding the crocheted cat is going to give it to her sister-in-law as a birthday present. Originally the cat cost $4.40. But the cat is now 25 percent off. Reitz puts the woman's money in the cash register and carefully wraps the cat.

Draw Conclusions   What is the sales price of the cat? (Calculate without tax.)

Continued on page 249

Example 1

Need Help? Go to...
- ▶ Workshop 14: Finding a Percentage, page 30
- ▶ Workshop 5: Subtracting Decimals, page 12
- ▶ Skill 30: Finding the Percentage, page 757
- ▶ Skill 6: Subtracting Decimals, page 733
- ▶ Application A: Formulas, page 760

Debralee Medford has a 25 percent off coupon and is purchasing a watch that has a regular price of $125.00. What is the sale price for the watch? What is the sale price using the percent paid method?

STEP 1: Find the markdown.

Regular Selling Price × Markdown Rate

$125.00   ×   25%   = $31.25

STEP 2: Find the sale price.

Regular Selling Price − Markdown

$125.00   − $31.25   = **$93.75 sale price**

STEP 3: Find the percent paid.

100% − Percent Off

100% −   25%   = 75%

STEP 4: Find the sale price.

Percent Paid × Regular Selling Price

75%   × $125   = **$93.75 sale price** (using percent paid method)

Living in the Real World

100% − 25% = 75%
75% × $4.40 = $3.30

USING CALCULATORS

The following sequence shows the use of the RM key to recall memory.
53.99 M+ × .20 =
10.798 M− RM 43.192
The sequence calculates 20 percent of 53.99 and subtracts the product from 53.99 to determine the sale price.

CONCEPT CHECK

 SELF-CHECK ✓

Complete the problems, then check your answers at the end of the chapter.

1. The regular selling price of men's jeans is $37.99. The markdown rate is 20 percent. Find the sale price. **Markdown = $37.99 × 20% = $7.598 = $7.60**
 Sale price = $37.99 − $7.60 = $30.39

2. The regular selling price of a fire safe is $329.99. The markdown rate is 30 percent. Find the sale price. **Markdown = $329.99 × 30% = $98.997 = $99.00**
 Sale price = $329.99 − $99.00 = $230.99

3. The regular selling price of a treadmill is $2,899. The markdown rate is 20 percent. Use the percent paid to determine the sale price.

4. The regular selling price of a cashmere sweater is $198. The markdown rate is 33 percent. Use the percent paid to determine the sale price.
 Percent Paid = 100% − 33% = 67%; Sale Price = 67% × $198 = $132.66

3. Percent Paid = 100% − 20% = 80%; Sale Price = 80% × $2,899 = $2,319.20

SECTION 6-7 PRACTICE

5. Rechargeable lantern.
 Regularly sells for $29.99.
 Markdown rate is 30 percent.
 What is the sale price? **$20.99**

6. Compact stereo.
 Regularly sells for $229.99.
 Markdown rate is 53 percent.
 What is the sale price? **$108.10**

7. Paint.
 Regularly sells for $22.99.
 Markdown rate is 20 percent.
 a. What is the percent paid? **80%**
 b. What is the sale price? **$18.39**

8. Sweeper.
 Regularly sells for $129.99.
 Markdown rate is 25 percent.
 a. What is the percent paid? **75%**
 b. What is the sale price? **$97.49**

9. Shoe Store has marked down men's work and outdoor boots 25 percent during its spring sale. What is the sale price of a pair of boots with a regular price of $149.99? **$112.49**

10. During an August back-to-school sale, Casual Clothes has marked down its line of dress shirts 30 percent. These shirts are regularly priced at $27.95 each. What is the sale price of these shirts? **$19.57**

11. Office Store has a computer drive for $99.99. The sale price is $69.99 and you have a manufacturer's coupon for $20.00. What is your final price? **$49.99**

12. The Pizza Shack discounts 15 percent off the regular selling price on the purchase of 3 or more pizzas. What is the sale price on the purchase of 3 pizzas that regularly sell for $9.75, $15.75, and $19.75? **$38.46**

13. A Danny's Department Store advertisement reads that you can save 50 percent to 66 percent off women's fall collections. Items with original prices of $44.00 to $152.00 are now $14.95 to $76.00. Determine if this ad is correct by verifying the markdowns. **($44.00 − $14.95) ÷ $44.00 = 0.66 = 66%**
 ($152 − $76) ÷ $152 = 0.50 = 50%

14. Best Deal has a phone on sale for $19.99. You can save $80.00. Determine the regular selling price. Determine the percent markdown.
 $99.99; $80 ÷ $99.99 = 0.80 = 80%

MAINTAINING YOUR SKILLS

Need Help? Go to...
→ Skill 30: Finding the Percentage, page 757
→ Skill 6: Subtracting Decimals, page 733

Find the percentage. Round answers to the nearest hundredth.

15. 25% of $74.80 **$18.70** 16. 7.5% of 425 **31.88** 17. 8% of 322 **25.76**

Subtract.

18. 471.814
 − 389.008
 82.806

19. 37
 − 26.321
 10.679

20. 0.016
 −0.0019
 0.0141

Section 6-7 Sale Price ▶ **247**

GLOBAL PERSPECTIVE

Currencies

Students work individually or in groups to create a list of the currencies in countries other than the United States. Ask one student to name all the countries that use the dollar as a basic unit of currency. **(United States, Australia, Canada, Hong Kong, New Zealand, Singapore, Taiwan.)** Ask students if the dollars used in other countries are the same as U.S. dollars. **No.** LS , CL

WRAP-UP

Go over any problem for which a wrong answer is given.

Assignment Guide
 Basic: 5–8
 Average: 9–12

20 min.

② TEACH

Have students make a list of the different ways stores usually give the markdown on sale items. For example, $10 off the regular selling price. Emphasize that the sale price of an item can be determined if the regular selling price and the markdown are given. Remind students that the discount can be given as a dollar amount or as a percent.

Review the two different ways to compute the sale price: Sale Price = Regular Selling price − Markdown; Sale Price = Percent Paid × Regular Selling Price.

In-Class Examples
1. A set of queen-size mattresses that regularly sells for $900 is on sale for 30 percent off. Find the sale price. **$630**
2. A 241-piece set of mechanic's tools sells for $225. The markdown rate is 40 percent. What is the sale price? **$135**

③ ASSESS

Error Analysis
Remind students that when they calculate the sale price using the percent paid, they must first compute the percent paid: Percent paid = 100% − Percent Off.

④ CLOSE

Closing Activity
1. $329.55 × 0.75 **$247.16**
2. $164.99 − $16.50 **$148.49**
3. A $90 weight bench with bar is on sale at a sporting goods store for 45 percent off. Find the sale price. **$49.50**
4. A music store is selling a set of drums for 25 percent off the regular price of $799. Use the percent paid to determine the sale price. **$599.25**

247

Quick Quiz

1. Sylvia Russell bought a hair dryer for $14.95 and a battery operated toothbrush for $16.99. The state sales tax rate is 4 percent, the county rate is 4.25 percent, and the city rate is 0.25 percent. What is the sales tax on these purchases? **$2.71**

2. Tanya Cramer buys a circular saw for $129.00, a cordless drill for $84.97, and a sander for $39.97. The state sales tax is 6.5 percent and the city tax rate is 0.5 percent. What is the total purchase price of these three items? **$271.72**

3. A hardware store is having a special sale on interior house paint. Buy 2 gallons, get 1 free. A gallon of paint costs $16.99. What is the unit price per gallon if you take advantage of the special price? Which is the better buy? **$16.99 for 1 gallon: $\frac{\$33.98}{3} = \$11.326666 = \$11.33$ per gallon; the special is the better buy.**

4. A local home center sells a gas grill for $179.99. What is the final price after the manufacturer's $25.00 rebate? **$154.99**

5. Outdoor furniture is on clearance for 60 percent off. The regular price for a table and a set of four chairs is $379.99. Find the sale price of the set. **$152.00**

SECTION 6-1 CONCEPT CHECK (p. 232)
1. $420 × 0.05 = **$21.00**
2. $2,520.00 × (6.00% + 1.00%) = $2,520.00 × 0.07 = **$176.40**

SECTION 6-2 CONCEPT CHECK (p. 234, 235)
1. a. Find the total selling price: $179.50 + $39.50 = $219.00
   b. Find the sales tax: $219.00 × 0.0825 = $18.0675 = $18.07
   c. Find the total purchase price: $219.00 + $18.07 = **$237.07**
2. a. Find the total selling price: (2 × $59.99) + (2 × $19.99) = $119.98 + $39.98 = $159.96
   b. Find the sales tax: $159.96 × 0.06 = $9.5976 = $9.60
   c. Find the total purchase price: $159.96 + $9.60 = **$169.56**

SECTION 6-3 CONCEPT CHECK (p. 238)
1. $3.69 ÷ 64 = $0.05765 = **$0.0577 or $0.06 per ounce**
2. $2.29 ÷ 20 = $0.1145 = **$0.115 or $0.12 per bag**

SECTION 6-4 CONCEPT CHECK (p. 239)
1. Coffee   22-ounce jar: $2.95 ÷ 22 = $0.13409 or $0.1341 per ounce
   16-ounce jar: $2.19 ÷ 16 = $0.136875 or $0.1369 per ounce
   22-ounce is the better buy
2. Cereal   14-ounce box: $2.50 ÷ 14 = $0.17857 or $0.1786 per ounce
   20-ounce box: $3.58 ÷ 20 = $0.179 or $0.1790 per ounce
   14-ounce is the better buy

SECTION 6-5 CONCEPT CHECK (p. 241, 242)
1. $3.39 − $0.55 = **$2.84 final price**
2. $2.59 − $0.35 = **$2.24 final price**
3. ($3.69 + $3.79) − $0.35 = $7.48 − $0.35 = **$7.13 final price**
4. ($4.19 × 2) − $1.00 = $8.38 − $1.00 = **$7.38 final price**

SECTION 6-6 CONCEPT CHECK (p. 243, 244)
1. $36.00 − $23.00 = **$13.00**
2. $1,899.99 − $1,789.99 = **$110.00**
3. $219.99 × 40% = $87.996 = **$88.00**
4. $239.99 × 50% = $119.995 = **$120.00**

SECTION 6-7 CONCEPT CHECK (p. 247)
1. Markdown = $37.99 × 20% = $7.598 = $7.60
   Sale price = $37.99 − $7.60 = **$30.39**
2. Markdown = $329.99 × 30% = $98.997 = $99.00
   Sale price = $329.99 − $99.00 = **$230.99**
3. Percent Paid = 100% − 20% = 80%; Sale Price = 80% × $2,899 = **$2,319.20**
4. Percent Paid = 100% − 33% = 67%; Sale Price = 67% × $198 = **$132.66**

Living in the Real World

Sifting through the Gently Used

Analyze the Story   Perhaps this chapter's story will make you check out your local secondhand store. Reitz makes good deals on odds and ends. Now, when was the last time you worked a deal? When was the last time you bargain shopped to get more for your money?

❶ Real-World Project. Suppose you have 20 dollars. How far can you make that money go?

 A. Select one item that you want or need to buy. Shop around to see who has that item for less.

 B. Take into account the taxes on that purchase. (So if your item is $19 then your total bill, with tax included, might come out to more than your allotted $20.)

 C. Comparison shopping makes you a smart consumer. Sometimes when you're in a pinch you might not always have time to shop around for an item. Yet if you do, how much did you save this one time just by shopping around? What is more important to you—saving money or saving time?

❷ Interview. Ask your family how often they comparison shop. How important is this to the family budget? Share with your class examples of when shopping around saved your family money.

Living in the Real World

1. Answers will vary depending on what item students select. Make sure students understand the value of comparison shopping (as they are supposed to do in part C of the problem).
2. Answers will vary depending on each student's home situation. Emphasize comparison shopping from selecting food at the grocery store to buying big-ticket items like televisions and vehicles.

REVIEW OF KEY WORDS

sales receipt (p. 234)   unit pricing (p. 237)   sale price (p. 246)
sales tax (p. 232)   coupons (p. 241)   markdown (p. 243)
total purchase price (p. 234)   rebates (p. 241)   markdown rate (p. 243)

Match one of the key words above with a definition below.

 1. the amount of money that is saved by buying an item at the sale price. **markdown**

 2. a product sold for a lower price than the regular selling price. **sale price**

 3. the markdown of an item expressed as a percent of the regular sale price. **markdown rate**

 4. a cash register tape or sales slip showing the selling price of items purchased, any sales tax, and the total purchase price. **sales receipt**

 5. the cost per unit of measure or count of an item. **unit pricing**

 6. a tax charged on the selling price of an item or service provided. **sales tax**

 7. in order to obtain them, a UPC label, sales slips, and a coupon must be mailed in to the manufacturer. **rebate**

 8. is equal to the selling price plus the sales tax. **total purchase price**

 9. redeemed at the time of purchase to obtain a discount. **coupons**

Study Guide and Assessment ▶ **249**

CHAPTER **Study Guide and Assessment**

6

Skills and Concepts

SECTION OBJECTIVE 6-1 AND EXAMPLES

Compute the sales tax.

Jeffrey Dahlin bought a backpack that had a selling price of $49.50. What is the sales tax on his purchase if he lives in a state where the sales tax rate is 6 percent?

STEP: Find the sales tax.

Total Selling Price × Sales Tax Rate

$49.50 × 0.06 = $2.97 sales tax

REVIEW EXERCISES

10. Joshua Okwy was planning to go camping with his family. He purchased a tent for $199.98, a lantern for $39.50 and an outdoor stove for $59.95. He lives in North Carolina, where the sales tax is 6 percent. What is the sales tax? **($199.98 + $39.50 + $59.95) × 6% = $17.97**

Compute the sales tax.

11. Total selling price $654.34; sales tax rate 5%.

12. Total selling price $1,238.45; sales tax rate $8\frac{1}{2}$%.

13. Total selling price $12.84; sales tax rate $7\frac{1}{4}$%.

11. $32.72
12. $105.27
13. $0.93

SECTION OBJECTIVE 6-2 AND EXAMPLES

Calculate the total purchase price.

Anderson's Country Store advertised wool blankets for $36.99. What is the sales tax if the state rate is 5.5 percent? What is the total purchase price?

STEP 1: Find the sales tax.

Total Selling Price × Sales Tax Rate

$36.99 × 0.055

= $2.03 sales tax

STEP 2: Find the total purchase price.

Total Selling Price + Sales Tax

$36.99 + $2.03

= $39.02 total purchase price

REVIEW EXERCISES

14. Gene DeWitt purchased a paper shredder for $99.95 and a case of computer paper for $24.95. The sales tax rate is 7.5 percent. What is the total purchase price? **($99.95 + $24.95) × 7.5% = $9.37 sales tax $124.90 + $9.37 = $134.27**

Complete the table below.

	Purchases	Selling Price	Sales Tax Rate	Sales Tax	Total Purchase Price
15.	Cat food Cat litter Flea powder	$ 9.58 4.59 5.33	6.50%	a. $1.27	b. $20.77
16.	Ski jacket Snowboard Snow hat	149.95 350.00 12.75	8.25%	a. $42.30	b. $555.00

17. Sales slip for Lester Gordon: shirt for $32.97, socks for $9.95, belt for $18.50. Sales tax rate is 4 percent. What is the total purchase price? **$63.88**

REINFORCEMENT

Section 6-1

1. Travis Irving bought a campfire grill for $79.96, a sleeping bag for $29.96, and a fishing rod for $34.99. He lives in Mississippi where the sales tax is 7 percent. What is the total selling price? **($144.91)** What is the sales tax on his purchases? **$10.14**

2. Elizabeth Gibbons bought a candle for $8, a picture frame for $15, and a CD rack for $11. The state sales tax is 2.9 percent and city tax is 2 percent. What is the sales tax on her purchases? **$1.67**

Section 6-2

1. Clayton Young buys 4 packages of alkaline batteries for $1.99 each, a bottle of sunscreen for $5.96, 2 boxes of adhesive bandages for $2.56 each, and a tube of toothpaste for $1.76. The combined state and city sales tax rate is 5.25 percent. What is the total purchase price? **$21.89**

23. 100 envelopes:
$2.19 ÷ 100 = $0.0219 =
2¢ per envelope
150 envelopes:
$2.59 ÷ 150 = $0.0172 =
1.7¢ per envelope
200 envelopes:
$2.99 ÷ 200 = $0.0149 =
1.4¢ per envelope
The 200 envelopes per box is
the best buy.

SECTION OBJECTIVE 6-3 AND EXAMPLES

Figure out the unit price.

Bret Franco purchased a 64-ounce bottle of shampoo for $3.99. What is the unit price of the shampoo (to the nearest tenth of a cent)?

STEP: Find the unit price.

Price per Item	÷	Measure or Count	
$3.99	÷	64	= $0.062343 or $0.0623 or 6.2¢ per ounce

REVIEW EXERCISES

18. Heather Burns takes a multivitamin each morning. She purchased a bottle at the drugstore for $11.58. It contained 500 vitamins. What is the price per vitamin?

19. James Johnson loves pretzels and takes a bag to work each day. He recently purchased a 32-ounce bag for $1.99. What is the unit price (to the nearest tenth of a cent)?

18. $\frac{\$11.58}{500} = $0.02316 = $0.023 = 2.3¢ per vitamin

19. $\frac{\$1.99}{32} = $0.062187 = $0.062 = 6.2¢ per ounce

Figure out the unit price. Round answers to the nearest tenth of a cent.

	Price per Item	Measure or Count	Unit Price
20.	$ 0.89	15 oz	$0.0593 = 5.9¢
21.	12.50	2 L	$6.25 per L

SECTION OBJECTIVE 6-4 AND EXAMPLES

Find the better buy based on unit price.

Pickles are sold in two sizes. The price of a 16-ounce jar is $2.49. The price of a 32-ounce jar is $3.15. Based on price alone, which size is the better buy?

STEP 1: Find the unit price for each item.

	Price per Item	÷	Unit of Measure	
16-ounce jar:	$2.49	÷	16	= $0.155625 or 15.56¢ per ounce
32-ounce jar:	$3.15	÷	32	= $0.09843 or 9.84¢ per ounce

STEP 2: Find the best buy.
The 32-ounce jar is the better buy.

22. 7.5-oz size: $2.50 ÷ 7.5 = $0.3333 − 33¢ per ounce
10.5-oz size: $3.29 ÷ 10.5 = $0.3133 = 31¢ per ounce (better buy)

REVIEW EXERCISES

22. A box of 7.5-ounce size crackers costs $2.50. Also advertised was the 10.5-ounce size for $3.29. Based on price alone, which one is the better buy?

23. A box of 100 envelopes cost $2.19. A box of 150 envelopes cost $2.59. A box of 200 envelopes cost $2.99. Based on price alone, which box is the best buy?

Find the better buy.

	Small Size	Large Size	Better Buy
24.	$12.69/30 count	$23.49/96 count	large size
25.	1.09/8-oz jar	1.69/12-oz jar	small size

REINFORCEMENT

Section 6-3

1. Diapers in a package of 30 for $10.88. Find the unit price per diaper. **$0.36 per diaper**

2. A roll of 600 labels costs $6.95. What is the unit cost per label? **$0.01 per label**

Section 6-4

1. Laundry detergent is sold in a 100-oz. plastic container for $7.07 or in a 200-ounce container for $10.57. Which is the better buy? $\frac{\$.0707}{100\text{-oz.}} = $.0707 = 7.07¢ per oz.; $\frac{\$10.57}{200\text{ oz.}} = $.05285 = 5.29¢ per oz.; **200-oz. container is the better buy.**

2. A local supermarket is running a special on facial tissues. A package of 3 boxes, which contains 216 tissues per box costs $3.98. An individual box, which also contains 216 tissues, costs $1.27. Which is the better buy? $\frac{\$3.98}{3 = \$1.3266666} = $1.33 per box $1.27 **for 1 box; $1.27 individual box is the better buy.**

SECTION OBJECTIVE 6-5 AND EXAMPLES

Work out the final price after using a coupon or rebate.

Barbara Bailey purchased a pair of pants for $24.99. She had a coupon for 25 percent off. What was the final price for the pants?

STEP: Find the final price.

Total Selling Price	−	Total Savings	
$24.99	×	25%	= $6.25
$24.99	−	$6.25	= **$18.74 final price**

REVIEW EXERCISES

26. As Peder Cruiz entered his favorite sporting goods store, he received a coupon for $10.00 off any item in the store. He decided to purchase a tennis racket that was selling for $125.98. What was the final price? **$125.98 − $10 = $115.98**

27. Carlos Ruiz purchased a water pitcher for $19.99. What is the price after the $2.50 manufacturer's rebate? **$19.99 − $2.50 = $17.49**

Compute the final price.

	Item	Total Selling Price	Coupon	Final Price
28.	Catsup	$ 1.98	$0.75	**$1.23**
29.	Dog food	15.97	1.25	**$14.72**

SECTION OBJECTIVE 6-6 AND EXAMPLES

Solve for the dollar amount of the markdown.

Nancy Britt purchased a vacuum cleaner on sale for $149.95. The regular selling price is $249.50. What was the markdown?

STEP: Find the markdown.

Regular Selling Price	−	Sale Price	
$249.50	−	$149.95	= **$99.55 markdown**

REVIEW EXERCISES

30. Jason Slaugh purchased a pair of golf shoes for $69.99. The regular selling price is $89.00. What was the markdown? **$89.00 − $69.99 = $19.01**

31. Shelly Ward purchased a mountain bike for 35 percent off the regular price of $899. How much is the markdown? **$899 × 35% = $314.65**

Find the markdown.

	Item	Regular Selling Price	Sale Price	Markdown
32.	Pillow	$34.99	$29.69	**$5.30**
33.	Lamp	95.59	40% off	**$38.24**

REINFORCEMENT

Section 6-5

1. A frozen yogurt costs $2.49. You have a $0.75 off store coupon that you clipped out of your school newspaper. What is the final price of your frozen yogurt? **$1.74**

2. A can of tennis balls sells for $3.59. You have a store coupon for $2.00 off if 2 cans are purchased. What is the final price for 2 cans of tennis balls? **$5.18**

3. A cordless telephone is advertised for $19.99. The manufacturer offers a $10.00 rebate. What is the final price of the phone? **$9.99**

Section 6-6

1. One store sells the industrial vacuum cleaner for $36.29, but a competitor has it on sale this week for $32.99. What is the markdown? **$3.30**

2. A video game system that usually sells for $299.99 is on sale for 15 percent off. What is the markdown if the game system is bought for the sale price? **$45.00**

SECTION OBJECTIVE 6-7 AND EXAMPLES

Compute the sale price when the markdown rate is known.

Lee Truk has a coupon for 30 percent off and is purchasing a 12-cup coffee maker that has a regular price of $19.99. What will he pay for the coffee maker?

STEP 1: Find the markdown.

Regular Selling Price × Markdown Rate

$19.99   ×   30%

= $6.00

STEP 2: Find the sale price.

Regular Selling Price − Markdown

$19.99   − $6.00

= **$13.99 sale price**

REVIEW EXERCISES

34. The regular selling price of a silk scarf is $49. The markdown rate is 38 percent. Use the percent paid to determine the sale price. $49.00 × 38% = $18.62

$49.00 − $18.62 = $30.38 sale price

Complete the table.

	Regular Selling Price	Markdown Rate		Markdown		Sale Price
35.	$ 349.75	25.0%	a.	$87.44	b.	$262.31
36.	23,450.00	8.5%	a.	$1,993.25	b.	$21,456.75
37.	123.45	35.0%	a.	$43.21	b.	$80.24

 38. Language Arts Dana Dickerson sells candles exclusively through her catalog. She found out that San Francisco has the highest tax rate in the state—8.5 percent. If a catalog customer from San Francisco purchased a dozen votive candles for 58¢ each, what would the total purchase price be, including sales tax? (See Section 6-2.) **$7.55**

 39. Social Science Jose Artillo is a general manager of a large department store chain. His research has shown that customers prefer at least 30 percent off an item when considering whether something is a good deal or not. This week he has decided to offer 33 percent off any item in the store. Find the markdown for the following items: wool pants, $65.95; leather shoes, $126.50; and straw purses, $19.95. (See Section 6-6.) **$21.76; $41.75; $6.58**

 40. Computer Technology Harvey Kellerman purchased a complete computer system for $1,436.88. He also received a manufacturer's rebate for $55.00. What was the final price he paid once he received the rebate? (See Section 6-5.) **$1,381.88**

 41. Science Jorge Mendez teaches family and consumer science. For this week's assignment, he is requiring his students to conduct a comparison-shopping activity. One of his students came back to class with the following: sweet peas, 10-ounce package, $1.09; 14-ounce package, $1.79; 16-ounce package, $2.29. Help the student find the best buy, based on price alone. (See Section 6-4.) **The 10-oz size is the best buy.**

REINFORCEMENT

Section 6-7

1. A children's apparel shop is having a sale on denim overalls for toddlers. The overalls usually sell for $24.99. The markdown rate is 20 percent. What is the sale price? **$19.99**

2. An auto repair shop has a special on car batteries. A battery with a warranty usually sells for $69.99. It is marked down 25 percent. Use the percent paid to determine the sale price. **$52.49**

3. An appliance store has a special on washers and dryers. Dryers are marked down 10 percent if a washer is also purchased. What is the sale price of a dryer that regularly sells for $349 if a washer is also bought? Use the percent paid to determine the sale price. **$314.10**

Aligned and verified by
The Princeton Review

Cumulative Test Prep

Test-Taking Tip
When taking a standardized test, you may be able to find the correct answer using estimation. Perform the proper operations with rounded numbers and look to see which answer choices are reasonable for the information given in the problem.

SECTION ONE: MULTIPLE CHOICE

There are eight multiple-choice questions in this section. After working each problem, write the letter of the correct answer on your paper.

1. Nick Bronson is paid $6 for each birdhouse he assembles. If he made 12 yesterday and 17 today, how much money did he earn? **B**

    Ⓐ $102   Ⓑ $174
    Ⓒ $198   Ⓓ $204

2. Tomas Olivera keeps records of his family's expenses. Total monthly expenses for September, October, and November were $1,787.43, $1,891.74, and $1,811.12 respectively. What was the average monthly expenditure? **C**

    Ⓐ $5,940.29   Ⓑ $5,490.29
    Ⓒ $1,830.10   Ⓓ $1,710.07

3. George Pinewood deposited $54.21 in currency and a check for $348.19 in his savings account. What was his total deposit? **B**

    Ⓐ $401.40   Ⓑ $402.40
    Ⓒ $403.40   Ⓓ $420.04

4. Jay Stone's gross weekly pay is $280.00. His earnings to date are $9,240.00. What amount is deducted from his pay this week for Social Security taxes? (Note: The rate is 6.2 percent.) **C**

    Ⓐ $4.06   Ⓑ $16.80
    Ⓒ $17.36   Ⓓ $17.64

5. In the Morenos' budget for this month, they had planned to spend $187.50 on transportation costs. They actually spent $212.45. How much more or less did they spend on transportation expenses than they originally planned? **B**

    Ⓐ $399.95 more than originally planned
    Ⓑ $24.95 more than originally planned
    Ⓒ $24.95 less than originally planned
    Ⓓ $12.45 less than originally planned

6. Martin Gillis compares the prices for paper towels. A 24-roll package is $19.99. A 12-roll package is priced at $11.99. A 3-roll package is priced at $2.89. A single roll is priced at $0.89. Based on price alone, which is the better buy? **A**

    Ⓐ 24-roll package
    Ⓑ 12-roll package
    Ⓒ 3-roll package
    Ⓓ single roll

7. Boston Savings Bank pays 6 percent interest compounded quarterly on regular savings accounts. Fred Pilliod deposited $1,800 in a regular savings account for $1\frac{1}{2}$ years. He made no other deposits or withdrawals. How much interest will he earn? (Note: Use the Compound Interest—Amount of $1.00 table on page 797.) **D**

    Ⓐ 1.09344   Ⓑ 1.07728
    Ⓒ $1,968.19   Ⓓ $168.19

8. Jill Dohr deposited a check for $701.32. She also deposited coins totaling $15.97 and currency totaling $108. What was her total deposit? **D**

    Ⓐ $717.29   Ⓑ $809.32
    Ⓒ $820.29   Ⓓ $825.29

SECTION TWO: FREE RESPONSE

This section contains eight questions for which you will supply short answers. Write your answers on your paper.

9. If a company pays 80 percent of a group insurance plan that costs $3,000 annually, how much is deducted from the employee's monthly paycheck? (Remember that the employee pays the remaining 20 percent.) **$50.00**

10. Commission: 4 percent first $2,000; 8 percent over $2,000. Find the total graduated commission on $8,800. **$624.00**

11. Maria Diaz statement balance is $952.64. Check numbers 901 and 905, in the amounts of $47.27 and $59.23, are outstanding. She also has an outstanding deposit of $200.00. She reconciles the statement. What should her adjusted balance be? **$1,046.14**

12. Tony Vivoni pays for a new surround sound system with a check in the amount of $763.45. Write the amount in words as it would appear on a check.

13. Bart Rodger's statement balance is $649.12. He has 2 outstanding checks in the amounts of $123.99 and $75.45. He also has an outstanding deposit of $125. He reconciles the statement. What should his adjusted balance be? **$574.68**

14. Taylor Cotton deposits $4,000 in an ordinary annuity after each quarter for 1 year. The account pays 6 percent interest compounded quarterly. What is the future value of the account in 1 year? (Note: Use the Future Value of an Ordinary Annuity for $1.00 per Period table on page 798.) **$16,363.60**

15. A brand of salad dressing that Sally Beckman prefers is on sale at Foodway. She can buy an 8-ounce bottle for $3.29 or a 12-ounce bottle for $3.89. What is the unit price of each package?

16. Andrea Cho purchased a new outfit at the back-to-school sale in August. All the clothing was marked down 25 percent. The outfit was regularly priced at $87.69. What was the sale price of the outfit? **$65.77**

15. 8-oz = $0.411; 12-oz = $0.324

SECTION THREE: OPEN-ENDED

This section contains four open ended questions. Demonstrate your knowledge by giving a clear, concise solution to each problem. Your score on these problems will depend on how well you do in the following:

- Explain your reasoning.
- Show your understanding of mathematics in an organized manner.
- Use charts, graphs, and diagrams in your explanation.
- Show the solution in more than one way or relate it to other situations.
- Investigate beyond the requirements of the problem.

17. Why might someone choose to have no withholding allowances when figuring taxes to withhold?

They may wish to put money in the bank to collect interest until the tax money is due.

12. Seven hundred sixty-three and $\frac{45}{100}$ dollars

18. What would you do if an unpredictable expense occurred and your emergency fund is not enough to cover it?

19. Why do you think it might be beneficial to compare interest rates and interest periods at several banks before you open your savings account?

20. What do state, county, and city governments do with the sales tax money they collect?

Mathematics Online

To learn more about cash purchases, visit the *Mathematics with Business Applications* Web site at www.busmath.glencoe.com.

18. You could try to cut back on budget items that are not fixed expenses, such as entertainment or dining out.

19. A higher interest rate can give you considerably more interest because of the compounding so it is important to get the highest rate. The interest periods are also important—the more times your money compounds the more interest you get.

20. The sales tax money is used for repairing roads, providing services to residents, and so on. State, county, and city governments use tax money for police and fire departments as well as roads and civic improvements.

National Standards for Business Education

Section Objectives	1. Mathematical Foundations	2. Number Relationships and Operations	3. Patterns, Functions, and Algebra	4. Measurements	5. Statistics and Probability	6. Problem-Solving Applications	
7-1 Account Statements (pp. 258–260) Calculate the new balance on a charge account.	X	X					
7-2 Finance Charge: Unpaid Balance Method (pp. 261–263) Find the finance charge by using the unpaid-balance method.	X	X					
7-3 Finance Charge: Average-Daily-Balance Method (No Purchases Included) (pp. 264–267) Calculate the finance charge based on the average-daily-balance method where no new purchases are included.	X	X					
7-4 Finance Charge: Average-Daily-Balance Method (New Purchases Included) (pp. 268–271) Compute the finance charge based on the average-daily-balance method where new purchases are included.	X	X			X	X	

(Source: Reprinted with permission from the National Standards for Business Education, copyright © 2001 by National Business Education Association, 1914 Association Drive, Reston, Virginia 21901-1596)

SCANS Correlation

Foundation Skills

Basic Skills	Reading	Writing	Math	Listening	Speaking	
Thinking Skills	Creative Thinking	Decision Making	Problem Solving	Seeing Things in the Mind's Eye	Knowing How to Learn	Reasoning
Personal Qualities	Responsibility	Self-Esteem	Sociability	Self-Management	Integrity/Honesty	

This chapter's highlighted blocks indicate the chapter's content coverage in the Student Edition and the Teacher Wraparound Edition.

1. Numbers & Operations	2. Algebra	3. Geometry	4. Measurement	5. Data Analysis & Probability	6. Problem Solving	7. Reasoning & Proof	8. Communication	9. Connections	10. Representations
X			X		X		X	X	
X			X		X		X	X	
X			X		X		X	X	
X			X		X		X	X	

SCANS Correlation

Workplace Competencies

Resources	Allocating Time	Allocating Money	Allocating Material and Facility Resources	Allocating Human Resources		
Information	Acquiring and Evaluating Information	Organizing and Maintaining Information	Interpreting and Communicating Information	Using Computers to Process Information		
Interpersonal Skills	Participating as a Member of a Team	Teaching Others	Serving Clients/Customers	Exercising Leadership	Negotiating to Arrive at a Decision	Working with Cultural Diversity
Systems	Understanding Systems	Monitoring and Correcting Performance	Improving and Designing Systems			
Technology	Selecting Technology	Applying Technology to Task	Maintaining and Troubleshooting Technology			

What You'll Learn

In this chapter you'll focus on charge (i.e., buy now and pay later) account statements and investigate various methods credit card companies use to compute finance charges.

Why It's Important

Many times consumers find themselves in a position where they would like to make a purchase but lack the necessary cash. Perhaps it is an emergency. Using a credit card to make purchases allows the cardholder the flexibility to "buy now, pay later." There is considerable responsibility in using a credit card, and it is important that the user understands how interest is calculated.

Key Word Review

Create a Quiz

Students create a fill-in-the-blank test for each key word. The tests may be shared and used as a review activity later in this chapter. If possible, have students create their test using a word processor.

CHAPTER 7

Charge Accounts and Credit Cards

What You'll Learn

Section 7-1 Calculate the new balance on a charge account.

Section 7-2 Find the finance charge by using the unpaid-balance method.

Section 7-3 Calculate the finance charge based on the average-daily-balance method where no new purchases are included.

Section 7-4 Compute the finance charge based on the average-daily-balance method where new purchases are included.

When Will You Ever Use This?

Credit is an agreement to get money, goods, or services now in exchange for a promise to pay in the future. When you buy on credit, you're delaying the payment for the purchase. You might use credit cards to purchase clothes, airline tickets, or other big-ticket items.

Key Words to Know
- credit card
- charge account
- finance charge
- unpaid-balance method
- average-daily-balance method
- account statement

Mathematics Online

To learn more about charge accounts and credit cards, visit the *Mathematics with Business Applications* Web site at **www.busmath.glencoe.com**.

256 ◀ Chapter 7 Charge Accounts and Credit Cards

CLASSROOM RESOURCES

Application and Enrichment
- ✍ *Teacher Wraparound Edition*
- ✍ *Teacher Resource Binder, Blackline Masters*
- 💿 *Interactive Lesson Planner* CD-ROM
- 💿 *PowerPoint® Presentations* CD-ROM

Review and Enforcement
- Mathematics Online
  www.busmath.glencoe.com
- ✍ *Teacher Resource Binder, Internet Resources*

- ✍ *Student Activity Workbook*
- ✍ *Student Activity Workbook, Teacher Annotated Edition*
- ✍ *School-to-Home Activity Workbook*

Assessment and Evaluation
- ✍ *Assessment Binder, Reproducible Tests*
- ✍ *Assessment Binder, Alternative Assessment Strategies*
- 💿 **Exam***View*® *Pro Test Generator* CD-ROM

For the Teacher
- ✍ *Student Activity Workbook, Teacher Annotated Edition*
- ✍ *Assessment Binder*
- 💿 *Interactive Lesson Planner* CD-ROM
- ✍ *Teacher Resource Binder*
- 🖥 Mathematics Online
  www.busmath.glencoe.com

For the Student
- ✍ *Student Activity Workbook*
- ✍ *School-to-Home Activity Workbook*

Living in the Real World

Story's Summary

Students learn the possible perils of credit card debt by following the story of José Yuma, a Southwest silversmith keeping his business buoyant with the use of credit cards. After speaking to his cousin Kimi, a banker, Yuma learns about finance charges, average daily balances, and the workings of a basic credit card statement. In the end, he sees the sense in trying to pay off his monthly credit card bill in full.

Living in the Real World

A Financial Gem?

José Yuma is a silversmith who works from his home at the foot of a mesa in the Four Corners region of the Southwest. Yuma fashions silver, gold, and turquoise into award-winning jewelry, which he sells to art dealers across the country. In this chapter you'll learn how Yuma keeps his business afloat with charge accounts and credit cards.

Read on. Go to . . .

257

Did You Know...

In one year the National Foundation for Credit Counseling counseled 1.6 million American households in need of assistance managing their debt. The average American household carries a balance of $5,900 on bank and store credit cards with a 15 percent interest rate.

Think about This

If you have a $1,000.00 balance on a credit card with a 15 percent interest rate and you only pay the minimum amount of $25.00 each month, how long will it take to pay off the debt in full? How much interest will you have paid? **It will take almost 11 years, with total interest of $757.98. Answer can be calculated using an online credit card calculator such as the one available at www.bankrate.com.**

LOCAL STANDARDS

National Standards for Business Education

Standard 1	Mathematical Foundations
Standard 2	Number Relationships and Operations
Standard 5	Statistics and Probability

National Council of Teachers of Mathematics Standards

Standard 1	Numbers and Operations
Standard 4	Measurement
Standard 6	Problem Solving
Standard 8	Communication
Standard 9	Connections

① FOCUS

Ask students if they know how a person actually pays for the purchases made with a credit card. Explain that a credit card company sends a monthly statement to the customer. In this lesson, students will compute the new balance on a charge account statement.

In-Class Examples

Work through these exercises with students before having them do the Self-Check.

1. $170.00 + $3.40 + $50.00 − $70.00 **$153.40**
2. $250.00 + 0 + $125.60 + $249.95 **$625.55**
3. $315.67 + $3.15 + $75.33 − $50.00 − $12.50 **$331.65**
4. $451.70 + $6.78 + $119.99 − ($70.00 + $11.92) **$496.55**
5. $629.73 + $91.47 + $32.48 − $355.00 + $99.51 **$498.19**

SECTION ⑺⁻¹ Account Statements

○ **Section Objective**

Calculate the new balance on a charge account.

With a **credit card** or a **charge account**, you receive a monthly **account statement,** which lists all the items you purchased during a one-month period. A credit card allows the cardholder to purchase goods and services on demand. A charge account is an existing line of credit, often at a particular business. If your previous bill was not paid in full, then the credit card or charge account company adds on a **finance charge**. A finance charge is interest that is charged for delaying payment. The formula you'll need to remember for this is:

$$\frac{\text{New}}{\text{Balance}} = \frac{\text{Previous}}{\text{Balance}} + \frac{\text{Finance}}{\text{Charge}} + \frac{\text{New}}{\text{Purchases}} - (\text{Payments} + \text{Credits})$$

▶**FYI**

Although the Federal Reserve Bank estimates that 60 percent of payments are made with checks, credit cards account for more than 12 billion transactions a year.

▶▶▶

Living in the Real World

A Financial Gem?

The Statement Yuma is self-employed, so he must keep careful records of what he spends and earns. Today he receives the monthly statement from his credit card company. Since several valuable pieces of his jewelry didn't sell quickly last month, he doesn't have enough money to pay for some of the materials he ordered.

Draw Conclusions What are the disadvantages of using credit cards?

Continued on page 261

Need Help? Go to...
▶ **Workshop 4:** Adding Decimals, page 10
▶ **Workshop 5:** Subtracting Decimals, page 12
▶ **Skill 6:** Subtracting Decimals, page 733
▶ **Skill 5:** Adding Decimals, page 732
▶ **Application A:** Formulas, page 760

(**Example 1**)

Martha Palmer received this charge account statement on October 2 (see Figure 7.1). What is her new balance?

STEP: Find the new balance.

$$\frac{\text{Previous}}{\text{Balance}} + \frac{\text{Finance}}{\text{Charge}} + \frac{\text{New}}{\text{Purchases}} - (\text{Payments} + \text{Credits})$$

$$\$332.64 + \$5.64 + \$173.03 - (\$50.00 + \$31.94)$$
$$= \qquad\qquad \$511.31 \qquad - \qquad\qquad \$81.94$$
$$= \$429.37 \text{ new balance}$$

332.64 [+] 5.64 [+] 173.03 [M+] 50.00 [M−] 31.94 [M−]
[RM] [=] 429.37

Living in the Real World

It can be easy to overextend yourself financially when using credit cards, which can then turn into a dangerous financial situation. Ringing up high debt means paying for items with money you've yet to earn.

COOPERATIVE LEARNING

Visit Businesses

Students visit banks and businesses to collect charge account applications. Students work in groups to look at the type of information required on the applications. Groups locate the annual fee, annual percentage rate (APR), grace period, incentives, finance charge, and any charges (transaction fees, late fees, cash advance fees, etc.). Groups display an application and the relevant information on a poster board. [CL], [LS], [P]

Figure 7.1

D&L Department Store

MAIL THIS PORTION WITH PAYMENT TO P.O. BOX 1027   PALMER'S ACCOUNT NUMBER

Martha Palmer
1234 Main St.
Toledo, OH 43605

☐ (IF ADDRESS IS INCORRECT,
PLEASE CHECK BOX AND
CORRECT ON REVERSE SIDE)

ACCOUNT NUMBER → 101-04076
NEW BALANCE
TOTAL MINIMUM AMOUNT NOW DUE $43.00
SEND PAYMENT TO REACH US BY 10/30/--

DATE	DEPT. NO.	DESCRIPTION	PURCHASES	CREDITS	PAYMENTS	ITEM NO.
09/07	162	SPORTSWEAR		$23.42		0-06-18005
09/10	363	SPORTSWEAR	$108.63			0-07-20015
09/17		PAYMENT—THANK YOU			$50.00	0-06-47023
09/19	214	JR SPORTSWEAR		8.52		0-07-45005
09/19	53	HOUSEWARES	19.53	CREDIT FOR ITEMS RETURNED	$50.00 PAYMENT TOWARD LAST MONTH'S BILL	0-07-45006
09/27	34	COSMETICS	25.62			0-07-64004
09/29	1	LINENS-TOWELS	19.25			0-07-70012

Bill Closing Date	Previous Balance	Finance Charge	Total Purchases This Month	Credits	Payment	New Balance
9/30	$332.64	$5.64	$173.03	$31.94	$50.00	$429.37

Pay new balance in full within 25 days of bill closing date to avoid finance charge next month. Finance charge, if any, is computed on the average daily balance of $375.72 by applying monthly periodic rates.
SUBJECT TO A MINIMUM FINANCE CHARGE OF $.50. **NOTICE:** SEE REVERSE SIDE FOR IMPORTANT INFORMATION.

LAST DATE TRANSACTIONS WERE PROCESSED

AMOUNT PALMER OWED LAST MONTH

AMOUNT PALMER NOW OWES

CONCEPT CHECK

Complete the problems, then check your answers at the end of the chapter. Find the new balance.

	Previous Balance	+	Finance Charge	+	New Purchases	−	(Payments + Credits)	=	New Balance
1.	$600.00	+	$7.50	+	$90.00	−	$100.00	=	**$597.50**
2.	278.75	+	4.18	+	35.85	−	48.00	=	**$270.78**

Example 2

3. $658.94 + $10.71 + $54.21 + $36.28 + $98.56 − ($100.00 + $145.81) = $858.78 − $245.81 = $612.89

4. $1,856.23 + $16.79 + $132.26 + $142.39 + $12.56 − ($160.00 + $32.21) = $2,169.23 − $192.21 = $1,977.02

Dante Green's charge account statement showed a previous balance of $157.80, a finance charge of $2.76, new purchases of $86.50 and $48.50, a payment of $40.00, and a credit of $37.85. What is the new balance?

STEP: Find the new balance.

$$\frac{\text{Previous}}{\text{Balance}} + \frac{\text{Finance}}{\text{Charge}} + \frac{\text{New}}{\text{Purchases}} - (\text{Payments} + \text{Credits})$$

$157.80 + $2.76 + ($86.50 + $48.50) − ($40.00 + $37.85)

= $295.56 − $77.85

= **$217.71 new balance**

CONCEPT CHECK

Complete the problems, then check your answers at the end of the chapter.

3. Rolo Stein's charge account statement showed a previous balance of $658.94, a finance charge of $10.71, new purchases of $54.21, $36.28, and $98.56, a credit of $145.81 and a $100.00 payment. What is the new balance?

4. Naomi Folsum's charge account statement showed a previous balance of $1,865.23, a finance charge of $16.79, new purchases of $132.26, $142.39, and $12.56, a credit of $32.21 and a $160.00 payment. What is the new balance?

PROBLEM SOLVING

Rate of Exchange

When you purchase items in another country with a credit card, the credit card company will figure the exchange rate on the day you made the purchase or the day your account was billed. Students choose a country to "visit." Students look up the current value of that country's currency in relation to the U.S. dollar using the *Wall Street Journal,* or searching online. As an example, using the current exchange rate students, find the cost in dollars of a necklace purchased in Italy for 6,140 euros. (**6,140 ÷ current exchange rate**) Assign students problems from Workshop 23 on page 48. LS , CL , P

SECTION 7-1

② TEACH

Explain that the format of monthly statements varies from company to company, but that the information given is the same. Stress that if the balance of the previous month had been paid in full, there would be no finance charge. Thus, you essentially can borrow the money for purchases without paying interest.

Mention that although a statement shows the minimum amount due, there is no penalty for paying more than this amount. The more you pay, the lower the finance charge.

Motivating the Lesson

Your car needs a new battery and 2 new tires. The battery costs $65, and 2 tires cost a total of $150. Since you are short on cash, you charge these items. When your monthly charge account statement arrives, it lists new purchases of $65 for the battery and $150 for the tires. Your previous balance on your statement was $0. What is the new balance? **$215**

In-Class Examples

1. $350.00 + $5.25 + $79.43 − $275.00 **$159.68**

2. $906.00 + $11.56 + $29.18 − $550.00 **$396.74**

3. $1,637.89 + $18.88 + $456.35 − $1,500.00 **$613.12**

4. Malcolm Turner's charge account statement showed a previous balance of $270.49, a finance charge of $4.05, new purchases of $44.62, and a payment of $225.00. What is the new balance? **$94.16**

3 ASSESS

Error Analysis

Remind students that the previous balance, the finance charge, and any new purchases on charge account statements are amounts owed. Have students total these amounts. From this total, have them subtract the payment and credits, if any. This amount is the new balance. If students are making errors, have them check their work for computational mistakes.

4 CLOSE

Closing Activity

1. $38.67 + $48.56 + $175.83 + $243.42 **$506.48**

2. $639.54 + $8.90 + $332.66 − $500 **$481.10**

3. Alice Newman received her credit card account statement. It showed a previous balance of $87.29, a finance charge of $1.31, new purchases of $44.60, $52.99, and $113.66, and a payment of $50.00. What is the new balance? **$249.85**

4. Penelope Barr's charge account statement showed a previous balance of $825.00, a finance charge of $10.75, no new purchases, and a payment of $450.00. What is the new balance? **$385.75**

5. Franklin Rhodes received his charge account statement. His previous balance was $86.79. His statement showed a finance charge of $1.30, new purchases of $46.80, $22.16, and $35.95, a credit of $46.80, and a payment of $25.00. What is the new balance? **$121.20**

SECTION 7-1 PRACTICE

What is the new balance for the credit statements shown?

	Billing Date	Previous Balance	Finance Charge	New Purchases	Payments & Credits	New Balance
5.	08/15/20--	$ 600.00	$ 9.00	$140.00	$100.00	**$649.00**
6.	01/22/20--	410.75	7.20	175.00	150.00	**$442.95**
7.	03/01/20--	450.95	6.75	39.95	160.00	**$337.65**
8.	09/04/20--	233.23	2.33	40.36	133.23	**$142.69**
9.	06/15/20--	675.19	—	416.34	675.19	**$416.34**
10.	08/01/20--	2,494.21	43.65	137.25	450.00	**$2,225.11**

11. Yukiko Naito's monthly credit card statement has a previous balance of $307.85. Naito made a payment of $40.00. This month's new purchases include the following charges: $9.50 and $41.75. The finance charge is $4.62. What is the new balance? **$323.72**

12. Bob Ross has a charge card. Ross's previous monthly balance is $144.79. He made a payment of $144.79. There is no finance charge. This month Ross has no new purchases. What is the new balance? **$0.00**

13. Andre Moore's charge card account has a previous balance of $787.29. Moore made a $100 payment. The new purchases include $47.97 and $49.28, with a finance charge of $11.81. What is the new balance? **$796.35**

14. Jane Cook has a monthly statement for her credit card. The previous balance is $529.78. Cook paid $85. This month's new purchases include $277.32 and $38.20, as well as a finance charge of $7.95. What is the new balance? **$768.25**

15. Marco Cassius received this charge account statement. Find his payments and credits, new purchases, and new balance.

Figure 7.2

Dept.	Description	Charges	Payment/Credit	Date	Ref. #
109	Garden Shop	$ 42.75		1/25	6004
85	Menswear	145.98		1/25	7018
	PAYMENT		$74.40	2/01	8014
71	Appliances	35.50		2/02	3113
Billing Date: 2/16					

Previous Balance	Payments & Credits	Unpaid Balance	Finance Charge	New Purchases	New Balance
$285.92	a. **$109.90**	—	$4.29	b. **$188.73**	c. **$369.04**

MAINTAINING YOUR SKILLS

Need Help? Go to...
► Skill 5: Adding Decimals, page 732
► Skill 6: Subtracting Decimals, page 733

Add.

16. $532.75 + $45.90 + $38.90 + $16.55 **$634.10**

17. $44.29 + $324.60 + $8.65 + $27.50 **$405.04**

Subtract.

18. $41.50 − $9.50 **$32.00**

19. $321.65 − $12.35 **$309.30**

20. $427.16 − $45.12 **$382.04**

ALTERNATIVE ASSESSMENT

Students with Orthopedic Impairments

If you have students who have orthopedic impairments, making sure they have access to the classroom can be one of the first steps you take to ensure their full participation in the class. Be aware that a barrier can be a stair, a curb, a narrow walkway, a heavy door, or an elevator door that does not allow time for a wheelchair exit.

WRAP-UP

Go over any problem for which a wrong answer is given.

Assignment Guide
   Basic: 5–10
   Average: 11–14

20 min.

SECTION **7-2** Finance Charge: Unpaid-Balance Method

Section Objective

Find the finance charge by using the unpaid-balance method.

Some companies use the **unpaid-balance method** to compute finance charges. This is when the finance charge is computed based on the portion of the previous balance you have not paid. The formula is:

Unpaid Balance = Previous Balance − (Payments + Credits)

Finance Charge = Unpaid Balance × Periodic Rate

New Balance = Unpaid Balance + Finance Charge + New Purchases

Living in the Real World

A Financial Gem?

How Do You Juggle Money? Yuma visits his cousin Kimi, the vice president at the local bank. He explains that he needs to continually buy materials to keep producing a steady supply of jewelry. Yet some months, especially when he creates particularly expensive pieces, it might take a while to sell his work. That means that occasionally he can't cover his business expenses completely.

Draw Conclusions Suppose his monthly invoice listed a balance of $1,220, but he only paid $900. Yuma would still owe $320. If the finance charge for an unpaid balance is 1.9 percent annual interest rate, what is the new balance?

Continued on page 264

(Example 1)

A portion of Lucille Sherman's charge account statement is shown. The monthly finance charge is 1.5 percent of the unpaid balance. What is the new account balance?

Figure 7.3

Charge Account Statement					
88	PAYMENT / Thank You	40.00			
Billing Date: 2/16					
Previous Balance	Payments & Credits	Unpaid Balance	Finance Charge	New Purchases	New Balance
$132.40	$40.00			$79.55	

Continued on next page

Section 7-2 Finance Charge: Unpaid-Balance Method ▶ **261**

Living in the Real World

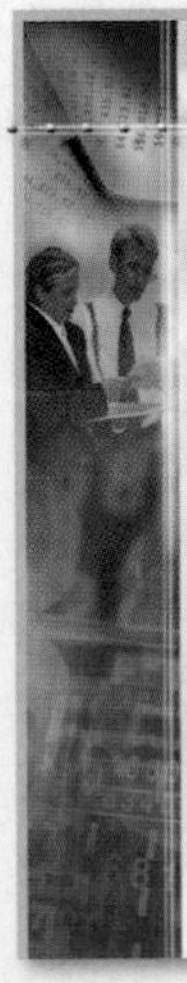

($1,220 − $900) × 1.9% =
$320 × 0.019 = $6.08
$320.00 + $6.08 = $326.08

COMMUNICATION SKILLS

Evaluate Advertising

Credit card companies compete for customers. Some companies use advertising, like direct mail to offer special introductory rates or credit protection services. Students bring in credit card ads or offers. Groups of students evaluate the way cards are advertised. Are some of the offers actually good deals? How often do the advertisements seem less appealing once students read the small print? Groups give a short presentation to the class. CL

National Standards for Business Education

Standard 1	Mathematical Foundations
Standard 2	Number Relationships and Operations

National Council of Teachers of Mathematics Standards

Standard 1	Numbers and Operations
Standard 4	Measurement
Standard 6	Problem Solving
Standard 8	Communication
Standard 9	Connections

1 FOCUS

Explain to students that there are different ways to calculate the finance charge. This lesson will focus on calculating the finance charge based on the unpaid-balance method. Write on the board the formula for calculating the finance charge based on this method: Finance Charge = Unpaid Balance × Periodic Rate. Have a student define the term *unpaid balance* (the portion of the previous balance that is not paid). Explain that there are other methods used to compute the finance charge that will be covered in Sections 7-3 and 7-4.

① FOCUS (cont'd)

In-Class Examples
Work through these exercises with students before having them do the Self-Check.

1. $71.40 − $21.40 **$50.00**
2. $415.20 − $200.00 **$215.20**
3. ($171.50 − $71.50) × 1.5% **$1.50**
4. ($478.50 − $24.90) × 2% **$9.07**
5. ($835.67 − $400.00) × 1.75% **$7.62**

② TEACH

Explain to students that just as the methods used to calculate the finance charge can vary, so, too, can the annual interest rates for finance charges.

Motivating the Lesson
Your charge card company calculates the finance charge based on the unpaid balance on your account. When your monthly account statement arrives, it shows you still owe $140.00 on a digital camera you purchased last month. The periodic interest rate is 1.5 percent. You have made no new purchases. What is the finance charge? **($2.10)** What is the new balance? **$142.10**

In-Class Example
Previous balance of $390. Payments and credits total $225. Periodic interest rate is 1.5 percent. What is the unpaid balance? **($165)** What is the finance charge? **($2.48)** New purchases of $60.98. What is the new balance? **$228.46**

Need Help? Go to...

Workshop 14: Finding a Percentage, page 30

Skill 30: Finding the Percentage, page 757

Application A: Formulas, page 760

STEP 1: Find the unpaid balance.

Previous Balance − (Payments + Credits)

$132.40 − $40.00 = $92.40

STEP 2: Find the finance charge.

Unpaid Balance × Periodic Rate

$92.40 × 1.5% = $1.386 or $1.39

STEP 3: Find the new balance.

Unpaid Balance + Finance Charge + New Purchases

$92.40 + $1.39 + $79.55

= **$173.34 new balance**

CONCEPT CHECK

SELF-CHECK ✓

Complete the problems, then check your answers at the end of the chapter. Find the unpaid balance, the finance charge, and the new balance. (The periodic rate is 1.5 percent.)

	Previous Balance	−	Payments + Credits	=	Unpaid Balance	Finance Charge	+	New Purchases	=	New Balance
1.	$600		$100		a.	b.		$70		c.
2.	220		150		a.	b.		95		c.

1.
a. Unpaid Balance = $600.00 − $100.00 = $500.00; b. Finance Charge = 1.5% × $500.00 = $7.50; c. New Balance = $500.00 + $7.50 + $70.00 = $577.50

2.
a. Unpaid Balance = $220.00 − $150.00 = $70.00; b. Finance Charge = 1.5% × $70.00 = $1.05; c. New Balance = $70.00 + $1.05 + $95.00 = $166.05

Example 2

Alejandro Martinez has a charge account at Diamond Jewelers, which uses the unpaid-balance method of computing finance charges. The periodic rate is 1.85 percent. If Martinez's previous balance is $478.68 and he had payments and credits of $250.00, find his unpaid balance and finance charge. If he has new purchases of $38.50, find his new balance.

STEP 1: Find the unpaid balance.

Previous Balance − (Payments + Credits)

$478.68 − $250.00 = $228.68

STEP 2: Find the finance charge.

Unpaid Balance × Periodic Rate

$228.68 × 1.85% = $4.23058 = $4.23

STEP 3: Find the new balance.

Unpaid Balance + Finance Charge + New Purchases

$228.68 + $4.23 + $38.50

= **271.41 new balance**

3. Unpaid Balance = $980.00 − $120.00 = $710.00; Finance Charge = 1.5% × $710.00 = $10.65; New Balance = $710.00 + $10.65 + $72.00 = $792.65

CONCEPT CHECK

SELF-CHECK ✓

Complete the problems, then check your answers at the end of the chapter. The periodic rate is 1.5 percent. Find the unpaid balance, the finance charge, and the new balance.

3. Previous balance of $980.00.
Credit of $120.00.
Payment of $150.
New purchases: $32.00 and $40.00.

4. Previous balance of $654.50.
Credit of $85.50.
Payment of $120.
New purchases: $32.50 and $54.50.

4. Unpaid Balance = $654.50 − $205.50 = $449.00; Finance Charge = 1.5% × $449.00 = $6.74; New Balance = $449.00 + $6.74 + $87.00 = $542.74

RETEACH / ENRICHMENT

Maximum Interest Rate
States regulate the maximum annual interest rate that may be charged for credit cards. In Connecticut the maximum is 19.8 percent. In New Jersey it's 30 percent. Marika Velasquez maintained a credit card balance of $750 for a year. If she lived in Connecticut, what is the amount of finance charge owed? **$750.00 × 0.198 = $148.50** What about in New Jersey? **$750.00 × 0.30 = $225.00** What is the amount if Velasquez lived in your state? **Answers will vary.**

5. a. Unpaid Balance: $400.00; **b.** Finance Charge: $6.00; **c.** new balance: $486.00

6. a. unpaid balance: $150.00; **b.** finance charge: $2.25; **c.** new balance: $197.25

7. a. unpaid balance: $275.00; **b.** finance charge: $4.13; **c.** new balance: $369.13

8. a. unpaid balance: $80.00; **b.** finance charge: $1.20; **c.** new balance: $123.70

9. a. unpaid balance: $380.00; **b.** finance charge: $5.70; **c.** new balance: $608.20

10. a. unpaid balance: $73.43; **b.** finance charge: $1.10; **c.** new balance: $202.44

11. a. unpaid balance: $372.87; **b.** finance charge: $5.59; **c.** new balance: $526.40

12. a. unpaid balance: $593.27; **b.** finance charge: $8.90; **c.** new balance: $802.12

Need Help? Go to...
▶ Skill 5: Adding Decimals, page 732
▶ Skill 6: Subtracting Decimals, page 733
▶ Skill 30: Finding the Percentage, page 757

SECTION 7-2 PRACTICE

For Problems 5–12, use a periodic rate of 1.5 percent and the unpaid-balance method to compute the finance charge.

	$\left(\begin{array}{c}\text{Previous}\\\text{Balance}\end{array}\right.$ $-$	Payments & Credits $=$	$\left.\begin{array}{c}\text{Unpaid}\\\text{Balance}\end{array}\right)$ $+$	Finance Charge $+$	New Purchases $=$	New Balance
5.	($500.00 $-$	$100.00 $=$ **a.**) $+$		**b.** $+$	$ 80.00 $=$	**c.**
6.	(300.00 $-$	150.00 $=$ **a.**) $+$		**b.** $+$	45.00 $=$	**c.**
7.	(350.00 $-$	75.00 $=$ **a.**) $+$		**b.** $+$	90.00 $=$	**c.**
8.	(125.50 $-$	45.50 $=$ **a.**) $+$		**b.** $+$	42.50 $=$	**c.**
9.	(437.50 $-$	57.50 $=$ **a.**) $+$		**b.** $+$	222.50 $=$	**c.**
10.	(173.43 $-$	100.00 $=$ **a.**) $+$		**b.** $+$	127.91 $=$	**c.**
11.	(491.87 $-$	119.00 $=$ **a.**) $+$		**b.** $+$	147.94 $=$	**c.**
12.	(738.27 $-$	145.00 $=$ **a.**) $+$		**b.** $+$	199.95 $=$	**c.**

Find the new balance.

13. Midge Duez's account statement. Previous balance of $1,280.00. Payment of $200.00. New purchases: $52.00 and $48.00. Periodic rate is 1.6 percent. **$1,197.28**

14. Liz Cole's account statement. Previous balance of $1,221.35. Payment of $300.00. New purchases: $25.90 and $18.53. Periodic rate is 1.75 percent. **$981.90**

15. Hideo Nagata's account statement. Previous balance of $948.00. Credit of $100.00. Payment of $200.00. New purchases: $72.00 and $88.00. Periodic rate is 1.5 percent. **$817.72**

16. Wyndolyn Brown's account statement. Previous balance of $419.70. Credit of $23.35. Payment of $200.00. New purchases: $49.90 and $32.48. Periodic rate is 1.25 percent. **$281.18**

17. A portion of Alvin Sujkowski's charge account statement is shown. The finance charge is 2 percent of the unpaid balance. What is the new balance?

Previous Balance	Payments & Credits	Unpaid Balance	Finance Charge	New Purchases	New Balance
$419.29	$45.00	**$374.29**	**$7.49**	$79.31	**$461.09**

18. A portion of Verda Buell's charge account statement is shown. The finance charge is 1.25 percent of the unpaid balance. What is the new balance?

Previous Balance	Payments & Credits	Unpaid Balance	Finance Charge	New Purchases	New Balance
$556.71	$147.55	**$409.16**	**$5.11**	$21.64	**$435.91**

MAINTAINING YOUR SKILLS

Add.

19. $425.10 + $38.75 + $29.51 + $4.22 **$497.58**

20. $5.95 + $38.75 + $71.19 + $314.75 **$430.64**

Subtract.

21. $499.24 − $88.31 **$410.93**

22. $391.37 − $79.43 **$311.94**

23. $523.89 − $154.79 **$369.10**

Find the percentage. Round answers to the nearest hundredth.

24. 4% of 220 **8.80**

25. 8% of 60 **4.80**

26. 3.9% of 500 **19.50**

Section 7-2 Finance Charge: Unpaid-Balance Method ▶ **263**

WRAP-UP

Go over any problem for which a wrong answer is given.

Assignment Guide
   Basic: 5–12
   Average: 13–16

20 min.

③ ASSESS

Error Analysis
Remind students that these problems require them to calculate the unpaid balance, the finance charge, and the new balance for monthly charge account statements. Emphasize that these calculations must be done in the correct order:
1. Find the unpaid balance.
2. Find the finance charge on the unpaid balance.
3. Find the new balance.

Sometimes the unpaid balance is given in the problem. If it is not, remind students that before calculating the finance charge, they must know the unpaid balance. Review how to find the unpaid balance: Previous Balance − (Payments + Credits). Then, have them multiply the periodic interest rate, for example, 1.75 percent or 0.0175 by the unpaid balance. Finally, add the finance charge and the amount of any new purchases to the unpaid balance. This is the new balance.

④ CLOSE

Closing Activity
1. ($543.18 − $466.00) × 1.5% **$1.16**
2. ($394.58 − $75.00) × 1.25% **$3.99**
3. Latrice Wallace had a previous balance of $494.50. Her payments and credits totaled $415.62. The periodic rate on the unpaid balance is 2 percent. What is the unpaid balance? **($78.88)** What is the finance charge? **($1.58)** What is the new balance? **$80.46**
4. Herbert Lancaster's charge account statement. Unpaid balance of $137.07. Periodic rate is 1.5 percent of the unpaid balance. What is the finance charge? **($2.06)** New purchases of $455.94. What is the new balance? **$595.07**

263

National Standards for Business Education

Standard 1	Mathematical Foundations
Standard 2	Number Relationships and Operations

National Council of Teachers of Mathematics Standards

Standard 1	Numbers and Operations
Standard 4	Measurement
Standard 6	Problem Solving
Standard 8	Communication
Standard 9	Connections

1 FOCUS

Lead students in a discussion of the meaning of average daily balance. Elicit from students the fact that the balance each day is the same until the day the credit card company makes a transaction. After that date, the balance again remains the same. Ask students how to find the average of the balances in a 30-day period. **(Find the sum of the daily balances and divide by 30.)** Explain that some credit card companies compute the finance charge by using the daily balances. In this section, the only transactions considered are payments.

○ **Section Objective**

Calculate the finance charge based on the average-daily-balance method where no new purchases are included.

SECTION 7-3 Finance Charge: Average-Daily-Balance Method (No New Purchases Included)

Many companies calculate the finance charge using the **average-daily-balance method** where *no new purchases* are included. The average daily balance is the average of the account balance at the end of each day of the billing period. For this method of computing finance charges, new purchases posted during the billing period are not included when figuring the balance at the end of the day. Calculating it looks like this:

$$\text{Average Daily Balance} = \frac{\text{Sum of Daily Balances}}{\text{Number of Days}}$$

If you need to calculate the finance charge, multiply the average daily balance by the periodic rate. Remember that:

$$\text{Finance Charge} = \text{Average Daily Balance} \times \text{Periodic Rate}$$

$$\text{New Balance} = \text{Unpaid Balance} + \text{Finance Charge} + \text{New Purchases}$$

Living in the Real World

A Financial Gem?

Do You Know What You're Being Charged? Credit card companies have more than one way of calculating finance charges. Kimi explains that his credit card company uses one particular method to figure his balance including a finance charge.

Draw Conclusions In your own words, what do you suppose a finance charge calculated on your average daily balance (with *no* new purchases included) means?

Continued on page 268

Example 1

A portion of Dewey Napp's credit card statement is shown in Figure 7.4 on page 265.

A finance charge was added to Napp's account balance because he did not pay his last bill in full. The finance charge was computed using the average daily balance where new purchases were not included. Only the payment of $44.85 affected the average daily balance. What is the average daily balance?

Living in the Real World

Answers will vary. New purchases posted during the billing period are not included when figuring the balance at the end of the day.

THINKING CRITICALLY

Businesses

Businesses usually have to pay credit card companies between 2 percent and 6 percent of each purchase charged. For example, if the charge to the business is 4 percent and you purchase jeans and a shirt for $78, how much does the business pay the credit card company? **($78 × 0.04 = $3.12)** Why are businesses willing to pay this fee?

Figure 7.4

Reference	Posting Date	Transaction Date	Description	Purchases & Advances	Payments & Credits
131809	9/05	8/24	Health Club	$48.75	
265118	9/18		PAYMENT		$44.85
407372	9/20	9/01	Wilson's	37.85	
329416	10/01	8/30	Ed's Discount	20.99	

Billing Period	Previous Balance	Periodic Rate	Average Daily Balance	Finance Charge
9/4–10/3	$194.85	2%	$170.93	$3.42

Payments & Credits	Purchases & Advances	New Balance	Minimum Payment	Payment Due
$44.85	$107.59	$261.01	$20.00	10/25

Need Help? Go to...

➤ Workshop 8:
Multiplying
Decimals, page 18

➤ Workshop 8:
Dividing Decimals,
page 16

➤ Skill 8:
Multiplying
Decimals, page 735

➤ Skill 11:
Dividing Decimals,
page 738

➤ Application G:
Elapsed Time
(Days), page 765

STEP 1: Find the sum of daily balances.

Dates	Payment	End-of-Day Balance	×	Number of Days	Sum of Balances
9/4–9/17		$194.85	×	14	$2,727.90
9/18	$44.85	150.00	×	1	150.00
9/19–10/3		150.00	×	15	2,250.00
			TOTAL	30	**$5,127.90**

STEP 2: Find the average daily balance.

Sum of Daily Balances ÷ Number of Days

$5,127.90　　÷　　30　= **$170.93 average daily balance**

194.85 ⊠ 14 = 2727.9 M+ 194.85 − 44.85 = 150
M+ 150 ⊠ 15 = 2250 M+ RM 5127.9 ÷ 30 = 170.93

CONCEPT CHECK

SELF-CHECK✓

Complete the problems, then check your answers at the end of the chapter. Find the average daily balance where no new purchases are included.

	Dates	Payment	End-of-Day Balance	×	Number of Days	Sum of Balances
1.	9/9–9/18		$500	×	10	a. $5,000
2.	9/19	$100	400	×	1	a. $400
3.	9/20–10/8		a. $400	×	b. 19	c. $7,600
4.				TOTAL	a. 30	b. $13,000

	Sum of Daily Balances	÷	Number of Days		= Average Daily Balance
5.	a. $13,000.00	÷	b. 30	=	c. $433.33

Section 7-3 Finance Charge: Average-Daily-Balance Method ▶ **265**

In-Class Examples

Work through these exercises with students before having them do the Self-Check.

1. (12 × $400) + (19 × $300)
   $10,500
2. (15 × $600) + (11 × $570)
   $15,270
3. $2754.85 ÷ 30 **$91.83**
4. $140 × 1.75% **$2.45**
5. $739 × 1.5% **$11.09**

(2) TEACH

Work through Example 1 on page 264 carefully with students. Finding the sum of daily balances may be confusing for some students. Emphasize the importance of setting up the computations in an orderly manner, such as the method shown in the solution.

Point out that the first date to use in finding the daily balances is the beginning date of the billing period. Explain also that the *posting* date is the date the payment is entered into the accounting records of the company.

Motivating the Lesson

Your credit card statement arrives in the mail. It covers the billing period of 8/15 through 9/15. You had a previous balance of $100. Your $50 payment was posted on 8/22. Your credit card company charges a periodic rate of 2 percent of the average daily balance. Your average daily balance was $59.68. You made no new purchases. What is the finance charge? **($1.19)** What is your new balance? **$51.19**

2 TEACH (cont'd)

In-Class Examples

1. Sadako Takahashi received her charge account statement for the billing period of 6/12 through 7/11. Her previous balance was $300. From 6/12 through 6/30, she had an end-of-day balance of $300. Her payment of $200 was posted on 7/1. From 7/2 through 7/11, her end-of-day balance was $100. What is the average daily balance? **$226.67**

2. Gabriel Kaplan received his charge account statement for the billing period of 7/21 through 8/20. His previous balance was $1,562.35. From 7/21 through 7/28, he had an end-of-day balance of $1,562.35. His payment of $1,200 was posted on 7/29. From 7/30 through 8/20, his end-of-day balance was $362.35. What is the average daily balance? **$672.03**

3 ASSESS

Error Analysis

Review why students need to find the average daily balance. **(Some credit card companies determine the finance charge based on the average daily balance.)** Students may find it helpful to use a calendar when computing average daily balance. For example, in Problem 1 of the In-Class Examples, have them use a calendar to count the number of days from 6/12 through 6/30. **(19 days)** Count the day that the payment was posted as 1 day. Then, count the days from 7/2 through 7/11 on the calendar. **(10 days)** Review the number of days in each month if necessary.

Ask why students need to know the number of days in each month. **(Divide the sum of the daily balances by the number of days in the month.)**

Dewey Napp (from Example 1) checks the finance charge and the new balance. The finance charge is 2 percent of the average daily balance. What is the new balance?

STEP 1: Find the unpaid balance.
Previous Balance − (Payments + Credits)
$194.85   − $44.85   = $150.00

STEP 2: Find the finance charge.
Average Daily Balance × Periodic Rate
$170.93   ×   2%   = $3.418 or $3.42

STEP 3: Find the new purchases.
$48.75 + $37.85 + $20.99 = $107.59

STEP 4: Find the new balance.
Unpaid Balance + Finance Charge + New Purchases
$150.00   + $3.42   + $107.59
= **$261.01 new balance**

CONCEPT CHECK

SELF-CHECK ✓

Complete the problems, then check your answers at the end of the chapter. The finance charge is 1.5 percent of the average daily balance.

Previous Balance	Purchases & Advances	Payments & Credits	Average Daily Balance	Finance Charge	New Balance
$180.00	$40.00	$30.00	$165.00		

6. Find the finance charge.
$165.00 × 0.015 = **$2.48**

7. Find the new balance.
$180.00 + $40.00 − $30.00 + $2.48 = **$192.48**

SECTION 7-3 PRACTICE

For Problems 8 and 9, fill in the table.

8.

Billing Periods	Payment	End-of-Day Balance	Number of Days	Sum of Balance		
6/01–6/15		$75.00	15	$1,125.00	d. What is the average daily balance?	average daily balance: $50
6/16	$50.00	25.00	1	25.00		
6/17–6/30		25.00	14	a. **$350**		
TOTAL			b. **30**	c. **$1,500**		

9.

Billing Periods	Payment	End-of-Day Balance	Number of Days	Sum of Balance		
7/15–8/2		$400.00	a. **19**	b. **$7,600**	i. What is the average daily balance?	average daily balance: $361.29
8/3	$100.00	300.00	c. **1**	d. **$300**		
8/4–8/14		300.00	e. **11**	f. **$3,300**		
TOTAL			g. **31**	h. **$11,200**		

TECHNOLOGY POWER

Many airlines and hotel chains issue credit cards that reward cardholders with "points" and rewards for dollars spent using their card. Marriott Hotels allows the points earned on their card to be redeemed for free hotel stays or entire vacation packages. American Express allows points to be transferred to airlines with which they maintain partnerships. Many companies let employees keep the points they earn while on business travel for personal use.

The finance charge is computed using the average-daily-balance method where no new purchases are included. Find the finance charge and the new balance for the following statements.

10.

Billing Period	Previous Balance	Periodic Rate	Average Daily Balance	Finance Charge
2/3–3/2	$196	2%	$156	a. $3.12

Payments & Credits	Purchases & Advances	New Balance	Minimum Payment	Payment Due
$60	0	b. $139.12	$15	3/20

11. A portion of Theo Clark's credit card account statement for March is shown. The finance charge is computed using the average-daily-balance method where new purchases are excluded. Find the average daily balance, the finance charge, and the new balance.

Figure 7.5

Reference	Posting Date	Transaction Date	Description	Purchases & Advances	Payments & Credits
450345	3/20		PAYMENT		$24.66
458343	3/27	3/14	Oil Co.	$81.30	

Billing Period	Previous Balance	Periodic Rate	Average Daily Balance	Finance Charge
3/4–4/3	$94.66	2%	a. $82.73	b. $1.65

Payments & Credits	Purchases & Advances	New Balance	Minimum Payment	Payment Due
$24.66	$81.30	c. $152.95	$10.00	4/21

12. Edith Bertelli received this statement from a department store. Find the average daily balance, the finance charge, and the new balance.

Figure 7.6

Reference	Posting Date	Transaction Date	Description	Purchases & Advances	Payments & Credits
1027485	4/11		PAYMENT		$40.00
4500298	4/15	4/1	Menswear	$39.95	
5473390	4/23	4/21	Housewares	15.99	
1376455	4/25		PAYMENT		50.00

Billing Period	Previous Balance	Periodic Rate	Average Daily Balance	Finance Charge
4/1–5/1	$175.00	1.2%	a. $136.61	b. $1.64

Payments & Credits	Purchases & Advances	New Balance	Minimum Payment	Payment Due
$90.00	$55.94	c. $142.58	$25.00	5/25

MAINTAINING YOUR SKILLS

Need Help? Go to...
▶ Skill 8: Multiplying Decimals, page 735
▶ Skill 10: Dividing (Decimal Remainder), page 737
▶ Application Q: Mean, page 770

Multiply.

13. 12 × 200 **2,400**   14. 18 × 150 **2,700**   15. 22 × 37.5 **825**

Divide. Calculate answers to the nearest hundredth.

16. 3,750 ÷ 30 **125**   17. 3,360 ÷ 28 **120**   18. 1,129.95 ÷ 31 **36.45**

Find the average.

19. 44, 73, 92, 88, 63 **72**   20. 324, 406, 958, 285, 785, 374 **522**

Section 7-3 Finance Charge: Average-Daily-Balance Method ▶ **267**

WRAP-UP

Go over any problem for which a wrong answer is given.

Assignment Guide
Basic: 8–9
Average: 10–11

20 min.

As students work through the problems computing the average daily balance, help them make a chart similar to the one in Step 1 of Example on page 264. Students may also need to review the four steps needed to find the new balance. Be sure they are adding the unpaid balance (*not the previous balance*), the finance charge, and the new purchases to find the new balance. Be sure they understand how to find the information needed to solve these problems.

4 CLOSE

Closing Activity

1. $2,208.30 ÷ 30 **$73.61**
Find the average.

2. 56, 48, 73, 23, 95 **59**

3. Darnell Jones examined his charge account statement for the billing period of 8/3 through 9/2. His previous balance was $317.29. From 8/3 through 8/8, he had an end-of-day balance of $317.29. His payment of $250.00 was posted on 8/9. From 8/10 through 9/2, his end-of-day balance was $67.29. What is the average daily balance? **$115.68**

4. Lenore Douglas received her charge account statement for the billing period of 6/20 through 7/19. Her previous balance was $181.32. From 6/20 through 7/5, she had an end-of-day balance of $181.32. Her payment of $140 was posted on 7/6. What was her end-of-day balance from 7/7 through 7/19? **($41.32)** What is the sum of the balances for the billing period of 6/20 through 7/19? **($3,479.60)** What is the average daily balance? **$115.99**

Finance Charge: Average-Daily-Balance Method
(New Purchases Included)

National Standards for Business Education

Standard 1	Mathematical Foundations
Standard 2	Number Relationships and Operations
Standard 5	Statistics and Probability
Standard 6	Problem-Solving Applications

National Council of Teachers of Mathematics Standards

Standard 1	Numbers and Operations
Standard 4	Measurement
Standard 6	Problem Solving
Standard 8	Communication
Standard 9	Connections

1 FOCUS

Ask students to suggest a way that a credit card company can compute the sum of daily balances to yield a higher finance charge. **(Include new purchases made during the billing, or posting, period.)** Explain that many charge accounts do use new purchases in computing the finance charge.

In-Class Examples

Work through these exercises with students before having them do the Self-Check.

1. $(10 \times \$350) + (20 \times \$425)$ **$12,000**
2. $(18 \times \$246) + (13 \times \$186)$ **$6,846**
3. $\$8,275.60 \div 30$ **$275.85**
4. $\$2892.50 \div 31$ **$93.31**
5. $\$91.55 \times 1.25\%$ **$1.14**

○ **Section Objective**

Compute the finance charge based on the average-daily-balance method where new purchases are included.

Some companies compute the finance charge using the average-daily-balance method where *new purchases are included* when figuring the daily balances during the billing period. Remember that:

$$\text{Average Daily Balance} = \frac{\text{Sum of Daily Balances}}{\text{Number of Days}}$$

Then you'll need to figure out the finance charge and the new balance. The finance charge is calculated by multiplying the average daily balance times the periodic rate. The new balance is comprised of an unpaid balance, a finance charge, and any new purchases. To do this, follow these formulas:

$$\text{Finance Charge} = \text{Average Daily Balance} \times \text{Periodic Rate}$$

$$\text{New Balance} = \text{Unpaid Balance} + \text{Finance Charge} + \text{New Purchases}$$

Living in the Real World

A Financial Gem?

Don't Take It to the Limit In case Yuma ever wants to get a different credit card, Kimi mentions he should remember to check if it calculates a finance charge based on your average daily balance (with *new* purchases included).

Draw Conclusions If you had a choice between paying a finance charge based on your average daily balance with or without new purchases, which one would you pick, and why?

Continued on page 273

Example 1

Aiesha Miller has a charge account where the finance charge is computed using the average-daily-balance method that includes new purchases. She checks to be sure the average daily balance is correct.

Living in the Real World

Answers may vary, but the most logical choice is without new purchases, as the finance charge would be higher if the additional cost of new purchases were added to the daily balance. Adding to the daily balance will increase the average daily balance, which will increase the finance charge.

COMMUNICATION SKILLS

Role-Play

Consumer should use the correct terms when communicating with a credit card company. Students role-play a phone inquiry between a customer and a credit card company using terms, such as APR, finance charge, interest rate, variable rate, fees, cash advance, and grace period.

`CL` , `LS`

Figure 7.7

Reference	Posting Date	Transaction Date	Description	Purchases & Advances	Payments & Credits
1-32734	12/10	12/8	Housewares	$25.85	
2-44998	12/20		PAYMENT		$70.00

Billing Period	Previous Balance	Periodic Rate	Average Daily Balance	Finance Charge
12/1–12/31	$125.80	2%	$117.05	$2.34

Payments & Credits	Purchases & Advances	New Balance	Minimum Payment	Payment Due
$70.00	$25.85	$83.99	$20.00	1/21

Need Help? Go to...

➤ Workshop 6:
   Multiplying
   Decimals, page 14
➤ Workshop 7:
   Dividing Decimals,
   page 16
➤ Skill 8: Multiplying
   Decimals, page 735
➤ Skill 11: Dividing
   Decimals, page 738
➤ Application G:
   Elapsed Time
   (Days), page 765

STEP 1: Find the sum of daily balances.

Dates	Payment	Purchases	End-of-Day Balance	×	Number of Days	Sum of Balances
12/1–12/9			$125.80	×	9	$1,132.20
12/10		$25.85	151.65	×	1	151.65
12/11–12/19			151.65	×	9	1,364.85
12/20	$70.00		81.65	×	1	81.65
12/21–12/31			81.65	×	11	898.15
			TOTAL		31	$3,628.50

STEP 2: Find the average daily balance.

Sum of Daily Balances ÷ Number of Days

$3,628.50 ÷ 31

= **$117.048 or $117.05 average daily balance**

125.8 [×] 9 [=] 1132.2 [M+] 125.8 [+] 25.85 [=]

151.65 [M+] [×] 9 [=] 1364.85 [M+] 151.65 [−]

70 [=] 81.65 [M+] [×] 11 [=] 898.15 [M+] [RM]

3628.5 [÷] 31 [=] 117.048

Section 7-4 Finance Charge: Average-Daily-Balance Method ▶ **269**

---

② TEACH

Encourage students to organize their computations in an orderly way, as is done in the examples. This will help to avoid errors when many transactions are added or subtracted.

Motivating the Lesson

Your charge account statement arrives in the mail for the billing period of 4/13 through 5/12. It shows a previous balance of $160. The statement lists new purchases of $30 on 4/16. It also states that your payment of $100 was posted on 4/20. Your credit card company uses new purchases to figure the average daily balance. What is the average daily balance? **$110.33**

In-Class Examples

1. Jan Schubert received her credit card statement for the billing period of 4/1 through 4/30. Her previous balance was $600. Her payment of $200 was posted on 4/8. On 4/12, a new purchase of $65 was posted. No other activity occurred during the billing period. What is the average daily balance (new purchases included)? **$487.83**

2. Wesley King's charge account statement arrived for the billing period of 7/30 through 8/29. His previous balance was $1,200. On 8/3 a new purchase of $100 was posted. On 8/10 his payment of $500 was posted. No other activity occurred during the billing period. What is the average daily balance (new purchases included)? **$964.52**

GLOBAL PERSPECTIVE

Credit around the World

Student groups research the kinds of consumer credit used in various countries. Groups find information about restrictions on the use of personal consumer credit and also the effect of credit use on savings. Each group presents its findings, and then the class converses if other nations could learn some credit lessons from Americans.

2 TEACH (cont'd)

3. Jan Schubert in Problem 1 (In-Class Examples, page 269) checks the finance charge and the new balance on her credit card statement. The finance charge is 1.75 percent of the average daily balance. What is the new balance? **$473.54**

4. Wesley King in Problem 2 (In-Class Examples, page 269) checks the finance charge and the new balance on his credit card statement. The finance charge is 2 percent of the average daily balance. What is the new balance? **$819.29**

5. Deepak Sankaran received his credit card statement for the billing period of 7/15 through 8/14. His previous balance was $820.47. His payment of $600 was posted on 7/22. On 8/4 new purchases of $144.39 were posted. No other transactions occurred during the billing period. The finance charge is 1.25 percent of the average daily balance. What is the average daily balance? **($407.19)** What is the finance charge? **($5.09)** What is the new balance (new purchases included)? **$369.95**

3 ASSESS

Error Analysis

If students are making mistakes in finding the average daily balance (new purchases included), have them make a chart similar to the one in Example 1 on page 269 to organize their work. Check that new purchases and the payment are correctly entered on the chart and that the sum of daily balances is correct for each transaction date or group of dates listed. Remind students to check that they have divided the sum of

---

CONCEPT CHECK

SELF-CHECK ✓

Complete the problems, then check your answers at the end of the chapter. Find the average daily balance, with new purchases included.

	Dates	Payment	Purchase	End-of-Day Balance	×	Number of Days	Sum of Balances
1.	9/9–9/15			$500	×	7	a. $3,500
2.	9/16		$100	600	×	1	a. $600
3.	9/17–9/21			a. $600	×	5	b. $3,000
4.	9/22	$150		a. $450	×	b. 1	c. $450
5.	9/23–10/8			a. $450	×	b. 16	c. $7,200
6.				TOTAL		a. 30	b. $14,750

Sum of Daily Balances	÷	Number of Days	=	Average Daily Balance
7. a. $14,750.00	÷ b. 30		= c. $491.67	

Example 2

Aiesha Miller (from Example 1) checks the finance charge and the new balance. The finance charge is 2 percent of the average daily balance. What is the new balance?

STEP 1: Find the unpaid balance.
Previous Balance − (Payments + Credits)
  $125.80   − $70.00   = $55.80

STEP 2: Find the finance charge.
Average Daily Balance × Periodic Rate
  $117.05   ×   2%   = $2.3418 or $2.34

STEP 3: Find the new purchases.
$25.85 new purchases

STEP 4: Find the new balance.
Unpaid Balance + Finance Charge + New Purchases
  $55.80   + $2.34   + $25.85
= **$83.99 new balance**

CONCEPT CHECK

SELF-CHECK ✓

Complete the problems, then check your answers at the end of the chapter.

Use the information in Self-Check Problems 1–7 to find the following if the finance charge is 1.5 percent of the average daily balance.

8. The unpaid balance. **Unpaid Balance = $500.00 − $150.00 = $350.00**

9. The finance charge. **Finance Charge = 1.5% × $491.67 = $7.38**

10. The new balance. **New Balance = $350.00 + $7.38 + $100.00 = $457.38**

COOPERATIVE LEARNING

Reasoning

Students work in pairs or small groups to visit the financial center of the *BusinessWeek* Web site. Groups explore different credit card types, and compare the features of each. `CL`, `LS`

SECTION 7-4 PRACTICE

Find the average daily balance, with new purchases included.

	Dates	Payment	Purchase	End-of-Day Balance	×	Number of Days	Sum of Balances
11.	9/6–9/17			$600	×	a. 12 days	b. $7,200
12.	9/18		$140	740	×	a. 1 day	b. $740
13.	9/19–9/24			a. $740	×	b. 6 days	c. $4,440
14.	9/25	$120		a. $620	×	b. 1 day	c. $620
15.	9/26–10/5			a. $620	×	b. 10 days	c. $6,200
16.				TOTAL		a. 30	b. $19,200

	Sum of Daily Balances	÷	Number of Days		=	Average Daily Balance
17.	a. $19,200	÷	b. 30 days		=	c. $640.00

18. Edith Bertelli received this statement from a department store. Find the average daily balance with new purchases including the finance charge and the new balance.

Figure 7.8

Reference	Posting Date	Transaction Date	Description	Purchases & Advances	Payments & Credits
1027485	4/11		PAYMENT		$40.00
4500298	4/15	4/01	Menswear	$39.95	
5473390	4/23	4/21	Housewares	15.99	
1374655	4/25		PAYMENT		50.00

Billing Period	Previous Balance	Periodic Rate	Average Daily Balance	Finance Charge
4/1–5/1	$175.00	1.2%	a. $163.16	b. $1.96

Payments & Credits	Purchases & Advances	New Balance	Minimum Payment	Payment Due
$90.00	$55.94	c. $142.90	$25.00	5/25

Need Help? Go to...
► Skill 7: Multiplying Whole Numbers, page 734
► Skill 8: Multiplying Decimals, page 735
► Skill 10: Dividing (Decimal Remainder), page 737
► Application Q: Mean, page 770

MAINTAINING YOUR SKILLS

Multiply.

19. 7×145 **1,015** **20.** 5×360 **1,800** **21.** 31×56.23 **1,743.13**

Divide. Round answers to the nearest hundredth.

22. $1,608.75 \div 30$ **53.63** **23.** $1,329.89 \div 31$ **42.90** **24.** $1,029 \div 28$ **36.75**

Find the average. Round answers to the nearest hundredth.

25. 36, 45, 58, 62, 48 **49.80** **26.** 456.2, 364.8, 471.5, 392.18 **421.17**

---

the daily balances by the correct number of days in the billing period. Finally, have them check for computational errors.

If students are having trouble computing the new balance, remind them to follow the steps listed in Example 2 on page 270:
1. Find the unpaid balance.
2. Find the finance charge.
3. Find the new purchases.
4. Find the new balance by totaling the unpaid balance, the finance charge, and the new purchases.

 CLOSE

Closing Activity

1. ($940 + $1,230 + $1,294 + $1,047 +$1,355) ÷ 30
   $195.53
2. ($1,514 + $1,598 + $1,634 + $1,300 + $1,479) ÷ 31
   $242.74
3. Sergei Romanov received his credit card statement for the billing period of 5/20 through 6/19. His previous balance was $535.46. On 5/24 new purchases of $49.95 were posted. On 5/29 his payment of $300.00 was posted. On 6/6 new purchases of $74.60 were posted. No other activity occurred during the billing period. What is the average daily balance (new purchases included)? **$399.75**
4. Sergei Romanov in Problem 3 checks the finance charge and the new balance on his credit card statement. The finance charge is 2 percent of the average daily balance. What is the finance charge? **($8.00)** What is the new balance? **$368.01**

PROBLEM SOLVING

Credit Limit
The maximum amount you can spend or charge on a credit account is your credit limit. If you have a $1,000 credit limit, you won't be able to charge more than that amount. If you pay your bills regularly, the creditor will often increase your credit limit. Pablo Diego has a $3,000 credit limit and has charged $1,287.17. Take a look at Workshop 29 on page 60 and then calculate how much more he can charge on the card.

WRAP-UP

Go over any problem for which a wrong answer is given.

Assignment Guide
  Basic: 11–17
Average: 18

20 min.

Quick Quiz

1. Melissa Johnson's charge account statement showed a previous balance of $773.16, a finance charge of $10.23, new purchases totaling $84.34, a credit of $27.76, and a payment of $360. What is the new balance? **$479.97**

2. Taylor Woods's charge account statement has an unpaid balance of $1,115. Periodic rate is 1.6 percent of the unpaid balance. What is the finance charge? **($17.84)** New purchases of $430.36. What is the new balance? **$1,563.20**

3. Andre DuPerow received his credit card statement for the billing period of 5/10 through 6/9. His previous balance was $906.54. From 5/10 through 5/23, he had an end-of-day balance of $906.54. His payment of $500.00 was posted on 5/24. What was his end-of-day balance on 5/24? **($406.54)** What is the sum of the daily balances? **($19,602.74)** What is the average daily balance? **$632.35**

4. Jackie Meyers received her charge account statement for the billing period of 4/29 through 5/28. She had a previous balance of $492.50. Her payment of $192.50 was posted on 5/10. Her average daily balance was $370.58. The finance charge is 2 percent of the average daily balance. New purchases are not included when figuring the average daily balance. New purchases total $50.25. What is the finance charge? **($7.41)** What is the new balance? **$357.66**

SECTION 7-1 **CONCEPT CHECK** (p. 259)

1. $597.50
2. $270.78
3. $658.94 + $10.71 + $54.21 + $36.28 + $98.56 − ($100.00 + $145.81) = $858.78 − $245.81 = **$612.89**
4. $1,856.23 + $16.79 + $132.26 + $142.39 + $12.56 − ($160.00 + $32.21) = $2,169.23 − $192.21 = **$1,977.02**

SECTION 7-2 **CONCEPT CHECK** (p. 262)

1. a. Unpaid Balance = $600.00 − $100.00 = **$500.00**
   b. Finance Charge = 1.5% × $500.00 = **$7.50**
   c. New Balance = $500.00 + $7.50 + $70.00 = **$577.50**
2. a. Unpaid Balance = $220.00 − $150.00 = **$70.00**
   b. Finance Charge = 1.5% × $70.00 = **$1.05**
   c. New Balance = $70.00 + $1.05 + $95.00 = **$166.05**
3. Unpaid Balance = $980.00 − $120.00 = **$710.00**
   Finance Charge = 1.5% × $710.00 = **$10.65**
   New Balance = $710.00 + $10.65 + $72.00 = **$792.65**
4. Unpaid Balance = $654.50 − $205.50 = **$449.00**
   Finance Charge = 1.5% × $449.00 = **$6.74**
   New Balance = $449.00 + $6.74 + $87.00 = **$542.74**

SECTION 7-3 **CONCEPT CHECK** (p. 265, 266)

1. a. $5,000
2. a. $400
3. a. $400   b. 19   c. $7,600
4. a. 30   b. $13,000
5. a. $13,000.00   b. 30   c. $433.33
6. $165.00 × 0.015 = **$2.48**
7. $180.00 + $40.00 − $30.00 + $2.48 = **$192.48**

SECTION 7-4 **CONCEPT CHECK** (p. 270)

1. a. $3,500
2. a. $600
3. a. $600   b. $3,000
4. a. $450   b. 1   c. $450
5. a. $450   b. 16   c. $7,200
6. a. 30   b. $14,750
7. a. $14,750.00   b. 30   c. $491.67
8. Unpaid Balance = $500.00 − $150.00 = **$350.00**
9. Finance Charge = 1.5% × $491.67 = **$7.38**
10. New Balance = $350.00 + $7.38 + $100.00 = **$457.38**

Living in the Real World

A Financial Gem?

Analyze the Story   Perhaps Yuma thinks using a credit card is the way to go when he is tight on cash. Charge it and the worries go away, right? Wrong. It only adds up and can lead to serious financial problems for years (or even decades). So, what's a self-employed person supposed to do?

1 Reasoning. If Yuma maintains a high daily balance on his credit card, would it be better for him to find a company that calculates the finance charge based on the unpaid balance?

2 Choosing a Method. Yuma's credit card company uses a finance charge of 1.2 percent for an unpaid balance. What does his statement really look like? Complete the credit card statement on your own piece of paper. Fill in the blanks. (**Note: Minimum payment is 12 percent of the previous balance.**)

Reference	Posting Date	Transaction Date	Description	Purchases & Advances	Payments & Credits
3727485	4/11		PAYMENT		$900.00
4565298	4/15	4/01	Metal	$250.95	
5473445	4/23	4/21	Stones	198.42	
3566455	4/25	4/23	Clips	55.74	

Billing Period	Previous Balance	Periodic Rate	Average Daily Balance	Finance Charge
4/1–5/1	$320.00	1.2%		

Payments & Credits	Purchases & Advances	New Balance	Minimum Payment	Payment Due
$900.00				5/25

3 Decision Making. The best thing to do is pay off your credit card statement at the end of each month. Yuma just sold several of his best pieces of jewelry to the Native American arts museum. What should Yuma do with the money when he receives it?

REVIEW OF KEY WORDS

account statement (p. 258)
charge account (p. 258)
finance charge (p. 258)
credit card (p. 258)
unpaid-balance method (p. 261)
average-daily-balance method (p. 264)

Match one of the key words above with a definition below.

1. a way of computing finance charges where the average of the charge account balance is averaged at the end of each day in the billing period. **average-daily-balance method**

2. a document you receive with a monthly listing of all transactions processed by the closing date of that month. **account statement**

3. allows the holder to buy things on demand by presenting it. **credit card**

4. a line of credit, often at a particular business. **charge account**

5. the interest charged on the amount you owe. **finance charge**

Study Guide and Assessment ▶ **273**

---

5. Walter Robinski received his credit card statement for the billing period of 7/25 through 8/24. He had a previous balance of $162.44. On 7/30 new purchases of $108.39 were posted. On 8/6 his payment of $120.00 was posted. On 8/22 new purchases of $56.95 were posted. The finance charge is 2 percent of the average daily balance (new purchases included). What is the average daily balance? (**$185.31**) What is the finance charge? (**$3.71**) What is the new balance? **$211.49**

Living in the Real World

1. If he pays his debt off in full, or close to it, each month. Otherwise, it won't make much of a difference, as a high unpaid balance could still incur a hefty finance charge.

2. Average daily balance: −$81.87 Purchases and advances: $505.11 Credit: $74.89 Minimum payment: $0

3. He should deposit it into a savings account for use as a safety net to cover expenses during inevitable slow-selling months. Or pay off credit card.

Skills and Concepts

SECTION OBJECTIVE 7-1 AND EXAMPLES

Calculate the new balance in a charge account.

Your monthly statement has a previous balance of $504.33, with a payment of $50.00, new purchases of $12.35 and $39.54, and a finance charge of $5.67. What is the new balance?

STEP: Find the new balance.

Previous Balance + Finance Charge + New Purchases − (Payments + Credits)

$504.33   + $5.67   + $12.35 + $39.54 − $50.00   = **$511.89**

REVIEW EXERCISES

What is the new balance for the credit card statements shown?

	Billing Date	Previous Balance	Finance Charge	New Purchases	Payments & Credits	New Balance
6.	9/27/--	$ 306.55	$ 6.75	$ 209.54	$175.00	**$347.84**
7.	6/29/--	985.66	9.06	1,239.44	300.00	**$1,934.16**
8.	5/25/--	121.09	2.35	219.30	53.00	**$289.74**
9.	6/15/--	1,239.92	18.56	500.00	895.00	**$863.48**

SECTION OBJECTIVE 7-2 AND EXAMPLES

Find the finance charge by using the unpaid-balance method.

Aldo Vazquez has a charge account at Robert's Bike Shop, which uses the unpaid-balance method of computing finance charges. The periodic rate is 1.25 percent. If Vazquez's previous balance was $569.32 and he had payments and credits of $150.00, find his unpaid balance and finance charges. He had new purchases of $97.50. Find his new balance.

STEP 1: Find the unpaid balance.

Previous Balance − (Payments + Credits)

$569.32   − $150.00   = $419.32

STEP 2: Find the finance charge.

Unpaid Balance × Periodic Rate

$419.32   ×   1.25%   = $5.2415 or $5.24

STEP 3: Find the new balance.

Unpaid Balance + Finance Charge + New Purchases

$419.32   + $5.24   + $97.50   = **$522.06 new balance**

REINFORCEMENT

Section 7-1

1. Colin Scott received his charge account statement. It showed a previous balance of $74.22, a finance charge of $1.11, new purchases of $351.38, a credit for $69.95, and a payment of $175.00. What is the new balance? **$181.76**
2. When Lynette Fagan's charge account statement arrived, it showed a previous balance of $426.67, a finance charge of $6.40, a payment of $300.00, and no new purchases. What is the new balance? **$133.07**

10. $210.94 × 1.85% = $3.90
    $210.94 + $3.90 + $341.22 = $556.06

REVIEW EXERCISES

10. Denise Shelby's account statement. Unpaid balance of $210.94. Periodic rate of 1.85 percent. What is the finance charge? New purchases of $341.22. What is the new balance?

11. $75.06 × 2% = $1.50
    $75.06 + $1.50 + $432.11 = $508.67

11. Fredericka Smith's account statement. Unpaid balance of $75.06. Periodic rate of 2 percent. What is the finance charge? New purchases of $432.11. What is the new balance?

Use a periodic rate of 1.25 percent and the unpaid-balance method of computing the finance charge for Problems 12 and 13.

	Previous Balance	Payments & Credits	Unpaid Balance	Finance Charge	New Purchases	New Balance
12.	$400.00	$200.00	a. $200	b. $2.50	$300.00	c. $502.50
13.	654.99	300.00	a. $354.99	b. $4.44	76.45	c. $435.88

SECTION OBJECTIVE 7-3 AND EXAMPLES

Calculate the finance charge based on the average-daily-balance method where no new purchases are included.

A portion of Jamal Johnson's credit card statement is shown. A finance charge was added to his account balance because he did not pay his last bill in full. The finance charge was computed using the average-daily-balance method where new purchases are not included. Find the average daily balance, finance charge, and the new balance.

Reference	Posting Date	Transaction Date	Description	Purchases & Advances	Payments & Credits
7044598	6/04	6/02	Pictures	$103.95	
7044791	6/13		PAYMENT		$50.00
7049810	6/22	6/18	Shirt	56.49	
7050002	6/27	6/22	Paint	19.95	

Billing Period	Previous Balance	Periodic Rate	Average Daily Balance	Finance Charge
6/1–6/30	$125.88	1.5%	a.	b.

Payments & Credits	Purchases & Advances	New Balance	Minimum Payment	Payment Due
$50.00	$180.39	c.	$25.00	7/31

Continued on next page

REINFORCEMENT

Section 7-2

1. Albert Ainslie's account statement has an unpaid balance of $765. Periodic rate is 1.75 percent of the unpaid balance. What is the finance charge? **($13.39)** New purchases of $238.24. What is the new balance? **$1,016.63**

2. Jacinto Espinosa's account statement has an unpaid balance of $86.45. Periodic rate is 1.25 percent of the unpaid balance. What is the finance charge? **($1.08)** New purchases of $56.70. What is the new balance? **$144.23**

STEP 1: Find the sum of the daily balances.

Dates	Payment	End-of-Day Balance	Number of Days	Sum of Balances
6/1–6/12		$125.88	12	$1,510.56
6/13	$50.00	75.88	1	75.88
6/14–6/30		75.88	17	1,289.96
		TOTAL	30	$2,876.40

STEP 2: Find the average daily balance.
Sum of Daily Balances ÷ Number of Days
$2,876.40 ÷ 30 = **$95.88 average daily balance**

STEP 3: Find the finance charge.
Average Daily Balance × Periodic Rate
$95.88 × 1.5% = **$1.438 or $1.44 finance charge**

STEP 4: Find the new balance.
Previous Balance − (Payments + Credits)
$125.88 − $50 = 75.88

Unpaid Balance + Finance Charge + New Purchases
$75.88 + $1.44 + $180.39 = **$257.71 new balance**

REVIEW EXERCISES

14. George Silas has a bank credit card. A portion of his account statement is shown below. Find the average daily balance excluding new purchases, the finance charge, and the new balance.

Reference	Posting Date	Transaction Date	Description	Purchases & Advances	Payments & Credits
2100091	3/07	3/06	Mower	$188.95	
2100187	3/17		PAYMENT		$75.00
2100766	3/20	3/18	Bicycle	58.88	
2100789	3/22	3/19	Work shoes	14.88	

Billing Period	Previous Balance	Periodic Rate	Average Daily Balance	Finance Charge
3/1–3/31	$651.20	1.75%	a. $614.91	b. $10.76

Payments & Credits	Purchases & Advances	New Balance	Minimum Payment	Payment Due
$75.00	$262.71	c. $849.67	$25.00	4/30

REINFORCEMENT

Section 7-3

1. Hannah Blake received her charge account statement for the billing period of 7/25 through 8/24. Her previous balance was $655.79. From 7/25 through 8/17, she had an end-of-day balance of $655.79. Her payment of $555.79 was posted on 8/18. What was her end-of-day balance from 8/19 through 8/24? **($100)** What is the sum of the daily balances for the billing period of 7/25 through 8/24? **($16,438.96)** What is the average daily balance? **$530.29**

2. Monique Rhodes previous charge account balance was $741.06. From 6/19 through 6/29, she had an end-of-day balance of $741.06. Her payment of $325.00 was posted on 6/30. What was her end-of-day balance from 7/1 through 7/18? **($416.06)** What is the sum of the daily balances for the billing period of 6/19 through 7/18? **($16,056.80)** What is the average daily balance? **$535.23**

REVIEW EXERCISES (continued)

The finance charge is computed using the average-daily-balance method where no new purchases are included. Find the finance charge and the new balance for the following statements.

15.

Billing Period	Previous Balance	Periodic Rate	Average Daily Balance	Finance Charge
7/01–7/31	$156.90	2%	$143.00	a. **$2.86**

Payments & Credits	Purchases & Advances	New Balance	Minimum Payment	Payment Due
$85.00	$35.00	b. **$109.76**	$10.00	8/15

16.

Billing Period	Previous Balance	Periodic Rate	Average Daily Balance	Finance Charge
9/01–9/30	$705.09	1.5%	$655.35	a. **$9.83**

Payments & Credits	Purchases & Advances	New Balance	Minimum Payment	Payment Due
$100.00	$0.00	b. **$754.92**	$25.00	10/10

Find the average daily balance, the finance charge, and the new balance.

17.

Reference	Posting Date	Transaction Date	Description	Purchases & Advances	Payments & Credits
6345666	10/25	10/20	Dept. store	$32.45	
6345788	11/4	11/1	PAYMENT		$40.00

Billing Period	Previous Balance	Periodic Rate	Average Daily Balance	Finance Charge
10/15–11/14	$45.66	1.5%	a. **$31.47**	b. **$0.47**

Payments & Credits	Purchases & Advances	New Balance	Minimum Payment	Payment Due
$40.00	$32.45	c. **$38.58**	$15.00	12/10

REINFORCEMENT

Section 7-3 (cont'd)

3. Aaron Foster received his charge account statement for the billing period of 6/24 through 7/23. He has a previous balance of $460.55. His payment of $290.00 was posted on 7/7. His average daily balance was $296.22. The finance charge is 1.5 percent of the average daily balance. New purchases totaled $63.50. What is the finance charge? (**$4.44**) What is the new balance? **$238.49**

4. Isaac Gates received his charge account statement for the billing period of 7/28 through 8/27. He has a previous balance of $1,425.77. His payment of $875.00 was posted on 8/6. His average daily balance was $804.80. The finance charge is 1.75 percent of the average daily balance. New purchases totaled $219.36. What is the finance charge? (**$14.08**) What is the new balance? **$784.21**

CHAPTER **Study Guide and Assessment**

7

SECTION OBJECTIVE 7-4 AND EXAMPLES

Compute the finance charge based on the average-daily-balance method where new purchases are included.

Martin Choi has a department store charge account where the finance charge is computed using the average-daily-balance method that includes new purchases. What is his average daily balance and his finance charge? What is his new balance?

Reference	Posting Date	Transaction Date	Description	Purchases & Advances	Payments & Credits
3809018	11/10	11/8	Fine art	$125.44	
3809117	11/20	11/15	PAYMENT		$200.00

Billing Period	Previous Balance	Periodic Rate	Average Daily Balance	Finance Charge
11/04–12/03	$623.11	1.25%	a.	b.

Payments & Credits	Purchases & Advances	New Balance	Minimum Payment	Payment Due
$200.00	$125.44	c.	$20.00	12/20

STEP 1: Find the sum of the daily balances.

Dates	Payment	Purchase	End-of-Day Balance	Number of Days	Sum of Balances
11/04–11/09			$623.11	6	$ 3,738.66
11/10		$125.44	748.55	1	748.55
11/11–11/19			748.55	9	6,736.95
11/20	$200.00		548.55	1	548.55
11/21–12/3			548.55	13	7,131.15
			TOTAL	30	$18,903.86

STEP 2: Find the average daily balance.

$$\text{Average Daily Balance} = \frac{\text{Sum of Daily Balances}}{\text{Number of Days}}$$

$18,903.86 \div 30 =$ **$630.13 average daily balance**

STEP 3: Find the finance charge.

$630.13 \times 1.25\% =$ **$7.88 finance charge**

STEP 4: Find the unpaid balance.

Previous Balance − (Payments + Credits)

$623.11　　−　　$200.00　　= $423.11

STEP 5: Find the new balance.

Unpaid Balance + Finance Charge + New Purchases

$423.11　　+　　$7.88　　+　　$125.44　　= **$556.43 new balance**

REINFORCEMENT

Section 7-4

1. Ernestina Cruz received her credit card statement for the billing period of 6/4 through 7/3. Her previous balance was $227.59. Her payment of $125.00 was posted on 6/19. On 6/24 new purchases of $137.04 were posted. On 6/30 new purchases of $72.16 were posted. No other activity occurred during the billing period. What is the average daily balance (new purchases included)? **$220.39**

2. Ernestina Cruz in Problem 1 examines her credit card statement. She checks the finance charge and the new balance. The finance charge is 1.5 percent of the average daily balance. What is the finance charge? **($3.31)** What is the new balance? **$315.10**

REVIEW EXERCISES

18. Drew Williams received this statement from his bank. Find the average daily balance (new purchases included), the finance charge, and the new balance.

Reference	Posting Date	Transaction Date	Description	Purchases & Advances	Payments & Credits
1238090	2/5	2/3	Home repairs	$ 75.66	
2789433	2/10	2/8	PAYMENT		$100.00
3459811	2/17	2/15	Discount store	198.33	
4334681	2/27	2/24	PAYMENT		50.00

Billing Period	Previous Balance	Periodic Rate	Average Daily Balance	Finance Charge
2/01–2/28	$36.54	2.1%	a. $114.96	b. $2.41

Payments & Credits	Purchases & Advances	New Balance	Minimum Payment	Payment Due
$150.00	$273.99	c. $162.94	$10.00	3/15

19. Freddie Vargo received this statement from the department store. Find the average daily balance (new purchases included), the finance charge, and the new balance.

Reference	Posting Date	Transaction Date	Description	Purchases & Advances	Payments & Credits
2034599	3/2		PAYMENT		$35.00
2034766	3/11	3/8	Housewares	$123.96	
2040009	3/20	3/12	Shoes	56.49	
2040065	3/25		PAYMENT		50.00

Billing Period	Previous Balance	Periodic Rate	Average Daily Balance	Finance Charge
3/1–3/31	$200.34	2%	a. $261.02	b. $5.22

Payments & Credits	Purchases & Advances	New Balance	Minimum Payment	Payment Due
$85.00	$180.45	c. $301.01	$25.00	4/30

20. Monica Sweeny received this statement from Market Street Bank. Find the average daily balance (new purchases included), the finance charge, and the new balance.

Reference	Posting Date	Transaction Date	Description	Purchases & Advances	Payments & Credits
1809008	9/20	9/15	Electronics	$25.44	
1809039	9/25		PAYMENT		$100.00
1809111	10/02	9/29	Sports Inc.	66.74	
1809388	10/10		PAYMENT		50.00

Billing Period	Previous Balance	Periodic Rate	Average Daily Balance	Finance Charge
9/15–10/14	$321.99	1.75%	a. $297.11	b. $5.20

Payments & Credits	Purchases & Advances	New Balance	Minimum Payment	Payment Due
$150.00	$92.18	c. $269.37	$15.00	11/10

Math Studio Overview

Students are asked to investigate a variety of credit card offers (from large corporate banks to local department stores) and decide which card is best for them. By doing research and polling family and friends about what prompted them to apply for the cards they carry, students will understand the importance of a knowledge-able credit card choice.

Bell Ringer Activity

Write on the board: "Write a sentence explaining why credit cards are beneficial and another sentence detailing how credit cards can be detrimental." Ask each student to read his or her sentence out loud, then lead a class discussion in response to the variety of opinions.

2 TEACH

Cooperative Learning

Break students into groups of four and give each set a blank credit card application. Have students fill out the application, asking them to pay special attention to the types of information requested and questions asked. Once all groups have finished filling out their forms, have the class regroup and discuss the necessity of the different application sections. Why are certain questions asked? How do the students think the answers affect the success or failure of a specific applicant to be issued a credit card?

A Creative Lab

Credit Where Credit Is Due

You have your first job, and you're thinking about applying for a credit card. One of the most important reasons you'd like to open a credit card account is to establish a good credit history. You know that if you pay your credit card bills promptly and fully, the good credit rating you earn now will help you borrow money in the future for large purchases, including a car and house.

Purpose

Credit card companies will inundate you with their applications. It's hard to know which company to choose since each one seems to offer different terms, conditions, and enticements. This activity will include interviewing, investigating, and comparing to help you in your decision-making process.

Supplies Needed

- Pen
- Paper
- Poster board
- Marker pens
- If possible, a computer spreadsheet program

Your Activity

Step 1: Make a list of several credit card companies that you would consider when deciding whether to open an account.

A. Try to find a variety of companies (such as corporate banks, department stores, single-purpose cards, multipurpose cards, etc.).

B. Organize the list alphabetically and include the customer service telephone number and Web address for each company.

Fold in thirds lengthwise.

Figure 7.9 Step 1: Fold in thirds.

Draw lines along folds and label as shown.

Step 2: Label.

COMMUNICATION SKILLS

Newsworthy Trend

According to the Consumer Credit Counseling Service of Britain, 60 percent of its clients between the ages of 25 and 39 will become disabled by debt at the outset of their economic lives.

Step 2: Ask your family and friends which credit cards they carry and try to find out why they chose that card.

Step 3: Try to find out if the people you talk with know and understand the terms of their credit card accounts.

A. Create a Foldable organizer before you start asking questions. (See **Figure 7.9** to see how it's done.)

B. Once you've created the Foldable, then you can write these questions on it and get started on your interviewing process. You might ask the following questions:

- What is the annual fee for this card?
- What is the credit limit?
- Is it a single-purpose or multipurpose card?
- What is the finance charge rate on the card?
- How is the finance charge calculated (previous-balance method or average daily-balance method)?
- Does this card have any special features such as cash back or frequent flier miles?

Step 4: Contact the credit card companies to ask them a few questions. Tell them you're inquiring about their services for a classroom assignment.

A. Go online or call customer service at each credit card company to determine:

- the annual fees,
- finance charges,
- benefits, and
- penalties for each card.

B. Compare this information with the answers given to you by your family and friends.

Step 5: Write a report that addresses the following questions:

- Do you think most people know enough about the terms of their credit cards? If not, does it matter? What are the risks of this lack of knowledge?
- What kinds of information are necessary for you to understand before you make a decision to obtain a credit card?
- If you decide to get a credit card, what do you need to know before choosing a particular card? Why?

Critique It

Given your decision to apply for this credit card, what are some questions you should ask the credit card company before signing on its dotted line and dreaming of that vacation to a distant land (courtesy of your credit card)?

MATH STUDIO

3 ASSESS

Enrichment

Divide the classroom in two and have each side stage a mock debate about the appropriate age for students to obtain a credit card. Ask one side to argue for a law making credit cards available only to those over 18. Have the other side debate the importance of letting minors secure credit cards.

4 CLOSE

Critique It

Perhaps the credit card you want offers free airplane mileage. Then you realize that it will require you to spend $25,000 in order to earn the 25,000 points necessary for a free ticket. It will take you a number of years to spend that much money and thus accumulate one free trip. Given your decision to apply for this credit card, what are some questions you should ask the credit card company before signing on its dotted line and dream of that vacation to a distant land? **It would be important to find out how long the promotion will run. For instance, if the credit card company ends the promotion before you earn the necessary points, will they cancel your accumulated miles? Is there a prohibitive annual fee attached to the card? If so, you may spend enough in annual fees over the time it takes to accumulate miles to pay for an airline ticket.**

National Standards for Business Education

Section Objectives	1. Mathematical Foundations	2. Number Relationships and Operations	3. Patterns, Functions, and Algebra	4. Measurements	5. Statistics and Probability	6. Problem-Solving Applications	
8-1 Single-Payment Loan (pp. 284–286) Compute the maturity value and interest rate of a single-payment loan.	X	X				X	
8-2 Installment Loans (pp. 287–289) Calculate the amount financed on an installment loan.	X	X				X	
8-3 Simple Interest Installment Loans (pp. 290–293) Figure out the monthly payment, total amount repaid, and finance charge on an installment loan.	X	X					
8-4 Installment Loans—Allocation of Monthly Payment (pp. 294–296) Work out the payment to interest, payment to principal, and the new balance.	X	X					
8-5 Paying Off Simple Interest Installment Loans (pp. 297–299) Compute the final payment when paying off a simple interest installment loan.	X	X					
8-6 Determining the APR (pp. 300–303) Use a table to find the annual percentage rate of a loan.	X	X					

(Source: Reprinted with permission from the National Standards for Business Education, copyright © 2001 by National Business Education Association, 1914 Association Drive, Reston, Virginia 21901-1596)

SCANS Correlation

Foundation Skills

Basic Skills	Reading	Writing	Math	Listening	Speaking	
Thinking Skills	Creative Thinking	Decision Making	Problem Solving	Seeing Things in the Mind's Eye	Knowing How to Learn	Reasoning
Personal Qualities	Responsibility	Self-Esteem	Sociability	Self-Management	Integrity/Honesty	

This chapter's highlighted blocks indicate the chapter's content coverage in the Student Edition and the Teacher Wraparound Edition.

1. Numbers & Operations	2. Algebra	3. Geometry	4. Measurement	5. Data Analysis & Probability	6. Problem Solving	7. Reasoning & Proof	8. Communication	9. Connections	10. Representations
X			X		X		X	X	
X			X		X		X	X	
X			X		X		X	X	
X			X		X		X	X	
X			X		X		X	X	
X			X		X		X	X	

SCANS Correlation

Workplace Competencies

Resources	Allocating Time	Allocating Money	Allocating Material and Facility Resources	Allocating Human Resources		
Information	Acquiring and Evaluating Information	Organizing and Maintaining Information	Interpreting and Communicating Information	Using Computers to Process Information		
Interpersonal Skills	Participating as a Member of a Team	Teaching Others	Serving Clients/Customers	Exercising Leadership	Negotiating to Arrive at a Decision	Working with Cultural Diversity
Systems	Understanding Systems	Monitoring and Correcting Performance	Improving and Designing Systems			
Technology	Selecting Technology	Applying Technology to Task	Maintaining and Troubleshooting Technology			

CHAPTER 8

CHAPTER 8

Loans

What You'll Learn
In this chapter you'll investigate loans, loan payments, interest payments, and how to compare the costs of taking out a loan.

Why It's Important
Many times consumers find themselves in a position where they would like to make a purchase but lack the necessary cash. Perhaps it is an emergency. Using a credit card to make purchases allows the cardholder the flexibility to "buy now, pay later." There is considerable responsibility in using a credit card and it is important that the user understands how interest is calculated.

Key Word Review
On-the-Job Skill
One important on-the-job skill is paying attention to detail and concentrating on completing a task. To practice this skill, here's your task: First, keep a notebook of new key words. Second, write each of the definitions in your own words as they are presented in the chapter.

What You'll Learn

Section 8-1 Compute the maturity value and interest rate of a single-payment loan.

Section 8-2 Calculate the amount financed on an installment loan.

Section 8-3 Figure out the monthly payment, total amount repaid, and finance charge on an installment loan.

Section 8-4 Work out the payment to interest, payment to principal, and the new balance.

Section 8-5 Compute the final payment when paying off a simple interest installment loan.

Section 8-6 Use a table to find the annual percentage rate of a loan.

When Will You Ever Use This?
Some day you might want to earn a college degree, buy a car, or purchase a home. Taking out a loan is a common way to borrow the money now and repay it later.

Key Words to Know
- single-payment loan
- promissory note
- maturity value
- term
- ordinary interest
- exact interest
- installment loan
- down payment
- amount financed
- simple interest installment loan
- annual percentage rate
- repayment schedule
- final payment

Mathematics Online
To learn more about loans, visit the *Mathematics with Business Applications* Web site at www.busmath.glencoe.com.

CLASSROOM RESOURCES

Application and Enrichment
- ✍ *Teacher Wraparound Edition*
- ✍ *Teacher Resource Binder, Blackline Masters*
- ⦿ *Interactive Lesson Planner* CD-ROM
- ⦿ *PowerPoint® Presentations* CD-ROM

Review and Enforcement
- Mathematics Online
  www.busmath.glencoe.com
- ✍ *Teacher Resource Binder, Internet Resources*

- ✍ *Student Activity Workbook*
- ✍ *Student Activity Workbook, Teacher Annotated Edition*
- ✍ *School-to-Home Activity Workbook*

Assessment and Evaluation
- ✍ *Assessment Binder, Reproducible Tests*
- ✍ *Assessment Binder, Alternative Assessment Strategies*
- ⦿ **Exam*View*® Pro Test Generator** CD-ROM

For the Teacher
- ✍ *Student Activity Workbook, Teacher Annotated Edition*
- ✍ *Assessment Binder*
- ⦿ *Interactive Lesson Planner* CD-ROM
- ✍ *Teacher Resource Binder*
- 🖥 Mathematics Online
  www.busmath.glencoe.com

For the Student
- ✍ *Student Activity Workbook*
- ✍ *School-to-Home Activity Workbook*

Living in the Real World

A Picture-Perfect Loan

Last winter photographer Al Chen hiked in the Chiricahua Mountains east of Tucson, Arizona. The area is not as high as many mountain ranges in North America (the summit of Chiricahua Peak is 9,795 feet above sea level). Chen hopes to return and tackle another week of camping and photography. He has four months before his trip and he knows he can't save enough money to pay for the equipment he wants. In this chapter learn how Chen contemplates taking out a small loan to afford a trip.

Read on. Go to . . .

283

Living in the Real World

Story's Summary

Freelance photographer Al Chen is considering taking out a small loan so he can return to the Chiricahua Mountains east of Tucson, Arizona, to enjoy a working week of camping and photography. Chen's parents loaned him money in the past to buy a car, which the young man conscientiously paid back in full, but this time he would like to go through a bank. His father thinks this is a good idea, as doing so will teach Chen further financial responsibility and start him on the road to good credit. Mr. Chen walks his son through the many things he must think about before signing on the dotted line.

Did You Know...

Most potential lenders require a visit to a local bank or credit union to secure a loan. However, online lenders are growing in popularity, cropping up in droves to take advantage of the increasingly computer-comfortable culture.

Think about This

How would life be different if loans didn't exist? What types of things would be more difficult or impossible for the average person to purchase?

LOCAL STANDARDS

National Standards for Business Education

Standard 1	Mathematical Foundations
Standard 2	Number Relationships and Operations
Standard 6	Problem-Solving Applications

National Council of Teachers of Mathematics Standards

Standard 1	Numbers and Operations
Standard 4	Measurement
Standard 6	Problem Solving
Standard 8	Communication
Standard 9	Connections

FOCUS

Ask students if they've ever loaned money to someone. How long did it take to be paid back? Was it paid back in one payment, or did the person repay a portion of the loan on different days? Explain that banks and other lending institutions grant loans to people; however, a bank charges interest. One type of loan is a single-payment loan, often called a promissory note, which is repaid in one payment.

In-Class Examples
Work through these exercises with students before having them do the Self-Check.
1. $1,000 × 12% × 30 ÷ 365
   $9.86
2. $1,000 × 12% × 30 ÷ 360
   $10.00

SECTION 8-1 Single-Payment Loans

○ **Section Objective**

Compute the maturity value and interest rate of a single-payment loan.

A **single-payment loan** is a loan that you repay with one payment after a specified period of time. A **promissory note** is a type of single-payment loan. It is a written promise to pay a certain sum of money on a certain date in the future. The **maturity value** of the loan is the total amount you must repay. It includes both the principal and the interest owed. To review Chapter 5 content remember that principal is the amount borrowed.

You'll need to know the **term** of a loan. This is the amount of time for which the loan is granted. For example, a single-payment loan may be granted for a number of years, months, or days. When the term is a certain number of days, the lending agency may calculate interest in one of two ways: (1) **ordinary interest** or (2) **exact interest**. Here is an explanation on both kinds of interest:

- ordinary interest is calculated by basing the time of the loan on a 360-day year.

- exact interest is calculated by basing the time of the loan on a 365-day year.

Ask yourself these questions as you work through the problems:

Important Questions	What Formulas Do I Use?
How do I calculate **interest**?	Interest = Principal × Rate × Time
Then ask yourself . . . what do I need to find— **ordinary interest** or **exact interest**?	Ordinary Interest = Principal × Rate × Time ÷ 360 Exact Interest = Principal × Rate × Time ÷ 365
How do I calculate **maturity value**?	Maturity Value = Principal + Interest Owed

Living in the Real World

A Picture-Perfect Loan

When Your Dad Doesn't Have Deep Pockets Chen's friend Liz was the one who suggested taking out a loan. He'd never borrowed money from a bank before. Liz tells him that he can take out the loan and then sell his photos from the trip to help pay back the loan. Chen decides to look into the possibility of getting a loan for his trip.

Draw Conclusions How might a loan from Chen's dad be different than a loan from a bank?

Continued on page 287

Living in the Real World

A loan from a family member may carry little or no interest, no fixed payment dates, and no structured financial arrangements.

BUSINESS NOTES

Current Interest Rate
Students investigate current interest rates for bank loans. They bring in ads from the business section of the newspaper, go online, or call or visit local banks. Groups create and then share a poster display. CL , LS , P

Example 1

Need Help? Go to...

➤ Workshop 13:
Fractions to
Decimals, Decimals
to Percent, page 28

➤ Skill 28: Writing
Percents as
Decimals, page 755

➤ Skill 14: Changing
Fractions/Decimals,
page 741

➤ Application J:
Fractional Parts of
a Year, page 766

Anita Sloane's bank granted her a single-payment loan of $7,200 for 91 days at 12 percent ordinary interest. What is the maturity value of the loan?

STEP 1: Find the ordinary interest owed.
Principal × Rate × Time
$7,200.00 × 12% × $\frac{91}{360}$ = $218.40

STEP 2: Find the maturity value.
Principal + Interest Owed
$7,200.00 + $218.40   = **$7,418.40 maturity value**

7200 M+ × 12 % × 91 ÷ 360 =

218.4 M+ RM 7418.4

CONCEPT CHECK

SELF-CHECK✓

Complete the problems, then check your answers at the end of the chapter.

1. Compute the ordinary interest and the maturity value.
$600 × 10% × 90 ÷ 360 = **$15, $615**

2. Compute the ordinary interest and the maturity value.
$800 × 12% × 75 ÷ 360 = **$20, $820**

Example 2

Suppose Anita Sloane's bank granted her a single-payment loan of $7,200 for 91 days at 12 percent exact interest. What is the maturity value of the loan?

STEP 1: Find the exact interest owed.
Principal × Rate × Time
$7,200.00 × 12% × $\frac{91}{365}$ = $215.408 or $215.41

STEP 2: Find the maturity value.
Principal + Interest Owed
$7,200.00 + $215.41   = **$7,415.41 maturity value**

CONCEPT CHECK

SELF-CHECK✓

Complete the problems, then check your answers at the end of the chapter.

3. Compute the exact interest and the maturity value.
$600 × 10% × 90 ÷ 365 = **$14.79, $614.79**

4. Compute the exact interest and the maturity value.
$800 × 12% × 75 ÷ 365 = **$19.73, $819.73**

2 TEACH

Spend ample time going over the key words presented in this lesson. Explain that single-payment loans are generally for short periods of time, usually less than one year.

Emphasize that when computing ordinary interest, the denominator in the fraction representing time is 360, which assumes that each month has 30 days. If a year is considered to have 365 days by a bank, as is the case for exact interest, the denominator is 365.

Motivating the Lesson

You worked all summer and will receive an income tax refund of $500. You plan to use the money to buy a new amp for your guitar. You borrow the money from your parents and agree to repay the $500 in a single payment in 90 days when you receive your refund. Your parents agree to lend you the money, but they will charge you interest of $5. How much will you owe your parents at the end of 90 days? **$505**

In-Class Examples

1. Single-payment loan of $6,425. Interest rate of 7 percent. Days of ordinary interest: 180 days. What is the interest owed? **($224.88)** What is the maturity value? **$6,649.88**

2. Single payment loan of $495. Interest rate of 8.5 percent. Days of ordinary interest: 68. What is the interest owed? **($7.95)** What is the maturity value? **$502.95**

COOPERATIVE LEARNING

Prime Rate
What is the prime rate? Research and report on the prime rate. Students can read the *Wall Street Journal* or *USA Today* to find the current prime rate. Discuss how the prime rate is used. **It affects the rate set for credit cards, home loans, and so on. The rate is determined by market forces. When a major bank moves its prime rate up or down, the banking industry follows. Major customers can get discounts on the prime rate.**

PROBLEM SOLVING

Days in the Year
Give each answer as a decimal:

1. Find 45 days as a fraction of 365 days. **0.12328767**

2. Find 180 days as a fraction of 360 days. **0.50**

3. Find 226 days as a fraction of 365 days. **0.61917808**

3 ASSESS

Error Analysis

As students calculate interest, remind them to read each problem carefully. Are they calculating ordinary interest or exact interest? Ordinary interest is calculated on 360 days. Exact interest is calculated on 365 days.

Have them check their calculations to see that they used the correct number in the denominator. For instance, to calculate ordinary interest for 45 days, multiply the principal × interest rate × 45 ÷ 360. To calculate exact interest, multiply the principal × interest rate × 45 ÷ 365. Some students may find it helpful if you review how to change fractions to decimals.

4 CLOSE

Closing Activity

1. $1,575 × 11% × 47 ÷ 365
   $22.31
2. $3,616 × 9% × 98 ÷ 360
   $88.59
3. Single payment loan of $5,955. Interest rate of 8.75 percent. Days of ordinary interest: 42. What is the interest owed? **($60.79)** What is the maturity value? **$6,015.79**
4. LaVar Brown borrowed $4,357. The bank granted him a single-payment loan at 8.75 percent exact interest for 250 days. Find the exact interest owed. **($261.12)** What is the maturity value of his loan? **$4,618.12**
5. Laura Johnson obtained a single-payment loan of $11,300. The bank is charging her 9.5 percent ordinary interest for 164 days. What is the interest owed? **($489.04)** What is the maturity value of her loan? **$11,789.04**

SECTION 8-1 PRACTICE

	Principal	Interest Rates Ordinary	Exact	Term	Interest		Maturity Value	
5.	$ 900	4%	—	45	a.	$4.50	b.	$904.50
6.	1,960	—	6%	30	a.	$9.67	b.	$1,969.67
7.	3,450	5%	—	72	a.	$34.50	b.	$3,484.50
8.	730	—	5%	75	a.	$7.50	b.	$737.50
9.	4,800	10%	—	123	a.	$164.00	b.	$4,964.00
10.	9,675	—	9%	275	a.	$656.04	b.	$10,331.04

11. Maria Rodriquez.
    Single-payment loan of $1,000.
    Interest rate of 7 percent.
    Ordinary interest for 108 days.
    a. What is the interest owed? **$21.00**
    b. What is the maturity value? **$1,021.00**

12. Manuel Bruins.
    Single-payment loan of $8,400.
    Interest rate of 12 percent.
    Exact interest for 146 days. **$403.20**
    a. What is the interest owed?
    b. What is the maturity value?
    $8,803.20

13. Joseph Henning borrowed $24,000 for new computers for his software production company. His bank granted him a single-payment loan of $24,000 for 144 days at an ordinary interest rate of 9 percent. What is the maturity value of his loan? **$24,864**

14. Vanessa Tackett borrowed $21,000 for new lawn care equipment for her landscape business. The bank granted her a single-payment loan of $21,000 for 45 days at an ordinary interest rate of 10 percent. What is the maturity value of her loan? **$21,262.50**

15. Jessie Ardella obtained a single-payment loan of $3,225.00 to pay a repair bill. He agreed to repay the loan in 31 days at an exact interest rate of 11.75 percent. What is the maturity value of his loan? **$3,257.18**

16. Suppose your bank has a minimum loan charge of $48 when you borrow at 6 percent ordinary interest for 90 days. What principal borrowed will result in a $48 interest charge? **$3,200**

MAINTAINING YOUR SKILLS

Need Help? Go to...
➤ Skill 28: **Writing Percents as Decimals,** page 755
➤ Skill 12: **Equivalent Fractions,** page 739
➤ Skill 14: **Changing Fractions/Decimals,** page 741

Write the percents as decimals.

17. 40% **0.40**
18. 90.5% **0.905**
19. 7% **0.07**

Reduce the fractions to lowest terms.

20. $\frac{40}{60}$ **$\frac{2}{3}$**
21. $\frac{180}{360}$ **$\frac{1}{2}$**
22. $\frac{90}{360}$ **$\frac{1}{4}$**

Change the fractions to decimals. Round to the nearest thousandth.

23. $\frac{40}{60}$ **0.667**
24. $\frac{45}{360}$ **0.125**
25. $\frac{126}{360}$ **0.35**

WRAP-UP

Go over any problem for which a wrong answer is given.

Assignment Guide
Basic: 5–10
Average: 11–12

20 min.

SECTION 8-2 Installment Loans

Section Objective

Calculate the amount financed on an installment loan.

An **installment loan** is a loan that you repay in several equal payments over a specified period of time. Usually when you purchase an item with an installment loan, you must make a down payment. The **down payment** is a portion of the cash price of the item you are purchasing. The **amount financed** is the portion of the cash price that you owe *after* making the down payment.

Ask yourself these questions as you work through the problems:

Important Questions	What Formulas Do I Use?
How do I calculate the amount financed?	Amount Financed = Cash Price − Down Payment
How do I find the down payment?	Down Payment = Amount × Percent

Living in the Real World

A Picture-Perfect Loan

A Little Fatherly Advice Chen tells his father about his dream to return to the rugged Chiricahua Mountains and photograph them for his freelance photography business. He mentions he won't be able to save enough money by February so he wants to take out a loan from a bank.

Mr. Chen thinks this is a great idea because it'll teach Chen financial responsibility, and require him to start paying the money back in installments (as opposed to whenever he feels like it).

Draw Conclusions Mr. Chen explains that taking out a loan is certainly possible but that there are restrictions on the amount of money Chen can borrow. Before the bank will give Chen a loan, what does he have to do first?

Continued on page 290

Need Help? Go to...

▶ Workshop 14: Finding a Percentage, page 30
▶ Workshop 13: Fractions to Decimals, Decimals to Percents, page 28
▶ Workshop 2: Rounding Numbers, page 6
▶ Application A: Formulas, page 760

Example 1

Tasheka Quintero is buying a new refrigerator for $1,399. Quintero made a down payment of $199 and financed the remainder. How much did Quintero finance?

STEP: Find the amount financed.

Cash Price − Down Payment
$1,399 $199   = $1,200 financed

Section 8-2 Installment Loans ▶ **287**

Living in the Real World

He will have to fill out an application, subject himself to a credit check, and likely put down a down payment.

National Standards for Business Education

Standard 1	Mathematical Foundations
Standard 2	Number Relationships and Operations
Standard 6	Problem-Solving Applications

National Council of Teachers of Mathematics Standards

Standard 1	Numbers and Operations
Standard 4	Measurement
Standard 6	Problem Solving
Standard 8	Communication
Standard 9	Connections

1 FOCUS

Have students suggest reasons for borrowing money. (**To buy a car, furniture, appliance, or other expensive consumer items.**) Explain that when purchasing consumer items, it is more likely that the purchase is made through an installment loan in which the amount borrowed is paid back in a series of equal payments over a specified time period. Ask students why they think people prefer this type of loan rather than a single-payment loan. (**They can pay back the loan in smaller portions.**) In this lesson, students will compute the amount financed on an installment loan.

SECTION 8-2

① FOCUS (cont'd)

In-Class Examples
Work through these exercises with students before having them do the Self-Check.
1. $162 × 30%$ **$48.60**
2. $387 × 35%$ **$135.45**
3. $959 × 20%$ **$191.80**
4. $6,327 × 10%$ **$632.70**
5. $800 − ($800 × 20%)$ **$640**

② TEACH

When a person uses a credit card, he or she can pay the account in full within a month or a finance charge is added to the unpaid balance. When purchasing an item through an installment loan, a person usually pays a small portion of the cash price as a down payment and then signs a contract to make equal weekly or monthly payments. The payments would include a finance charge, which is discussed in the next lesson. In both cases, the customer has immediate possession of the item.

Motivating the Lesson
You want to buy a digital camera that costs $1,099; however, you only have $200. You could use the $200 as a down payment and finance the remaining amount through the store's credit department. What amount must you finance? **$899**

In-Class Examples
1. Monique Wallace purchased a backyard swimming pool that costs $595. She made a 25 percent down payment and financed the remaining amount. What amount did
2. Michael and Javanna Griffin purchased new kitchen cabinets for $3,368. They made a 20 percent down payment and financed the remaining amount. What amount did they finance? **$2,694.40**

288

CONCEPT CHECK

SELF-CHECK✓

Complete the problems, then check your answers at the end of the chapter. Determine the amount financed.

1. Big-screen television set.
   Cash price of $1,999.99.
   Down payment of $199.99.
   $1,999.99 − $199.99 = $1,800

2. Office computer.
   Cash price of $3,950.
   Down payment of $150.
   $3,950 − $150 = $3,800

Example 2

Rebecca Clay purchased a washer and a dryer for $1,140. She used the store's installment credit plan to pay for the items. She made a down payment and financed the remaining amount. What amount did she finance if she made a 20 percent down payment?

STEP 1: Find the 20 percent down payment.
$1,140 × 20% = $228

STEP 2: Find the amount financed.
Cash Price — Down Payment
$1,140 — $228 = **$912 financed**

1140 **M+** **×** 20 **%** 228 **M−** **RM** 912

CONCEPT CHECK

SELF-CHECK✓

Complete the problems, then check your answers at the end of the chapter. Find the down payment and the amount financed.

3. Waterbed.
   Cash price of $1,360.
   Twenty percent down payment.
   $1,360 × 0.20 = $272;
   $1,360 − $272 = $1,088

4. Television set.
   Cash price of $725.
   Thirty percent down payment.
   $725 × 0.30 = $217.50;
   $725 − $217.50 = $507.50

SECTION 8-2 PRACTICE

	Cash Price	Down Payment (Cash)	Down Payment (Percent)	Down Payment (in Dollars)	Amount Financed
5.	$ 640	$ 120	—	a. $120	b. $520
6.	4,860	1,400	—	a. $1,400	b. $3,460
7.	9,774	1,500	—	a. $1,500	b. $8,274
8.	3,600	—	40%	a. $1,440	b. $2,160
9.	9,480	—	15%	a. $1,422	b. $8,058
10.	5,364	—	25%	a. $1,341	b. $4,023

ALTERNATIVE ASSESSMENT

Amount Financed
Another way to find the amount financed is to multiply the cash price by the complement of the percent down. For example, if the down payment is 20 percent, then the amount financed is 100 percent minus 20 percent. The complement means that 20 percent down implies 80 percent financed. What is the amount financed if the loan amount is $1,140 and the down payment is 25 percent? **0.75 × $1,140 = $855**

COMMUNICATION SKILLS

Contracts
Installment loan contracts can be lengthy and the language difficult to understand. When signing a contract, however, it is very important to know what the contract actually states. Bring in to class a typical installment contract from a bank or other lending source. Together, read the contract and discuss exactly what it states. **LS** , **CL**

▶FYI

What influences
your credit rating?
Timely payments
and the amount
of debt you're
carrying affect it.
▶▶▶

11. Cash price of $1,265.
Down payment of $100.
What amount is financed? **$1,165**

12. Cash price of $14,470.
Down payment of $3,000.
What amount is financed? **$11,470**

13. Cash price of $8,371.39.
Down payment of 15 percent.
What amount is financed? **$7,115.68**

14. Cash price of $18,936.50.
Down payment of 30 percent.
What amount is financed?
$13,255.55

15. Milt Gibson purchased computer equipment for $4,020. He used the store's credit plan. He made a 20 percent down payment. What amount did he finance? **$3,216**

16. Linda Chevez purchased a stereo for her car. The stereo cost $279.50. Using the store's credit plan, she made a $50.00 down payment. What amount did she finance? **$229.50**

17. Ardella Haubert purchased living room furniture for $3,987.95. She made a down payment of 20 percent and financed the remaining amount using the store's installment plan. What amount did she finance? **$3,190.36**

18. Bev and Tom Hoffman went on a two-week vacation at a total cost of $2,876. They financed the trip through State Bank. They made a 25 percent down payment and financed the remaining amount on the installment plan. What amount did they finance? **$2,157**

19. Amy and Cliff Martin want to remodel their kitchen. They would like to finance part of the cost but do not want the amount financed to be more than $9,000. The total cost of remodeling the kitchen is $12,000. What percent of the total cost should their down payment be? **25%**

20. Mack Casey wants to purchase a car costing $14,590. He will finance the car with an installment loan from the bank but would like to finance no more than $10,000. What percent of the total cost of the car should his down payment be? **31.5%**

MAINTAINING YOUR SKILLS

Need Help? Go to...
▶ Skill 28: Writing
   Percents as
   Decimals, page 755
▶ Skill 30: Finding
   the Percentage,
   page 757
▶ Skill 2: Rounding
   Numbers, page 729

Write the percents as decimals.

21. 32% **0.32**

22. 45% **0.45**

23. 25% **0.25**

Find the percentage.

24. 440 × 30% **132**

25. 325 × 20% **65**

26. 1,240 × 25% **310**

Round to the nearest cent.

27. $49.9638 **$49.96**

28. $178.3813 **$178.38**

29. $413.995 **$414.00**

WRAP-UP

Go over any problem for which a wrong answer is given.

Assignment Guide
   Basic: 5–10
   Average: 11–14

20 min.

3. Derrick Simmons purchased an outdoor storage building for $399. He made a 10 percent down payment and financed the remaining amount. How much did he finance? **$359.10**

③ ASSESS

Error Analysis

Review the concept of percent. Stress that percent means so many parts in one hundred. For example, if a person owns 100 DVDs and 28 of them are action/adventure movies, then 28 percent of the DVDs are action/adventure movies.

You may also wish to review how to convert a percent to a decimal. To change a percent to a decimal, first write the percent as a fraction with a denominator of 100, then divide by 100.
16% = 16 ÷ 100 = 0.16

④ CLOSE

Closing Activity

1. Cash price of $1,145. Down payment: $250. What amount is financed? **$895**

2. Laura Alvarez purchased a new convertible for $27,382. She made a down payment of 30 percent and financed the remaining amount. What amount did she finance?
$19,167.40

3. Patrick and Colleen McNamara bought new carpeting for their home. The carpeting cost $3,450. They made a down payment of 15 percent and financed the remaining amount. Find the down payment and the amount financed.
$517.50; $2,932.50

National Standards for Business Education

Standard 1	Mathematical Foundations
Standard 2	Number Relationships and Operations

National Council of Teachers of Mathematics Standards

Standard 1	Numbers and Operations
Standard 4	Measurement
Standard 6	Problem Solving
Standard 8	Communication
Standard 9	Connections

 **FOCUS**

Discuss the meaning of *interest* with students. Point out that a person can *earn* interest (on a savings account) or *pay* interest (on a loan). Point out that interest is always paid to the person who owns the money and is letting someone else use it. In this lesson, the finance charge is the interest paid on the installment loan.

In-Class Examples
Work through these exercises with students before having them do the Self-Check.
1. ($1,240 ÷ $100) × $6 **$74.40**
2. ($6,875 ÷ $100) × $5.50 **$378.13**
3. (6 × $146.63) − $850 **$29.78**
4. (24 × $79.85) − $1,600 **$316.40**
5. $2,500 − ($2,500 × 20%) **$2,000**

○ **Section Objective**
Figure out the monthly payment, total amount repaid, and finance charge on an installment loan.

SECTION 8-3 Simple Interest Installment Loans

When you obtain a **simple interest installment loan**, you must pay finance charges for the use of the money. You repay the loan with equal monthly payments, where part of each payment is used to pay the interest on the unpaid balance of the loan. And the remaining part of the payment is used to reduce the balance.

Usually you repay the amount financed plus the finance charge in equal monthly payments. The amount of each monthly payment depends on the amount financed, the number of payments, and the **annual percentage rate** (APR). The annual percentage rate is an index showing the relative cost of borrowing money.

Ask yourself these questions as you work through the problems:

Important Questions	What Formulas Do I Use?
How do I find the **monthly payment?**	Monthly Payment = $\frac{\text{Amount of Loan}}{\$100}$ × Monthly Payment for a $100 Loan
How do I calculate the **total amount paid?**	Total Amount Repaid = Number of Payments × Monthly Payments
How do I find the **finance charge?**	Finance Charge = Total Amount Repaid − Amount Financed

Living in the Real World

A Picture-Perfect Loan

A Model for Improvement Mr. Chen uses a home remodeling loan as a model for his son. "It's important to understand that with a simple interest installment loan, you'll be paying back the amount you borrow plus finance charges each month," Mr. Chen says.

Draw Conclusions What do you think a bank looks for in a client who wants to take out a personal loan?

Continued on page 294

Example 1

Clara Hart obtained an installment loan of $1,800.00 to purchase some new furniture. The annual percentage rate is 8 percent. She must repay the loan in 18 months. What is the finance charge?

Living in the Real World

A stable income, good credit rating, proven financial responsibility with previous loans, etc.

GLOBAL PERSPECTIVE

Interest Rates in Other Countries
Students research interest rates for loans in Canada, Mexico, and a third country that they're interested in visiting. How do the rates compare? Do these countries have Truth-in-Lending Laws that require the lender to disclose the method of computing any unearned finance charge?

Need Help? Go to...

► **Workshop 6:**
Multiplying
Decimals, page 14

► **Workshop 5:**
Subtracting
Decimals, page 12

► **Workshop 18:**
Reading Tables and
Charts, page 38

► **Application C:**
Tables and Charts,
page 762

STEP 1: Find the monthly payment. (Refer to the Monthly Payment on a Simple Interest Installment Loan of $100 table on page 799.)

$$\frac{\text{Amount of Loan}}{\$100} \times \frac{\text{Monthly Payment}}{\text{for a }\$100\text{ Loan}}$$

$$\frac{\$1800.00}{\$100.00} \times \$5.91 = \$106.38$$

STEP 2: Find the total amount repaid.

Number of Payments × Monthly Payment
18 × $106.38 = $1,914.84

STEP 3: Find the finance charge.

Total Amount Repaid − Amount Financed
$1,914.84 − $1,800.00 = **$114.84 finance charge**

1800 M+ ÷ 100 × 5.91 = 106.38 × 18 =

1914.84 − RM 1800 = 114.84

CONCEPT CHECK

SELF-CHECK ✓

Complete the problem, then check your answers at the end of the chapter.

1. Find the monthly payment, total amount repaid, and the finance charge for a $1,600.00 installment loan at 10 percent for 24 months.
Monthly Payment: ($1,600.00 ÷ $100.00) × $4.61 = $73.76; Total Repaid: 24 × 73.76 = $1,770.24; Finance Charge: $1,770.24 − $1,600.00 = $170.24

Example 2

Tulio and Lupe Fernandez are purchasing a side-by-side refrigerator with an installment loan that has an APR of 12 percent. The refrigerator sells for $1,399.99. The store financing requires a 10 percent down payment and 12 monthly payments. What is the finance charge?

STEP 1: Find the amount financed.

Selling Price − Down Payment
$1,399.99 − (0.10 × $1,399.99)
$1,399.99 − $140.00 = $1,259.99

STEP 2: Find the monthly payment. (Refer to the Monthly Payment on a Simple Interest Installment Loan of $100 table on page 799.)

$$\frac{\text{Amount of Loan}}{\$100} \times \frac{\text{Monthly Payment}}{\text{for a }\$100\text{ Loan}}$$

$$\frac{\$1259.99}{\$100.00} \times \$8.88$$

= $111.887 or $111.89 monthly payment

STEP 3: Find the total amount repaid.

Number of Payments × Monthly Payment
12 × $111.89 = $1,342.68

STEP 4: Find the finance charge.

Total Amount Repaid − Amount Financed
$1,342.68 − $1,259.99 = **$82.69 finance charge**

---

2 TEACH

Discuss the Monthly Payment on a Simple Interest Installment Loan of $100 table on page 799. Make sure they understand that the dollar amounts in the tables are for a $100 loan. Therefore, when using the table, first divide the total amount of the loan by 100. Next, multiply the answer by the appropriate number from the table. Review the fact that dividing a number by 100 has the effect of moving the decimal point in the number two places to the left.

Discuss the three formulas, and ask students what the finance charge represents (the interest charged on the amount financed). The annual percentage rate will be discussed in detail in Section 8-6. You might wish to point out that if the monthly interest rate for a loan is known, then the APR is 12 times the monthly rate.

Motivating the Lesson

Suppose you want to borrow $5,000 to buy a used car. Your bank will give you an installment loan of $5,000 for 2 years at 10 percent interest annually. Your monthly payments would be $230.50 for 24 months. What is the total amount of money you would have repaid at the end of 2 years if you accept the loan? **$5,532**

RETEACH / ENRICHMENT

Using a Computer

You're starting in a new apartment. When you buy an expensive item in installments, you often have to make a down payment. Create a spreadsheet to compute the down payment for each of the items in the table at the right and find the total. **LS** , **CL** , **P**

Item	Price	Required Down Payment	Amount of Down Payment
TV	$ 435	10%	$43.50
Refrigerator	430	20%	$86.00
Used car	8,000	25%	$2,000.00
Sofa	995	17%	$169.15
Total			$2,298.65

2 TEACH (cont'd)

In-Class Examples

Refer to the Monthly Payment on a Simple Interest Installment Loan of $100 table on page 799 for Problems 1 and 2.

1. Installment loan to buy a new piano: $3,500. Plan of 18 monthly payments, with an APR of 8 percent. What are the monthly payments? **($206.85)** What is the finance charge? **$223.30**

2. Installment loan for bathroom remodeling: $7,000. Plan of 24 monthly payments, with an APR of 10 percent. What are the monthly payments? **($322.70)** What is the finance charge? **$744.80**

3 ASSESS

Error Analysis

Review the terms *finance charge, monthly payment,* and *total amount repaid.* Computing the *finance charge* requires that students must first know the *monthly payment* and the *total amount repaid.*

For loan amounts greater than $100, divide the amount of the loan by 100. Then multiply the answer times the monthly payment for a $100 loan. This will give you the *monthly payment.*

Be sure students understand that they must then multiply the monthly payment times the total number of payments to find the *total amount repaid.*

Only then can they compute the *finance charge* by subtracting the amount of the loan from the total amount repaid. Emphasize that these steps must be done in the correct order when calculating the finance charge. Have students check their work to be sure they have not skipped any steps when computing finance charge.

292

CONCEPT CHECK

SELF-CHECK ✓ Complete the problem, then check your answers at the end of the chapter.

2. Find the down payment, amount financed, monthly payment, total amount repaid, and the finance charge for a $4,000.00 used boat, with a 20 percent down payment and an installment loan at an APR of 10 percent interest for 36 months.
   Down Payment: $4,000.00 − ($4,000.00 × 0.20) = $800.00; Amount Financed: $4,000.00 − $800.00 = $3,200.00; Monthly Payment: ($3,200.00 ÷ $100.00) × $3.23 = $103.36; Total Repaid: 36 × 103.36 = $3,720.96; Finance Charge: $3,720.96 − $3,200.00 = $520.96

SECTION 8-3 PRACTICE

Use the Monthly Payment on a Simple Interest Installment Loan of $100 table on page 799 to solve the following.

3. b. $171.60
   c. $1,029.60
   d. $29.60
4. b. $122.00
   c. $2,196.00
   d. $196.00
5. b. $253.12
   c. $6,074.88
   d. $474.88
6. b. $393.03
   c. $11,790.90
   d. $1,890.90
7. b. $298.92
   c. $10,761.30
   d. $1,211.12

	APR	Term (Months)	Table Value	Amount Financed	Monthly Payment	Total Repaid	Finance Charge
3.	10%	6	a. $17.16	$1,000	b.	c.	d.
4.	12%	18	a. $6.10	2,000	b.	c.	d.
5.	8%	24	a. $4.52	5,600	b.	c.	d.
6.	14%	30	a. $3.97	9,900	b.	c.	d.
7.	8%	36	a. $3.13	9,550	b.	c.	d.

8. Hazel Basnett.
   Installment loan of $2,000.
   Requires 12 monthly payments.
   APR is 8 percent.
   a. What are the monthly payments?
   b. What is the finance charge?
   a. $174.00; b. $88.00

9. Brian Anderson.
   Installment loan of $1,250.
   Requires 24 monthly payments.
   APR is 10 percent.
   a. What are the monthly payments?
   b. What is the finance charge?
   a. $57.63; b. $133.12

10. Used boat loan for $12,000.
    Down payment of 25 percent.
    A 14 percent APR for 36 months.
    $3,000.00 a. What is the down payment?
    $9,000.00 b. What is the amount of the loan?
    $307.80 c. What are the monthly payments?
    $2,080.80 d. What is the finance charge?

11. Equipment loan for $20,000.
    Down payment of 20 percent.
    A 12 percent APR for 30 months.
    a. What is the down payment?
    b. What is the amount of the loan?
    c. What are the monthly payments?
    d. What is the finance charge?
    11. a. $4,000; b. $16,000; c. $619.20; d. $2,576.00

12. Bob Wozniak obtained an installment loan of $2,400 to put a new roof on his house. The APR is 12 percent. The loan is to be repaid in 36 monthly payments. (You may need to refer to the Monthly Payment on a Simple Interest Installment Loan of $100 table on page 799.) What is the finance charge?
    $468.48

13. Jim Wilson obtained an installment loan of $1,450 to pay for some new furniture. He agreed to repay the loan in 18 monthly payments at an APR of 15 percent. What is the finance charge? **$178.64**

THINKING CRITICALLY

Monthly Payment
Ludmilla Felman put a $795 down payment on a computer system that cost $2,795. What is the principal of the loan? **($2,000)** The interest rate on her loan is 12 percent and the length of the loan is one year. What will Felman's monthly payment be?
($2,000 ÷ $100) × $8.88 = $177.60

14. Mark and Pam Voss obtained an installment loan of $2,460. The APR is 15 percent for 12 monthly payments. What is the finance charge? **$205.68**

15. Herb and Marci Rahla are purchasing a dishwasher with an installment loan that has an APR of 18 percent. The dishwasher sells for $699.95. They agree to make a down payment of 20 percent and to make 12 monthly payments. What is the finance charge? **$56.26**

16. Adolfo Ramirez obtained an installment loan of $6,800 for a used car. He made an $800 down payment. He financed the purchase with a finance company and agreed to repay the loan in 24 monthly payments at an APR of 18 percent. What is the finance charge? **$1,185.60**

17. Aurora Kaylow obtained an installment loan of $6,000 on a used sailboat. She financed the purchase through the boat dealer and agreed to repay the loan in 48 monthly payments at an APR of 18 percent. What is the finance charge? **$2,467.20**

18. Andrew and Ruth Bacon would like to obtain an installment loan of $1,850 to repair the gutters on their home. They can get the loan at an APR of 15 percent for 24 months or at an APR of 18 percent for 18 months. How much do the Bacons save by taking the loan with the lowest finance charge?
Save $28.98 w/ 18%

19. Lola Samaria would like an installment loan of $1,200 for auto repairs. Walton Savings and Loan will loan her the money at 15 percent for 12 months. Horton Finance Company will loan her the money at 18 percent for 24 months. How much will she save by taking the loan with the lowest finance charge? **Save $136.80 w/ 15%**

20. Pauline and Eldon Kharche would like to obtain an installment loan of $9,800 for replacement windows in their home. They can get the loan at an APR of 15 percent for 24 months or at an APR of 18 percent for 18 months. Which loan costs less? How much do the Kharches save by taking the loan that costs less? **Save $152.88 w/ 18%**

21. Lucretia and Don Protsman would like an installment loan of $12,900. City Loan will loan the money at 18 percent for 24 months. Economy Line Finance Company will loan the money at 17 percent for 30 months. Which loan costs less? How much will be saved by taking the loan that costs less?
Save $456.66 w/ 18% for 24 months

Need Help? Go to...
▶ Skill 30: **Finding the Percentage,** page 757
▶ Skill 20: **Multiplying Fractions/Mixed Numbers,** page 747
▶ Skill 6: **Subtracting Decimals,** page 733

MAINTAINING YOUR SKILLS

Multiply. Round to the nearest thousandth.

22. 4,000.00 ÷ 100.00 × 3.33 **13.200**   **23.** 1,240.00 ÷ 250.00 × 5.09 **25.246**

Subtract.

24.	**25.**	**26.**
4,200	1,240	1,224.50
− 42	− 15.50	− 15.31
4,158	1,224.50	1,209.19

Section 8-3 Simple Interest Installment Loans ▶ **293**

Closing Activity
Refer to the Monthly Payment on a Simple Interest Loan on $100 table on page 799 as needed.

1. Andrew Greene obtains an installment loan for the amount of $3,200 at an APR of 10 percent for 12 months. What is the finance charge? **$175.36**

2. Lisa Reed buys a new car for $19,000. She makes a down payment of 25 percent and finances the remaining amount on an installment loan at an APR of 8 percent for 36 months.
   a. What is the down payment? **$4,750**
   b. What is the amount of the loan? **$14,250**
   c. What are the monthly payments? **$446.03**
   d. What is the finance charge? **$1,806.90**

3. Frank Mintz can obtain an installment loan for $12,000 at an APR of 14 percent for 48 months or get a loan for the same amount at the same APR that must be repaid in 24 months. How much money in interest will he save if he takes the loan that must be repaid in 24 months? **$1,900.80**

WRAP-UP

Go over any problem for which a wrong answer is given.

Assignment Guide
   Basic: 3–7
   Average: 8–11

20 min.

National Standards for Business Education

Standard 1	Mathematical Foundations
Standard 2	Number Relationships and Operations

National Council of Teachers of Mathematics Standards

Standard 1	Numbers and Operations
Standard 4	Measurement
Standard 6	Problem Solving
Standard 8	Communication
Standard 9	Connections

FOCUS

Introduce the objective of this lesson by asking students to suppose they borrowed $500 from a bank. Then ask them if they would have to pay interest on the loan. **(Yes)** Would they pay back more or less than $500? **(More)** What is the amount of $500 called? **(The principal)** How could they find the total amount of interest paid? **Subtract $500 from the total amount repaid on the loan.**

In-Class Examples

Work through these exercises with students before having them do the Self-Check.
1. $1,575 − $12.55 **$1,562.45**
2. $2,000 − $16.67 **$1,983.33**
3. $2,000 × 10% **$200**
4. $4,449.38 × 12% **$533.93**
5. $1,417.23 × 15% **$212.58**

Installment Loans— Allocation of Monthly Payment

○ **Section Objective**

Work out the payment to interest, payment to principal, and the new balance.

As you learned in Section 8-3, a simple interest installment loan is repaid in equal monthly payments. Part of each payment is used to pay the interest on the unpaid balance of the loan and the remaining part is used to reduce the balance. The interest is calculated each month using the simple interest formula. The amount of principal that you owe *decreases* with each monthly payment. A **repayment schedule** shows the distribution of interest and principal over the life of the loan. The repayment schedule in **Figure 8.1** shows the interest and principal on an installment loan of $1,800 for 6 months at 8 percent.

Figure 8.1

Repayment Schedule for a $1,800 Loan at 8.0% for 6 Months				
Payment Number	Monthly Payment	Amount for Interest	Amount for Principal	Balance $1,800.00
1	$307.08	$12.00	$295.08	$1,504.92
2	307.08	10.03	297.05	1,207.87
3	307.08	8.05	299.03	908.85
4	307.08	6.06	301.02	607.82
5	307.08	4.05	303.03	304.80
6	307.08	2.03	305.05	−0.25

Note that the last payment would be reduced by $0.25 in order to zero out the loan.

Important Questions	What Formulas Do I Use?
What's the formula for **interest**?	Interest = Principal × Rate × Time
How do I find the **payment to principal**?	Payment to Principal = Monthly Payment − Interest
How do I find the **new principal**?	New Principal = Previous Principal − Payment to Principal

Living in the Real World

A Picture-Perfect Loan

It's Payback Time Chen reads the bank's brochure. The pamphlet contains a chart that shows a repayment schedule for a $2,000 loan at 6.0 percent interest for 8 months.

Each month you pay proportionately less for interest and more on your principal as you approach the end of your loan period.

Draw Conclusions Why is it important to get a copy of your repayment schedule?

Continued on page 297

Living in the Real World

It's vital to know exactly how much is being paid and how it's being broken down between principal and interest.

Great Ideas from the Classroom Of...

Marge Garneau Central High School Grand Junction, Colo.

Loan for Furniture

Imagine students want to buy furniture. Research the price of something they want to buy. They bring home $1,900 a month. Subtract $695 for rent and utilities. How much will be borrowed? Be sure to calculate their monthly payments, interest, and discounts (if paid off early).

Example 1

Need Help? Go to...
▶ Workshop 5:
Subtracting
Decimals, page 12
▶ Workshop 6:
Multiplying
Decimals, page 14
▶ Workshop 14:
Finding a
Percentage, page 30
▶ Application A:
Formulas, page 760

Stephanie and Donald Cole obtained the loan of $1,800 at 8 percent for 6 months shown in the repayment schedule in Figure 8.1 on page 294. Show the calculation for the first payment. What is the interest? What is the payment to principal? What is the new principal?

STEP 1: Find the interest.
Principal × Rate × Time
$1,800.00 × 8% × $\frac{1}{12}$ = **$12.00 interest**

STEP 2: Find the payment to principal.
Monthly Payment − Interest
$307.08 − $12.00 = **$295.08 payment to principal**

STEP 3: Find the new principal.
Previous Principal − Payment to Principal
$1,800.00 − $295.08 = **$1,504.92 new principal**

CONCEPT CHECK

SELF-CHECK✔

Complete the problems, then check your answers at the end of the chapter.

1. Interest the second month is: $1,504.92 × 8% × $\frac{1}{12}$ = **$10.03**

2. Payment to principal is: $307.08 − ? = **$297.05**

3. The new balance is: $1,504.92 − ? = **$1,207.87**

Example 2

Carlo Blanco obtained a home improvement loan of $6,000.00 at 8 percent for 36 months. The monthly payment is $187.80. The balance of the loan after 20 payments is $2,849.08. What is the interest for the first payment? What is the interest for the 21st payment? Why is the interest so much different for the two payments?

STEP 1: Find the interest for the first payment.
Principal × Rate × Time
$6,000.00 × 8% × $\frac{1}{12}$ = **$40.00**

STEP 2: Find the interest for the 21st payment.
Principal × Rate × Time
$2,849.08 × 8% × $\frac{1}{12}$ = **$18.99**

The interest is reduced by more than half. The principal is much greater for the first payment than the second payment.

CONCEPT CHECK

SELF-CHECK✔

Complete the problem, then check your answers at the end of the chapter.

4. You take out a loan of $8,000.00 at 12 percent for 24 months. The monthly payment is $376.80. The balance of the loan after 15 payments is $3,222.44.
   a. What is the interest for the first payment? $8,000 × 0.12 × $\frac{1}{12}$ = **$80.00**
   b. What is the interest for the 16th payment?
   $3,222.44 × 0.12 × $\frac{1}{12}$ = **$32.22**

TECHNOLOGY POWER

Use *BusinessWeek* Online to determine how much can be borrowed and to calculate monthly payments. There is a calculator to enter current wages, taxes and other loans, and it returns the amount you can safely borrow. Various down payment amounts can be entered into a different calculator, and monthly payments are calculated based on user-entered interest rates, taxes, and insurance. Estimates for other costs, such as closing costs and insurance or refinancing are also available.

---

2 TEACH

Discuss the repayment schedule for the $1,800 loan. Have students check the figures for payment No. 1. **$307.08 − $12.00 = $295.08; $1,800 − $295.08 = $1,504.92**

Motivating the Lesson

Suppose you borrow $1,000. The bank charges you an interest rate of 8 percent for 12 months. You agree to pay $87 per month for 12 months until your loan is repaid.

You might think that the entire $87.00 of your first monthly payment goes toward reducing the principal, or the amount you owe the bank; however, out of the first $87.00 monthly payment, $6.67 is interest. The remainder of the $87.00 is used toward paying off the principal.

How much of your first monthly payment of $87.00 goes toward paying off the principal? (**$80.33**) After you make your first monthly payment, how much money will you still owe the bank? **$919.67**

In-Class Example

Isabel Rosario obtained a home improvement loan for $11,000 at 14 percent for 48 months. The monthly payment is $300.30. How much of the first monthly payment is for interest? (**$128.33**) How much of the first monthly payment is for principal? (**$171.97**) What is the new balance? **$10,828.03**

3 ASSESS

Error Analysis

Review the major concepts covered in this lesson. Be sure students understand that a portion of each monthly payment on a loan is interest, and the other portion is payment toward the principal.

SECTION 8-4

③ ASSESS (cont'd)

Review the formula for computing interest (**Principal × Rate × Time**). Explain that students are calculating monthly interest, so Time is always $\frac{1}{12}$, which represents $\frac{1}{12}$ of a year, or one month.

Have students note that the interest and the payment to the principal will change each month. Point out the correlation between the interest and the payment to the principal, noting that as the interest on a monthly payment decreases, the payment to the principal increases.

Remind students to carefully follow the steps in Example 1 in the order given. They must find the monthly interest (Step 1) before they can calculate the payment to the principal (Step 2). Likewise, they must find the payment to principal (Step 2) before they can calculate the new principal, or new balance (Step 3). This lesson may require extensive practice before students fully understand the concepts covered.

④ CLOSE

Closing Activity

1. Shane Norris has a college tuition loan for $14,000. Interest rate of 10 percent for 42 months. Monthly payment is $396.20. How much of the first monthly payment is interest? **($116.67)** How much of the first monthly payment goes toward the principal? **($279.53)** What is the new balance? **$13,720.47**

SECTION 8-4 PRACTICE

	Loan Balance	Interest Rate	Monthly Payment	Amount for Interest	Amount for Principal	New Principal
5.	$1,200	12%	$106.56	$12.00	$94.56	a. $1,105.44
6.	2,400	15%	149.76	30.00	a. $119.76	b. $2,280.24
7.	3,460	10%	207.95	a. $28.83	b. $179.12	c. $3,280.88
8.	1,011	10%	207.95	a. $8.43	b. $199.52	c. $811.48
9.	7,200	15%	349.20	a. $90.00	b. $259.20	c. $6,940.80
10.	3,599	15%	349.20	a. $44.99	b. $304.21	c. $3,294.79

For Problems 11–17, complete the repayment schedule for a loan of $2,400 at 12 percent for 12 months.

	Repayment Schedule for a $2,400 Loan at 12% for 12 Months				
	Payment Number	Monthly Payment	Amount for Interest	Amount for Principal	New Principal
	1	$213.12	$24.00	$189.12	$2,210.88
	2	213.12	22.11	191.01	2,019.87
	3	213.12	20.20	192.92	1,826.95
	4	213.12	18.27	194.85	1,632.10
	5	213.12	16.32	196.80	1,435.30
11.	6	213.12	14.35	198.77	a. $1,236.53
12.	7	213.12	12.37	a. $200.75	b. $1,035.78
13.	8	213.12	a. $10.36	b. $202.74	c. $833.02
14.	9	213.12	a. $8.33	b. $204.79	c. $628.23
15.	10	213.12	a. $6.28	b. $206.84	c. $421.39
16.	11	213.12	a. $4.21	b. $208.91	c. $212.48
17.	12	a. $214.60	b. $2.12	c. $212.48	d.

d. $0.00; You need to adjust the last payment to $214.60 in order to zero out the loan.

MAINTAINING YOUR SKILLS

> **Need Help? Go to...**
> ➤ **Skill 30: Finding the Percentage,** page 757

Find the percentage.

18. 12% of $5,000 **$600**   **19.** 15% of $6,000 **$900**   **20.** 8% of $8,400 **$672**

21. 22% of $1,282.15 **$282.07**   **22.** 26% of $2,348.90 **$610.71**   **23.** 20% of $456.21 **$91.24**

24. 6% of $340.80 **$20.45**   **25.** 15% of $9,845.20 **$1,476.78**   **26.** 7% of $12,346.97 **$864.29**

COMMUNICATION SKILLS

Truth-in-Lending Law
Lenders are required by the Truth-in-Lending Law to inform borrowers of the finance charge and the APR. Students research the Truth-in-Lending Law and report their findings to the class. Bring in a contract. Students identify what parts of the contract are covered by the Truth-in-Lending Law. **Finance charge and APR.**

WRAP-UP

Go over any problem for which a wrong answer is given.

Assignment Guide
  Basic: 5–10
  Average: 11–16

20 min.

SECTION 8-5 Paying Off Simple Interest Installment Loans

○ Section Objective

Compute the final payment when paying off a simple interest installment loan.

When you have a simple interest installment loan, you pay interest on the unpaid balance. If you pay off a simple interest installment loan before the end of the term, you just pay the previous balance plus the current month's interest. This is the **final payment**.

One reason to pay off a simple interest installment loan before the end of the term is to pay less interest. The amount of interest saved depends on the total payback minus the sum of the previous payments and the final payment.

Ask yourself these questions as you work through the problems:

Important Questions	What Formulas Do I Use?
How do I calculate interest?	Interest = Principal × Rate × Time
How do I find the final payment?	Final Payment = Previous Balance + Current Month's Interest
How do I determine the interest saved?	Interest Saved = Total Payback − (Sum of Previous Payments + Final Payment)

Living in the Real World

A Picture-Perfect Loan

You Need a Plan Chen thinks he could pay off this loan early if he sells some of his photographs from his trip as soon as he gets back.

Mr. Chen smiles, "Make sure you talk with the loan officer about that possibility. The bank will explain how a payoff works. Generally, the bank still gets some interest on the loan on the final payoff."

Draw Conclusions Why might a bank not encourage you to pay off a loan early?

Continued on page 300

Example 1

The first 3 months of the repayment schedule for Doug and Donna Collins's loan of $1,800 at 12 percent interest for 6 months is shown in Figure 8.2 on page 298. What is the final payment if they pay the loan off with the fourth payment?

Continued on next page

Section 8-5 Paying Off Simple Interest Installment Loans ▶ **297**

Living in the Real World

Paying off the loan early means the bank earns less interest from the loan.

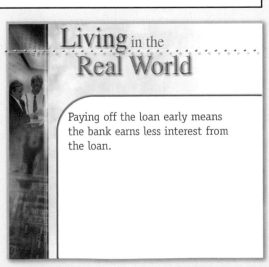

SECTION 8-5

National Standards for Business Education

Standard 1	Mathematical Foundations
Standard 2	Number Relationships and Operations

National Council of Teachers of Mathematics Standards

Standard 1	Numbers and Operations
Standard 4	Measurement
Standard 6	Problem Solving
Standard 8	Communication
Standard 9	Connections

1 FOCUS

Ask students if they had a loan, would they like the option of paying if off early. **(Yes)** Why? **(Save on interest)** Tell them that in this lesson they will learn how to compute a final payment on an installment loan.

In-Class Examples

Work through these exercises with students before having them do the Self-Check.

1. $4,800 × 12% × $\frac{1}{12}$ **$48**
2. $3,200 × 15% × $\frac{1}{12}$ **$40**
3. $6,480 × 18% × $\frac{1}{12}$ **$97.20**
4. $3,256 × 9% × $\frac{1}{12}$ **$24.42**
5. $728.42 + $8.79 **$737.21**
6. $1,368.51 + $15.97 **$1,384.48**
7. (12 × $196.27) − [(6 × $196.27) + $1,075.08] **$102.54**
8. (24 × $294.98) − [(20 × $294.98) + $1,016.80] **$163.12**

Figure 8.2

Payment Number	Monthly Payment	Amount for Interest	Amount for Principal	Balance $1,800.00
Repayment Schedule for a $1,800 Loan at 12.0% for 6 Months				
1	$310.50	$18.00	$292.50	$1,507.50
2	310.50	15.08	295.42	1,212.08
3	310.50	12.12	298.38	913.70

Need Help? Go to...

▶ **Workshop 4:** Adding Decimals, page 10

▶ **Workshop 5:** Subtracting Decimals, page 12

▶ **Workshop 6:** Multiplying Decimals, page 14

▶ **Workshop 14:** Finding a Percentage, page 30

STEP 1: Find the previous balance.
= $913.70.

STEP 2: Find the interest for the fourth month.
Principal × Rate × Time
$913.70 × 12% × $\frac{1}{12}$ = $9.137 or $9.14

STEP 3: Find the final payment.
Previous Balance + Current Month's Interest
$913.70 + $9.14 = **$922.84 final payment**

CONCEPT CHECK

SELF-CHECK ✓

Complete the problems, then check your answers at the end of the chapter.

1. Find the interest for a month and then the final payment for a previous balance of $800 at 15 percent interest. **$800 × 0.15 × $\frac{1}{12}$ = $10.00; $800 + $10 = $810.00**

2. You have a 12-month loan of $1,200.00 at 12 percent interest with a balance of $816.04 after the fourth payment. What is the final payment if you pay off the loan with the fifth payment?
$816.04 × 0.12 × $\frac{1}{12}$ = $8.16; $816.04 + $8.16 = $824.20

Example 2

How much would the Collinses in Example 1 save by paying off the loan early?

STEP: Find the interest saved.

Total Payback	−	(Sum of Previous Payments	+	Final Payment)
(6 × $310.50)	−	[(3 × $310.50)	+	$922.84]
= $1,863.00	−	[$931.50	+	$922.84]
= $1,863.00	−			$1,854.34
= **$8.66 saved**				

CONCEPT CHECK

SELF-CHECK ✓

Complete the problem, then check your answer at the end of the chapter.

3. In Problem 2 you had a 12-month loan of $1,200.00 at 12 percent interest with a balance of $816.04 after the fourth payment of $106.56. How much do you save by paying off the loan with the fifth payment?
(12 × $106.56) − [(4 × $106.56) + $824.20] = $1,278.72 − [$425.24 + $824.20]; $1,278.72 − $1,250.24 = $28.28

Students should understand that the primary advantage of a simple interest installment loan is that you always know exactly how much you owe after each monthly payment. Thus, you can pay off the loan by simply paying the new principal after the last payment plus any interest due. In the examples, if the loan were paid off with the third payment, then the final payment would be the new balance after payment two (**$1,212.08**), plus the interest for payment three (**$12.12**). Thus, the final payment is $1,212.08 + $12.12 = $1,224.20.

Motivating the Lesson

You have a simple interest installment loan for $1,400 at 10 percent for 6 months. After 3 payments, you owe a balance of $708.55. You decide to pay off the loan early when you make your fourth payment. Your final payment is the balance you still owe plus the fourth month's interest of $5.90. What is the final payment? **$714.45**

In-Class Example

The balance on a simple interest installment loan is $3,600. The annual interest rate is 8 percent. What is the interest? **($24)** What is the final payment? **$3,624**

Error Analysis

In problems where students are asked to compute final payment and interest saved by paying off the loan early, emphasize the importance of following each step in the correct order. First, students must compute current monthly interest on the previous balance. Second, they must then add the current monthly interest

COOPERATIVE LEARNING

Promissory Note

Work in pairs. Imagine that you've agreed to lend $100 to a friend. You want to make sure you get repaid. Write a promissory note for the loan using a word processing program. The note should include the date, lender's name, borrower's name, loan amount, interest rate, repayment date, any conditions of repayment (for example, monthly installments), and lines for the signatures of both parties. Pairs check each other's promissory notes.

SECTION 8-5 PRACTICE

Find the interest and the final payment.

	Interest Rate	Previous Balance		Interest		Final Payment
4.	12%	$4,800.00	a.	$48.00	b.	$4,848
5.	15%	3,000.00	a.	$37.50	b.	$3,037.50
6.	10%	1,460.80	a.	$12.17	b.	$1,448.63
7.	18%	3,987.60	a.	$59.81	b.	$4,047.41
8.	22%	3,265.87	a.	$59.87	b.	$3,325.74

9. Willard Hudson took out a simple interest loan of $6,000.00 at 10 percent interest for 24 months. His monthly payment is $276.60. After 4 payments the balance is $5,082.21. He pays off the loan when the next payment is due. What is the interest? What is the final payment? How much is saved by paying the loan off early? **$42.35; $5,124.56; $407.44**

10. Lillian Hartwick took out a simple interest loan of $3,600.00 at 18 percent for 12 months with a payment of $330.12. After 6 payments the balance is $1,879.90. She pays off the loan when the next payment is due. What is the interest? What is the final payment? How much is saved by paying the loan off early? **$28.20; $1,908.10; $72.62**

11. Scott DuBois took out a simple interest loan of $1,800.00 for home repairs. The loan is for 12 months at 8 percent interest with a payment of $156.60. After 8 months, the balance is $615.87. He pays off the loan when the next payment is due. What is the final payment? How much is saved by paying the loan off early? **$619.98; $6.42**

12. Nicholas and Dorothea Schrodt were looking over the repayment schedule for their boat loan of $5,500.00 at 15 percent interest for 42 months with a payment of $168.85. They note the following:
- Balance after payment 18 is $3,493.39.
- Balance after payment 24 is $2,718.43.
- Balance after payment 30 is $1,883.50.

How much is saved by paying off the loan early at payment 19, 25, and 31? **pymt 18: $515.34; pymt 24: $286.89; pymt 30: $119.16**

MAINTAINING YOUR SKILLS

Need Help? Go to...
▶ Skill 8: Multiplying Decimals, page 735
▶ Skill 30: Finding the Percentage, page 757

Multiply.

13. $5,489 \times 0.15$ **823.35** **14.** $2,729 \times 0.22$ **600.38** **15.** $9,032 \times 0.18$ **1,625.76**

Find the percentage.

16. $430 \times 18\%$ **77.4** **17.** $3,561.90 \times 9\%$ **320.57** **18.** $\$10,907.45 \times 15\%$ **1,636.12**

Section 8-5 Paying Off Simple Interest Installment Loans ▶ **299**

---

to the previous principal to determine the final payment. Only after they know the final payment, can they calculate interest saved by paying off the loan early. Review the formula for computing interest saved on early payment of the loan.

④ CLOSE

Closing Activity

1. ($2,761 \times 11\% \times \frac{1}{12}$) + $891.18 **$916.49**

2. $755 \times 8\% \times \frac{1}{12}$ + $1,580.67 **$1,585.70**

3. Previous balance of $679.36. Interest rate of 15 percent. What is the interest? **($8.49)** What is the final payment? **$687.85**

4. Eleanor Wojek took out a simple interest installment loan of $1,525 at 8 percent for 6 months. Her monthly payment on the loan is $260.17. After 3 payments, the balance is $769.98. If she pays off the loan when the next payment is due, what is the final payment? **($775.11)** How much is saved by paying off the loan early? **$5.40**

5. Arthur Senn obtained a simple interest installment loan for $6,370 at 17 percent for 12 months. His monthly payment on the loan is $580.94. After 9 payments, the balance is $1,695.01. If he pays off the loan when the next payment is due, what is the final payment? **($1,719.02)** How much is saved by paying off the loan early? **$23.80**

USING CALCULATORS

Many calculators have a STO key that allows you to recall a value several times in a problem. The stored value is usually retrieved using the recall RCL key. Have students explain what happens in the following sequence of keystrokes. 735 [STO] [×] .15 [×] 1 [÷] 12 [=] [+] [RCL]

WRAP-UP

Go over any problem for which a wrong answer is given.

Assignment Guide
   Basic: 4–8
   Average: 9–11

20 min.

National Standards for Business Education

Standard 1	Mathematical Foundations
Standard 2	Number Relationships and Operations

National Council of Teachers of Mathematics Standards

Standard 1	Numbers and Operations
Standard 4	Measurement
Standard 6	Problem Solving
Standard 8	Communication
Standard 9	Connections

① FOCUS

Ask students if they have seen the APR of loans advertised in newspapers. Ask also which APR they would prefer for a loan of their own: 14 percent or 16 percent? Why? **(Fourteen percent is better because interest on the loan would be less.)** The focus of this lesson is to use a table to find the APR of a loan.

In-Class Examples

Work through these exercises with students before having them do the Self-Check.

1. $(12 \times \$25) - \$240$ **$60**
2. $(24 \times \$15.25) - \$305$ **$61**
3. $\$100 \times (\$40 \div \$800)$ **$5**
4. $\$100 \times (\$35 \div \$75)$ **$46.67**
5. $\$100 \times (\$125 \div \$946.10)$ **$13.21**

SECTION 8·6 Determining the APR

○ **Section Objective**

Use a table to find the annual percentage rate of a loan.

Figure 8.3

If you know the number of monthly payments and the finance charge per $100 of the amount financed, you can use a table to find the annual percentage rate (APR) of the loan. You can use the APR of loans to compare the relative cost of borrowing money.

Annual Percentage Rate for Monthly Payment Plans											
	Annual Percentage Rate										
	10.00%	10.25%	10.50%	10.75%	11.00%	11.25%	11.50%	11.75%	12.00%	12.25%	12.50%
Term	Finance Charge per $100 of Amount Financed										
6	$ 2.94	$ 3.01	$ 3.08	$ 3.16	$ 3.23	$ 3.31	$ 3.38	$ 3.45	$ 3.53	$ 3.60	$ 3.68
12	5.50	5.64	5.78	5.92	6.06	6.20	6.34	6.48	6.62	6.76	6.90
18	8.10	8.31	8.52	8.73	8.93	9.14	9.35	9.56	9.77	9.98	10.19
24	10.75	11.02	11.30	11.58	11.86	12.14	12.42	12.70	12.98	13.26	13.54

Note: An expanded table can be found in the Appendices on pages 794–795.

As you work through the problems, you will need this important formula:

$$\text{Finance Charge per } \$100 = \$100 \times \frac{\text{Finance Charge}}{\text{Amount Financed}}$$

Living in the Real World

A Picture-Perfect Loan

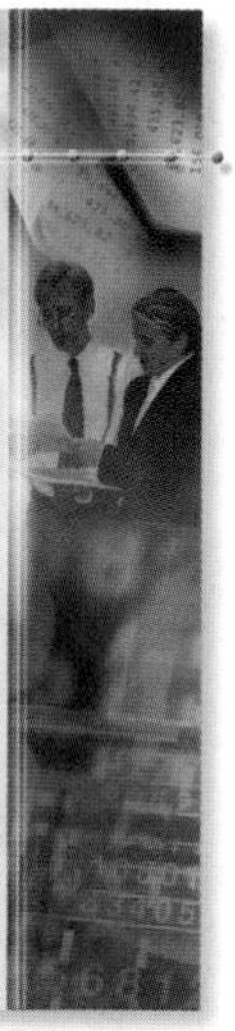

How Much Are Your Dreams Worth? Still studying the brochure, Chen finds one chart that shows the annual percentage rates (APR) of the home improvement loan Chen's parents borrowed. The chart shows various finance charges per $100 borrowed. The figures vary according to the length of the loan and the annual percentage rate of the loan. He figures out the APR and term of loan that will suit his needs best, and tomorrow he'll talk with the bank's loan officer to negotiate a loan.

Draw Conclusions Given Chen's situation, do you think it's a good idea to take out a loan for a vacation? Or should he wait and save up money in order to afford the trip?

Continued on page 305

(**Example 1**)

Paul Norris obtained an installment loan of $1,500.00 to pay for a computer. The finance charge is $146.25. He agreed to repay the loan in 18 monthly payments. What is the annual percentage rate?

Living in the Real World

Chen's trip is part vacation, part work assignment. It is likely he will make income on the photographs he shoots while in Arizona, so taking out the loan makes financial sense.

STEP 1: Find the finance charge per $100.

$$\$100 \times \frac{\text{Finance Charge}}{\text{Amount Financed}}$$

$$\$100 \times \frac{\$146.25}{\$1,500.00}$$

$$\$100 \times \quad 0.0975 \qquad = \$9.75$$

STEP 2: Find the APR. (Refer to Figure 8.3, the Annual Percentage Rate for Monthly Payment Plans table on page 300.)

In the row for 18 payments, find the number closest to $9.75. It is $9.77. Read the APR at the top of the column. **APR is 12.00 percent.**

Need Help? Go to...

➤ **Workshop 7:**
  Dividing Decimals,
  page 16
➤ **Workshop 2:**
  Rounding Numbers,
  page 6
➤ **Skill 11: Dividing**
  Decimals, page 738
➤ **Skill 2: Rounding**
  Numbers, page 729

CONCEPT CHECK

Complete the problems, then check your answers at the end of the chapter.
Find the finance charge per $100 and the APR.

1. A 6-month loan.
   Finance charge: $24.64.
   Amount financed of $800.

   Finance charge ÷ 100 = $3.08
   APR = 10.5%

2. A 24-month loan.
   Finance charge: $96.22.
   Amount financed of $850.

   Finance charge ÷ 100 = $11.32
   APR = 10.5%

Example 2

A 54-inch HDTV is for sale for $1,899.92 cash or $177.83 per month for 12 months. What is the APR?

STEP 1: Find the finance charge.

Total Payback	—	Amount Financed	
(12 × $177.83)	—	$1,899.92	=
$2,133.96	—	$1,899.92	= $234.04

STEP 2: Find the finance charge per $100.

$$\$100 \times \frac{\text{Finance Charge}}{\text{Amount Financed}}$$

$$\$100 \times \frac{\$234.04}{\$1,899.92}$$

$$\$100 \times \quad 0.12318 \qquad = \$12.32$$

STEP 3: Find the APR. (Refer to the Annual Percentage Rate for Monthly Payment Plans table on pages 794–795.)

In the row of 12 payments, find the number closest to $12.32. It is $12.31. Read the APR at the top of the column. **APR is 22.00 percent.**

CONCEPT CHECK

Complete the problem, then check your answer at the end of the chapter.

3. A home improvement loan of $4,000.00 has payments of $186.00 per month for 24 months. What is the APR?
   Finance charge = (24 × $186) − $4,000 = $4,464 − $4,000 = $464
   Finance charge per $100 = $100 × ($464 ÷ $4,000) = $11.60
   Row for 24 payments, number closest to $11.60 is $11.58.
   The APR is 10.75%.

Section 8-6 Determining the APR ▶ **301**

---

2 TEACH

As an enticement to buy a product, many stores will couple the cost of a product with the finance charge. They might advertise, for example, "12 monthly payments of $149" instead of stating the cost of the product plus the Annual Percentage Rate (APR) to finance it. Here, the APR is the cost of financing something. Use the chart to show students how an APR can be found if the finance charge and term are known. For example, a finance charge of $9.77 for a term of 18 months yields an APR of 12 percent.

Ask students to think about the number that results from dividing the finance charge by the amount financed. What does it represent? **(Finance charge per one dollar of the loan)** Why is the number multiplied by $100? **The APR chart gives the finance charge per $100 of amount financed.**

Motivating the Lesson

Suppose you wanted to borrow $5,000 for 12 months. Delco Finance will lend you the money at an APR of 7.5 percent. Starr Finance will charge you an APR of 8 percent. Which loan will cost you less in interest? Remember that the formula for computing interest is Principal × Rate × Time.

$5,000 × 7.5% × 1 = $375
$5,000 × 8% × 1 = $400
$400 − $375 = $25 The loan of $5,000 at an APR of 7.5 percent costs $25 less in interest than the same loan at an APR of 8 percent.

THINKING CRITICALLY

Interest
Ask students why the amount for interest goes down each month on an installment loan. **(The principal is decreasing each month.)** Also ask if they think many people pay off loans early, and if not, why not? **No. They have to come up with the full amount needed to pay off the loan. They might pay off the car loan early if they sell the car.**

2 TEACH (cont'd)

In-Class Examples
Use the Annual Percentage Rate Table for Monthly Payment Plans on pages 794 and 795 for the following problems.

1. Installment loan of $5,000. Finance charge of $580. Monthly payments: 24. What is the APR? **10.75%**

2. Installment loan of $7,200. Finance charge of $1,008. Monthly payments: 36. What is the APR? **8.75%**

3. Ahmad Abdul took out an 18-month installment loan for $3,600. The finance charge was $450. What is the APR? **15.25%**

3 ASSESS

Error Analysis
Remind students to read each question carefully. If the finance charge is given in the problem, then students divide the finance charge by the amount financed and multiply the result by $100. Have students review their work to see if they have correctly placed the finance charge in the *numerator* and the amount finance in the *denominator* before they divide. Then they find the APR by looking up the dollar amount on the corresponding monthly row of an APR table on pages 794 and 795.

If the finance charge is not given in the problem, students must first compute the finance charge before they can figure the APR. Review the formula: Finance Charge = Total Payback − Amount Financed. Remind students that the total payback is found by multiplying the monthly payment times the number of months of the loan. Then have students follow the steps for finding the finance charge per $100 and looking up the APR on one of the APR tables.

Complete the table. Using the Annual Percentage Rate for Monthly Payment Plans table on pages 794–795, find the finance charge per $100 and the APR.

	Finance Charge	Amount Financed	Finance Charge per $100	Number of Payments	Annual Percentage Rate
4.	$ 33.10	$1,000	a. $3.31	6	b. 11.25%
5.	434.16	2,400	a. $18.09	24	b. 16.5%
6.	421.50	3,000	a. $14.05	18	b. 17%
7.	1,652.00	5,400	a. $30.59	36	b. 18.25%
8.	597.66	4,200	a. $14.23	30	b. 10.5%

9. Ed Naiman.
   Installment loan of $2,500.00.
   Finance charge of $430.50.
   Requires 24 monthly payments.
   What is the APR? **15.75%**

10. Betty Arca.
    Installment loan of $800.00.
    Finance charge of $170.40.
    Requires 36 monthly payments.
    What is the APR? **13%**

11. Webster Larkin.
    Installment loan of $3,000.00.
    Requires 6 monthly payments of $511.18.
    What is the APR? **7.75%**

12. Kenneth Bryant.
    Installment loan of $9,365.
    Requires 36 monthly payments of $330.
    What is the APR? **16.25%**

13. Marie Brenson obtained an installment loan of $460.00 to purchase computer software. The finance charge is $19.32. She agreed to repay the loan in 6 monthly payments. What is the APR rate? **14.25%**

14. Herb Stanley acquired an installment loan of $6,800.00 to pay his daughter's college tuition. The finance charge is $731. He agreed to repay the loan in 24 monthly payments. What is the APR? **10%**

15. Jeff Stapleton acquired an installment loan of $1,995.00 to pay for truck transmission repairs. He agreed to repay the loan in 12 monthly payments of $186.20. What is the APR? **21.5%**

16. Julia Bourne obtained an installment loan of $3,800.00 to purchase a lawn and garden tractor. She agreed to repay the loan in 24 monthly payments of $186.20. What is the APR? **16%**

17. Oneta Correy wants to obtain an installment loan of $9,900.00 to purchase a used truck. The bank has agreed to loan her the money for 24 months at $480.15 per month. What is the APR of her loan? **15%**

ALTERNATIVE ASSESSMENT

Oral Presentations
Oral presentations in class help you get over a fear of public speaking. The many opportunities for students to give oral presentations both as individuals and in groups, leads to increased comfort later on when they must speak in front of an audience.

24. Dealer:
FC: $128.00
APR: 12.25%
TP: $2,115
Credit Union:
FC: $155.42
APR: 10.00%
TP: $2,142
Based on APR the loan should come from the credit union. Based on finance charge the loan should come from the dealer. The times are different so you really cannot compare.

25. Computer:
FC: $501.52
APR: 17.5%
TP: $3,750.81
Small business loan:
FC: $343.72
APR: 16%
TP: $3,593.01
Based on APR the loan should be a small business loan. Based on finance charge the loan should come from the computer company. The times are different so you really cannot compare.

18. Helen Olson needs an installment loan of $999.00 to purchase a power washer from a paint store. She must repay the loan in 24 months. The finance charge is $48.50. What is the APR of her loan? **17.24%**

19. Brent and Lola Miller are buying a washer that costs $399.95 and a dryer that costs $249.99. To use the store's installment plan, they need a down payment of $49.94. They must make 18 monthly payments of $37.08 each. What is the APR on their installment loan? **13.75%**

20. Jorge Holland is having a new furnace installed. The furnace costs $3,500.00. The bank requires a down payment of 20 percent and 36 monthly payments of $91.84 each. What is the APR on his loan? **18.08%**

21. Ty Chin is buying a new 32-inch television set that costs $599.99 plus 6 percent sales tax. To use the installment plan available at the electronics store, he must make a down payment of 25 percent and make 30 monthly payments of $19.46 each. What is the APR on his loan? **16.25%**

22. Chef Andrew Stachowick is buying a gas range. He would like an installment loan of $5,000 to be repaid in 36 months. Nathaniel Loan Company will grant the loan with a finance charge of $1,215.60. City Finance Company will grant the loan with a finance charge of $1,332.50. What is the APR on each loan? **NLC: 14.75% APR; CFC: 15.75% APR**

23. Wayne Charles is financing the replacement of kitchen cupboards with an installment loan of $8,000 to be repaid in 24 months. ABC Finance Company will grant the loan with a finance charge of $1,984. Atco Financial Service will grant the loan with a finance charge of $2,010. What is the APR on each loan? **ABC: 22.25%; Atco: 22.50%**

24. Eleanor Penny had a $1,987.00 water softener installed. She made a down payment of $87.00. She can finance the remainder through the dealer at $169.00 a month for 12 months. She could also obtain a credit union loan at $114.19 per month for 18 months. Find the following for each loan: the finance charge, the APR, and the total amount paid. Which payment plan is the best deal? Why?

25. Kathleen Dunn purchased a laptop computer for $3,249.29. She made a down payment of $649.29. She can finance the remainder by agreeing to pay $129.23 per month for 24 months to the computer company. She could also obtain a small business loan at $163.54 per month for 18 months. Find the following for each loan: the finance charge, the APR, and the total amount paid. Which payment plan is the best deal? Why?

Need Help? Go to...
➤ Skill 2: **Rounding Numbers**, page 729
➤ Skill 10: **Dividing (Decimal Remainder)**, page 737
➤ Skill 11: **Dividing Decimals**, page 738

MAINTAINING YOUR SKILLS

Round to the nearest cent.

26. $19.439 **$19.44**   **27.** $12.4162 **$12.42**   **28.** $40.3072 **$40.31**

Divide. Round answers to the nearest hundredth.

29. 510 ÷ 17 **30**   **30.** 1,060 ÷ 24 **44.17**   **31.** 2,642 ÷ 47 **56.21**

---

4 CLOSE

Closing Activity
Round to the nearest hundredth.
1. 100 × $65 ÷ $3,680 **$1.77**
2. 100 × $250 ÷ $4,090 **$6.11**
Use the Annual Percentage Rate Table for Monthly Payment Plans on pages 794 and 795 for Problems 3–5.

3. Grace Reid obtained an installment loan from her bank for $2,836 for 24 months. The finance charge for the loan was $329. What is the APR? **10.75%**

4. Aaron Russell took out an installment loan for $13,600 to purchase a used car. The bank will loan him the money for 30 months at $502 per month. What is the APR? **8%**

5. Robin Young purchased a bedroom set for $6,000. She made a down payment of 25 percent and financed the remainder at $165 per month for 30 months. What is the APR? **7.5%**

WRAP-UP

Go over any problem for which a wrong answer is given.

Assignment Guide
  Basic: 4–8
  Average: 9–12

20 min.

Quick Quiz

1. Jong Lee borrowed $7,329. He agreed to repay this single-payment loan in 64 days. His bank charged him 10.25 percent exact interest. What is the exact interest owed? **($131.72)** What is the maturity value of his loan? **$7,460.72**

2. Franklin Hayes obtained a loan for $4,800 at 8 percent for 24 months. The monthly payment is $216.96. Compute the interest, payment toward the principal, and the new balance for the first two monthly payments on the loan.

   a. How much of the first monthly payment is interest? **$32**

   b. How much of the first monthly payment is for principal? **$184.96**

   c. What is the new balance? **$4,615.04**

   d. How much of the second monthly payment is interest? **$30.77**

   e. How much of the second monthly payment is for principal? **$186.19**

   f. What is the new balance? **$4,428.85**

SECTION 8-1 **CONCEPT CHECK** (p. 285)

1. $15, $615
2. $20, $820
3. $14.79, $614.79
4. $19.73, $819.73

SECTION 8-2 **CONCEPT CHECK** (p. 288)

1. $1,999.99 − $199.99 = **$1,800**
2. $3,950 − $150 = **$3,800**
3. $1,360 × 0.20 = **$272**; $1,360 − $272 = **$1,088**
4. $725 × 0.30 = **$217.50**; $725 − $217.50 = **$507.50**

SECTION 8-3 **CONCEPT CHECK** (p. 291, 292)

1. Monthly Payment: ($1,600.00 ÷ $100.00) × $4.61 = **$73.76**
   Total Repaid: 24 × 73.76 = **$1,770.24**
   Finance Charge: $1,770.24 − $1,600.00 = **$170.24**

2. Down Payment: $4,000.00 − ($4,000.00 × 0.20) = **$800.00**
   Amount Financed: $4,000.00 − $800.00 = **$3,200.00**
   Monthly Payment: ($3,200.00 ÷ $100.00) × $3.23 = **$103.36**
   Total Repaid: 36 × 103.36 = **$3,720.96**
   Finance Charge: $3,720.96 − $3,200.00 = **$520.96**

SECTION 8-4 **CONCEPT CHECK** (p. 295)

1. $10.03
2. $297.05
3. $1,207.87
4. a. $8,000 × 0.12 × $\frac{1}{12}$ = **$80.00**
   b. $3,222.44 × 0.12 × $\frac{1}{12}$ = **$32.22**

SECTION 8-5 **CONCEPT CHECK** (p. 298)

1. $800 × 0.15 × $\frac{1}{12}$ = **$10.00**; $800 + $10 = **$810.00**
2. $816.04 × 0.12 × $\frac{1}{12}$ = **$8.16**; $816.04 + $8.16 = **$824.20**
3. (12 × $106.56) − [(4 × $106.56) + $824.20]
   = $1,278.72 − [$425.24 + $824.20]
   $1,278.72 − $1,250.24 = **$28.28**

SECTION 8-6 **CONCEPT CHECK** (p. 301)

1. Finance charge ÷ $100 = **$3.08**
   APR = **10.5%**

2. Finance charge ÷ $100 = **$11.32**
   APR = **10.5%**

3. Finance charge = (24 × $186) − $4,000 = $4,464 − $4,000 = **$464**
   Finance charge per $100 = $100 × ($464 ÷ $4,000) = **$11.60**
   Row for 24 payments, number closest to $11.60 is $11.58.
   The APR is 10.75%.

Living in the Real World

A Picture-Perfect Loan

Analyze the Story As Chen found out, dreams do have a price tag attached. Depending on whether or not you're willing to save or get a loan, you'll need to contemplate the type of loan to take out. Now that you've read about Chen's situation, answer these questions as they pertain to your life.

Negotiating to Arrive at a Decision What are you willing to take out a loan for?

a. Create a list of expensive items that you might need a loan for in the future. Pick one to pursue.

b. Use the Internet to find out about your item's expense. Find out how much you'd need to spend in order to get it.

c. On a sheet of paper, estimate how long it might take if you took out a loan like Chen was looking at. (See Section 8-4 on page 294.)

d. Discuss with classmates if the item is worth taking out a loan and paying interest on over a number of years.

e. Put together a pro and con list after openly talking with your friends. Make a decision about purchasing the item in the future.

REVIEW OF KEY WORDS

single-payment loan (p. 284)
promissory note (p. 284)
maturity value (p. 284)
term (p. 284)
ordinary interest (p. 284)

exact interest (p. 284)
installment loan (p. 287)
annual percentage rate (p. 290)
down payment (p. 287)
amount financed (p. 287)

simple interest installment loan (p. 290)
repayment schedule (p. 294)
final payment (p. 297)

Determine if the following statements are true or false.

1. A **loan** is money that you have borrowed and must repay. **True**

2. A **single-payment loan** is a loan for which you pay a portion of the loan and a portion of the interest in several installments. **False**

3. The total amount of money you repay is called the **maturity value**. **True**

4. The **term** of the loan is the amount borrowed. **False**

5. **Ordinary interest** is calculated by basing the time on a 365-day year. **False**

6. The **down payment** is a portion of the cash price of the item you are purchasing. **True**

7. The formula for the **amount financed** is the cash price plus the exact interest. **False**

8. For a **simple interest installment loan,** you usually repay the amount financed plus the finance charge in equal monthly payments. **True**

9. The **annual percentage rate** is interest calculated by basing the time of the loan on a 31-day month. **False**

10. A **repayment schedule** shows a plan to distribute interest and principal over the life of the loan. **True**

Study Guide and Assessment ▶ **305**

---

3. Lisa Engels took out a simple interest installment loan for $2,000 at 10 percent interest for 6 months. The monthly payment is $343.20. After 2 payments, the balance is $1,344.22. She pays off the loan when the next payment is due. What is the final payment? **($1,355.42)** How much is saved by paying off the loan early? **$17.38**

Living in the Real World

Analyze the Story
Answers will vary depending on students. Push students to think about bigger ticket items, such as a vehicle loan, higher education, vocational training, and so on.

CHAPTER 8 Study Guide and Assessment

Skills and Concepts

SECTION OBJECTIVE 8-1 AND EXAMPLES

Compute the maturity value and interest rate of a single-payment loan.

Ricardo Lopez's bank granted him a single-payment loan of $3,500 for 80 days at 11 percent ordinary interest. What is the maturity value of the loan?

STEP 1: Find the ordinary interest.

    Principal × Rate × Time

    $3,500 × 11% × $\frac{80}{360}$

    = $85.56

STEP 2: Find the maturity value.

    Principal + Interest Owed

    $3,500 + $85.56

    = **$3,585.56 maturity value**

REVIEW EXERCISES

12. $6,000 × 15.25% × $\frac{60}{365}$ = $150.41; $6,000 + $150.41 = $6,150.41

11. Dee Thomas obtained a single-payment loan of $21,400 to purchase a diamond necklace and bracelet set. She agreed to repay the loan in 120 days at an ordinary interest rate of 8.5 percent. What is the maturity value of her loan? **$22,006.33**

12. Bert Burruezo obtained a single-payment loan from University Bank for $6,000. He agreed to repay the loan in 60 days at an exact interest rate of $15\frac{1}{4}$ percent. What is the maturity value of his loan?

	Principal	Interest Rates Ordinary	Interest Rates Exact	Term	Interest	Maturity Value
13.	$1,540	—	5%	60	a. $12.66	b. $1,552.66
14.	2,500	5%	—	72	a. $25.00	b. $2,525.00

SECTION OBJECTIVE 8-2 AND EXAMPLES

Calculate the amount financed on an installment loan.

Theresa Traurig is buying a new copy machine for $635.88. She made a down payment of 15 percent and will finance the remainder. How much did Traurig finance?

STEP 1: Find the down payment.

    $635.88 × 15%

    = $95.38

STEP 2: Find the amount financed.

    Cash Price − Down Payment

    $635.88 − $95.38

    = **$540.50 financed**

REVIEW EXERCISES

15. Daleen Aragon purchased a DVD player and speaker system for her home. The total cost of her purchases was $587.33. Using the store's credit plan, she made a $147.00 down payment. What amount did she finance? **$587.33 − $147.00 = $440.33**

16. Levi Lemke wants to purchase a car costing $21,000. He will finance the car with an installment loan from the bank, but he would like to finance no more than $14,280. What percent of the total cost of the car should his down payment be?
$21,000 − $14,280 = $6,720
$6,720 ÷ $21,000 = 0.32 = 32%

REINFORCEMENT

Section 8-1

1. Andrea Nguyen borrowed $14,200 to expand her carpentry business. The bank granted her a single-payment loan of $14,200 for 120 days at ordinary interest. The interest rate is 12.75 percent. What is the maturity value of her loan? **$14,803.50**

2. Javier Alvarez borrowed $3,346 for new business equipment. He agreed to repay the loan in 87 days at an exact interest rate of 10.5 percent. What is the maturity value of his loan? **$3,429.74**

Section 8-2

1. Matt Yokohama purchased a fountain for his newly landscaped backyard. The fountain cost $677. He made a down payment of 15 percent. What amount did he finance? **$575.45**

REVIEW EXERCISES (continued)

	Cash Price	Down Payment (Cash)	Down Payment (Percent)	Down Payment (in Dollars)	Amount Financed
17.	$ 789	$300	—	a. $300	b. $489
18.	4,500	—	25%	a. $1,125	b. $3,375

SECTION OBJECTIVE 8-3 AND EXAMPLES

Figure out the monthly payment, total amount repaid, and finance charge on an installment loan.

Andria Berger obtained an installment loan of $2,200 to purchase a fence for her home. The annual percentage rate is 10 percent. She must repay the loan in 24 months. What is the finance charge?

STEP 1: Find the monthly payment. (Refer to the Monthly Payment on a Simple Interest Installment Loan of $100 table on page 799.)

$$\frac{\text{Amount of Loan}}{\$100} \times \frac{\text{Monthly Payment}}{\text{for a }\$100 \text{ loan}}$$

$$\frac{\$2,200.00}{\$100.00} \times \$4.61 = \$101.42$$

STEP 2: Find the total amount repaid.

Number of Payments × Monthly Payment

24 × $101.42 = $2,434.08

STEP 3: Find the finance charge.

Total Amount Repaid − Amount Financed

$2,434.08 − $2,200.00 = **$234.08 finance charge**

19. ($3,500 ÷ 100) × $3.87 = $135.45; 30 × $135.45 = $4,063.50; $4,063.50 − $3,500 = $563.50

20. $2,896 × 20% − $579.20 down payment; $2,896 − $579.20 = $2,316.80 amount financed; ($2,316.80 ÷ 100) × $9.03 = $209.21 monthly payment; 12 × $209.21 = $2,510.52 amount repaid; $2,510.52 − $2,316.80 = $193.72 finance charge

REVIEW EXERCISES

For these problems, you might need to refer to the Monthly Payment on a Simple Interest Installment Loan of $100 table on page 799.

19. James Proctor obtained an installment loan of $3,500 to have some trees removed from his yard. The APR is 12 percent. The loan is to be repaid in 30 months. What is the finance charge?

20. Rick and Annette Evans purchased a new living room set at Allied Furniture Store for $2,896.00. They agreed to make a down payment of 20 percent and finance the remainder for 12 monthly payments. The APR is 15 percent. What is the finance charge?

21. a. $17.06
b. $255.90
c. $1,535.40
d. $35.40
22. a. $17.16
b. $394.68
c. $2,368.08
d. $68.08

	APR	Term (Months)	Table Value	Amount Financed	Monthly Payment	Total Repaid	Finance Charge
21.	8%	6	a.	$1,500	b.	c.	d.
22.	10%	6	a.	2,300	b.	c.	d.

REINFORCEMENT

Section 8-3

1. A new heating and air conditioner will cost the Sangjun family $4,800. They make a down payment of 20 percent and finance the remaining amount. They obtain an installment loan for 36 months at an APR of 14 percent.
   a. What is the down payment? **$960**
   b. What is the amount of the loan? **$3,840**
   c. What are the monthly payments? **$131.33**
   d. What is the finance charge? **$887.88**

Refer to the Monthly Payment on a Simple Interest Installment Loan of $100 table on page 799.

SECTION OBJECTIVE 8-4 AND EXAMPLES

Work out the payment to interest, payment to principal, and the new balance.

Jorge Ortega obtained a loan of $2,800.00 at 8 percent for 1 year. The monthly payment was $243.60. For the first payment, what is the interest? What is the payment to principal? What is the new principal?

STEP 1: Find the interest.

Principal × Rate × Time

$2,800.00 × 8% × $\frac{1}{12}$ = **$18.67 interest**

STEP 2: Find the payment to principal.

Monthly Payment − Interest

$243.60 − $18.67 = **$224.93 payment to principal**

STEP 3: Find the new principal.

Previous Principal − Payment to Principal

$2,800.00 − $224.93 = **$2,575.07 new principal**

REVIEW EXERCISES

	Loan Balance	Interest Rate	Monthly Payment	Amount for Interest	Amount for Principal	New Principal
23.	$3,900	12%	$303.55	a. $39.00	b. $264.55	c. $3,635.45
24.	1,800	15%	249.86	a. $22.50	b. $227.36	c. $1,572.64
25.	1,300	8%	105.43	a. $8.67	b. $96.76	c. $1,203.24
26.	2,600	10%	189.45	a. $21.67	b. $167.78	c. $2,432.22

27. Daniel Orrange obtained an installment loan of $8,500 at 14 percent for 42 months. The balance of the loan after 26 payments is $3,733.55. What is the interest for payment 27?

28. Bill Nanz obtained a loan for porch furniture. The loan is for $2,500 at 12.5 percent. The monthly payment is $118.23. What is the interest for the first payment? What is the payment to principal? What is the new principal?

27. $43.56, found by $3,733.55 × 14% × $\frac{1}{12}$ = $43.558 or $43.56

28. Interest $26.04, found by $2,500 × 12.5% × $\frac{1}{12}$ = $26.0417 or $26.04
Payment to principal $92.19, found by 118.23 − $26.04
New principal $2,407.81, found by $2,500 − $92.19

SECTION OBJECTIVE 8-5 AND EXAMPLES

Compute the final payment when paying off a simple interest installment loan.

You have a 6-month loan of $1,000.00 at 10 percent with a balance of $338.89 after payment 4. What is the final payment if you pay off the loan with payment 5?

STEP 1: Find the previous balance.

= $338.89

REINFORCEMENT

Section 8-4

1. Cathleen Brooks obtained an 18-month loan for $3,200. The interest rate is 15 percent. Her monthly payment is $199.68. The balance of the loan after 6 payments is $2,341.45.
   a. What is the interest for the first payment? **$40.00**
   b. What is the interest for the seventh payment? **$29.27**
   c. How much more goes toward the principal on the seventh payment compared to the first payment? **$10.73**

Section 8-5

1. Raymond Harris took out a simple interest loan of $4,300 at 10 percent for 30 months. His monthly payment is $162.54. After 6 payments the balance is $3,523.75. If he pays off the loan when the next payment is due, what is the final payment? **($3553.11)** How much is saved by paying off the loan early? **$347.85**

STEP 2: Find the interest for the fifth month.

Principal $\times$ Rate $\times$ Time

$338.89 $\times$ 10% $\times$ $\frac{1}{12}$ = $2.82

STEP 3: Find the final payment.

Previous Balance + Current Month's Interest

$338.89   + $2.82   = **$341.71 final payment**

REVIEW EXERCISES

	Interest Rate	Previous Balance	Interest	Final Payment
29.	10%	$3,600.00	a. $30.00	b. $3,630.00
30.	8%	2,400.00	a. $16.00	b. $2,416.00
31.	12%	4,860.80	a. $48.61	b. $4,909.41
32.	18%	2,984.50	a. $44.77	b. $3,029.27

SECTION OBJECTIVE 8-6 AND EXAMPLES

Use a table to find the annual percentage rate of a loan.

Paula Simms obtained an installment loan of $900.00 to purchase a digital camera to use at work. The finance charge is $45.55. She agreed to repay the loan in 6 months. What is the annual percentage rate?

STEP 1: Find the finance charge per $100.

$100 \times \dfrac{\text{Finance Charge}}{\text{Amount Financed}}$

$100 \times \dfrac{\$45.55}{\$900.00}$

$100 \times$ 0.0506   = $5.06

STEP 2: Find the APR. (Refer to the Annual Percentage Rate for Monthly Payment Plans table on pages 794–795.)

In the row for 6 payments, find the number closest to $5.06. It is $5.09. Read the APR at the top of the column. **APR is 17.25 percent.**

REVIEW EXERCISES

For Problems 33–36, refer to the Annual Percentage Rate for Monthly Payment Plans table on pages 794–795.

	Finance Charge	Amount Financed	Finance Charge per $100	Number of Payments	Annual Percentage Rate
33.	$ 45.20	$2,000	a. $2.26	6	b. 7.75%
34.	343.61	3,600	a. $9.54	12	b. 17.25%
35.	399.83	2,500	a. $15.99	18	b. 19.25%
36.	665.03	4,500	a. $14.78	18	b. 18%

REINFORCEMENT

Section 8-5 *(cont'd)*

2. Chanelle Thompson took out a simple interest loan of $2,200 at 15 percent for 6 months. Her monthly payment on the loan is $382.80. After 3 payments the balance is $1,120.72.
   a. What is the interest? **$14.01**
   b. What is the final payment? **$1,134.73**
   c. How much is saved by paying off the loan early? **$13.67**

Section 8-6

1. Brenda Richards obtained an installment loan for $2,125. She agreed to repay the loan in 12 monthly payments of $189. What is the APR? **12.25%**

2. Arthur Tanimoto took out an installment loan for $4,650. He agreed to make 24 monthly payments of $227. What is the APR? **15.75%**

Aligned and verified by

The Princeton Review

Cumulative Test Prep

Test-Taking Tip
On most tests you can get as much credit for correctly answering the easy questions as you do for correctly answering the difficult ones. Answer the easy questions first and then spend time on the more challenging questions.

SECTION ONE: MULTIPLE CHOICE

This section contains six multiple-choice questions. After working each problem, write the letter of the correct answer on your paper.

1. Alma Ying used her bank charge card to purchase a sound system. The system cost $995.99 plus 6 percent sales tax. What was the total purchase price on the sales receipt? **C**

   (A) $59.76   (B) $936.23
   (C) $1,055.75   (D) $1,055.76

2. Find the new balance on the charge account statement. **C**

Previous Balance	Closing Date This Month	Closing Date Last Month
$175.41	November 13, 20--	October 14, 20--

Total Purchases	Payments & Credits	Finance Charge	New Balance	Minimum Payment
$72.59	$50.00	$1.90		—

   (A) $150.92   (B) $154.72
   (C) $199.90   (D) $299.99

3. Tom DuVall obtained a 36-month loan of $4,350 for a used car. The interest rate is 15 percent. His monthly payment is $150.95. What is the payment to principal for the first payment? **B**

   (A) $96.56   (B) $96.57
   (C) $96.65   (D) $96.75

4. Charles Quick's bank granted him a single-payment loan of $3,240 for 100 days at an exact interest rate of 14 percent. What is the maturity value of his loan? **C**

   (A) $124.27   (B) $125.96
   (C) $3,364.27   (D) $3,365.96

5. Valerie Beecher purchased a car for $4,000. She will finance the car with an installment loan from the bank but would like to finance no more than $2,500. What percent of the total cost of the car should her down payment be? **C**

   (A) 25 percent   (B) 35 percent
   (C) 37.5 percent   (D) 40.5 percent

6. Lisa Snow obtained an installment loan of $2,300. The annual percentage rate is 18 percent. She plans to repay the loan in 24 months. (Use the table to find the finance charge.) What is the monthly payment? **B**

	Monthly Payment on a $100 Loan			
Term in Months	Annual Percentage Rate			
	15.00%	16.00%	17.00%	18.00%
6	17.40	17.45	17.50	17.55
12	9.03	9.07	9.12	9.17
18	6.24	6.29	6.33	6.38
24	4.85	4.90	4.94	4.99
30	4.02	4.07	4.11	4.16

   (A) $114.77   (B) $454.48
   (C) $507.63   (D) $2,754.48

7. Interest: $15.40; payment to principal: $121.35; new principal: $1,418.65
8. Interest: $14.41; final payment: $974.89

SECTION TWO: FREE RESPONSE

This section contains four questions for which you will supply short answers. Write your answer on your paper.

7. Rocky Butler obtained a 12-month loan of $1,540.00. The interest rate is 12 percent. His monthly payment is $136.75. For the first payment, what is the interest? What is the payment to principal? What is the new principal?

8. Linda Hartman took out a simple interest loan of $3,600.00 at 18 percent for 12 months. After 9 payments, the balance is $960.48. She pays off the loan when the next payment is due. What is the interest? What is the final payment?

9. Juan Corvez obtained an installment loan of $625.00 to pay for a new stove. The finance charge is $102.44. He agreed

to make 24 payments of $30.31 each. Find the annual percentage rate. (Use this table.)   **15%**

Finance Charge per $100 Financed

Number of Payments	APR 14.50%	14.75%	15.00%
6	$ 4.27	$ 4.35	$ 4.42
12	8.03	8.17	8.31
18	11.87	12.08	12.29
24	15.80	16.08	16.37

10. Jane Tripp had a previous balance of $4,532.66 on an installment loan through her bank. The interest rate is 14 percent. What is the interest for the next payment? What is the final payment if she decides to pay off the loan as she makes this payment?
Interest: $52.88; final payment: $4,585.54

SECTION THREE: OPEN-ENDED

This section contains four open-ended questions. Demonstrate your knowledge by giving a clear, concise solution to each problem. Your score on these problems will depend on how well you do on the following:

- Explain your reasoning.
- Show your understanding of mathematics in an organized manner.
- Use charts, graphs, and diagrams in your explanation.
- Show the solution in more than one way or relate it to other situations.
- Investigate beyond the requirements of the problem.

11. Why should you review your charge account statement when you receive it? What should you look for?

12. Create a sample problem and compute the finance charge using the average-daily-balance method (with no new purchases) and the unpaid-balance

method. Which one is less expensive to the consumer?

13. The use of credit is widespread. Some people use credit cards and take out loans for emergencies only. Others believe credit is necessary for everyday living. Explain your position.

14. Explain how can you use the APR of loans to compare the relative cost of borrowing money.

Mathematics Online

To learn more about loans, visit the *Mathematics with Business Applications* Web site at www.busmath.glencoe.com.

11. **To check for accuracy, check to see if the payments and new purchases are covered.**
12. **Answers will vary.**

Cumulative Test Prep ▶ **311**

13. Credit cards are important today, since most people do not like to carry a lot of cash. However, the pervasive use of credit cards has riddled the nation in debt, causing an increase in personal bankruptcy. The cost of keeping a high balance can be expensive. Generally, answers will vary.

14. APR is a uniform measure of the cost of borrowing money. There are a number of ways that interest rates can be determined. APR is a way to measure interest rates.

National Standards for Business Education

Section Objectives	1. Mathematical Foundations	2. Number Relationships and Operations	3. Patterns, Functions, and Algebra	4. Measurements	5. Statistics and Probability	6. Problem-Solving Applications
9-1 Purchasing a New Vehicle (pp. 314–316) Compute the sticker price of a new vehicle.	X	X				
9-2 Dealer's Cost (pp. 317–319) Calculate the dealer's cost of a new vehicle.	X	X				
9-3 Purchasing a Used Vehicle (pp. 320–322) Figure out the average retail price of a used vehicle.	X	X				
9-4 Vehicle Insurance (pp. 323–326) Use tables to compute the annual premium for vehicle insurance.	X	X				
9-5 Operating and Maintaining a Vehicle (pp. 327–329) Compute the total cost per mile of operating and maintaining a vehicle.	X	X				
9-6 Leasing a Vehicle (pp. 330–332) Calculate the total cost of leasing a vehicle.	X	X				
9-7 Renting a Vehicle (pp. 333–335) Figure out the cost per mile of renting a vehicle.	X	X				

(Source: Reprinted with permission from the National Standards for Business Education, copyright © 2001 by National Business Education Association, 1914 Association Drive, Reston, Virginia 21901-1596)

SCANS Correlation

Foundation Skills

Basic Skills	Reading	Writing	Math	Listening	Speaking	
Thinking Skills	Creative Thinking	Decision Making	Problem Solving	Seeing Things in the Mind's Eye	Knowing How to Learn	Reasoning
Personal Qualities	Responsibility	Self-Esteem	Sociability	Self-Management	Integrity/Honesty	

This chapter's highlighted blocks indicate the chapter's content coverage in the Student Edition and the Teacher Wraparound Edition.

National Council of Teachers of Mathematics Standards

1. Numbers & Operations	2. Algebra	3. Geometry	4. Measurement	5. Data Analysis & Probability	6. Problem Solving	7. Reasoning & Proof	8. Communication	9. Connections	10. Representations
X			X		X		X	X	
X			X		X		X	X	
X			X		X		X	X	
X			X		X		X	X	
X			X		X		X	X	
X			X		X		X	X	
X			X		X		X	X	

SCANS Correlation

Workplace Competencies

Resources	Allocating Time	Allocating Money	Allocating Material and Facility Resources	Allocating Human Resources		
Information	Acquiring and Evaluating Information	Organizing and Maintaining Information	Interpreting and Communicating Information	Using Computers to Process Information		
Interpersonal Skills	Participating as a Member of a Team	Teaching Others	Serving Clients/Customers	Exercising Leadership	Negotiating to Arrive at a Decision	Working with Cultural Diversity
Systems	Understanding Systems	Monitoring and Correcting Performance	Improving and Designing Systems			
Technology	Selecting Technology	Applying Technology to Task	Maintaining and Troubleshooting Technology			

What You'll Learn

In this chapter you'll focus on costs involved in buying, leasing, or renting a vehicle. You'll also investigate costs of running a vehicle, such as insurance and maintenance.

Why It's Important

One of the first major purchases that many people make is a vehicle. This purchase involves many decisions—new versus used, lease versus purchase, payments versus paid-in-full, comprehensive insurance versus collision-only insurance, etc. Determining the cost of operating a vehicle is also an important factor in acquiring one.

Key Word Review
Speaking

Ask teams of five students to take turns on a mock panel. A student from the "audience" reads out loud one of this chapter's key words from the Glossary. A panel member earns a point by repeating in his or her own words the definition.

CHAPTER 9
Vehicle Transportation

What You'll Learn

Section 9-1 Compute the sticker price of a new vehicle.

Section 9-2 Calculate the dealer's cost of a new vehicle.

Section 9-3 Figure out the average retail price of a used vehicle.

Section 9-4 Use tables to compute the annual premium for vehicle insurance.

Section 9-5 Compute the total cost per mile of operating and maintaining a vehicle.

Section 9-6 Calculate the total cost of leasing a vehicle.

Section 9-7 Figure out the cost per mile of renting a vehicle.

When Will You Ever Use This?

There are almost too many choices when it comes to purchasing a vehicle. Learn how to narrow your search by calculating the costs in relation to your budget.

Key Terms to Know

- sticker price
- base price
- options
- destination charge
- dealer's cost
- used-vehicle guides
- liability insurance
- comprehensive insurance
- collision insurance
- deductible clause
- variable costs
- fixed costs
- depreciation
- lease
- rent

Mathematics Online

To learn more about buying and insuring a vehicle, visit the *Mathematics with Business Applications* Web site at www.busmath.glencoe.com.

CLASSROOM RESOURCES

Application and Enrichment
- Teacher Wraparound Edition
- Teacher Resource Binder, Blackline Masters
- Interactive Lesson Planner CD-ROM
- PowerPoint® Presentations CD-ROM

Review and Enforcement
Mathematics Online
www.busmath.glencoe.com
- Teacher Resource Binder, Internet Resources

- Student Activity Workbook
- Student Activity Workbook, Teacher Annotated Edition
- School-to-Home Activity Workbook

Assessment and Evaluation
- Assessment Binder, Reproducible Tests
- Assessment Binder, Alternative Assessment Strategies
- Exam*View*® Pro Test Generator CD-ROM

For the Teacher
- Student Activity Workbook, Teacher Annotated Edition
- Assessment Binder
- Interactive Lesson Planner CD-ROM
- Teacher Resource Binder
- Mathematics Online www.busmath.glencoe.com

For the Student
- Student Activity Workbook
- School-to-Home Activity Workbook

Living in the Real World

Story's Summary

Melita Gomez is the owner and sole employee of an organic farm in western Illinois. Her '73 pickup has taken her a long way in business, but it's time to invest in a new vehicle for hauling her vegetables. Gomez has never owned another vehicle, so her first visit to the dealership is a lesson in base prices, lease options, and test drives. She also pays a visit to an insurance agent friend and learns that insurance costs will be higher with a new truck.

Living in the Real World

A Hard One to Pick

Melita Gomez owns an organic farm in western Illinois. The Good Earth produces tomatoes, squash, green beans, and other vegetables, which Gomez sells to trendy restaurants in Chicago. Each year she also puts a half-acre of land into flowers, which she sells every Thursday at the local Farmer's Market.

Since Gomez's farm is a one-woman operation, she has put a lot of miles on her '73 Ford pickup. While business is good, her truck isn't. It's time for a new one. In this chapter you'll read more about Gomez's truck shopping venture.

313

Did You Know...

Most states have laws in place that protect consumers from buying newly manufactured automobiles with defects that can't be corrected despite numerous attempts by the car dealer or manufacturer. These types of cars are called "lemons," and lemon laws provide consumers with the right to have the manufacturer either replace or buy back defective automobiles.

Think about This

Why would it be important to conduct research about automobile loans before visiting the car dealership?

LOCAL STANDARDS

National Standards for Business Education

Standard 1	Mathematical Foundations
Standard 2	Number Relationships and Operations

National Council of Teachers of Mathematics Standards

Standard 1	Numbers and Operations
Standard 4	Measurement
Standard 6	Problem Solving
Standard 8	Communication
Standard 9	Connections

1 FOCUS

In-Class Examples

Work through these exercises with students before having them do the Self-Check.

1. $7,400 + $919 + $80 + $150 **$8,549**
2. $8,500 + $3,070 + $440 + $148 **$12,158**
3. $12,450 + $2,196 + $319 + $297 **$15,262**
4. $5\% \times $12,400 **$620**
5. $6\frac{1}{2}\% \times $18,360 **$1193.40**

2 TEACH

Have students name other features that can be considered as standard equipment. Point out that some items of standard equipment may vary from model to model. Have students name other features that are considered optional. Advertisements found in newspapers or magazines may be helpful.

SECTION 9-1 Purchasing a New Vehicle

○ **Section Objective**

Compute the sticker price of a new vehicle.

Vehicle manufacturers are required by law to place a **sticker price** on a new vehicle's window. What's included in the sticker price?

- **Base price.** This is the price of the engine, chassis (that is, the vehicle's frame), and any other piece of standard equipment for a particular model.
- **Options.** These are extras for convenience, safety, or appearance, such as a sunroof, air-conditioning, and tinted glass.
- **Destination charge.** This is the cost of shipping the vehicle from the factory to the dealer.

Therefore, the sticker price is the total of the base price, options, and destination charge.

Sticker Price = Base Price + Options + Destination Charge

Living in the Real World

A Hard One to Pick

You've Got Options When Gomez was in high school, she bought a used truck from a friend. It's the same truck she's using now. Since Gomez has never owned another vehicle, she's never paid much attention to the sticker prices for new cars or trucks. Today she is shopping for her new vehicle at Tucker Motors. As she walks around the dealership, she reads the sticker information taped to each car's back window. She notices two different prices on the sticker—base and optional.

Draw Conclusions What do you think is included in the base price?

Continued on page 317

Example 1

Scott Huber is shopping for a sports car. A portion of the sticker for a convertible is shown below. What is the sticker price for this vehicle?

Figure 9.1

Convertible Vehicle	
Base Price	$23,140
Optional Equipment Description	
Anti-Lock Brakes (ABS)	730
Automatic Transmission (ATO)	815
Destination Charge	499

Living in the Real World

The base price is the cost of the truck without options. This means the truck will have only the basics of standard equipment, but no extras, such as air conditioning, power steering, CD player, etc.

Need Help? Go to...
➤ Workshop 4: Adding Decimals, page 10
➤ Skill 5: Adding Decimals, page 732

STEP 1: Find the options price.
$730 + $815 = $1,545

STEP 2: Find the sticker price.

Base Price + Options + Destination Charge

$23,140 + $1,545 + $499 = $25,184 sticker price

730 + 815 = 1545 M+ 23140 + RM

1545 + 499 = 25184

Ask your local auto dealer for a window sticker for classroom use. Point out that if a new car is ordered, you have a choice as to the optional equipment, not just what is listed on the sticker. Point out that the destination charge is not taxed in some states.

CONCEPT CHECK

SELF-CHECK ✓

Complete the problems, then check your answers at the end of this chapter. Find the sticker price.

	Model	Base Price	Options	Destination Charge
1.	Four-door vehicle	$11,080	$340; $800; $925	$499
2.	Two-door truck	13,655	1,220; 650	749

1. $11,080 + ($340 + $800 + $925) + $499 = $13,644
2. $13,655 + ($1,220 + $650) + $749 = $16,274

Example 2

Carlos and Marta Alvarez are shopping for a new family vehicle. They are pricing a minivan with all-wheel drive. The base price is listed at $25,535. The options are the touch-screen DVD navigation system at $1,225, a heavy duty engine cooling system at $154, trailer tow package at $568, and a keyless entry system at $132. The destination charge is $349. What is the sticker price?

STEP: Find the sticker price.

Base Price + Options + Destination Charge

$25,535 + $1,225 + $154 + $568 + $132 + $349
= $27,963 sticker price

CONCEPT CHECK

SELF-CHECK ✓

Complete the problems, then check your answers at the end of this chapter. Find the sticker price.

3. Cargo van
Base price: $22,245
Options:
  4.6L EFI V8 $1,186
  Speed control: $204
  Trailer towing package: $336
Destination charge: $715
$22,245 + ($1,186 + $204 + $336) + $715 = $24,686

4. Sports coupe
Base price: $16,725
Options:
  4-speed elect. trans: $860
  Leather trim: $710
  AM/FM w/CD player: $220
Destination charge: $465
$16,725 + ($860 + $710 + $220) + $465 = $18,980

Section 9-1 Purchasing a New Vehicle ▶ **315**

Motivating the Lesson
You took a new SUV for a test drive and want to buy it. The sticker price on this vehicle is $23,055. You would like to upgrade the sound system, which is an additional $510. The destination charge is $625 and is not optional. What is the total sticker price if you add the upgraded sound system? **$24,190**

In-Class Examples
1. Hatchback base price is $19,750. Options: automatic transmission $864, sports luxury package $1,435, sound system package $287, destination charge is $550. What is the sticker price? **$22,886**

2. Front Wheel Drive vehicle, base price is $18,755. Options: automatic transmission $759, radio/compact disc player $92, power moon roof $547, airbags $322, destination charge is $590. What is the sticker price? **$21,065**

COOPERATIVE LEARNING

Is it Fair?
Insurance companies rely on the laws of probability. These laws enable an insurance mathematician, called an actuary, to determine the likelihood that an event will actually take place. Teenagers pay more than other age groups for vehicle insurance. Teenage boys usually pay more than teenage girls. Why do you think this is the case? Is it fair? Groups of students find out about actuarial figures and create a poster display of their findings.

PROBLEM SOLVING

Visit a Dealership
Students visit a dealership, go online, or research a vehicle issue of *Consumer Reports* to find the cost of various new vehicles, options, and destination charges. Students check that the sticker price equals the base price plus options plus destination charge. Students also list other types of information available on new vehicles, such as types of safety features and performance ratings.

LS , CL

 **ASSESS**

Error Analysis

If students are making errors, have them check that they've aligned the numbers correctly in vertical columns before they add. Then, have them review their addition for computational errors. Also, remind them to check that they have totaled all the options, as well as the destination charge, when computing the sticker price.

4 CLOSE

Closing Activity

1. $38,306 + $380 + $715 + $565 **$39,966**
2. $15,342 + $1,225 + $319 + $90 **$16,976**
3. Base Price is $17,745. Options: cruise control costs $217, electronic four-speed automatic transmission $747, destination charge $610. What is the sticker price? **$19,319**
4. A coupe has a base price of $16,725. Two-tone leather seat trim is available for $710. The anti-lock brake system costs an additional $495. The destination charge is $465. What is the sticker price if both options are purchased? **$18,395**
5. Bill Landry is pricing an SUV with a base price of $36,728. A second row of bucket seats is an option that costs $431. The digital communication system costs $612. A rear door system is available for $220. A trailer package costs $229. The destination charge is $790. Find the sticker price if Landry buys the SUV with these four options. **$39,010**

SECTION 9-1 PRACTICE

Find the sticker price.

	Base Price	Options	Destination Charge	Sticker Price
5.	$ 9,000	$1,600	$400	$11,000.00
6.	9,900	2,400	350	$12,650.00
7.	21,540	1,260	345	$23,145.00
8.	32,654	2,865	338	$35,857.00
9.	49,842	3,861	425	$54,128.00

10. Sedan.
    Base price is $13,868.
    Options:
    Anti-lock brakes for $550.
    Automatic transmission for $815.
    Air conditioning for $575.
    Tinted glass for $195.
    Destination charge is $345.
    What is the sticker price? **$16,348.00**

11. Sports car.
    Base price is $17,495.
    Options:
    Anti-lock brakes for $500.
    Automatic transmission for $995.
    Destination charge is $400.
    What is the sticker price?
    $19,390.00

12. Dalton Slade is interested in a sports utility vehicle that has a base price of $31,145. Factory-installed options total $1,245. The destination charge from its assembly plant in River Rouge, Michigan, is $352. What is the sticker price for this car? **$32,742.00**

13. Andy Dunn sees a small pickup that he is interested in buying. There is a 5 percent state sales tax on the purchase of the truck. If Dunn pays the sticker price of $16,069, how much sales tax must he pay? **$803.45**

MAINTAINING YOUR SKILLS

Need Help? Go to...
➤ **Skill 5: Adding Decimals,** page 732

Add.

14. 8,850 + 995 + 660 + 242 **10,747**

15. 6,770 + 1,217 + 648 + 344 + 85 **9,064**

16. 19,453 + 2,540 + 199 + 60 **22,252**

17. 9,851 + 2,889 + 401 + 75 + 90 **13,306**

18. 15,237 + 78.50 + 421.60 + 92 **15,829**

19. 7,575.20 + 1,243.26 + 791.24 **9,609.70**

WRAP-UP

Go over any problem for which a wrong answer is given.

Assignment Guide
Basic: 5–9
Average: 10–11

20 min.

SECTION 9·2 Dealer's Cost

○ **Section Objective**
Calculate the dealer's cost of a new vehicle.

Vehicle dealers pay less than the sticker price for both the basic vehicle and the options. Consumer magazines often report the **dealer's cost** as a percent of the sticker price. You may save money when purchasing a new vehicle by making an offer that is higher than the estimated dealer's cost but lower than the sticker price. Keep this in mind as you work through this section:

Important Questions	What Formulas Do I Use?
How do I find the **dealer's cost**?	Percent of Base Price Percent of Options Price + Destination Charge ————————— Dealer's Cost
How do I find the **percent of the base price**?	Base Price × Percent of Dealer's Cost on Base Price ————————— Percent of the Base Price
How do I find the **percent of the options price**?	Total Price of Options × Percent of Dealer's Cost on Options ————————— Percent of the Options Price

Living in the Real World

A Hard One to Pick

It Pays to Do Your Homework As a sharp businesswoman, Gomez knows that well-informed customers usually strike the best deals. Even before coming to Tucker's, she researched the dealer's cost for several truck models. She found these figures in consumer magazines and on Web sites. These sources list dealer's costs as a percent of the sticker price.

Draw Conclusions Once Gomez has the dealer's costs, what can she figure out?

Continued on page 320

Example 1

Chin and Lisa Weng want to purchase a new car. The car has a base price of $12,905, options totaling $2,010, and a destination charge of $360. They read in a consumer magazine that the dealer's cost for the car is about 95 percent of the base price and 89 percent of the options price. What should they estimate as the dealer's cost?

Continued on next page

Section 9-2 Dealer's Cost ▶ **317**

Living in the Real World

She can compare the dealer's cost to the sticker price and determine how much the dealer paid for the vehicle. Using subtraction, she can figure out the dealer's profit, which helps her conclude how much he might be willing to negotiate on cost.

National Standards for Business Education

Standard 1	Mathematical Foundations
Standard 2	Number Relationships and Operations

National Council of Teachers of Mathematics Standards

Standard 1	Numbers and Operations
Standard 4	Measurement
Standard 6	Problem Solving
Standard 8	Communication
Standard 9	Connections

1 FOCUS

Ask students if they've ever accompanied anyone to buy a new car. Did the buyer offer less than the sticker price? Dealers may sometimes be willing to accept an offer less than the sticker price, because they paid less to the manufacturer for the car.

In-Class Examples
Work through these exercises with students before having them do the Self-Check.
1. 90% × $12,000 **$10,800**
2. 85% × $15,000 **$12,750**
3. 81% × $17,780 **$14,401.80**
4. 72% × $28,900 **$20,808**
5. ($28,515 × 83%) + ($2,416 × 80%) + $655 **$26,255.25**

② TEACH

The amount of markup on a car will differ from dealer to dealer. The sticker price is a suggested starting price in negotiating a final selling price that is acceptable to both the dealer and the customer.

Point out that the percent used for options and the percent used for the base price can be different. These figures can be found in consumer magazines. Have students notice that there was no markup on the destination charge. This part of the price is not negotiable.

Motivating the Lesson

A convertible has a base price of $24,080 and options that total $1,645. The destination charge is $520. The dealer's cost includes 100 percent of the destination charge, about 92 percent of the base price, and 85 percent of the options. What is the dealer's estimated cost for this car? **$24,071.85**

In-Class Examples

1. Base price is $15,840. Options total $1,910. Destination charge is $515. Dealer pays 94 percent of base price and 89 percent of options. What is the dealer's cost? **$17,104.50**

2. Luxury sports car. Base price is $33,200. Options total $5,225. Destination charge is $645. Dealer pays 90 percent of base price and 89 percent of options. What is the dealer's cost? **$35,175.25**

3. Full-size pickup. Base price is $24,550. Options total $4,820. Destination charge is $740. Dealer pays about 89 percent of base price and 88 percent of options. What is the dealer's cost? **$26,831.10**

Need Help? Go to...
▶ Workshop 14:
  Finding a
  Percentage,
  page 30
▶ Skill 30:
  Finding the
  Percentage,
  page 757

STEP 1: Find the percent of base price.
$12,905.00 × 95% = $12,259.75

STEP 2: Find the percent of options price.
$2,010.00 × 89% = $1,788.90

STEP 3: Find the dealer's cost.

Percent of Base Price	+	Percent of Options Price	+	Destination Charge
$12,259.75	+	$1,788.90	+	$360.00

= **$14,408.65 dealer's cost**

12905 ⊠ 95 ％ 12259.75 M+ 2010 ⊠ 89 ％ 1788.9
M+ RM 14048.65 + 360 = 14408.65

CONCEPT CHECK

SELF-CHECK✔

Complete the problems, then check your answers at the end of this chapter.

1. The dealer's cost on a sport utility vehicle (SUV) is 88 percent of the base price of $53,105, 90 percent of the options price of $1,785, plus a destination charge of $340. Find the dealer's cost for the SUV.
($53,105 × 88%) + ($1,785 × 90%) + $340 = $48,678.90

Example 2

The truck sticker shows a base price of $41,036.00, with options totaling $2,425.00 and a destination charge of $450. *Consumer Reports* shows the dealer cost as 87.7 percent of the base price and 90.2 percent of the options. What is the dealer's cost?

STEP 1: Find the percent of base price.
$41,036.00 × 87.7% = $35,988.57

STEP 2: Find the percent of options price.
$2,425.00 × 90.2% = $2,187.35

STEP 3: Find the dealer's cost.

Percent of Base Price	+	Percent of Options Price	+	Destination Charge
$35,988.57	+	$2,187.35	+	$450.00

= **$38,625.92 dealer's cost**

CONCEPT CHECK

SELF-CHECK✔

Complete the problem, then check your answer at the end of this chapter.

2. The truck shows a base price of $23,855, with options totaling $2,256 and a destination charge of $610. The dealer's cost is 90.5 percent of the base price and 87 percent of the options. What is the dealer's cost?
($23,855 × 90.5%) + ($2,256 × 87%) + $610 = $24,161.50

ALTERNATIVE ASSESSMENT

Students with Behavior Disorders

Students with behavior disorders of any type require a class environment with support and structure. For example, a visual learner will benefit from having material presented photographs or graphics. Using computer software engages students when they are required to give a written response to an activity. Allow students who act out in class spend time on the computer to build their enthusiasm in completing assignments.

SECTION 9-2 PRACTICE

$\left(\begin{matrix}\text{Base} \\ \text{Price}\end{matrix}\right.$	$\times$	$\left.\begin{matrix}\text{Dealer's} \\ \text{Percent}\end{matrix}\right)$	$+$	$\left(\begin{matrix}\text{Option} \\ \text{Price}\end{matrix}\right.$	$\times$	$\left.\begin{matrix}\text{Dealer's} \\ \text{Percent}\end{matrix}\right)$	$+$	$\begin{matrix}\text{Destination} \\ \text{Charge}\end{matrix}$	$=$	$\begin{matrix}\text{Dealer's} \\ \text{Cost}\end{matrix}$
3. ($8,000	$\times$	80%)	+	($2,200	$\times$	75%)	+	$360	=	**$8,410**
4. ($17,000	$\times$	85%)	+	($3,400	$\times$	80%)	+	$342	=	**$17,512**
5. ($14,300	$\times$	82%)	+	($1,200	$\times$	78%)	+	$465	=	**$13,127**

6. Station wagon.
Base price is $37,125.
Options total is $1,075.
Destination charge is $870.
Dealer pays 93 percent of the
base price and 96 percent of
the options price.
What is the dealer's cost? **$36,428.25**

7. Sedan.
Base price is $29,375.
Options total is $1,200.
Destination charge is $350.
Dealer pays 91.7 percent of the
base price and 83.3 percent of
the options price.
What is the dealer's cost? **$28,286.48**

8. Paul Dempsey is looking at a new sedan that has a base price of $22,680,
options totaling $1,495, and a destination charge of $380. The dealer's cost is
about 92.5 percent of the base price and 88.3 percent of the options price.
What is the sticker price of the car? What should Dempsey estimate as the
dealer's cost? **$22,679.09**

9. Poloma Sokanon is considering the purchase of a large sports utility vehicle.
She sees one with a base price of $35,988 and options totaling $1,275. The
destination charge is $435. She estimates that the dealer's cost is 88 percent
of the base price and 80 percent of the options price. If Sokanon offers the
dealer $250 above the estimated dealer's cost, what is her offer? **$33,374.44**

10. Julia Brown offered an automobile dealer $150 over the estimated dealer's
cost on a car that has a base price of $24,495 and options totaling $600. The
dealer's cost is about 89.7 percent of the base price and 81 percent of the
price of the options. The destination charge is $720. What was her offer?
$23,328.02

11. Evander Harris is ordering a luxury coupe convertible built to his
specifications. The base price is $81,975 and options total $2,180. There
is a destination charge of $890. The dealer's cost is about 90 percent of
the base price and 88 percent of the options price. The dealer will sell
him the car for $200 more than the estimated dealer's cost plus a 6 percent
sales tax. What is the total cost of the car? **$81,393.05**

MAINTAINING YOUR SKILLS

Need Help? Go to...
→ Skill 30: Finding
the Percentage,
page 757

Find the percentage.

12. 8% of 700 **56**

13. 15% of 980 **147**

14. 22% of 756 **166.32**

15. 24% of 1,520 **364.8**

16. 45% of 9,800 **4,410**

17. 78% of 3,440 **2,683.2**

(3) ASSESS

Error Analysis
The types of errors students make
when finding the percent of a
number are either computational
(i.e., they multiply incorrectly)
or they result from putting the
decimal point in the wrong place
in the answer. Both types of errors
are easy to identify and correct. If
errors in addition are occurring,
remind students to check that they
have vertically aligned numbers
correctly before adding.

(4) CLOSE

Closing Activity

1. ($37,419 × 89%) +
($2,946 × 85%) + $715
$36,522.01

2. ($15,294 × 93%) + ($830 ×
90%) + $595 **$15,565.42**

3. A minivan's base price is
$19,575. The options total
$3,130. It has a destination
charge of $665. If the dealer
pays an estimated 94 percent
of the base price and 88 percent of the options, what is
the dealer's estimated cost?
$21,819.90

4. A luxury car has a base price
of $45,240. The options total
$1,900. The destination charge
is $770. If the dealer pays
about 91.75 percent of the
base price and 87 percent of
the options, what is the
dealer's cost? **$43,930.70**

WRAP-UP

Go over any problem for which a wrong
answer is given.

Assignment Guide
  Basic: 3–5
  Average: 6–7

20 min.

National Standards for Business Education

| Standard 1 | Mathematical Foundations |
| Standard 2 | Number Relationships and Operations |

National Council of Teachers of Mathematics Standards

Standard 1	Numbers and Operations
Standard 4	Measurement
Standard 6	Problem Solving
Standard 8	Communication
Standard 9	Connections

① FOCUS

Many students may have had experience shopping for, owning, or selling a used vehicle. Ask students to share their experiences of trying to find a price agreeable to both the buyer and the seller.

In-Class Examples
Work through these exercises with students before having them do the Self-Check.
1. $4,000 + $500 + $50 − $200 **$4,350**
2. $8,000 + $250 + $475 − $125 **$8,600**
3. $9,500 + $75 + $25 − $100 **$9,500**
4. $1,250 + $125 + $75 − $75 − $75 **$1,300**
5. $13,700 + $475 + $125 + $300 − $295 **$14,305**

SECTION 9-3 Purchasing a Used Vehicle

○ Section Objective

Figure out the average retail price of a used vehicle.

Vehicle dealers usually advertise used vehicles for prices that are higher than what they expect you to pay. **Used-vehicle guides** published monthly by the National Automobile Dealers Association (NADA) or Vehicle Market Research (VMR) give the average prices for vehicles that were purchased from dealers during the previous month. The information can help you make decisions about how much to pay for a used vehicle. Remember to ask yourself this question:

Important Question	What Formula Do I Use?
How do I find the **average retail price** of a used car?	Average Retail Value + Additional Options − Options Deductions − Mileage Deduction ‾‾‾‾‾‾‾‾‾‾‾‾‾ Average Retail Price

Living in the Real World

A Hard One to Pick

Do Yourself a Favor: Be Smart about It Like any good consumer, Gomez did a lot of research before going to the car dealership. For information about used trucks, she read used-vehicle guides published by the National Automobile Dealers Association (NADA) and Vehicle Market Research (VMR).

Draw Conclusions Why is it smart to do research on a car before buying the first one you see?

Continued on page 324

Example 1

Jackie Morris would like to purchase a used Palamino V8 four-door car, which is advertised for $15,450. It has no air conditioning. It has power seats, premium sound system, leather seats, and a power sunroof. It has been driven 51,760 miles. The used-vehicle guide indicates that $575 should be subtracted if the mileage is from 45,001 to 52,500 miles. What average retail price should Morris keep in mind when she makes an offer for the vehicle?

Living in the Real World

Knowledge is power. Research can help a consumer understand how well a car is made, any problems other owners have had with the same model, and the fairest possible purchase price.

GLOBAL PERSPECTIVE

Pros and Cons
Many cars are manufactured in countries overseas. Some have a higher gas mileage, so are considered more economical. Some "wear well" and keep their value better. The price and availability of repair parts may make these cars more costly to repair and insure. When you buy a vehicle, will it be a foreign or domestic car? Consider the pros and cons of domestic vehicles and foreign vehicles. Students create a chart listing the pros and cons. LS , CL , P

Figure 9.2

Palamino Four-Year-Old Vehicles	Average Retail Value	Average Wholesale Value
V6 Four-Door	$13,050	$11,090
V8 Four-Door	14,675	11,740
V8 Sport	15,000	12,000
Deduct w/o Air-Conditioning	800	675
Add Power Seats	125	100
Add Premium Sound System	200	175
Add Leather Seats	340	300
Add Sunroof—Manual	225	200
Add Sunroof—Power	450	375
Add Aluminum Wheels	125	100

SECTION 9-3

2 TEACH

Make sure students understand the differences between *average wholesale value* and *average retail value* in the table. The average wholesale value is based on the trade-in value of hundreds of cars of that particular model. Point out that the average wholesale value is always less than the average retail. Have students explain why this is so. **(Emphasize that having certain optional features adds to the value of the car, while not having others subtracts from the value.)**

If possible, bring to class one of the used vehicle guides, such as the N.A.D.A., and show students how to use it. Point out the low mileage and high mileage tables that are used to adjust the price of a vehicle. Explain that each vehicle is given a mileage classification from I–IV. At the beginning of each manufacturer's list, a classification is given for each model of vehicle. Remind students to find the exact year, make, model and style of vehicle they are pricing. Note how prices change with different styles and options.

In-Class Example
1. Sedan. Average retail value is $22,475. Add $350 for aluminum/alloy wheels. Add $700 for power sunroof. Add $500 for leather seats. Deduct $675 for manual transmission. What is the average retail price? **$23,350**

Need Help? Go to...
- Workshop 4: Adding Decimals, page 10
- Workshop 5: Subtracting Decimals, page 12
- Skill 5: Adding Decimals, page 732
- Skill 6: Subtracting Decimals, page 733
- Application C: Tables and Charts, page 762

STEP: Find the average retail price.

$$\underset{\text{Retail Value}}{\text{Average}} + \text{Additional Options} - \underset{\text{Deductions}}{\text{Options}} - \underset{\text{Deductions}}{\text{Mileage}}$$

$$\$14,675 + (\$125 + 200 + 340 + 450) - \$800 - \$575$$
$$\$14,675 + \$1,115 - \$800 - \$575$$
$$= \$14,415 \text{ average retail value}$$

125 + 200 + 340 + 450 M+ 1115

14675 + RM 1115 − 800 − 575 = 14415

CONCEPT CHECK

SELF-CHECK✓

Complete the problem, then check your answer at the end of this chapter.

1. Using **Figure 9.2,** find the average retail price for a four-year old V6 four-door vehicle that has air conditioning, power seats, leather seats, manual sunroof, and aluminium wheels. It has been driven only 36,500 miles. The used-vehicle guide indicates that $525 should be added if the mileage is from 30,001 to 37,500 miles. What is the average retail price for this vehicle?
$13,050 + ($125 + $340 + $225 + $125) + $525 = $14,390

Example 2

Using Figure 9.2, find the average wholesale price for a four-year-old V8 Sport that has no air conditioning, but does have the premium sound system and a power sunroof. It has 63,580 miles. The used-vehicle guide indicates that $1,400 should be deducted if the mileage is from 60,001 to 67,500 miles. What is the average wholesale price for this vehicle?

STEP: Find the average wholesale price.

$$\underset{\text{Retail Value}}{\text{Average}} + \underset{\text{Options}}{\text{Additional}} - \underset{\text{Deductions}}{\text{Options}} - \underset{\text{Deductions}}{\text{Mileage}}$$

$$\$12,000 + (\$175 + 375) - \$675 - \$1,400$$
$$= \$12,000 + \$550 - \$675 - \$1,400$$
$$= \$10,475 \text{ average wholesale price}$$

Section 9-3 Purchasing a Used Vehicle ▶ **321**

RETEACH / ENRICHMENT

Odometer Reading

Mileage traveled, or the odometer reading, affects a car's value. When you buy a used car, the seller is required by law to provide you with an odometer disclosure statement. How the odometer reading affects a car's value is shown in the "bluebook" guide. Students graph the effect of mileage on the value of a used car. **LS** , **P**

3 ASSESS

Error Analysis

If students are making errors, remind them that when they compute the average retail price of a vehicle, they must consider two things: the cost of options that increase a car's value and the cost of options that are missing, which decrease the value of the vehicle.

Have students group all the options that increase the car's value in one column and total them. Then, add the total to the average retail price for the base vehicle. Next, have them group the options that decrease the vehicle's value, including possible adjustments for mileage, in another column and total them. Now, subtract this amount from the previous total. This is the average retail price of the vehicle.

4 CLOSE

Closing Activity

1. $8,900 + $550 +$250 + $100
   $9,800

2. $14,500 − $200 − $150
   $14,150

3. Sport truck with miles 42,306 driven on it. Average retail value is $19,600. Add $275 for 7/8 passenger seating. Add $375 for rear air conditioning. Deduct $225 for mileage 40,001 to 45,000. What is the average retail value? **$20,025**

4. Sport truck with 57,309 miles driven on it. Average retail price is $13,100. Add $650 for trim. Add $200 for stereo system. Add $150 for power seat. Add $550 for power sunroof. Deduct $150 without cruise control. Deduct $100 without tilt wheel. Deduct $425 for mileage 55,001 to 60,000. What is the average retail value? **$13,975**

SELF-CHECK ✓

3. a. Average retail value: **$13,050**
   b. Average retail price: **$13,700**
4. a. Average retail value: **$15,000**
   b. Average retail price: **$14,790**
5. a. Average retail value: **$14,675**
   b. Average retail price: **$15,465**

CONCEPT CHECK

Complete the problem, then check your answer at the end of this chapter.

2. Use Figure 9.2 to find the average wholesale price for a used V8 Sport, with air conditioning, power seats, leather seats, power sunroof, and aluminium wheels. It has 65,500 miles so you must deduct $1,400 for excessive mileage.
   $12,000 + ($100 + $300 + $375 + $100) − $1,400 = $11,475

SECTION 9-3 PRACTICE

Use Figure 9.2 on page 321 to find the average retail price. All the vehicles have from 37,501 to 45,000 miles for which there is zero adjustment.

	Model	Average Retail Value	A/C	Power Seats	Premium Sound System	Leather Seats	Power Sunroof	Aluminum Wheels	Retail Price
3.	V6 4-dr	a.	Yes	No	Yes	No	Yes	No	b.
4.	V8 Sport	a.	No	Yes	No	Yes	No	Yes	b.
5.	V8 4-dr	a.	Yes	Yes	Yes	Yes	No	Yes	b.

6. Three-year-old hatchback. Average retail value is $16,750. Add $175 for tilt steering wheel. Add $800 for air-conditioning. Deduct $550 for manual transmission. Deduct $450 for excessive mileage. What is the average retail price?
   $16,725

7. One-year-old sedan. Average retail value is $19,100. Add $200 for CD player. Deduct $800 for no air-conditioning. Deduct $525 for excessive mileage. What is the average retail price?
   $17,975

8. Sue Soto owns a used four-door sedan that she wants to sell so she can purchase a new vehicle. One used-vehicle guide shows that the average retail value for it is $3,900. She adds $50 for having a vinyl top, $125 for a cassette player, $25 for power windows, and $25 for power locks. Soto deducts $175 for having no air-conditioning. She adds $450 for having less than the expected mileage. What is the average retail price for her vehicle? **$4,400**

9. Use Figure 9.2 on page 321 for Kordell Bryant who owns a four-year-old Palamino V6 four-door. The four-door has power leather seats, premium sound system, manual sunroof, aluminum wheels, and no air conditioning. There are 26,540 miles on Bryant's vehicle, which means it falls in the 22,501 to 30,000 category and calls for a deduction of $450. What is the average retail price for Bryant's vehicle? **$12,690**

MAINTAINING YOUR SKILLS

Need Help? Go to...
➤ Skill 3: Adding Whole Numbers, page 730
➤ Skill 4: Subtracting Whole Numbers, page 731

Add.

10. 4,225 + 1,200 + 375 + 245   **6,045**

11. 4,060 + 225 + 3,950 + 325 + 75   **8,635**

Subtract.

12. 8,450 − 475 **7,975**   13. 3,890 − 2,530 **1,360**   14. 2,205 − 225 **1,980**

WRAP-UP

Go over any problem for which a wrong answer is given.

Assignment Guide
Basic: 3–5
Average: 6–7

20 min.

SECTION 9-4 Vehicle Insurance

○ Section Objective

Use tables to compute the annual premium for vehicle insurance.

If your vehicle is involved in an accident, it can cause bodily injury and property damage. For this reason, you need to have **liability insurance.** Your insurance company might offer bodily injury limits of 25/100. What does 25/100 mean?

| The insurance company will pay up to **$25,000** to any *one* person injured. | → 25/100 ← | The insurance company pays up to **$100,000** if *more than one* person is injured. |

Besides liability insurance on your vehicle, you'll also need to consider:

- **Comprehensive insurance.** This protects you from losses due to fire, vandalism, theft, and so on.
- **Collision insurance.** This pays to repair your vehicle if it's in an accident.

Each kind of insurance may have a **deductible clause.** This is the amount you're required to pay for any repair bill. For example, if your insurance policy states that you have a $50-deductible clause, then this means that you pay the first $50 of the repair bill. If your total repair bill is, say, $400, you have to pay only $50 and the insurance company pays the remaining amount (or $350 in this example).

So how much is your vehicle insurance going to cost you a year? This is determined by the annual *base premium*. This involves three factors:

- the amount of insurance you want,
- how old your vehicle is, and
- the insurance-rating group, (which depends on the size and value of your vehicle).

The *annual premium* is the amount you pay each year for insurance coverage. Your annual premium depends on the:

- annual base premium. (This depends on the amount of coverage you want.)
- driver-rating factor. (This depends on your age, marital status, the amount you drive each week, and so on.)

If several people drive your vehicle, the highest driver-rating factor among those who drive your vehicle is used to determine the annual premium. Insurance companies use tables to determine your base premium. Here's how to remember all of this:

Important Questions	What Formulas Do I Use?
How do I find the **annual base premium?**	Liability Premium Comprehensive Premium + Collision Premium —————————— Annual Base Premium
How do I calculate the **annual premium?**	Annual Base Premium × Driver-Rating Factor —————————— Annual Premium

▶ FYI

The federal government has estimated that driver distraction, which includes eating, dialing radio buttons, and talking, causes 20 to 30 percent of all accidents.

▶▶▶

Living in the Real World

Older car models don't need collision insurance, as they're no longer worth enough money to warrant the extra cost of paying for the coverage. Collision insurance is always needed with a new vehicle.

COMMUNICATION SKILLS

Used Cars

A very practical out-of-class project is when students investigate and report on the various used-car guides. Some are available online, and several different guides are carried in bookstores. Most auto dealers use the "bluebook" published by the National Automobile Dealers Association. Specifically, students determine the value of various cars owned by family and friends. **LS**

National Standards for Business Education

Standard 1	Mathematical Foundations
Standard 2	Number Relationships and Operations

National Council of Teachers of Mathematics Standards

Standard 1	Numbers and Operations
Standard 4	Measurement
Standard 6	Problem Solving
Standard 8	Communication
Standard 9	Connections

1 FOCUS

The focus of this section is to use tables to compute the annual premium for vehicle insurance. In many states, it is against the law to drive a car without auto insurance. This is an additional cost that needs to be considered when purchasing a vehicle.

In-Class Examples

Work through these exercises with students before having them do the Self-Check.

1. $180 × 1.20 **$216**
2. $70.00 × 3.10 **$217**
3. ($140 + $64) × 4.10 **$836.40**
4. ($180.00 + $90.20) × 2.90 **$783.58**
5. ($232.00 + $126.00 + $84.00) × 3.1 **$1,370.20**

② TEACH

Define the key words: *liability, bodily injury, property damage, comprehensive,* and *collision insurance.* Point out that many states require liability insurance, but make comprehensive insurance optional. An older car may not be worth enough to have comprehensive coverage. If you have a loan on a car, the bank often requires full coverage for the term of the loan to safeguard its money in case of damage or loss to the car.

Annual premiums also can be paid semiannually, quarterly, or monthly. There is sometimes a small handling fee charged if the payments are made quarterly or monthly. Point out that a prior driving record can also affect a person's insurance rating group.

Motivating the Lesson

Congratulations! You just bought your first vehicle, but before you can drive it, you need to purchase vehicle insurance. Your insurance agent recommends a policy that has an annual base premium of $692. Based on your gender, age, and marital status, your driver-rating factor is 2.9. Your agent explains that you multiply your annual base premium ($692) × your driver-rating factor (2.9) to get the total cost of insurance for one year. What will one year's insurance cost you? **$2,006.80**

In-Class Examples

1. Driver-rating factor is 2.15. Age, rating group is B, 13. Coverage: 100/200 bodily injury, $50,000 property damage, $50-deductible comprehensive, and $50-deductible collision. What is the annual base premium? **($632.80)** What is the annual premium? **$1,360.52**

Living in the Real World

A Hard One to Pick

Cover Your Bumper (and More) Gomez discusses insurance with her friend, Jorge Leon, who is an insurance agent. Leon tells Gomez that with the purchase of a new vehicle, the cost of her insurance will increase. She's driven her truck for so long, she has no idea how much it costs to insure a new vehicle. In fact, she's never even had collision insurance and now she'll need comprehensive insurance.

Draw Conclusions Why might Gomez never have had collision insurance on her old truck?

Continued on page 327

Example 1

Della Welch is the principal operator of her vehicle. Her driver-rating factor is 2.20. Her insurance includes 50/100 bodily injury and $50,000 property damage. Her vehicle is in age group A and insurance-rating group 13 (or A, 13). She has $50-deductible comprehensive and $50-deductible collision insurance. What is her annual base premium? What is her annual premium? (You'll need to use Figure 9.3 to find important information for the problem.)

Figure 9.3

Liability Premium

Property Damage Limits	Bodily Injury Limits					
	25/50	25/100	50/100	100/200	100/300	300/300
$ 25,000	$206.40	$218.80	$213.20	$252.00	$258.00	$286.80
50,000	212.40	224.80	237.20	258.00	264.00	293.20
100,000	220.80	233.20	245.60	266.40	272.40	301.20

Physical Damage Premium

Coverage	Age Group	Insurance-Rating Group					
		10	11	12	13	14	15
Comprehensive $50-Deductible	A	$76.80	$81.60	$95.20	$108.00	$122.00	$135.60
	B	65.20	77.60	90.40	102.40	115.60	128.40
	C	62.00	74.00	86.00	98.00	110.40	122.80
	D	59.20	70.40	82.00	93.20	105.20	116.80
Collision $50-Deductible	A	$225.60	$246.00	$266.80	$287.20	$307.60	$328.00
	B	214.00	233.20	253.20	272.40	291.60	311.20
	C	204.00	222.80	241.60	260.00	278.40	296.80
	D	194.40	212.00	230.00	247.60	265.20	282.80

THINKING CRITICALLY

 Lower Insurance Premiums There are a number of things you can do to lower your vehicle insurance premium. Look at factors, such as type of vehicle, vehicle usage, geographic location, deductible amount, and so on. Contact a local insurance broker, or use a Web site such as www.insure.com, to get tips on how to save on your insurance. Make a table or chart of your findings.

LS , P

Need Help? Go to...

▶ Workshop 6:
Multiplying
Decimals, page 14
▶ Skill 8: Multiplying
Decimals, page 735

STEP 1: Find the annual base premium.

Liability Premium	+	Comprehensive Premium	+	Collision Premium
$237.20	+	$108.00	+	$287.20

= **$632.40 annual base premium**

STEP 2: Find the annual premium.

Base Premium × Driver-Rating Factor
$632.40 × 2.20

= **$1,391.28 annual premium**

237.2 + 108 + 287.2 = 632.4 × 2.2 = 1391.28

CONCEPT CHECK

SELF-CHECK✔

Complete the problem, then check your answers at the end of this chapter. Find the annual base premium and the annual premium.

1. Bodily injury 25/100 and $100,000 property damage.
Car is in age group C and insurance-rating group 10 (or C, 10).
A $50-deductible comprehensive and a $50-deductible collision.
Driver-rating factor is 1.50. **Annual base premium: $499.20,**
Annual premium: $748.80

Example 2

Soseki Nagamatus has a driver-rating factor of 3.1. His insurance includes 100/300 bodily injury limits and $100,000 property damage limits. His vehicle is in age group B and insurance-rating group 15 (B, 15). He has a $50-deductible comprehensive and a $50-deductible collision insurance. What is his annual base premium? What is his annual premium? (You'll need to use Figure 9.3 on page 324 to find important information for the problem.)

STEP 1: Find the annual base premium.

Liability + Comprehensive + Collision
$272.40 + $128.40 + $311.20

= **$712.00 annual base premium**

STEP 2: Find the annual premium.

Base Premium × Driver-Rating Factor
$712.00 × 3.1

= **$2,207.20 annual premium**

CONCEPT CHECK

SELF-CHECK✔

Complete the problem, then check your answers at the end of this chapter.

2. J.J. Briner has a driver rating factor of 4.10. His insurance includes 25/50 bodily injury limits and $25,000 property damage limits. His truck is in age group D and insurance rating group 12. He has a $50-deductible comprehensive and a $50-deductible collision insurance. What is his annual base premium? What is his annual premium?
Annual base premium: $206.40 + $82.00 + $230.00 = $518.40,
Annual premium: $518.40 × 4.10 = $2,125.44

Section 9-4 Vehicle Insurance ▶ **325**

2. Driver-rating factor is 3.10.
Age, rating group is C, 14.
Coverage: 50/100 bodily injury, $50,000 property damage, $50 deductible comprehensive, and $50-deductible collision. What is the annual base premium? **($626)** What is the annual premium? **$1,940.60**

3. Driver-rating factor is 1.35.
Age, rating group is A, 11.
Coverage: 25/100 bodily injury, $25,000 property damage, $50-deductible comprehensive, and $50-deductible collision. What is the annual base premium? **($546.40)** What is the annual premium? **$737.64**

③ ASSESS

Error Analysis

Be sure students know how to read the tables in **Figure 9.3** on page 324. Explain that the first table combines the cost of insurance for bodily injury and property damage into one amount. Find the amount of coverage you want and then read the corresponding amount. Explain that as the amount of coverage increases, so does the annual base premium.

Explain that the second part of the table lists two types of insurance: comprehensive and collision. Be sure students know how to find the cost of insuring a car based on the age of the car and the group it belongs in. Vehicles in group A cost more to insure than vehicles in group D.

After students have obtained three figures from the tables (bodily injury/property, comprehensive, and collision), have them add these amounts. Then, multiply by the driver-rating group to find the annual premium. Breaking down this process into smaller steps can help students pinpoint their errors.

Great Ideas from the Classroom Of...

Doug McCreath
East Union High School
Manteca, Calif.

Car Buying

Have students cut out car advertisements from the newspaper. When they have the price of the car, decide on a down payment amount they can log onto a lender Web site, and fill in a loan application. To complete the exercise, they calculate the monthly loan payments based on the cost of the car and the amount of their down payment.

4 **CLOSE**

Closing Activity

1. ($245.60 + $135.00 + $278.00) × 2.4 **$1,580.64**

2. ($212.40 + $81.60 + $246) × 1.35 **$729**

Refer to **Figure 9.3** on page 324 for Problems 3 and 4.

3. Driver-rating factor is 1.9. Age, rating group is B, 10. Coverage: 100/200 bodily injury, $100,000 property damage, $50-deductive comprehensive, and $50-deductible collision. What is the annual base premium? **($545.60)** What is the annual premium? **$1,036.64**

4. Henry Rolland has a vehicle insurance policy that contains $50-deductible comprehensive, $50-deductible collision, 25/100 bodily injury, and $50,000 property damage. His driver-rating factor is 2.2 and his vehicle is classified at D, 13. What is his annual base premium? **($565.60)** What is his annual premium? **$1,244.32**

---

3. a. **Annual Base Premium:** $642.80
   b. **Annual Premium:** $835.64

4. a. **Annual Base Premium:** $576.00
   b. **Annual Premium:** $921.60

5. **Annual Base Premium: $622.40**
   Annual Premium: $622.40

6. **Annual Base Premium: $740.80**
   Annual Premium: $2,481.68

7. **Annual Base Premium: $683.60**
   Annual Premium: $1,469.74

8. **Annual Base Premium: $628.40**
   Annual Premium: $1,948.04

9. **Annual Base Premium: $472.40**
   Annual Premium: $1,488.06

10. **Annual Base Premium: $696.40**
    Annual Premium: $3,377.54

Need Help? Go to...

▶ Skill 5: **Adding Decimals,** page 732
▶ Skill 8: **Multiplying Decimals,** page 735

SECTION 9-4 PRACTICE

3. Driver-rating factor is 1.30. Age group A and insurance-rating group 14. Coverage: 50/100 bodily injury. Has $25,000 property damage. Has $50-deductible comprehensive. Has $50-deductible collision.
   a. What is the annual base premium?
   b. What is the annual premium?

4. Driver-rating factor is 1.60. Age group D and insurance-rating group 12. Coverage: 100/300 bodily injury. Has $50,000 property damage. Has $50-deductible comprehensive. Has $50-deductible collision.
   a. What is the annual base premium?
   b. What is the annual premium?

5. Paula Williams uses her vehicle primarily for pleasure. She has $50-deductible comprehensive, $50-deductible collision, 100/200 bodily injury, and $25,000 property damage coverage. Because of her excellent driving record, her driver-rating factor is 1.00. Her vehicle is classified as D, 14. What is her annual base premium? What is her annual premium?

6. Scott Hanson uses his minivan primarily for business. He has $50-deductible comprehensive, $50-deductible collision, 300/300 bodily injury, and $100,000 property damage coverage. Because of his business use, his driver-rating factor is 3.35. His vehicle is classified B, 15. What is his annual base premium? What is his annual premium?

7. Magdalena Diaz uses her sports utility vehicle (SUV) mainly for pleasure. She has $50-deductible comprehensive, $50-deductible collision, 100/300 bodily injury, and $50,000 property damage coverage. Her driver-rating factor is 2.15 and her SUV is classified as C, 15. What is her annual base premium? What is her annual premium?

8. Carl Adams uses his station wagon to deliver office supplies. He has $50-deductible comprehensive, $50-deductible collision, 100/200 bodily injury, and $50,000 property damage coverage. Because of the business use of his wagon, his driver-rating factor is 3.10. His station wagon is classified as D, 14. What is his annual base premium? What is his annual premium?

9. Henry Rodriguez delivers bundles of firewood to retail outlets in his pickup truck. His driver-rating factor is 3.15. His insurance coverage includes 25/100 bodily injury and $25,000 property damage. He has $50-deductible comprehensive and $50-deductible collision. His truck is in age group D and insurance-rating group 10. What is his annual base premium? What is his annual premium?

10. Esther Miller-Kruse drives to and from work in her red sports car. Her driver-rating factor is 4.85. Her insurance coverage includes 300/300 bodily injury and $100,000 property damage. She has $50-deductible comprehensive and $50-deductible collision. Her car is in age group A and insurance-rating group 13. What is her annual base premium? What is her annual premium?

MAINTAINING YOUR SKILLS

Add.

11. 429.45 + 87.92 + 6.48 + 73.35 **597.2**

12. 49.55 + 2.82 + 4.59 + 733.20 **790.16**

Multiply.

13. 1.25 × 79.90 **99.875**

14. 2.40 × 360 **864**

15. 3.90 × 67.70 **264.03**

WRAP-UP

Go over any problem for which a wrong answer is given.

Assignment Guide
  Basic: 3–4
  Average: 5–8

20 min.

SECTION 9-5 Operating and Maintaining a Vehicle

Section Objective

Compute the total cost per mile of operating and maintaining a vehicle.

Many costs are involved in operating and maintaining a vehicle. You'll need to take these costs into consideration.

- **Variable costs** (such as gasoline and tires) increase the more you drive.
- **Fixed costs** (such as vehicle insurance, registration fees, and depreciation) remain about the same regardless of how many miles you drive.
- **Depreciation** is a decrease in the value of your vehicle because of its age and condition.

Remember that:

$$\text{Cost per Mile} = \frac{\text{Annual Variable Cost} + \text{Annual Fixed Cost}}{\text{Number of Miles Driven}}$$

Living in the Real World

A Hard One to Pick

Don't Forget about the Other Fees Involved Gomez continues to shop for various trucks at Tucker Motors. She keeps in mind the true cost of the truck is more than the just the sticker price and insurance.

Draw Conclusions What are some of the other costs she needs to take into consideration before buying a vehicle?

Continued on page 330

Example 1

Need Help? Go to...

- ➤ Workshop 1: Dividing Decimals, page 16
- ➤ Workshop 2: Rounding Numbers, page 6
- ➤ Skill 11: Dividing Decimals, page 738
- ➤ Skill 2: Rounding Numbers, page 729

Ann Jones purchased a used vehicle for $4,000 one year ago. She drove 9,000 miles during the year and kept a record of all her expenses. She estimates the vehicle's present value at $3,200. What was the cost per mile for Jones to operate her vehicle last year?

Variable Costs		Fixed Costs	
Gasoline	$345.24	Insurance	$ 385.40
Oil changes	71.85	License/registration	76.25
Maintenance	114.36	Depreciation	800.00
New tire	41.75	($4,000 − $3,200)	
Total	**$573.20**	**Total**	**$1,261.65**

Continued on next page

Living in the Real World

Automobiles don't run on air alone. Gasoline is a major expense over the life of a car, as well as regular maintenance, depreciation, and the occasional repair bill. The more Gomez uses her truck, the higher these costs will climb.

TECHNOLOGY POWER

There are a number of Internet sites that can be used to check the value of a new or used car. Edmunds.com and KBB.com (Kelly Blue Book) are examples of two sites that provide this information. You can enter the information (features, mileage, etc.) about your existing vehicle, and based on your zip code a trade-in value and a resale value is returned. Invoice prices on new vehicles are available by model and option packages.

National Standards for Business Education

Standard 1	Mathematical Foundations
Standard 2	Number Relationships and Operations

National Council of Teachers of Mathematics Standards

Standard 1	Numbers and Operations
Standard 4	Measurement
Standard 6	Problem Solving
Standard 8	Communication
Standard 9	Connections

1 FOCUS

Ask students to name the costs they or their families have encountered in operating and maintaining an automobile. List items on the board as they are named. Tell students that in today's lesson, they will learn to compute the cost per mile of operating and maintaining an automobile.

In-Class Examples

Work through these exercises with students before having them do the Self-Check. Round to the nearest cent.

1. $67 + $33 + $24 + $136 **$260**
2. ($150 + $140) + ($35 + $75) **$400**
3. ($113 + $250 + $300 + $200) ÷ 4,000 **$0.22**
4. ($219 + $385 + $172 + $1,424) ÷ 8,000 **$0.28**

327

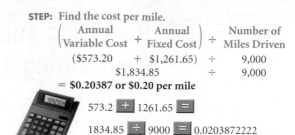

STEP: Find the cost per mile.

$$\left(\begin{array}{c}\text{Annual} \\ \text{Variable Cost}\end{array} + \begin{array}{c}\text{Annual} \\ \text{Fixed Cost}\end{array}\right) \div \begin{array}{c}\text{Number of} \\ \text{Miles Driven}\end{array}$$

$$(\$573.20 \quad + \quad \$1,261.65) \div \quad 9,000$$

$$\$1,834.85 \qquad \div \quad 9,000$$

$$= \$0.20387 \text{ or } \$0.20 \text{ per mile}$$

573.2 [+] 1261.65 [=]

1834.85 [÷] 9000 [=] 0.0203872222

CONCEPT CHECK

SELF-CHECK ✓

Complete the problems, then check your answers at the end of this chapter. Find the total cost and the cost per mile.

	Variable Cost	Fixed Cost	Miles Driven	
1.	$1,900.00	$1,700.00	10,000	Total cost: $3,600, Cost per mile: $0.36
2.	$2,137.26	$2,491.24	12,000	Total cost: $4,628.50, Cost per mile: $0.3857 or $0.39

Example 2

Lucas Perry purchased a new four-door car 2 years ago at a price of $21,750. *Kiplinger* estimates it is worth $13,920 today. The *Complete Car Cost Guide* computes the annual variable cost to be $595.20 per year with insurance costing $1,461 per year. Perry paid $112.60 for license and registration fees and drove 16,500 miles during the year. After computing the depreciation and the total annual cost, find the cost per mile.

STEP 1: Find the depreciation.

$$\frac{\text{Purchase Price} - \text{Today's Worth}}{\text{Number of Years Owned}}$$

$$\frac{(\$21,750.00 - \$13,920.00)}{2}$$

$$\frac{\$7,830.00}{2} = \$3,915.00$$

STEP 2: Find the total annual cost.

$$\$595.20 + (\$1,461.00 + \$3,915.00 + \$112.60) = \$6,083.80$$

STEP 3: Find the cost per mile.

$$\left(\begin{array}{c}\text{Annual} \\ \text{Variable Cost}\end{array} + \begin{array}{c}\text{Annual} \\ \text{Fixed Cost}\end{array}\right) \div \begin{array}{c}\text{Number of} \\ \text{Miles Driven}\end{array}$$

$$\$6,083.80 \qquad \div \quad 16,500$$

$$= \$0.3687 \text{ or } \$0.37 \text{ per mile}$$

3. Depreciation: $4,800 ÷ 3 = $1,600
Variable cost: $795.60
Fixed cost: ($1,600.00 + $2,350.00 + $132.50 + $1,080.00) = $5,162.50
Total cost: $5,958.10
Cost per mile: $0.44

CONCEPT CHECK

SELF-CHECK ✓

Complete the problem, then check your answers at the end of this chapter.

3. Sylvia McDowell purchased a new car 3 years ago for $23,500.00. It's estimated worth now is $18,700.00. Annual variable costs this year were $795.60. This year insurance cost $2,350.00, registration was $132.50, and loan interest totalled $1,080.00. She drove 13,540 miles this year. Compute the depreciation, annual costs, and cost per mile.

---

2 TEACH

Emphasize the difference between variable cost and fixed cost. Use the list on the board to have students categorize each item named earlier. Make sure that depreciation is included in the list if it wasn't already named. Students may be surprised to find out how much a car depreciates the first year. Contact a car dealer and a bank in your area for more information. If payments are going to be made, the finance charge paid to the bank should be listed as one of the fixed costs.

Point out that keeping accurate records are important for many people who use their cars in their businesses. Part of these operating expenses can be deducted at tax time. For other people, the prior year's expenses of operating and maintaining an automobile can be used as a basis for preparing a budget for the new year. A large increase in the cost per mile driven is a signal to some individuals that they may need to consider trading for a car that is cheaper to own and operate.

Motivating the Lesson

Last year you drove your sport coupe 10,000 miles. You kept track of all your expenses for the year. Your fixed expenses included insurance $1,260, license and registration $98, and depreciation $1,190. Your variable expenses included gas $731, oil changes $86, parking $273, and repairs $142. What were your total expenses for one year? **($3,780)** What was your cost per mile to drive your car? **$0.38 per mile**

In-Class Examples

1. This year Jeff Stillman drove his luxury car 10,300 miles. Fixed costs totaled $3,858. Variable costs totaled $1,480. What was the total annual cost? **($5,338)** What was the cost per mile? **$0.52 per mile**

COMMUNICATION SKILLS

Car Expenses

Students check with friends and relatives to find their typical yearly car expenses, such as gasoline, maintenance, insurance, depreciation, and so on. Students share their findings in class and record them on the board. Decide as a class the typical annual cost of running a car.

SECTION 9-5 PRACTICE

Find the total annual cost and the cost per mile to the nearest cent.

	(Annual Variable Cost	+	Annual Fixed Costs	=	Total Annual Cost)	÷	Miles Driven	=	Cost per Mile
4.	$1,000.00	+	$1,250.00	=	a. $2,250	÷	9,000	=	b. $0.25
5.	$1,530.00	+	$1,275.00	=	a. $2,805	÷	11,000	=	b. $0.255 ≐ $0.26
6.	$2,114.00	+	$3,786.00	=	a. $5,900	÷	14,700	=	b. $0.401 ≐ $0.40
7.	$1,584.00	+	$ 934.35	=	a. $2,518.35	÷	6,800	=	b. $0.370 ≐ $0.37
8.	$2,312.50	+	$4,321.90	=	a. $6,634.40	÷	20,415	=	b. $0.324 = $0.32

9. A student drove 9,500 miles in his car last year.
Fixed costs totaled $1,215.
Variable costs totaled $1,985.
   a. What was the total annual cost? **Total cost: $3,200**
   b. What was the cost per mile? **Cost per mile: $0.336 = $0.34**

10. A salesperson drove 34,500 miles in his car last year.
Fixed costs totaled $3,860.
Variable costs totaled $3,940.
   a. What was the total annual cost? **Total cost: $7,800**
   b. What was the cost per mile? **Cost per mile: $0.226 = $0.23**

11. Hope Kocinski drove 12,200 miles in her car last year. Her variable costs totaled $780.35. Her fixed costs totaled $2,439.00. What was the cost per mile for her to operate her car? **Cost per mile: $0.263 = $0.26**

12. Alice Powers drove 13,550 miles in her car last year. Her variable costs totaled $1,776.90. Her fixed costs totaled $2,457.15. What was the cost per mile for her to operate her car? **Cost per mile: $0.312 = $0.31**

13. J. J. Olmstead drove 11,400 miles in his SUV last year. His variable costs totaled $2,965.89. His fixed costs totaled $2,884.26. What was the cost per mile for him to operate his SUV? **Cost per mile: $0.513 = $0.51**

MAINTAINING YOUR SKILLS

Need Help? Go to...
▶ Skill 2: **Rounding Numbers,** page 729
▶ Skill 10: **Dividing (Decimal Remainder),** page 737

Round to the nearest hundredth.

14. 21.751 **21.75**   15. 15.352 **15.35**   16. 4.3981 **4.40**

17. 15.9061 **15.91**   18. 0.04126 **0.04**   19. 0.3179 **0.32**

Divide. Round answers to the nearest hundredth.

20. 641 ÷ 200 **3.21**   21. 1,500 ÷ 500 **3**   22. 850 ÷ 9,000 **0.09**

Section 9-5 Operating and Maintaining a Vehicle ▶ **329**

2. Gloria Alvarado drove her car 12,000 miles. Fixed costs totaled $2,793. Variable costs totaled $1,190. What was the total annual cost? **($3,983)** What was the cost per mile? **$0.33 per mile**

3. Rajeesh Chaturvedi drove his van 15,000 miles. Fixed costs totaled $3,650. Variable costs totaled $1,640. What was the total annual cost? **($5,290)** What was the cost per mile? **$0.35 per mile**

(3) ASSESS

Error Analysis

If students are making errors, they are usually computational. Have them recheck their addition of variable costs plus fixed costs. Then remind them to divide this amount by the annual mileage to arrive at the annual cost per mile of driving a particular vehicle. Review how to round a dollar amount to the nearest cent.

(4) CLOSE

Closing Activity

Round to the nearest hundred.
1. ($1,480 + $3,195) ÷ 11,000 **$0.43**
2. ($1,974 + $2,450) ÷ 13,000 **$0.34**
3. Denise Irwin drove her vehicle 10,500 miles. Fixed costs totaled $2,452. Variable costs totaled $893. What was the total annual cost? **($3,345)** What was the cost per mile? **$0.32 per mile**
4. Mario Palazzo drove his sport car 11,200 miles. Fixed costs totaled $6,237. Variable costs totaled $2,125. What was the total annual cost? **($8,362)** What was the cost per mile? **$0.75 per mile**

WRAP-UP

Go over any problem for which a wrong answer is given.

Assignment Guide
   Basic: 4–8
   Average: 9–10

20 min.

National Standards for Business Education

Standard 1	Mathematical Foundations
Standard 2	Number Relationships and Operations

National Council of Teachers of Mathematics Standards

Standard 1	Numbers and Operations
Standard 4	Measurement
Standard 6	Problem Solving
Standard 8	Communication
Standard 9	Connections

1 FOCUS

Ask students what a lease in reference to an apartment means. Point out that leasing an automobile has become a common business practice.

In-Class Examples

Work through these exercises with students before having them do the Self-Check.
1. 48 × $199 **$9,552**
2. 36 × $275 **$9,900**
3. 24 × $399.95 **$9,598.80**
4. 9,360 + 1,200 + 125 + 60 **10,745**
5. 13,740 + 1,500 + 400 + 75 **15,715**

SECTION 9·6 Leasing a Vehicle

Section Objective

Calculate the total cost of leasing a vehicle.

Rather than purchase a vehicle, you might want to **lease** one. When you lease a vehicle, you make monthly payments to the leasing company, the dealer, or the bank for two to five years. You don't own the car; you're essentially renting the car. At the end of the lease, you either return the vehicle to the leasing company or you may purchase it.

The most common lease is a *closed-end lease*. With a closed-end lease, you make a specified number of payments, return the vehicle, and owe nothing (unless you damage the vehicle beyond fair wear and tear or exceed the mileage limit). If you do damage the vehicle or exceed the mileage limit, then you owe money to the leasing company.

Another type of lease is an *open-end lease*. At the end of an open-end lease, you can buy the vehicle for its residual value. The residual value is the expected value of the vehicle at the end of the lease period. The residual value is often established at the signing of the lease. With either lease—the closed-end lease or the open-end lease—you must pay all the monthly payments, a security deposit, title fee, and license fee.

Important Question	What Formula Do I Use?
How do I calculate the **total cost** of the lease?	$\text{Total Lease Cost} = \left(\text{Number of Payments} \times \text{Amount of Payment} \right) + \text{Deposit} + \text{Title Fee} + \text{License Fee}$

Living in the Real World

A Hard One to Pick

Do You Want It to Be "Yours" or Not? Gomez also knows that leasing a new truck is an option. She's not sure if it makes financial sense for her, considering that she uses her truck so much for work.

Draw Conclusions Why might she lease a vehicle instead of buying one?

Continued on page 333

Example 1

Ralph Dunn leased a pickup truck for use in his lawn care business. He pays $199 per month for 60 months. His deposit was $2,500. He paid an $80 title fee and a $45 license fee. What is his total lease cost?

Living in the Real World

Leasing can be a good option if Gomez doesn't have enough to pay for a down payment or can't afford to buy a higher-end model.

COOPERATIVE LEARNING

Group Report

Students work in groups to use a vehicle operation and maintenance manual and a warranty to write a report on the following: (1) parts of an automobile covered under a typical warranty, (2) parts included under an extended warranty, and (3) maintenance schedules that are recommended by the manufacturer.

 LS , CL

STEP: Find the total lease cost.

$$\left(\begin{array}{c}\text{Number of} \\ \text{Payments}\end{array} \times \begin{array}{c}\text{Amount of} \\ \text{Payment}\end{array}\right) + \text{Deposit} + \begin{array}{c}\text{Title} \\ \text{Fee}\end{array} + \begin{array}{c}\text{License} \\ \text{Fee}\end{array}$$

$$(60 \times \$199) + \$2,500 + \$80 + \$45$$
$$\$11,940 \qquad + \$2,500 + \$80 + \$45$$
$$= \$14,565 \text{ total lease cost}$$

60 ⊗ 199 ▣ 11940 ⊞ 2500 ⊞ 80 ⊞ 45 ▣ 14565

CONCEPT CHECK

 SELF-CHECK ✓

Complete the problems, then check your answers at the end of this chapter. Find the total lease cost.

1. Convertible.
Pays $349.00 per month for
36 months.
Deposit of $3,000.00.
Title fee of $80.00.
License fee of $112.86. **$15,756.86**

2. Sedan.
Pays $250.00 per month for
39 months.
Deposit of $900.00.
Title fee of $75.00.
License fee of $54.95. **$10,779.95**

(**Example 2**)

Tashira Conley leased a minivan for family use. She pays $229.00 per month for 39 months. Her deposit was $1,000.00. She paid a $57.50 title fee and a $48.50 license fee. What is her total lease cost?

STEP: Find the total lease cost.

$$(39 \times \$229.00) + \$1,000.00 + \$57.50 + \$48.50$$
$$\$8,931.00 \qquad + \$1,000.00 + \$57.50 + \$48.50$$
$$= \$10,037.00 \text{ total lease cost}$$

CONCEPT CHECK

SELF-CHECK ✓

Complete the problem, then check your answer at the end of this chapter.

3. Marie Storholder leased a car for $179 per month for 36 months. Her deposit was $2,000, with a title fee of $85 and a license fee of $79. What is her total lease cost? **$8,608.00**

USING CALCULATORS

Have students explain what the following keystroke sequence accomplishes:
415.21 [M+] 36.59 [M+]
127.43 [M+] 312.95 [M+]
[MRC] [÷] 9512 [=]

ALTERNATIVE ASSESSMENT

Real World
Relate this lesson to the real world by using a car dealer's newspaper ad. Ads are a good source of current prices. They usually give such pertinent information as payment amount, number of payments, and down payment. Rework the examples using a title fee and license fee typical to your area.

(2) TEACH

For the closed end lease, point out that the mileage limit is generally set at 12,000 to 14,000 miles. After that limit, there is an additional charge per mile. The car may not be purchased at the end of the closed-end lease.

The open-end lease may be preferable if the car is to be purchased. The lease payments are often less than the purchase payments when you finance all or most of the price of the car.

In addition to the security deposit, title fee, and license fee, you must also qualify for credit. Sales tax must sometimes be paid at the time of purchase. These problems assume the sales tax is part of the lease payment. **(Note: the prices on leasing vehicles used in the TWE do not include sales tax.)**

Motivating the Lesson
You've been out car shopping and may decide to lease a car instead of purchasing one. For a deposit of $2,316 and 36 monthly payments of $191, you can lease a vehicle. In addition, you also must pay a title fee of $65 and a license fee of $125. At the end of the three-year period, you must return the vehicle. How much will the lease cost you over the three-year period, including the title and license? **$9,382**

In-Class Examples
1. Lease a SUV for 48 payments of $294. Deposit of $1,189. Title fee of $90. License fee of $125. What is the total lease cost? **$15,516**
2. Lease a sedan for 36 payments of $260 per month. Deposit of $2,685. Title fee of $65. License fee of $85. What is the total lease cost? **$12,195**

③ ASSESS

Error Analysis

Review students' written work to identify the kinds of errors they may be making. Very often errors in basic multiplication and addition facts are common. Have students check their work to correct these types of errors.

④ CLOSE

Closing Activity

1. (60 × $499) + $135 + $85
    $30,160
2. (48 × $329) + $75 +$150
    $16,017
3. Truck leased for 36 payments of $399. Deposit of $799. Title fee of $35. License fee of $135. What is the total lease cost? **$15,333**
4. Sedan leased for 60 payments of $225. Deposit of $0. Title fee of $15. License fee of $60. What is the total lease cost? **$13,575**

For Problems 4–8, find the total of payments and the total lease cost.

	Number of Payments	×	Amount of Payment	=	Total of Payments	+ Deposit +	Title Fee	+	License Fee	=	Total Lease Cost
a. $5,256 **4.**	(24	×	$219	=	a.)	+ $ 419 +	$ 8	+	$36	=	b. $5,719
a. $9,552 **5.**	(48	×	199	=	a.)	+ 749 +	15	+	15	=	b.$10,331
a. $5,712 **6.**	(48	×	119	=	a.)	+ 1,200 +	60	+	75	=	b. $7,047
a. $9,720 **7.**	(54	×	180	=	a.)	+ 1,200 +	35	+	96	=	b.$11,051
a. $22,440 **8.**	(60	×	374	=	a.)	+ 1,500 +	66	+	55	=	b.$24,061

9. Luxury car.
    Agreed to 48 payments of $475.
    Deposit of $475.
    Title fee of $65.
    License fee of $85.
    What is the total lease cost? **$23,425**

10. SUV.
    Agreed to 39 payments of $279.95.
    Deposit of $900.00.
    Title fee of $60.00.
    License fee of $69.95.
    What is the total lease cost? **$11,948**

11. Magarita Cervantes leased a truck for personal use. She pays $239 a month for 48 months. She also paid a deposit of $1,100, a title fee of $90, and a license fee of $125. What is the total lease cost? **$12,787**

12. Nadine Daniels leased a convertible for $499 a month for 36 months. She paid a deposit of $3,000, a title fee of $125, and a license fee of $365. What is the total lease cost? **$21,454**

13. Teneshia Cooper has an open-end lease for a SUV, which she uses for her fabric store. The lease costs $339 a month for 60 months. She paid a deposit of $2,500, a title fee of $35, and a license fee of $135. At the end of the lease, she can buy the vehicle for its residual value of $9,446. What is the total lease cost? What is the total cost if she buys the vehicle? **Total lease cost: $23,010; Total cost to purchase: $32,456**

14. Homer Gill leased a vehicle for $199.00 a month for 48 months. He paid a deposit of $225.00, a title fee of $15.00, and a license fee of $60.00. The lease carried a stipulation that there would be a $0.10 per mile charge for all miles over 60,000. He drove the vehicle 68,515 miles. What is the total cost of leasing the vehicle? **$10,703.50**

15. Alicia Harper can lease a sedan for $254.95 a month for 48 months. She must pay a deposit of $250.00, a title fee of $75.00, and a license fee of $120.00. At the end of the 48 months, the vehicle is expected to be worth $4,117.00. Instead of leasing, she can purchase the vehicle for $278.96 a month for 48 months plus a $978.00 down payment and the same title and license fees. What is less expensive: to lease or to purchase?
    $16,799.60 to lease; $14,563.08 to purchase; best to purchase

---

MAINTAINING YOUR SKILLS

Need Help? Go to...
➤ Skill 8: **Multiplying Decimals**, page 735

Multiply.

16. 33.90 × 5 **169.5**   17. 29.95 × 4 **119.8**   18. 7 × 54.65 **382.55**

WRAP-UP

Go over any problem for which a wrong answer is given.

Assignment Guide
  Basic: 4–8
Average: 9–12

20 min.

SECTION (9-7) Renting a Vehicle

Section Objective

Figure out the cost per mile of renting a vehicle.

From time to time you may need to **rent** a vehicle. Some vehicle rental agencies charge a daily rate plus a per-mile rate. Others charge a daily rate with no mileage charge. In either case, you pay for the gasoline used.

You might also have to pay for insurance on the rented vehicle. Often the insurance generally has a collision deductible clause that states that you will pay for a portion of any damage to the vehicle if it is in an accident. You can obtain complete insurance coverage with a collision waiver by paying an additional charge per day. How do you figure out how much you're paying per mile? Use this formula:

$$\text{Cost per Mile} = \frac{\text{Total Cost}}{\text{Number of Miles Driven}}$$

Living in the Real World

A Hard One to Pick

Take It for a Test Drive By now, Gomez is fairly certain she knows what model truck she wants to buy, the features she wants on it, and the price she's willing to pay. She'd just like to try it out for a week or so to get an idea if it's exactly what she needs for work. So she decides to rent the truck the way people rent cars.

Draw Conclusions Why is it important to test drive or rent the truck she is interested in buying?

Continued on page 337

Example 1

Joe Wozniak rented a car for 3 days at $39.95 per day plus $0.20 per mile. He purchased the collision waiver for $10.00 per day. Wozniak drove 468 miles and paid $21.70 for gasoline. What was the total cost of renting the car? What was the total cost per mile to rent the car?

STEP 1: Find the total cost.

Daily cost: $39.95 × 3 =	$119.85
Mileage cost: $0.20 × 468 =	93.60
Gasoline cost:	21.70
Collision waiver: $10.00 × 3 =	30.00
Total cost	**$265.15 total cost**

STEP 2: Find the cost per mile.

$$\text{Total Cost} \div \frac{\text{Number of}}{\text{Miles Driven}}$$

$$\$265.15 \div 468 = \$0.566 \text{ or } \$0.57 \text{ per mile}$$

39.95 [×] 3 [=] 119.85 [M+] .20 [×] 468 [=]

93.6 [M+] 10 [×] 3 [=] 30 [M+] [RM] 243.45 [+] 21.70 [=]

265.15 [÷] 468 [=] .0566559829

Living in the Real World

Purchasing a new truck is a big investment. By test driving the pickup truck, Gomez gets an idea of whether this is the right truck for her.

National Standards for Business Education

Standard 1	Mathematical Foundations
Standard 2	Number Relationships and Operations

National Council of Teachers of Mathematics Standards

Standard 1	Numbers and Operations
Standard 4	Measurement
Standard 6	Problem Solving
Standard 8	Communication
Standard 9	Connections

(1) FOCUS

Ask students if any of their families have ever rented a vehicle either while on vacation or while the family car was being repaired. The focus of this lesson is to compute the cost per mile of renting a vehicle.

In-Class Examples

Work through these exercises with students before having them do the Self-Check.

1. $79 × 4 **$316**
2. $15 × 8 **$120**
3. $0.24 × 600 **$144**
4. $420 ÷ 800 **$0.525**
5. ($39.95 × 4) + (0.20 × 206) + ($8.95 × 4) + $36.97 **$273.77**

333

② TEACH

Go over each of the four components of the total cost in the examples. Emphasize that the insurance is charged per day. Some rental companies offer a flat fee, then charge an additional per mile fee if you drive over a set limit of miles. The cost of renting a vehicle varies from agency to agency. It also varies on the type of vehicle, with compact cars renting for the least and luxury cars, vans, and SUVs for the most. Most agencies require either a deposit or a valid credit card.

Motivating the Lesson

Your family wants to rent a minivan for a week's vacation. You've checked the cost of rental companies and have found a special weekly rate of $299, which includes unlimited mileage. You want the collision waiver at an additional cost of $10.50 per day. You plan to drive the van about 722 miles. You estimate that gasoline will cost approximately $68 for the week. What is the total cost of renting the minivan for a week? **($440.50)** What is the cost per mile? **$0.61 per mile**

In-Class Examples

1. Tony Gianolli rented a sedan for 4 days at $99 per day with unlimited mileage. He paid $15 per day for the collision waiver. Gasoline cost him $41.60. He drove the vehicle 468 miles. Find the total cost and the cost per mile for renting the vehicle. **$497.60; $1.06**

2. Dale Sanders rented a truck for 1 week at a special rate of $199 per week. There is a $0.25 per mile charge for miles over 700. He drove the pickup 817 miles. He paid $12.95 per day for the collision waiver and gasoline cost $48.05. Find the total cost and the cost per mile for renting the truck. **$366.95; $0.45 per mile**

SELF-CHECK✓ Complete the problems, then check your answers at the end of this chapter.

Winona Simms rented a car for $30.00 a day for 4 days plus $0.22 per mile. Simms drove 430 miles and spent $18.90 on gasoline.

1. Find the total cost.
   ($30.00 × 4) + ($0.22 × 430) + $18.90 = $233.50

2. Find the cost per mile.
   $233.50 ÷ 430 = $0.543 or $0.54

Example 2

Miguel Alvarez rented a sedan for $41.95 a day for 3 days. He paid $0.20 per mile for all miles over 150 miles per day. He drove 186 miles the first day, 78 miles the second day, and 210 miles the third day. Gasoline cost him $22.68. He paid $12.50 per day for the collision waiver. Find the total cost and cost per mile for renting the sedan.

STEP 1: Find the total cost.
   ($41.95 × 3) + [$0.20 × (36 + 0 + 60)] + $22.68 + ($12.50 × 3)
   $125.85   + $19.20   + $22.68 + $37.50
   = **$205.23 total cost**

STEP 2: Find the cost per mile.
   $205.23 ÷ (186 + 78 + 210)
   $205.23 ÷   474   = **$0.43297 or $0.43 cost per mile**

CONCEPT CHECK

SELF-CHECK✓ Complete the problem, then check your answers at the end of this chapter.

3. William LaFrance rented a van for $45.50 a day for 5 days. The mileage charge was $0.25 a mile over 120 miles per day. He drove 112, 162, 95, 180, and 144 miles for the days rented. Gasoline cost $77.88. He paid $15.50 per day for the collision waiver. Find the total cost and cost per mile for renting the van. **($45.50 × 5) + ($0.25 × 126) + $77.88 + ($15.50 × 5) = $227.50 + $31.50 + $77.88 + $77.50 = $414.38**
   $414.38 ÷ (112 + 162 + 95 + 180 + 144) = $414.38 ÷ 693 = $0.59795 or $0.60

SECTION 9-7 PRACTICE

Solve. Find the cost per mile to the nearest cent.

	Total Daily Cost	+	Total Mileage Cost	+	Gasoline Cost	=	Total Cost	÷	Miles Driven	=	Cost per Mile
4.	($160.00	+	$94.00	+	$23.89	=	a.	) ÷	500	=	b.
5.	(119.95	+	74.40	+	30.53	=	a.	) ÷	620	=	b.
6.	(159.95	+	63.55	+	41.67	=	a.	) ÷	420	=	b.

4. a. $277.89; b. $0.555 = $0.56
5. a. $224.88; b. $0.362 = $0.36
6. a. $265.17; b. $0.631 = $0.63

GLOBAL PERSPECTIVE

Overseas Car Rental

Students pick a country they would like to visit. They contact a travel agent, research a travel magazine, or go on the Internet to find out how much it costs to rent a car in that country. Are there different rates for three days, a week, and a month? Does the rate include insurance? How much does gas cost? Is it important to purchase travel vehicle insurance when you're driving in another country?

Find the cost per mile to the nearest cent. (No mileage charge.)

	Rental Cost	+	Gasoline Cost	=	Total Cost	÷	Miles Driven	=	Cost per Mile
7.	($ 66.50	+	$10.39	=	a. $76.89)	÷	240	=	b.
8.	(96.00	+	25.98	=	a.$121.98)	÷	300	=	b.
9.	(154.75	+	28.27	=	a.$183.02)	÷	476	=	b.
10.	(89.95	+	41.38	=	a.$131.33)	÷	518	=	b.

7. b. $0.320 = $0.32
8. b. $0.406 = $0.41
9. b. $0.384 = $0.38
10. b. $0.253 = $0.25

11. Sedan.
It cost $28.00 a day for 4 days.
He drove 520 miles at $0.33 a mile.
Gasoline cost $20.78.
a. What was the total cost? **$304.38**
b. What was the cost per mile?
$0.585 = $0.59

12. Truck.
It cost $32.00 a day for 5 days.
He drove 1,100 miles at $0.37 a mile.
Gasoline cost $54.95.
a. What was the total cost? **$621.95**
b. What was the cost per mile?
$0.565 = $0.57

13. Sanchez Corado rented a minivan for 4 days at $38.00 a day plus $0.30 a mile. He purchased collision waiver insurance for $8.50 per day. He drove 420 miles and paid $49.64 for gasoline. What was the total cost of renting the minivan? What was the cost per mile? **$361.64; $0.861 = $0.86**

14. Freda Rochetti rented a car for 2 days at $32.95 a day plus $0.33 a mile. She purchased collision waiver insurance for $7.50 per day. She drove 140 miles and paid $8.39 for gasoline. What was the total cost of renting the car? What was the cost per mile? **$135.49; $0.967 = $0.97**

15. The Car Rental Company has a 5-day rate of $208.34 for compact cars, with no charge for mileage. One is driven 450 miles and uses $22.90 in gasoline. What is the cost per mile? **$0.513 = $0.51**

16. Alice Coopersmith is moving to a new home. She can rent a 14-foot panel truck for $40.00 a day plus $0.26 a mile or an 18-foot truck for $55.00 a day plus $0.29 a mile. It would take 4 trips to make the move in the 14-foot truck, but only 3 trips in the larger truck. She estimates that gasoline would cost about $45.00 for either truck. A round-trip to her new home is 60 miles. Regardless of the number of trips, she would need the truck for only 1 day. To save on expenses, which size truck should Coopersmith rent? How much would it cost per mile to rent each truck?
14-foot truck: $147.40 < 18-foot truck: $152.20;
14-foot: $0.614 = $0.61/mile; 18-foot: $0.845 = $0.85

MAINTAINING YOUR SKILLS

Need Help? Go to...
▶ Skill 5: Adding
Decimals, page 732
▶ Skill 11: Dividing
Decimals, page 738

Add.

17. 7.94 + 34.67 + 86.75 + 378.99 **508.35**

18. 86.03 + 8.75 + 94.01 + 378.19 **566.98**

Divide. Round answers to the nearest hundredth.

19. 762.20 ÷ 32 **23.818 = 23.82**

20. 684.26 ÷ 42.2 **16.214 = 16.21**

21. 502.00 ÷ 361.9 **1.39**

22. 801.83 ÷ 15.5 **51.73**

USING CALCULATORS

The parentheses keys can be useful when some of the numbers being added in a list need to be multiplied first. For example, the sequence
(57 × 2) + 32 + 47 +
(22 × 3) = will ensure that the expression is simplified using the correct order of operations.

WRAP-UP

Go over any problem for which a wrong answer is given.

Assignment Guide
Basic: 4–10
Average: 11–15

20 min.

3 ASSESS

Error Analysis
Remind students to read each problem carefully. Point out that some rental agreements, include unlimited mileage while others charge per mile or for the number of miles driven over a certain amount. Have students check that they have totaled the cost of daily or weekly rental, the cost of the collision waiver, the mileage charge, if any, and the cost of gasoline.

When students are computing the cost per mile of renting a vehicle, remind them to divide the total cost by the number of miles driven. For example, a car that cost $387.32 to rent was driven 674 miles. The cost per mile is $387.32 ÷ 674, or $0.57 per mile.

4 CLOSE

Closing Activity
1. ($69.95 × 4.00) + ($14.95 × 4.00) + ($0.20 × 39) + $35.28 **$382.68**
2. ($79.00 × 3.00) + ($12.95 × 3.00) + $36.75 **$312.60**
3. Evander Young rented a car with unlimited mileage. He received a special weekly rate of $249. He took the collision waiver at $10.50 per day. He drove the car 994 miles and spent $72.29 for gasoline. What was the total cost of renting the car for the week? **($394.79)** What was the cost per mile? **$0.40 per mile**

335

Quick Quiz

1. Rob Carson is pricing sport utility vehicles. One has a base price of $27,189. He is considering the optional leather package for $1,590 and the entertainment system for $1,147. The destination charge is $540. What is the sticker price if he purchases the vehicle with these two options? **$30,466**

2. A truck has a base price of $22,830 and options that total $1,870. The destination charge is $650. If the dealer pays an estimated 92.6 percent of base price and 92 percent of the options, what is the dealer's cost? **$23,510.98**

3. A Coupe has an average retail value of $11,400. Add $100 for CD player. Add $350 for leather seats. Add $150 for power seat. Add $550 for power sunroof. Deduct $150 without cruise control. No adjustment for mileage. What is the average retail price? **$12,400**

Refer to **Figure 9.3** on page 324 for Problem 4.

4. Driver-rating factor is 3.3. Age, rating group is C, 14. Coverage: 100/300 bodily injury, $50,000 property damage, $50-deductible comprehensive, and $50-deductible collision. What is the annual base premium? **($652.80)** What is the annual premium? **$2,154.24**

CHAPTER 9 Self-Check Answers

SECTION 9-1 CONCEPT CHECK (p. 315)

1. $11,080 + ($340 + $800 + $925) + $499 = **$13,644**
2. $13,655 + ($1,220 + $650) + $749 = **$16,274**
3. $22,245 + ($1,186 + $204 + $336) + $715 = **$24,686**
4. $16,725 + ($860 + $710 + $220) + $465 = **$18,980**

SECTION 9-2 CONCEPT CHECK (p. 318)

1. ($53,105 × 88%) + ($1,785 × 90%) + $340 = **$48,678.90**
2. ($23,855 × 90.5%) + ($2,256 × 87%) + $610 = **$24,161.50**

SECTION 9-3 CONCEPT CHECK (p. 321, 322)

1. $13,050 + ($125 + $340 + $225 + $125) + $525 = **$14,390**
2. $12,000 + ($100 + $300 + $375 + $100) − $1,400 = **$11,475**

SECTION 9-4 CONCEPT CHECK (p. 325)

1. Annual base premium: **$499.20**, Annual premium: **$748.80**
2. Annual base premium: $206.40 + $82.00 + $230.00 = **$518.40**, Annual premium: $518.40 × 4.10 = **$2,125.44**

SECTION 9-5 CONCEPT CHECK (p. 328)

1. Total cost: **$3,600**, Cost per mile: **$0.36**
2. Total cost: **$4,628.50**, Cost per mile: **$0.3857 or $0.39**
3. Depreciation: $4,800 ÷ 3 = **$1,600**
   Variable cost: **$795.60**
   Fixed cost: ($1,600.00 + $2,350.00 + $132.50 + $1,080.00) = **$5,162.50**
   Total cost: **$5,958.10**
   Cost per mile: **$0.44**

SECTION 9-6 CONCEPT CHECK (p. 331)

1. **$15,756.86**   2. **$10,779.95**   3. **$8,608.00**

SECTION 9-7 CONCEPT CHECK (p. 334)

1. ($30.00 × 4) + ($0.22 × 430) + $18.90 = **$233.50**
2. $233.50 ÷ 430 = **$0.543 or $0.54**
3. ($45.50 × 5) + ($0.25 × 126) + $77.88 + ($15.50 × 5)
   $227.50 + $31.50 + $77.88 + $77.50 = **$414.38**
   $414.38 ÷ (112 + 162 + 95 + 180 + 144) =
   $414.38 ÷ 693 = **$0.59795 or $0.60**

Living in the Real World

A Hard One to Pick

Analyze the Story Gomez's new truck will depreciate in value most rapidly since it's new. You can estimate how your vehicle will depreciate by looking at the value of older vehicles of the same model. Depreciation is often expressed as a percent of the purchase price.

Maintenance and repair costs tend to increase as a vehicle ages. You can estimate these costs by talking with mechanics and with people who own the same model. Consumer and automobile magazines sometimes have articles comparing these costs for various models.

1 **Calculating.** Imagine Gomez loses 18 percent of the truck's purchase price (less tax) the first year, 15 percent of its purchase price (less tax) the second year, and 12 percent the third year.
- What is the total percent?
- How much will the truck be worth in 3 years?
- What is the average depreciation a month?

2 **Determining.** Gomez plans to drive it 12,000 miles per year. Gasoline costs $1.295 per gallon. Her new truck gets 20 miles per gallon. What is the cost of her gasoline per month?

REVIEW OF KEY WORDS

sticker price (p. 314)
base price (p. 314)
options (p. 314)
destination charge (p. 314)
dealer's cost (p. 317)

used-vehicle guides (p. 320)
liability insurance (p. 323)
comprehensive insurance (p. 323)
collision insurance (p. 323)
deductible clause (p. 323)

variable costs (p. 327)
fixed costs (p. 327)
depreciation (p. 327)
lease (p. 330)
rent (p. 333)

Use one of the key words above in each of the sentences.

1. A decrease in the value of your car because of its age or condition is called **depreciation**

2. If you do not own an automobile but need to use one on occasion, you can **rent** one from a rental agency.

3. The _____ in your insurance policy states that you must pay a portion of any repair bill. **deductible clause**

4. The _____ is the cost of shipping the vehicle from the factory to the dealership.

5. The total of the base price, the options price, and the destination charge is the **sticker price**.

6. The _____ is often reported as a percent of the sticker price. **dealer's cost**

7. The _____ give the average prices for vehicles that were purchased from dealers during the previous month. **used-vehicle guides**

8. _____ on your vehicle protects you from losses caused by fire, vandalism, and theft.

9. Gasoline and tires are examples of _____.

10. Insurance, registration fees, and depreciation are examples of **fixed costs**

8. comprehensive insurance
9. variable costs

4. destination charge

5. Mark Adams drove his sedan 11,700 miles last year. Fixed costs totaled $3,563. Variable costs totaled $1,288. What was the total annual cost? **($4,851)** What was the cost per mile? **$0.41 per mile**

6. Lease a sports car for 48 payments of $499. Deposit of $4,000. Title fee of $55. License fee of $90. What is the total lease cost? **$28,079**

7. Selene Byrne rented a full size car for 4 days at the rate of $44.97 per day. The rental agreement included unlimited mileage. She took the collision waiver for $11.95 per day. She drove the car 368 miles and paid $34.63 for gasoline. What is the total cost of renting the car? **($262.31)** What is the rate per mile? **$0.71 per mile**

Living in the Real World

1. What is the total percent? 45%
How much will the truck be worth in three years? 55% of purchase price
What is the average depreciation a month? 1.25%

2. $64.75

CHAPTER 9 Study Guide and Assessment

Skills and Concepts

SECTION OBJECTIVE 9-1 AND EXAMPLES

Compute the sticker price of a new vehicle.

Timothy Darling wants to buy a new car. He has been pricing a new car that has a base price of $18,705.00. He is interested in several options that total $4,326.54. The destination charge is $654.00. Find the sticker price.

STEP: Find the sticker price.

Base Price + Options + Destination Charge = **$23,685.54**
$18,705.00 + $4,326.54 + $654.00   sticker price

REVIEW EXERCISES
Find the sticker price.

	Base Price	Options	Destination Charge	Sticker Price
11.	$11,500	$1,750	$450	**$13,700**
12.	12,430	2,390	340	**$15,160**
13.	15,400	3,244	458	**$19,102**
14.	21,000	4,459	654	**$26,113**

SECTION OBJECTIVE 9-2 AND EXAMPLES

Calculate the dealer's cost of a new vehicle.

Hal O'Brien wants to purchase a new sports car. The car has a base price of $25,000, options totaling $2,190, and a destination charge of $643. He read in a consumer magazine that the dealer's cost for the car was about 91 percent of the base price and 87.5 percent of the options price. What should he estimate as the dealer's cost?

STEP 1: Find the percent of the base price. $25,000.00 × 91.0% = **$22,750.00** base price

STEP 2: Find the percent of the options price. $2,190.00 × 87.5% = **$1,916.25** options price

STEP 3: Find the dealer's cost.

Percent of Base Price + Percent of Options Price + Destination Charge = **$25,309.25**
$22,750.00 + $1,916.25 + $643.00   dealer's cost

REVIEW EXERCISES
Find the dealers cost.

	Base Price	×	Dealer's Percent	+	Options Price	×	Dealer's Percent	+	Destination Charge	=	Dealer's Cost
15.	$13,500	×	90%	+	$3,500	×	85%	+	$450	=	**$15,575**
16.	11,600	×	88%	+	2,300	×	91%	+	362	=	**$12,663**
17.	21,500	×	82%	+	4,500	×	76%	+	782	=	**$21,832**
18.	32,000	×	86%	+	3,400	×	81%	+	654	=	**$30,928**

REINFORCEMENT

Section 9-1
1. Sports car, base price is $19,015. Options: sport appearance package $1,224, power driver's seat $246, premium sound system $319, removable hatch roof panels $905, destination charge is $600. What is the sticker price? **$22,309**
2. Sports utility vehicle, base price is $26,630. Options: power sunroof $704, supplemental side airbags $431, security alarm $132, destination charge is $625. What is the sticker price? **$28,522**

Section 9-2
1. A hatchback's base price is $10,249. The options total $910. The destination charge is $495. Dealer pays about 93.5 percent of base price and 77 percent of options. What is the dealer's cost? **$10,778.52**

SECTION OBJECTIVE 9-3 AND EXAMPLES

Figure out the average retail price of a used vehicle.

A used vehicle is advertised for $13,490. It has air-conditioning, power seats, and a power sunroof. These options add an additional $1,020. It has 85,000 miles and the used-vehicle guide recommends $540 be subtracted if the mileage exceeds 30,000. What is the average retail price for this used vehicle?

STEP: Find the average retail price.

$$\underset{\$13,490}{\underset{\text{Retail Value}}{\text{Average}}} + \underset{\$1,020}{\underset{\text{Options}}{\text{Additional}}} - \underset{\$0}{\underset{\text{Deductions}}{\text{Option}}} - \underset{\$540}{\underset{\text{Deduction}}{\text{Mileage}}} = \$13,970 \text{ average retail price}$$

19. $14,500 + $150 + $700 − $600 − $560 = $14,190

20. $2,600 + $100 + $50 − $600 = $2,150

REVIEW EXERCISES

19. A four-wheel drive vehicle has an average retail price of $14,500. Add $150 for a tilt steering wheel. Add $700 for air conditioning. Deduct $600 for manual transmission. Deduct $560 for excessive mileage. What is the average retail price?

20. Donald Alsott owns a compact car, which he wants to trade in for a new car. He is interested in knowing the average wholesale price. He uses the Internet and finds out that the average wholesale price is $2,600. He adds $100 for power windows and $50 for a tilt steering wheel. He deducts $600 for no air-conditioning. What is the average wholesale price?

21. A two-year-old convertible has an average retail value of $14,800. Add $300 for a sunroof. Add $150 for a CD player. Deduct $560 for excessive mileage. What is the average retail price? **$14,690**

22. A five-year-old luxury vehicle has an average retail value of $17,800. Add $450 for a tilt steering wheel. Add $400 for a surround-sound speaker system. Deduct $660 for excessive mileage. What is the average retail price? **$17,990**

23. Carol Pelfrey owns a three-year-old sedan. One used-vehicle guide shows that the average retail value of her car is $8,500. She adds $100 for power windows and $125 for power seats. She also adds $450 for low mileage. However, she deducts $150 for a broken trunk lock. What is the average retail price for her car? **$9,025**

SECTION OBJECTIVE 9-4 AND EXAMPLES

Use tables to compute the annual premium for vehicle insurance.

Use Figure 9.3 on page 324 to solve the following problems.

Sheryl Edwards has a driver-rating factor of 2.1. Her insurance includes 100/200 bodily injury and $25,000 property damages. Her vehicle is in age group C and insurance-rating group 12 (C, 12). She has a $50-deductible comprehensive and $50-deductible collision insurance. What is her annual base premium? What is her annual premium?

STEP 1: Find the annual base premium.

$$\underset{\$252.00}{\text{Liability Premium}} + \underset{\$86.00}{\text{Comprehensive Premium}} + \underset{\$241.60}{\text{Collision Premium}} = \$579.60 \text{ annual base premium}$$

Continued on next page

REINFORCEMENT

Section 9-3

1. Minivan. Average retail value is $13,375. Add $500 for left sliding door. Add $175 for power seat. Add $375 for rear air conditioning. Deduct $175 without cruise control. Deduct $125 without tilt wheel. No adjustment for mileage. What is the average price? **$14,125**

Section 9-4

Refer to **Figure 9.3** on page 324.

1. Driver-rating factor is 2.0. Age, rating group is C, 15. Coverage: 300/300 bodily injury, $100,000 property damage, $50-deductible comprehensive, and $50-deductible collision. What is the annual base premium? **($720.80)** What is the annual premium? **$1,441.60**

28. $1,589.56 + $245.98 + $548.11 = $2,383.65 variable expenses; $1,105.32 + $85 = $1,190.32 fixed expenses; $\frac{\$2,383.65 + \$1,190.32}{13,569}$ = **$0.26 per mile**

24. $237.20 + $77.60 + $233.20 = $548 annual base premium
$548 × 1.45 = $794.60

25. $272.40 + $122.00 + $307.60 = $702 annual base premium

STEP 2: Find the annual premium. $702 × 3.85 = $2,702.70

Base Premium × Driver-Rating Factor
$579.60 × 2.10 = **$1,217.16 annual premium**

REVIEW EXERCISES

24. Driver-rating factor is 1.45. Age and rating group is B, 11. Coverage: 50/100 bodily injury. $50,000 property damage. $50-deductible comprehensive. $50-deductible collision. What is the annual base premium? What is the annual premium?

25. Yvette Ramirez uses her car to drive to and from work. Her driver-rating factor is 3.85. Her insurance coverage includes 100/300 bodily injury and $100,000 property damage. Her car is in age group A and insurance-rating group 14. What is her annual base premium? What is her annual premium?

Use Figure 9.3 on page 324 to solve these problems.

	Driver-Rating Factor	Age, Rating Group	Bodily Injury	Property Damage	Comprehensive (Deductible)	Collision (Deductible)	Annual Base Premium	Annual Premium
26.	3.2	B, 12	50/100	$ 50,000	$50	$50	a.	b.
27.	1.2	D, 14	100/300	100,000	50	50	a.	b.

26. a. $580.80
b. $1,858.56

27. a. $642.80
b. $771.36

SECTION OBJECTIVE 9-5 AND EXAMPLES

Compute the total cost per mile of operating and maintaining a vehicle.

Jackson McCormick purchased a used car a year ago. He drove 8,564 miles during the year and kept a record of all his expenses. He figured the annual variable cost to be $1,342.90. His annual fixed costs were $905.44. Find the cost per mile.

STEP: Find the cost per mile. $\frac{\text{Annual Variable Cost} + \text{Annual Fixed Cost}}{\text{Number of Miles Driven}}$

$$\frac{\$1,342.90 + \$905.44}{8,564} = \frac{\$2,248.34}{8,564} = \$0.2625 \text{ or } \$0.26 \text{ per mile}$$

REVIEW EXERCISES

28. Two years ago Ernest Dorsey purchased a 1997 vehicle for $8,000.00, and it is worth $6,000.00 today. Last year he drove it 13,569 miles and kept a record of all his expenses. His variable costs included gasoline, $1,589.56; oil changes, $245.98; and repairs, $548.11. His fixed costs were insurance, $1,105.32; and license, $85.00. What is the cost per mile?

	Annual Variable Cost	Annual Fixed Cost	Total Annual Cost	Miles Driven	Cost per Mile
29.	$1,300.00	$3,287.33	a. $4,587.33	9,500	b. $0.48
30.	1,549.98	1,200.31	a. $2,750.29	11,500	b. $0.24
31.	1,139.45	2,300.88	a. $3,440.33	14,546	b. $0.24

REINFORCEMENT

Section 9-4 *(cont'd)*

2. Janet O'Rourke uses her car primarily for business. She has $50-deductible comprehensive, $50-deductible collision, 100/200 bodily injury, and $50,000 property damage. Her driver-rating factor is 3.2 and her vehicle is classified as C, 14. What is her annual base premium? **($646.80)** What is her annual premium? **$2,069.76**

Section 9-5

1. Kim Leung drove a SUV 11,500 miles. Fixed costs totaled $3,343. Variable costs totaled $1,511. What was the total annual cost? **($4,854)** What was the cost per mile? **$0.42 per mile**

2. Lester Mantano drove his compact pickup 10,400 miles. Fixed costs totaled $2,671. Variable costs totaled $1,090. What was the total annual cost? **($3,761)** What was the cost per mile? **$0.36 per mile**

SECTION OBJECTIVE 9-6 AND EXAMPLES

Calculate the total cost of leasing a vehicle.

Penny Fountain leased a vehicle. She pays $403.50 per month for 48 months. Her deposit was $1,600. She paid a $75 title fee and a $55 license fee. What is her total lease cost?

STEP: Find the total lease cost.

$$\left(\begin{array}{c} \text{Number of} \\ \text{Payments} \end{array} \times \begin{array}{c} \text{Amount of} \\ \text{Payment} \end{array}\right) + \text{Deposit} + \begin{array}{c} \text{Title} \\ \text{Fee} \end{array} + \begin{array}{c} \text{License} \\ \text{Fee} \end{array}$$

$$(48 \quad \times \quad \$403.50) + \$1,600 + \$75 + \$55 = \$21,098 \text{ total least cost}$$

REVIEW EXERCISES
Find the total of payments and the total lease cost.

	(Number of Payments	×	Amount of Payment	=	Total of Payments)	+	Deposit	+	Title Fee	+	License Fee	=	Total Lease Cost
32.	(24	×	$189	=	a.	) +	$ 660	+	$10	+	$35	=	b.
33.	(24	×	208	=	a.	) +	590	+	15	+	39	=	b.
34.	(30	×	316	=	a.	) +	1,240	+	35	+	55	=	b.
35.	(36	×	185	=	a.	) +	1,500	+	65	+	89	=	b.

32. a. $4,536
    b. $5,241
33. a. $4,992
    b. $5,636
34. a. $9,480
    b. $10,810
35. a. $6,660
    b. $8,314

SECTION OBJECTIVE 9-7 AND EXAMPLES

Figure out the cost per mile of renting a vehicle.

Wheels & Deals had a rental car special last weekend on sedans for $9.99 per day plus $0.33 per mile. If Tonya Strickler rented one for 3 days, drove 865 miles, and paid $32.08 for gas, what was the total cost of renting the sedan? What was the total cost per mile to rent the vehicle?

STEP 1: Find the total cost.

$9.99 × 3 days =	$ 29.97
$0.33 × 865 miles =	285.45
Gasoline =	32.08
	$347.50 total cost

STEP 2: Find the cost per mile.

$$\frac{\text{Total Cost}}{\text{Number of Miles Driven}}$$

$347.50 ÷ 865 =

$0.40 cost per mile

REVIEW EXERCISES
Find the cost per mile to the nearest cent.

	(Total Daily Cost	+	Total Mileage Cost	+	Gasoline Cost	=	Total Cost)	÷	Miles Driven	=	Cost per Mile
36.	($ 45.95	+	$35.00	+	$12.54	=	a.	) ÷	365	=	b.
37.	(110.00	+	39.95	+	18.87	=	a.	) ÷	865	=	b.

36. a. $93.49
    b. $0.26
37. a. $168.82
    b. $0.20

Find the cost per mile to the nearest cent (no mileage charge).

	Rental Cost	Gasoline Cost	Total Cost	Miles Driven	Cost per Mile
38.	$ 65.35	$25.49	a. $90.84	409	b. $0.22
39.	115.85	54.39	a. $170.24	875	b. $0.19

REINFORCEMENT

Section 9-6
1. Lease a four-door car for 48 payments of $269.69 per month. Deposit of $269.69. Title fee of $60. License fee of $75. What is the total lease cost? **$13,349.81**

Section 9-7
1. Gina Durkin rented a car for 3 days at the cost of $35 per day plus $0.20 per mile. She took the collision waiver for $9.95 per day. She drove the car 652 miles. Gasoline cost $57. What was the total cost of renting the car? **($322.25)** What was the cost per mile **$0.49 per mile**

2. Guadalupe Hernandez rented a car for 1 week at the weekly rate of $229 plus $0.25 per mile. She took the collision waiver for $10.75 per day. She drove 373 miles. Gasoline cost $23.87. What was the total cost of renting the car? **($421.37)** What was the cost per mile? **$1.13 per mile**

National Standards for Business Education

Section Objectives	1. Mathematical Foundations	2. Number Relationships and Operations	3. Patterns, Functions, and Algebra	4. Measurements	5. Statistics and Probability	6. Problem-Solving Applications
10-1 Mortgage Loans (pp. 344–345) Compute the mortgage loan amount.	X	X				
10-2 Monthly Payment and Total Interest (pp. 346–348) Determine the monthly payment, total amount paid, and total interest charged.	X	X				
10-3 Closing Costs (pp. 349–350) Figure out the total closing costs.	X	X				
10-4 The Monthly Payment (pp. 351–354) Compute the allocation of monthly payment toward principal, interest, and the new principal.	X	X				
10-5 Real Estate Taxes (pp. 355–356) Calculate the assessed value and real estate taxes.	X	X				
10-6 Homeowners Insurance (pp. 357–358) Work out the amount of coverage.	X	X				
10-7 Homeowners Insurance Premium (pp. 359–360) Calculate the annual homeowners insurance premium.	X	X				
10-8 Other Housing Costs (pp. 361–363) Compute the total housing cost and compare it with suggested guidelines.	X	X				

(Source: Reprinted with permission from the National Standards for Business Education, copyright © 2001 by National Business Education Association, 1914 Association Drive, Reston, Virginia 21901-1596)

SCANS Correlation

Foundation Skills

Basic Skills	Reading	Writing	Math	Listening	Speaking	
Thinking Skills	Creative Thinking	Decision Making	Problem Solving	Seeing Things in the Mind's Eye	Knowing How to Learn	Reasoning
Personal Qualities	Responsibility	Self-Esteem	Sociability	Self-Management	Integrity/Honesty	

This chapter's highlighted blocks indicate the chapter's content coverage in the Student Edition and the Teacher Wraparound Edition.

1. Numbers & Operations	2. Algebra	3. Geometry	4. Measurement	5. Data Analysis & Probability	6. Problem Solving	7. Reasoning & Proof	8. Communication	9. Connections	10. Representations
X			X		X		X	X	
X			X		X		X	X	
X			X		X		X	X	
X			X		X		X	X	
X			X		X		X	X	
X			X		X		X	X	
X			X		X		X	X	
X			X		X		X	X	

SCANS Correlation

Workplace Competencies

Resources	Allocating Time	Allocating Money	Allocating Material and Facility Resources	Allocating Human Resources		
Information	Acquiring and Evaluating Information	Organizing and Maintaining Information	Interpreting and Communicating Information	Using Computers to Process Information		
Interpersonal Skills	Participating as a Member of a Team	Teaching Others	Serving Clients/Customers	Exercising Leadership	Negotiating to Arrive at a Decision	Working with Cultural Diversity
Systems	Understanding Systems	Monitoring and Correcting Performance	Improving and Designing Systems			
Technology	Selecting Technology	Applying Technology to Task	Maintaining and Troubleshooting Technology			

What You'll Learn

In this chapter you'll investigate costs associated with owning a home, such as a mortgage, insurance, and maintenance.

Why It's Important

The single, largest purchase that most people make in their lifetime is that of a home. Purchasing a home and making a mortgage payment requires significant planning. There are many costs in owning a home that aren't readily apparent. Knowledge of all the costs will ensure that you're prepared to purchase.

Key Word Review

Home Buyer's Vocabulary

Students produce a "Home Buyer's Vocabulary" pamphlet listing the key words in alphabetical order, with their definition. Students may use word processing or publishing software and illustrate their pamphlet with graphics.
`LS` , `CL` , `P`

CHAPTER 10

Housing Costs

What You'll Learn

Section 10-1 Compute the mortgage loan amount.

Section 10-2 Determine the monthly payment, total amount paid, and total interest charged.

Section 10-3 Figure out the total closing costs.

Section 10-4 Compute the allocation of monthly payment toward principal, interest, and the new principal.

Section 10-5 Calculate the assessed value and real estate taxes.

Section 10-6 Work out the amount of coverage.

Section 10-7 Calculate the annual homeowners insurance premium.

Section 10-8 Compute the total housing cost and compare it with suggested guidelines.

When Will You Ever Use This?

Shelter is one of life's basic needs, right after water and food. At some point in your life you might want to buy a house and make it your home. In doing so you'll need to take into consideration all the costs involved in buying a house.

Key Words to Know

- mortgage loan
- interest
- closing costs
- principal
- real estate taxes
- assessed value
- tax rate
- market value
- rate of assessment
- homeowners insurance
- loss-of-use coverage
- personal liability
- medical coverage
- replacement value
- premium
- fire protection class
- utility costs

Mathematics Online

To learn more about buying a house, visit the *Mathematics with Business Applications* Web site at www.busmath.glencoe.com.

CLASSROOM RESOURCES

Application and Enrichment

- 🖘 *Teacher Wraparound Edition*
- 🖘 *Teacher Resource Binder, Blackline Masters*
- 💿 *Interactive Lesson Planner* CD-ROM
- 💿 *PowerPoint® Presentations* CD-ROM

Review and Enforcement

Mathematics Online
  www.busmath.glencoe.com
- 🖘 *Teacher Resource Binder, Internet Resources*

- 🖘 *Student Activity Workbook*
- 🖘 *Student Activity Workbook, Teacher Annotated Edition*
- 🖘 *School-to-Home Activity Workbook*

Assessment and Evaluation

- 🖘 *Assessment Binder, Reproducible Tests*
- 🖘 *Assessment Binder, Alternative Assessment Strategies*
- 💿 **Exam***View®* *Pro Test Generator* CD-ROM

For the Teacher

- 🖘 *Student Activity Workbook, Teacher Annotated Edition*
- 🖘 *Assessment Binder*
- 💿 *Interactive Lesson Planner* CD-ROM
- 🖘 *Teacher Resource Binder*
- 🖥 Mathematics Online
    www.busmath.glencoe.com

For the Student

- 🖘 *Student Activity Workbook*
- 🖘 *School-to-Home Activity Workbook*

Living in the Real World

The Hunt to Find a Home

Sometimes finding the right house at the right price in the right location is nothing short of a miracle. In this chapter you'll follow a family searching for a home.

Read on. Go to . . .

343

Living in the Real World

Story's Summary
Shereen and Torian Sultan are first-time homebuyers looking for a house in a safe neighborhood with a nearby school for their kids. By reading about the Sultans' experience, students learn about interest rates, monthly mortgage payments, homeowners insurance, and additional housing costs.

Did You Know...
According to U.S. Census Bureau, 67.8 percent of residents own their home.

Think about This
For most people, buying a home is a sound investment that makes financial sense. Why is this true? When is it not? **Home prices usually continue to climb after purchase, so a seller can make money when it's time to sell. There are tax incentives to buying a home, and mortgage interest is tax deductible. If a person moves a lot for job reasons, buying a house may not make financial sense.**

LOCAL STANDARDS

National Standards for Business Education

Standard 1	Mathematical Foundations
Standard 2	Number Relationships and Operations

National Council of Teachers of Mathematics Standards

Standard 1	Numbers and Operations
Standard 4	Measurement
Standard 6	Problem Solving
Standard 8	Communication
Standard 9	Connections

① FOCUS

Bring to class the real estate section of your local newspaper. Read a variety of advertisements of houses for sale. Select one home in the $100,000 range, and ask students if they know anyone who could pay for the house in cash. Explain that very few homes today are purchased outright. Instead, most people need to borrow money. In this section, students will compute the amount that is borrowed, which is called a mortgage loan.

In-Class Examples

Work through these exercises with students before having them do the Self-Check.

1. 20% of $40,000 **$8,000**
2. 25% of $30,000 **$7,500**
3. 30% of $120,000 **$36,000**
4. $60,000 − $12,000 **$48,000**

SECTION 10-1 Mortgage Loans

○ Section Objective

Compute the mortgage loan amount.

When you purchase a home, first you'll make a down payment. Generally, the down payment is between 10 percent and 40 percent of the selling price, although many first-time homeowners put down 5 percent.

You finance the remaining portion of the selling price with a **mortgage loan** from a lender, such as a bank, savings and loan association, credit union, or mortgage company. The mortgage gives the lender the right to seize and sell the property if you fail to make the payments. The mortgage loan is usually repaid with interest in equal monthly payments. Remember that:

Mortgage Loan Amount = Selling Price − Down Payment

Living in the Real World

The Hunt to Find a Home

Looking at Life 15 or 30 Years from Now Shereen and Torian Sultan are driving through the various neighborhoods in their Texas town to look at houses. They have two children and want to buy a house in a safe neighborhood close to a school.

Draw Conclusions Why do you think a majority of homeowners take out 15- to 30-year mortgages as opposed to a 5-year mortgage?

Continued on page 346

Example 1

Need Help? Go to...
- ► **Workshop 14: Finding a Percentage**, page 30
- ► **Skill 30: Finding the Percentage**, page 757
- ► **Skill 4: Subtracting Whole Numbers**, page 731
- ► **Skill 6: Subtracting Decimals**, page 733

Jessica and Kirk Cramer consider purchasing a new home for $140,000. A 15 percent down payment is required. What is the amount of the mortgage loan needed to finance the purchase?

STEP 1: Find the down payment.
$140,000 \times 15\% = \$21,000$

STEP 2: Find the mortgage loan amount.
Selling Price − Down Payment
$140,000 \quad - \quad \$21,000 \quad = \textbf{\$119,000 mortgage loan amount}$

140000 ⊠ 15 % 21000   140000 ⊟ 21000 ⊟ 119000

Living in the Real World

A 15- or 30-year mortgage will allow smaller, more manageable monthly payments than a 5-year mortgage.

BUSINESS NOTES

Home Values

A number of factors affect the value of a house, including its size, age, condition, and location. Location is especially important. A house that seems like a bargain might turn out to be in a bad neighborhood or in the flight path of a nearby airport. Students check out local home price listings in the newspaper or online. Students discuss in class why some homes cost more than others.

CONCEPT CHECK

SELF-CHECK ✓

Complete the problems, then check your answers at the end of the chapter.
Find the down payment and the amount of the mortgage.

1. It has a $80,000 selling price.
You put down 25 percent.

2. It has a $200,000 selling price.
You put down 30 percent.

1. $80,000 × 0.25 = $20,000; $80,000 − $20,000 = $60,000

2. $200,000 × 0.30 = $60,000; $200,000 − $60,000 = $140,000

SECTION 10-1 PRACTICE

Buyer	Selling Price	Portion of Down Payment	Amount of Down Payment	Mortgage Loan Amount
3. Sumika Ganet	$ 87,000	20%	$17,400	a. $69,600
4. Carla Gonzalez	62,500	25%	a. $15,625	b. $46,875
5. Albert Nash	298,800	$\frac{1}{4}$	a. $74,700	b. $224,100
6. Dario Valencia	156,000	$\frac{2}{5}$	a. $62,400	b. $93,600

7. David and Peggy Chin. Modular home is priced at $77,400. They made a 20 percent down payment. What is the mortgage loan amount? **$61,920**

8. Alvira and Berry Fukunaga. Home is priced at $280,000. They put down $\frac{2}{5}$. What is the mortgage loan amount? **$168,000**

9. Rita and Alfred Johnson offered $85,000 for a home that had been priced at $90,000. The Johnsons and the seller agreed on a selling price of $86,500. What is the amount of the mortgage loan if they make a 20 percent down payment? **$69,200**

10. Richard Darman offered $112,500 for a home that had been priced at $125,000. The seller agreed to the offer. A bank is willing to finance the purchase if he can make a down payment of $\frac{1}{4}$ of the selling price. What is the amount of his mortgage loan? **$84,375**

11. The Hasbros have purchased a duplex. They would use the rental income from one part of the duplex to help meet the mortgage payments. A selling price of $100,800 was agreed upon. What is the amount of the mortgage loan if a down payment of 30 percent is required? **$70,560**

12. Dan and Sue Willingham have saved $14,000 for a down payment on their future home. Their bank has informed them that the minimum down payment required to obtain a mortgage loan is 20 percent. What is the most that they can spend for a home and expect to receive bank approval for their loan? **$70,000**

MAINTAINING YOUR SKILLS

Need Help? Go to...
➤ Skill 30: Finding the Percentage, page 757
➤ Skill 4: Subtracting Whole Numbers, page 731

Find the percentage.

13. 15% of 40,000 **$6,000** **14.** $\frac{1}{4}$ of 84,000 **$21,000** **15.** 20% of 90,000 **$18,000**

Subtract.

16. 40,000 − 8,400 **31,600** **17.** 94,000 − 18,000 **76,000** **18.** 180,000 − 36,000 **144,000**

Section 10-1 Mortgage Loans ▶ **345**

COOPERATIVE LEARNING

Dollars Down
Find the dollar amount of the down payment and the mortgage loan amount:

	Cash Price	Percent Down	Amount Down	Mortgage Loan Amount
1.	120,000	25%	$30,000	$90,000
2.	160,000	30%	$48,000	$112,000

WRAP-UP

Go over any problem for which a wrong answer is given.

Assignment Guide
Basic: 3–6
Average: 7–8

20 min.

② TEACH

When discussing the examples, point out to students that the complement of the down payment of 15 percent is 85 percent, which can be used to find the mortgage amount. Write on the board: 85 percent of $140,000 is _?_. Ask a volunteer to work the problem at the board. Suggest that students check their answers to mortgage amounts by using the complement method.

In-Class Example
Selling price: $105,000.
Down payment: 15 percent.
What is the down payment? ($15,750) What is the amount of the mortgage? $89,250

③ ASSESS

Error Analysis
Review with students how to change a percent to a decimal. Remind them that a percent is a part of 100. For example, 25 percent is the same as $\frac{25}{100}$, or 0.25. To find 25 percent of 200, multiply 0.25 × 200. The answer is 50.

④ CLOSE

Closing Activity
1. The Quintos bought a home for $232,000. They made a down payment of 30 percent. What is the down payment? ($69,600) What is the mortgage amount? **$162,400**

2. The Jennets bought a home for $147,500. They made a down payment of 20 percent. What is the down payment? ($29,500) What is the mortgage amount? **$118,000**

National Standards for Business Education

Standard 1	Mathematical Foundations
Standard 2	Number Relationships and Operations

National Council of Teachers of Mathematics Standards

Standard 1	Numbers and Operations
Standard 4	Measurement
Standard 6	Problem Solving
Standard 8	Communication
Standard 9	Connections

FOCUS

When applying for a mortgage loan, it is smart to shop around for the lowest rate available. Ask students why people shop for a low rate. In this lesson, the answer to this question will be clear after students learn how to compute the total payment, amount paid, and total interest charged.

In-Class Examples
Work through these exercises with students before having them do the Self-Check.

1. $10.67 × 42 **$448.14**
2. $384.84 × 300 **$115,452**
3. $448.14 × 20 × 12 **$107,553.60**
4. $683.43 × 30 × 12 **$246,034.80**
5. (120 × $450) − $30,000 **$24,000**
6. (180 × $1,274.60) − $146,244 **$83,184**

○ **Section Objective**

Determine the monthly payment, total amount paid, and total interest charged.

SECTION 10-2 Monthly Payment and Total Interest

Lenders that make mortgage loans charge **interest**. This is the amount of money paid for the use of the lender's money. The interest rate will vary from lender to lender, so it pays to shop around. If you know the annual interest rate, the amount of the loan, and the length of the loan, you can use a table to find the monthly payment, total amount paid, and total interest charged. It looks like this:

Figure 10.1

Interest Rate	Length of Loan in Years		
	20	25	30
5.00%	$6.60	$5.85	$5.37
5.50%	6.88	6.14	5.68
6.00%	7.16	6.44	6.00
6.50%	7.46	6.75	6.32
7.00%	7.75	7.07	6.65
7.50%	8.06	7.39	6.99
8.00%	8.36	7.72	7.34
8.50%	8.68	8.05	7.69

Monthly Payment for a $1,000 Loan*

*An expanded form can be found in the Appendices on page 799.

$$\text{Monthly Payment} = \frac{\text{Amount of Mortgage}}{\$1,000} \times \text{Monthly Payment for } \$1,000 \text{ Loan}$$

Amount Paid = Monthly Payment × Number of Payments

Total Interest Charged = Amount Paid − Amount of Mortgage

Living in the Real World

The Hunt to Find a Home

Curb Appeal Torian slows down their car, and he and Shereen look at a small stone house with shutters and a flower garden. They are so excited, neither of them notices the front porch is sagging and the roof needs replacing.

"I'm just hoping interest rates will go down soon," Shereen says, "so we won't have to pay so much each month."

Draw Conclusions Can you shop around for mortgage rates or are they all the same no matter where you go?

Continued on page 349

Living in the Real World

Mortgage interest rates often vary between banking institutions. An astute homebuyer will shop around and compare rates at several different lenders.

PROBLEM SOLVING

What Can You Afford?
The first step in buying a home is to determine what you can afford. You will need to decide how much you can put down and how much of a monthly payment you can afford. The rule of thumb is that you should pay no more than 30 percent of your gross income per month. If your gross income is $2,000 a month, what can you afford in monthly mortgage payments?
$2,000 × 0.30 = **$600 a month**

Example 1

Need Help? Go to...
→ Workshop 6: Multiplying Decimals, page 14
→ Workshop 5: Subtracting Decimals, page 12
→ Skill 8: Multiplying Decimals, page 735
→ Skill 6: Subtracting Decimals, page 733

Carol and Adam Burke have applied for an $80,000.00 mortgage loan at an annual interest rate of 8.00 percent. The loan is for a period of 30 years and will be paid in equal monthly payments that include interest. What is the total amount of interest charged?

STEP 1: Find the monthly payment. (Refer to the Monthly Payment for a $1,000 Loan table on page 799.)

$$\frac{\text{Amount of Mortgage}}{\$1,000} \times \frac{\text{Monthly Payment}}{\text{for } \$1,000 \text{ Loan}}$$

$$\frac{\$80,000.00}{\$1000.00} \times \$7.34$$

$$= \$587.20$$

STEP 2: Find the amount paid.

Monthly Payment × Number of Payments
$587.20 × (12 months × 30 years)
$587.20 × 360
$$= \$211,392.00$$

STEP 3: Find the total interest charged.

Amount Paid − Amount of Mortgage
$211,392.00 − $80,000.00 = **$131,392.00 total interest**

1. $\frac{\$90,000.00}{\$1,000.00} \times \$9.65$
= $868.50 monthly payment; $868.50 × 12 × 20 = $208,440.00 amount paid; $208,440.00 − $90,000.00 = $118,440.00 interest charged

80000 ÷ 1000 × 7.34 = 587.2 × 12 × 30 =

211392 − 80000 = 131392

CONCEPT CHECK

SELF-CHECK ✓

Complete the problem, then check your answers at the end of the chapter. Use the Monthly Payment for a $1,000 Loan table on page 799.

1. Find the monthly payment, amount paid, and interest charged for a $90,000 mortgage loan at an annual interest rate of 10 percent for 20 years.

SECTION 10-2 PRACTICE

Use the Monthly Payment for a $1,000 Loan table on page 799 to solve.

2. a. $387.50
   b. $93,000.00
   c. $43,000.00
3. a. $540.40
   b. $162,120.00
   c. $92,120.00
4. a. $764.75
   b. $275,310.00
   c. $180,310.00
5. a. $2,151.00
   b. $387,180.00
   c. $162,180.00
6. a. $3,468.10
   b. $1,248,516.00
   c. $853,516.00

	Mortgage	Years	Rate	Payment	Amount Paid	Total Interest
2.	$ 50,000	20	7.00%	a.	b.	c.
3.	70,000	25	8.00%	a.	b.	c.
4.	95,000	30	9.00%	a.	b.	c.
5.	225,000	15	8.00%	a.	b.	c.
6.	395,000	30	10.00%	a.	b.	c.

Continued on next page

---

2 TEACH

After working through the examples, students will be surprised at the total amount paid for the loan. Point out that in Example 1, the total amount paid is over $1\frac{1}{2}$ times the amount of the original loan of $80,000.

Although the difference in a monthly payment for a loan having an interest rate of 7 percent and one having an 8 percent rate may seem relatively small, when the amount and time period of a loan are great, the difference can be substantial. Have students compute the loan of Example 1 using a 7 percent interest rate. (**$532 monthly payment; $191,520 total amount paid; $111,520 interest paid.**) Ask them also to find the amount saved if the interest rate was 7 percent rather than 8 percent. **$19,872 saved in interest**

In-Class Examples

For Problems 1–7, refer to Monthly Payment for $1,000 Loan on page 799.

1. Mortgage: $110,000.
   Terms: 5.5 percent for 30 years.
   a. What is the monthly payment? **$624.80**
   b. What is the total amount paid? **$224,928**
   c. What is the interest charged? **$114,928**
2. Mortgage: $165,000.
   Terms: 6.5 percent for 25 years.
   a. What is the monthly payment? **$1,113.75**
   b. What is the total amount paid? **$334,125**
   c. What is the interest charged? **$169,125**
3. Selling price: $195,000.
   Down payment: 20 percent.
   Terms: 6 percent for 30 years.
   What is the total interest charged? **$180,960**

ALTERNATIVE ASSESSMENT

Strategies

Have each student choose one concept presented in this chapter and teach it to someone outside the class—perhaps a friend or family member. Ask students to also teach the concept to the class. If possible, take a photograph of each student as he or she presents the lesson. Have students type an account of their teaching strategy, including their name and their photograph to place on a bulletin-board display. LS , CL , P

COMMUNICATION SKILLS

Chart or Diagram

Charts or diagrams clearly and quickly communicate information to a reader. Students choose a country and find what percent of the total population lives in different kinds of housing, such as single-family homes, apartment buildings, mobile homes, or condominiums. Students compile the data and prepare a chart summarizing the results. LS , CL , P

③ ASSESS

Error Analysis

A review of the concepts taught in Example 1 on page 347 will help students identify any errors they may be making.

Be sure students understand the Monthly Payment for $1,000 Loan on page 799. To get the monthly payment on a specific loan amount, they must divide the amount of the mortgage loan by $1,000 and multiply the answer by the dollar amount given on the table.

Once students have found the monthly payment, they find the total amount paid on the loan by multiplying the monthly payment by the total number of payments required to pay off the loan. They find the total number of payments by taking the number of years of the mortgage and multiplying it by 12. For example, a 30-year mortgage has 12 × 30 payments, or 360 payments. A 15-year loan has 12 × 15 payments, or 180 payments. When students know the total amount paid, they can subtract the amount of the mortgage from the total amount paid to get the total interest charged. Students may need additional practice before they feel comfortable working with these concepts.

④ CLOSE

Closing Activity

1. Mortgage: $180,000.
   Terms 5 percent for 30 years.
   a. What is the monthly payment? **$966.60**
   b. What is the total amount paid? **$347,976**
   c. What is the total interest charged? **$167,976**

2. Selling price: $114,000.
   Down payment: 20 percent.
   Terms: 6 percent for 25 years.
   What is the total interest charged? **$84,998.40**

▶ **FYI**

Today the Department of Housing and Urban Development is the federal agency charged with the mission of securing "a decent, safe, and sanitary home and suitable living environment for every American."

▶▶▶

7. Charles and Sandy Compton.
   Mortgage: $80,000.
   Terms: 8.5 percent for 25 years.
   a. What is the monthly payment? **$644.00**
   b. What is the total amount paid? **$193,200.00**
   c. What is the total interest charged? **$113,200.00**

8. Abigail and Karlis Krisjanis.
   Mortgage: $70,000.
   Terms: 7 percent for 20 years.
   a. What is the monthly payment? **$542.50**
   b. What is the total amount paid? **$130,200.00**
   c. What is the total interest charged? **$60,200.00**

9. Julie Hardy.
   Selling price: $150,000.
   Down payment: 10 percent.
   Terms: 8.5 percent for 20 years.
   What is the total interest charged? **$146,232**

10. Diane Novak.
    Selling price: $250,000.
    Down payment: 25 percent.
    Terms: 9.5 percent for 30 years.
    What is the total interest charged? **$380,175.00**

11. Ivan and Vicki Egan have obtained a $60,000 mortgage loan at an annual interest rate of 7.5 percent for 15 years. What is the monthly payment? What is the total amount to be paid? **$556.20; $100,116.00**

12. Salma and Coron Broomall have reached an agreed-upon selling price of $197,000. They plan to make a 30 percent down payment and finance the rest at 8.5 percent for 15 years. What is the monthly payment? What is the total amount to be paid? **$1,358.32; $244,496.70**

13. Ellen and Clyde Perez reached an agreed-upon price of $124,000 for the purchase of a house. They made a down payment of $14,000 and could finance the remaining amount in one of two ways: at 11.5 percent for 25 years or at 12 percent for 20 years. Which mortgage results in a larger amount of interest paid? How much greater? **11.5% for 25 years; $44,286**

MAINTAINING YOUR SKILLS

> **Need Help? Go to...**
> ➤ Skill 8: **Multiplying Decimals**, page 735
> ➤ Skill 6: **Subtracting Decimals**, page 733

Multiply.

14. 24 × 120.50 **2,892**   15. 36 × 431.2 **15,523.2**   16. 12 × 832.40 **9,988.8**

Subtract.

17. 75,500 − 22,200   18. 92,461 − 12,420   19. 453,821.50 − 100,000
    53,300   **80,041**   **353,821.50**

WRAP-UP

Go over any problem for which a wrong answer is given.

Assignment Guide
Basic: 2–6
Average: 7–10

20 min.

SECTION 10-3 Closing Costs

Section Objective

Figure out the total closing costs.

At the time you sign the documents transferring ownership of the home to you, the lender charges **closing costs**. Closing costs may include fees for lawyers, credit checks and title searches, surveys, taxes, and the preparation of the documents. Some lenders charge a flat fee regardless of the amount of the loan. Some lenders charge a percent of the amount of the loan. Other lenders charge itemized fees at the closing. Remember that:

$$Closing\ Costs = Sum\ of\ Bank\ Fees$$

Living in the Real World

The Hunt to Find a Home

That Will Cost You The Sultans decide to make an offer on the house. The young couple is at the bank to discuss the cost of borrowing money for a mortgage. Bud Ayala, one of the mortgage officers at their Texas bank, talks about how much of a down payment they should put toward the house and how different down payments will change what they borrow, and therefore affect their monthly payments. Then he mentions additional costs.

Draw Conclusions Why might the lender charge additional costs (over and above the loan documents)?

Continued on page 351

Example 1

Need Help? Go to...
Skill 3: Adding Whole Numbers, page 730

Trudy and Germane Hallett have been granted a mortgage loan at an annual interest rate of 8 percent for 25 years by State Bank. The home has a selling price of $95,500. They need a 15 percent down payment. State Bank will allow them to finance the closing costs as part of the mortgage.

What are the total closing costs? What is the actual amount financed with the mortgage?

STEP 1: Find the down payment.
$95,500 × 15% = $14,325

STEP 2: Find the amount of the mortgage.
$95,500 − $14,325
= $81,175

STEP 3: Find the closing costs. (See the Closing Costs table.)

STEP 4: Find the actual amount financed.

Closing Costs	
Credit report	$ 65.00
Loan origination	2% of mortgage
Abstract of title	120.00
Attorney fee	250.00
Documentation stamp	0.3% of mortgage
Processing fee	1.10% of mortgage
Total Closing Costs	**$3,194.96**

Amount of Mortgage + Closing Costs
$81,175   + $3,194.96   = **$84,369.96 financed**

Living in the Real World

Banks and credit unions charge settlement fees that cover the time and effort they must put in to prepare a loan and transfer a house title from the current owner to the buyer.

RETEACH / ENRICHMENT

Closing Costs
Students investigate and write a report on closing costs for a home. Some sources of information are banks, real estate offices, or friends or relatives in the real estate field. Students choose a topic: (1) listing the various closing costs; (2) how a specific fee is computed; or (3) the purpose or description of a closing cost not discussed in class.

CL , **LS** , **P**

---

① FOCUS

This lesson will explain how closing costs are computed.

In-Class Examples
Work through these exercises with students before having them do the Self-Check.
1. $80 + $1900 + $150 + $250 + $325 + $740 **$3,445**
2. 2% of $20,000 **$400**
3. 0.5% of $40,000 **$200**

② TEACH

Explain to students that lenders, such as banks, can have different fees for closing costs. Just as it is important to shop around for a mortgage with low interest rates, it is also important to find a lender whose fees for closing costs are low.

National Standards for Business Education

Standard 1	Mathematical Foundations
Standard 2	Number Relationships and Operations

National Council of Teachers of Mathematics Standards

Standard 1	Numbers and Operations
Standard 4	Measurement
Standard 6	Problem Solving
Standard 8	Communication
Standard 9	Connections

2 TEACH (cont'd)

See Problem 1 answer on page 364.

Motivating the Lesson

You're making a 20 percent down payment on a home that costs $200,000. Your bank has granted you a mortgage for the remaining amount. The bank charges 3 percent of the mortgage amount for closing costs. What are the closing costs for your mortgage loan? **$4,800**

In-Class Example

Use the list of Closing Costs on page 349 from Example 1 to solve Problem 1.

1. Mortgage loan of $75,000. What are the closing costs? **$2,985**

3 ASSESS

Error Analysis

Review the concept that percent means a part of 100. Five percent means $\frac{5}{100}$ and is written as 0.05; 0.5 percent means $\frac{0.5}{1,000}$ and is written as 0.005.

4 CLOSE

Closing Activity

1. The Monroes purchase a home for $172,000. They put a 25 percent down payment. They will finance the remainder. Their bank charges the following closing costs: loan origination fee, 1.75 percent of mortgage amount; title search, $175; appraisal fee, $225; credit report, $75; legal fees, $375; property tax, $1,080; documentation stamp, 0.3 percent of mortgage amount. What are the closing costs? **$4,574.50**

SELF-CHECK✓ Complete the problem, then check your answer at the end of the chapter.

1. Kyung Ja and Hideo Hakola have been granted a mortgage loan at an annual interest rate of 7.5 percent for 15 years by USA Mortgage. The home has a selling price of $105,000. They need a 10 percent down payment. USA Mortgage will allow them to finance the closing costs as part of the mortgage. Use the closing costs from **Figure 10.2** on page 351 to find the total closing costs. What is the actual amount financed with the mortgage?

SECTION 10-3 PRACTICE

Use the Closing Costs table on page 349 to solve.

2. Jeremy Roberts.
   Mortgage loan of $50,000.
   What are the total closing costs? **$2,035**

3. Vincent and Sue Hemsley.
   Mortgage loan of $95,000.
   What are the total closing costs? **$3,665**

4. Ralph and Cristi Sheen.
   Mortgage loan of $271,000.
   a. What are the total closing costs?
   b. What is the total amount of the mortgage if the closing costs are financed? **a. $9,649; b. $280,649**

5. Jack and Dina King.
   Mortgage loan of $420,000.
   a. What are the total closing costs?
   b. What is the total amount of the mortgage if the closing costs are financed? **a. $14,715; b. $434,715**

6. Lateefah and Eric Lewis have been granted a mortgage loan at an annual interest rate of 9.5 percent for 15 years. The home has a selling price of $175,000, and they need a 20 percent down payment. The bank will allow them to finance the closing costs as part of the mortgage. The total closing costs are 3.5 percent of the mortgage. What is the total of the closing costs? What is the actual amount financed with the mortgage? **$4,900; $144,200**

7. Barry and Ella Ellerbee have agreed to purchase a house for $96,500. Universal Savings and Loan Association is willing to lend the money at 8.25 percent for 25 years, provided they can make a $10,000 down payment. The total closing costs are 3.25 percent of the amount of the mortgage loan. What is the total of the closing costs? What is the total of the mortgage if they finance the closing costs? **$2,811.25; $89,311.25**

8. Rene and Jefferson Franklin are interested in purchasing a $60,000 home. They plan to make a 20 percent down payment and finance the remaining amount through Peabody Savings Association. Peabody Savings has these closing costs: credit report, $80; appraisal report, $255; title insurance, $190; survey and photographs, $325; recording fee, $65; legal fees, $280; and property taxes, $789. If the loan is approved, how much cash will the Franklins need to secure the loan, including the down payment? **$13,984.00**

MAINTAINING YOUR SKILLS

Need Help? Go to...
➤ Skill 30: **Finding the Percentage,** page 757

Find the percentage.

9. 15% of 9,000 **1,350**
10. 4% of 86,000 **3,440**
11. 7% of 252,000 **17,640**
12. 2.4% of 78,000 **1,872**
13. 3.3% of 83,000 **2,739**
14. 1.2% of 30,000 **360**
15. 0.3% of 92,000 **276**
16. 0.15% of 85,100 **127.65**
17. 0.04% of 22,300 **8.92**

GLOBAL PERSPECTIVE

Cost of Housing
Have students pick a country where they'd like to live and research the cost of housing there. What is the average cost of a house? What is the average cost of an apartment? Why do they think the cost of housing is higher or lower than in the United States? **Main reasons, include societal preferences, differences in wages, differences in the cost of living, availability of jobs, and availability of land.**

WRAP-UP

Go over any problem for which a wrong answer is given.

Assignment Guide
  Basic: 2–5
  Average: 6–7

20 min.

SECTION (10-4) The Monthly Payment

Section Objective

Compute the allocation of monthly payment toward principal, interest, and the new principal.

Most mortgage loans are repaid in equal monthly payments. Each payment includes an amount for payment of interest and an amount for payment of the **principal** of the loan, or the amount borrowed to finance the mortgage. The amount of interest is calculated using the simple interest formula:

$$\text{Interest} = \text{Principal} \times \text{Rate} \times \text{Time}$$

The amount of principal that you owe decreases with each payment that you make. The chart shows the interest and principal paid in the first 4 months of an $80,000 mortgage loan. (See **Figure 10.2**.)

Figure 10.2

Payment Number	Monthly Payment	Amount for Interest	Amount for Principal	Balance $80,000.00
1	$587.20	$533.33	$53.87	$79,946.13
2	587.20	532.97	54.23	79,891.90
3	587.20	532.61	54.59	79,837.31
4	587.20	532.25	54.95	79,782.36

$80,000 Mortgage Loan at 8% for 30 Years

Ask yourself these questions in order to solve the answers:

Important Questions	What Formulas Do I Use?
How do I find **simple interest**?	Interest = Principal × Rate × Time
How do I figure out the **payment to principal** amount?	Payment to Principal = Monthly Payment − Interest
How do I figure out the **new principal**?	New Principal = Previous Balance − Payment to Principal

Living in the Real World

The Hunt to Find a Home

How Much Can You Afford a Month? The Sultans and Ayala also discuss monthly payments. Monthly payments include interest and a portion of the principal. However, Ayala explains that since the amount of principal decreases after each monthly payment, the proportion of principal-to-interest also changes each month.

Draw Conclusions Why would most people be interested in the proportion of principal-to-interest for their monthly payments?

Continued on page 355

National Standards for Business Education

Standard 1	Mathematical Foundations
Standard 2	Number Relationships and Operations

National Council of Teachers of Mathematics Standards

Standard 1	Numbers and Operations
Standard 4	Measurement
Standard 6	Problem Solving
Standard 8	Communication
Standard 9	Connections

1 FOCUS

Remind students that the interest charged is included in the monthly payment. Ask if they think the interest portion will be greater than, equal to, or less than the portion toward the mortgage amount. Why? Recall that the total interest charged in that example on the $80,000 mortgage was $131,392—a great deal more than the mortgage itself.

In-Class Examples

Work through these exercises with students before having them do the Self-Check.
1. $40,000 − $379.79 **$39,620.21**
2. $12,000 − $360 **$11,640**
3. $42,000 × 10% **$4,200**

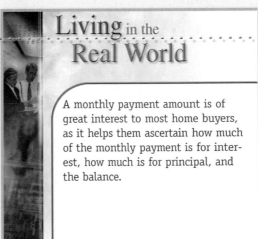

Living in the Real World

A monthly payment amount is of great interest to most home buyers, as it helps them ascertain how much of the monthly payment is for interest, how much is for principal, and the balance.

2 TEACH

As you go over **Figure 10.3** on page 352, ask students what they notice about the "amount for principal" and "amount for interest" columns. **(The amount for principal increases as the amount for interest decreases.)**

Explain that during the early years of a mortgage, the payment toward the original mortgage amount is very small. If you should have to sell the house in one year, you may lose money. In Example 1 when calculating the payments for 1 year, the new balance, which has to be paid to the bank if the house is sold, is $79,329.34. Only $670.66 was paid toward the principal.

Motivating the Lesson
You obtain a 30-year $120,000 mortgage at 8 percent. Your monthly payment is $880.80. The interest on your first payment is $800. How much of your first payment will be used to reduce the principal? **($80.80)** What will the new principal be after your first payment? **$119,919.20**

In-Class Examples
1. Mortgage loan of $92,000. Interest rate is 10 percent for 30 years. Monthly payment is $807.76. How much of the first monthly payment is for interest? **$766.67**
2. Mortgage loan of $118,000. Interest rate is 6.5 percent for 30 years. Monthly payment is $745.76. How much of the first monthly payment is for interest? **($639.17)** How much of the first monthly payment is for principal? **($106.59)** What is the new principal? **$117,893.41**

Need Help? Go to...
➤ **Workshop 5:** Subtracting Decimals, page 12
➤ **Workshop 6:** Multiplying Decimals, page 14
➤ **Skill 6: Subtracting** Decimals, page 733
➤ **Skill 8: Multiplying** Decimals, page 735

Example 1

Rod and Carey Finn obtained a 30-year, $80,000.00 mortgage loan from State Bank and Trust. The interest rate is 8 percent. Their monthly payment is $587.20. For the first payment, what is the interest? What is the payment to principal? What is the new principal?

STEP 1: Find the interest.
Principal × Rate × Time
$80,000.00 × 8% × $\frac{1}{12}$
= **$533.33 interest**

STEP 2: Find the payment to principal.
Monthly Payment − Interest
$587.20 − $533.33
= **$53.87 payment to principal**

STEP 3: Find the new principal.
Previous Balance − Payment to Principal
$80,000.00 − $53.87
= **$79,946.13 new principal**

80000 × 8 % 6400 × 1 ÷ 12 = 533.33 M+ 587.20 − RM 533.33 = 53.87   80000 − 53.87 = 79946.13

CONCEPT CHECK

SELF-CHECK ✓

Complete the problems, then check your answers at the end of the chapter. In the example above, the new principal is $79,946.13. For the second payment, find:

1. The interest on $79,946.13.
   Interest on $79,946.13: $79,946.13 × 8% × $\frac{1}{12}$ = $532.97
2. The payment to principal.
   Payment to principal: $587.20 − $532.97 = $54.23
3. The new balance.
   New balance: $79,946.13 − $54.23 = $79,891.90

Example 2

The amount of principal that you owe decreases with each payment that you make. The chart shows the interest and principal paid for payment numbers 325, 326, and 327 on an original $80,000 mortgage loan. For payment number 328, what is the interest? What is the payment to principal? What is the new principal?

Figure 10.3

$80,000 Mortgage Loan at 8% for 30 Years				
Payment Number	Monthly Payment	Amount for Interest	Amount for Principal	Balance $18,517.69
325	$587.20	$123.45	$463.75	$18,053.94
326	587.20	120.36	466.84	17,587.10
327	587.20	117.25	469.95	17,117.15

THINKING CRITICALLY

 Percent to Decimal
What is 8 percent expressed as a decimal? **(0.08)** Express each of the following as a decimal:
1. 12% **(0.12)**
2. 10% **(0.10)**
3. 6% **0.06**

STEP 1: Find the interest.
　　Principal × Rate × Time
　　$17,117.15 × 8% × $\frac{1}{12}$
　　= **$114.11 interest**

STEP 2: Find the payment to principal.
　　Monthly Payment − Interest
　　　$587.20 　　− 　$114.11
　　= **$473.09 payment to principal**

STEP 3: Find the new principal.
　　Previous Balance − Payment to Principal
　　　$17,117.15 　− 　　　$473.09
　　= **$16,644.06 new principal**

CONCEPT CHECK

In the example above, the new principal is $16,644.06. For payment number 329, find:

4. The interest on $16,644.06.
　　Interest on $16,644.06: $16,644.06 × 8% × $\frac{1}{12}$ = $110.96
5. The payment to principal.
　　Payment to principal: $587.20 − $110.96 = $476.24
6. The new balance.
　　New balance: $16,644.06 − $476.24 = $16,167.82

SECTION 10-4 PRACTICE

	Mortgage Amount	Interest Rate	1st Monthly Payment	Amount for Interest	Amount for Principal	New Principal
7.	$ 50,000	8.0%	$ 478.00	$333.33	$144.67	a.$49,855.33
8.	70,000	9.0%	563.50	a. $525.00	b. $38.50	c.$69,961.50
9.	60,000	9.5%	559.80	a. $475.00	b. $84.80	c.$59,915.20
10.	120,000	8.5%	922.80	a. $850.00	b. $72.80	c.
11.	225,000	10.0%	2,418.75	a.	b. $543.75	c.

10. c. $119,927.20
11. a. $1,875.00
　　c. $224,456.25

12. Lois Larczyk.
　　Mortgage loan of $46,000.00.
　　Interest rate is 12 percent.
　　Monthly payment is $506.92.
　　How much of the first monthly payment is for interest? **$460**

13. Patrick Yunker.
　　Mortgage loan of $84,000.
　　Interest rate is 10 percent.
　　Monthly payment is $714.
　　How much of the first monthly payment is for interest? **$700**

Continued on next page

---

3. Mortgage loan of $66,000. Interest rate is 8.5 percent for 30 years. Monthly payment is $507.54. How much of the first monthly payment is for interest? **($467.50)** How much of the first monthly payment is for principal? **($40.04)** What is the new principal? **$65,959.96**

3 ASSESS

Review the formula for finding the monthly payment on a loan. **(Amount of the loan ÷ $1,000) × Monthly Payment for a $1,000 Loan.** Then direct them to Monthly Payments of a $1,000 Loan on page 799.

Remind students to complete the steps for finding interest, payment to principal, and new balance in the correct order. Explain that they must first know the interest before they can find the payment to principal and that in order to find the new balance, they must know the payment to principal.

Review the formula for finding interest. Be sure students understand that they multiply the Principal × Rate × $\frac{1}{12}$ because they are computing monthly interest. To find the payment to principal, remind them to subtract the interest from the monthly payment. To find the new principal, have them subtract the payment to principal from the previous balance.

4 **CLOSE**

Closing Activity

1. $72,000 × 8% × $\frac{1}{12}$ **$480.00**
2. $159,000 − $416.00
   $158,584.00
3. Mortgage amount: $200,000.
   Interest rate is 6.5 percent
   for 30 years. First monthly
   payment: $1,264.00
   Amount for interest? **$1,083.33**
   Amount for principal? **$180.67**
   New principal? **$199,819.33**
4. Mortgage amount: $137,000.
   Interest rate is 9 percent
   for 30 years. First monthly
   payment? **$1,102.85**
   Amount for interest? **$1,027.50**
   Amount for principal? **$75.35**
   New principal? **$136,924.65**
5. Mortgage amount $59,000.
   Interest rate is 7 percent
   for 15 years. First monthly
   payment? **$530.41**
   Amount for interest? **$344.17**
   Amount for principal? **$186.24**
   New principal? **$58,813.76**

14. Matthew Roberts.
    Mortgage loan of $38,600.00.
    Interest rate is 8.5 percent.
    Monthly payment is $335.05.
    a. How much of the first monthly payment is for interest? **$273.42**
    b. How much of the first payment is for principal? **$61.63**
    c. What is the new principal? **$38,538.37**

15. Dee Pollom.
    Mortgage loan of $98,000.00.
    Interest rate is 7.5 percent.
    Monthly payment is $686.00.
    a. How much of the first monthly payment is for interest? **$612.50**
    b. How much of the first payment is for principal? **$73.50**
    c. What is the new principal? **$97,926.50**

16. Jill Barley obtained a 25-year, $60,000.00 mortgage loan from University Savings and Loan Association. The interest rate is 9 percent. The monthly payment is $503.40. For the first payment, what is the interest? What is the payment to principal? What is the new balance? **$450.00; $53.40; $59,946.00**

17. Norman Foster obtained a 30-year, $180,000.00 mortgage loan from American Savings and Loan Association. The interest rate is 10 percent. His monthly payment is $1,580.40. For the first payment, what is the interest? What is the payment to principal? What is the new balance?
    $1,500; $80.40; $179,919.60

18. Amelia McGuire obtained a 20-year, $36,000.00 mortgage loan from Society Trust Company. The interest rate is 11.5 percent. Her monthly payment is $383.76. Use this portion of the repayment schedule to find the remaining debt after the payment numbers 42 and 43.

Payment Number	Monthly Payment	Amount for Interest	Amount for Principal	New Balance
41	$383.76	$70.78	$312.98	$7,072.32
42	383.76	a. $67.78	b. $315.98	c. $6,756.34
43	383.76	d. $64.75	e. $319.01	f. $6,437.33

MAINTAINING YOUR SKILLS

Need Help? Go to...
► Skill 6: **Subtracting Decimals,** page 733

Subtract.

19. 48,000 − 29.46
    47,970.54
20. 91,800 − 39.55
    91,760.45
21. 24,400 − 23.12
    24,376.88
22. 78,902 − 22.98
    78,879.02
23. 18,185 − 45.11
    18,139.89
24. 14,915 − 107.7
    14,809.30

WRAP-UP

Go over any problem for which a wrong answer is given.

Assignment Guide
   Basic: 7–11
Average: 12–15

20 min.

SECTION (10-5) Real Estate Taxes

○ **Section Objective**

Calculate the assessed value and real estate taxes.

When you own a home, you'll have to pay city or county **real estate taxes.** The money collected is used to operate and maintain roads, parks, schools, government offices, and other city expenses. The amount of real estate tax that you pay in one year depends on:

- the **assessed value** of your property (this is the dollar value assigned to a property by a tax assessor for taxation purposes).
- the **tax rate.**

The assessed value is found by multiplying the **market value** of your property by the **rate of assessment.** The market value is the price at which a house can be bought or sold. An assessor hired by the municipality determines the market value. The rate of assessment is a percent.

The tax rate is sometimes expressed in *mills* per dollar of assessed value of property. A mill is $0.001. A tax rate of 80 mills is a tax rate of $80 per $1,000 of assessed value. When working with mills, it is often convenient to express mills in dollars by dividing by 1,000.

You might ask yourself again:

Important Questions	What Formulas Do I Use?
How do I find the **assessed value**?	Assessed Value = Market Value × Rate of Assessment
How do I find the **real estate tax**?	Real Estate Tax = Tax Rate × Assessed Value
How do I calculate **mills** per dollar of valuation?	Mill = $0.001 or Mill = $1.00 ÷ 1,000

Living in the Real World

The Hunt to Find a Home

You Have Other Costs to Consider   Later that evening, after their children are in bed, the Sultans sit at their kitchen table and talk about their finances and whether they'll be able to swing the cost of buying a house. Their housing costs include principal, interest, and closing costs. In addition, they must have enough money to pay for insurance and real estate taxes.

Draw Conclusions   What are the benefits of spreading out tax payments?

Continued on page 357

(**Example 1**)

The Fulton County tax assessor determined that the market value of Courtland Farm is $340,000.00. The rate of assessment in Fulton County is 40 percent of market value. The tax rate is 50.73 mills. What is the real estate tax on Courtland Farm?

Continued on next page

Section 10-5 Real Estate Taxes ▶ **355**

Living in the Real World

Smaller monthly payments are much more manageable for many home-owners than one lump yearly sum. Paying a little each month doesn't make taxes and insurance any cheaper, but it does make it easier to pay.

National Standards for Business Education

Standard 1	Mathematical Foundations
Standard 2	Number Relationships and Operations

National Council of Teachers of Mathematics Standards

Standard 1	Numbers and Operations
Standard 4	Measurement
Standard 6	Problem Solving
Standard 8	Communication
Standard 9	Connections

(1) FOCUS

Ask students to name some different taxes that people have to pay. Discuss what these taxes are based on (**income, purchases**) and how they are computed (**tax table, taxable wages, and tax rate**). Explain that if you own a home, you also will pay another tax. In this lesson, students will learn how to compute real estate taxes, often referred to as property taxes, based on the assessed value of a home.

In-Class Examples

Work through these exercises with students before having them do the Self-Check.
1. 86.72 ÷ 1,000 **0.08672**
2. 75.4 ÷ 1,000 **0.0754**
3. $50,000 × 40% **$20,000**
4. $30,000 × 50% **$15,000**
5. 0.075 × $20,000 **$1,500**
6. 0.05 × $15,000 **$750**

② TEACH

Point out that a tax rate of 50.73 mills means the same as a tax rate of $50.73 per $1,000 of assessed value. Demonstrate the following alternative method of finding the real estate tax in the Example 1:

$136,000 ÷ $1,000 = 136
136 × $50.73 = $6,899.28

In-Class Example

1. The home of Claire Adams. Market value is $312,000. Rate of assessment is 34 percent. What is the assessed value? **$106,080**

③ ASSESS

Error Analysis

Students may be confused when the tax rate is expressed in mills per dollar of valuation. Review the concept that a tax rate of 75 mills is the same as a tax rate of $75 per $1,000 of assessed value. Seventy-five mills can be written as $\frac{75}{1,000}$ or as its decimal equivalent of 0.075.

④ CLOSE

Closing Activity

1. Market value is $50,800. Rate of assessment is 40 percent. Tax rate is 65.5 mills What is the assessed value? **($20,320)** What is the annual real estate tax rate? **$1,330.96**
2. Market value is $245,000. Rate of assessment is 50 percent. Tax rate is 72.35 mills. What is the assessed value? **($122,500)** What is the annual real estate tax rate? **$8,862.88**
3. Market value is $625,000. Rate of assessment is 80 percent. Tax rate is 25.13 mills. What is the annual real estate tax rate? **$12,565**

STEP 1: Find the assessed value.

Market Value × Rate of Assessment
$340,000.00 × 40% = $136,000.00 assessed value

STEP 2: Express the tax rate as a decimal.
50.73 mills ÷ 1,000.00 = 0.05073 tax rate

STEP 3: Find the real estate tax.
Tax Rate × Assessed Value
0.05073 × $136,000.00 = **$6,899.28 real estate tax**

1. $70,000 × 0.40 = $28,000
2. 65.50 ÷ 1,000 = 0.0655
3. 0.0655 × $28,000 = $1,834

340000 ⊠ 40 % 136000 M+ 50.73 ÷ 1000 =

0.05073 ⊠ RM 136000 = 6899.28

CONCEPT CHECK

SELF-CHECK ✓

Complete the problems, then check your answers at the end of the chapter. The tax rate is 65.50 mills, market value is $70,000.00, and rate of assessment is 40 percent. Find the following:

1. The assessed value. 2. The tax rate as a decimal. 3. The real estate tax.

SECTION 10-5 PRACTICE

4. Lima's home. Market value is $72,000. Rate of assessment is 30 percent. What is the assessed value? **$21,600**

5. The Simms' condominium. Market value is $159,800. Rate of assessment is 40 percent. What is the assessed value? **$63,920**

6. Brenda Roth's home is located in Columbus, Ohio, where the rate of assessment is 35 percent of market value. The tax rate is $59.56 per $1,000 of assessed value. Her home has a market value of $392,000.00. What is its assessed value? What is the property tax? **$137,200; $8,171.63**

7. The rate of assessment in Foster, Rhode Island, is 50 percent. The tax rate is $40.20 per $1,000 of assessed value. What is the real estate tax on a piece of property that has a market value of $236,000.00? **$4,743.60**

$2,904.77 8. Ali and Jackie Erwin live in Providence, Rhode Island, where the tax rate is 29.52 mills. The rate of assessment is 100 percent. The property that the Erwins own has a market value of $98,400.00. What is their real estate tax for a year?

9. Jose and Trudy Engstrom own a home that has a market value of $675,000.00. They live in Richmond, Virginia, where the rate of assessment is 80 percent and the tax rate is 25.13 mills. What is the annual real estate tax? **$13,570.20**

10. Gina and Tony Jasinski received a tax statement showing that their land has an assessed value of $7,500 and their buildings have an assessed value of $42,300. The rate of assessment in their locality is 40 percent. What is the market value of their property? **$124,500**

Need Help? Go to...
▶ Skill 8: Multiplying Decimals, page 735
▶ Skill 30: Finding the Percentage, page 757

MAINTAINING YOUR SKILLS

Multiply.

11. 37.3 × 78.4 **2,924.32** 12. 13.18 × 9.42 **124.1556** 13. 13.30 × 4.37 **58.121**

Find the percentage.

14. 90,000 × 20% **18,000** 15. 140,000 × 45% **63,000** 16. 45,500 × 33% **15,015**

356 ◀ Chapter 10 Housing Costs

COMMUNICATION SKILLS

Tax Rate

To express 84.32 mills as a decimal, move the decimal point to the left by the number of zeros in 1,000. **(3)** Since there are only two digits to the left of the decimal point in 84.32, a zero needs to be written in front of the 8 in the tenths place. Also, for a number less than 1, a zero is written in the ones place: 84.32 ÷ 1,000 = 0.08432. Students work in pairs to create, share, and solve similar conversions. LS , CL , P

WRAP-UP

Go over any problem for which a wrong answer is given.

Assignment Guide
  Basic: 4–5
  Average: 6–9

20 min.

SECTION (10-6) Homeowners Insurance

Section Objective

Work out the amount of coverage.

Once you're a homeowner, you'll want to protect yourself from losses such as fire, theft, and personal liability. To be covered for this protection, you'll want to buy **homeowners insurance**. This policy also includes **loss-of-use coverage**. Let's say that your house is damaged and unlivable, so you're forced to live in a hotel for a couple of weeks. The loss-of-use coverage pays for the expenses of living away from home while the reparations are being completed.

What else does homeowners insurance protect you against? What if a neighbor falls off the deck of your house and breaks her leg? Are you responsible for her accident? Maybe. Just in case that neighbor thinks you are at fault, then **personal liability** and **medical coverage** will protect you from financial losses.

To receive full payment for any loss up to the amount of the policy, you must insure your home for at least 80 percent of its **replacement value**. The replacement value is the amount required to reconstruct your home if it's destroyed. Insurance companies use the amount of coverage on your home to calculate the amount of coverage you receive on your garage, personal property, and for loss of use.

Remember to ask yourself this question:

Figure 10.4

Coverage	Percent Covered
Garage and other structures	10%
Loss of use	20%
Personal property	50%

Important Question	What Formula Do I Use?
How do I find the **amount of coverage** for each type of protection?	Amount of Coverage = $\dfrac{\text{Amount of Coverage on Home}}{} \times$ Percent

Living in the Real World

The Hunt to Find a Home

Protect Yourself "What did Mr. Ayala say would be covered in homeowners insurance?" Sheridan asks.

"He said it would cover losses due to fire and theft," Torian says. "And if we can't live in the house for a while, it should cover the expense of renting a place."

Draw Conclusions Suppose that someone comes onto their property and falls on the droopy porch and gets hurt. How will they protect themselves against a lawsuit?

Continued on page 359

Example 1

The replacement value of Joy and Ron Amodeo's home is estimated at $94,000. They have insured their home for 80 percent of its replacement value. According to the guidelines above and using Figure 10.4, what is the amount of coverage on the Amodeo's personal property?

Continued on next page

Section 10-6 Homeowners Insurance ▶ **357**

Living in the Real World

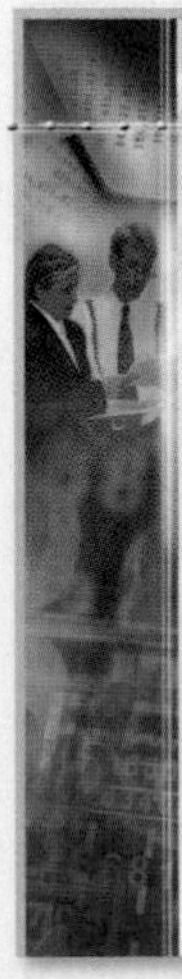

Homeowners insurance covers situations like this and protects owners from liability and lawsuit.

COOPERATIVE LEARNING

Service Opportunity

Habitat for Humanity builds houses for families in need. Its mission is to make decent shelter a matter of conscience and action. Work in small groups to find out about Habitat for Humanity's plans for the future. Is there an opportunity for you to make a difference?

National Standards for Business Education

Standard 1	Mathematical Foundations
Standard 2	Number Relationships and Operations

National Council of Teachers of Mathematics Standards

Standard 1	Numbers and Operations
Standard 4	Measurement
Standard 6	Problem Solving
Standard 8	Communication
Standard 9	Connections

① FOCUS

Ask students if anyone has ever witnessed a house burning or seen the damage fire can do to the contents of a home. How can the owners of a home damaged by a fire replace the home and their personal belongings? In this lesson, students will learn about homeowners insurance and how to compute the amount of coverage.

② TEACH

Stress to students that the key computation in the example is finding the amount of coverage on a home, which is a percent of the replacement value. The answer is the base for all other insurance coverages on the home.

357

2 TEACH (cont'd)

In-Class Example

Refer to **Figure 10.4** on page 357.
1. Replacement value of home is $260,000. Coverage of the house: 90 percent.
   a. What is the insurance coverage on the home? **$234,000**
   b. What is the amount of insurance for personal property? **$117,000**

3 ASSESS

Error Analysis

Emphasize that before students can calculate the separate insurance coverage on a homeowners policy, such as personal property, loss of use, etc., they must first determine the insurance coverage on the house. All the other insurance coverages are based on a percent of this amount. Have students check their work to see that they have figured the additional insurance coverages on the insurance coverage of the house, not on its replacement value, unless the insurance coverage is 100 percent of the replacement value.

4 CLOSE

Closing Activity

Refer to **Figure 10.4** on page 357.
1. The townhouse's replacement value is $230,000. Coverage of the home: 90 percent.
   a. What is the insurance coverage on the home? **$207,000**
   b. What is the coverage on loss of use? **$41,400**
   c. What is the amount of coverage on personal property? **$103,500**

358

STEP 1: Find the amount of coverage on the home.

Replacement Value × Percent

$94,000 × 80% = $75,200 coverage on home

STEP 2: Find the amount of coverage on personal property.

Amount of Coverage on Home × Percent

$75,200 × 50%

= **$37,600 coverage on personal property**

94000 × 80 % = 75200 × 50 % = 37600

CONCEPT CHECK

 SELF-CHECK ✓

Complete the problems, then check your answers at the end of the chapter. A home is insured for 90 percent of its replacement value of $120,000, or $108,000. Using the percents from Figure 10.4 on page 357, find the coverage for:

1. Personal property. **$54,000**
2. Loss of use. **$21,600**
3. Garage. **$10,800**

SECTION 10-6 PRACTICE

Use Figure 10.4 on page 357 for the percent of coverage.

4. Replacement value of the home is $70,000. Eighty percent of the home is covered. What is the amount of insurance? **$56,000**

5. Replacement value of the home is $95,000. One hundred percent of the home is covered. What is the amount of insurance? **$95,000**

6. Replacement value of the home is $38,500. Ninety percent of the home is covered.
   a. What is the amount of insurance? **$34,650**
   b. What is the amount of coverage for personal property? **$17,325**

7. Replacement value of the home is $144,000. Eighty percent of the home is covered.
   a. What is the amount of insurance? **$115,200**
   b. What is the amount of coverage for loss of use? **$23,040**

8. A home has a replacement value of $324,000. The owners insure the new home for 90 percent of its replacement value.
   a. What is the amount of insurance on their home? **$291,600**
   b. What is the amount of coverage on their garage? **$29,160**

9. A home has a replacement value of $324,000. The owners insure the new home for 80 percent of its replacement value.
   a. What is the amount of insurance on their home? **$259,200**
   b. What is the amount of coverage for personal property? **$129,600**
   c. What is the amount of coverage for loss of use? **$51,840**
   d. What is the amount of coverage on their garage? **$25,920**

MAINTAINING YOUR SKILLS

Need Help? Go to...
➤ Skill 30: Finding the Percentage, page 757

Find the percentage.

10. 10% of $90,000 **$9,000**
11. 80% of $30,000 **$24,000**
12. 50% of 140,000 **$70,000**

THINKING CRITICALLY

Renter's Insurance
You're living in an apartment and someone breaks in and steals your video player. Is there anything you can do about it? **(You can buy renter's insurance to cover any loss or damage to your personal possessions.)** What does it cover? **Televisions, clothing, and furniture from loss due to fire, theft, and smoke. Also includes liability protection.**

WRAP-UP

Go over any problem for which a wrong answer is given.

Assignment Guide
   Basic: 4–5
Average: 7–8

20 min.

Homeowners Insurance Premium

○ **Section Objective**

Calculate the annual homeowners insurance premium.

What matters the most when buying a home? As they say in real estate: location, location, location. Are you living in a crime-ridden area? Or what about on a mountain vista? Your location even affects your homeowners policy **premium**—the amount you have to pay for insurance coverage. Also the type of house—brick masonry veneer or wood frame—affects your premium. The home will be assigned a number that reflects how fire resistant your house is and how close you are to a water source. This number is called your **fire protection class**.

Living in the Real World

The Hunt to Find a Home

The Insurer Assures You Coverage The Sultans include the cost of homeowners insurance in their total. They look through the information they got at the bank and find the estimated premium for their homeowners insurance on the house they hope to buy.

Draw Conclusions How does an insurance company compute the amount of your premium?

Continued on page 361

Figure 10.5

Homeowners Insurance Premiums										
Annual Premiums for a Typical Homeowners Policy										
Amount of Insurance Coverage	Brick/Masonry Veneer Fire Protection Class					Wood Frame Fire Protection Class				
	1–6	7–8	9	10	11	1–6	7–8	9	10	11
$ 40,000	$ 166	$ 170	$ 225	$ 237	$ 270	$ 178	$ 183	$ 237	$ 248	$ 285
45,000	173	178	233	244	280	187	191	248	260	298
50,000	178	183	241	254	290	190	195	254	265	304
60,000	191	196	259	273	313	205	211	273	287	328
70,000	213	216	285	299	343	225	231	299	315	360
80,000	241	248	328	343	394	257	265	343	363	415
90,000	268	276	365	384	441	289	296	384	403	464
100,000	298	307	407	426	490	320	329	426	449	515
120,000	354	364	484	508	584	381	391	508	534	614
150,000	459	471	625	657	755	493	506	657	692	794
200,000	616	633	841	884	1,017	662	680	884	931	1,070
250,000	737	754	961	1,021	1,167	780	798	1,021	1,086	1,243
300,000	879	901	1,147	1,218	1,394	931	953	1,218	1,295	1,483
400,000	1,021	1,045	1,331	1,413	1,617	1,067	1,105	1,413	1,504	1,723
500,000	1,309	1,340	1,707	1,812	2,074	1,385	1,418	1,812	1,929	2,209

Living in the Real World

Many factors are taken into consideration by the insurance company, including the type of insurance you want and the amount of coverage, the location and age of the house, and from what type of material it's built.

GLOBAL PERSPECTIVE

Move across the World

Scenario: Imagine you want to move somewhere such as Paris or Tokyo. How would you go about buying a home or finding an apartment there?

Students work in pairs to contact a real estate agent or a travel agent, or go online to find out what steps and costs are involved. Students present a short presentation to illustrate their findings.

LS , CL , P

National Standards for Business Education

Standard 1	Mathematical Foundations
Standard 2	Number Relationships and Operations

National Council of Teachers of Mathematics Standards

Standard 1	Numbers and Operations
Standard 4	Measurement
Standard 6	Problem Solving
Standard 8	Communication
Standard 9	Connections

(1) FOCUS

Ask students which of the three houses—straw, sticks, or brick—they would prefer to insure if employed by an insurance company. Point out that insurance companies consider the material used in the construction of a house to compute the premium.

In-Class Examples

Work through these exercises with students before having them do the Self-Check.
1. 90% of $50,000 **$45,000**
2. 80% of $150,000 **$120,000**
3. 80% of $260,00 **$208,000**
4. 90% of $375,000 **$337,500**

TEACH

When reviewing **Figure 10.5** on page 359, ask students to determine whether the lower numbers or higher numbers reflect a better fire protection class and how they came to their conclusion. **(The lower numbers have lower premiums, which imply less risk for an insurance company.)** Students should recognize also that the premium is less for a brick house than for a wood-frame house.

In-Class Examples
Refer to **Figure 10.5** Homeowners Insurance Premiums on page 359.
1. The wood-frame house's replacement cost is $125,000. Insured at 80 percent. Fire protection class 3. What is the annual premium? **$320**
2. The brick home's replacement cost is $300,000. Insured at 100 percent. Fire protection class 7. What is the annual premium? **$901**

ASSESS

Error Analysis
Emphasize the three factors which affect the cost of insuring a home: *the amount of coverage desired, the home's proximity to a good fire station, and whether the home is constructed of wood or brick.* Show students how to locate these factors on **Figure 10.5** on page 359.

CLOSE

Closing Activity
1. The brick home. Homeowners policy: $80,000. Fire protection in class 5. What is the annual premium? **$241**
2. The wood-frame home. Replacement cost is $150,000. Insured at 80 percent. Fire protection in class 9. What is the annual premium? **$508**

360

SELF-CHECK ✓

1. Coverage is $100,000 × 80% = $80,000; Wood frame, class 5, premium is $257
2. Coverage is $200,000 × 75% = $150,000; Brick, class 11, premium is $755

$1,147; $1,394

7. Mortgage payment: $1,003.20 per month; insurance: $459 ÷ 12 = $38.25 per month; taxes: $2,707.95 ÷ 12 = $222.66 per month

Need Help? Go to...
➤ Skill 30: Finding the Percentage, page 757

Example 1

The replacement value of Marcia Syke's home is $150,000. She has insured her home for 80 percent of its replacement value. The home is of wood-frame construction and has been rated in fire protection class 4. What is the annual premium?

STEP 1: Find the amount of coverage.

$$\text{Replacement Value of Home} \times \text{Insured Percent of Replacement Value}$$

$$\$150,000 \times 80\% = \$120,000 \text{ coverage on home}$$

STEP 2: Find the annual premium. (See Figure 10.5 on page 359.)
- Find the column, Wood Frame.
- Find the Fire Protection Class 1–6 column.
- Find the Amount of Insurance Coverage row with 120,000.
- Follow across the row and down the column to where 120,000 and 1–6 meet.

= **$381 annual premium**

CONCEPT CHECK

Complete the problems, then check your answers at the end of the chapter. For Problems 1 and 2, find the annual insurance premium. Use Figure 10.5 on page 359.

1. Replacement cost is $100,000. Insured at 80 percent. Wood frame, protection class 5.
2. Replacement cost is $200,000. Insured at 75 percent. Brick, protection class 11.

SECTION 10-7 PRACTICE

Use Figure 10.5 on page 359 to find the annual premium.

3. The Campbells' $50,000 wood frame house. A $40,000 homeowners policy. Fire protection class 8. What is the annual premium? **$183**
4. Kuen Yee's $100,000 brick home. A $80,000 homeowners policy. Fire protection class 11. What is the annual premium? **$394**

5. The Smiths own a wood-frame home in an area rated fire protection class 1. Their two-family home has a replacement value of $250,000 and is insured for 80 percent. What is their annual premium? **$662**

6. The Quicks own a brick home that has a replacement value of $375,000. They purchased a homeowners policy for 80 percent of its replacement value. They live in an area rated fire protection class 9. What is their annual policy premium? What would the premium be if they were in class 11?

7. Nelia and Gary Penn own a brick home with a market value and replacement value of $150,000.00. They insured their home for 100 percent of its replacement value. The Penns live in an area where the rate of assessment is 35 percent, the tax rate is 51.58 mills, and the fire protection is rated class 6. They have a $120,000.00 mortgage at 8 percent for 20 years. How much is the monthly payment for the mortgage, real estate taxes, and insurance?

MAINTAINING YOUR SKILLS

Find the percentage.

8. 70% of 90,000 **63,000**
9. 80% of 140,000 **112,000**
10. 96% of 148,000 **142,080**
11. 50% of 70,000 **35,000**
12. 40% of 84,500 **33,800**
13. 15% of 71,400 **10,710**

USING CALCULATORS

When adding or subtracting lists of numbers on a calculator, you might introduce errors by accidentally hitting the wrong key or forgetting to insert a decimal point. It is wise to check your results by entering the numbers again to see if you get the same result.

WRAP-UP

Go over any problem for which a wrong answer is given.

Assignment Guide
Basic: 3–4
Average: 5–6

20 min.

SECTION (10-8) Other Housing Costs

Section Objective

Compute the total housing cost and compare it with suggested guidelines.

In addition to your monthly mortgage payment, real estate taxes, and insurance payment, you'll have expenses for utilities, maintenance, and home improvements. **Utility costs** may include charges for electricity, gas, water, telephone, cell phone, cable TV, Internet service, repairs, and heating fuel. The Federal Housing Administration (FHA) recommends that your total monthly housing cost be less than 35 percent of your monthly net pay or take home pay.

Living in the Real World

The Hunt to Find a Home

What Else Do You Have to Pay For? Before they call it a night, the Sultans estimate the other costs of a new house. These will include gas and electricity; water, sewer, and trash collection; telephone, cable, and Internet service; and repairs.

Draw Conclusions Currently, who pays for their apartment's repairs? Who pays for the repairs once they own a home?

Continued on page 365

Example 1

Figure 10.6

Housing Expenses for May	
Mortgage payment	$698.24
Insurance ($303 ÷ 12)	25.25
Real estate taxes ($1,885 ÷ 12)	157.08
Electricity	65.90
Heating fuel	54.20
Telephone	36.18
Water	26.20
Cell phone	29.95
Satellite TV service	39.95
Loan payment on oven	50.00
Repair storm door	38.68

Sue and Paul Kwan have a combined monthly take-home pay of $3,320. The list of expenses for May is shown. Were their housing costs for May within the FHA guidelines?

STEP 1: Find the total monthly cost.
Sum of expenses:
= $1,221.63

STEP 2: Find the recommended maximum.
$3,320.00 × 35%
= $1,162.00

STEP 3: Compare. Is the total monthly cost less than the recommended maximum?
Is $1,221.63 less than $1,162.00?
No, the Kwans are not within the guidelines.

698.24 **+** 25.25 **+** 157.08 **+** 65.9 **+** 54.2 **+** 36.18

+ 26.2 **+** 29.95 **+** 39.95 **+** 50 **+** 38.68 **=** 1221.63

3320 **×** 35 **%** 1,162

Living in the Real World

One major difference between being a renter and an owner is general repairs. A landlord pays for all repairs in a rental; homeowners are responsible for all repair costs.

COOPERATIVE LEARNING

Rent or Own?
Students work in groups to create a poster-size Venn Diagram comparing the advantages and disadvantages of renting an apartment as opposed to owning a home. **Rent: Mobility. Less costly. Don't pay property taxes. Both: Pay property insurance. Pay utilities. Own: A good investment. Security and stability. Tax breaks. Pay mortgage. Pay property taxes. Maintenance costs. Value of home may give equity or profit.**

National Standards for Business Education

Standard 1	Mathematical Foundations
Standard 2	Number Relationships and Operations

National Council of Teachers of Mathematics Standards

Standard 1	Numbers and Operations
Standard 4	Measurement
Standard 6	Problem Solving
Standard 8	Communication
Standard 9	Connections

1 FOCUS

Review with students the three costs of owning a home. (**Mortgage payments, real estate taxes, and homeowner's insurance**) Ask students to name some other costs of owning a home (**e.g., utilities, repairs, purchases of large appliances, such as a refrigerator**).

In-Class Examples
Work through these exercises with students before having them do the Self-Check.
1. $500.00 + $35.50 + $26.50 + $48.00 **$610.00**
2. $480.00 + $220.00 + $65.45 + $22.35 **$787.80**
3. 35% of $600 **$210**
4. 35% of $1,020 **$357**
5. 35% of $3,742 **$1,309.70**

2 TEACH

Explain to students that monthly housing costs can be separated into two categories: (1) fixed costs, which are the same each month, and (2) variable costs, which can vary each month. Have students determine which of the costs in the example are fixed **(mortgage, taxes, and insurance)** and which are variable **(all others—the loan payment could also be considered fixed for the length of the loan).** Ask why the utilities costs are variable. **(They can change based on usage.)**

Motivating the Lesson

You've moved into a condominium and have kept track of your monthly expenses for June: mortgage payment, $630; insurance, $21.29; taxes, $188; condo association fee, $205; electricity, $67; telephone service, $26.75; cell phone, $29.95; Internet connection, $19.95. What are your total housing expenses for June? **$1,187.94**

In-Class Examples

For Problems 1 and 2, find the recommended FHA maximum.

1. Monthly net pay: $2,645. **$925.75**

2. Monthly net pay: $5,148. **$1,801.80**

3. Cheryl Emory has monthly take-home pay of $3,564. Here is a list of her monthly housing expenses for May: mortgage payment, $539; insurance, $33; taxes, $226; electricity, $60; phone service, $38; gas heat, $47; water, $23; internet connection, $22; new kitchen faucet, $207. The list of expenses for May is shown. Find the total monthly housing cost. **($1,195)** Is it within the FHA guidelines? **Yes.**

CONCEPT CHECK

SELF-CHECK ✓ Complete the problem, then check your answer at the end of the chapter.

Housing Expenses for April	
Mortgage payment	$644.00
Insurance ($490 ÷ 12)	40.83
Real estate taxes ($2,740 ÷ 12)	228.38
Electricity	66.24
Heating fuel	78.26
Telephone	39.62
Water	45.25
Cell phone	39.95
Satellite service	51.50
Home equity loan	75.00
Miscellaneous repairs	59.65

1. Dan Hosteler has a monthly take-home pay of $4,100. The list of expenses for April is shown. Were his housing costs for April within the FHA guidelines?

   Total monthly cost = $1,368.68; Recommended maximum = $4,100 × 35% = $1,435; $1,435 > $1,368.68; Total monthly cost is less than recommended maximum, therefore, within the guidelines.

SECTION 10-8 PRACTICE

Find the recommended FHA maximum. (Round to nearest $1.)

	Monthly Net Pay	Recommended FHA Minimum
2.	$1,100	$385
3.	3,900	$1,365
4.	880	$308
5.	4,284	$1,499
6.	5,439	$1,903.65
7.	7,942	$2,780

Figure 10.7

Housing Expenses for June	
Rent payment	$450.00
Renters insurance	12.50
Electricity	55.44
Gas—heat	44.00
Basic cable service	22.50
Telephone service	44.98
Appliance loan	82.35

8. Joshua and Peg Ryder. Monthly net pay is $1,980.
   $711.77 a. Find the total housing cost. (See **Figure 10.7**.)
   b. Is it within the FHA recommendation? **No; $711.77 > $693.00**

Figure 10.8

Condo Expenses for March	
Mortgage payment	$533.50
Insurance	19.75
Home equity loan	132.40
Electricity	75.80
Gas—heat	85.00
Satellite TV	51.00
Telephone service	29.45
Condo fee	155.00
Water	22.00

9. Frank and Yvette Shelby. Monthly net pay is $3,200.
   a. Find the total housing **$1,103.90** cost. (See **Figure 10.8**.)
   b. Is it within the FHA recommendation? **Yes; $1,103.90 < $1,120.00**

COMMUNICATION SKILLS

Dream Home

Create and display a poster of your dream home. Use magazines, the Internet, or your own drawings to depict what features it will have, where it will be located, and what it will look like. Then use the newspaper or the Internet to locate a real home that might look like the one you designed. Use the real home's price to create a reasonable estimate of the purchase price of your home.

BUSINESS NOTES

Real Estate Career

Research careers associated with the real-estate profession. Choose one: sales agent, broker, real-estate lawyer, appraiser, urban planner, or real-estate researcher. Interview someone in the profession. What skills does it take for that job? What training do you need for that job? What are the opportunities in the field? What is the typical range of earnings? Write a one-page paper with your findings. **LS**, **P**

10. Fara Pinkston recorded her housing expenses for the month of August: mortgage payment, $347.90; insurance, $17.00; taxes, $84.00; electricity, $64.40; phone service, $33.50; fuel, $98.25; water, $17.44; and repairs, $79.87. Her monthly take-home pay is $2,150.00. What is her total monthly cost? Is it within the FHA recommendation? **$742.36; Yes**

11. Melvin Hayashi recorded his housing expenses for the month of December: $548.36 for mortgage payment, $29.50 for insurance premium, $122.50 for real estate taxes, $46.75 for refrigerator installment payment, $104.70 for electricity, $34.40 for telephone service, $86.70 for home heating oil, and $21.80 for water. His monthly take-home pay is $2,500.00. What is his total monthly housing cost? Is it within the FHA recommendation? **$994.71; No; $875**

12. David and Helen Voss have a combined monthly net income of $4,750.00. Their records show that for last year they paid $10,789.20 in mortgage payments, $281.00 for insurance premiums, and $2,085.00 in real estate taxes. In addition, they had the expenses shown. What was their average monthly housing cost for last year? Was it within the FHA recommendation? **$1,734.62; No; $1,662.50**

Annual Home Expenses	
Water/sewer charges	$ 292.00
Electricity	940.00
Telephone service	559.92
Water heater	490.32
Repair windows	580.10
New air conditioner	2,458.68
Replace gutters	1,760.00
New lawn mower	579.20
Total	

For Problem 13, use Figure 10.1 on page 346 to find the loan payment and Figure 10.5 on page 359 to find the insurance premium.

13. Molly and Chris Spaulding recently purchased a brick house for $150,000.00. They made a 20 percent down payment and financed the remaining amount at 8 percent for 30 years. The tax rate in their area is 71.57 mills and the rate of assessment is 40 percent. They purchased a homeowners insurance policy for the purchase price of the house. The fire protection in the neighborhood is rated class 9. For the month of August, they recorded the following housing expenses: $69.20 for electricity, $44.85 for telephone service, $39.95 for cable TV, $18.80 for water, and $74.65 to repair a door. They have a combined monthly net income of $5,400.00. What is their monthly mortgage payment? What is the monthly insurance premium? What are their monthly taxes? What was their total monthly housing cost for August? Is it within the FHA recommendation? **Mortgage: $880.80; insurance: $52.08; taxes: $357.85; total: $1,538.18; FHA: Yes**

MAINTAINING YOUR SKILLS

Need Help? Go to...
➤ Skill 1: **Numbers,** page 727
➤ Skill 5: **Adding Decimals,** page 732
➤ Skill 30: **Finding the Percentage,** page 757

Which number is greater?

14. 2,109.8 or 2,107.9 **2,109.8**

15. 7,484.08 or 74,846.50 **74,846.50**

Add.

16. 85.89 + 74.84 + 35.30 + 306.24 **502.27**

17. 456.26 + 24.98 + 24.50 + 9.39 **515.13**

Find the percentage. Round answers to the nearest hundredth.

18. 35% of 8,300 **2,905**

19. 40% of 4,600 **1,840**

WRAP-UP

Go over any problem for which a wrong answer is given.

Assignment Guide
  Basic: 2–7
  Average: 8–10

20 min.

---

3 ASSESS

Error Analysis

Remind students to vertically align decimal points as they add the monthly housing costs. Have them check for computational errors in their work.

Emphasize that FHA guidelines suggest that total monthly housing costs remain less than 35 percent of monthly income. Have students check to be sure that they are multiplying the monthly income (not total monthly expenses) by 0.35. They can then compare 35 percent of the monthly income with the monthly expenses to determine if they are within FHA guidelines.

4 CLOSE

Closing Activity

1. Which number is greater: 3,114 or 3,029? **3,114**
2. $487.56 + $18.12 + $140.17 + $62.90 + $44.88 + $70.27 **$823.90**
3. Monthly take-home pay is $2,860. Total monthly housing cost is $996.78. Is the total monthly housing cost within FHA guidelines? **Yes**
4. Amanda and Chang Yoon have a monthly take-home pay of $7,016.33. They have the following monthly housing expenses for February: mortgage payment, $1,426; insurance, $39; taxes, $584.63; electricity, $90.41; phone service, $35.60; gas heat, $124.35; water, $18.19; Internet connection, $19.95; replace ceiling fan, $99.67. Find the total monthly housing cost. **($2,437.80)** Is it within the FHA guidelines? **Yes**

Quick Quiz

1. Peter and Colleen Chadwick bought a home for $388,000. They made a down payment of 40 percent. What is the down payment? **($155,200)** What is the amount of the mortgage? **$232,800**

2. Dave and Kathleen Madonia have reached an agreed-upon selling price of $172,000. They plan to make a 20 percent down payment and finance the rest at 6 percent for 20 years. What is the monthly payment? **($985.22)** What is the total amount to be paid? **($236,452.80)** What is the total interest charged? **$98,852.80**

3. Juan and Rosario Albertez have agreed to purchase a home for $326,000. They plan to make a 30 percent down payment and finance the rest. Their bank charges the following closing costs: loan origination fees, 1.75 percent of the mortgage amount; title search, $175; appraisal fee, $200; credit report, $70; legal fees, $350; property tax, $932; documentation stamp, 0.3 percent of mortgage amount. What are the closing costs? **$6,405.10**

For Problem 4, refer to Monthly Payments on a $1,000 Loan on page 799.

4. Mortgage amount of $144,000. Interest rate of 8 percent for 30 years. What is the first monthly payment? **($1,056.96)** What is the interest for the first payment? **($960)** What is the payment to the principal? **($96.96)** What is the new principal after the first payment? **$143,903.04**

CHAPTER 10 Self-Check Answers

SECTION 10-1 CONCEPT CHECK (p. 345)
1. $80,000 × 0.25 = **$20,000**; $80,000 − $20,000 = **$60,000**
2. $200,000 × 0.30 = **$60,000**; $200,000 − $60,000 = **$140,000**

SECTION 10-2 CONCEPT CHECK (p. 347)
1. $\frac{\$90,000.00}{\$1,000.00} × \$9.65 =$ **$868.50 monthly payment**
$868.50 × 12 × 20 =$ **$208,440.00 amount paid**
$208,440.00 − $90,000.00 =$ **$118,440.00 interest charged**

SECTION 10-3 CONCEPT CHECK (p. 350)
1. Find the mortgage amount. $105,000 × 0.10 = $10,500
$105,000 − $10,500 = $94,500
Find the sum of the bank fees.

Credit report	$ 65.00
Loan origination: $94,500 × 2%	1,890.00
Abstract of title	120.00
Attorney fee	250.00
Documentation stamp: $94,500 × 0.3%	283.50
Processing fee: $94,500 × 1.10%	1,039.50
Total Closing Costs	$3,648.00

Amount of Mortgage + Closing Costs
$94,500.00 + $3,648.00 = **$98,148.00 amount financed**

SECTION 10-4 CONCEPT CHECK (p. 352, 353)
1. Interest on $79,946.13: $79,946.13 × 8% × $\frac{1}{12}$ = **$532.97**
2. Payment to principal: $587.20 − $532.97 = **$54.23**
3. New balance: $79,946.13 − $54.23 = **$79,891.90**
4. Interest on $16,644.06: $16,644.06 × 8% × $\frac{1}{12}$ = **$110.96**
5. Payment to principal: $587.20 − $110.96 = **$476.24**
6. New balance: $16,644.06 − $476.24 = **$16,167.82**

SECTION 10-5 CONCEPT CHECK (p. 356)
1. $70,000 × 0.40 = **$28,000**   2. 65.50 ÷ 1,000 = **0.0655**
3. 0.0655 × $28,000 = **$1,834**

SECTION 10-6 CONCEPT CHECK (p. 358)
1. **$54,000**   2. **$21,600**   3. **$10,800**

SECTION 10-7 CONCEPT CHECK (p. 360)
1. Coverage is $100,000 × 80% = $80,000; Wood frame, class 5, **premium is $257**
2. Coverage is $200,000 × 75% = $150,000; Brick, class 11, **premium is $755**

SECTION 10-8 CONCEPT CHECK (p. 362)
1. Total monthly cost = $1,368.68; Recommended maximum = $4,100 × 35% = $1,435; $1,435 > $1,368.68; **Total monthly cost is less than recommended maximum, therefore, within the guidelines.**

Living in the Real World

The Hunt to Find a Home

Analyze the Story The Sultans had a lot to consider before signing the dotted line and turning over a down payment. They had to consider a feasible monthly mortgage, the cost of utilities and other services, and taxes and insurance.

1 **Drawing.** As a class come up with your own plan to purchase a home. Make a table or chart showing your monthly expenses and annual expenses (like taxes and insurance). Ask friends and family members what are typical costs involved based upon living in your area.

2 **Examining.** Buying a home requires many trade-offs. For example, the house you might want to live in is close to work, but it's too expensive. Different life situations will require different housing choices. What might be a wise housing choice for a single parent—buying or renting?

REVIEW OF KEY WORDS

mortgage loan (p. 344)
interest (p. 346)
closing costs (p. 349)
principal (p. 351)
real estate taxes (p. 355)
assessed value (p. 355)

tax rate (p. 355)
market value (p. 355)
rate of assessment (p. 355)
homeowners insurance (p. 357)
loss-of-use coverage (p. 357)
personal liability (p. 357)

medical coverage (p. 357)
replacement value (p. 357)
premium (p. 359)
fire protection class (p. 359)
utility costs (p. 361)

Match one of the key words above with a definition below.

1. an amount paid for an insurance policy. **premium**

2. a loan whereby the lender has the right to sell the property if payments are not made.

3. fees paid at the time documents are signed transferring ownership of a home. **closing costs**

4. public services such as water, phone, electricity, and garbage pickup. **utility costs**

5. an amount owed upon which interest charged is calculated. **principal**

6. fees collected on the ownership of property used to support the operation of government.
real estate taxes

2. mortgage loan

7. the price at which a house can be bought or sold. **market value**

8. pays for the expenses of living away from home while home reparations are being completed. **loss-of-use coverage**

9. the amount required to reconstruct your home if it is destroyed. **replacement value**

10. a number that reflects the quality of fire protection in your area. **fire protection class**

Refer to **Figure 10.4** on page 357 to determine the amount of homeowners insurance coverage for Problem 5.

5. Replacement value of home is $190,000. Coverage of the house: 90 percent.

  a. What is the insurance coverage on the home? **$171,000**

  b. What is the amount of insurance coverage for personal property? **$85,500**

  c. What is the amount of insurance coverage for loss of use? **$34,200**

  d. What is the amount of insurance coverage on the garage? **$17,100**

Refer to **Figure 10.5** on page 359 for Problem 6.

6. The wood-frame house. Replacement cost is $250,000. Insured at 80 percent. Fire protection class 9. What is the annual premium? **$884**

Living in the Real World

1. Answers will vary. Make sure they research the costs for living in your area—median home pricing, property taxes, etc.

2. Depends on financial stability, job security, savvy with home repairs, space needed, location, and so on.

CHAPTER Study Guide and Assessment

10

SECTION OBJECTIVE 10-1 AND EXAMPLES

Compute the mortgage loan amount.

Desiree Ramsey is considering the purchase of a new condominium for $95,500. A 20 percent down payment is required. What is the amount of the mortgage loan needed to finance the purchase?

STEP 1: Find the down payment.
$95,500 × 20% = $19,100

STEP 2: Find the mortgage loan amount.
Selling Price − Down Payment
$95,500 − $19,100
= $76,400 mortgage loan amount.

REVIEW EXERCISES
Complete the table below.

	Selling Price	Down Payment		Down Payment		Mortgage Loan Amount
11.	$132,600	25.0%	a.	$33,150	b.	$99,450
12.	87,500	15.0%	a.	$13,125	b.	$74,375
13.	306,200	$17\frac{1}{2}$%	a.	$53,585	b.	$252,615
14.	198,000	$\frac{1}{8}$	a.	$24,750	b.	$173,250

SECTION OBJECTIVE 10-2 AND EXAMPLES

Determine the monthly payment, total amount paid, and total interest charged.

Dee and Cissy White have applied for a $125,500 mortgage loan at an annual interest rate of 6 percent. The loan is for a period of 25 years and will be paid in equal monthly payments that include interest. What is the total amount of interest charged?

STEP 1: Find the monthly payment. (Refer to Figure 10.1 on page 346.)

$$\frac{\text{Amount of Mortgage}}{\$1,000} \times \begin{array}{c}\text{Monthly}\\ \text{Payment for}\\ \text{a } \$1,000 \text{ Loan}\end{array}$$

$$\frac{\$125,500}{\$1,000} \times \$6.44$$

= $808.22 monthly payment

STEP 2: Find the amount paid.

$$\begin{array}{c}\text{Monthly}\\ \text{Payment}\end{array} \times \begin{array}{c}\text{Number of}\\ \text{Payments}\end{array}$$
$808.22 × (12 months × 25 years)
$808.22 × 300
= $242,466 amount paid

STEP 3: Find the total interest charged.
Amount Paid − Amount of Mortgage
$242,466 − $125,000
= $116,966 total interest charged

REVIEW EXERCISES
Complete the table below.

	Mortgage	Years	Rate	Monthly Payment	Total Amount Paid	Total Interest Charged
15.	$ 75,500	25	5.5%	a. $463.57	b. $139,071.00	c. $63,571.00
16.	83,900	20	6.0%	a. $600.72	b. $144,172.80	c. $60,272.80
17.	123,900	25	6.5%	a. $836.33	b. $250,899.00	c. $126,999.00
18.	156,000	30	7.5%	a. $1,090.44	b. $392,558.40	c. $236,558.40

REINFORCEMENT

Section 10-1
1. Home priced at $260,000. Down payment: 30 percent. **($78,000)** What is the mortgage loan amount? **$182,000**
2. Santos and Anna Rivera made an offer of $158,000 on a home that was priced at $164,000. Their offer was accepted. They made a down payment of 25 percent and financed the remaining amount. What is the amount of the mortgage? **$118,500**

Section 10-2
1. Selling price: $276,000. Down payment: 25 percent. Terms: 8 percent for 15 years. What is the total interest charged? **$149,205.60**
2. Jordan Lytle has obtained a $90,000 mortgage loan at an annual interest rate of 7 percent for 20 years. What is the monthly payment? **($697.50)** What is the total amount to be paid? **($167,400)** What is the total interest charged? **$77,400**

SECTION OBJECTIVE 10-3 AND EXAMPLES

Figure out the total closing costs.

Shannon and Glenn Shelton have been granted a $150,000 loan. When they sign the papers to purchase their new home, they will have to pay the closing costs shown. What is the total of their closing costs? What is the actual amount financed with the mortgage?

STEP 1: Find the closing costs. (Refer to the chart next to this problem.)
$250 + $75 + $275 + ($150,000 \times 1.3\%) + $295 = **$2,845**$

STEP 2: Find the actual amount financed.
Amount of Mortgage + Closing Costs
$150,000 + $2,845
= **$152,845 amount financed**

Closing Costs	
Appraisal fee	$250
Credit report	75
Title search	275
Service fee	1.3% of mortgage
Legal fees	295

REVIEW EXERCISES

Use the list of closing costs for Problems 19–22.

19. Sung and Mu Lee. **$8,946.80**
Mortgage loan of $245,600.
What are the total closing costs?

20. Greg and Kaye Meiers. **$3,874.38**
Mortgage loan of $97,500.
What are the total closing costs?

21. Josh and Judy Jones. **$4,929.28**
Mortgage loan of $128,300.
What are the total closing costs?

22. Rochelle St. James. **$3,549**
Mortgage loan of $88,000.
What are the total closing costs?

Closing Costs	
Credit report	$ 55
Loan origination	2% of mortgage
Abstract of title	155
Attorney fee	325
Documentation stamp	0.325% of mortgage
Processing fee	1.10% of mortgage

SECTION OBJECTIVE 10-4 AND EXAMPLES

Compute the allocation of monthly payment toward principal, interest, and the new principal.

Rowena Tinley obtained a 30-year $90,000.00 mortgage from State Bank. The interest rate is 7.5 percent. Her monthly payment is $629.10. For the first payment, what is the interest? What is the payment to principal? What is the new principal?

STEP 1: Find the interest. Principal $\times$ Rate $\times$ Time
$90,000.00 \times 7.5\% \times \frac{1}{12} = **$562.50 interest**$

STEP 2: Find the payment to principal. Monthly Payment − Interest
$629.10 − $562.50 = **$66.60 payment to principal**$

STEP 3: Find the new principal. Previous Balance − Payment to Principal
$90,000.00 − $66.60 = **$89,933.40 new principal**$

REVIEW EXERCISES
Complete the table below.

	Mortgage Amount	Interest Rate	First Monthly Payment	Amount for Interest	Amount for Principal	New Principal
23.	$ 60,000	8.5%	$ 483.14	a.	b. $58.14	c. $59,941.86	a. $425.00
24.	130,000	9.0%	1,090.96	a.	b. $115.96	c. $129,884.04	a. $975.00
25.	145,500	12.0%	1,496.63	a.	b. $41.63	c. $145,458.37	a. $1,455.00
26.	159,900	10.0%	1,403.24	a.	b. $70.74	c. $159,829.26	a. $1,332.50

REINFORCEMENT

Section 10-3

1. Seung-Hoon Lee bought a house for $218,000. He made a down payment of 20 percent and applied for a mortgage for the remaining amount. He will finance the closing costs as part of the mortgage. What are the total closing costs? **($6,364.60)** What is the actual amount financed with the mortgage? **$180,764.60**

Section 10-4

1. Mortgage loan of $154,000. Interest rate is 8 percent for 30 years. Monthly payment is $1,130.36. How much of the first monthly payment is for interest? **($1,026.67)** How much of the first monthly payment is for principal? **($103.69)** What is the new principal? **$153,896.31**

27. $95,000 × 45% = $42,750 assessed value 54.5 ÷ 1,000 = 0.0545 tax rate as decimal 0.0545 × $42,750 = $2,329.88 real estate tax
28. $229,500 × 30% = $68,850 assessed value $43.46 ÷ 1,000 = 0.04346 tax rate expressed as decimal 0.04346 × $68,850 = $2,992.22 property tax

---

SECTION OBJECTIVE 10-5 AND EXAMPLES

Calculate the assessed value and real estate taxes.

The Orange County tax assessor stated that the market value of the Marvin Hotel is $950,000. The rate of assessment in Orange County is 55 percent of market value. The tax rate is 34.50 mills. What is the real estate tax on the Marvin Hotel?

STEP 1: Find the assessed value. Market Value × Rate of Assessment
$950,000 × 55% = $522,500 assessed value

STEP 2: Express the tax rate as a decimal. 34.50 mills ÷ 1,000 = 0.0345 tax rate

STEP 3: Find the real estate tax. Tax Rate × Assessed Value
0.0345 × $522,500.00 = **$18,026.25 real estate tax**

REVIEW EXERCISES

27. The tax rate is 54.5 mills, the market value is $95,000, and the rate of assessment is 45 percent. Find the assessed value, the tax rate as a decimal, and the real estate tax.

28. Se Ri Pak's home is located in a town where the rate of assessment is 30 percent of market value. The tax rate is $43.46 per $1,000 of assessed value. His home has a market value of $229,500. What is the assessed value? What is the property tax?

29. **$7,095.61**

29. Harvey and Marie Levan own a home with a market value of $542,000. The rate of assessment is 60 percent and the tax rate is 24.31 mills. What is the annual real estate tax?

30. Steve and Shelia Hitt own a home in a retirement community. The home has a market value of $87,400. The rate of assessment is 50 percent and the tax rate is $30.45 per $1,000 of assessed value. What is their yearly real estate tax? **$1,330.67**

SECTION OBJECTIVE 10-6 AND EXAMPLES

Work out the amount of coverage.

Use Figure 10.4 on page 357 to answer the problems in this section. The replacement value of Todd and Melissa Dewey's home is $86,500. They have insured their home for 80 percent of the replacement value. According to the guidelines found in Figure 10.4, what is the amount of coverage on the Deweys' personal property?

STEP 1: Find the amount of coverage on the home. Replacement Value × Percent
$86,500 × 80% = $69,200

STEP 2: Find the amount of coverage on personal property.
Amount of Coverage on Home × Percent
$69,200 × 50% = **$34,600 coverage on personal property**

REVIEW EXERCISES

Find the amount of coverage and the amount of insurance.

	Replacement Value	Percent Covered	Amount of Coverage	Amount of Insurance (for Garage, Personal Property, Loss of Use)
31.	$124,500	90%	a. $112,050	—
32.	65,000	75%	a. $48,750	—
33.	250,000	85%	a. $212,500	b. $21,250
34.	87,000	80%	a. $69,600	—

REINFORCEMENT

Section 10-5

1. A townhouse's market value is $163,000. Rate of assessment is 36 percent. Tax rate is $75 per $1,000. What is the annual real estate tax? **$4,401**

Section 10-6

1. The duplex's replacement value is $78,000. Coverage of the home: 80 percent.
   a. What is the insurance coverage on the home? **$62,400**
   b. What is the amount of coverage on personal property? **$31,200**
2. The home's replacement value is $136,000. Coverage of the home: 90 percent.
   a. What is the insurance coverage on the home? **$122,400**
   b. What is the loss of use insurance coverage? **$24,480**
   c. What is the insurance coverage on the garage? **$12,240**

SECTION OBJECTIVE 10-7 AND EXAMPLES

Calculate the annual homeowners insurance premium.

The Cunninghams' wood-frame house. Replacement value of $150,000. Fire protection class 10. What is the annual premium? (Use Figure 10.5 on page 359 to answer the problem.)

Answer: $692

REVIEW EXERCISES

Complete the table below. (Use Figure 10.5 on page 359 to answer the problems.)

	Type of Construction	Replacement Value	Percent Covered	Fire Protection Class	Annual Premium
35.	Brick	$100,000	80%	5	$241
36.	Brick	100,000	90%	11	$441
37.	Wood frame	120,000	100%	8	$391
38.	Wood frame	200,000	75%	10	$692

SECTION OBJECTIVE 10-8 AND EXAMPLES

Compute the total housing cost and compare it with suggested guidelines.

Peter and Lucy Cole have a combined monthly take-home pay of $2,550. They keep a record of their monthly housing expenses. The list of expenses for April is shown. Were their housing costs for April within FHA guidelines?

Housing Expenses for April	
Rent payment	$886.50
Renters insurance	36.00
Gas—heat	54.00
Electricity	108.20
Telephone service	35.50

STEP 1: Find the monthly cost.
$886.50 + $36.00 + $54.00 + $108.20 + $35.50 = $1,120.20

STEP 2: Find the recommended maximum.
$2,550.00 × 35% = $892.50

STEP 3: Compare. Is the total monthly cost less than the recommended maximum?
Is $1,120.20 less than $892.50? **No, the Coles are not within the guidelines.**

REVIEW EXERCISES

Find the recommended FHA maximum. (Round to nearest $1.)

	Monthly Net Pay	Recommended FHA Maximum
39.	$2,540	$889
40.	3,298	$1,154.30
41.	1,298	$454.30
42.	5,496	$1,923.60

REINFORCEMENT

Section 10-7

Use **Figure 10.5** on page 359.

1. Carmen Guerrero owns a brick home that has a replacement value of $500,000. She purchased a homeowners policy for 80 percent of its replacement value. She lives in an area rated fire protection class 8. What is the annual premium? **$1,045**

Section 10-8

1. Dwight and Autumn Higgins recorded their housing expenses for the month of June: mortgage payment, $1,053; insurance, $38.35; taxes, $362; electricity, $101.74; gas heat, $18.37; garbage pick-up, $14.25; telephone service, $53.33; satellite TV, $44.99; cell phone, $35; high-speed Internet service, $45.99. Their combined monthly take-home pay is $5,328. What is their total housing cost for June? **($1,767.02)** Is it within the FHA recommendation? **Yes**

National Standards for Business Education

Section Objectives	1. Mathematical Foundations	2. Number Relationships and Operations	3. Patterns, Functions, and Algebra	4. Measurements	5. Statistics and Probability	6. Problem-Solving Applications	
11-1 Health Insurance Premiums (pp. 372–374) Compute health insurance premiums.	X	X			X		
11-2 Health Insurance Benefits (pp. 375–377) Calculate the amount that the patient pays for health care.	X	X			X		
11-3 Term Life Insurance (pp. 378–380) Utilize tables to compute the annual premium for term life insurance.	X	X			X		
11-4 Other Types of Life Insurance (pp. 381–383) Apply tables to data to compute the annual premiums for three types of life insurance.	X	X			X		

(Source: Reprinted with permission from the National Standards for Business Education, copyright © 2001 by National Business Education Association, 1914 Association Drive, Reston, Virginia 21901-1596)

SCANS Correlation

Foundation Skills

Basic Skills	Reading	Writing	Math	Listening	Speaking	
Thinking Skills	Creative Thinking	Decision Making	Problem Solving	Seeing Things in the Mind's Eye	Knowing How to Learn	Reasoning
Personal Qualities	Responsibility	Self-Esteem	Sociability	Self-Management	Integrity/Honesty	

This chapter's highlighted blocks indicate the chapter's content coverage in the Student Edition and the Teacher Wraparound Edition.

National Council of Teachers of Mathematics Standards

1. Numbers & Operations	2. Algebra	3. Geometry	4. Measurement	5. Data Analysis & Probability	6. Problem Solving	7. Reasoning & Proof	8. Communication	9. Connections	10. Representations
X			X		X		X	X	
X			X		X		X	X	
X			X		X		X	X	
X			X		X		X	X	

SCANS Correlation

Workplace Competencies

Resources	Allocating Time	Allocating Money	Allocating Material and Facility Resources	Allocating Human Resources		
Information	Acquiring and Evaluating Information	Organizing and Maintaining Information	Interpreting and Communicating Information	Using Computers to Process Information		
Interpersonal Skills	Participating as a Member of a Team	Teaching Others	Serving Clients/Customers	Exercising Leadership	Negotiating to Arrive at a Decision	Working with Cultural Diversity
Systems	Understanding Systems	Monitoring and Correcting Performance	Improving and Designing Systems			
Technology	Selecting Technology	Applying Technology to Task	Maintaining and Troubleshooting Technology			

What You'll Learn

In this chapter you'll focus on finding the cost of health insurance and life insurance premiums. You'll also explore the amount the patient pays for medical care.

Why It's Important

Health and life insurance protect you and your dependents against financial loss in case of illness or death. Knowing what type of insurance policy you need or want can help you make a wise choice in purchasing coverage for you and your family.

Key Word Review

Make Learning Easy

Drawing sketches, diagrams, and charts helps you to learn. To get ready to make learning easy in this chapter, make two charts—Health Insurance (with headings corresponding to Sections 11-1 and 11-2) and Life Insurance (with the headings Term, Life, and Other). Write the key words from each section and their definitions in the correct area of your chart.

CHAPTER 11

Insurance

What You'll Learn

Section 11-1 Compute health insurance premiums.

Section 11-2 Calculate the amount the patient pays for health care.

Section 11-3 Utilize tables to compute the annual premium for term life insurance.

Section 11-4 Apply tables to data to compute the annual premiums for three types of life insurance.

When Will You Ever Use This?

When tragedy strikes, who's there to comfort you? Hopefully you can lean on your friends and family. Although emotional support is needed, so is financial support. Having insurance is a way to financially protect you and your loved ones when you're faced with illness and death and dying.

Key Words to Know

- health insurance
- preferred provider organization (PPO)
- health maintenance organization (HMO)
- deductible
- co-insurance
- co-payment
- life insurance
- term life insurance
- beneficiary
- whole life insurance
- cash value
- limited payment policy
- universal life insurance

Mathematics Online

To learn more about insurance, visit the *Mathematics with Business Applications* Web site at www.busmath.glencoe.com.

CLASSROOM RESOURCES

Application and Enrichment
- Teacher Wraparound Edition
- Teacher Resource Binder, Blackline Masters
- Interactive Lesson Planner CD-ROM
- PowerPoint® Presentations CD-ROM

Review and Enforcement
- Mathematics Online
  www.busmath.glencoe.com
- Teacher Resource Binder, Internet Resources

- Student Activity Workbook
- Student Activity Workbook, Teacher Annotated Edition
- School-to-Home Activity Workbook

Assessment and Evaluation
- Assessment Binder, Reproducible Tests
- Assessment Binder, Alternative Assessment Strategies
- ExamView® Pro Test Generator CD-ROM

For the Teacher
- Student Activity Workbook, Teacher Annotated Edition
- Assessment Binder
- Interactive Lesson Planner CD-ROM
- Teacher Resource Binder
- Mathematics Online
  www.busmath.glencoe.com

For the Student
- Student Activity Workbook
- School-to-Home Activity Workbook

Living in the Real World

Insuring Your Life

When Jeremy Waldschmidt was in a car accident last year, his health insurance covered most of his hospital emergency room expenses, follow-up doctor's visits, and rehabilitation. Waldschmidt is a freelance artist, so his health insurance is a nongroup plan. After his leg healed, Waldschmidt began considering how he could get better insurance. Once you've read this story, you might have a different outlook on the necessity of health insurance.

Read on. Go to . . .

371

Living in the Real World

Story's Summary
When freelance artist Jeremy Waldschmidt was involved in an automobile accident, his insurance covered much of the cost of his healthcare and rehabilitation, but he was still faced with a hefty bill. His plan is a non-group policy and the time has come to shop around for better coverage. His sister Louise, a mother of two children, is shopping around for life insurance. Students learn the ins and outs of insurance by reading about the two siblings' search for indemnity.

Did You Know...
According to the U.S. Census Bureau, roughly 14 percent of the U.S. population is without health insurance coverage. That translates to nearly 39 million individuals who are uninsured.

Think about This
How do people without insurance coverage pay for medical expenses related to accidents or a life-threatening disease?

LOCAL STANDARDS

National Standards for Business Education

Standard 1	Mathematical Foundations
Standard 2	Number Relationships and Operations
Standard 5	Statistics and Probability

National Council of Teachers of Mathematics Standards

Standard 1	Numbers and Operations
Standard 4	Measurement
Standard 6	Problem Solving
Standard 8	Communication
Standard 9	Connections

1 FOCUS

Use a number cube or die. Ask a student to choose a number he or she thinks the cube will land on when rolled. If the cube doesn't land on the number, would you be willing to give up your most valued possession? **Explain that not having some type of health insurance also is taking a big risk.**

In-Class Examples

Work through these exercises with students before having them do the Self-Check. Divide. Round to the nearest hundredth.

1. $\frac{544}{12}$ **45.33**
2. $\frac{1,195}{52}$ **22.98**

Add.

3. $42.60 + $153.82 + $16.96 **$213.38**

○ **Section Objective**

Compute health insurance premiums.

An accident or illness could cut off your income, wipe out your savings, and leave you in debt. Just as important as vehicle insurance is **health insurance**. It protects *you* against overwhelming medical expenses.

Many types of health care coverage plans exist. Let's focus on just three group health insurance plans—a *traditional* plan, a **preferred provider organization** (PPO), and a **health maintenance organization** (HMO). A traditional plan offers health care coverage when the health care provider is paid a predetermined dollar amount for the service given. You may use any health care provider. A PPO is a group of selected health care providers who offer comprehensive services at preset reimbursement levels. You are required to use these "network" providers (that is, a selected group of doctors) unless you are willing to pay additional costs to non-network providers. An HMO is a prepaid health plan in which the care providers either contract with or are employees of the HMO to provide you with services. You may select a "primary care" physician and agree to receive all non-emergency services from the physician. This physician may refer you to a specialist (such as an obstetrician, a psychiatrist, a cardiologist, and so on).

Often times the selected employer's health insurance group pays for 75 to 80 percent of the costs and you, the policyholder, pay for the remaining 20 or 25 percent. Given this, how do you budget for health insurance?

Important Questions to Ask Yourself	What Formula Do I Use?
How do you calculate the **percent** that you'll be paying?	Employee's Percent = 100% − Employer's Percent
How do you calculate how much you'll **contribute** each paycheck to health insurance?	$\text{Employee's Contribution} = \text{Total Premium} \times \text{Employee's Percent}$

Living in the Real World

Insuring Your Life

Find a New Plan Waldschmidt needs new health insurance and asks his older sister Louise for some advice. She suggests that he join a professional organization of artists who are part of a group plan. This way the organization will pay part of his premium or at least offer a reduced premium.

Draw Conclusions What's the purpose of an insurance premium?

Continued on page 375

BUSINESS NOTES

Insurance Industry

There are over 900 insurance companies in the United States. These companies employ people in many different kinds of jobs from sales to claims adjusters. The employees who help insurance companies set up their premium rates are called actuaries. Students create a chart to keep track of their skills and education. Students use these headings or add their own: interests, abilities, values, education, experience, job options. **LS** , **CL**

Living in the Real World

It is the cost of an insurance policy that must be paid to ensure coverage.

Example 1

Need Help? Go to...
- ▶ **Workshop 7:**
  Dividing Decimals,
  page 16
- ▶ **Skill 11: Dividing**
  Decimals, page 738
- ▶ **Skill 30: Finding**
  the Percentage,
  page 757
- ▶ **Application K:**
  Chronological
  Expressions,
  page 766

Sean Derricotte has a family membership in a group medical insurance program. The annual premium is $6,180. Derricotte's employer pays 80 percent of the total cost. His contribution is deducted monthly from his paycheck. What is Derricotte's annual contribution? What is his monthly deduction?

STEP 1: Find the employee's percent.
$100\% - 80\% = 20\%$ employee's percent

STEP 2: Find the employee's annual contribution.

Total Premium	×	Employee's Percent		
$6,180.00	×	20%	=	$1,236.00 employee's annual contribution

STEP 3: Find the employee's monthly deduction.
Employee's Contribution ÷ 12
$1,236.00 ÷ 12 = $103.00 employee's monthly deduction

100 − 80 = 20

6180 × 20 % = 1236 ÷ 12 = 103

CONCEPT CHECK

SELF-CHECK ✓

Complete the problems, then check your answers at the end of the chapter. Find the employee's total annual contribution and the employee's monthly deduction.

1. Dorsey Williams, single plan. PPO annual premium is $4,325. Employer pays 65 percent.

   $100\% - 65\% = 35\%$
   $\$4,325 \times 35\% = \$1,513.75$
   $\$1,513.75 \div 12 = \$126.15$

2. Rubina Shaw, family plan. HMO annual premium is $11,473. Employer pays 73 percent.

   $100\% - 73\% = 27\%$
   $\$11,473 \times 27\% = \$3,097.71$
   $\$3,097.71 \div 12 = \$258.14$

SECTION 11-1 PRACTICE

		Insurance Plan	Annual Premium	Employer's Percent	Employee's Percent	Employee's Contribution	Monthly Premium
b. $1,192.00	3.	Single PPO	$ 2,980	60%	a. 40%	b.	c. $99.33
b. $473.60	4.	Single HMO	2,368	80%	a. 20%	b.	c. $39.47
b. $1,516.50	5.	Family Trad	6,066	75%	a. 25%	b.	c. $126.38
b. $1,254.00	6.	Family HMO	12,540	90%	a. 10%	b.	c. $104.50
b. $2,190	7.	Family PPO	14,600	85%	a. 15%	b.	c. $182.50

Continued on next page

COOPERATIVE LEARNING

Health Insurance Plans
There are many types of health insurance plans available. Students work in groups to report on different plans. Students talk to family members or insurance agents to find information. In addition to deductible and co-insurance, students report on terms such as: first-dollar coverage; customary, usual, and reasonable (CUR); maximum out of pocket expense; and self-insure.

PROBLEM SOLVING

Table
Make a table to calculate the income for each pay period for the following annual income amounts: **$22,000, $34,000, and $56,000. $22,000: $1,833.33, $916.67, $846.15, $423.08. $34,000: $2,833.33, $1,416.67, $1,307.69, $653.85. $56,000: $4,666.67, $2,333.33, $2,153.85, $1,076.92** P

SECTION 11-1

② TEACH

Explain that most people are covered by some type of health insurance. Discuss the various health plans insurance companies offer and mention that the less costly insurance usually is provided by an employer through a group plan.

You might want to review the term *deduction*, as well as different pay periods, such as biweekly and semimonthly.

Motivating the Lesson
You are single and enrolled in a traditional group medical insurance plan where you work. Your employer pays 80 percent of the annual premium of $5,450. Your contribution is deducted from your weekly paycheck. What is your weekly deduction for medical insurance? **$20.96**

In-Class Examples
1. Darrell Morris, single plan. PPO annual premium: $5,060. Employer pays 75 percent. Find the employee's total annual contribution. **($1,265)** Find the employee's monthly deduction. **$105.42**
2. Odell Porter, family plan. HMO annual premium: $12,240. Employer pays 90 percent. Find the employee's total annual contribution. **($1,224)** Find the employee's semi-monthly deduction. **$51**
3. Cleona Wilkins, single plan. Traditional medical plan. Premium: $5,248. Employer pays 80 percent of cost.
   a. How much does she pay annually? **$1,049.60**
   b. How much is deducted from her biweekly paycheck? **$40.37**

SECTION 11-1

ASSESS

Error Analysis

Review the concept that percent is a fraction of 100. For example, 85 percent means $\frac{85}{100}$ and can be written as the decimal 0.85. Once students know what percent of the annual premium the employer pays, remind them to subtract that percent from 100 to find the percent the employee must pay. If an employer pays 85 percent, the employee pays 100 percent less 85 percent, or 15 percent (100% − 85% = 15%). To determine the employee's annual cost of insurance, change 15 percent to a decimal **(0.15)** and multiply 0.15 by the annual premium **(0.15 × Annual Premium)**.

Some students may benefit from a review of monthly **(12)**, semimonthly **(24)**, biweekly **(26)**, and weekly **(52)** pay periods.

CLOSE

Closing Activity

1. What percent of $200 is $80?
    40%

    Find the percentage.
2. 94% × $10,635 **$9,996.90**
3. Jocelyn Scully is enrolled in a traditional family medical plan. The annual premium is $8,094. Her employer pays 80 percent of the total cost. What is her total annual contribution? **$1,618.80** What is her bi-weekly contribution? **$62.26**
4. Randy Gramer, single plan. HMO premium costs him $57.30 monthly. Annual dental costs him $578. Annual vision costs him $195. What is his monthly deduction for all insurance? **$121.72**

8. Sing-Chi Chow, single plan.
    PPO premium is $5,436.
    Employer pays 85 percent of cost.
    a. How much does Chow pay annually? **$815.40**
    b. How much is deducted from his weekly paycheck? **$15.68**

9. Kelli Lenz, family plan.
    HMO premium is $8,500.
    Employer pays 65 percent of cost.
    a. How much does Lenz pay annually? **$2,975.00**
    b. How much is deducted from her semimonthly paycheck? **$123.96**

10. Luisa Hernandez has a family membership in her company's traditional group medical insurance program. The total cost is $6,288 annually and the employer pays 75 percent of the total cost. She also pays for the optional annual dental premium of $880 and the optional vision premium of $324. Her contribution is deducted biweekly from her paycheck. How much is her total annual contribution? How much is her biweekly deduction? **$2,776, $103.77**

11. Boris Heban is single and pays into an HMO. The total cost is $8,190 annually, and the employer pays 90 percent of the total cost. He also pays 50 percent of the optional annual dental premium of $662 and 50 percent of the optional vision premium of $188. How much is deducted each week from his paycheck? **$23.92**

12. Rachel and Dustin Lutts are self-employed photographers. They pay 100 percent of the PPO insurance premium of $7,640 annually. They also have a dental plan that costs $566 annually and a vision plan that costs $244 annually. The premiums are paid quarterly (every three months). How much do they pay each quarter? **$2,112.50**

13. Placido Lucero is retired and covered by Medicare Part A & B. His retirement plan covers 67 percent of his Medicare HMO annual premium of $4,200. His retirement plan covers 50 percent of his wife's Medicare HMO annual premium of $4,200. Also, Lucero has a dependent grandchild who has an HMO annual premium of $1,600, of which 40 percent is covered by his retirement plan. What is the monthly amount deducted from his retirement check for health care? **$370.50**

Need Help? Go to...
► Skill 31: **Finding the Rate,** page 758
► Skill 30: **Finding the Percentage,** page 757

MAINTAINING YOUR SKILLS

Find the percent.

14. What percent of $60 is $3? **5%**
15. What percent of $150 is $60? **40%**
16. What percent of $475 is $95? **20%**
17. What percent of $210.00 is $73.50? **35%**

Find the percentage.

18. 367 × 55% **201.85**
19. 940 × 14.2% **133.48**
20. 4,200 × 13.65% **573.30**
21. 3,500 × 4.81% **168.35**

WRAP-UP

Go over any problem for which a wrong answer is given.

Assignment Guide
Basic: 3–7
Average: 8–9

20 min.

SECTION (11-2) Health Insurance Benefits

Section Objective

Calculate the amount the patient pays for health care.

Just because you have health insurance doesn't mean all procedures are covered. In fact, the insurance plan and the state you live in determine the services provided. For example, you might have difficulty securing health insurance to cover infertility treatment and pre-existing conditions (for example, congenital heart disease).

Health insurance policies have an annual **deductible**, which is the amount of money you must pay each year before your insurance company starts paying. Some health care services also have a **co-insurance** clause. This requires you to pay a certain percent of medical expenses after a deductible has been paid. For example, an 80 percent co-insurance clause means your insurance company pays 80 percent of the cost and you pay 20 percent of the cost. You might also hear about a **co-payment**. This is usually a predetermined flat fee you pay for health care services. (This is usually *not* specified by a percent like a co-insurance clause.) For example, you might have a $10 co-payment for visiting the doctor regardless of the type of service provided.

You'll need to remember that:

$$\text{Amount Paid by Patient} = \text{Deductible} + \text{Co-payments} + \text{Co-insurance Amount} + \text{Hospital Charges}$$

Living in the Real World

Insuring Your Life

How Risky Do You Want to Be? Waldschmidt knows that health insurance doesn't cover all the costs of medical care. In fact, he thought his part of the bill for his broken leg was pretty high. He is now exploring insurance policy options that might reduce his costs in the future.

Draw Conclusions What are some ways for Waldschmidt to reduce his costs?

Continued on page 378

Example 1

Brooke Kolodie is single and has a health insurance plan with the benefits shown in Figure 11.1 on page 376. Her recent network health care costs include co-payments for 8 physician visits and 9 specialist visits. Following hospital surgery, she made co-payments for 12 physical therapy visits, and she had 75 home visits from a nurse at $55 each. Her hospital admission charge was $200 and her hospital bill was $14,560. What amount did she pay?

Continued on next page

National Standards for Business Education

Standard 1	Mathematical Foundations
Standard 2	Number Relationships and Operations
Standard 5	Statistics and Probability

National Council of Teachers of Mathematics Standards

Standard 1	Numbers and Operations
Standard 4	Measurement
Standard 6	Problem Solving
Standard 8	Communication
Standard 9	Connections

(1) FOCUS

If you have available a medical insurance claim form, pass it around for the class to see. Explain that when medical costs are incurred (such as doctor visits, hospital charges, or sometimes even medical prescriptions), you must complete a claim form and send it with the total bill to the insurance company. The insurance company will compute the amount of the total cost they pay, and the amount you, the patient, must pay.

In-Class Examples

Work through these exercises with students before having them do the Self-Check.
1. $465.18 − $50 **$415.18**
2. $1,249 − $300 **$949**
3. (67 × $75) × 30% **$1,507.50**

ALTERNATIVE ASSESSMENT

Students with Learning Disabilities
Processing information in written or verbal form can be difficult for students with learning disabilities. Visual representations, such as graphs, charts, and tables help the students understand the information. Remind students that to better understand material they can make their own study guides with graphs and diagrams. `LS`, `CL`

Living in the Real World

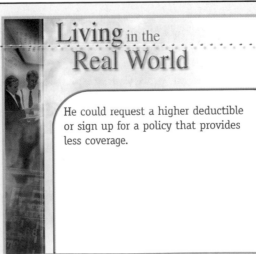

He could request a higher deductible or sign up for a policy that provides less coverage.

② TEACH

Be sure students understand the meanings of the terms *deductible clause* and *co-insurance clause*.

Remind students to add the deductible amount to the co-insurance amount that the patient pays when finding the total amount paid by the patient. Although the deductible was subtracted in finding the amount subject to co-insurance, the actual dollars still have to be paid toward the medical bill itself.

You might want to mention that in most major medical plans, the deductible amount is used on an annual basis. That is, once a patient has paid the full deductible within one year, any other bills during that same year are not subject to the deductible—only the co-insurance clause applies.

Motivating the Lesson

You have a medical insurance plan at work with a $300 annual deductible. After your deductible has been paid, your insurance covers physician visits at $10 co-payment and specialist visits at $20 co-payment. You have already paid your $300 annual deductible. In addition, you have 9 visits to your physician and 3 visits to a specialist. What is the total amount you paid this year for medical expenses including your deductible? **$450**

In-Class Examples

Use **Figure 11.1** for Problems 1–3.
1. Single, Network. Co-payments: physician visits, 15 specialist visits, 8 physical therapy, 12 ambulance, 1 emergency room, 1 hospital charges, $13,862. Find the total amount paid by the insured. **$2,251.20**

Figure 11.1

Health Care Benefits Schedule

		Network	Non-Network*
Annual Deductible	Single	$300	$ 600
	Family	$900	$1,800
Hospital Charges	—	90% **	70% **
Home Health Care	First 50 visits	100% **	80% **
	Over 50 visits	80% **	80% **
Co-insurance/ Co-payments	Physician visit	$ 10	$ 12
	Specialist visit	$ 20	$ 25
	Physical Therapy		
	First 15 visits	$ 15	70% **
	Over 15 visits	80% **	70% **
	Emergency Room	$ 50	$ 50
	Ambulance	$ 25	$ 25

*Non-Network refers to a health care provider that doesn't have a contract with the health plan administrator.
**Percent of total cost that is covered by the health care company.

Need Help? Go to...
➤ **Skill 4:** Subtracting Whole Numbers, page 731
➤ **Skill 30:** Finding the Percentage, page 757

1. The deductible is $900. Find the cost of the co-payments.
($10.00 × 22) + ($20 × 12) + ($15 × 15) + $50 = $220 + $240 + $225 + $50 = $735
Find the hospital charges.
$1,260 × (100% − 90%) = $1,260 × 10% = $126
Find the total amount paid by the patient.
$900 + $735 + $126 = $1,761

STEP 1: Find the deductible.
The deductible is $300.

STEP 2: Find the cost of the co-payments.
Physician + Specialist + Physical Therapy
($10 × 8) + ($20 × 9) + ($15 × 12) =
$80 + $180 + $180 = $440

STEP 3: Find the co-insurance amount for home health care.
(Note: Co-insurance requires the insurance company to pay 80 percent of the costs and the patient pays 20 percent of the costs.)
$55 × (75 − 50) × 20% =
$55 × 25 × 0.20 = $275

STEP 4: Find the hospital charges. (Note: The patient pays a small percent of the hospital charge, such as 10 percent.)
$14,560 × (100% − 90%) =
$14,560 × 10% = $1,456

STEP 5: Find the total amount paid by patient.

Deductible + Co-payments + Co-insurance Amount + Hospital Charges
$300 + $440 + $275 + ($1,456 + $200)
= **$2,671 total paid**

CONCEPT CHECK

SELF-CHECK ✓

Complete the problem, then check your answers at the end of the chapter. Determine the total health care charges using Figure 11.1.

1. Determine a family's network plan costs, with the following co-payments: 22 physician visits, 12 specialist visits, 15 physical therapy appointments, and 1 emergency room visit. There is also a hospital charge of $1,260 to consider.

376 ◀ **Chapter 11 Insurance**

COMMUNICATION SKILLS

Column Graph

Students make a column graph with the following statistics of persons not covered by health insurance: Under 18 years is 13.9 percent; 18 to 24 years is 29 percent; 25 to 34 years is 23.2 percent; 35 to 44 years is 16.5 percent; 45 to 64 years is 13.8 percent; and 65 years and over 1.3 percent. (*Source:* Bureau of the Census.) Which age group has the lowest percent of uninsured persons? **(65 years and over)** Which age group has the highest percent? **(18 to 24 year olds)**

SECTION 11-2 PRACTICE

	Deductible Amount	Number of Co-payments at $10.00 Each	Amount of the Co-payments	Amount Subject to Co-insurance	Insured Co-insurance Rate	Amount of Co-insurance	Total Paid by Insured
c. $2,950 2.	$300	25	a. $250	$12,000	20%	b. $2,400	c.
c. $5,400 3.	200	40	a. $400	24,000	20%	b. $4,800	c.
c. $5,670 4.	350	52	a. $520	16,000	30%	b. $4,800	c.
c. $22,520 5.	600	32	a. $320	54,000	40%	b. $21,600	c.

For Problems 6 and 7, find the deductible, co-payment amount, co-insurance amount, hospital charges, and total paid by the insured. (Use Figure 11.1 on page 376 for the following problems.)

6. Sofia Carbondale
Single plan, Network
Co-payments: 18 physician visits
15 specialist visits
15 physical therapy appointments
1 ER visit
Hospital charge of $6,560

Deductible: $300; **Co-payment:** $180 + $300 + $225 = $705; **Hospital charges:** $656 + $50 = $706; **Total paid:** $300 + $705 + $706 = $1,711

7. Jacobi Duarte
Family, Non-network
Co-payments: 22 physician visits
12 specialist visits
25 physical therapy appointments at $55 each
1 ER visit
Hospital charge of $15,600

Deductible: $1,800; **Co-payments:** $264 + $300 + $412.50 = $976.50; **Hospital charges:** $4,680 + $50 = $4,730; **Total paid:** $1,800 + $976.50 + $4,730 = $7,506.50

Ded: $300
Co-pay: $825
Hosp: $1,364
$2,489

8. Wanda Orsini broke her leg playing basketball, which resulted in numerous medical bills. She is covered by the family network insurance plan with the benefits shown in Figure 11.1 on page 376. Her recent health care costs include co-payments for 4 physician visits, 9 orthopedic bone specialist visits, and hospital costs of $12,940. She had 40 physical therapy visits at $60 each. She had 12 home visits from a nurse at $55 each. Orsini's hospital admission charge was $200 and she had an ER charge of $950. She also had 8 generic drug prescriptions with a co-payment of $10.00 each. Find the deductible, co-payment amount, co-insurance amount, hospital charges, and total paid by the insured.

MAINTAINING YOUR SKILLS

Need Help? Go to...
▶ Skill 30: Finding the Percentage, page 757
▶ Skill 4: Subtracting Whole Numbers, page 731

Find the percentage. Round answers to the nearest hundredth.

9. 20% of $2,490 **$498**

10. 31.4% of 952 **298.93**

Subtract.

11. 978 − 865 **113**

12. 77,521 − 66,842 **10,679**

13. 997,341 − 942,876 **54,465**

14. 955 − 827 **128**

15. 82,321 − 32,966 **49,355**

16. 793,450 − 89,890 **703,560**

Section 11-2 Health Insurance Benefits ▶ **377**

WRAP-UP

Go over any problem for which a wrong answer is given.

Assignment Guide
Basic: 2–5
Average: 6–7

20 min.

2. Family, Non-Network. Co-payments: physician visits, 40 specialist visits, 18 emergency room, 1 prescription at $10 co-payment, 15 co-insurance, home health care visits at $55 each, 20 hospital charges, $12,526. Find the total amount paid by the insured. **$6,907.80**

3. Family, Network. Co-payments: physician visits, 34 specialist visits, 16 physical therapy appointments at $60 each, 42 co-insurance, home health care visits and 25 hospital charges, $28,456. Find the deductible, co-payment amount, co-insurance amount, hospital charges, and amount paid by the insured. **$900; $885.00; $0.00; $2,845.60; $4,954.60**

Error Analysis

When computing health care benefits, students may find it helpful to review how to read **Figure 11.1** on page 376. Students must subtract that percent from 100 percent to figure the amount the insured must pay.

Closing Activity

Use **Figure 11.1** on page 376.

1. Single, Non-Network. Co-payments: physician, 17 specialist, 8 Physical therapy, 29 appointments at $65 each 10 prescriptions at $10 co-payment ambulance trip, 1 co-insurance, home health care visits at $55 each, 16 hospital charges, $23,266. Find the deductible, co-payment amount, co-insurance amount, hospital charges, and amount paid by the insured. **$600.00; $1069.50; $176.00; $25.00; $6,979.80; $8,850.30**

National Standards for Business Education

Standard 1	Mathematical Foundations
Standard 2	Number Relationships and Operations
Standard 5	Statistics and Probability

National Council of Teachers of Mathematics Standards

Standard 1	Numbers and Operations
Standard 4	Measurement
Standard 6	Problem Solving
Standard 8	Communication
Standard 9	Connections

FOCUS

Call on various students to explain what they think the purpose of life insurance is. Point out that unlike other types of insurance, which provide financial protection *if* a certain event (such as an accident or illness) happens, life insurance provides financial protection *when* a person dies.

In-Class Examples

Work through these exercises with students before having them do the Self-Check.

1. $\frac{40,000}{1,000}$ **40**
2. $\frac{65,000}{1,000}$ **65**
3. $\frac{100,000}{1,000}$ **100**

○ Section Objective

Utilize tables to compute the annual premium for term life insurance.

When the breadwinner of the family dies, what do you do financially? If this happens to a family with children, then it's the classic case of financial setback. **Life insurance**, however, can soften the financial blow. This is financial protection for the family in case the breadwinner dies.

There are a couple of different insurance policies you need to know about. First, **term life insurance** is the least expensive form of life insurance that you can buy. You buy term life insurance for a specified term, such as five years, or to a specified age. Unless you renew your policy at the end of each term, the insurance coverage ends. The annual premium depends on your age at the time you buy the policy and the number of *units*. (One unit of insurance has a face value of $1,000.) The annual premium for term life insurance usually increases with each new term.

The person whose name is on the policy chooses the **beneficiary**. The beneficiary will receive the *face value* of the policy. The face value is the amount of insurance coverage that you buy.

$$\text{Annual Premium} = \text{Number of Units Purchased} \times \text{Premium per } \$1,000$$

Living in the Real World

Insuring Your Life

Someone Else's Life Depends on It Talking to her brother about health insurance has reminded Louise that she wants to purchase life insurance. She has two young children whom she wants to protect financially in case she dies. Today, Louise is talking to an insurance agent.

Draw Conclusions What is the difference between term and life insurance?

Continued on page 381

Example 1

Need Help? Go to...
- ► Skill 11: **Dividing Decimals**, page 738
- ► Skill 8: **Multiplying Decimals**, page 735
- ► Application C: **Tables and Charts**, page 762

Kenny Calloway is 30 years old. He wants to purchase a $50,000, 5-year term life insurance policy. What is his annual premium?

STEP 1: Find the number of units purchased.
$50,000 \div \$1,000 = 50$ units purchased

STEP 2: Find the premium per $1,000.
Refer to **Figure 11.2** on page 379. Read the table.
Male, age 30 = $2.47

STEP 3: Find the annual premium.
Number of Units Purchased × Premium per $1,000
  50   × $2.47
= **$123.50 annual premium**

Living in the Real World

Term life insurance provides protection for a set period and pays a benefit only if the insured dies while the coverage is in effect. Permanent life insurance provides long-term coverage.

RETEACH / ENRICHMENT

Term Life Insurance
Students use the Internet or contact an insurance company to obtain a quote for term life insurance for themselves. What are the lifestyle choices that might impact the cost of term life insurance? What are other factors?

Figure 11.2

Annual Premiums per $1,000 of Life Insurance: 5-Year Term*		
Age	Male	Female
18–30	$ 2.47	$2.13
35	2.70	2.29
40	3.27	2.67
45	4.17	3.54
50	5.84	4.82
55	8.81	6.60
60	13.22	9.71
*Minimum amount is $50,000		

3. Premium at age 40.
$60 \times \$2.67 = \$160.20$
Premium at age 45.
$60 \times \$3.54 = \$212.40$
Percent increase in premium.
$\dfrac{\$212.40 - \$160.20}{\$160.20} =$
$\dfrac{\$52.20}{\$160.20} = 0.3258 =$
32.6%

$50000 \div 1000 = 50 \times 2.47 = 123.5$

CONCEPT CHECK

 SELF-CHECK ✓

Complete the problems, then check your answers at the end of the chapter. Use Figure 11.2 above to find the annual premium for a 5-year term policy.

1. A $50,000, 5-year term policy, female, age 18.
$50 \times \$2.13 = \$106.50$

2. A $60,000, 5-year term policy, male, age 45.
$60 \times \$4.17 = \$250.20$

Example 2

Maria Rita Gomez took out an $80,000, 5-year term policy at age 30. She will be 35 years old this year. What will the annual premium be at age 35? What was the annual premium at age 30? How much is the increase? What is the percent increase?

4. Premium at age 55.
$100 \times \$8.81 = \$881$
Premium at age 60.
$100 \times \$13.22 = \$1,322.00$
Percent increase in premium.
$\dfrac{\$1,322 - \$881}{\$881} =$
$\dfrac{\$441}{\$881} = 0.501 =$
50.1%

STEP 1: Find premium at age 35.
$\dfrac{\$80,000}{\$1,000} \times \$2.29 = \$183.20$ annual premium at 35

STEP 2: Find premium at age 30.
$\dfrac{\$80,000}{\$1,000} \times \$2.13 = \$170.40$ annual premium at 30

STEP 3: Find the annual increase.
$\$183.20 - \$170.40 = \$12.80$ annual increase

STEP 4: Find the percent increase.
$$\dfrac{\text{Increase}}{\text{Original Amount}}$$
$$\dfrac{\$12.80}{\$170.40} = 0.075 \text{ or } 7.5\% \text{ increase}$$

CONCEPT CHECK

 SELF-CHECK ✓

Complete the problems, then check your answers at the end of the chapter. What is the percent increase in premiums for a 5-year term policy?

3. A $60,000, 5-year term policy, female, age 40. Now age 45.

4. A $100,000, 5-year term policy, male, age 55. Now age 60.

② TEACH

Spend ample time discussing the basic concepts of term life insurance. When discussing **Figure 11.2,** ask students what two facts can be deduced from the table. **(Rates for men are higher than for women and the amounts increase with age.)** Elicit their reason as to why. **(The risk to an insurance company is greater for men because women generally live longer.)**

Stress the use of units when computing the annual premium. Remind students that when dividing by 1,000, simply drop the same number of zeros in the dividend.

Motivating the Lesson

At age 30 Samantha Roland has a five-year term life insurance policy with $50,000 coverage. Her annual premium is $106.50. At age 35 her premium will increase and she will pay $114.50 per year for the same coverage. What is the percent increase? **7.5%**

In-Class Examples

Use **Figure 11.2** to find the annual premium for a five-year term life policy for Problems 1–3.

1. Female: age 21.
Five-year term life.
Coverage: $90,000.
What is the annual premium?
$191.70

2. Male: age 35.
Five-year term life.
Coverage: $100,000.
What is the annual premium?
$270

3. Female: age 40.
Five-year term life.
Coverage: $175,000.
What is the annual premium?
$467.25

GLOBAL PERSPECTIVE

Health Care in other Countries
Have students pick a country and research to answer the question: Does the government provide health care or do the people provide their own health insurance? **(In many cases, the government provides health care.)** Students discuss which they think is better—the government providing health care or people buying their own health insurance—and why. **With government-provided health care, everyone has access to health care.**

ASSESS

Error Analysis

Some students may benefit from a review of the steps needed to find the percent increase in premiums. Remind them first to find the premium for the lower age and the premium for the higher age. Then subtract the *lower* premium from the *higher* one. Finally, divide the difference by the *lower* premium to find the percent increase.

4 CLOSE

Closing Activity

1. $8.81 × 500 **$4,405**
2. $\frac{(547 - 489)}{489}$ **12%**
3. Female: was 40, now 45. Five-year term life. Coverage: $75,000. What is the percent increase in the premium? **33%**
4. Male: was 55, now 60. Five-year term life. Coverage: $250,000. What is the percent increase in the premium? **50%**
5. Jay Allen was 35 years old when he first purchased an $85,000, five-year term life insurance policy. He will be 40 years old this year.
   a. What will his annual premium be if he increases the policy to $140,000? **$457.80**
   b. What is his monthly premium? **$38.15**
   c. What total amount did he pay during the previous five-year term? **$1,147.50**
   d. What total amount will he pay for the next five years? **$2,289**

SECTION 11-3 PRACTICE

Use Figure 11.2 on page 379 to answer the following:

	Insured	Age	Coverage	Number of Units	×	Annual Premium per $1,000	=	Annual Premium
5.	Lianna Torrez	20	$ 60,000	60	×	a. $2.13	=	b. $127.80
6.	John O'Neill	45	85,000	a. 85	×	b. $4.17	=	c. $354.45
7.	Kate Owens	35	95,000	a. 95	×	b. $2.29	=	c. $217.55
8.	Debra Green	50	200,000	a. 200	×	b. $4.82	=	c. $964.00

For Problems 9 and 10, what is the percent increase in the premium?

9. Phil Davis purchased a $75,000, 5-year term life insurance policy when he was 40. Now he is 45. **27.5%**

10. Marica Deerfoot purchased a $120,000, 5-year term life insurance policy when she was 55. Now she is 60. **47.1%**

11. Joni Hauck wants to purchase a $65,000, 5-year term life insurance policy. She is 25 years old. What is her annual premium? **$138.45**

12. Peter and Edith Lichtner have a child. Peter is a career counselor, and Edith is a child psychologist. Peter is 30 years old, and Edith is 25 years old. Both want to purchase $80,000, 5-year term life insurance policies. What is Edith's annual premium? What is Peter's annual premium? **$170.40; $197.60**

13. Sam and Kolleen Hastings have two children. Sam was 30 years old when he first purchased a $125,000, 5-year term life insurance policy. He will be 35 years old this year.
    a. What will his annual premium be if he increases the policy to $200,000?
    b. What is his monthly premium? **$45** ... **$540**
    c. What total amount did he pay during the previous 5-year term? **$1,543.75**
    d. What total amount will he pay for the next 5-year term? **$2,700**

MAINTAINING YOUR SKILLS

Need Help? Go to...
➤ Skill 11: **Dividing Decimals**, page 738
➤ Skill 8: **Multiplying Decimals**, page 735

Divide. Round answers to the nearest thousandth.

14. 8.216 ÷ 6.12 **1.342**　　15. 76.26 ÷ 0.14 **544.714**

16. 1.025 ÷ 0.05 **20.5**　　17. 21,624 ÷ 1,000 **21.624**

18. 93.40 ÷ 100.00 **0.934**　　19. 18,400 ÷ 1,000 **18.400**

Multiply. Round answers to the nearest hundredth.

20. 34.362 × 100 **3,436.2**　　21. 0.95 × 0.16 **0.152**

22. 3.49 × 0.035 **0.12**　　23. 42.6 × 32.914 **1,402.14**

24. 0.052 × 1,000 **52**　　25. 3.481 × 1,000 **3,481**

WRAP-UP

Go over any problem for which a wrong answer is given.

Assignment Guide
Basic: 5–8
Average: 9–11

20 min.

SECTION (11-4) Other Types of Life Insurance

○ Section Objective

Apply tables to data to compute the annual premiums for three types of life insurance.

Whole life insurance, also known as permanent insurance, offers financial protection for your entire life. You pay a specific premium for the entire duration that you hold the policy. When you die, the insurance company pays your beneficiary a declared sum. The amount of the premium depends on your age at the time you purchased the policy.

Not only does whole life provide your dependents financial coverage, but it can also be used as an investment. In addition to the face value that your beneficiary will receive, whole life insurance has a **cash value** and *loan value.* The cash value is the amount of money you'll receive if you cancel your policy. Think of whole life insurance as both a death benefit and a savings account. You can borrow money on the policy and then pay interest on the loan. The insurance company will lend you the same amount as the cash value if you request it.

Insurance companies have your needs in mind. That's why there are different kinds of whole life insurance policies available to you—**limited payment policy** and **universal life insurance**. Limited payment policy offers lifetime protection. You pay premiums only for a specified number of years or until you reach a certain age. Universal life insurance is a combination of a life insurance policy and a savings plan. The policy covers you for your entire life. You pay a minimum premium, but anything over the minimum goes into an investment account that earns interest.

When you calculate annual premiums, remember that:

Annual Premium = Number of Units Purchased × Premium per $1,000

Living in the Real World

Insuring Your Life

Prepare for the Future   When it comes to life insurance, Louise has options. She knows that at the end of each month she wants extra money to help Jeremy pay off his medical bills for that broken leg.

Draw Conclusions   What are the two other forms of insurance where you get back some of the money you spent on premiums?

Continued on page 385

─────── (**Example 1**) ───────

Phyllis Saul is 25 years old. She wants to purchase a whole life policy valued at $125,000. What is her annual premium?

Continued on next page

Section 11-4 Other Types of Life Insurance ▶ **381**

Living in the Real World

Limited-payment insurance, whole life, and universal insurance.

THINKING CRITICALLY

Reading Insurance Tables
Invite an insurance agent to visit the class. Ask the agent to bring real-world insurance tables to help students become more comfortable with reading complicated insurance tables. Use the tables for Practice problems.

`CL` , `LS`

National Standards for Business Education

Standard 1	Mathematical Foundations
Standard 2	Number Relationships and Operations
Standard 5	Statistics and Probability

National Council of Teachers of Mathematics Standards

Standard 1	Numbers and Operations
Standard 4	Measurement
Standard 6	Problem Solving
Standard 8	Communication
Standard 9	Connections

1 FOCUS

Review with students the fact that the purpose of term life insurance is to provide money to the beneficiary in case of a disaster. Explain that there are other types of life insurance coverage, which combine life insurance and a savings plan, but that the premiums are higher for the latter. The focus of this lesson is to compute the annual premiums for these types of insurance.

In-Class Examples
Work through these exercises with students before having them do the Self-Check.
1. $\frac{80,000}{1,000}$ **80**
2. $\frac{200,000}{1,000}$ **200**
3. 25 × $38.14 **$953.50**

2 TEACH

Due to the complexity of the insurance business, this lesson only briefly discusses the other types of life insurance. The key ideas and terms presented are necessary to understand the basic concepts of life insurance. If time permits, you might ask a local insurance agent to address the class and answer any questions students may have.

Students should feel comfortable with the computations in this lesson, as it is a continuation of the previous lesson. The key skill here is reading a more complicated insurance table.

Motivating the Lesson

You take out a $50,000 universal life insurance policy at age 20. Your monthly premium is $19. What is your annual premium? **$228**

In-Class Examples

1. Thirty-five-year old female. Paid up at age 65. Coverage: $60,000. What is the annual premium? **$1,080**
2. Twenty-five-year old male. Universal life: $50,000. What is the annual premium? **$288**
3. Twenty-year-old female. Paid up at age 65. Coverage: $70,000. What is the annual premium? **($682.50)** What is the quarterly premium? **$174.04**

Figure 11.3

| Age | Annual Premiums per $1,000 of Life Insurance | | | | Monthly Premium |
| | Paid Up at Age 65 | | Whole Life | | $50,000 Universal Life |
	Male	Female	Male	Female	Male or Female
20	$11.75	$ 9.75	$ 8.00	$ 6.25	$ 19.00
25	13.75	11.50	9.50	7.50	24.00
30	17.00	14.50	11.75	9.25	29.00
35	21.50	18.00	15.00	11.50	37.50
40	29.75	25.00	19.50	14.50	52.00
45	39.50	32.50	25.50	18.75	69.50
50	56.25	45.75	34.00	24.25	93.50
55			46.50	32.25	126.00

Need Help? Go to...
- ▶ Skill 11: Dividing Decimals, page 738
- ▶ Skill 8: Multiplying Decimals, page 735
- ▶ Application C: Tables and Charts, page 762

STEP 1: Find the number of units purchased.
$125,000 ÷ $1,000 = 125 units purchased

STEP 2: Find the premium per $1,000. (Refer to **Figure 11.3**.)
Female, age 25 = $7.50

STEP 3: Find the annual premium.
Number of Units Purchased × Premium per $1,000
125 × $7.50 = $937.50 annual premium

125000 ÷ 1000 = 125 × 7.5 = 937.5

CONCEPT CHECK

SELF-CHECK ✔

Complete the problems, then check your answers at the end of the chapter. Find the annual premium.

1. Thirty-year-old male, with a $70,000 whole life policy.
2. Forty-year-old female, with a limited payment policy until age 65 of $90,000.

Figure 11.4

1. Units: $70,000 ÷ $1,000 = 70
   Premium per $1,000: $11.75
   Annual premium: 70 × $11.75 = $822.50
2. Units: $90,000 ÷ $1,000 = 90
   Premium per $1,000: $25.00
   Annual premium: 90 × $25.00 = $2,250

| Optional Payment Plans | | |
Percent of Annual Premium		
Semi-annual Premiums	=	50.5%
Quarterly Premiums	=	25.5%
Monthly Premiums	=	8.5%

Rather than make one annual payment, many insurance companies will allow you to make smaller payments. Because of the additional expense of collecting and handling the payments several times a year, a small fee is charged. Many companies use the guidelines shown in **Figure 11.4**.

Example 2

Suppose Phyllis Saul (from Example 1), wants to pay the $937.50 annual premium monthly. What are her monthly payments? How much can she save in one year by paying the premium annually?

STEP 1: Find the monthly premium. (Note: Refer to Figure 11.4 on page 382 for percent of monthly premium.)

Annual Premium × 8.5%

$937.50 × 0.085 = $79.6875 = **$79.69 pays premium per month**

STEP 2: Find how much she can save.

(12 × $79.69) − $937.50 =

$956.28 − $937.50 = **$18.78 amount saved**

CONCEPT CHECK

SELF-CHECK ✓

Complete the problems, then check your answers at the end of the chapter. Determine how much can be saved by paying annually. (Refer to Figure 11.4 on page 382 for optional premium plans.)

3. An annual premium of $1,700 paid monthly.

4. An annual premium of $1,080 paid quarterly.

SECTION 11-4 PRACTICE

Use Figure 11.3 on page 382 to solve the following.

	Type	Gender	Age	Face Value	Number of Units	Cost per $1,000	Annual Premium	Monthly Premium
5.	Whole Life	Female	20	$ 50,000	a. **50**	b.	c.	d.
6.	Paid at 65	Male	30	120,000	a. **120**	b.	c.	d.
7.	Paid at 65	Female	40	200,000	a. **200**	b.	c.	d.
8.	Whole Life	Male	45	200,000	a. **200**	b.	c.	d.

9. Ann Gosik's insurance policy. Whole life, $50,000. a. **$725.00** She is 40 years old. b. **$366.13**
   a. What is her annual premium?
   b. What is her semi-annual premium?

10. James Dolby's insurance policy. Paid up at age 65, $50,000. He is 20 years old. a. **$587.50**
   a. What is his annual premium?
   b. What is his quarterly premium?
   b. **$149.81**

11. Terrance Gonzales is 30 years old and wants to purchase a $50,000 life insurance policy. He is considering a universal life insurance policy. What is his monthly premium? What is his annual premium? **$29.00; $348.00**

12. Robert and Lucy Dubbs each purchase a $100,000 whole life insurance policy. Both are 25 years of age. What are their total annual premiums? How much more is Robert Dubbs's annual premium than his wife's? **$950; $750; $1,700 total; $200 more**

13. Leona Sowinski purchased a $50,000 universal life insurance policy at the age of 20. What is her annual premium? If Leona pays $150 a month, how much is she saving annually? **$228.00; $1,572.00**

MAINTAINING YOUR SKILLS

Divide. Round answers to the nearest hundredth.

14. 18.4 ÷ 0.032 **575**   **15.** 47.614 ÷ 15.62 **3.05**   **16.** 0.098 ÷ 1.9 **0.05**

Multiply. Round answers to the nearest hundredth.

17. 0.31 × 0.84 **0.26**   **18.** 7.81 × 8.1 **63.26**   **19.** 6.511 × 0.05 **0.33**

Section 11-4 Other Types of Life Insurance ▶ **383**

Sidebar left:

3. Monthly premium: $1,700 × 0.085 = $144.50
Saves: (12 × $144.50) − $1,700 = $1,734 − $1,700 = $34

4. Quarterly premium: $1,080 × 0.255 = $275.40
Saves: (4 × $275.40) − $1,080 = $1,101.60 − $1,080 = $21.60

5. b. $6.25
   c. $312.50
   d. $26.56

6. b. $17.00
   c. $2,040
   d. $173.40

7. b. $25.00
   c. $5,000
   d. $425

8. b. $25.50
   c. $5,100
   d. $433.50

Need Help? Go to...
▶ Skill 11: Dividing Decimals, page 738
▶ Skill 8: Multiplying Decimals, page 735

WRAP-UP

Go over any problem for which a wrong answer is given.

Assignment Guide
   Basic: 5–8
   Average: 9–11

20 min.

SECTION 11-4

3 ASSESS

Error Analysis

If students are making errors, they may be reading **Figure 11.4** on page 382 incorrectly. Be sure students understand that the chart provides information on the cost of three different types of life insurance: paid up at age 65, whole life, and a $50,000 universal life policy. Both the paid up at age 65 and the whole life rates listed in **Figure 11.4** can be used to calculate various amounts of coverage. However, the monthly premium listed for the universal life policy is based on $50,000 coverage. Point out, too, that while the rates for paid up at age 65 and whole life have separate rates for men and women, universal life has one rate.

Help students with **Figure 11.4** "optional payment plans." Point out that the least expensive way to pay insurance is to make an annual payment. For example, a life insurance policy with an annual premium of $500.00 would cost $252.50 semiannually or a total of $505.00 a year if paid in two installments. If paid quarterly, it would cost $127.50 or a total of $510.00 per year. If paid monthly, it would cost $42.50 or a total of $510.00 per year.

4 CLOSE

Closing Activity

Use **Figures 11.3** and **11.4** for Problems 1 and 2.

1. Male: age 35.
   Paid up at age 65.
   Coverage: $150,000. What is the annual premium?
   ($3,225) What is the quarterly premium? **$822.38**

2. Margarita Orlando is 25 years old. She purchases a $50,000 universal life insurance policy. What is her monthly premium? **($24)** What is her annual premium? **$288**

Quick Quiz

1. Family HMO. Annual premium is $11,300. Employer pays 70 percent. What percent does the employee pay? **(30%)** Employee's contribution? **($3,390)** Monthly premium? **$282.50**

Use **Figure 11.1** on page 376 for Problem 2.

2. Family, Network. Co-payments: physician visits, 33 specialist visits, 16 prescriptions at $10 co-payment, 27 emergency room visit, 1 co-insurance, home health care visits at $55 each, 45 hospitalization charges, $54,190. Find the deductible, co-payment amount, co-insurance amount, hospital charges, and amount paid by the insured. **$900; $970; $0.00; $5,419; $1,200; $3,070**

Use **Figure 11.2** on page 379 to find the premium for Problem 3.

3. Rosemary Briggs. Five-year term life insurance. Coverage: $170,000. Was 35, now 40. What is the percent increase in the premium? **17%**

Use **Figures 11.3** and **11.4** on page 382 for Problems 4 and 5.

4. Max Devlin, age 20. Whole life. Coverage: $75,000. What is the annual premium? **($600)** What is the semiannual premium? **$303**

5. Rachel LaCrosse, age 30. Paid up at age 65. Coverage: $140,000. What is the annual premium? **($2,030)** What is the quarterly premium? **($517.65)** How much is saved by making an annual payment instead of quarterly payments? **$40.60**

CHAPTER 11 Self-Check Answers

SECTION 11-1 CONCEPT CHECK (p. 373)

1. $100\% - 65\% = 35\%$
   $\$4,325 \times 35\% = \mathbf{\$1,513.75}$
   $\$1,513.75 \div 12 = \mathbf{\$126.15}$

2. $100\% - 73\% = 27\%$
   $\$11,473 \times 27\% = \mathbf{\$3,097.71}$
   $\$3,097.71 \div 12 = \mathbf{\$258.14}$

SECTION 11-2 CONCEPT CHECK (p. 376)

1. The deductible is $900.
   Find the cost of the co-payments.
   $(\$10.00 \times 22) + (\$20 \times 12) + (\$15 \times 15) + \$50 =$
   $\quad \$220 \quad + \quad \$240 \quad + \quad \$225 \quad + \$50 = \$735$
   Find the hospital charges.
   $\$1,260 \times (100\% - 90\%) =$
   $\$1,260 \times \quad 10\% \quad = \$126$
   Find the total amount paid by the patient.
   $\$900 + \$735 + \$126 = \mathbf{\$1,761}$

SECTION 11-3 CONCEPT CHECK (p. 379)

1. $50 \times \$2.13 = \mathbf{\$106.50}$

2. $60 \times \$4.17 = \mathbf{\$250.20}$

3. Premium at age 40. $60 \times \$2.67 = \$160.20$
   Premium at age 45. $60 \times \$3.54 = \$212.40$
   Percent increase in premium. $\dfrac{\$212.40 - \$160.20}{\$160.20} = \dfrac{\$52.20}{\$160.20} = 0.3258 = \mathbf{32.6\%}$

4. Premium at age 55. $100 \times \$8.81 = \$881$
   Premium at age 60. $100 \times \$13.22 = \$1,322.00$
   Percent increase in premium. $\dfrac{\$1,322 - \$881}{\$881} = \dfrac{\$441}{\$881} = 0.501 = \mathbf{50.1\%}$

SECTION 11-4 CONCEPT CHECK (p. 382, 383)

1. Units: $\$70,000 \div \$1,000 = 70$
   Premium per $1,000: $11.75
   Annual premium: $70 \times \$11.75 = \mathbf{\$822.50}$

2. Units: $\$90,000 \div \$1,000 = 90$
   Premium per $1,000: $25.00
   Annual premium: $90 \times \$25.00 = \mathbf{\$2,250}$

3. Monthly premium: $\$1,700 \times 0.085 = \$144.50$
   Saves: $(12 \times \$144.50) - \$1,700 = \$1,734 - \$1,700 = \mathbf{\$34}$

4. Quarterly premium: $\$1,080 \times 0.255 = \$275.40$
   Saves: $(4 \times \$275.40) - \$1,080 = \$1,101.60 - \$1,080 = \mathbf{\$21.60}$

Living in the Real World

Insuring Your Life

Analyze the Story Insurance may not be a big issue for you now, but once you're no longer covered under your parents' or guardian's policies or you start full-time employment, you'll need to know your options. Here's an opportunity to test your knowledge. Write your answers to the following questions on a separate piece of paper.

1. Health insurance is only available as a benefit from an employer.   True   False

2. You can continue your health insurance even if you leave a job.   True   False

3. A co-payment is an amount you pay for a doctor's visit or prescription.   True   False

4. In general, the younger you are, the less expensive life insurance is.   True   False

5. Life insurance can also be used as an investment for retirement.   True   False

6. Life insurance companies can cancel policies if you develop a serious illness after you're insured.   True   False

7. You can collect life insurance benefits before you die.   True   False

Living in the Real World

1. False
2. True
3. True
4. True
5. True
6. False
7. True
8. True

REVIEW OF KEY WORDS

health insurance (p. 372)
preferred provider organization (PPO) (p. 372)
health maintenance organization (HMO) (p. 372)
deductible (p. 375)
co-payment (p. 375)
co-insurance (p. 375)
life insurance (p. 378)

term life insurance (p. 378)
beneficiary (p. 378)
whole life insurance (p. 381)
cash value (p. 381)
limited payment policy (p. 381)
universal life insurance (p. 381)

For Problems 1–10, write your own definitions for 10 of the key words above.

1–10. Definitions will vary. Evaluate based on the students' understanding of the term and their ability to put the definition into their own words.

Study Guide and Assessment ▶ **385**

CHAPTER **Study Guide and Assessment**

11

Skills and Concepts

SECTION OBJECTIVE 11-1 AND EXAMPLES

Compute health insurance premiums.

Pedro Martinez is employed by the Wise and Wonderful Gift Corporation. He has a family membership in a traditional group medical insurance program. The annual premium is $8,540. Martinez's employer pays 90 percent of the total cost. His contribution is deducted monthly from his paycheck. What is Martinez's annual contribution? What is his monthly deduction?

STEP 1: Find the employee's percent.
100% − Employer's Percent
100% − 90% = 10% employee's percent

STEP 2: Find the employee's annual contribution.
Total Premium × Employee's Percent
$8,540 × 10% = $854 employee's contribution

STEP 3: Find the employee's monthly deduction.
Employee's Contribution ÷ 12
$854 ÷ 12 = $71.17 employee's monthly deduction

REVIEW EXERCISES
Complete the table below.

	Insurance Plan	Annual Premium	Employer's Percent	Employee's Percent	Employee's Contribution	Monthly Premium	
11.	Single PPO	$ 3,006	65%	a. 35%	b.	c. $87.68	b. $1,052.10
12.	Family PPO	3,259	50%	a. 50%	b.	c. $135.79	b. $1,629.50
13.	Family Trad.	5,832	75%	a. 25%	b. $1,458	c. $121.50	
14.	Family PPO	15,600	90%	a. 10%	b. $1,560	c. $130	
15.	Single HMO	2,560	85%	a. 15%	b. $384	c. $32	
16.	Family HMO	13,650	70%	a. 30%	b. $4,095	c. $341.25	

SECTION OBJECTIVE 11-2 AND EXAMPLES

Calculate the amount the patient pays for health care.

Use Figure 11.1 on page 376 to solve the example and problems.

Tawney Manuel is single and has a health insurance plan with the benefits shown in Figure 11.1. Her recent network health care costs include co-payments for 4 physician visits and 6 specialist visits. She also had 56 home visits from a nurse at $45 each. What was the total amount she paid?

REINFORCEMENT

Section 11-1

1. Amita Ghandi's monthly PPO costs her $236. Annual dental costs her $575. Annual vision costs her $205. What is the total monthly premium for all the insurance? **$301**

2. Paul Esnerado has a family PPO group medical insurance plan. The total cost is $13,900. His employer pays 85 percent of the total cost. He also has the optional annual dental (which costs $950) and the optional vision care (which costs $315). His employer pays 50 percent of dental and vision costs. How much is deducted each week from his paycheck for medical, dental, and vision insurance? **$52.26**

STEP 1: Find the deductible.
The deductible is $300.

STEP 2: Find the cost of co-payments.
Physician + Specialist + Physical Therapy
($10 × 4) + ($20 × 6)   = $160 cost of co-payments

STEP 3: Find the co-insurance amount for home health care.
$45 × (56 − 50) × 20% = $54 co-insurance amount

STEP 4: Find the total amount paid by patient.

Deductible + Co-payments + Co-insurance + Hospital
                             Amount   Charges

   $300   + $160   + $54
= $514 total amount paid

REVIEW EXERCISES
Complete the table below.

	Deductible Amount	Number of Co-payments at $10.00 Each	Amount of the Co-payments	Amount Subject to Co-insurance	Insured Co-insurance Rate	Amount of Co-insurance	Total Paid by Insured	
17.	$500	15	a. $150	$15,000	20%	b. $3,000	c.	c. $3,650
18.	300	25	a. $250	10,000	30%	b. $3,000	c.	c. $3,550
19.	200	45	a. $450	25,000	40%	b. $10,000	c.	c. $10,650
20.	100	56	a. $560	12,000	35%	b. $4,200	c.	c. $4,860
21.	150	41	a. $410	35,000	45%	b. $15,750	c.	c. $16,310
22.	550	35	a. $350	55,000	25%	b. $13,750	c.	c. $14,650

SECTION OBJECTIVE 11-3 AND EXAMPLES

Utilize tables to compute the annual premium for term life insurance.

Yamid Haad purchased a 5-year term life insurance policy. It provides $100,000 coverage. He is 35 years old. What is his annual premium?

STEP 1: Find the number of units purchased.
$100,000 ÷ $1,000 = 100 units purchased

STEP 2: Find the premium per $1,000. (Refer to Figure 11.2 on page 379.)
Male, age 35 = $2.70 premium per $1,000

STEP 3: Find the annual premium.
Number of Units Purchased × Premium per $1,000
        100   × $2.70   = $270 annual premium

Continued on next page

REINFORCEMENT

Section 11-2
Use **Figure 11.1** on page 376.
1. Single, Non-Network. Co-payments: 28 physician visits, 11 specialist visits, physical therapy at $65 each, and 1 emergency room. Co-insurance: 14 home health care visits at $55 each, and $17,394 of hospital charges. Find the deductible, co-payment amount, co-insurance amount, hospital charges, and amount paid by the insured.
$600; $1,040.00; $154.00; $5,218.20; $7,062.20

CHAPTER Study Guide and Assessment

(11)

24. $150,000 ÷ 1,000 = 150 units purchased; $2.29 premium per $1,000; 150 × $2.29 = $343.50 annual premium; 200 × $2.29 = $458 annual premium if she increases the policy to $200,000; $343.50 ÷ 12 = $28.63 monthly payment

REVIEW EXERCISES

23. Paul Lopez has a 5-year term life insurance policy with $125,000 coverage. He is 50 years old. What is his annual premium?
$125,000 ÷ 1,000 = 125 units purchased
$5.84 premium per $1,000
125 x $5.84 = $730 annual premium

24. Alexis Finley is 35 years old and has $150,000, 5-year term life insurance policy. What is her annual premium? What would it be if she increases the policy to $200,000? What is her monthly premium?

Use Figure 11.2 on page 379 to answer the following:

	Insured	Age	Coverage	Number of Units	Annual Premium per $1,000	Annual Premium
25.	Caesar Morales	25	$ 50,000	a. 50	b. $2.47	c. $123.50
26.	Rose McNerney	30	75,000	a. 75	b. $2.13	c. $159.75
27.	David Rotunno	45	80,000	a. 80	b. $4.17	c. $333.60
28.	Erin McCamie	55	100,000	a. 100	b. $6.60	c. $660.00
29.	Terrie Creek	60	200,000	a. 200	b. $9.71	c. $1,942.00
30.	John Kim	40	500,000	a. 500	b. $3.27	c. $1,635.00

SECTION OBJECTIVE 11-4 AND EXAMPLES

Apply tables to data to compute the annual premiums for three types of life insurance.

Gretchen Kuhn is 30 years old. She wants to purchase a whole life insurance policy valued at $150,000. What is her annual premium?

STEP 1: Find the number of units purchased.
$150,000 ÷ $1,000 = 150 units purchased

STEP 2: Find the premium per $1,000. (Refer to Figure 11.3 on page 382.)
Female, age 30 = $9.25

STEP 3: Find the annual premium.
Number of Units Purchased × Premium per $1,000
150 × $9.25 = $1,387.50 annual premium

REVIEW EXERCISES

Use Figure 11.3 on page 382 to solve the following:

	Type	Gender	Age	Face Value	Number of Units	Cost per $1,000	Annual Premium	Monthly Premium
31.	Paid at 65	Male	20	$ 50,000	a. 50	b.	c.	d.
32.	Whole Life	Female	40	125,000	a. 125	b.	c.	d.
33.	Paid at 65	Male	25	150,000	a. 150	b.	c.	d.
34.	Universal	Male	35	50,000	a. 50	b.	c.	d.

31. b. $11.75
c. $587.50
d. $49.94

32. b. $14.50
c. $1,812.50
d. $154.06

33. b. $13.75
c. $2,062.50
d. $175.31

34. b. $37.50
c. $1,875
d. $159.38

REINFORCEMENT

Section 11-3

Use **Figure 11.2** on page 379 to find the annual premium for a five-year term life policy for Problems 1 and 2.

1. Male, age 45. Five-year term life. Coverage: $150,000. What is the annual premium at age 45? **($625.50)** What will be the annual premium at age 50? **($876)** How much is the increase? **($250.50)** What is the percent increase? **40%**

2. Male. Five-year term life. Coverage: $50,000. Was 35, now 40. What is the percent increase in the premium? **21%**

Section 11-4

1. Male: 40 years old. Whole life. Coverage: $100,000. What is the annual premium? **($1,950)** What is the semiannual premium? **($984.75)** What will he pay in total premiums in a year? **$1,969.50**

Alternative Assessment

Count Me In: *How You'll Use Math*

No More House Calls Health insurance is one of the largest and most important industries in the United States. The cost of researching and delivering high quality health care is growing every year, and insurance coverage must stretch even more each year.

Some insurance companies and physicians have worked to form preferred provider organizations (PPO) or health maintenance organizations (HMO) to try to make health care more affordable. The days of the family physician making house calls are long gone; the days of the family physician in solo practice are rapidly disappearing.

Doctor can take a vacation and can share cost of equipment and office.

35. What are some of the financial advantages of group practice? In order to answer this question, you'll need to do a little research on the Internet or in the library to find out the benefits of a physician's group practice. You might also call your local hospital to see if you can talk with an administrator.

Answers will vary.

36. What other advantages benefit doctors who join such practices? You might interview a doctor or nurse to get his or her take on this.

Answers will vary.

37. Some patients prefer solo practice doctors. What are the advantages to patients of solo practitioners?

Answers will vary.

38. Why would the group practice and prepaid health plans of an HMO benefit insurance companies?

Thinking Critically
- How often do you take your health for granted? Find a story in the media about how *not* having health insurance affects families.
- Find out how many single people and families don't carry health insurance in your state.
  - Compare this to one other state.
  - What did you find? Explain your findings.

Portfolio

Select one of the assignments from this chapter that you found especially challenging and place it in your portfolio.

THINKING CRITICALLY

Find a story in the media about how *not* having health insurance affects families. Find out how many single people and families don't carry health insurance in your state. **According to the U.S. Census Bureau, among the entire population of 18 to 64 years old in 2000, workers (both full- and part-time) were more likely to have health insurance coverage (83.8 percent) than nonworkers (76.4 percent); but among the poor, workers were less likely to be covered (54.5 percent) than nonworkers (63.4 percent).**

A Creative Lab

1 FOCUS

Math Studio Overview

Students are asked to research the controversial Human Genome Project and then role-play a script with two other classmates. Include in the conversation a patient (undergoing an annual physical), the patient's physician, and the patient's insurance agent. They are asked to think about the ethical issues surrounding testing and how each party perceives them differently.

Bell Ringer Activity

Ask students to make a list of professions where ethics play an important role. They will likely choose obvious ones, like accounting, law, or politics; encourage them to think creatively and come up with examples of ethical dilemmas in less obvious careers, such as a truck driver or restaurant owner.

2 TEACH

Cooperative Learning

Have students work in groups to discuss the implications of unethical practices in business. Have them list recent examples of news items that uncovered unethical practices in a local business or larger, national corporation. Using the library and Internet as a research tool, ask each group to write a report and prepare an oral presentation on the news item of their choice. How did the company or individual they chose to research act unethically? What was the consequence of their unethical behavior? Were they brought to task for their actions? What type of punishment did they receive, if any?

How Much Is Your Health Worth?

The Human Genome Project is the government-led project to "map" all the human genes' packages. Already, scientists have discovered the location of certain genes that cause health problems either at birth or later in life. With such knowledge, doctors may be able to treat or even prevent certain diseases.

The medical, social, and economic effects of this project will be profound. In addition, biotechnology companies are working to provide doctors with the tools to change the gene structure of humans.

QUICK FACTS ON THE HUMAN GENOME PROJECT
- The federal government and university and private researchers began this collaborative effort in the early '90s.
- It identifies approximately 30,000 genes in human DNA.
- Researchers used super-computers to organize its 3 billion bits of research.
- More than 1,100 scientists around the world worked on this project.

Purpose

Providing good health care involves collaboration between many different professionals, including medical professionals, hospitals, group insurance plans, and medical researchers. One problem can spark many different answers, depending on the person's perspective. In this Math Studio, you're asked to role-play with two other participants.

Supplies Needed

- Pen
- Paper
- Public library
- Internet
- Props and simple costumes, if desired

Your Activity

Step 1: In this role-play exercise, you and two other participants will write a brief script concerning three characters—a patient undergoing a standard annual physical, the patient's physician, and the patient's insurance agent. Decide now who you want to be for the purposes of this Math Studio.

Begin by researching the Human Genome Project and its effect on the health insurance industry. You should consult your local library and also the Internet. Several federal agencies that are funding the Project have excellent Web sites.

Step 2: In this role-play, the patient is undergoing a routine physical. Carefully read the following bulleted points. You will need to refer to these in order to complete Step 3.

- Since the Human Genome Project began, it has become easier to find genetic alterations associated with human disease. The physician recommends a simple blood test to determine the risk of disease and cancer.

NEWSWORTHY TREND

Human Cloning

The Human Genome Project isn't the only scientific advancement to stir controversy and raise an ethical dilemma. Human cloning has also caused heated debate and much research has taken place specifically about the ethics of the development.

Human cloning is, simply, the production of genetically identical human beings, made possible by either embryo splitting or nuclear transfer. Reasons for cloning include reproduction for infertile couples and the hope that one day scientists could supply new organs for humans in need of them.

MATH STUDIO

- The patient wants the test, but doesn't want the results provided to the insurance company. Like every patient, this one has signed an information release form that says that personal medical information will be given to the insurance company in order for the patient to collect health insurance.

- The doctor thinks the genetic test is worthwhile. If it comes out positive, the patient will know that there is a greater risk of getting cancer and may be able to take steps now to avoid that problem. On the other hand, if the test results are negative, the patient will have peace of mind.

- The doctor knows that the insurance company needs information about patient's health in order to assess how much risk that person would be to insure. On the other hand, since this patient does not have cancer, the doctor is wondering whether the insurer should receive the genetic test results. The physician knows that insurance companies sometimes increase the premiums or even cancel policies of people who are high risk.

- The insurance company needs information about its clients' health and lifestyle. Companies generally do not want to insure high-risk individuals.

Step 3: As part of this role-play, you need to take the bulleted points listed in Step 2 and weigh them against your answers to the following questions:

- What are the ethical issues involved?

- Do those ethical issues or the perspective on them change depending on which role you are in?

- Who owes an ethical obligation to whom? Should an insurance company be ethically obliged to help anyone who can pay the premium? If so, could this policy conflict with any obligation they might have to shareholders in the company?

- If an insurance company agrees to insure everyone regardless of risk, could this affect the cost of a policy? If so, would it mean only the wealthy could afford insurance?

- Is there a difference between refusing to give information to insurers about a genetic test on a healthy person and giving information about a risky lifestyle?

Step 4: Finish the role-play. Among the participants

- discuss the issues you explored.

- explore how your views changed during the course of the skit.

- decide if you are better able to understand a view you do not share.

Critique It

How do all of you resolve your conflicting points of view in order to benefit all parties involved?

Math Studio How Much Is Your Health Worth? ▶ **391**

3 ASSESS

Enrichment
Ask students to write a persuasive essay starting with the sentence, "Unethical business practices are wrong because…" Have them include a clear hypothesis statement and supporting evidence that leads to a logical conclusion.

4 CLOSE

Critique It

How do all of you resolve your conflicting points of view in order to the benefit of all parties involved? **Answers will vary depending on each group's experience. Conflict resolution is a vital skill that all students will use throughout their lifetimes. It's important to find a way to resolve disagreements in a civil manner. Sometimes one can only agree to disagree, but if this is done in a reasonable, respectful way, both parties should come away with an understanding of the other person's views.**

NEWSWORTHY TREND

Sides to the Human Cloning Argument

As is true with so many difficult issues, there are two sides to the human cloning argument—both with valid concerns regarding human cloning. Groups in favor of continued research into human cloning cite the importance of helping infertile couples have children and the future possibilities of saving human lives with needed organs and nerve cells.

Those who believe advancements in human cloning should be quelled argue that it is a dangerous science and meddles medically with something that should be left alone to run its natural course.

National Standards for Business Education

Section Objectives	1. Mathematical Foundations	2. Number Relationships and Operations	3. Patterns, Functions, and Algebra	4. Measurements	5. Statistics and Probability	6. Problem-Solving Applications	
12-1 Certificate of Deposit (pp. 394–396) Use tables to compute interest on a certificate of deposit.	X	X			X		
12-2 Effective Annual Yield (pp. 397–399) Determine the effective annual yield.	X	X			X		
12-3 Stocks (pp. 400–402) Solve for the total cost of a stock investment.	X	X					
12-4 Stock Dividends (pp. 403–405) Compute the yield and annual dividend of a stock investment.	X	X			X		
12-5 Selling Stocks (pp. 406–408) Calculate the profit or loss from a stock sale.	X	X			X		
12-6 Bonds (pp. 409–411) Compute the annual interest and annual yield of a bond investment.	X	X					

(Source: Reprinted with permission from the National Standards for Business Education, copyright © 2001 by National Business Education Association, 1914 Association Drive, Reston, Virginia 21901-1596)

SCANS Correlation

Foundation Skills

Basic Skills	Reading	Writing	Math	Listening	Speaking	
Thinking Skills	Creative Thinking	Decision Making	Problem Solving	Seeing Things in the Mind's Eye	Knowing How to Learn	Reasoning
Personal Qualities	Responsibility	Self-Esteem	Sociability	Self-Management	Integrity/Honesty	

This chapter's highlighted blocks indicate the chapter's content coverage in the Student Edition and the Teacher Wraparound Edition.

National Council of Teachers of Mathematics Standards

1. Numbers & Operations	2. Algebra	3. Geometry	4. Measurement	5. Data Analysis & Probability	6. Problem Solving	7. Reasoning & Proof	8. Communication	9. Connections	10. Representations
X			X		X		X	X	
X			X		X		X	X	
X			X		X		X	X	
X			X		X		X	X	
X			X		X		X	X	
X			X		X		X	X	

SCANS Correlation

Workplace Competencies

Resources	Allocating Time	Allocating Money	Allocating Material and Facility Resources	Allocating Human Resources		
Information	Acquiring and Evaluating Information	Organizing and Maintaining Information	Interpreting and Communicating Information	Using Computers to Process Information		
Interpersonal Skills	Participating as a Member of a Team	Teaching Others	Serving Clients/Customers	Exercising Leadership	Negotiating to Arrive at a Decision	Working with Cultural Diversity
Systems	Understanding Systems	Monitoring and Correcting Performance	Improving and Designing Systems			
Technology	Selecting Technology	Applying Technology to Task	Maintaining and Troubleshooting Technology			

What You'll Learn

In this chapter you'll focus on investments, such as certificates of deposit, stocks, and bonds.

Why It's Important

Burying your money in a jar in the backyard will only ensure that you have the amount of money you've buried. Investing in stocks, bonds, or certificates of deposit is a way to earn interest on your money, while enabling you to afford your dreams in the future.

Key Word Review

Quiz Bowl

Divide the class into teams to play Quiz Bowl. Each team writes questions about the key words on the front of index cards. Possible questions include: "Supply the correct word for [insert a given glossary definition]"; "Give an example of [insert key word here]." Include key words from three or four other chapters.

LS , **CL**

CHAPTER 12

Investments

What You'll Learn

Section 12-1 Use tables to compute interest on certificates of deposit.

Section 12-2 Determine the effective annual yield.

Section 12-3 Solve for the total cost of a stock investment.

Section 12-4 Compute the annual yield and annual dividend of a stock investment.

Section 12-5 Calculate the profit or loss from a stock sale.

Section 12-6 Compute the annual interest and annual yield of a bond investment.

When Will You Ever Use This?

Do you want your money to work for you? Become a savvy investor by learning how to invest and diversify your personal portfolio.

Key Words to Know
- certificate of deposit
- annual yield
- stocks
- stock certificate
- dividend
- profit
- loss
- bonds

Mathematics Online

To learn more about investing, visit the *Mathematics with Business Applications* Web site at www.busmath.glencoe.com.

CLASSROOM RESOURCES

Application and Enrichment
- 📖 *Teacher Wraparound Edition*
- 📖 *Teacher Resource Binder, Blackline Masters*
- 💿 *Interactive Lesson Planner* CD-ROM
- 💿 *PowerPoint® Presentations* CD-ROM

Review and Enforcement
- Mathematics Online
  www.busmath.glencoe.com
- 📖 *Teacher Resource Binder, Internet Resources*

- 📖 *Student Activity Workbook*
- 📖 *Student Activity Workbook, Teacher Annotated Edition*
- 📖 *School-to-Home Activity Workbook*

Assessment and Evaluation
- 📖 *Assessment Binder, Reproducible Tests*
- 📖 *Assessment Binder, Alternative Assessment Strategies*
- 💿 **Exam***View*® *Pro Test Generator* CD-ROM

For the Teacher
- 📖 *Student Activity Workbook, Teacher Annotated Edition*
- 📖 *Assessment Binder*
- 💿 *Interactive Lesson Planner* CD-ROM
- 📖 *Teacher Resource Binder*
- 💻 Mathematics Online
  www.busmath.glencoe.com

For the Student
- 📖 *Student Activity Workbook*
- 📖 *School-to-Home Activity Workbook*

Living in the Real World

Life after Working Shifts

Picking up 1,280 dirty forks, wiping 320 tables, taking 2,000 orders for coffee, and wearing out 2 pairs of shoes earned Ruth Doucette "Waitress of the Month" in her short tenure on the job. She knows there is more to life than a night shift and its leftovers. In this chapter learn how Doucette is looking ahead by learning how to invest in her future.

Read on. Go to . . .

393

Living in the Real World

Story's Summary

Ruth Doucette is a hard-working waitress who has scrimped and saved and now has $900 she'd like to invest. By watching Doucette go through the process, students learn about certificates of deposit, stocks, dividends, mutual funds, and bonds. What began as a quick trip to the bank to buy a certificate of deposit has instead opened the door to several savings options, and Doucette must carefully weigh them before making a decision.

Did You Know...

According to a survey by the Securities Industry Association, 50 percent of American investors are between the ages of 30 and 49.

Think about This

How has the Internet changed the way people invest their money?

LOCAL STANDARDS

SECTION (12-1) **Certificates of Deposit**

National Standards for Business Education

Standard 1	Mathematical Foundations
Standard 2	Number Relationships and Operations
Standard 5	Statistics and Probability

National Council of Teachers of Mathematics Standards

Standard 1	Numbers and Operations
Standard 4	Measurement
Standard 6	Problem Solving
Standard 8	Communication
Standard 9	Connections

 **FOCUS**

Banks will sometimes advertise their interest rates for certificates of deposit. Use such an advertisement or copy the rates posted at a local bank to motivate the computation of interest on certificates of deposit.

In-Class Examples

Work through these exercises with students before having them do the Self-Check.
1. 1.208796 × $5,000 **$6,043.98**
2. $6,043.98 − $5,000 **$1,043.98**
3. 1.184242 × $10,000 **$11,842.42**

○ Section Objective

Use tables to compute interest on certificates of deposit.

One way to invest your money is to purchase a **certificate of deposit** (CD), which earns interest at a higher rate than a regular savings account. You buy CDs for specific amounts, such as $500 or $1,000, and you must leave the money on deposit for a specified time (ranging from 3 months to 30 years). You're penalized for early withdrawal. Most CDs earn interest compounded daily, monthly, or quarterly. Although banks use computers to calculate interest earned, you can use a table.

Important Questions to Ask Yourself	What Formula Do I Use?
How do I figure out the **amount** of my CD?	Amount = Original Principal × Amount per $1.00
How do I calculate the **interest earned** on my CD?	Interest Earned = Amount − Original Principal

Living in the Real World

Life after Working Shifts

Find the Best Rate For the last 18 months, Ruth Doucette has saved $50 from each of her monthly paychecks as a waitress at the Inn Restaurant. She wants to invest this $900 but doesn't want to tie it up for years to come. Doucette decides her best choice is a certificate of deposit (CD) with her local bank.

Draw Conclusions If you want to find the best rate for a CD, is it best to consult only your neighborhood bank?

Continued on page 397

(**Example 1**)

Paul Crates invests $4,000 in a 1-year certificate of deposit that earns interest at an annual rate of 5 percent compounded monthly. How much interest will he earn at the end of 1 year? (Refer to the Amount of $1.00 Invested—Daily, Monthly, and Quarterly Compounding table on page 800.)

BUSINESS NOTES

Growth and Income

Some stocks are classified as "growth and income" stocks. "Growth" anticipates the price of the stock increasing, while "income" would be represented by the dividend the stock pays. Using the stock exchange reports from a newspaper, students find the dividend for various stocks and verify that the annual yield given is correct. LS , CL , P

Living in the Real World

No. It's best to shop around, as different banks offer different rates and a person can deposit their savings into any bank of their choice across the country.

STEP 1: Find the amount.

Original Principal × Amount per $1.00

$4,000.00 × 1.051162 = $4,204.648 or $4,204.65

STEP 2: Find the interest earned.

Amount − Original Principal

$4,204.65 − $4,000.00 = **$204.65 interest earned**

4000 [M+] [×] 1.051162 [=] 4204.648 [−] [RM] [=] 204.648

CONCEPT CHECK

 SELF-CHECK

Complete the problems, then check your answers at the end of the chapter. Find the interest earned.

1. Eight thousand dollar CD for 1 year.
   Four percent annual interest rate compounded quarterly.
   $8,000 × 1.040604 = $8,324.83, $8,324.83 − $8,000 = $324.83
2. Fifty thousand dollar CD for 4 years.
   Five and a quarter percent annual interest rate compounded daily.
   $50,000 × 1.233659 = $61,682.95; $61,682.95 − $50,000 = $11,682.95

Example 2

Ching-Hsia Chan can invest $5,000 in a 1-year CD at 4 percent compounded monthly or a 1-year CD compounded daily. What is the difference earned in each investment?

> **STEP 1:** Find the interest earned in each investment.
>
> Monthly: $5,000 × 1.040742 = $5,203.71
>
> $5,203.71 − $5,000 = $203.71
>
> Daily: $5,000 × 1.040808 = $5,204.04
>
> $5,204.04 − $5,000 = $204.04
>
> **STEP 2:** Find the difference earned in each investment.
>
> Difference: $204.04 − $203.71 = **$0.33 difference earned**

3. $1,000 × 1.046025
   = $1,046.025;
   $1,046.03 − $1,000
   = $46.03
   $1,000 × 1.045765
   = $1,045.765;
   $1,045.77 − $1,000
   = $45.77
   $46.03 − $45.77 =
   $0.26

CONCEPT CHECK

 SELF-CHECK

Find the difference in the amount of interest for each investment.

3. One thousand dollars at 4.50 percent for 1 year compounded daily or 1 year compounded quarterly.

4. Forty thousand dollars at 5 percent for 4 years compounded monthly or 4 years compounded quarterly.
   $40,000 × 1.220895 = $48,835.80; $48,835.80 − $40,000 = $8,835.80
   $40,000 × 1.219890 = $48,795.60; $48,795.60 − $40,000 = $8,795.60
   $8,835.80 − $8,795.60 = $40.20

Section 12-1 Certificates of Deposit ▶ **395**

TECHNOLOGY POWER

Rather than just cutting costs, companies can save money by investing in new technology that makes certain processes more efficient. The Internet allows smaller suppliers to plug in, whereas previous systems required expensive hardware to allow them to communicate electronically with big retailers. This software will automatically feed forecasts directly into the manufacturers' production schedules.

COMMUNICATION SKILLS

Five Questions

Students work in small groups to develop a five-question quiz for this lesson. Groups prepare an answer sheet to their quiz and check that their answers are correct. Groups pass their quiz to another group. They take each other's quiz and check their answers with the answer sheet. **LS**, **CL**

SECTION 12-1

② TEACH

Instruct students on how to read the interest table (the Amount of $1.00 Invested—Daily, Monthly, Quarterly Compounding table on page 800) before discussing the examples. Point out that money invested in a CD earns interest for the life of the CD. This is not the case with a regular savings account because a bank can set new rates at any time.

Tell students that interest rates for CDs can vary over time (i.e., they can go up or down in any given time period). Then, ask them if they see any advantages or disadvantages to being locked-in to a specific rate for a long period of time, say, for two to five years.

Motivating the Lesson

You have $1,500 to invest. You decide to put your money in a CD with a guaranteed rate of interest. Your money will earn 4.75 percent interest compounded daily for 4 years. Your $1,500.00 investment will be worth $1,813.85 after 4 years. How much interest will your CD have earned? **$313.85**

In-Class Examples

Use the Amount of $1.00 Invested—Daily, Monthly, Quarterly Compounding table on page 800 as needed to compute interest for Problems 1–3.

1. Invested $3,000 CD for 4 years. Received 3.25 percent interest compounded monthly. Find the interest earned. **$415.88**

2. Invested $12,000 CD for 1 year. Received 6.5 percent interest compounded daily. Find the interest earned. **$805.84**

3. Invested $5,000 at 3.75 percent for 4 years compounded daily or 4 years compounded quarterly. Find the difference in the amount of interest for each investment. **$4.01 more for daily**

395

3 ASSESS

Error Analysis

Students may encounter difficulty in reading the table on page 800. Review percent, interest period, and how interest is compounded. Encourage students to use a straight edge or ruler as a guide in finding the correct rate per $1 invested. Be sure students understand that they must multiply the original principal times the rate per $1 to figure the interest earned over a specific time period at a specific rate.

Remind students to check their work for computational errors.

4 CLOSE

Closing Activity

1. $16,844.39 − $16,500 **$344.39**
2. 1.030416 × $2,350 **$2,421.48**

Use the Amount of $1.00 Invested—Daily, Monthly, Quarterly Compounding table on page 800 for Problems 3–5.

3. Invest $9,200 CD for 4 years. Received 6.75 percent interest compounded daily. Find the interest earned. **$2,851.37**

4. Invested $3,400 at 5 percent for 1 year compounded daily or 1 year compounded monthly. What is the amount of the CD at each rate at maturity? **($3,574.31 daily; $3,573.95 monthly)** What is the difference in the interest earned? **A difference of $0.36.**

5. Invested $30,000 at 8 percent for 4 years compounded daily or 8.25 percent for 4 years compounded quarterly. What is the amount of the CD at each rate at maturity? Which CD earns the most interest? By how much? **8% compounded daily is worth $41,312.37; 8.25% compounded quarterly is worth $41,589.18; 8.25% compounded quarterly earns $276.81 more than 8% compounded daily**

Use the Amount of $1.00 Invested—Daily, Monthly, and Quarterly Compounding table on page 800.

	Annual Rate	Interest Period	Original Principal	×	Amount per $1.00	=	Amount	Interest Earned
5.	5.00%	1 year quarterly	$ 4,500	×	a. 1.050945	=	b. $4,729.25	c. $229.25
6.	3.50%	4 years daily	18,000	×	a. 1.150266	=	b. $20,704.79	c. $2,704.79
7.	4.75%	4 years monthly	9,000	×	a. 1.208796	=	b. $10,879.16	c. $1,879.16
8.	4.25%	1 year quarterly	140,000	×	a. 1.043182	=	b. *b. $146,045.48*	c. $6,045.48

9. Genet Spurlock can invest $25,000 at 9.25 percent in a 1-year CD compounded quarterly or a 1-year CD compounded daily. What is the amount of the CD at maturity for each rate? What is the difference in the interest earned? **$27,393.95 quarterly; $27,422.50 daily; $28.55 difference**

10. Clifford and Hazel Ida can purchase a 4-year certificate of deposit for $10,000 at a rate of 8.75 percent compounded daily or compounded monthly. What is the amount of the CD at each rate at maturity? What is the difference in the interest earned? **$14,190.08 daily; $14,172.67 monthly; $17.41 difference**

11. The LaGelleys have $25,000 that they want to invest in a certificate of deposit. Granite Trust offers a 4-year certificate that earns interest at a rate of 8.50 percent compounded quarterly. Hancock Cooperative Bank offers a 4-year certificate of deposit that earns interest at a rate of 8.25 percent compounded daily. Which CD earns the most interest? By how much? **$9,998.80 interest on Granite; $9,772.90 interest on Hancock; $225.90 more at Granite**

MAINTAINING YOUR SKILLS

Need Help? Go to...
➤ Skill 2: Rounding Numbers, page 729
➤ Skill 6: Subtracting Decimals, page 733
➤ Skill 8: Multiplying Decimals, page 735

Round to the nearest ten.

12. 78 **80**   13. 144 **140**   14. 3,045 **3,050**

Subtract.

15. 0.099 − 0.032 **0.067**   16. 921.7285 − 336.94 **584.7885**   17. 5.435 − 0.794 **4.641**

Multiply.

18. 0.073 × 8 **0.584**   19. 1.42 × 1543 **2,191.06**   20. 26.49 × 85.76 **2,271.78**

WRAP-UP

Go over any problem for which a wrong answer is given.

Assignment Guide
  Basic: 5–8
  Average: 9–10

20 min.

SECTION (12-2) Effective Annual Yield

Section Objective

Determine the effective annual yield.

Banks advertise not only their annual interest rates, but also the effective annual yields on certificates of deposit. The **annual yield** is the rate at which your money earns simple interest in one year. Remember that even money has a price. So, *interest* is the price that is paid for the use of another's money.

In the real world though, you'll run into *effective* annual yield. Effective annualized interest earned is affected by the frequency of compounding. Yield is the rate of return, usually stated as a percent, earned by an investor who holds it over a period of time. To figure out what your effective annual yield is on your investment, remember that:

Important Questions to Ask Yourself	What Formula Do I Use?
Which yield uses **simple interest?**	Annual Yield
Which yield uses **compound interest** in its calculation?	Effective Annual Yield
How do I calculate **effective annual yield?**	Effective Annual Yield $= \dfrac{\text{Interest for 1 Year}}{\text{Principal}}$

Living in the Real World

Life after Working Shifts

How Much Will You Profit? The last time she was in the bank, Doucette picked up a brochure about certificates of deposit. The bank is having a "special" on 18-month CDs, which will earn a higher interest rate than certificates invested for a shorter or longer period of time.

Draw Conclusions A table in the brochure indicates that the interest rate on an 18 month CD is 5.65 percent. Doucette also notices another rate called the annual yield. What do you suppose this means?

Continued on page 401

Example 1

Randall Raye invested $5,000 in a certificate of deposit for 3 years. The certificate earns interest at an annual rate of 6.25 percent compounded quarterly. What is the effective annual yield to the nearest thousandth of a percent?

Continued on next page

Section 12-2 Effective Annual Yield ▶ **397**

Living in the Real World

The annual yield is the rate at which money earns simple interest in one year. Similar to compound interest on a savings account, the annual yield is always higher than the interest rate because as interest is added to the CD daily, monthly, or quarterly, the interest also earns interest.

National Standards for Business Education

Standard 1	Mathematical Foundations
Standard 2	Number Relationships and Operations
Standard 5	Statistics and Probability

National Council of Teachers of Mathematics Standards

Standard 1	Numbers and Operations
Standard 4	Measurement
Standard 6	Problem Solving
Standard 8	Communication
Standard 9	Connections

(1) FOCUS

Ask students this question: If you have $1,000 to invest for one year, would you invest it at 4 percent compounded daily or 4 percent compounded weekly? Explain your choice. In this lesson, students will learn how to compute the effective annual yields.

In-Class Examples

Work through these exercises with students before having them do the Self-Check. Multiply. Round answers to nearest hundredth.

1. $1.210620 \times 4,000$ **4,842.48**
2. $1.009125 \times 3,000$ **3,027.38**
3. $\$12,250.10 - \$11,382.95$ **$867.15**

2 TEACH

Students need to understand that a valid comparison of the yields of two or more investments can be made only by using the effective annual yields of the investments. The use of a calculator is highly recommended for working the problems in this lesson.

Motivating the Lesson

You have $5,000 to invest. You can put the money in a 4-year CD that pays 5 percent interest compounded daily or 5.25 percent compounded quarterly. The CD that pays 5 percent interest compounded daily has an effective annual yield of 5.127 percent while the CD that pays 5.25 percent compounded quarterly has an effective annual yield of 5.354 percent. Compare the two effective annual yields. Which investment is the better deal? **The investment that pays 5.25% compounded quarterly is the better deal because it has a higher effective annual yield.**

In-Class Examples

In Problems 1–3, round effective annual yield to the nearest thousandth of a percent.

1. CD: $8,000. Six percent annual interest rate compounded daily. What is the effective annual yield? **6.183%**
2. CD: $12,500. Annual interest compounded quarterly: 5.25 percent. What is the effective annual yield? **5.354%**
3. CD: $6,000. Annual interest rate compounded quarterly 3-year certificate: 8.5 percent What is the effective annual yield? **8.775%**

---

1. ($10,000 × 1.059040) − $10,000; $10,590.40 − $10,000 = $590.40 ($590.40 ÷ $10,000) = 0.05904 or 5.904%

SELF-CHECK✔

3. **Find the interest for 1 year and the annual yield.**
Daily: ($20,000 × 1.035618) − $20,000; $20,712.36 − $20,000.00 = $712.36
Yield: $712.36 ÷ $20,000.00 = 0.035618 or 3.562%
Monthly: ($20,000 × 1.038151) − $20,000; $20,763.02 − $20,000.00 = $763.02
Yield: $763.02 ÷ $20,000.00 = 0.038151 or 3.82%
The better investment is 3.75 percent monthly.

4. Quarterly: ($20,000.00 × 1.045765) − $20,000; $20,915.30 − $20,000.00 = $915.30
Yield: $915.30 ÷ $20,000.00 = 0.045765 or 4.577%
Monthly: ($20,000.00 × 1.043338) − $20,000; $20,866.76 − $20,000.00 = $866.76
Yield: $866.76 ÷ $20,000.00 = 0. 043338 or 4.334%
The better investment is 4.5 percent quarterly.

STEP 1: Find the interest for 1 year. (Refer to the Amount of $1.00 Invested—Daily, Monthly, and Quarterly Compounding table on page 800.)

Amount	− Principal	
($5,000.00 × 1.063980)	− $5,000.00	
$5,319.90	− $5,000.00	= $319.90

STEP 2: Find the effective annual yield.

$$\frac{\text{Interest for 1 Year}}{\text{Principal}} = \frac{\$319.90}{\$5,000.00} = \textbf{0.06398 or 6.398\% effective annual yield}$$

CONCEPT CHECK

Complete the problems, then check your answers at the end of the chapter. Find the effective annual yield. (Refer to the Amount of $1.00 Invested—Daily, Monthly, and Quarterly Compounding table on page 800.)

1. You own a $10,000 certificate of deposit at 5.75 percent annual interest rate compounded monthly.

2. You own a $25,000 certificate of deposit at 5 percent annual interest rate compounded quarterly.
($25,000 × 1.050945) − $25,000; $26,273.63 − $25,000 = $1,273.63 ($1,273.63 ÷ $25,000) = 0.050945 or 5.0945%

Example 2

Galeno Villarreal can invest $10,000 at either 4.75 percent compounded daily for 4 years or 5 percent compounded quarterly for 4 years. Based on an effective annual yield, which is the better investment?

STEP 1: Find the interest for 1 year and the annual yield.

Daily:	($10,000 × 1.048643)	− $10,000.00	
	$10,486.43	− $10,000.00	= $486.43
Yield:	$486.43	÷ $10,000.00	= 0.048643 or 4.864%
Quarterly:	($10,000 × 1.050945)	− $10,000.00	
	$10,509.45	− $10,000.00	= $509.45
Yield:	$509.45	÷ $10,000.00	= 0.050945 or 5.095%

STEP 2: Compare the two.
The better investment is 5 percent quarterly.

CONCEPT CHECK

Complete the problems, then check your answers at the end of the chapter.

Luisa Hernandez wants to invest $20,000. Which 4-year investment is the best deal?

3. Compounded daily at 3.5 percent or compounded monthly at 3.75 percent.

4. Compounded quarterly at 4.5 percent or compounded monthly at 4.25 percent.

COOPERATIVE LEARNING

Compare

The effective annual yield is the index to use to compare various savings plans. Just as the annual percentage rate (APR) was used to compare consumer credit plans, the effective annual yield plays a similar role with savings plans. Students collect financial institutions' ads and verify those that fit the rates and terms given in the tables in the text. **CL**, **LS**

SECTION 12-2 PRACTICE

Find the amount per $1.00 invested by using the Amount of $1.00 Invested—Daily, Monthly, and Quarterly Compounding table on page 800.

	Annual Rate	Interest Period	Original Principal	×	Amount per $1.00	=	Amount	Interest Earned	Effective Annual Yield
5.	7.25%	1 year quarterly	$6,000	×	1.074495	=	a. $6,446.97	b. $446.97	c. 7.450%
6.	8.00%	1 year quarterly	8,100	×	a. 1.082432	=	b. $9,092.43	c. $692.43	d. 8.243%
7.	9.25%	1 year monthly	5,000	×	a. 1.096524	=	b. $5,482.62	c. $482.62	d. 9.652%
8.	7.50%	1 year daily	1,800	×	a. 1.077876	=	b. $1,940.18	c. $140.18	d. 7.788%

9. Ollie Gibson is considering investing $10,000 in a certificate of deposit for 4 years at an annual interest rate of 8.25 percent compounded daily or 8.25 percent compounded monthly. Based on the effective annual yield, which one is the better investment? **8.25% compounded daily**

10. May Wattson has $50,000 to invest in a 4-year certificate of deposit that earns interest at a rate of 7.75 percent compounded monthly or 7.50 percent compounded daily. Based on annual yield, which one is the better investment? **7.75% compounded monthly**

11. Paul Durant invested $10,000 at 6 percent compounded daily for 4 years and $10,000 at 6 percent compounded monthly for 1 year. What is the interest earned for 1 year on each investment? What is the effective annual yield for each investment? **6% daily: $618.31 (interest); 6.1831% (effective annual yield)**
6% monthly: $616.78 (interest); 6.1678% (effective annual yield)

12. **5% daily: $769.01 (interest); 5.1267% (effective annual yield) 5.25% daily: $4,662.26 (interest); 5.378% (effective annual yield)** 12. Ben Garison invested $15,000 at 5 percent compounded daily in a Golden Buckeye account that matures in 1 year. He also invested $20,000 at 5.25 percent compounded monthly in a Silver Screen account that matures in 4 years. What is the interest earned at maturity for both accounts? What is the effective annual yield for each account?

13. Ricardo Torres invests $10,000 at 4 percent compounded daily for 1 year. At the end of the year, Torres reinvests the amount in the account for another year at the same rate. He repeats this process for 2 more years. Compare the amount in the account at the end of 4 years with what he would have if he had invested the $10,000 at 4 percent compounded daily for 4 years. **$11,734.98 vs. $11,735.01 (the amount is about the same)**

MAINTAINING YOUR SKILLS

Need Help? Go to...
▶ Skill 26: Writing Decimals as Percents, page 753
▶ Skill 11: Dividing Decimals, page 738

Write as a percent. Round answers to the nearest hundredth percent.

14. 0.089146 **8.91%**　　15. 1.25642 **125.64%**　　16. 2.0 **200%**

Divide.

17. 1,500 ÷ 0.05 **30,000**　　18. 28.42 ÷ 1.2 **23.68**　　19. 679.2 ÷ 0.02 **33,960**

USING CALCULATORS

A calculator will give any percent answer as a decimal. It is important that you move the decimal point two places to the right to convert a decimal to a percent. For example: 0.00412 becomes 0.412 percent.

WRAP-UP

Go over any problem for which a wrong answer is given.

Assignment Guide
　Basic: 5–8
　Average: 9–11

20 min.

(3) ASSESS

Error Analysis

Students may mistakenly use the wrong interest period when calculating effective annual yield. Review the concept that effective annual yield refers to the amount of compound interest accrued over a *one-year period*. Therefore, students should read *only* the portion of Amount of $1.00 Invested—Daily, Monthly, and Quarterly Compounding table that lists the rate for a *one-year interest period*.

　Remind students that to change a decimal to a percent, move the decimal point two places to the right. Students may also benefit from a review of how to round numbers to the thousandth place value.

(4) CLOSE

Closing Activity

Round to the nearest cent.
1. $5,000 × 1.038031 **$5,190.16**
2. $\frac{\$190.16}{\$5,000}$ **0.038032**
3. CD: $6,700. Interest compounded monthly: 3.75 percent. What is the effective annual yield? **3.815%**
4. Dave Rigsby has $9,000 to invest. Which 4-year investment is the better deal based on effective annual yield? Compounded daily at 4.25 percent or compounded quarterly at 4.5 percent. **4.5% compounded quarterly is the better investment.**

National Standards for Business Education

Standard 1	Mathematical Foundations
Standard 2	Number Relationships and Operations
Standard 5	Statistics and Probability

National Council of Teachers of Mathematics Standards

Standard 1	Numbers and Operations
Standard 4	Measurement
Standard 6	Problem Solving
Standard 8	Communication
Standard 9	Connections

1 FOCUS

You can motivate the study of stocks by opening a discussion in starting a new business. Ask students to think about starting a business of their own. Who would invest in their business? If the business were successful, how would they raise more money? Point out that both small and large businesses issue stocks to raise money. In this lesson, students compute the total cost of a stock investment.

In-Class Examples

Work through these exercises with students before having them do the Self-Check.
Calculate.
1. 100 × $49.62 **$4,962.00**
2. 220 × $14.10 **$3,102.00**
3. 300 × $37.30 **$11,190.00**

SECTION 12-3 Stocks

○ **Section Objective**

Solve for the total cost of a stock investment.

You can invest your money in shares of **stocks**. When you purchase a share of stock, you become a part owner of the corporation that issues the stock. Nearly each day you'll find the stock prices published in newspapers and on Web sites. Stock prices are usually quoted in dollars and cents. You may receive a **stock certificate** as proof of ownership. The total amount you pay for the stock depends on the cost per share, the number of shares you purchase, and the stockbroker's commission. A *stockbroker* is a registered representative with the Commodity Futures Trading Commission (CFTC)—an agency created by Congress in 1974. This person takes your money and invests it for you. In return for investing your money, this person keeps a small percent, such as 1 percent, of the investment, which is known as earning a *commission*.

First, you'll need to know how to read a stock table. You'll find these in the newspaper or online.

Figure 12.1

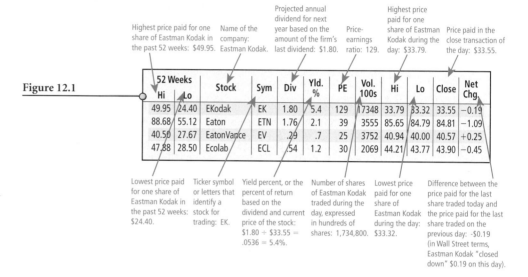

When you're thinking about investing in stocks, you might ask yourself these questions:

Important Questions to Ask Yourself	What Formula Do I Use?
How do I calculate the **cost of a stock**?	Cost of Stock = Number of Shares × Cost per Share
How do I know how much I've paid in **total** for a stock?	Total Paid = Cost of Stock + Commission

---

THINKING CRITICALLY

Stock Tables

Students bring to class a sample of stock listings from the business section of a newspaper. Students make a display of a typical stock listing with the different parts clearly labeled. **For example: name of stock, change from previous day, sales in thousands, and so on.**

Living in the Real World

Life after Working Shifts

Are You A Risk Taker? As Doucette is studying the bank brochure about CDs, she wonders if she should consider other investment options, such as stocks.

Draw Conclusions Imagine the stock market has dropped 20 percent since the last quarter. The market experts are optimistic. If you were Doucette, what would you do with your money?

Continued on page 403

►FYI

Perhaps the largest pool of personal investment money in the world is in China, where a billion-plus individuals control $845 billion-worth of personal savings. Although most Chinese citizens invest their savings in state-owned banks, those institutions offer only minimal interest.

►►►

Example 1

Melanie Lambert purchased 100 shares of stock at $106.30 per share. Her Internet online stockbroker charged her a $15.95 commission. What is the total amount that she paid for the stock?

STEP 1: Find the cost of a stock.

Number of Shares × Cost per Share

100 × $106.30 = $10,630

STEP 2: Find the total paid.

Cost of Stock + Commission

$10,630 + $15.95 = **$10,645.95 total paid**

CONCEPT CHECK

SELF-CHECK ✓

Complete the problems, then check your answers at the end of the chapter. Find the total paid.

1. One hundred fifty shares of stock at $36.21 per share. Commission of $29.95.
150 × $36.21 = $5,431.50 + $29.95 = $5,461.45
2. Four hundred shares of stock at $58.80 per share. Commission of $19.95.
400 × $58.80 = $23,520.00 + $19.95 = $23,539.95

SECTION 12-3 PRACTICE

3. a. $11,050.00
  b. $11,059.99
4. a. $41,310.00
  b. $41,360.00
5. a. $17,800.00
  b. $17,845.50
6. a. $156,125.00
  b. $156,200.00

	Company	Number of Shares	×	Cost per Share	=	Cost of Stock	+ Commission =	Total Paid
3.	Nelson Inc.	100	×	$110.50	=	a.	+ $ 9.99 =	b.
4.	Galvin Co.	900	×	45.90	=	a.	+ 50.00 =	b.
5.	Dunkle LTD	500	×	35.60	=	a.	+ 45.50 =	b.
6.	Warncke Co.	2,500	×	62.45	=	a.	+ 0.03/share −	b.

Continued on next page

Living in the Real World

Answers will vary depending on the student. Many people would keep their money invested in hope that the stock market would rebound; others would cut their losses and get out before it dropped even further.

ALTERNATIVE ASSESSMENT

The Right Résumé

An insurance company in your area is advertising for a payroll clerk. You'd like to get this job, but you're afraid that you don't have the right qualifications. A friend suggests that you "enhance" your résumé to make yourself look better. Do you agree with your friend or not? **Your résumé should highlight your skills and knowledge that a potential employer would find valuable, but it doesn't need to point out your weaknesses.**

② **TEACH**

Ask students what they think a business does with money raised from the issue of new stock. Ask them also to think about the reasons a person would buy stocks. **Students should understand that the sale of stocks can provide a business with new money for expansion into new markets, replace old equipment, hire people to do research and development, improve existing products, and so on. Individuals buy stocks in the hope that their value will increase and thus can be sold for a profit. Some stocks pay dividends and are a source of income.**

Motivating the Lesson
You plan to buy stock in XYZ Corporation. The stock costs $17.66 per share. An online broker charges a commission of $9.99 for the transaction. How much will 20 shares of this stock cost? **($353.20)** What is the total amount you will pay for the stock including the broker's commission? **$363.19**

In-Class Examples
1. Purchase 100 shares at $32.05 per share. Commission of $12.95. What is the total amount paid for the stock? **$3,217.95**
2. Purchase 300 shares at $17 per share. Commission is $19.95.
  a. What is the cost of the stock? **$5,100**
  b. What is the total paid? **$5,119.95**
3. Purchase 1,000 shares at $48.95 per share. Online commission is $0.03 per share.
  a. What is the cost of the stock? **$48,950**
  b. What is the total paid? **$48,980**

 **ASSESS**

Error Analysis

Review students' work to see what kind of errors they may be making. Computational errors may occur when multiplying decimals to determine the cost of the stock. When students add the cost of the stock to the commission, remind them to vertically align decimal points.

4 **CLOSE**

Closing Activity

1. $49.09 × 600 **$29,454**
2. $16,360 + $39.95 **$16,399.95**
3. Purchase 400 shares at $34.75 per share. Commission of $49.
   a. What is the cost of the stock? **$13,900**
   b. What is the total paid? **$13,949**
4. Kendall Adams bought 1,900 shares at $29.33 per share. Her online broker charges $29.95 for fewer than 1,000 shares or $0.02 per share for 1,000 or more shares.
   a. What is the cost of the stock? **$55,727**
   b. What is the total paid? **$55,765**

Use **Figure 12.2** for Problem 5.
5. After consulting with her broker, Mary Engle purchases 500 shares at $18.98 per share and 200 shares of another company for $116.65 per share. What is the total cost of the stocks including the commission? **$33,079.60**

---

7. Trudy Fahringer.
   Owns 500 shares of Waverson Inc.
   Cost per share is $32.90.
   Commission is $65.00.
   $16,450.00 a. What is the cost of the stock?
   $16,515.00 b. What is the total paid?

8. David Daly.
   Owns 215 shares of Atwood Tire.
   Cost per share is $18.90.
   Online commission is $14.95.
   a. What is the cost of the stock?
   b. What is the total paid?
   a. **$4,063.50;** b. **$4,078.45**

9. Enice Brudley purchased 3,000 shares of GTI Petroleum at $6.30 per share. The broker's commission was $19.95 for fewer than 1,000 shares, or $0.02 per share for 1,000 or more. What was the cost of the stock? What was the total paid? **$18,900; $18,960**

10. Linda and Martin Sonoma purchased 300 shares of Hampton Publishing at $31.94 per share and 150 shares of Company R at $29.19 per share. The broker charged $19.95 for each transaction. What was the total paid? **$14,000.40**

Figure 12.2

Broker Assisted Commissions					
Minimum Charge $39 per Trade					
Transaction Size		Commission			
$ 0	–	$ 2,999	$ 30	+	1.70%
3,000	–	6,999	56	+	0.66%
7,000	–	19,999	76	+	0.34%
20,000	–	49,999	100	+	0.22%
50,000	+		155	+	0.11%

Use **Figure 12.2** for Problems 11–13.

11. After consulting with his broker, Dan Hostetler purchases 2,000 shares of Ballon Synergy stock at $4.10 per share. He also purchased 500 shares of Matell Scientific at $26.76 per share. What is the total cost of the stocks including the commission? **$21,805.37**

12. Yukiko Nakata, after consulting with her broker, purchases 10,000 shares of McQuire Internet Inc. at $24.52 per share. He also purchased 5,000 shares of Smithmeyer Capital Group at $45.25 a share. What is the total cost of the stocks including the commission? **$472,278.60**

13. Calculate the difference between the commission on a $7,000 stock sale and a $6,999 stock sale. Comment on the difference.
    It costs $2.39 more to buy $6,999 of stock than to buy $7,000 of stock.

MAINTAINING YOUR SKILLS

Need Help? Go to...
▶ Skill 5: **Adding Decimals,** page 732
▶ Skill 8: **Multiplying Decimals,** page 735

Add.

14. $55,289 + $39.95 **$55,328.95**
15. $5,863 + $19.95 **$5,882.95**
16. $980 + $9.95 **$989.95**

Multiply.

17. $45.50 × 400 **$18,200**
18. $12.75 × 200 **$2,550**
19. $57.38 × 400 **$22,952**

WRAP-UP

Go over any problem for which a wrong answer is given.

Assignment Guide
Basic: 3–6
Average: 7–9

20 min.

SECTION (12-4) Stock Dividends

Section Objective

Compute the annual yield and annual dividend of a stock investment.

When you buy stock, you may receive a **dividend**. A dividend is the money you receive as a shareholder of the company. You may receive an amount specified by the corporation for each share of stock that you own. The annual yield is your annual return for holding a stock; it's expressed as a percent of the price. Generally remember that the higher your yield, the greater the return on your investment during the year. Throughout the chapter, remind yourself of these important equations:

Important Questions to Ask Yourself	What Formula Do I Use?
How do I find the **total annual dividend**?	$\text{Total Annual Dividend} = \text{Annual Dividend per Share} \times \text{Number of Shares}$
How do I find the annual **yield**?	$\text{Annual Yield} = \dfrac{\text{Annual Dividend per Share}}{\text{Cost per Share}}$

Living in the Real World

Life after Working Shifts

Tolerance for Risk If she invests in a company that's doing well, Doucette could receive dividends. Then she might be able to re-invest that money in something else, such as real estate.

Doucette also decides that she will look over all her finances to see if she can draw on other sources to buy the land and still put her savings into stock.

Draw Conclusions Which do you think is more important to Doucette as an investor—steady income or steady income and growth?

Continued on page 406

Example 1

Pam Schmidt bought 80 shares of Network Associates stock at $24 per share. The company paid annual dividends of $0.38 per share. What is the total annual dividend? What is the annual yield to the nearest hundredth of a percent?

STEP 1: Find the total annual dividend.

Annual Dividend per Share × Number of Shares

$\$0.38 \qquad \times \qquad 80$

= **$30.40 annual dividend**

STEP 2: Find the annual yield.

Annual Dividend per Share ÷ Cost per Share

$\$0.38 \qquad \div \qquad \$24.00$

= **0.0158 or 1.58% annual yield**

Section 12-4 Stock Dividends ▶ **403**

1 FOCUS

Assume each student has $5,000 to invest in stocks. Ask how they would decide which stocks to buy. **Introduce the idea of a dividend and point out that many people choose to buy stocks of companies that pay high dividends. The focus of this lesson is on computing the annual dividend and annual yield of a stock investment.**

In-Class Examples

Work through these exercises with students before having them do the Self-Check.

Write the decimals as percents.

1. 0.357 **35.7%**
2. 2.15 **215%**

Divide. Round to the nearest hundredth of a percent.

3. $\dfrac{0.73}{67.42}$ **1.08%**
4. $\dfrac{1.16}{41.35}$ **2.81%**

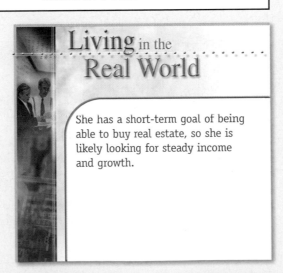

Living in the Real World

She has a short-term goal of being able to buy real estate, so she is likely looking for steady income and growth.

SECTION 12-4

SELF-CHECK ✓

Complete the problem, then check your answers at the end of the chapter.

1. One hundred eighty shares at $41.00 per share, receiving $1.23 annual dividend per share. Find the total annual dividend and the annual yield.
   180 × $1.23 = $221.40, $1.23 ÷ $41 = 0.03 or 3%

② TEACH

The annual yield of a stock can be used to compare its performance with other stocks or other investments, such as a CD. Students need to understand that there is a risk in investing in stocks. The price of a stock can go down and thus be worth less than an investor paid for it, or a company may have a poor year and decide not to pay a dividend. In such a case, the value of its stock would almost certainly go down.

Of course you can also make money by buying and selling stocks. You might wish to have some students keep a daily record of the stocks of five or six different companies for about one month. Then the risks of investing in the stock market can be made real for students.

Motivating the Lesson

You have researched stocks that pay annual dividends and bought 200 shares of a particular company. The annual dividend is $2 per share. What is the total amount of money you receive in dividends at the end of the year for your stock? **$400**

In-Class Examples

1. The cost of a share of stock in a printing and publishing business is $64.50. Dividends are $0.92 per share. What is the annual yield? **1.43%**

2. The cost of a share of stock in a pharmaceutical company is $41.74. Dividends are $1.40 per share. What is the annual yield? **3.35%**

3. Tyra Burns owns 500 shares of stock in a department store. Purchase price is $31.92 per share. Dividends are $0.24 per share. What are the annual dividends? **($120)** What is the annual yield? **0.75%**

(Example 2)

Susana Valasco owns 100 shares of Wagoneer Inc. stock. The stock ranged from a low of $37.26 to a high of $52.86 last year. The annual dividend is $1.10. What is the annual yield based on the high and the low? What is the total annual dividend?

STEP 1: Find the annual yield based on the high and the low.

Annual yield on high price $\frac{\$1.10}{\$52.86} = $ **0.02080 or 2.08%**

Annual yield on low price $\frac{\$1.10}{\$37.26} = $ **0.02952 or 2.95%**

STEP 2: Find the total annual dividend.
100 × $1.10 = **$110.00 total annual dividend**

SELF-CHECK ✓

Complete the problem, then check your answers at the end of the chapter.

2. Higginbotham Network Design stock had a high of $49.88 and a low of $32.64 during the year. The annual dividend is $1.34. What is the annual yield based on the high? What is the annual yield based on the low?
   $1.34 ÷ $49.88 = 0.02686 or 2.69%; $1.34 ÷ $32.64 = 0.04105 or 4.11%

SECTION 12-4 PRACTICE

Find the annual yield.

		Annual Dividend per Share	÷	Cost per Share	=	Annual Yield
3.	Webpage Inc.	$1.24	÷	$73.36	=	0.01690 = 1.69%
4.	Foster Mfg.	2.80	÷	83.20	=	0.03365 = 3.37%
5.	Brown Oil	0.20	÷	18.37	=	0.01088 = 1.09%
6.	Hyundia LLC	1.10	÷	44.23	=	0.02486 = 2.49%

Great Ideas from the Classroom Of...

Barbara Motley McGill
T. Wingate Andrews High School
High Point, N.C.

Investments

Invite a stockbroker to teach students the value of investing early in life. The broker might share that money invested over long periods of time will generally pay greater dividends. Show students several different types of stocks and then decide as a class, which ones to hypothetically invest in for the duration of the course. At the end of the course, "sell" the stocks and ration out the earnings.

▶FYI

You may have heard the expressions "bear market" and "bull market." A bear market is one that is tending downward, usually over a period of time. When more people want to sell than buy, prices fall. A bull market, on the other hand, is moving upward. When more people want to buy than sell, prices of stocks rise.

▶▶▶

Round the annual yield to the nearest hundredth of a percent.

7. Purchase price: $15.53 per share.
   Dividends are $1.48 per share.
   What is the annual yield? **9.53%**

8. Purchase price: $36.91 per share.
   Dividends are $0.14 per share.
   What is the annual yield? **0.38%**

9. Christine Gony owns 400 shares.
   Purchase price: $55.99 a share.
   Dividends were $1.52 per share.
   a. What are her annual dividends?
   b. What is the annual yield?
      a. **$608.00; b. 2.71%**

10. Woody Davenport owns 850 shares.
    High and low prices for the year were
    $74.46 and $47.50.
    Dividends are $1.36 per share.
    a. What are his annual dividends?
    b. What are the annual yields for the
       high and low prices?
       a. **$1,156; b. high 1.83%; low 2.86%**

11. Joyce Kronecki bought 350 shares of KOW Inc. at $42.50 per share. Last year
    the company paid annual dividends of $0.58 per share. What were her
    annual dividends? What is the annual yield? **$203; 1.36%**

12. Reed Hopkins purchased 400 shares of Barber Industries at $11.93 per share.
    Recently the company paid annual dividends of $0.10 per share. What were
    his annual dividends? What is the annual yield? **$40.00; 0.84%**

13. Duane Hartley owns 2,000 shares of Heban Oil stock, which he purchased
    for $28.40 each. Recently he read that the average selling price of his stock
    was $37.90. The company paid annual dividends of $1.80 per share last year.
    What is the annual yield on his stock? For an investor who purchased the
    stock at $37.90 per share, what is the annual yield? **6.34%; 4.75%**

14. The Racitis own 300 shares of Clayton Manufacturing, which they purchased
    at $36.30 per share. They also purchased 200 shares at $22.50 per share. The
    dividend per share paid by the company is $0.72. What is the average price
    per share? What were the Racitis' annual dividends? What is the average
    annual yield? **$30.78; $360.00; 2.34%**

MAINTAINING YOUR SKILLS

Need Help? Go to...
▶ Skill 11: **Dividing**
   Decimals, page 738
▶ Skill 26: **Writing**
   Decimals as
   Percents, page 753

Divide. Round answers to the nearest hundredth.

15. $24.0 \div 200$ **0.12**

16. $32.61 \div 35$ **0.93**

17. $0.587 \div 0.009$ **65.22**

18. $16.7 \div 1.1$ **15.18**

Write the decimals as percents.

19. 0.2583 **25.83%**

20. 0.017 **1.7%**

21. 0.03126 **3.126%**

22. 1.125 **112.5%**

Section 12-4 Stock Dividends ▶ **405**

WRAP-UP

Go over any problem for which a wrong answer is given.

Assignment Guide
  Basic: 3–6
  Average: 7–10

20 min.

Error Analysis

Students may benefit from a review of the major concepts presented in this section. Remind students that the *annual dividend* is a dollar amount earned on each share of stock a person owns. The more stock a person owns, the greater the total annual dividend. For instance, 100 shares of stock with an annual dividend of $0.64 per share would earn a total annual dividend of $64.00, while 2,000 shares of the same stock would earn a total annual dividend of $1,280.00.

The *annual yield* is the dividend expressed as a percent of the price paid for the stock. Compute the annual yield by dividing the annual dividend by the price paid for the stock. For instance, if you paid $41.75 per share of stock that had an annual dividend of $0.64, your annual yield would be $\frac{\$0.64}{\$41.75}$, which is 1.53 percent. However, if you paid $29.00 per share for the same stock with the same annual dividend of $0.64, the annual yield would be $\frac{\$0.64}{\$29}$, or 2.21 percent. Students should see that if the annual dividend is the same, the annual yield fluctuates with the price paid for the stock.

4 CLOSE

Closing Activity

1. Purchase 280 shares of a candy company at $57.36 per share. Annual dividend is $1.21.
   a. What is the total annual dividend? **$338.80**
   b. What is the annual yield?
      2.11%

405

National Standards for Business Education

Standard 1	Mathematical Foundations
Standard 2	Number Relationships and Operations
Standard 5	Statistics and Probability

National Council of Teachers of Mathematics Standards

Standard 1	Numbers and Operations
Standard 4	Measurement
Standard 6	Problem Solving
Standard 8	Communication
Standard 9	Connections

1 FOCUS

Using the financial page from a newspaper or from an online site, select a few stocks that had gone down the day before and, assuming a higher purchase price, calculate the loss for 100 shares. Then, select a few stocks that had gone up and calculate the profit made. Use your real-world examples to lead into the topic of computing the profit or loss from a stock sale.

In-Class Examples

Work through these exercises with students before having them do the Self-Check.

1. $41.00 × 50 **$2,050**
2. $6,550 − $5,440 **$1,110**
3. Write the amount that is greater: $4,080 or $6,660. **$6,660**

○ **Section Objective**

Calculate the profit or loss from a stock sale.

When you sell your stocks, the sale can result in either a **profit** or a **loss**. Think: profit = good; loss = not so good. What is profit on a stock? It's the amount of money you make over and above the initial money you invested. In business lingo it means that if the amount you receive for the sale minus the sales commission is greater than the total amount you paid for the stocks, then you made a profit. (See the equation below as a visual cue, since the last sentence was a lot to grasp.)

On the other hand, loss on a stock is just the opposite of profit—you lose some of the money that you invested. If the amount you receive from the sale minus the sales commission is less than the total you paid, you lost money on the sell. (Again, see the equation below if you're a little confused.)

In order to compute the profit and loss of stocks, use the following calculations. (Note: Remember that "commission" is the fee charged by the brokerage firm buying and/or selling your stock.)

Important Questions to Ask Yourself	What Formula Do I Use?
How do I find the **net sale** of a stock?	Net Sale = Amount of Sale − Commission
How do I calculate the **profit** on my stock?	Profit = Net Sale − Total Paid
How do I calculate the **loss** on my stock?	Loss = Total Paid − Net Sale

Living in the Real World

Life after Working Shifts

Expert Advice Needed Doucette decides to start reading a national newspaper to see if she can learn more about several stocks she is considering investing in. She decides to pick three companies that deal in different products and pretend that she has invested her $900 in them. Watching their performance over a few weeks, she decides she isn't good at picking stocks on her own. She decides to hire a stockbroker.

Draw Conclusions Investors buy stocks in the hopes of earning a large return on their investment. What causes the demand for a stock to change?

Continued on page 409

Living in the Real World

Many things cause stock prices to rise and fall, including news of expected sales revenues, earnings, losses, company expansions, and mergers.

Example 1

Bill Tennyson paid a total of $3,738.43 for 75 shares of Watson Parcel Service.
He sold the stock for $51.50 a share and paid a sales commission of $39.45.
What is the profit or loss from the sale?

STEP 1: Find the net sale.
Amount of Sale − Commission
($51.50 × 75) − $39.45
$3,862.50 − $39.45 = $3,823.05 net sale

STEP 2: Is net sale greater than total paid?
Yes, $3,823.05 is greater than $3,738.43.

STEP 3: Find the profit.
Net Sale − Total Paid
$3,823.05 − $3,738.43 = **$84.62 profit**

51.5 × 75 =

3862.5 − 39.45 = 3823.05 − 3738.43 = 84.62

2 TEACH

Tell students that stocks are bought and sold through a person called a *broker*. A broker executes a buy or sell order through his or her brokerage firm. The brokerage firm must be a member of a stock exchange to buy or sell stocks. A stock exchange, such as the New York Stock Exchange, does not buy or sell stocks; it is simply a marketplace where the brokerage firms can buy and sell stocks.

Motivating the Lesson

You buy 100 shares of an international telecommunications stock for $1,400.00. Later you sell the stock for $17.00 per share. You pay a commission of $9.99. What is your profit or loss on the sale? **$290.01 profit**

In-Class Examples

1. Paid a total of $17,885.00 for 500 shares of stock and sold the stock at $42.00 per share. Paid a sales commission of $19.99. What is the profit or loss? **$3,095.01 profit**
2. Bought 270 shares for a total of $8,802.00 and sold at $27.85 per share. Paid a commission of $39.95. What is the profit or loss? **$1,322.45 loss**
3. Bought 700 shares of stock and paid a total of $12,110 and sold at $22.49 per share. Commission of $49.95. What is the profit or loss? **$3,583.05 profit**

CONCEPT CHECK

SELF-CHECK ✓

Complete the problems, then check your answers at the end of the chapter.
Find the profit or loss.

1. Paid $1,829 for 40 shares of stock. ($61.50 × 40) − $35.50;
Sold for $61.50 per share. $2,460.00 − $35.50 = $2,424.50
Commission of $35.50. $2,424.50 − $1,829.00 = $595.50 profit

2. Paid $24,000 for 1,000 shares of stock. ($22.50 × 1,000) − $49.95;
Sold for $22.50 per share. $22,500.00 − $49.95 =
Commission of $49.95. $22,450.05 net sale
$24,000.00 − $22,450.05 =
$1,549.95 loss

SECTION 12-5 PRACTICE

3. a. $7,170
b. $1,970 profit
4. a. $11,950
b. $1,950 profit
5. a. $6,480
b. $280 loss
6. a. $1,560
b. $150 loss

	Stock	Total Paid	Selling Price per Share	×	Number of Shares	−	Commission	=	Net Sale	Profit or Loss
3.	Sargent Inc.	$ 5,200	$72.00	×	100	−	$30.00	=	a.	b.
4.	Putman Co.	10,000	30.00	×	400	−	50.00	=	a.	b.
5.	Western Packing	6,760	32.50	×	200	−	20.00	=	a.	b.
6.	St. Clair Land	1,710	10.50	×	150	−	15.00	=	a.	b.

7. Garlan and Kesia Green.
Bought 180 shares of stock.
Paid a total of $4,512.
Sold at $30 per share.
Paid a $40 sales commission.
What was the profit or loss?
$848 profit

8. Jasmine and Eric Walton.
Bought 280 shares of stock.
Paid a total of $9,788.50.
Sold at $23.00 per share.
Paid a $60.00 sales commission.
What was the profit or loss?
$3,408.50 loss

Continued on next page

TECHNOLOGY POWER

While most companies use their Internet sites to show off products, the fashion design store Prada has invested heavily in a system that uses the Internet to boost customer service. Sales associates are equipped with a "staff device," a handheld computer that accesses information stored on the Web. The machine can scan tags on garments so the salesperson can access the item in different colors or fabrics and find accessories. The "staff device" also controls video monitors located throughout the store, where salespeople can call up original designer sketches of the garment. All the information is stored on the Web so the customer can visit the Web site from home to review items that were tried on, get opinions from others, and make a purchase.

3 ASSESS

Error Analysis

Be sure students understand the basic concepts taught in this lesson. Remind students that when selling stock, it is possible to lose money as well as to make a profit. Review how to compute Net Sale. **(Net Sale = Amount of Sale – Commission)** Emphasize the importance of comparing the net sale to the total paid for the stock. If the net sale is *greater* than the total paid, then the seller has made a profit. However, if the net sale is *less* than the total paid, then the seller has lost money on the transaction. Have students review their work for computational errors.

4 CLOSE

Closing Activity

1. ($21.50 × 900) – $69.00
   $19,281

2. $47.70 × 175) – $19.99
   $8,327.51

3. Bought 2,000 shares of a stock for a total of $123,500. Sold at $65.90 per share. Paid a commission of $60 for each transaction. What is the profit or loss? **$8,300 profit**

4. Janet and Russell Siegel bought 600 shares of a stock. They paid $15.40 per share. They sold the stock for $14.23 per share. Their sales commission was $19.99 for each transaction. What was their profit or loss? **$702 loss**

5. Ahmed Patel bought 3,000 shares of stock for a total of $48,000. He sold the stock at $14.60 per share. He paid a sales commission of $0.03 per share for each transaction. What was his profit or loss from the sale? **$4,200 loss**

---

11. $73,000.00 +
   ($49.95 + $40.00)
   = $73,089.95
   $96,500.00 –
   ($49.95 + $40.00)
   = $96,410.05
   Net amount of sale:
   $96,410.05
   Profit: $23,320.10

12. $33,660.00 +
   ($40.00 + $24.00)
   = $33,664.00
   $31,200.00 –
   ($30.00 + $36.00)
   = $31,134.00
   Net amount of sale:
   $31,134.00
   Loss: $2,530.00

13. $2,430.00 + $48.60 =
   $2,478.60
   $5,670.00 – $170.10
   = $5,499.90
   Profit: $3,021.30

> **Need Help? Go to...**
> ► Skill 1: Numbers, page 727
> ► Skill 6: Subtracting Decimals, page 733
> ► Skill 8: Multiplying Decimals, page 735

408 ◄ Chapter 12 Investments

---

9. Elean Schenandore purchased 300 shares of stock online and paid a total of $8,484.95. She sold the stock at $39.94 per share and paid a $39.95 sales commission. What was the net amount of the sale? What was the profit or loss from the sale? **$11,942.05 sale; $3,457.10 profit**

10. Bruce and Shelita Maron own 850 shares of a pizza chain's stock. They originally paid $28.75 per share for the stock. They needed cash so they sold at the current price of $23.40 per share. Their sales commission was $14.95 for each transaction. What was the profit or loss? **$24,437.50 + $14.95 = $24,452.45; $19,890.00 – $14.95 = $19,875.05; Loss: $4,577.40**

11. Alfredo Gutierrez bought 2,000 shares of a phone company's stock at $36.50 a share. He sold his stock at $48.25 per share. Each transaction paid a sales commission of $49.95 plus $0.02 per share. What was the net amount of the sale? What was the profit or loss from the sale?

12. Enrico and Eve Marcucci bought 1,200 shares of a paint store's stock at $28 per share and paid a sales commission of $40 plus $0.02 per share. They sold the stock at $26 per share plus a sales commission of $30 plus $0.03 per share. What was the net amount of the sale? What was the profit or loss from the sale?

13. Tony Sanchez owned 180 shares of an architecture company's stock, for which he paid $13.50 per share plus a 2 percent commission on the principal. He sold at $31.50 and paid a 3 percent sales commission on the principal. What was the profit or loss from the sale?

14. The Montvilles purchased 150 shares of Allen Pharmaceuticals stock at $34.00. A year later they bought an additional 300 shares at $38.75. They paid a commission of $29.95 on each transaction. A year later they sold the original 150 shares plus 100 shares from the second purchase of 300 shares at $46.71. They paid a sales commission of $40.00 when they sold the stock. What was the profit or loss from the sale of the 250 shares?

Stock:	Shares	Cost/Share	Cost of Stock	Commission	Total Cost
Allen	150	$34.00	**$5,100.00**	$29.95	**$5,129.95**
	300	$38.75	**$11,625.00**	$29.95	**$11,654.95**
	100 shares = 1/3 cost of 300 =				**$3,884.98**
			Cost of 250 Shares =		**$9,014.93**
Sales					
Allen	250	$46.71	**$11,677.50**	$40.00	**$11,677.50**
			Profit	Total	**$2,622.57**

MAINTAINING YOUR SKILLS

Which number is greater?

15. 381 or 381.6 **381.6**

16. $21.19 or $21.91 **$21.91**

17. $219.84 or $218.94 **$219.84**

Subtract.

18. 88.35 – 81.15 **7.2**

19. 53.83 – 38.91 **14.92**

20. $8,244.50 – $3,398.49 **$4,846.01**

Multiply.

21. 471.2 × 0.035 **16.492**

22. 100 × 3.141 **314.1**

23. 15.058 × 7.2 **108.4176**

BUSINESS NOTES

Investment Clubs

One inexpensive and informative way to invest in stocks is to join an investment club. For perhaps $25 a month, about a dozen club members research stocks, choose purchases, and pool their money to make purchases. Some investment clubs have done remarkably well. Ask students to research investment clubs in your state. **LS** , **CL** , **P**

WRAP-UP

Go over any problem for which a wrong answer is given.

Assignment Guide
   Basic: 3–6
   Average: 7–10

20 min.

SECTION (12·6) Bonds

○ **Section Objective**

Compute the annual interest and annual yield of a bond investment.

Many corporations and governments raise money by issuing **bonds.** The bond is a written pledge that you'll be repaid your specified amount of money plus interest. Unlike stocks, when you invest in a bond, you don't become a part owner of the corporation. Instead, bonds lend money to the corporation or government. In return for the loan, the corporation or government pays you interest.

Eventually a bond "matures." This means that you get your money back after a certain amount of time passes. Maturity dates range from 10 to 30 years, and interest is paid every 6 months. What influences the value of your bond? Two things: (1) how long you keep the bond (despite its maturity date) and (2) when the corporation or government pays interest (it may not be every 6 months). When you redeem your bond, you'll receive the amount printed on the bond. The cost of a bond is usually a percent of the value. A bond price of 90 on a $1,000 bond means that the bond sells for 90 percent of $1,000 (or $900). The interest that you receive from a bond is calculated on its face value. Here's another way to remember all of this:

Important Questions to Ask Yourself	What Formula Do I Use?
How do I calculate the **bond cost**?	Bond Cost = Face Value × Percent
How do I find the **annual interest**?	Annual Interest = Face Value × Interest Rate
How do I find the **annual yield** on a bond?	Annual Yield = $\frac{\text{Annual Interest}}{\text{Bond Cost}}$

Living in the Real World

Life after Working Shifts

In Whose Best Interest? Doucette is utterly confused now that she has all these investment options. CDs. Stocks. And now bonds. If she buys bonds from a corporation, it has to repay her in the future (unlike if she were a stockholder). Companies are required to pay interest on bonds (unlike if she were a stockholder).

Draw Conclusions Do you think bonds are less risky than stocks? Justify your answer.

Continued on page 413

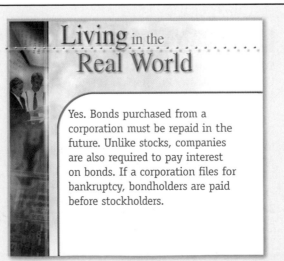

Living in the Real World

Yes. Bonds purchased from a corporation must be repaid in the future. Unlike stocks, companies are also required to pay interest on bonds. If a corporation files for bankruptcy, bondholders are paid before stockholders.

National Standards for Business Education

Standard 1	Mathematical Foundations
Standard 2	Number Relationships and Operations
Standard 5	Statistics and Probability

National Council of Teachers of Mathematics Standards

Standard 1	Numbers and Operations
Standard 4	Measurement
Standard 6	Problem Solving
Standard 8	Communication
Standard 9	Connections

(1) FOCUS

Some students may be familiar with U.S. government bonds, and you can use these types of bonds to initiate the discussion of this lesson. Students should understand that even the United States government borrows money to pay its bills by issuing bonds. In this lesson, the focus is on computing the cost of a bond, along with the annual interest and annual yield of a bond investment.

In-Class Examples

Work through these exercises with students before having them do the Self-Check.
Change to decimals.

1. $\frac{1}{2}$ **0.5**
2. $\frac{5}{8}$ **0.625**

Calculate.

3. $95\frac{1}{2}\% \times \$1,000$ **$955**

2 TEACH

Work through the examples step by step with students. Discuss the meaning of *face value* of a bond. Ask students why a person would want to buy bonds rather than putting the money in a bank savings account. **(He or she could earn more interest.)** Point out to students that cities can also sell bonds, which are used to finance city projects, including the building of new schools.

Motivating the Lesson
You have the opportunity to buy a $1,000.00 bond. The bond pays 6.25 percent annual interest. If you purchase the bond, how much annual interest will you earn?
$62.50

In-Class Examples
1. Jamal Walker purchased a $5,000.00 bond at the quoted price of 96.25. The bond paid annual interest of $5\frac{7}{8}$ percent. What is the annual yield rounded to the nearest hundredth of a percent? **6.1%**
2. A $10,000 bond at 91.13. Pays $7\frac{3}{4}$ percent interest.
   a. What is the annual interest? **$775.00**
   b. What is the cost of the bond? **$9,113.00**
3. A $1,000 bond at 87.25. Pays 9.15 percent interest.
   a. What is the annual interest? **$91.50**
   b. What is the cost of the bond? **$872.50**

George Vanderhill purchased a $1,000 bond at the quoted price of $89\frac{1}{2}$. The bond paid interest at a rate of 6 percent. Find the interest, the cost of the bond, and the annual yield.

STEP 1: Find the annual interest.
Face Value × Interest Rate
$1,000.00 × 6% = **$60.00 interest**

STEP 2: Find the bond cost.
Face Value × Percent
$1,000.00 × $89\frac{1}{2}$% = **$895.00 bond cost**

STEP 3: Find the annual yield.
$$\frac{\text{Annual Interest}}{\text{Bond Cost}}$$
$$\frac{\$65}{\$895} = 0.072625 \text{ or } 7.26\% \text{ annual yield}$$

CONCEPT CHECK

SELF-CHECK ✓

Complete the problems, then check your answers at the end of the chapter.
Find the interest and the cost of the bond.
1. Interest: $1,000 × 6% = $60.00; Cost: $1,000 × 0.805 = $805
1. One thousand dollar bond at $80\frac{1}{2}$. Pays 6 percent interest.

2. Ten thousand dollar bond at 92. Pays $7\frac{1}{4}$ percent interest.
Interest: $10,000 × 0.0725 = $725.00; Cost: $10,000 × 0.92 = $9,200
Find the annual yield.

3. Annual interest is $60.
Cost is $805.
Annual yield = $60 ÷ $805 = 0.074534 or 7.45%

4. Annual interest is $725.
Cost is $9,200.
Annual yield = $725 ÷ $9,200 = 0.0788 or 7.88%

SECTION 12-6 PRACTICE

Find the bond cost and annual yield.

Source	Face Value of Bond	Quoted Price	Cost of Bond	Interest Rate	Annual Interest	Annual Yield
5. Galvin Controls	$10,000	$70\frac{1}{4}$	a. $7,025	8.0%	b. $800	c. 11.39%
6. Johnson Fruit Farms	1,000	96	a. $960	6.4%	b. $64	c. 6.67%
7. Geiser Interiors	10,000	104	a. $10,400	7.9%	b. $790	c. 7.60%
8. Eleven Cord Embroidery	5,000	$104\frac{3}{8}$	a. $5,218.75	7.8%	b. $390	c. 7.47%

GLOBAL PERSPECTIVE

Stock Markets
United States stockbrokers sometimes buy and sell stock in the middle of the night in order to do business as soon as Japanese markets open each day. Suggest that students consult the business section of the local newspapers to find the Japanese and London equivalents of the Dow Jones Industrial average. **(Nikkei 225; FTSE 100, often called "Footsy.")** Have students find out the time differences between the three countries.

9. Celinda Vasquez.
   Purchased a $10,000 bond at $99\frac{1}{2}$.
   Pays 7 percent annual interest.

   $700   **a.** What is the annual interest?

   $9,950   **b.** What was the cost of the bond?

   7.04%   **c.** What is the annual yield?

10. Giuseppe Caviness.
    Purchased a $10,000 bond at 102.
    Pays 9 percent annual interest.

    a. What is the annual interest?   **$900**

    b. What was the cost of the bond?

    c. What is the annual yield?
         b. **$10,200;** c. **8.82%**

11. Sandy and Morry Doran purchased a $50,000 bond at a quoted price of $94\frac{3}{8}$. The bond pays annual interest at a rate of 3 percent. What is the annual interest earned? What was the cost of the bond? What is the annual yield?
    $1,500, $47,187.50, 3.18%

12. The Sonoma Housing Authority is offering $5,000 bonds that pay 7.4 percent annual interest. The quoted price of each bond is 92.125. Rollin Kowalski purchased 8 bonds through a broker who charges a 1.75 percent sales commission. What is the total cost of his purchase? What total interest will he earn yearly? What is the annual yield?
    $37,494.88 total purchase; $2,960.00 total interest; 7.89% yield

13. Many newspapers give up-to-date bond information in the financial section. In the hypothetical listing shown, the name of the corporation is given, then the annual interest rate the bond is paying, the year the bond matures, and so on. In the third column "M," the number "13" means the bond matures in the year 2013.

    Alex Wosick purchased six $5,000 bonds of the ITB Corporation at the closing price for the day. He had to pay a broker's commission of 2.25 percent. What was the total cost of his purchase? What will be his total yearly earnings? In what year will his bond mature?

New York Bonds						
Bond	Rate	M	Cur Yld	Vol	Close	Net Chg
ITB	$7\frac{1}{4}$	13	6.8	15	$110\frac{1}{4}$	$-1\frac{3}{4}$
NJ Tel	6.7	23	6.9	30	$97\frac{3}{4}$	$+\frac{5}{8}$

$33,819.19 total purchase; $2,175.00 yearly earnings; 2013 bond matures

---

MAINTAINING YOUR SKILLS

Need Help? Go to...

► Skill 30: **Finding the Percentage,** page 757

► Skill 11: **Dividing Decimals,** page 738

Find the percentage.

14. $6\frac{1}{2}$% of $700   **$45.50**

15. $93\frac{1}{4}$% of $15,000   **$13,987.50**

16. $\frac{1}{2}$% of 40   **0.2**

17. 120% of 900   **1,080**

18. $15\frac{1}{4}$% of 350   **53.375**

19. 110% of 940   **1,034**

Divide. Round answers to the nearest hundredth.

20. $2.22\overline{)56.80}$ **25.59**

21. $19.4\overline{)608}$ **31.34**

22. $0.004\overline{)96.28}$ **24,070**

THINKING CRITICALLY

Stocks and Bonds
Emphasize the difference between stocks and bonds. With stocks you're a part owner of the company; with bonds you're lending the company money. Stock prices are per share; bond prices are given as a percent of the face value. What would a $30,000 bond at 105 percent sell for? **($31,500)** Why would anyone pay a premium of $31,500 (over 100 percent) for a bond with a face value of $30,000? **High return.**

WRAP-UP

Go over any problem for which a wrong answer is given.

Assignment Guide
   Basic: 5–8
   Average: 9–11

20 min.

⓷ ASSESS

Error Analysis
If students are making errors that are not computational mistakes, they may need to review the three formulas for finding the *annual interest,* the *bond cost,* and the *annual yield.*

Be sure students understand that the *annual interest* is based on the *face value* of the bond (not the bond cost). The interest is $50.

The *bond cost* is also based on the *face value* of the bond. For instance, if a bond with a face value of $1,000 costs 95 percent, compute the bond cost by multiplying the face value ($1,000) by the percent (0.95), which is $950. If a $1,000 bond costs 102 percent, then multiply the face value ($1,000) by 1.02 which is $1,020.

The *annual yield,* however, is based on the *bond cost* (not the face value). This means that if a $1,000 bond costs $950, compute the annual yield by dividing the *annual interest* by the *bond cost* ($50 ÷ $950, which is 5.26 percent).

Students may find it helpful to write each of the three formulas for *annual interest, bond cost,* and *annual yield* on separate 3" by 5" note cards. They can then refer to these note cards as they work through the problems in this lesson.

⓸ CLOSE

Closing Activity
1. $10,000 × 6.75% **$675**
2. $675 ÷ $9,000 **0.075**
3. A $5,000 bond at 97.13. Pays $4\frac{1}{4}$% interest.
   a. What is the annual interest? **$212.50**
   b. What is the cost of the bond? **$4,856.50**

Quick Quiz

For Problems 1–2, use the Amount of $1.00 Invested—Daily, Monthly, and Quarterly Compounding table on page 800.

1. Purchased $7,000 at 4.75 percent for 4 years compounded daily or 4 years compounded quarterly. What is the amount of the CD at each rate of maturity? What is the difference in the interest rate? **$8,464.64 daily; $8,455.28 quarterly; a difference of $9.37**

2. Daryll Warner can invest $11,000 at either 4 percent compounded daily for 1 year or 4.25 percent compounded monthly for 1 year. What is the effective annual yield on each investment? Based on effective annual yield, which is the better deal? **4% compounded daily has an effective annual yield of 4.081%; 4.25% compounded monthly has an effective annual yield of 4.334 percent. The better investment is 4.25 percent compounded monthly.**

3. Purchased 1,700 shares at $26.57 per share. Online broker charges $29.95 for fewer than 1,000 shares or $0.03 per share for 1,000 or more shares. What is the cost of the stock? **($45,169)** What is the total paid? **$45,220**

4. Masahiko Takamiya owns 1,200 shares of a stock. The high and low prices for the year were $40.20 and $28.50. Dividends are $2.50 per share.
    a. What is his total annual dividend? **$3,000**
    b. What is the annual yield based on the high? **6.22%**

SECTION 12-1   **CONCEPT CHECK** (p. 395)

1. $8,000 × 1.040604 = $8,324.83, $8,324.83 − $8,000 = **$324.83**
2. $50,000 × 1.233659 = $61,682.95; $61,682.95 − $50,000 = **$11,682.95**
3. $1,000 × 1.046025 = $1,046.025; $1,046.03 − $1,000 = $46.03
    $1,000 × 1.045765 = $1,045.765; $1,045.77 − $1,000 = $45.77
    $46.03 − $45.77 = **$0.26**
4. $40,000 × 1.220895 = $48,835.80; $48,835.80 − $40,000 = $8,835.80
    $40,000 × 1.219890 = $48,795.60; $48,795.60 − $40,000 = $8,795.60
    $8,835.80 − $8,795.60 = **$40.20**

SECTION 12-2   **CONCEPT CHECK** (p. 398)

1. ($10,000 × 1.059040) − $10,000; $10,590.40 − $10,000 = $590.40
    ($590.40 ÷ $10,000) = **0.05904 or 5.904%**
2. ($25,000 × 1.050945) − $25,000; $26,273.63 − $25,000 = $1,273.63
    ($1,273.63 ÷ $25,000) = **0.050945 or 5.0945%**
3. Find the interest for 1 year and the annual yield.
    Daily: ($20,000 × 1.035618) − $20,000; $20,712.36 − $20,000.00 = $712.36
    Yield: $712.36 ÷ $20,000.00 = 0.035618 or 3.562%
    Monthly: ($20,000 × 1.038151) − $20,000; $20,763.02 − $20,000.00 = $763.02
    Yield: $763.02 ÷ $20,000.00 = 0.038151 or 3.82%
    The better investment is 3.75 percent monthly.
4. Quarterly: ($20,000.00 × 1.045765) − $20,000; $20,915.30 − $20,000.00 = $915.30
    Yield: $915.30 ÷ $20,000.00 = 0.045765 or 4.577%
    Monthly: ($20,000.00 × 1.043338) − $20,000; $20,866.76 − $20,000.00 = $866.76
    Yield: $866.76 ÷ $20,000.00 = 0. 043338 or 4.334%
    The better investment is 4.5 percent quarterly.

SECTION 12-3   **CONCEPT CHECK** (p. 401)

1. 150 × $36.21 = $5,431.50 + $29.95 = **$5,461.45**
2. 400 × $58.80 = $23,520.00 + $19.95 = **$23,539.95**

SECTION 12-4   **CONCEPT CHECK** (p. 404)

1. 180 × $1.23 = **$221.40**, $1.23 ÷ $41 = **0.03 or 3%**
2. $1.34 ÷ $49.88 = **0.02686 or 2.69%**; $1.34 ÷ $32.64 = **0.04105 or 4.11%**

SECTION 12-5   **CONCEPT CHECK** (p. 407)

1. ($61.50 × 40) − $35.50; $2,460.00 − $35.50 = $2,424.50
    $2,424.50 − $1,829.00 = **$595.50 profit**
2. ($22.50 × 1,000) − $49.95; $22,500.00 − $49.95 = $22,450.05 net sale
    $24,000.00 − $22,450.05= **$1,549.95 loss**

SECTION 12-6   **CONCEPT CHECK** (p. 410)

1. Interest: $1,000 × 6% = **$60.00;** Cost: $1,000 × 0.805 = **$805**
2. Interest: $10,000 × 0.0725 = **$725.00;** Cost: $10,000 × 0.92 = **$9,200**
3. Annual yield = $60 ÷ $805 = **0.074534 or 7.45%**
4. Annual yield = $725 ÷ $9,200 = **0.0788 or 7.88%**

Living in the Real World

Life after Working Shifts

Deciding to Spend or Invest Whether you're a saver or a spender, it's part of your personality. Being a saver or a spender isn't good or bad on its own, but either personality can cause problems if not managed properly. Here's a chance to test your financial personality.

Pretend someone gave you $200, what would you do with it? Read the options below and choose three.

_____ Take my closest friend out to eat and to the movies. (5 points)

_____ Spend $50 on fun items and save the rest. (3 points)

_____ Put the money toward my next vehicle payment. (1 point)

_____ Buy new clothes for school. (3 points)

_____ Hit the nearest music store and buy several CDs. (5 points)

_____ Buy a portable CD player. (3 points)

_____ Get a cell phone. (5 points)

_____ Buy a savings bond. (1 point)

_____ Put it in a savings account for future education. (1 point)

_____ Buy the hottest new concert tickets. (5 points)

What do your choices say about you?

Big Saver: If you scored 3–5 points, you're willing to give up things today so you can buy something you want more tomorrow.

Middle of the Roader: If you scored 7–11 points, you know how to use your money for current needs while keeping an eye on the future.

Big Spender: If you scored 13–15 points, wow . . . do you like to spend money!

REVIEW OF KEY WORDS

certificate of deposit (p. 394)
annual yield (p. 397)
stocks (p. 400)

stock certificate (p. 400)
dividend (p. 403)
profit (p. 406)

loss (p. 406)
bonds (p. 409)

For Problems 1–8, write your own definitions for the terms above.

1–8. Definitions will vary. Evaluate based on the students' understanding of the term and their ability to put the definition into their own words.

---

c. What is the annual yield based on the low? **8.77%**

5. Lupe Gomez bought 250 shares of stock for a total of $3,825. She sold the stock at $18 per share. Gomez paid a commission of $14.95 for each transaction. What is her profit or loss from the sale? **$675 profit**

6. Tim Brooks purchased a $1,000 bond at 97.38. The bond pays 6.5 percent annual interest.
   a. What is the annual interest? **$61.25**
   b. What was the cost of the bond? **$973.80**
   c. What is the annual yield? Round to the nearest hundredth percent. **6.29%**

Living in the Real World

Answers will vary. Make sure students are diligent about checking their chosen stock each day. Students will need to compare and contrast the value of the stock from beginning to end and in relation to other students' stocks.

CHAPTER Study Guide and Assessment

12

Skills and Concepts

SECTION OBJECTIVE 12-1 AND EXAMPLES

Use tables to compute the interest on certificates of deposit.

Celine Hocking invests $3,500 in a 1-year certificate of deposit that earns interest at an annual rate of 4.5 percent compounded quarterly. How much interest will she earn at the end of 1 year?

STEP 1: Find the amount.

Original Principal × Amount per $1.00

$3,500 × 1.045765 = $3,660.18 amount

STEP 2: Find the interest earned.

Amount − Original Principal

$3,660.18 − $3,500.00 = $160.18 interest earned

REVIEW EXERCISES

Use the Amount of $1.00 Invested—Daily, Monthly, and Quarterly Compounding table on page 800 to find the amount per $1.00 invested.

9. a. 1.030416
   b. $6,697.70
   c. $197.70
10. a. 1.161825
   b. $11,618.25
   c. $1,618.25
11. a. 1.053899
   b. $3,688.65
   c. $188.65
12. a. 1.053899
   b. $3,688.65
   c. $188.65
13. a. 1.172579
   b. $41,040.27
   c. $6,040.27

	Annual Rate	Interest Period	Original Principal	Amount per $1.00	Amount	Interest Earned
9.	3.00%	1 year; monthly	$ 6,500	a.	b.	c.
10.	3.75%	4 years; daily	10,000	a.	b.	c.
11.	5.25%	1 year; daily	3,500	a.	b.	c.
12.	4.25%	4 years; monthly	90,000	a.	b.	c.
13.	4.00%	4 years; quarterly	35,000	a.	b.	c.

SECTION OBJECTIVE 12-2 AND EXAMPLES

Determine the effective annual yield.

Andy Eyre invested $3,000 in a CD for 1 year. The certificate earns interest at an annual rate of 5.00 percent compounded monthly. What is the effective annual yield rounded to the nearest thousandth of a percent?

STEP 1: Find the interest for 1 year. (Refer to the Amount of $1.00 Invested—Daily, Monthly, and Quarterly Compounding table on page 800.)

$3,000 × 1.051162 = $3,153.49

Amount − Principal

$3,153.49 − $3,000.00 = $153.49 interest for 1 year

REINFORCEMENT

Section 12-1

Use the Amount of $1.00 Invested—Daily, Monthly, and Quarterly Compounding table on page 800 to compute interest for the problems.

1. Invested $25,000 at 7.75 percent for 1 year compounded daily or 1 year compounded monthly. Find the difference in the amount of interest for each investment. **$6.50**

2. Invested $12,000 at 5.25 percent for 4 years compounded daily or 4 years compounded quarterly. What is the amount of the CD at each rate of maturity? **($14,803.91 daily; $14,783.93 quarterly)** What is the difference in the interest earned? **a difference of $19.98**

STEP 2: Find the effective annual yield.

$$\frac{\text{Interest for 1 Year}}{\text{Principal}}$$

$$\frac{\$153.49}{\$3,000.00} = 0.05116 \text{ or } 5.116\% \text{ effective annual yield}$$

REVIEW EXERCISES

Use the Amount of $1.00 Invested—Daily, Monthly, and Quarterly
Compounding table on page 800 to find the amount per $1.00 invested.

	Annual Rate	Interest Period	Original Principal	Amount per $1.00	Amount	Interest Earned	Effective Annual Yield
14.	7.25%	1 year; monthly	$ 8,500	a.	b.	c.	d. 7.496%
15.	8.00%	1 year; quarterly	4,500	a.	b.	c.	d. 8.243%
16.	8.75%	4 years; daily	15,000	a.	b.	c.	d. 9.143%
17.	9.00%	4 years; quarterly	25,500	a.	b.	c.	d. 9.381%
18.	7.75%	1 year; daily	2,300	a.	b.	c.	d. 8.057%
19.	9.25%	1 year; monthly	10,000	a.	b.	c.	d. 9.652%

14. a. 1.074958
    b. $9,137.14
    c. $637.14
15. a. 1.082432
    b. $4,870.94
    c. $370.94
16. a. 1.419008
    b. $21,285.12
    c. $6,285.12
17. a. 1.427621
    b. $36,404.33
    c. $10,904.33
18. a. 1.080573
    b. $2,485.32
    c. $185.32
19. a. 1.096524
    b. $10,965.24
    c. $965.24

SECTION OBJECTIVE 12-3 AND EXAMPLES

Solve for the total cost of a stock investment.

Derek Abreu purchased 200 shares of stock at $35.11 per share. His full-service
stockbroker charged a $50.00 commission for the transaction. What is the total
amount he paid for the stock?

STEP 1: Find the cost of a stock.

Number of Shares × Cost per Share

200　　　×　　$35.11　　= $7,022.00

STEP 2: Find the total paid.

Cost of Stock + Commission

$7,022.00 + $50.00 = $7,072.00 total paid

20. a. $59,140
    b. $59,147
21. a. $7,318.50
    b. $7,368.50
22. a. $2,931.50
    b. $2,955.49
23. a. $135,907
    b. $135,946.50
24. a. $41,454.50
    b. $41,466
25. a. $120,020
    b. $120,042

REVIEW EXERCISES

	Company	Number of Shares	Cost per Share	Cost of Stock	Commission	Total Paid
20.	Forestry Inc.	1,000	$59.14	a.	$ 7.00	b.
21.	Safety Lmt.	150	48.79	a.	50.00	b.
22.	Ross Bank	55	53.30	a.	12.99	b.
23.	Cantwell Co.	2,300	59.09	a.	39.50	b.
24.	Ott & Assoc.	850	48.77	a.	11.50	b.
25.	GIS Mapping	2,000	60.01	a.	22.00	b.

REINFORCEMENT

Section 12-2

In Problems 1 and 2, round effective annual yield to the nearest hundredth of a percent.

1. Derek Carter can invest $20,000 at either 4.5 percent compounded daily for 1 year
    or 4.75 percent compounded monthly for 1 year. Based on an effective annual yield,
    which is the better investment? **4.75% compounded monthly is the better investment.**

Section 12-3

1. Purchased 500 shares at $51.14 per share. Broker fee is $30.00 for fewer than 1,000
    shares or $0.02 per share for 1,000 or more shares.
    a. What is the cost of the stock? **$25,570**
    b. What is the total paid? **$25,600**

SECTION OBJECTIVE 12-4 AND EXAMPLES

Compute the annual yield and annual dividend of a stock investment.

Patty Slade bought 250 shares of Pine Nursery stock at $32.57 per share. The company paid annual dividends of $1.12 per share. What is the total annual dividend? What is the annual yield to the nearest hundredth of a percent?

26. $0.52 × 50 = $26 annual dividend; $0.52 ÷ $38.00 = 0.01368 or 1.37% annual yield

STEP 1: Find the annual dividend.

Annual Dividend per Share × Number of Shares
$1.12   ×   250   = **$280 annual dividend**

STEP 2: Find the annual yield.

Annual Dividend per Share ÷ Cost per Share
$1.12   ÷ $32.57   = **0.034387 or 3.44% annual yield**

REVIEW EXERCISES

26. Julian Lopez bought 50 shares of stock at $38.00 per share. The company paid annual dividends of $0.52 per share. What is the total annual dividend? What is the annual yield to the nearest hundredth of a percent?

27. Rose Wallace owns 200 shares of stock. The stock ranged from a low of $44.45 to a high of $54.54 last year. The annual dividend is $2.31 per share. What is the annual yield based on the high and the low? What is the total annual dividend?

	Stock	Annual Dividend per Share	Cost per Share	Annual Yield
28.	Stone Products	$0.60	$ 38.00	1.579%
29.	OFA Education	1.40	57.36	2.441%
30.	Lazenby Inc.	1.36	34.86	3.901%
31.	Cornell Supply	2.48	121.93	2.034%

SECTION OBJECTIVE 12-5 AND EXAMPLES

Calculate the profit or loss from a stock sale.

Frank Walden paid a total of $3,066.54 for 88 shares of stock. He sold the stock for $57.10 per share and paid a sales commission of $49.50. What is the profit or loss from the sale?

STEP 1: Find the net sale.

Amount of Sale   −   Commission
($57.10 × 88)   − $49.50
$5,024.80   − $49.50   = $4,975.30

STEP 2: Is the net sale greater than total paid?

Yes, $4,975.30 is greater than $3,066.54.

STEP 3: Find the profit.

Net Sale   −   Total Paid
$4,975.30   − $3,066.54   = **$1,908.76 profit**

27. Annual yield on high price:

$\frac{\$2.31}{\$54.54} = 0.04235$ or 4.24%

Annual yield based on low price:

$\frac{\$2.31}{\$44.45} = 0.05196$ or 5.20%

Total annual dividend: 200 × $2.31 = $462

REINFORCEMENT

Section 12-4

1. Lionel LeGrand owns 200 shares of stock in a food manufacturer. The stock had a high of $43.95 and a low of $30.00 during the year. The stock paid an annual dividend of $0.52 per share.

  a. What is the annual yield based on the high? **1.18%**

  b. What is the annual yield based on the low? **1.73%**

  c. What is his total annual dividend? **$104**

Section 12-5

1. Bought 375 shares of stock and paid a total of $4,252.50. Sold at $14.90 per share. Paid a commission of $39 for each transaction. What is the profit or loss? **$1,335 profit**

2. Bought 1,000 shares of a company's stock for $45,000. Sold at $46.10 per share. Paid a commission of $79.00 for each transaction. What is the profit or loss? **$1,100 profit**

REVIEW EXERCISES

	Stock	Total Paid	Selling Price per Share	Number of Shares	Commission	Net Sale	Profit or Loss
32.	Tanner Co.	$ 6,787	$26.42	150	$39.95	a.	b.
33.	Maloney Inc.	5,800	39.01	200	45.50	a.	b.
34.	Elden Mfg.	24,000	42.12	600	9.99	a.	b.
35.	S&R Electric	1,800	10.52	50	12.50	a.	b.
36.	PAE Internet	4,800	58.87	100	55.00	a.	b.
37.	Aquailla Imp.	3,250	11.70	250	7.00	a.	b.

38. Carlos and Jade Enrique bought 2,000 shares of stock at $18.80 a share and paid a sales commission of $50.00 plus $0.02 a share. They sold the stock at $21.95 per share plus a sales commission of $45.00 plus $0.03 per share. What was the net amount of the sale? What was the profit or loss from the sale?

32. a. $3,923.05
  b. $2,863.95 loss
33. a. $7,756.50
  b. $1,956.50 profit
34. a. $25,262.01
  b. $1,262.01 profit
35. a. $513.50
  b. $1,286.50 loss
36. a. $5,832
  b. $1,032 profit
37. a. $2,918
  b. $332 loss
38. $43,795.00; $6,105 profit

SECTION OBJECTIVE 12-6 AND EXAMPLES

Compute the annual interest and annual yield of a bond investment.

Graeme Williams purchased a $1,500 bond at the quoted price of $79\frac{3}{4}$. The bond paid interest at a rate of 5 percent. What is the annual yield to the nearest hundredth of a percent?

STEP 1: Find the annual interest.
  Face Value × Interest Rate
    $1,500 × 5% = $75 annual interest

STEP 2: Find the bond cost.
  Face Value × Percent
    $1,500 × 79.75% = $1,196.25 bond cost

STEP 3: Find the annual yield.
  $$\frac{\text{Annual Interest}}{\text{Bond Cost}} = \frac{\$75}{\$1,196.25} = 0.06269 \text{ or } 6.27\% \text{ annual yield}$$

REVIEW EXERCISES
Find the bond cost and annual yield.

	Source	Face Value of Bond	Quoted Price	Cost of Bond	Interest Rate	Annual Interest	Annual Yield
39.	Diamond Co.	$ 3,000	103.50	a.	6.50%	b.	c.
40.	Gable Inc.	1,000	82.90	a.	7.75%	b.	c.
41.	Lawns Inc.	5,000	75.25	a.	8.00%	b.	c.
42.	Bunde Sales	2,000	96.50	a.	5.50%	b.	c.
43.	Locksmith Co.	10,000	101.00	a.	9.00%	b.	c.
44.	Latrell Mfg.	2,500	92.75	a.	11.00%	b.	c.

39. a. $3,105
  b. $195
  c. 6.3%
40. a. $829.00
  b. $77.50
  c. 9.3%
41. a. $3,762.50
  b. $400
  c. 10.6%
42. a. $1,930
  b. $110
  c. 5.7%
43. a. $10,100
  b. $900
  c. 8.9%
44. a. $2,318.75
  b. $275
  c. 11.9%

REINFORCEMENT

Section 12-5 *(cont'd)*
3. Bought 80 shares of stock at $3,544. Sold at $37.24 per share. Paid a commission of $9.99 for each transaction. What is the profit or loss? **$564.80 loss**

Section 12-6
1. A $50,000 bond from Bayview at 103. Pays $9\frac{1}{8}$ percent annual interest.
  a. What is the annual interest? **$4,562.50**
  b. What was the cost of the bond? **$51,500**
  c. What is the annual yield? **9.125%**

1 FOCUS

Math Studio Overview

Students imagine they are a financial planner. They're giving a presentation on investing for retirement at an annual meeting for electrical workers labor union. The speech must persuade younger workers of the importance of saving for retirement. By writing biographies for four electrical workers and creating several charts displaying the outcomes of different saving strategies, the students will learn about the importance of saving for retirement.

Bell Ringer Activity

Write on the board: "Your older sibling has decided that saving for retirement is unnecessary and would rather have more money to spend today. What do you tell him or her about the importance of investing for the future?"

2 TEACH

Cooperative Learning

What would the country's economy be like if there were no stock market? Break students into groups of four and ask them to discuss the ramifications of closing the New York Stock Exchange or the Chicago Stock Exchange. Have two members of each group argue that this would be a good idea; ask the remaining two members to debate the opposite opinion. After 20 minutes of discussion, ask each group to give an oral presentation that outlines the points made by each side.

3 ASSESS

Enrichment

Have students read an article that mentions how to be a smart investor. Ask them to share information about the article with the class.

Investing in Your Future

Retirees draw on their investments to help them meet their cost of living. Retirement investing is investing for the long term. In general, the longer the term of your investment, the more you will have earned when it comes time to retire.

Purpose

Although you know that people who invest for a longer period of time generally earn more, it's important to understand what that actually means in numerical terms. Financial planners must be able to show younger people that it's well worth their while to invest for retirement now, even though it is many years in the future.

Supplies Needed

- Pen
- Paper
- Chart
- Computer or word processor, if available
- Photocopy machine or overhead projector

Your Activity

Step 1: You are a financial planner. You have been asked to give a talk about retirement investment at an annual meeting of electrical workers labor union. You know that the union members represent a wide range of ages, from 19 to 62. You want to convince these younger workers that it's important for them to save now. You decide your talk will be most convincing if you use four of your clients as examples. The people you'll talk about include:

- Diego lives in Hilton Head, South Carolina. He is a 22-year-old caddy

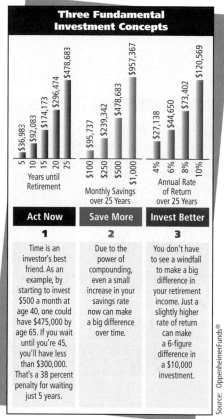

Figure 12.3

NEWSWORTHY TREND

Online Trading

The Internet has had a profound effect on investing in recent years. In its most simple form, the Internet has helped make it much easier to research investment options. But the bigger impact of the Internet on investing has been the invention of online trading.

Online investing began in 1994, as K. Aufhauser & Co., Inc., became the first brokerage firm to offer Internet trading. A glut of other online investment Web sites soon joined the fray, and by 2001 there were roughly 1 million trades being made via the Internet every day. According to Deutsche Bank Securities, 45 percent of all stock trading in 2001 took place online.

at a trendy golf course. He has started saving some of his earning and is putting them into a retirement account known as a 401(k).

- Harry lives in Denver. He is 36 years old and also just started a 401(k). He works as a taxi driver.
- Bena lives in Binghamton, New York. She is a city reporter for her local paper. Bena started saving for retirement with a new 401(k) account. She is 48 years old.
- Comeca lives in Centralia, Illinois, where she has been a daycare worker for most of her life. She is now 65 and ready to retire. She only began saving in a 401(k) ten years ago, when she was 55.

Step 2: Many financial planners can provide a chart that compares how much wealth you can accumulate depending on when you invest. (Use **Figure 12.3** as an example for you to follow in order to create a graph for each client.) Create a graph for impact.

A. Using Figure 12.3, figure out for each client the number of years until retirement. (Note: The retirement age is increasing. For those born before 1959, the retirement age is 65. For those born after 1959, the retirement age will gradually increase to 67; therefore, use that number.)

B. Create three fundamental investment concepts for each client. On your chart, create the three different concepts: Act Now, Save More, and Invest Better. (Note: As in Figure 12.3, assume a fixed rate of return on continuing investment of 8 percent.)

Step 3: With all 12 graphs in front of you (remember that there are 4 clients and each has 3 graphs representing himself or herself), compare how much each client will earn.

Step 4: Create an effective graphic display to use during your presentation.

Step 5: Using the profiles of your four clients as a springboard for your presentation, prepare the rest of your speech. Incorporate references to the chart to show your audience how much more they'll earn if they invest earlier in life. Your talk should be about seven minutes or less.

Critique It

Re-create this table on a separate piece of paper. Use it to review each person's presentation. Be positive and critical at the same time. Remember you'll be critiqued, too!

Speech Qualities	Your Comments on ____'s Presentation
Volume (too soft, hard to hear, easy to hear)	
Pitch (monotone, lively, etc.)	
Tone (cheerful, pleasant, disagreeable, etc.)	
Tempo (spoke too fast, too slow, just right, etc.)	

NEWSWORTHY TREND

Issues on Online Investing

Some advantages of online trading for individuals includes low flat-rate commissions on trades, easy-to-use trading tools, accessibility of trading from remote locations, instant quotes and account summaries, and convenient account access.

The economy has benefited from the growth in online trading because significantly more money has been invested in recent years than ever before.

The steep rise in popularity of online investing has even made after-hours trading a reality. Historically, trades could only be made during the regular business hours of the major stock exchanges. Now, trading can occur at anytime during the day or night, with any personal computer and an online trading account. But after-hours trading is a tricky proposition for most small investors. Many of the advantages of trading during regular business hours—when most of the large institutions are trading—disappear during after-hours trading.

MATH STUDIO

Independent Practice

L1 Have students prepare a graphic that shows different types of investment strategies. Encourage them to be creative and think of images other than pie, bar, or line charts.

L2 Ask students to research the process of becoming a licensed stockbroker, and give an oral report on their findings. Is a college education necessary to become a stockbroker? Which exams must be passed before a person can become a licensed stockbroker?

L3 Ask students to find two articles about investing from a money magazine or book—one that is recent and another that is many years old. Are there any differences in the advice given? Have students write a report comparing and contrasting the two articles.

 **4 CLOSE**

Critique It

Many people count public speaking among their worst fears in life and avoid it at all costs. The best solution to a paralyzing fear of public speaking is simply by practicing. Discuss with students any fears they have about public speaking.

419

PART ③ Business Math

Part Overview

In Part 3, Business Math, students will explore mathematical applications in typical business situations, from figuring out traveler's expenses to purchasing discounts to depreciating items. This part gets students in the "inside" of how a business functions.

Key to Descriptive Icons

The following designations will help you decide which activities are appropriate for your students.

L1   **Level 1** activities should be within the ability range of all students.

L2   **Level 2** activities should be within the ability range of the average to above-average students.

L3   **Level 3** activities are designed for the ability range of above-average students.

ELL   Activities should be within the ability range of the **English Language Learner.**

LS   **Learning Styles** designation represents activities designed to address different learning styles.

CL   **Cooperative Learning** activities are designed for small group work.

P   **Portfolio** designation represents student products that can be placed into a best-work portfolio.

Living in the Real World

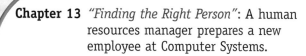

In Part 3 students will read the following stories about applying math in life:

Chapter 13 *"Finding the Right Person"*: A human resources manager prepares a new employee at Computer Systems.

Chapter 14 *"Tracking Tractors"*: An accounting manager meets with an industrial engineer to evaluate the company's productivity.

Chapter 15 *"Restoring Vintage Vehicles"*: A teenager learns how his family's multi-generational owned custom car repair shop stays in business.

Chapter 16 *"Markups in the Enchanted Forest"*: A master gardener and shop owner decides how to sell her inventory.

Chapter 17 *"The Campaign for Dozie D'Oats"*: A market researcher and product developer team up to figure out how to advertise a new cereal.

Chapter 18 *"Auto Do It Right"*: Learn a father-and-son business's approach to their auto parts store.

Chapter 19 *"Just the Write Thing"*: A writer's success drives her looking for new space.

Chapter 20 *"A Well-Sprung Business"*: A medical doctor decides to hire an accountant to help run this practice.

Chapter 21 *"Jojoba Healing"*: An aromatherapy products entrepreneur figures out how to expand her business.

Chapter 22 *"Roundtable Discussion"*: A board of directors meets to discuss the financial future of a steel company.

Chapter 23 *"Vintage Vamp"*: A vintage clothing shop owner contemplates the current sales and the store's future.

Teacher Resources

Incorporating Technology

Do you need a little extra help in the classroom? Take a look at the program resources that might make your life easier. These program resources are correlated to technology standards, with your time and efficiency in mind.

Teacher Program Resources

Technology Standard	Technology Resources				
	Mathematics Online	Interactive Lesson Planner	Exam View Pro Test Generator	Student Activity Workbook, TAE CD-ROM	PowerPoint Presentations
Proficiency in operating equipment	✓			✓	✓
Using technology for research	✓	✓	✓	✓	
Problem solving and collaboration	✓	✓	✓	✓	
Using computers and software to support lessons	✓	✓	✓	✓	✓

Part 3 Intervention and Assessment

Continuing Needs	pp. 422, 456, 484, 516, 550, 580, 608, 632, 656, 680, 704	Student Activity Workbook, Teacher Annotated Edition w/ CD-ROM Mathematics Online www.busmath.glencoe.com Teacher Resource Binder, Blackline Masters Teacher Resource Binder, Lesson Plans Teacher Resource Binder, Internet Resources
Cumulative Test Prep	pp. 454–455, 578–579, 630–631, 724–725	Exam View® Pro Test Generator Assessment Binder, Reproducible Tests Mathematics Online www.busmath.glencoe.com, Quizzes
Open-Ended Assessment	pp. 482–483, 548–549	Assessment Binder, Alternative Assessment Strategies
Chapter Study Guide and Assessment	pp. 443–446, 477–481, 509–515, 541–546, 571–577, 603–607, 625–629, 651–655, 675–679, 699–703	Student Activity Workbook School-to-Home Activity Workbook
Alternative Assessment	pp. 453, 547	Assessment Binder, Alternative Assessment Strategies Teacher Resource Binder, Internet Resources

Introduction

Use Part 3, Business Math, to evaluate how wages reflect inflation. How do you compare wages earned over time? Teach the concept of inflation as it applies to the students' daily life (e.g., part-time jobs, rent/mortgage, and so on.)

Assessment Options

Part 3 Diagnostic Test
See diagnostic tests in the Assessment Binder. Select from the following diagnostic tests on workshops, skills, and applications. Gauge the students' skills on the fundamentals.

PART 3

Business Math

Measure a Dollar

Have you ever wondered where that dollar in your wallet has been? Who else has had it? What did it buy? The U.S. dollar bill has a lifespan of about 18 months. Either it falls apart or the government takes it out of circulation.

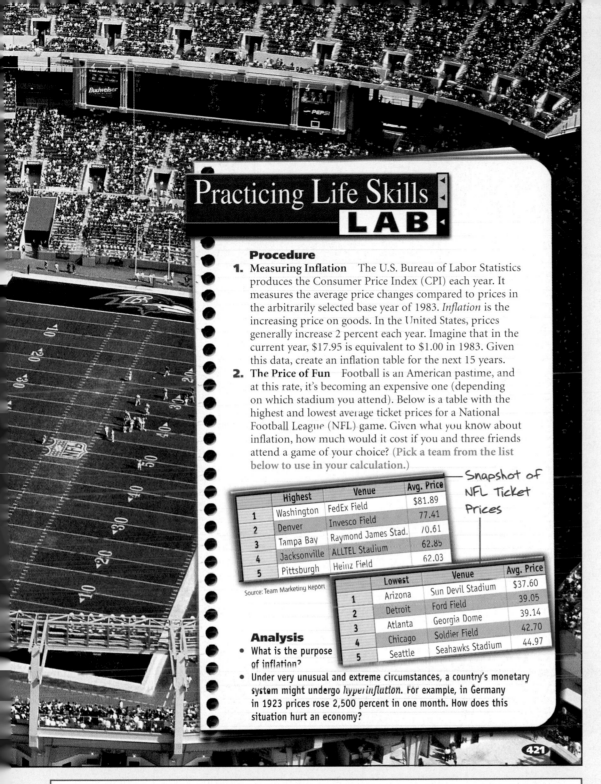

Practicing Life Skills LAB

Procedure

1. Measuring Inflation The U.S. Bureau of Labor Statistics produces the Consumer Price Index (CPI) each year. It measures the average price changes compared to prices in the arbitrarily selected base year of 1983. *Inflation* is the increasing price on goods. In the United States, prices generally increase 2 percent each year. Imagine that in the current year, $17.95 is equivalent to $1.00 in 1983. Given this data, create an inflation table for the next 15 years.

2. The Price of Fun Football is an American pastime, and at this rate, it's becoming an expensive one (depending on which stadium you attend). Below is a table with the highest and lowest average ticket prices for a National Football League (NFL) game. Given what you know about inflation, how much would it cost if you and three friends attend a game of your choice? (Pick a team from the list below to use in your calculation.)

Snapshot of NFL Ticket Prices

	Highest	Venue	Avg. Price
1	Washington	FedEx Field	$81.89
2	Denver	Invesco Field	77.41
3	Tampa Bay	Raymond James Stad.	70.61
4	Jacksonville	ALLTEL Stadium	62.85
5	Pittsburgh	Heinz Field	62.03

Source: Team Marketing Report

	Lowest	Venue	Avg. Price
1	Arizona	Sun Devil Stadium	$37.60
2	Detroit	Ford Field	39.05
3	Atlanta	Georgia Dome	39.14
4	Chicago	Soldier Field	42.70
5	Seattle	Seahawks Stadium	44.97

Analysis

- What is the purpose of inflation?
- Under very unusual and extreme circumstances, a country's monetary system might undergo *hyperinflation*. For example, in Germany in 1923 prices rose 2,500 percent in one month. How does this situation hurt an economy?

421

VOCABULARY BUILDER

Vocabulary Builder
During the next week, ask students to bring in business articles. Have them circle words or concepts that they don't understand. Use the Part 3 Business Math to apply the real-world concepts to mathematics in the course.

Practicing Life Skills LAB

Teaching Suggestion
This activity allows students to apply math to entertainment, such as a professional sporting event. Ask them how long it would take them to pay for a ticket to one of the NFL games? For those students who work, how many hours would they work to pay for the ticket? **Breaking down an item's price into hours worked is a good lesson for budgeting, efficiency with money, and personal finance.**

Analysis Answer
What is the purpose of inflation? **Inflation is the general rise int he level of prices for goods and services over time. It stimulates business and helps wages to rise. In times of inflation, it takes more money to purchase the same amount of goods and services. For example, if the rate of inflation is 5 percent, then a computer that cost $1,000 last year would now cost $1,050.** How does hyperinflation hurt an economy? **Wages go up, producers raise prices again to pay for the higher wages. The situation spirals out of control. It crushes a nation's monetary system; consumers can't afford to buy goods or service; hence, creates a downward spiral of layoffs, closings, and bankruptcy.**

National Standards for Business Education

Section Objectives	1. Mathematical Foundations	2. Number Relationships and Operations	3. Patterns, Functions, and Algebra	4. Measurements	5. Statistics and Probability	6. Problem-Solving Applications
13-1 Hiring New Employees (pp. 424–426) Calculate the cost of recruiting new employees.	X	X				X
13-2 Administering Wages and Salaries (pp. 427–429) Compute the new salary after merit increase and cost-of-living adjustment.	X	X				X
13-3 Employee Benefits (pp. 430–432) Work out the rate of employee benefits based on annual gross pay.	X	X				X
13-4 Disability Insurance (pp. 433–435) Figure out disability benefits under independent retirement systems and under Social Security.	X	X				X
13-5 Workers Compensation and Unemployment Insurance (pp. 436–439) Compute the employer cost for workers compensation and unemployment insurance	X	X				X
13-6 Travel Expense (pp. 440–442) Calculate total business travel expenses.	X	X				X
13-7 Employee Training (pp. 443–445) Compute total employee training costs.	X	X				X

(Source: Reprinted with permission from the National Standards for Business Education, copyright © 2001 by National Business Education Association, 1914 Association Drive, Reston, Virginia 21901-1596)

SCANS Correlation

Foundation Skills

Basic Skills	Reading	Writing	Math	Listening	Speaking	
Thinking Skills	Creative Thinking	Decision Making	Problem Solving	Seeing Things in the Mind's Eye	Knowing How to Learn	Reasoning
Personal Qualities	Responsibility	Self-Esteem	Sociability	Self-Management	Integrity/Honesty	

This chapter's highlighted blocks indicate the chapter's content coverage in the Student Edition and the Teacher Wraparound Edition.

1. Numbers & Operations	2. Algebra	3. Geometry	4. Measurement	5. Data Analysis & Probability	6. Problem Solving	7. Reasoning & Proof	8. Communication	9. Connections	10. Representations
X					X		X		
X					X		X		
X					X		X		
X					X		X		
X					X		X		
X					X		X		
X					X		X		

SCANS Correlation

Workplace Competencies

Resources	Allocating Time	Allocating Money	Allocating Material and Facility Resources	Allocating Human Resources		
Information	Acquiring and Evaluating Information	Organizing and Maintaining Information	Interpreting and Communicating Information	Using Computers to Process Information		
Interpersonal Skills	Participating as a Member of a Team	Teaching Others	Serving Clients/Customers	Exercising Leadership	Negotiating to Arrive at a Decision	Working with Cultural Diversity
Systems	Understanding Systems	Monitoring and Correcting Performance	Improving and Designing Systems			
Technology	Selecting Technology	Applying Technology to Task	Maintaining and Troubleshooting Technology			

What You'll Learn

Companies need to hire and train employees and provide employee benefits. In this chapter you'll focus on how companies figure out the costs involved.

Why It's Important

Increasing the quality and consistency of hiring and providing generous health insurance and retirement benefits can help attract and retain the right people. This in turn reduces workloads, controls costs, and improves employee job satisfaction. Employees are motivated to focus their attention on the job and not worry about their own financial security.

Key Word Review

Creative Sentences

Write a sentence for each key word but replace each key word with a nonsense word. Volunteers read out loud the sentence while others insert the correct word.

LS

CHAPTER 13
Personnel

What You'll Learn

Section 13-1 Calculate the cost of recruiting new employees.

Section 13-2 Compute the new salary after merit increase and cost-of-living adjustment.

Section 13-3 Work out the rate of employee benefits based on annual gross pay.

Section 13-4 Figure out disability benefits under independent retirement systems and under Social Security.

Section 13-5 Compute the employer cost for workers compensation and unemployment insurance.

Section 13-6 Calculate total business travel expenses.

Section 13-7 Compute total employee training costs.

When Will You Ever Use This?

When you work for a company, know that you're an investment to the company. The company is paying for you in more ways than just your income. Knowing about the employee benefits helps you understand how the company treats its people.

Key Words to Know
- recruiting
- salary scale
- cost-of-living adjustment
- merit increase
- employee benefits
- disability insurance
- workers compensation insurance
- unemployment insurance
- travel expenses
- release time

Mathematics Online

To learn more about calculating the costs of personnel, visit the *Mathematics with Business Applications* Web site at www.busmath.glencoe.com.

CLASSROOM RESOURCES

Application and Enrichment
- *Teacher Wraparound Edition*
- *Teacher Resource Binder, Blackline Masters*
- *Interactive Lesson Planner* CD-ROM
- *PowerPoint® Presentations* CD-ROM

Review and Enforcement
Mathematics Online
www.busmath.glencoe.com
- *Teacher Resource Binder, Internet Resources*

- *Student Activity Workbook*
- *Student Activity Workbook, Teacher Annotated Edition*
- *School-to-Home Activity Workbook*

Assessment and Evaluation
- *Assessment Binder, Reproducible Tests*
- *Assessment Binder, Alternative Assessment Strategies*
- **Exam***View*® Pro Test Generator CD-ROM

For the Teacher
- *Student Activity Workbook, Teacher Annotated Edition*
- *Assessment Binder*
- *Interactive Lesson Planner* CD-ROM
- *Teacher Resource Binder*
- Mathematics Online
www.busmath.glencoe.com

For the Student
- *Student Activity Workbook*
- *School-to-Home Activity Workbook*

Living in the Real World

Story's Summary

Yoshi Takahashi is a recent college graduate and a human resource manager. In this chapter, students get a glimpse into Takahashi's daily responsibilities, which include recruiting, hiring, training, and (sometimes) firing employees at this software company.

Living in the Real World

Finding the Right Person

Three months ago, Yoshi Takahashi graduated from college with a degree in psychology and began a new job as a human resource manager at Computer Systems. He is in charge of hiring, training, and if necessary, firing employees for the software company, which creates and markets graphic design programs. This chapter introduces you to Takahashi's responsibilities.

Read on. Go to . . .

423

Did You Know...

The cost to hire and train each new employee can be very high. Most companies prefer to have long-term workers and a low turnover rate.

Think about This

Why is it so important for a company to carefully select its employees—to be sure it hires the best people for each particular job position?

LOCAL STANDARDS

SECTION 1

National Standards for Business Education

Standard 1	Mathematical Foundations
Standard 2	Number Relationships and Operations
Standard 6	Problem-Solving Strategy

National Council of Teachers of Mathematics Standards

Standard 1	Numbers and Operations
Standard 6	Problem Solving
Standard 8	Communication

1 FOCUS

Ask students what expenses they encountered when they looked for part-time jobs. **These may include the cost of a newspaper to look for advertisements or the cost of transportation to an interview. Point out that those employers also have expenses when hiring employees.**

In-Class Examples

Work through these exercises with students before having them do the Self-Check.
1. $205.12 + $124.49 + $1,700 **$2,029.61**
2. $1,842.27 + $11,075.63 + $4,299.45 + $967.81 **$18,185.16**
3. $394.55 + $557.60 + $225.32 + $198.46 **$1,375.93**

Hiring New Employees

○ Section Objective

Calculate the cost of recruiting new employees.

In order for a business to succeed, it must have a sufficient number of people to make it run. Finding qualified individuals to perform a business's duties is an important function. In order to meet the competitive edge of today's marketplace, a company needs to hire people who will enhance its mission.

To fill openings in your business, you may recruit new employees. **Recruiting** is the act of soliciting qualified people to work for your company. The cost of recruiting includes advertising fees, interviewing expenses (such as travel expenses), and hiring expenses (such as moving expenses). Here's what it looks like as a mathematical equation:

$$\text{Total Recruiting Cost} = \text{Advertising Expenses} + \text{Interviewing Expenses} + \text{Hiring Expenses}$$

Living in the Real World

Finding the Right Person

It Offered a Good Package Takahashi recruited Iris Curry to be a data manager in the information technology section of Computer Systems. Recruiting top employees is one of the most important functions of the human resources department. Curry was a top prospect who brought to the company a degree in computer science and four years of experience at a competitor company. This morning, Curry and Takahashi will discuss her salary and benefits package.

Draw Conclusions Why are benefits just as important as a good salary?

Continued on page 427

Example 1

Talbot Manufacturing Company is searching for a person to head its production department. The personnel department placed advertisements for a total cost of $6,495 and employed Empire Executive Search Company to locate candidates. Empire recommended Alice Welch, Tomas Valdez, and Cleveland Adams. Talbot paid the candidates' travel expenses (i.e., transportation, lodging, and meals) for interviews.

Alice Welch	Total travel expenses: $517
Tomas Valdez	Total travel expenses: $735
Cleveland Adams	Total travel expenses: $674

Living in the Real World

A good salary can't compensate for a lack of adequate health coverage, a safe work environment, vacation time, job security, or retirement planning.

BUSINESS NOTES

Workplace Trends
Have students read an article mentioning corporate culture or diversity in the workplace. Ask students to summarize the article and draw attention to any trends mentioned. Ask students to identify two trends in corporate culture. **Answers may include an increased awareness of diversity issues and more informal corporate cultures.**

LS , CL , P

After the interviews, Talbot hired Cleveland Adams at an annual salary of $154,900. Talbot paid these expenses to hire him:

Moving expenses	$3,600
Sale of home (real estate broker's fee)	$9,470
Empire's fee (25 percent of Adams's first-year salary)	$38,725

What was the total expense of recruiting Cleveland Adams?

STEP: Find the total recruiting cost.

$$\begin{array}{ccccc} \text{Advertising} & + & \text{Interviewing} & + & \text{Hiring} \\ \text{Expenses} & & \text{Expenses} & & \text{Expenses} \end{array}$$

$\$6,495 \quad + \quad (\$517 + \$735 + \$674) \quad + \quad (\$3,600 + \$9,470 + \$38,725)$

$= \$6,495 \quad + \quad \$1,926 \quad + \quad \$51,795$

$= \$60,216$ total expense

6495 M+ 517 + 735 + 674 = 1926 M+

3600 + 9470 + 38725 = 51795 M+ RM 60216

CONCEPT CHECK

 SELF-CHECK ✓

Complete the problem, then check your answer at the end of the chapter. Find the total recruiting cost.

1. Advertising expenses: $2,150.
Interviewing expenses: $245 and $315.
Hiring expenses: $1,240 and $2,170.

$2,150 + ($245 + $315) +
($1,240 + $2,170) = $2,150 +
$560 + $3,410 = $6,120

Example 2

A northern New Jersey financial services firm searched and found a senior-level investment banker, with corporate finance and transaction experience. Advertising for the position totaled $12,500. The firm narrowed the search down to 3 finalists; it spent $3,890 on interviewing expenses (e.g., transportation, lodging, and meals). It decided to hire Jane McNally. The firm paid $5,000 in moving expenses and a 6 percent realtor's fee on the selling price of her home. The home sold for $348,000. What is the total recruiting cost?

STEP: Find the total recruiting cost.

$$\begin{array}{ccccc} \text{Advertising} & + & \text{Interviewing} & + & \text{Hiring} \\ \text{Expenses} & & \text{Expenses} & & \text{Expenses} \end{array}$$

2. $1,975 + ($470 +
$860) + ($475 +
$8,600 + $11,415)
= $1,975 + $1,330
+ $20,490 =
$23,795

$\$12,500 \quad + \quad \$3,890 \quad + \quad [\$5,000 + (6\% \times \$348,500)]$

$= \$12,500 \quad + \quad \$3,890 \quad + \quad [\$5,000 + \$20,910]$

$= \$12,500 \quad + \quad \$3,890 \quad + \quad \$25,910$

$= \$42,300$ total recruiting cost

CONCEPT CHECK

 SELF-CHECK ✓

Complete the problem, then check your answer at the end of the chapter. Find the total recruiting cost.

2. Advertising expenses: $1,975.
Interviewing expenses: $470 and $860.
Hiring expenses: $475, $8,600, and 6 percent on a $190,250 home.

Section 13-1 Hiring New Employees ▶ **425**

② TEACH

Discuss each of the different expenses in the formula for finding the total recruiting cost. For each expense category, students list possible expenses. **(To begin the list, point out that one of advertising expenses may be a fee for placing an advertisement online.)** Interviewing expenses may include travel expenses, lodging, and meals. Hiring expenses may include relocation assistance, such as moving expenses or temporary lodging.

Motivating the Lesson

Ruby Electronics recently hired Bonnie Fay as an engineer. The list below gives the expenses involved to recruit her. Organize the list into three categories: advertising expenses, interviewing expenses, and hiring expenses. Find the sum of the expenses in each category. **(Moving $945.57; Newspaper ads $452.75; Temporary lodging $1,695.41; Travel $359.60; Online ads $224.99)** What is the total recruiting cost? **$3,678.32**

In-Class Examples

Find the total recruiting cost.

1. Advertising expense: $569.52. Interviewing expense: $85.20. Hiring expense: $229.34. **$884.06**

2. Advertising expense: $1,297.80. Interviewing expense: $321.15. Hiring expense: $432.67. **$2,051.62**

3. Advertising expenses: $254.75 and $329.55. Interviewing expenses: $238.44, $195.29, and $206.45 Hiring expense: 7% of $185,000. **$14,174.48**

COOPERATIVE LEARNING

Job Application

Students obtain employment application forms from local businesses. Students work in groups filling out the job applications. Judging by the questions on the application, what kinds of workers does this business want? Are there any questions on the application that would tell a human resources manager about an applicant's character? Groups share their findings with the class. **CL**, **LS**, **P**

PROBLEM SOLVING

New Employee Training

If the new employee orientation workshop costs the company $565 per employee, how much will the company spend during a 12-month period if they train 136 new employees? **$565 × 136 = $76,840**

425

3 ASSESS

Error Analysis

Remind students that when they see the word "of" in a math problem, they should think of multiplication. For the problems that involve finding the percent of a number, encourage students to write the percent expression in words first. Then students can easily replace the words with numbers and symbols.

Since calculating the total recruiting cost may involve addition and multiplication, review the importance of using parentheses and following the order of operations in mathematical expressions that contain more than one operation.

4 CLOSE

Closing Activity

1. $1,590.55 + $765.99 + $992.25 + $2,637.25
$5,986.04

2. $280 + (20% × $36,865) + $572 + $681 **$8,906**

3. What is the formula for finding the total recruiting cost?
Advertising Expense + Interviewing Expense + Hiring Expense

4. A company spends $375.90 on advertising, $298.35 on interviewing, and $1,256.26 on hiring to recruit an employee. What is the total recruiting cost? **$1,930.51**

5. Three candidates from the Green Placement Agency are interviewed by Holden Enterprises for a position that pays a starting salary of $37,280.00. Their travel costs are $165.25, $98.40, and $221.67. Holden spends $490.50 on advertising and pays Green 20 percent of the starting salary. What is the total recruiting cost? **$8,431.82**

Celestial Seasonings is one of the most renowned and successful start-ups in the country. The company began in 1969, when 19-year-old Mo Siegel began gathering wild herbs in the Rocky Mountains and packaging them for tea. Today, the Boulder, Colorado, company is the largest herb tea producer in North America and serves 1.2 billion cups of tea per year.

▶▶▶

	Advertising Costs	+	Interviewing Costs	+	Hiring Costs	=	Total Recruiting Cost
3.	$420.70	+	$41.20	+	$517.20	=	**$979.10**
4.	$315.85	+	$79.80	+	$847.72	=	**$1,243.37**
5.	$789.16	+	$415.25	+	$1,213.49	=	**$2,417.90**
6.	$1,412.71	+	$614.91	+	$1,971.44	=	**$3,999.06**
7.	$8,761.43	+	$971.84	+	$3,147.43	=	**$12,880.70**

8. A tire company recruits a district sales manager.
Advertising cost: $917.45.
Interviewing cost: $694.74.
Hiring cost: $2,191.47.
What is the total recruiting cost? **$3,803.66**

9. A manufacturing company recruits a data processing manager.
Advertising cost: $1,475.00.
Interviewing cost: $861.79.
Hiring cost: $3,791.86.
What is the total recruiting cost? **$6,128.65**

10. The cellular communications department hired Marilyn Curtis as its new national distribution manager at an annual salary of $154,950.
Advertising costs: $2,247.50.
Interviewing expenses: Marilyn Curtis, $647.43; Tom Hart, $816.94.
Finder agency fee: 20 percent of first year's salary.
What was the total cost of hiring the national distribution manager?
$34,701.87

11. Novi Discount Brokers hired Wall Street Search Service to locate candidates for the position of manager, investment bonds. The agency's fee is 25 percent of the first year's salary if one of its candidates is hired. Novi also ran several advertisements at a total cost of $2,816.40. Novi interviewed three people:
   • Hakeem Golden applied through the agency. His travel costs were $948.75.
   • Nancy Cooper answered the advertisement. Her travel costs were $516.40.
   • Henry Little applied through the agency. His travel costs were $671.80.
   Novi hired Henry Little at an annual salary of $94,760. Novi paid his moving expenses of $1,419.20 and his real estate broker's fee of 7 percent to sell his $249,000 home. What was the recruiting cost including the costs for the two candidates not hired? **$47,492.55**

Need Help? Go to...
▶ Skill 5: Adding Decimals, page 732

Add.

12. $148 + $74 + $865 **$1,087**

13. $615 + $419 + $1,291 **$2,325**

14. $1,484 + $815 + $11,650 **$13,949**

15. $2,241 + $915 + $14,542 **$17,698**

16. $715.80 + $523.40 + $3,120.50 **$4,359.70**

17. $746.50 + $319.20 + $4,314.70 **$5,380.40**

WRAP-UP

Go over any problem for which a wrong answer is given.

Assignment Guide
Basic: 5–7
Average: 8–10

20 min.

SECTION 13-2 Administering Wages and Salaries

Section Objective

Compute the new salary after merit increase and cost-of-living adjustment.

Your business may have a **salary scale** for any position. This is a table of wages or salaries used to compare various jobs in a company. You can use the information to compare various jobs or to estimate the cost of giving an employee a **cost-of-living adjustment** or a **merit increase.** A cost-of-living adjustment is a raise in your salary to help you keep up with inflation. A merit increase is a raise in your salary to reward you for the quality of your work. How might this formula look?

New Salary = Present Salary + Cost-of-Living Adjustment + Merit Increase

Living in the Real World

Finding the Right Person

The Scales of Worth While Takahashi waits for Curry to arrive, he reviews the company's salary scales for cost-of-living recommendations he is preparing for company executives. The executive will then estimate employees' cost-of-living increases for the next fiscal year. Takahashi hears a knock on the door.

Draw Conclusions What items might be included in a cost-of-living index?

Continued on page 430

Example 1

Elaine Taylor is a systems analyst (salary level 2 position) for EPD Inc. The executive board of EPD voted to give all employees a cost-of-living adjustment of 2.8 percent. In addition, Taylor was awarded a merit increase of 3.5 percent for excellent work during the year. What will Taylor's salary be for the coming year?

Figure 13.1

Salary Level	Data Entry	Computer Operator	Systems Analyst	Systems Team Leader
1	$28,500	$30,000	$35,000	$45,000
2	32,500	34,000	40,000	55,000
3	36,500	38,500	47,500	65,000

Continued on next page

Living in the Real World

A cost-of-living index provides a measure of living cost differences among cities, giving a percent differential used to figure the after-taxes income needed in a particular city to maintain a standard of living currently held in another city.

SECTION 13-2

National Standards for Business Education

Standard 1	Mathematical Foundations
Standard 2	Number Relationships and Operations
Standard 6	Problem-Solving Strategy

National Council of Teachers of Mathematics Standards

Standard 1	Numbers and Operations
Standard 6	Problem Solving
Standard 8	Communication

1 FOCUS

Ask students if they know how raises are calculated. Tell students that two types of salary increases will be discussed in this lesson: cost-of-living adjustments and merit increases.

In-Class Examples

Work through these exercises with students before having them do the Self-Check.
1. $28,220 + $1,185.24 + $338.64 **$29,743.88**
2. $43,692 + $1,747.68 + $1,485.53 **$46,925.21**
3. $29,000 × 4% **$1,160**

427

Discuss the meaning of inflation as it applies to the cost of living. Explain that in order to keep up with increases in the cost of living, companies often give employees raises based on the rate of inflation. Mention that some companies also give raises based on an employee's performance, or merit. Explain that sometimes these raises are given at the same time as the cost-of-living adjustment, and sometimes they are given separately at another time.

Make sure that students understand that not all employees with the same job title will have the same salary. In the example, there are four different levels and four different salaries for each job title. Explain that salary is often based on an employee's past experience and education. Even though two people may have the same job title, it does not necessarily mean that they will have the same salary.

Motivating the Lesson

Below is a list of some of Bill Lin's monthly living expenses:
Rent: $850.
Food: $604.
Utilities: $394.70.
Transportation: $231.68.
Adjust each expense for a 4 percent cost-of-living increase. If Lin's salary is $42,900, what should his new salary be to reflect this increase? **($44,616)** Rent **($884)** Food **($628.16)** Utilities **($410.49)** Transportation **$240.95**

STEP 1: Find the present salary. (Note: Retrieve this number from Figure 13.1 on page 427.)
The present salary is $40,000.

STEP 2: Find the cost-of-living adjustment.
Salary × Cost-of-Living Adjustment Percent
$40,000 ×   2.8%   = $1,120

STEP 3: Find the merit increase.
Salary ×   Merit Increase Percent
$40,000 ×   3.5%   = $1,400

STEP 4: Find the new salary.

Present Salary +	Cost-of-Living Adjustment +	Merit Increase	
$40,000 +	$1,120 +	$1,400	= **$42,520 new salary**

40000 [+] 40000 [×] .028 [+] 40000 [×] .035 [=] 42520

CONCEPT CHECK

SELF-CHECK✓

Complete the problem, then check your answer at the end of the chapter.

1. A systems team leader (salary level 1 position) for EPD Inc. receives a 2.8 percent cost-of-living adjustment and a 2 percent merit increase. Find the new salary. (Use Figure 13.1 on page 427.)
$45,000 + (2.8% × $45,000) + (2% × $45,000) = $45,000 + $1,260 + $900 = $47,160

Example 2

D'Marco Mullin is a computer operator, salary level 3, for EPD Inc. He received a 2.8 percent cost-of-living adjustment and a merit increase of 4 percent. What is Mullin's new salary?

STEP 1: Find the present salary. (Note: Retrieve this number from Figure 13.1 on page 427.)
The present salary is $38,500.

STEP 2: Find the cost-of-living adjustment.
Salary × Cost-of-Living Adjustment Percent
$38,500 ×   2.8%   = $1,078

STEP 3: Find the merit increase.
Salary ×   Merit Increase Percent
$38,500 ×   4%   = $1,540

STEP 4: Find the new salary.

Present Salary +	Cost-of-Living Adjustment +	Merit Increase	
$38,500 +	$1,078 +	$1,540	= **$41,118 new salary**

CONCEPT CHECK

SELF-CHECK✓

Complete the problem, then check your answer at the end of the chapter.

2. Angel Martinez, a systems analyst (salary level 2 position), receives a cost-of-living adjustment of 3 percent and a merit increase of 3.8 percent. What is her new salary? (Use Figure 13.1 on page 427.)
$40,000 + (3% × $40,000) + (3.8% × $40,000) = $40,000 + $1,200 + $1,520 = $42,720

ALTERNATIVE ASSESSMENT

Today's Students
Given the central role of computer technology in many of the best-paying jobs, general education must be supplemented with current, hands-on computer knowledge. Encourage students to commit to developing and maintaining their computer skills by taking classes regularly, volunteering to learn new programs, and familiarizing themselves with as many computer applications as possible. **LS**

SECTION 13-2 PRACTICE

Use Figure 13.1 on page 427 for Problems 3–7.

3. May Song.
Systems team leader, level 3.
Cost-of-living adjustment:
2.8 percent.
Merit increase: 3.6 percent.
What is her new salary? **$69,160**

4. Beatrice Apple.
Data entry, level 3.
Merit increase: 7.6 percent.
What is her new salary? **$39,274**

5. Robert Moore, systems analyst (level 1 position) received a 4.7 percent cost-of-living adjustment and a 4.5 percent merit increase. What is his new salary?
$38,220

6. Ruth Tomasi is a computer operator (level 1 position). She receives a 4.8 percent cost-of-living adjustment and a 7.4 percent merit increase. What is her new salary? **$33,660**

7. Mike Rossi is in data entry (level 2 position). He receives a 3.7 percent cost-of-living adjustment and a 0.7 percent merit increase. What is his new salary?
$33,930

8. Malik Brooks works 40 hours a week 52 weeks per year for Metro Delivery Company. He earns $9.15 an hour.
a. What is his annual gross pay? **$19,032**
b. If he receives a 4.9 percent merit increase, what will be his new annual gross pay? **$19,964.568 = $19,964.57**
c. What will be his new hourly rate? **$9.59835 = $9.60**

9. Nick Antonelli sells for Discount Appliance, Inc. His weekly base salary is $400 plus 5 percent of all his sales. One week he had $9,860 in sales.
a. What was his gross pay for that week? **$893**
b. If he received a 6 percent merit increase in his base salary, what would his gross pay be in a week in which he had $9,860 in sales? **$917**
c. If he received a 10 percent merit increase in his rate of commission but had the same $400 weekly base, what would his gross pay be in a week in which he had $9,860 in sales? **$942.30**

10. Emily Penn sells for Maumee Electronics. Her base salary is $500 or 7 percent of all sales. One week she had sales of $7,280.
a. What is her gross pay for that week? **$509.60**
b. If she receives a 5 percent merit increase in her base salary, what would her gross pay be in a week in which she had $7,280 in sales? **$525.00**
c. If her rate of commission is increased to 7.5 percent, but her base remains $500, what would her gross pay be for a week when she had sales of $7,280?
$546.00

MAINTAINING YOUR SKILLS

Need Help? Go to...
► Application C:
Tables and Charts,
page 762
► Skill 30: Finding
the Percentage,
page 757

Find the present salary by using Figure 13.1 on page 427.

11. System analyst, level 3 **$47,500**

12. Data entry, level 1 **$28,500**

13. Systems team leader, level 2 **$55,000**

Find the percentage.

14. $17,740 × 4.5%
$798.30

15. $21,510 × 8.6%
$1,849.86

16. $15,100 × 3.1%
$468.10

COMMUNICATION SKILLS

Word Processing
Students select a job, research its requirements, and write a short job description for it. Then, students write a newspaper want ad for the job. Students use word processing software to attractively format both items and print out the results. **LS** , **CL** , **P**

WRAP-UP

Go over any problem for which a wrong answer is given.

Assignment Guide
Basic: 3–7
Average: 8–9

20 min.

In-Class Examples
Find the new salary.
1. Present salary: $25,000.
Cost-of-living adjustment:
4 percent.
Merit increase: 2 percent.
$26,500
2. Present salary: $33,560.
Cost-of-living adjustment:
4.1 percent.
Merit increase: 1.8 percent.
$35,540.04
3. Present salary: $37,226.
Cost-of-living adjustment:
3.9 percent.
Merit increase: 3 percent.
$39,794.59

③ ASSESS

Error Analysis
Remind students that since they are dealing with money, there should be only two decimal places. Some calculations may result in decimals with more than two decimal places. Review place value and rounding to the nearest cent.

Students may have difficulty understanding that the cost-of-living adjustment can be different for several employees even though the rate is the same. Emphasize that the adjustment is a percent of the salary. Since employees have different salaries, there will be different adjustments. You may want to give an example.

④ CLOSE

Closing Activity
Find the new salary.
1. Present salary: $32,800.
Cost-of-living adjustment:
4.1 percent. **$34,144.80**
2. Present salary: $22,355.
Merit increase: 3.8 percent.
$23,204.49
3. Present salary: $41,608.
Cost-of-living adjustment:
4.2 percent. Merit increase:
2 percent. **$44,187.70**

National Standards for Business Education

Standard 1	Mathematical Foundations
Standard 2	Number Relationships and Operations
Standard 6	Problem-Solving Strategy

National Council of Teachers of Mathematics Standards

Standard 1	Numbers and Operations
Standard 6	Problem Solving
Standard 8	Communication

 **FOCUS**

Employers consider employee benefits as part of the cost of employing someone. This lesson focuses on computing the rate of benefits based on annual gross pay.

In-Class Examples

Work through these exercises with students before having them do the Self-Check.

1. $7,953 \div 28,900$ **0.275**
2. $6,505 \div 31,075$ **0.209**
3. What is 5.2 percent of $24,780? **$1,288.56**

○ **Section Objective**

Work out the rate of employee benefits based on annual gross pay.

Your business may offer several **employee benefits.** Employee benefits may include the following:

- health insurance
- vision insurance
- dental insurance
- group life insurance
- retirement plans
- Social Security (FICA)
- Medicare
- stock purchase plans
- paid vacations and holidays
- unemployment insurance
- disability insurance
- sick leave

The total of the benefits may be figured as a percent of annual gross pay. It looks like this:

$$\text{Rate of Benefits} = \frac{\text{Total Benefits}}{\text{Annual Gross Pay}}$$

Living in the Real World

Finding the Right Person

Important Considerations Takahashi and Curry spend the next hour discussing her benefits package, travel expectations, and the possibility of future job training. Unlike her previous job, her new position offers generous benefits, including excellent medical, vision, and dental coverage for her and her family. This is especially important to Curry because she has a child who is partially disabled and requires regular medication.

Draw Conclusions What is included in a company's benefits package?

Continued on page 433

Example 1

The personnel department of Commercial Credit Company is preparing annual reports on employee benefits. Tamika Rey's total annual benefits are what percent of her annual salary?

Tamika Rey   Annual salary: $41,340   Weekly salary: $795

Vacation: 2 weeks @ $795/week	$ 1,590.00
Holidays: 8 days @ $159/day	1,272.00
Health insurance: 12 months @ $162.50/mo	1,950.00
Sick leave policy: 30 days @ $159/day	4,770.00
Unemployment insurance: 4.6% × $41,340	1,901.64
Social Security (FICA): 6.2% × $41,340	2,563.08
Medicare: 1.45% × $41,340	+ 599.43
Total:	$14,646.15

Living in the Real World

Usually included are vacation, sick leave, insurance, a retirement investment plan, and/or the opportunity to buy stock in the company. (See list in opening paragraph.)

RETEACH / ENRICHMENT

Benefits

Many small businesses cannot offer a wide range of employee benefits because of the costs involved. Students discuss the benefit they would consider most essential if they worked for a small business.

STEP: Find the rate of benefits.

    Total Benefits ÷ Annual Gross Pay

       $14,646.15 ÷ $41,340.00

             = **0.3542 or 35.4% of her annual salary**

14646.15 ÷ 41340 = 0.354285195

CONCEPT CHECK

Complete the problem, then check your answer at the end of the chapter.

1. Annual salary is $32,000. Total benefits are $9,600. Find the rate of benefits.
   $9,600 ÷ $32,000 = 30%

Example 2

Compute the rate of employee benefits based on annual gross pay for Tamika Rey (from Example 1) if she now receives 3 weeks of vacation. Everything else stays the same.

    STEP 1: Find the *total* benefits.

        Amount for Week of Vacation + Total Annual Benefits

           $795.00   + $14,646.15   = $15,441.15

    STEP 2: Find the *rate* of benefits.

        Total Benefits ÷ Annual Gross Pay

           $15,441.15 ÷ $41,340.00   = **0.3735 or 37.4% rate of benefits**

CONCEPT CHECK

Complete the problem, then check your answers at the end of the chapter.

2. A stock clerk's annual salary is $21,860.

    Benefits: Vacation and holidays: $840.77

                Health insurance: $1,275.00

                Unemployment insurance: $1,005.56

                Social Security (FICA): $1,355.32

                Medicare: $316.97

                Compensation insurance: $486.26

    a. What are the total benefits?

    b. What is the rate of benefits? (Round to nearest tenth percent.)

    a. Total benefits:
   $840.77 + $1,275.00 + $1,005.56 + $1,355.32 + $316.97 + $486.26 = $5,279.88

    b. Rate of benefits:
   $5,279.88 ÷ $21,860.00 = 24.153% − 24.2%

SECTION 13-3 PRACTICE

Calculate rate of benefits. Round to the nearest tenth of a percent.

	Total Benefits	÷	Annual Gross Pay	=	Rate of Benefits
3.	$11,870	÷	$ 43,748	=	27.1%
4.	15,610	÷	64,600	=	24.2%
5.	2,940	÷	14,700	=	20%
6.	11,392	÷	35,600	=	32%
7.	39,860	÷	124,650	=	31.98%

Continued on next page

SECTION 13-3

② TEACH

Ask students to list some employee benefits. Add to the list any benefits that students do not mention. Describe different types of health plans, dental plans, and life insurance plans. Mention that some benefits are fully paid for by the employer, and some are fully paid for by the employee. Other benefits are paid for partially by the employer and partially by the employee. One benefit that students may have heard of is a 401(k) plan. Remind students that they learned about different types of investments in Chapter 12. In particular, you may want to review stocks when you talk about 401(k) plans.

Motivating the Lesson
Sara Gold's annual gross pay is $28,450. Her benefits are listed below:
Health insurance: $3,116.04.
Vacation: $1,094.23.
social Security: $1,763.90.
Medicare: $412.53. **22.4%**

In-Class Examples
Find the rate of benefits. Round to the nearest whole percent.
1. Total benefits: $628.
   Annual gross pay: $28,600. **2%**
2. Total benefits: $915.
   Annual gross pay: $32,561. **3%**

GLOBAL PERSPECTIVE

Exchange Rates
Since companies of all sizes conduct business around the world, employees often need to understand how to figure currency exchange rates. Look up exchange rates in the newspaper or online and convert a U.S. $1 to Japanese, Canadian, German, and English currency.

SECTION 13-3

③ ASSESS

Error Analysis

In this lesson, students will need to calculate daily, monthly, and annual rates of pay. Students may need to practice this skill before they calculate the rate of benefits. Review the process for finding each rate of pay. To find an annual salary given a monthly salary, multiply by 12. To find a weekly rate given an annual salary, divide by 52. To find a daily rate given an annual salary, find the weekly salary and divide by 5. Give students some basic conversions to practice.

④ CLOSE

Closing Activity

Hilda Brooks has an annual salary of $42,305. Her employer pays the following benefits: health insurance at $359.50 monthly, 10 personal days, 2 weeks vacation, Social Security (6.2 percent), and Medicare (1.45 percent). What are the total benefits? **($10,804.53)** What is the rate of benefits? **25.5%**

---

9. a. Manager:
   a. $1,830.00
   b. $1,712.88
   c. $1,464.00
   d. $2,949.96
   e. $ 689.91
   f. $8,646.75
   Counter 1:
   a. $1,060.00
   b. $992.16
   c. $848.00
   d. $1,708.72
   e. $399.62
   f. $5,008.50
   Counter 2:
   a. $870.00
   b. $814.32
   c. $696.00
   d. $1,402.44
   e. $327.99
   f. $4,110.75
   Cleanup:
   a. $560.00
   b. $524.16
   c. $448.00
   d. $902.72
   e. $211.12
   f. $2,646.00

10. a. Lab tech:
   a. $1,598.00
   b. $1,438.20
   c. $1,911.21
   d. $2,575.98
   e. $602.45
   f. $8,125.84
   Lab analyst:
   a. $1,725.96
   b. $1,553.37
   c. $2,064.25
   d. $2,782.25
   e. $650.69
   f. $8,776.52
   Receptionist:
   a. $634.62
   b. $571.15
   c. $759.00
   d. $1,023.00
   e. $239.25
   f. $3,227.02

> **Need Help? Go to...**
> ➤ Skill 30: **Finding the Percentage,** page 757
> ➤ Skill 31: **Finding the Rate,** page 758

---

8. Mary Chambers teaches in Central City Schools. Her annual salary is $43,862. Her benefits include:

State Teachers Retirement System:	$5,921.37
Group life insurance:	$647.50
Health insurance:	$875.00
Vision and dental insurance:	$548.45

   a. What are the total benefits? **Total benefits: $7,992.32**
   b. What is the rate of benefits? (**Round to nearest tenth percent.**) **Rate of benefits: 18.2%**

9. a. Complete the benefits chart for French Coffee Shoppe's employees. (**Round to the nearest cent.**)

Position	Annual Wage	2-Week Vacation	3.6% Workers Comp.	8-Day Sick Leave	6.2% FICA	1.45% Medicare	Total Benefits
Manager	$47,580	a.	b.	c.	d.	e.	f.
Counter 1	27,560	a.	b.	c.	d.	e.	f.
Counter 2	22,620	a.	b.	c.	d.	e.	f.
Cleanup	14,560	a.	b.	c.	d.	e.	f.

   b. What is the rate of benefits for each employee? (**Round to the nearest tenth percent.**) **18.2%**

10. a. Complete the benefits chart for Pathology Lab's staff.

Position	Annual Wage	2-Week Vacation	9 Holidays	4.6% Unemp. Ins.	6.2% FICA	1.45% Medicare	Total Benefits
Lab tech	$41,548	a.	b.	c.	d.	e.	f.
Lab analyst	44,875	a.	b.	c.	d.	e.	f.
Receptionist	16,500	a.	b.	c.	d.	e.	f.

   b. What is the rate of benefits for each employee? (**Round to the nearest tenth percent.**) **19.6%**
   c. How much does the lab pay in benefits for the employees? **$20,129.38**
   d. How much more would it cost the lab to give each employee a 3-week vacation? **$1,979.29**

MAINTAINING YOUR SKILLS

Find the percentage.

11. $24,700 × 7.51% **$1,854.97**

12. $18,960 × 4.6% **$872.16**

13. $26,418 × 3.6% **$951.05**

Find the rate.

14. Six thousand five hundred is what percent of $32,500? **20%**

15. Six thousand seven hundred twenty is what percent of $16,800? **40%**

WRAP-UP

Go over any problem for which a wrong answer is given.

Assignment Guide
   Basic: 3–7
Average: 8–9

20 min.

SECTION 13-4 Disability Insurance

Section Objective

Figure out disability benefits under independent retirement systems and under Social Security.

You might not think of disability as something that could actually happen to you, but the chances of becoming disabled are probably greater than you realize. Studies show that a 20-year-old worker has a 30 percent chance of becoming disabled before reaching retirement age.

Disability insurance pays benefits to individuals who must miss work because of an illness or injury. Short-term disability is covered by an employer's sick leave policy or by a private insurance company. Long-term or permanent disability coverage is provided by Social Security or by an independent retirement system. Most independent retirement systems compute disability benefits based on a percent of the final average salary. Remember that:

$$\begin{array}{c}\text{Annual} \\ \text{Disability} \\ \text{Benefit}\end{array} = \left(\begin{array}{c}\text{Years} \\ \text{Worked}\end{array} + \begin{array}{c}\text{Expected} \\ \text{Retirement} \\ \text{Age}\end{array} - \begin{array}{c}\text{Present} \\ \text{Age}\end{array}\right) \times \begin{array}{c}\text{Rate of} \\ \text{Benefits}\end{array} \times \begin{array}{c}\text{Final} \\ \text{Average} \\ \text{Salary}\end{array}$$

Living in the Real World

Finding the Right Person

In Case of an Injury Takahashi's next job of the day is to review a file submitted by an employee who is seeking to use his disability insurance. Because he works at a software company, on-the-job risks for employees are very low. Nevertheless, disability insurance also covers employees who are injured or otherwise disabled while off the job. The case Takahashi is reviewing, however, involves an on-the-job incident. Harold Zenor, a shipping department employee, is claiming disability because he injured his back loading Computer Systems boxes onto a truck.

Draw Conclusions What is the purpose of disability insurance?

Continued on page 436

Example 1

Alicia Walmsley had been working at Northern State University for 21 years when she became permanently disabled and could not continue to work. She was 52 years old and had planned to retire in 13 years at Northern State's normal retirement age of 65. Her final average salary was $38,740. Northern State's rate of benefits is 2 percent. What is her monthly disability benefit?

STEP 1: Find the annual disability benefit.

$$\left(\begin{array}{c}\text{Years} \\ \text{Worked}\end{array} + \begin{array}{c}\text{Expected} \\ \text{Retirement} \\ \text{Age}\end{array} - \begin{array}{c}\text{Present} \\ \text{Age}\end{array}\right) \times \begin{array}{c}\text{Rate of} \\ \text{Benefits}\end{array} \times \begin{array}{c}\text{Final} \\ \text{Average} \\ \text{Salary}\end{array}$$

$$(21 + 65 - 52) \times 2\% \times \$38,740$$
$$= \quad 34 \quad \times 0.02 \times \$38,740$$
$$= \$26,343.20 \text{ annual disability benefit}$$

Continued on next page

Section 13-4 Disability Insurance ▶ **433**

Great Ideas from the Classroom Of...

Robin Carline
East Iberville High School
Saint Gabriel, La.

Travel Expenses

Create a travel itinerary to teach students about a personnel department. Their assignment is to search the Internet and find a conference to attend. Also, have them search for airfare, hotel accommodations, airport transportation, and other expenses. Put the information into an Excel spreadsheet.

Living in the Real World

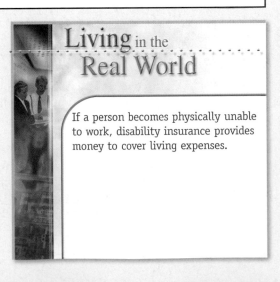

If a person becomes physically unable to work, disability insurance provides money to cover living expenses.

National Standards for Business Education

Standard 1	Mathematical Foundations
Standard 2	Number Relationships and Operations
Standard 6	Problem-Solving Strategy

National Council of Teachers of Mathematics Standards

Standard 1	Numbers and Operations
Standard 6	Problem Solving
Standard 8	Communication

1 FOCUS

Disability insurance provides benefits to employees who must miss work either on a short term or long term basis due to an illness or injury. Point out that unlike other employee benefits that are just based on salary, disability benefits are based on several factors.

In-Class Examples

Work through these exercises with students before having them do the Self-Check.

1. $37 \times 2\% \times \$29,975$ **$22,181.50**
2. $23 \times 2.3\% \times \$43,655$ **$23,093.50**
3. $(31 + 65 - 49) \times 1.9\% \times \$61,045$ **$54,513.19**
4. $(35 + 70 - 61) \times 1.8\% \times \$54,422.75$ **$43,102.82**

② TEACH

Have students discuss reasons why an employee may need to leave on short-term or long-term disability. Point out that maternity leave is often paid by a short-term disability plan.

Since there are many different types of disability plans, discuss how plans pay different amounts. Some plans pay a flat fee while others pay a percent of the last salary. In order to receive benefits, many plans require a doctor's written instructions that an employee should abstain from working. Point out that plans pay less than an employee's last salary. This discourages employees from remaining on disability longer than is actually needed.

Motivating the Lesson

Jane Tosti worked for 42 years before becoming disabled at age 63. She had expected to retire at age 65. Her final salary was $43,112. Her rate of disability benefits is 2.2 percent. What is her annual disability benefit? **$41,732.42**

In-Class Examples

Find the annual and monthly disability benefit.

1. Employee age: 61.
   Years worked: 40.
   Final average salary: $62,058.
   Expected retirement age: 65.
   Rate of benefits: 2.1 percent.
   $57,341.59; $4,778.47
2. Employee age: 39.
   Years worked: 17.
   Final average salary: $38,760.
   Expected retirement age: 65.
   Rate of benefits: 1.8 percent.
   $30,000.24; $2,500.02
3. Employee age: 47.
   Years worked: 24.
   Final average salary: $35,048.20.
   Expected retirement age: 70.
   Rate of benefits: 2 percent.
   $32,945.31; $2,745.44

STEP 2: Find the monthly disability benefit.
$26,343.20 ÷ 12 = **$2,195.266 or $2,195.27 per month**

21 `+` 65 `-` 52 `=` 34 `×` .02 `×` 38740 `=`

26343.2 `÷` 12 `=` 2195.266667

CONCEPT CHECK

 SELF-CHECK ✓

Complete the problem, then check your answers at the end of the chapter.

1. Final average salary is $47,800, you've worked for 15 years, you'll retire in 10 years when you're 60. The rate of benefits is 1.8 percent. Find the annual and monthly disability benefits.
   Annual disability benefit: $21,510.00; Monthly benefit: $1,792.50

DISABILITY INSURANCE UNDER SOCIAL SECURITY Disability under Social Security is based on your inability to work. Your disability also must last or be expected to last for at least a year, or to result in death. Generally you need 20 quarter credits (5 years) earned in the last 10 years to qualify for disability. The amount of your monthly disability benefit is based on your lifetime average earnings covered by Social Security.

If you would like an estimate of your disability benefit, request a Social Security statement, which displays your earnings record and provides an estimate of your disability benefit. Supplemental Security Income (SSI) is a program run by Social Security for the elderly, the blind, and people with disabilities. The basic monthly SSI check is $531 for one person and $796 for a couple. This may vary if the state adds to the SSI check.

(Example 2)

John Crawford has contributed to Social Security for the past 15 years. He becomes disabled while working. If he qualifies for SSI, what will his monthly disability benefit be for him and his wife?

STEP: Find the monthly disability benefit.
Crawford qualifies for SSI disability benefits under Social Security. Because they're a couple, they'll receive **$796 per month.**

CONCEPT CHECK

SELF-CHECK ✓

Complete the problem, then check your answer at the end of the chapter.

2. Maria Ramos has worked at Riverside Extended Care Facility for the past 6 years. Her employment has been covered by Social Security. She becomes disabled and qualifies for SSI. If she is single with no dependents, how much will she receive monthly in disability benefits? **$531 (one person)**

THINKING CRITICALLY

Employer Costs

Companies must take into account not only what the company will pay employees in wages and benefits, but also what percentage of these earnings will be paid to the government for legally required programs, such as Social Security and Medicare. The Statistical Abstracts of the United States give the average employer costs for employee compensation as: wages and salaries 72 percent, paid leave (vacation, holiday, and sick) 7 percent, supplementary pay 3 percent, insurance 6 percent, retirement and savings 3 percent (legally required payments 9 percent). Students create a pie graph using the data. How many times greater is the amount paid in wages and salaries than the amount paid for legally required programs? **72% ÷ 9% = 8 times greater.**

3. a. $20,000
  b. $1,666.67
4. a. $37,632
  b. $3,136
5. a. $20,563.20
  b. $1,713.60
6. a. $33,836
  b. $2,819.67
7. a. $21,932.40
  b. $1,827.70
8. a. $61,914.51
  b. $5,159.54

In Problems 3–8, find the annual and monthly disability benefits.

	Years Worked		Expected + Retirement − Age		Present Age	×	Rate of Benefits	×	Final Average Salary	=	Annual Disability Benefit	Monthly Disability Benefit
3.	(20	+	65	−	60)	×	2.00%	×	$40,000	=	a.	b.
4.	(26	+	60	−	54)	×	2.10%	×	56,000	=	a.	b.
5.	(14	+	62	−	44)	×	1.80%	×	35,700	=	a.	b.
6.	(16	+	65	−	37)	×	2.00%	×	38,450	=	a.	b.
7.	(3	+	70	−	31)	×	1.75%	×	29,840	=	a.	b.
8.	(30	+	65	−	54)	×	2.10%	×	71,910	=	a.	b.

9. Keshawn Brooks worked for 26 years covered by Social Security. He becomes disabled and qualifies for Supplemental Security Income. He is not married and has no dependents. What is his monthly SSI disability benefit? **$531**

10. Ishiro Nagayama has worked under Social Security coverage for the past 7 years. He becomes disabled and qualifies for SSI. What is the monthly SSI disability benefit for Nagayama and his wife? **$796**

11. Paul Thornton had worked for the state Department of Transportation for 18 years. He suffered a stroke and became disabled at age 49. His final average salary was $36,947.80. Normal retirement age is 65. The rate of benefits is 2.1 percent.
  a. What is Thornton's annual disability benefit? **$26,380.73**
  b. What is his monthly disability benefit? **$2,198.39**

12. Theresa Cole had worked for Central State University for 13 years when she suffered a heart attack and became disabled. Cole was 54 years of age and had planned to retire at the normal retirement age of 60. Her final average salary was $41,247.86. Central State's rate of benefits is 2 percent. What is her monthly disability benefit? **$1,306.18**

13. Richard Wexler, age 58, was an employee of Central Pacific Railroads for 16 years when he became permanently disabled. Normal retirement age for Central Pacific is 60. The rate of benefits is 2.2 percent. Wexler's final average salary was $41,870. Find his monthly disability benefit. **$1,381.71**

14. Henrietta Jordon, age 60, was an employee of Giant Department Stores for 38 years when she became permanently disabled. She was covered under Social Security for all 38 years and qualified for SSI. Find the monthly SSI disability benefit for her and her husband. **$796**

MAINTAINING YOUR SKILLS

Need Help? Go to...
▶ Skill 5: **Adding Decimals**, page 732
▶ Skill 6: **Subtracting Decimals**, page 733
▶ Skill 30: **Finding the Percentage**, page 757

Add.

15. 18 + 17 **35**   **16.** 21 + 12 **33**   **17.** 7 + 32 **39**

Solve.

18. 17 + (65 − 56) **26**   **19.** 9 + (60 − 31) **38**   **20.** 23 + (62 − 54) **31**

Find the percentage. Round to the nearest cent.

21. 2% of $47,965 **$959.30**   **22.** 2.1% of $36,741 **$771.56**   **23.** 1.8% of $29,176 **$525.17**

SECTION 13-4

3 ASSESS

Error Analysis

Students may have difficulty with the formula for benefits. Remind them that they need to first do the addition and subtraction inside the parentheses, then do the multiplications. Also point out that the rate of benefits percent must be changed to a decimal.

4 CLOSE

Closing Activity

1. (42 + 70 − 60) × 1.8% × $49,282 **$46,127.95**

2. (37 + 65 − 58) × 2% × $51,032.60 **$44,908.69**

Find the annual and monthly disability benefit.

3. Employee age: 41.
Years worked: 20.
Final average salary: $32,159.
Expected retirement age: 65.
Rate of benefits: 2.1 percent
$29,714.92; $2,476.24

4. Employee age: 56.
Years worked: 35.
Final average salary: $52,900.
Expected retirement age: 70.
Rate of benefits: 2 percent
$51,842; $4,320.17

WRAP-UP

Go over any problem for which a wrong answer is given.

Assignment Guide
  Basic: 3–8
  Average: 9–10

20 min.

SECTION **13-5** Workers Compensation and Unemployment Insurance

National Standards for Business Education

Standard 1	Mathematical Foundations
Standard 2	Number Relationships and Operations
Standard 6	Problem-Solving Strategy

National Council of Teachers of Mathematics Standards

Standard 1	Numbers and Operations
Standard 6	Problem Solving
Standard 8	Communication

FOCUS

Ask students to think about what a person working full time would do for income if he or she were hurt on the job. What if the person were laid off?

In-Class Examples

Work through these exercises with students before having them do the Self-Check.
1. $4.49 \times \$2,700$ **$12,123**
2. $2.99 \times \$50,246$ **$150,235.54**
3. $0.020 \times \$8,500$ **$170**
4. $0.052 \times \$4,680$ **$243.36**

○ **Section Objective**

Compute the employer cost for workers compensation and unemployment insurance.

SECTION 13-5 Workers Compensation and Unemployment Insurance

Unless you're in Texas, employers need **workers compensation insurance**. It's required in every state but the Lone Star; it covers employees' medical expenses and lost wages if they're hurt on the job. The premiums for workers compensation insurance are paid to the state by the employer, not the employee. The premiums vary by state but are based on the total payroll of a company, normally in blocks of $100, and the type of business. The state classifies every business according to the frequency and severity of accidents. Roofers who have a high exposure to injuries will have a higher premium than office personnel who have a low exposure to injuries. In most states the premium for workers compensation insurance is computed by multiplying a base rate by the total payroll.

Premium for Workers Compensation Insurance = Base Rate × Total Payroll

Living in the Real World

Finding the Right Person

How a Company Calculates Possible Injuries Delivery persons and data entry personnel have the same company rights. Yet employees with a high exposure to injuries will have a higher premium than office personnel who have a low exposure to injuries.

Draw Conclusions What do you know about your state's workers compensation program?

Continued on page 440

(**Example 1**)

The base rate for workers compensation insurance for underground coal mining in one state is $19.89 per $100 paid to employees. The total monthly payroll for a small underground mine is $76,800. What is the monthly premium for workers compensation insurance?

STEP: Find the premium for workers compensation insurance.
Base Rate × (Total Payroll ÷ 100)
$19.89 × ($76,800 ÷ $100) = **$15,275.52 premium**

19.89 ☒ 76800 ÷ 100 ═ 15275.52

Living in the Real World

Answers will vary depending on the student and the state they live in.

Complete the problem, then check your answer at the end of the chapter.

1. In the same state as Example 1, the owner of a toy store pays the base rate of only $2.12 per $100 paid in wages. The payroll for the Fun-n-Sun Toy Store for September is $21,780. What is the monthly premium for workers compensation insurance? **$2.12 × ($21,780 ÷ $100) = $461.736 = $461.74**

Unemployment insurance is a federal and state program jointly financed through federal and state employer payroll taxes. Unemployment insurance provides financial aid to qualified persons who, through no fault of their own, become unemployed. Generally, employers must pay both state and federal unemployment taxes if: (1) they pay wages to employees totaling $1,500, or more, in any quarter of a calendar year; or (2) they had at least one employee during any day of a week during 20 weeks in a calendar year (regardless of whether or not the weeks were consecutive).

The federal unemployment tax (FUTA) rate is 6.2 percent of taxable wages. The taxable wage base is the first $7,000 paid in wages to each employee during the calendar year. Employers who pay the state unemployment tax (SUTA) on a timely basis will receive an offset credit of up to 5.4 percent regardless of the rate of tax they pay to the state. Therefore, the net federal tax rate is generally 0.8 percent (6.2% − 5.4%). This would be equal to a maximum of $56.00 per employee, per year (0.008 × $7,000.00 = $56.00) in federal tax. Remember that:

State Tax Amount = State Tax Rate × First $7,000 of Annual Wages

Federal Tax Rate = 6.2% − First 5.4% of State Tax Rate

Federal Tax Amount = Federal Tax Rate × First $7,000 of Annual Wages

Example 2

A sewer contractor has four employees. The firm has some unemployment during the year, especially during the winter months, and must pay a state unemployment tax (SUTA) of 5.4 percent. That leaves 0.8 percent (6.2% − 5.4%) for the federal unemployment tax (FUTA). Compute the federal and state unemployment tax on the annual wage given below.

STEP 1: Find the federal unemployment tax.

Federal Tax Rate = 6.2% − 5.4%
= 0.8% (federal tax rate)

Federal Tax Amount = Federal Tax Rate × First $7,000 of Annual Wages
0.8% × $7,000
= $56.00 federal unemployment tax

Employee	Annual Wage	Amount Taxed	Federal Tax (0.8%)	State Tax (5.4%)
Art Webster	$24,750	$7,000	$56.00	

Continued on next page

COOPERATIVE LEARNING

Career Day
Set up a committee system in your class to plan and put on a career day for the school. Activities to be planned, scheduled, and executed include: gaining permission from school administration, canvassing parent and community volunteers, contacting career professionals to set up booths, and advertising the career day. Emphasis can be placed on careers involving math. **LS** , **CL** , **P**

---

2 TEACH

Have students discuss why not all companies pay the same amount for worker's compensation insurance. Some jobs are considered high risk for injuries while other jobs are extremely low risk. Have students name some businesses that would most likely have high premiums and some that would most likely have low premiums.

In Example 2, be sure that students understand that the taxable wage base is the first $7,000 paid in wages to each employee during the calendar year. The wages of the first two employees are more than $7,000, so the taxable wage base is $7,000. Since the wages of the other employees are less than $7,000, the taxable wage base is the actual amount of wages earned.

Motivating the Lesson
The base rate for workers compensation insurance for a particular business is $9.85 per $100.00 paid to employees. The total monthly payroll is $31,450.00. What is the monthly premium for workers compensation insurance? **$3,097.83**

In-Class Examples
Find the monthly premium for workers compensation insurance.
1. Base rate: $5.89 per $100.00. Total monthly payroll: $34,800.00. **$2,049.72**
2. Base rate: $3.50 per $100.00. Total annual payroll: $189,345.00. **$552.26**
3. The owner of a hat store pays the base rate of only $2.05 per $100.00 paid in wages. The payroll for the Tops Hat Store for one month is $11,220.00. What is the monthly premium for workers compensation insurance? **$230.01**

 **ASSESS**

Error Analysis

When finding the state and federal unemployment tax, students may make mistakes in calculating the federal unemployment tax because they forget to subtract the credit. Have students practice finding the federal unemployment tax rate for different companies.

In Example 2 on page 437, the federal unemployment tax rate is 0.8 percent. Make sure students know that 0.8 percent is equivalent to 0.008. Students make mistakenly write 0.8 percent as 0.08.

2. Moore:
FUTA—(6.2% − 1.1%) × $7,000.00 = $357
SUTA—1.1% × $7,000.00 = $77.00
Kinder:
FUTA—(6.2% − 1.1%) × $7,000.00 = $357
SUTA—1.1% × $7,000.00 = $77.00
Bender:
FUTA—(6.2% − 1.1%) × $5,378.90 = $274.32
SUTA—1.1% × $5,378.90 = $59.17

STEP 2: Find the state unemployment tax.

State Tax Amount = State Tax Rate × First $7,000 of Annual Wages
= 5.4% × $7,000
= $378.00 state unemployment tax

Employee	Annual Wage	Amount Taxed	Federal Tax (0.8%)	State Tax (5.4%)
Art Webster	$24,750	$7,000	$56.00	$378.00

CONCEPT CHECK

SELF-CHECK ✓

Complete the problem, then check your answers at the end of the chapter.

2. A small manufacturer of ceramic products has good experience with respect to layoffs. The firm pays a state tax of only 1.1 percent on the first $7,000 of each employee's annual wage. What is the federal and state unemployment insurance tax paid on the wages of the three employees?

Employee	Annual Wage
Shaquille Moore	$43,976.00
Elizabeth Kinder	21,654.00
Robert Bender	5,378.90

SECTION 13-5 PRACTICE

For Problems 3–6, find the monthly premium for workers compensation insurance.

	Type of Business	Monthly Payroll	Base Rate per $100	Monthly Premium
3.	Janitorial service	$ 980	$ 4.90	$48.02
4.	Window washer service	3,960	16.54	$654.98
5.	Painting contractor	7,860	6.10	$479.46
6.	Clothing store	4,650	2.73	$126.95

7. The base rate for a state's workers compensation insurance for a service station attendant is $5.12 per $100.00 paid in wages. The payroll for Scott Park Service Station for March is $5,784.00. What is the monthly premium for workers compensation insurance? **$296.14**

8. Maria and Enzo Farelli operate a bakery. The base rate for the state's workers compensation insurance is $2.90 per $100.00 paid in wages. The monthly payroll for the bakers employed by the Farellis is $13,870.00. What is the monthly premium for workers compensation insurance? **$402.23**

9. a. $7,000
   b. $490.00
   c. 0.8%
   d. $56.00
10. a. $5,700
    b. $307.80
    c. 0.8%
    d. $456.00
11. a. $4,800
    b. $105.60
    c. 4.0%
    d. $192.00
12. a. $7,000
    b. $280.00
    c. 2.2%
    d. $154.00
13. a. $7,000
    b. $70.00
    c. 5.2%
    d. $364.00
14. a. $7,000
    b. $455.00
    c. 0.8%
    d. $560.00

For Problems 9–14, the maximum annual wage taxed for both federal and state unemployment insurance is $7,000. Find the amount taxed, the federal and state unemployment insurance tax rates, and the amounts in federal and state taxes. Remember that a maximum of 5.4 percent state tax rate can be applied toward the 6.2 percent federal tax rate.

	Employee	Annual Wage	Amount Taxed	State Tax Rate	State Tax Amount	Federal Tax Rate	Federal Tax Amount
9.	Sam Bass	$42,600	a.	7.0%	b.	c.	d.
10.	Tammy Shore	5,700	a.	5.4%	b.	c.	d.
11.	Akili Jones	4,800	a.	2.2%	b.	c.	d.
12.	Mao Tsu	9,240	a.	4.0%	b.	c.	d.
13.	Dave Priest	24,890	a.	1.0%	b.	c.	d.
14.	Luis Rojas	17,450	a.	6.5%	b.	c.	d.

15. City Central Cab Company pays a state tax of 9.1 percent on the first $7,000 of each employee's annual wage. What is the federal and state unemployment insurance tax paid on the wages of the eight employees of City Central Cab Company?

Employee	Annual Wage	Amount Taxed	Federal Tax	State Tax
Larry Koster	$43,876	a. $7,000	b. $56.00	c. $637.00
Hakeem Ahmed	25,916	a. $7,000	b. $56.00	c. $637.00
Miguel Morales	32,908	a. $7,000	b. $56.00	c. $637.00
Alice Gallos	28,540	a. $7,000	b. $56.00	c. $637.00
Tula Haddad	7,248	a. $7,000	b. $56.00	c. $637.00
Leotis Brown	6,850	a. $6,850.00	b. $54.80	c. $623.35
Julio Lopez	6,240	a. $6,240.00	b. $49.92	c. $567.84
Fumiko Woo	4,650	a. $4,650.00	b. $37.20	c. $423.15

MAINTAINING YOUR SKILLS

Need Help? Go to...
➤ Skill 8: Multiplying Decimals, page 735

Multiply.

16. $3.14 × 320 **$1,004.80**

17. $6.24 × 576 **$3,594.24**

18. $23.85 × 230 **$5,485.50**

19. $17.89 × 63 **$1,127.07**

20. 0.022 × $7,000 **$154.00**

21. 0.054 × $5,428 **$293.11**

---

4 CLOSE

Closing Activity

Find the monthly premium for workers compensation insurance.

1. Base rate: $4.97 per $100.00. Total monthly payroll: $46,950.00. **$2,333.42**

2. Base rate: $2.60 per $100.00. Total annual payroll: $294,137.00. **$637.30**

3. The owner of a landscaping company pays the base rate of $15.75 per $100.00 paid in wages. The payroll for the Verde Landscaping for one month is $27,995.00. What is the monthly premium for workers compensation insurance? **$4,409.21**

4. A company pays a state tax of 3.1 percent on the first $7,000 of each employee's annual wage. What is the federal and state unemployment insurance tax paid on an employee that earns annual wages of $38,000? **$217; $217**

WRAP-UP

Go over any problem for which a wrong answer is given.

Assignment Guide
  Basic: 2–6
  Average: 7–8

20 min.

National Standards for Business Education

Standard 1	Mathematical Foundations
Standard 2	Number Relationships and Operations
Standard 6	Problem-Solving Strategy

National Council of Teachers of Mathematics Standards

Standard 1	Numbers and Operations
Standard 6	Problem Solving
Standard 8	Communication

 **FOCUS**

Discuss reasons why employees travel for business. Point out that travel expenses are often reimbursed. **Mention that sometimes travel is mandatory, such as to sell a product, and sometimes it is optional, such as to attend a workshop.**

In-Class Examples
Work through these exercises with students before having them do the Self-Check.
1. 39 × $0.24 **$9.36**
2. 121 × $0.20 **$24.20**
3. 319 × $0.22 **$70.18**
4. $10.35 + $28.32 + $12.38 + $17.15 + $26.08 **$94.28**

SECTION 13-6 Travel Expenses

○ **Section Objective**

Calculate total business travel expenses.

If you travel for your business, you'll probably be reimbursed, or paid back, for all authorized expenses during your trip. **Travel expenses** usually include transportation, lodging, and meals. Remember that:

$$\begin{array}{l}\text{Total Travel} \\ \text{Expenses}\end{array} = \begin{array}{l}\text{Cost of} \\ \text{Transportation}\end{array} + \begin{array}{l}\text{Cost of} \\ \text{Lodging}\end{array} + \begin{array}{l}\text{Cost of} \\ \text{Meals}\end{array} + \begin{array}{l}\text{Additional} \\ \text{Costs}\end{array}$$

Living in the Real World

Finding the Right Person

Expense Account Takahashi drives 230 miles to a meeting. Computer Systems compensates Takahashi for all his out-of-pocket expenses, including gasoline and food expenses.

Draw Conclusions After the meeting ended, Takahashi was stranded in town because of a blizzard. Do you think Computer Systems pays for his hotel and restaurant expenses in a situation like this?

Continued on page 443

(**Example 1**)

The accounting department of Diversified Sales Company will reimburse Roger Martin for attending a 3-day marketing conference. He drove to the conference, so Diversified will pay him $0.35 per mile. Martin's expenses included the following:

Expense Category	Amount
Hotel (9/6)	$174.50
Hotel (9/7)	174.50
Tolls	7.20
Conference Reg.	95.00
Meals (9/6)	29.12
Meals (9/7)	48.20
Meals (9/8)	19.37
Mileage	(240 miles round-trip)

What is the total cost of sending Martin to the conference?

Living in the Real World

It's very likely. If an employee is traveling for business and is delayed for any reason beyond his or her control, most companies would reimburse them for any additional travel expenses.

TECHNOLOGY POWER

Companies use corporate cards such as American Express to track business expenses. Employees can complete expense reports online and have the ability to import the transactions directly from American Express. American Express sends summary reports showing expenditures in various areas. The company is then able to negotiate special rates with airlines, hotel chains, and car rental companies.

STEP 1: Find the cost of transportation.
$$(240 \times \$0.35) + \$7.20 =$$
$$\$84.00 \quad + \$7.20 = \$91.20$$

STEP 2: Find the cost of lodging.
$$2 \times \$174.50 = \$349.00$$

STEP 3: Find the cost of meals.
$$\$29.12 + \$48.20 + \$19.37 = \$96.69$$

STEP 4: Find the additional costs.
Conference registration = $95.00

STEP 5: Find the total travel expenses.

Cost of Transportation	+	Cost of Lodging	+	Cost of Meals	+	Additional Costs
$91.20	+	$349.00	+	$96.69	+	$95.00

= **$631.89 total travel expenses**

240 ⨉ .35 = 84 ＋ 7.2 = 91.20 M+ 2 ⨉ 174.5 =

349 M+ 29.12 ＋ 48.20 ＋ 19.37 = 96.69 M+

95 ＋ RM = 631.89

CONCEPT CHECK

SELF-CHECK ✔

Complete the problem, then check your answer at the end of the chapter.

1. Cost of transportation, $476; cost of lodging, $219; cost of meals, $147.80; additional costs, $89. Find the total travel expenses.
$476.00 + $219.00 + $147.80 + $89.00 = $931.80

SECTION 13-6 PRACTICE

Complete the table for these business trips.

	Name	Miles Traveled	Transportation Cost (at $0.32/mile)	Meals	Hotel Room	Total Expenses
2.	T. Willis	48	$15.36	$ 27.80	$ 65.48	a. **$108.64**
3.	B. Henry	80	a. **$25.60**	46.90	0.00	b. **$72.50**
4.	M. Diaz	240	a. **$76.80**	71.95	189.40	b. **$338.15**
5.	V. Tarski	180	a. **$57.60**	70.40	210.00	b. **$338.00**
6.	T. Lanza	417	a. **$133.44**	238.51	314.90	b. **$686.85**
7.	B. Pappas	623	a. **$199.36**	291.94	516.85	b. **$1,008.15**

Continued on next page

USING CALCULATORS

In problems that require a large number of steps to complete, it may not be wise or practical to perform all operations in one keystroke sequence. Break larger problems into smaller steps. Be careful not to round irrational answers until all calculations are completed. The "store" key on your calculator may be useful.

② TEACH

Have students discuss each of the costs in the travel expense formula. Have students give examples of expenses involved in transportation, lodging, and meals. Then have students list additional costs that may arise when traveling on business. Point out some expenses that would not likely be reimbursed. Mention that it is usually the responsibility of the employee to keep track of travel expenses. Sometimes there are limits for certain expenses like meals. Employees may need to provide receipts from their travel expenses to their employer. Often there are specific forms that need to be completed and approved before an employee is reimbursed.

Motivating the Lesson

Mandy Katz attended a 2-day workshop for professional development. She spent $128.50 on train fare, $205.90 on lodging, $251.25 on meals, and $128.00 on registration. What was Katz's total travel expense? **$713.65**

In-Class Examples

Find the total travel expense.
1. Transportation: $298.
   Lodging: $412.
   Meals: $98.65.
   Additional costs: $50. **$858.65**
2. Airfare: $426.60.
   Hotel: 2 nights at $112.50 each.
   Meals: $108.46. **$760.06**
3. Transportation: 30 miles at $0.22 per mile.
   Lunch: $14.28.
   Conference registration: $65.
   $85.88

3 ASSESS

Error Analysis

Finding total travel expenses can involve several calculations. Encourage students to identify each type of cost, and find the individual sum for that cost category before combining with other costs.

Students need to make sure when they calculate mileage expenses that they are using the appropriate units. If a problem states that mileage reimbursement is 22 cents per mile, students should know they need to write this as $0.22 since the other expenses will be given in terms of dollars.

4 CLOSE

Closing Activity

Find the total travel expense.

1. Transportation: $329.04.
   Lodging: $385.44.
   Meals: $149.53.
   Additional costs: $108.29.
   $972.30
2. Train fare: $90.65.
   Hotel: 3 nights at $98.75 each.
   Meals: $87.88.
   Registration: $82. **$556.78**
3. Mileage: 52 miles at $0.24 per mile.
   Hotel: 1 night at $89.55.
   Meals: $67.43. **$169.46**
4. Airfare: $290.78.
   Hotel: 5 nights at $88.65 each.
   Meals: $197.58.
   Additional costs: $89.50.
   $1,021.11

8. Tomas Englasias.
   Airfare: $488.
   Hotel: 3 nights at $174.50 each.
   Meals: $117.45.
   Registration: $275.
   What are his total travel expenses? **$1,403.95**

9. Carol Cipriani.
   Train: $147.85.
   Hotel: 2 nights at $110 each.
   Meals: $71.85.
   Conference registration: $85.
   What are her total travel expenses? **$524.70**

10. Kobe Landis is a software troubleshooter for Advanced Software, Inc. He travels to various installations to de-bug their programs. This month his travel expenses included airplane fares of $617.60 and $347.80, 156 miles of driving at $0.33 per mile, taxicab fares of $17.25 and $14.50, and meals totaling $176.85. What were his total travel expenses for the month? **$1,225.48**

11. Cho Wan Sey, a sales representative for Curry Corporation, flew to New York City to make a sales presentation. Airfare was $515. She rented a car for 3 days for $51.40 a day plus $0.32 a mile. She drove a total of 70 miles. Her hotel bill was $184.50 a night for 2 nights. Her meals cost $11.90, $24.85, $9.76, $14.91, $37.80, $9.80, and $14.90. What were Sey's total travel expenses? **$1,184.52**

12. Phil Fitzenrider spent 3 days in Fargo, North Dakota, doing computer training as a consultant. His airfare was $548.52 and he rented a car for 3 days at $39.95 a day, plus $9.56 for gasoline. His hotel was $139.95 a night for 2 nights. His meals were $35.32 the first day, $45.68 the second day, and $17.44 the third day. Find the total travel expenses. **$1,056.27**

MAINTAINING YOUR SKILLS

Need Help? Go to...
▶ Skill 8: **Multiplying Decimals**, page 735
▶ Skill 5: **Adding Decimals**, page 732

Multiply.

13. 350 × $0.21 **$73.50**

14. 900 × $0.23 **$207.00**

15. 620 × $0.22 **$136.40**

16. 145 × $0.21 **$30.45**

17. 540 × $0.20 **$108.00**

18. 450 × $0.22 **$99.00**

19. 422 × $0.33 **$139.26**

20. 2 × $74.90 **$149.80**

21. 3 × $110.80 **$332.40**

22. 5 × $85.71 **$428.55**

23. 3 × $93.47 **$280.41**

24. 4 × $86.90 **$347.60**

Add.

25. $55 + $190 + $100 **$345**

26. $74 + $87 + $219 **$380**

27. $74.85 + $217.47 + $117.95 **$410.27**

28. $184.73 + $67.52 + $347.85 **$600.10**

WRAP-UP

Go over any problem for which a wrong answer is given.

Assignment Guide
   Basic: 2–7
Average: 8–9

20 min.

SECTION 13-7 Employee Training

○ **Section Objective**

Compute total employee training costs.

Your business may pay the expenses involved in training employees. Your company may send you to special job-related programs or may offer special training programs within the company. Expenses for training during regular work hours include the cost of **release time.** When you are granted release time, you are paid your regular wages or salary while you are away from your job. Remember that.

$$\text{Total Training Costs} = \text{Cost of Release Time} + \text{Cost of Instruction} + \text{Additional Costs}$$

Living in the Real World

Finding the Right Person

How a Company and its Employees Help Each Other
Computer Systems encourages its employees to participate in continuing education. If the training will benefit the company, it pays for the education.

Draw Conclusions Why might a company pay for training and higher education?

Continued on page 447

Example 1

Acme Manufacturing Company chose eight employees to attend a training program in computer assisted manufacturing (CAM) held within the company. The employees were paid their regular wages while attending the 2-day program. Their combined wages amounted to $512 per day. The production control manager, who earns $168 per day, was the course instructor. Refreshments were brought in twice a day at a cost of $45.70 per day. Supplies and equipment for the program amounted to $35 per person. What was the total cost for the training program?

STEP 1: Find the cost of release time.
2 days × $512.00 = $1,024.00 release time

STEP 2: Find the cost of instruction.
2 days × $168.00 = $336.00 instruction cost

STEP 3: Find the additional costs.
(2 × $45.70) + (8 × $35.00) =
91.40   + $280.00   = $371.40 additional costs

Continued on next page

Section 13-7 Employee Training ▶ **443**

Living in the Real World

Training and higher education can contribute to making the employee a better, more knowledgeable, more effective worker, which obviously benefits the company.

National Standards for Business Education

Standard 1	Mathematical Foundations
Standard 2	Number Relationships and Operations
Standard 6	Problem-Solving Strategy

National Council of Teachers of Mathematics Standards

Standard 1	Numbers and Operations
Standard 6	Problem Solving
Standard 8	Communication

① FOCUS

Ask students why they think an employer may pay for employees to undergo training. Discuss various types of training as they apply to different professions. List the costs that may be involved with each type.

In-Class Examples
Work through these exercises with students before having them do the Self-Check.
1. $124.50 + $208.95 + $49.62
   $383.07
2. (2 × $128.65) + $523.45
   $780.75
3. (3 × $238.87) + (3 × $87.50)
   $979.11

② TEACH

Point out the similarities between the total training cost formula and the total travel expense formula. Mention that employee training can take place at a location other than the location of the employer. Therefore, employees undergoing training can sometimes incur travel expenses. Give students an example where the two formulas can be used together.

Students may not be familiar with the concept of *release time*. Make sure that students understand that this is a cost to the employer. Even though employees are away from their job to attend training, they are still getting paid their regular salary.

Motivating the Lesson

An employer trains 3 new employees. The training lasts 5 days, and the employees are paid $150.65 per day. The total cost for instruction is $675, and supplies for the training cost are $43.35 per person. What is the total training cost? **$3,064.80**

In-Class Examples

Find the total training cost.
1. Cost of release time: $1,052.
   Cost of instruction: $568.
   $1,620
2. Cost of release time: $2,380.
   Cost of instruction: $436.
   Additional costs: $250. **$3,066**
3. Cost of release time: $1,034.75.
   Cost of instruction: $674.51.
   Total travel expenses: $1,673.36.
   $3,382.62

STEP 4: Find the total training cost.

Cost of Release Time	+	Cost of Instruction	+	Additional Costs
$1,024.00	+	$336.00	+	$371.40

= **$1,731.40 total training cost**

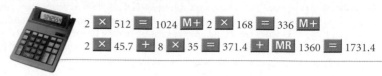

CONCEPT CHECK

SELF-CHECK ✓

Complete the problem, then check your answer at the end of the chapter.

1. Cost of release time, $1,247; cost of instruction, $250; additional costs, $140. Find the total training cost. **$1,247 + $250 + $140 = $1,637**

SECTION 13-7 PRACTICE

Determine the total training cost.

	Number of Days	Daily Cost of Release Time	Daily Cost of Instruction	Daily Cost of Supplies	Total Training Cost
2.	1	$417	$ 75	$ 50	**$542**
3.	1	545	250	120	**$915**
4.	4	345	175	100	**$2,480**
5.	3	716	200	30	**$2,838**
6.	2	96	150	25	**$542**
7.	5	176	100	15	**$1,455**

8. Three orthopedic surgeons attend a 2-day seminar.
   Release time: $980 per surgeon per day.
   Instruction: $675 per surgeon per day.
   Supplies: $425 per surgeon per day.
   What is the total training cost? **$12,480.00**

9. Five marketing representatives attend 3-day workshops to learn about a new product.
   Release time: $930 per day.
   Instruction: $85 per person.
   Travel expense: $285 per person.
   Meal expense: $50 per person per day.
   What is the total training cost? **$5,390.00**

THINKING CRITICALLY

Earnings Disparity

Although the amount women earn in weekly wages has steadily increased over the years, women still earn less than men on the average. To illustrate this disparity, convert the data in the table below into a column graph. If possible, use a spreadsheet program and the chart tool. LS , P

Year	Women	Men
5	$413	$605
10	432	599
15	441	559
20	490	646

10. The tax department of National Brokerage, Inc., is sending 8 tax advisors to a 2-day seminar on the new Economic Growth and Tax Relief Reconciliation Act. Three of the advisors earn $252 per day, while the other 5 earn $360 per day. Registration costs $350 per person. Materials cost $125 per person. What will the 2-day seminar cost National Brokerage, Inc.? **$8,912**

11. Laser Research, Inc., is sending their 5-person research team to a 3-day conference to learn a new automated lab procedure. One researcher earns $336 daily, 2 earn $360 daily, and 2 earn $390 daily. What will the 3-day conference cost Laser Research, Inc., in lost productivity for the 5 researchers? **$5,508**

12. Six employees of the Solar Energy Company underwent a 5-day sales training program. Their wage rate averaged $19.65 per hour for an 8-hour day. The sales manager, at a daily salary of $246.53, conducted the 5-day session. Refreshments cost $57.50 per day. Sales kits were provided for each of the 6 employees at a cost of $86.45 each. What was the total cost of the sales training program? **$6,754.85**

13. Adelphia Brokers, a full service brokerage house, brought in William N. Thomas, a specialist in financial stock, to meet with their 15 brokers. Mr. Thomas charged a fee of $2,500 for the 4-hour session. The average hourly rate for the 15 brokers was $50.00 per hour. Lunch for the 15 brokers and Mr. Thomas was $14.50 per person. What was the total cost for the 4-hour financial stock training session? **$5,732**

14. Forestry Consultants brought in Tom Collins, an expert on pruning trees, to train 8 summer employees. Collins charged a fee of $350.00 for a hands-on, 8-hour training session. The summer employees are paid $10.50 an hour. Lunch was $6.50 per person. Each trainee was furnished with a pruning saw that sells for $56.25 each. What is the total cost of the training? **$1,530.50**

MAINTAINING YOUR SKILLS

Need Help? Go to...
➤ Skill 8: **Multiplying Decimals**, page 735
➤ Skill 10: **Dividing (Decimal Remainder)**, page 737
➤ Skill 5: **Adding Decimals**, page 732

Multiply.

15. $4 \times \$145$ **$580**

16. $5 \times \$112$ **$560**

17. $8 \times \$74$ **$592**

18. $3 \times \$716$ **$2,148**

Divide. Round answers to the nearest cent.

19. $\$47,650 \div 52$ **$916.35**

20. $\$34,840 \div 52$ **$670**

21. $\$28,645 \div 260$ **$110.17**

Add.

22. $\$1,076 + \$345 + \$130$ **$1,551**

23. $\$916 + \$718 + \$215$ **$1,849**

24. $\$1,240.76 + \$337.50 + \$27.85$ **$1,606.11**

25. $\$3,167.25 + \$175.86 + \$47.95$ **$3,391.06**

 **ASSESS**

Error Analysis

Since many of the employee training problems involve multiple employees attending training on more than one day, students need to remember to multiply. Have students first practice finding only the cost of release time and cost of instruction. Give students some basic exercises. For example, find the cost of release time for 3 people earning $98.50 a day being trained for 2 days. By practicing these types of exercises, students will be more confident when they have to calculate the total training cost. Remind students to read each problem carefully and pick out all of the relevant information.

4 CLOSE

Closing Activity

Find the total training cost.
1. Cost of release time: $1,805.68. Cost of instruction: $229.77. Additional costs: $139.82. **$2,175.27**
2. Cost of release time: $845.79. Cost of instruction: $127.30. Additional costs: $91.42. **$1,064.51**
3. Cost of release time: $8,270.31. Cost of instruction: $1,245. Total travel expenses: $2,328.45. **$11,843.76**
4. Six employees earning $124.80 per day attend a training program for 3 days. The training costs $185.00 per person plus a total of $35.25 for supplies. What is the total training cost? **$3,391.65**

WRAP-UP

Go over any problem for which a wrong answer is given.

Assignment Guide
  Basic: 2–7
  Average: 8–9

20 min.

Quick Quiz

1. A company spends $295.70 on advertising, $394.32 on interviewing, and $2,268.65 on hiring to recruit an employee. What is the total recruiting cost? **$2,958.67**

2. John Roderick earns $12.75 an hour. He receives a merit increase of 3.5 percent. What is his new hourly rate? **$13.20**

3. An employee's annual gross pay is $32,450 with total benefits of $742.00. What is the rate of benefits? **2.3%**

4. Allen Viro is 48 years old and now disabled after working for 28 years. He was expected to retire at age 65. His final average salary is $53,280 and his rate of benefits is 2 percent. What is his monthly disability benefit? **$3,996**

5. Four employees undergo training for 2 days. The employees each earn $32,620 per year. The cost of instruction is $850. What is the total training cost? **$1,853.69**

SECTION 13-1 **CONCEPT CHECK** (p. 425)

1. $2,150 + ($245 + $315) + ($1,240 + $2,170) =
   $2,150 + $560 + $3,410 = **$6,120**

2. $1,975 + ($470 + $860) + ($475 + $8,600 + $11,415) =
   $1,975 + $1,330 + $20,490 = **$23,795**

SECTION 13-2 **CONCEPT CHECK** (p. 428)

1. $45,000 + (2.8% × $45,000) + (2% × $45,000) =
   $45,000 + $1,260 + $900 = **$47,160**

2. $40,000 + (3% × $40,000) + (3.8% × $40,000) =
   $40,000 + $1,200 + $1,520 = **$42,720**

SECTION 13-3 **CONCEPT CHECK** (p. 431)

1. $9,600 ÷ $32,000 = **30%**

2. **a.** Total benefits: $840.77 + $1,275.00 + $1,005.56 + $1,355.32 + $316.97 + $486.26 = **$5,279.88**
   b. Rate of benefits: $5,279.88 ÷ $21,860.00 = 24.153% = **24.2%**

SECTION 13-4 **CONCEPT CHECK** (p. 434)

1. Annual disability benefit: **$21,510.00;** Monthly benefit: **$1,792.50**

2. **$531 (one person)**

SECTION 13-5 **CONCEPT CHECK** (p. 437, 438)

1. $2.12 × ($21,780 ÷ $100) = $461.736 = **$461.74**

2. Moore: FUTA—(6.2% − 1.1%) × $7,000.00 = **$357**
   SUTA—1.1% × $7,000.00 = **$77.00**
   Kinder: FUTA—(6.2% − 1.1%) × $7,000.00 = **$357**
   SUTA—1.1% × $7,000.00 = **$77.00**
   Bender: FUTA—(6.2% − 1.1%) × $5,378.90 = **$274.32**
   SUTA—1.1% × $5,378.90 = **$59.17**

SECTION 13-6 **CONCEPT CHECK** (p. 441)

1. $476.00 + $219.00 + $147.80 + $89.00 = **$931.80**

SECTION 13-7 **CONCEPT CHECK** (p. 444)

1. $1,247 + $250 + $140 = **$1,637**

Living in the Real World

Finding the Right Person

Assessment You learned the duties of Takahashi. He enjoys his job, which requires understanding company policy development, reading charts, calculating wages and benefits, and making projections about the company's future personnel costs. Takahashi has been writing a want ad for a graphic artist.

1 Defining. Research newspapers or online job boards for a graphic artist. What qualifications must a person have for this position? Write an ad of your own.

2 Creating. At this stage of your life, you might not have a lot of work experience. Show a future employer you're still qualified for the job even if you've never done it before. To showcase your qualifications, create a *functional résumé*. This highlights your skills and related accomplishments, while de-emphasizing your work history.

Living in the Real World

1. Answers will vary depending on what position students pick.
2. Each functional résumé will vary depending on students' experiences. An objective, skill qualifications (e.g., computer skills, administration skills, and organizational skills), work experience, and education are all categories common on the functional résumé.

REVIEW OF KEY WORDS

recruiting (p. 424)
salary scale (p. 427)
cost-of-living adjustment (p. 427)
merit increase (p. 427)
employee benefits (p. 430)

disability insurance (p. 433)
workers compensation insurance (p. 436)
unemployment insurance (p. 437)
travel expenses (p. 440)
release time (p. 443)

Use the key words above to fill in the sentences below.

1. The personnel department may use a **salary scale** to compare the salaries of various jobs.

2. **recruiting** may include the cost of advertising in a newspaper.

3. Paid vacation and holidays are **employee benefits** that most businesses give their employees.

4. When training sessions are held during work hours, the cost of **release time** is one of the expenses.

5. If a job requires travel, the employee may be reimbursed for **travel expenses** such as transportation, lodging, and meals.

6. A _____ is a raise in an employee's salary based on economic factors.

7. _____ pays benefits to an individual who must miss work because of an illness or injury.

8. A **merit increase** is a raise in your salary to reward you for doing good work.

6. cost-of-living adjustment
7. disability insurance

Study Guide and Assessment ▶ **447**

Skills and Concepts

SECTION OBJECTIVE 13-1 AND EXAMPLES

Calculate the cost of recruiting new employees.

Goosen Department Store is searching for a person to head its human resources department. Goosen placed advertisements in newspapers all over the Southeast for a total cost of $5,432.34. Goosen's interviewed 3 candidates and paid the travel expenses for each. These expenses totaled $3,245.90. After the interviews Goosen hired Monica Cain at an annual salary of $85,400 and paid her moving expenses of $4,598. What was the total expense of recruiting Cain?

STEP: Find the total recruiting cost.

$$\begin{array}{ccccc} \text{Advertising} & & \text{Interviewing} & & \text{Hiring} \\ \text{Expenses} & + & \text{Expenses} & + & \text{Expenses} \\ \$5,432.34 & + & \$3,245.90 & + & \$4,598 \end{array} = \$13,276.24 \text{ total recruiting cost}$$

REVIEW EXERCISES

Find the total recruiting cost.

	Advertising Cost	Interviewing Cost	Hiring Cost	Total Recruiting Cost
9.	$ 526.15	$ 87.54	$ 398.45	$1,012.14
10.	784.33	98.45	983.22	$1,866.00
11.	1,540.23	432.98	976.54	$2,949.75
12.	2,690.99	873.09	1,002.87	$4,566.95

SECTION OBJECTIVE 13-2 AND EXAMPLES

Compute the new salary after merit increase and cost-of-living adjustment.

Lorena Irwin is a stockbroker for a firm in Topeka, Kansas. Her current salary is $43,260 per year. This year she received a cost-of-living adjustment of 2.8 percent and a merit increase of 4.7 percent for excellent work during the year. What will Irwin's salary be for the coming year?

STEP 1: Find the present salary.
The present salary is $43,260.00

STEP 2: Find the cost-of-living adjustment.

$$\begin{array}{ccc} \text{Salary} & \times & \text{Cost-of-Living Adjustment Percent} \\ \$43,260.00 \times & & 2.8\% \end{array} = \$1,211.28$$

REINFORCEMENT

Section 13-1

1. Trebor Technology is recruiting for a programmer position that pays an annual salary of $38,000.00. The company spends $859.50 in advertisements and hires the Quality Employment Agency to search for candidates. Quality's fee is 25 percent of the first-year salary. Trebor spends $1,287.98 on interviews and hires one of Quality's candidates. What is Trebor's total recruiting cost? **$11,647.48**

STEP 3: Find the merit increase.

Salary × Merit Increase Percent

$43,260.00 × 4.7% = $2,033.22

STEP 4: Find the new salary.

Present Salary + Cost-of-Living Adjustment + Merit Increase

$43,260 + $1,211.28 + $2,033.22 = **$46,504.50 new salary**

REVIEW EXERCISES

Find the new salary.

	Present Salary	Cost-of-Living Adjustment	Merit Increase	New Salary
13.	$ 28,500	$1,140	$1,500	**$31,140**
14.	43,900	1,756	0	**$45,656**
15.	56,900	2,276	1,000	**$60,176**
16.	65,000	2,600	1,500	**$69,100**
17.	101,500	4,060	3,500	**$109,060**
18.	28,650	1,146	1,900	**$31,696**

19. a. $2,511.54
b. $2,350.80
c. $2,260.35
d. $4,048.60
e. $946.85
f. $12,118.17
g. 18.55769

20. a. $1,230.77
b. $1,152
c. $1,107.69
d. $1,984.00
e. $464
f. $5,938.46
g. 18.55769

21. a. $846.15
b. $792
c. $761.54
d. $1,364.00
e. $319
f. $4,082.69
g. 18.55768

22. a. $1,211.54
b. $1,134
c. $1,090.35
d. $1,953.00
e. $456.75
f. $5,845.64
g. 18.55768

SECTION OBJECTIVE 13-3 AND EXAMPLES

Work out the rate of employee benefits on annual gross pay.

Rena Tanaka earns an annual salary of $54,320. Her benefits total $20,641.60. Tanaka's total annual benefits are what percent of her annual salary?

STEP: Find the rate of benefits.

Total Benefits ÷ Annual Gross Pay

$20,641.60 ÷ $54,320 – 38%

23. a. $1,361.54 **e.** $513.30
b. $1,274.40 **f.** $7,082.65
c. $1,225.38 **g.** 20.01%
d. $2,708.10

REVIEW EXERCISES

Complete the benefits chart for the OMY Music Store employees.

	Position	Annual Wage	2-Week Vacation	3.6% Workers Comp.	9-Day Sick Leave	6.2% FICA	1.45% Medicare	Total Benefits	Rate of Benefits
19.	Manager	$65,300	a.	b.	c.	d.	e.	f.	g.
20.	Technician	32,000	a.	b.	c.	d.	e.	f.	g.
21.	Cashier	22,000	a.	b.	c.	d.	e.	f.	g.
22.	Instructor	31,500	a.	b.	c.	d.	e.	f.	g.
23.	Marketing mgr	35,400	a.	b.	c.	d.	e.	f.	g.

REINFORCEMENT

Section 13-2

1. Mark Webb earns $10.70 an hour. He receives a merit increase of 4.5 percent. What is his new hourly rate? **$11.18**

2. Kendra Gomez earned $48,214.00 last year. This year she receives a cost-of-living adjustment of 4.2 percent and a merit increase of 2.9 percent. What is her new salary? **$51,637.19**

Section 13-3

1. 30 × ($425 ÷ 5) **$2,550**

2. $3,400 is what percent of $42,800? **7.9%**

SECTION OBJECTIVE 13-4 AND EXAMPLES

Figure out disability benefits under independent retirement systems and under Social Security.

Bernice Martin had worked at the Pacific Train Station for 19 years when she became permanently disabled and couldn't continue to work. Martin was 43 years of age and had planned to work until she was 65. Her final average salary was $31,298. The rate of benefits is 1.9 percent. What is Martin's monthly disability benefit?

STEP 1: Find the annual disability benefit.

$$\left(\begin{array}{c} \text{Years} \\ \text{Worked} \end{array} + \begin{array}{c} \text{Expected} \\ \text{Retirement} \\ \text{Age} \end{array} - \begin{array}{c} \text{Present} \\ \text{Age} \end{array} \right) \times \begin{array}{c} \text{Rate of} \\ \text{Benefits} \end{array} \times \begin{array}{c} \text{Final} \\ \text{Average} \\ \text{Salary} \end{array}$$

$$(19 \ + \ 65 \ - \ 43) \ \times \ 1.9\% \ \times \ \$31,298$$
$$= \$24,381.14 \text{ annual disability benefit}$$

STEP 2: Find the monthly disability benefit.
$$\$24,381.14 \div 12 = \$2,031.76 \text{ monthly disability benefit}$$

REVIEW EXERCISES

Find the annual and monthly disability benefits.

	Years Worked	Expected Retirement Age	Present Age	Rate of Benefits	Average Salary	Annual Disability Benefit	Monthly Disability Benefit
24.	10	65	30	2.00%	$45,000	a.	b.
25.	15	60	35	1.80%	38,000	a.	b.
26.	18	62	40	2.10%	56,000	a.	b.
27.	24	55	50	2.20%	65,000	a.	b.
28.	29	65	62	1.75%	98,000	a.	b.
29.	12	62	45	2.10%	36,800	a.	b.

24. a. $40,500
    b. $3,375

25. a. $27,360
    b. $2,280

26. a. $47,040
    b. $3,920

27. a. $41,470
    b. $3,455.83

28. a. $54,880
    b. $4,573.33

29. a. $22,411.20
    b. $1,867.60

SECTION OBJECTIVE 13-5 AND EXAMPLES

Compute the employer cost for workers compensation and unemployment insurance.

The base rate for workers compensation insurance for miners in one state is $22.50 per $100 paid to employees. The total monthly payroll for a small underground mine is $125,000. What is the monthly premium for workers compensation insurance?

STEP: Find the premium for workers compensation insurance.
$$\text{Base Rate} \times \quad (\text{Total Payroll} \div 100)$$
$$\$22.50 \quad \times \quad (\$125,000.00 \div \$100.00)$$
$$= \$28,125.00 \text{ premium}$$

REINFORCEMENT

Section 13-4

1. Joe Yanni worked for 31 years before becoming disabled at age 59. His expected retirement age was 70 and his final salary was $65,285. His rate of benefits is 2.0 percent. What is Yanni's disability benefit? **$54,839.40**

A Midwestern contractor firm has some unemployment during the year and must pay a state unemployment tax (SUTA) of 5.4 percent. That leaves 0.8 percent (6.2% − 5.4%) for the federal unemployment tax (FUTA). Compute the federal and state unemployment tax for Leotis Brown who has annual wages of $22,875.

STEP 1: Find the federal unemployment tax.

Federal Tax Rate = 6.2% − 5.4%
= 0.8% (federal tax rate)

Federal Tax Amount = Federal Tax Rate × First $7,000 of Annual Wages
= 0.8% × $7,000
= $56.00 federal unemployment tax

STEP 2: Find the state unemployment tax.

State Tax Amount = State Tax Rate × First $7,000 of Annual Wages
= 5.4% × $7,000
= $378.00 state unemployment tax

Employee	Annual Wage	Amount Taxed	Federal Tax (0.8%)	State Tax (5.4%)
Leotis Brown	$22,875	$7,000	$56.00	$378.00

REVIEW EXERCISES

Find the monthly premium for workers compensation insurance.

	Type of Business	Monthly Payroll	Base Rate per $100	Monthly Premium
30.	Building construction	$52,100	$13.42	$6,991.82
31.	Delivery service	2,450	4.05	$99.23

Find the federal and state unemployment tax.

	Employee	Annual Wage	Amount Taxed	Federal Tax (0.8%)	State Tax (5.4%)
32.	Julio Lopez	$6,895	$6,895	$55.16	$372.33
33.	Fumiko Woo	4,650	4,650	$37.20	$251.10

SECTION OBJECTIVE 13-6 AND EXAMPLES

Calculate the total business travel expenses.

The network department of Taylor Medical Corporation will reimburse Belinda Smith for attending a 2-day conference. Smith drove to the conference, so Taylor will pay her $0.32 per mile. Smith's expenses include: hotel, $89.50 for 1 night; meals, $83.21; and registration, $125. She drove 185 miles round trip. What is the total cost of sending Smith to the conference?

Continued on next page

REINFORCEMENT

Section 13-5
1. A company pays a state tax of 4.2 percent on the first $7,000 of each employee's annual wage. What are the federal and state unemployment insurance taxes paid on an employee that earns annual wages of $25,690? **$140; $294**

Section 13-6
1. Joseph Sandis, a marketing representative for Sully Seafood, recently traveled out of town for a sales conference. His travel expenses included $358.00 for airfare, a car rental for 4 days at $24.25 a day, plus a fuel charge of $16.00. His hotel bill was $429.60 and his meals cost $84.38. What was Sandis's total travel expense? **$984.98**

STEP: Find the total cost of travel expenses.

$$\underset{\text{Transportation}}{\text{Cost of}} + \underset{\text{Lodging}}{\text{Cost of}} + \underset{\text{Meals}}{\text{Cost of}} + \underset{\text{Costs}}{\text{Additional}}$$

$$(185 \times \$0.32) \; + \; \$89.50 \; + \; \$83.21 \; + \; \$125 \; = \$356.91 \text{ total cost of travel expenses}$$

REVIEW EXERCISES
Complete the table for these business trips.

	Name	Miles	Cost at $0.32/mile	Meals	Hotel Room	Total Expenses
34.	J. Wheaton	58	a. $18.56	$ 21.50	$ 88.58	b. $128.64
35.	C. Dunn	103	a. $32.96	35.43	101.22	b. $169.61
36.	M. Glenn	324	a. $103.68	84.33	154.23	b. $342.24
37.	L. Dalton	194	a. $62.08	54.22	75.34	b. $191.64
38.	S. Jenkins	459	a. $146.88	109.33	187.33	b. $443.54
39.	C. Raymer	742	a. $237.44	119.34	256.44	b. $613.22

SECTION OBJECTIVE 13-7 AND EXAMPLES

Compute the total employee training costs.

BR and Associates, an animal research company, plans to train two of its employees on new accounting software. The employees were paid their regular wages while attending the 2-day training. Their combined wages totaled $623.50 per day. A consultant was hired to conduct the training. She was paid $300.00 per day. The cost of supplies was $39.54 per day. What was the cost for the training program?

STEP: Find the total training cost.

$$\underset{\text{Release Time}}{\text{Cost of}} + \underset{\text{Instruction}}{\text{Cost of}} + \underset{\text{Costs}}{\text{Additional}}$$

$$(623.50 \times 2) \; + \; (\$300.00 \times 2) + (\$39.54 \times 2) \; = \$1,926.08 \text{ total training cost}$$

REVIEW EXERCISES
Find the total training cost.

	Number of Days	Daily Cost of Release Time	Daily Cost of Instruction	Daily Cost of Supplies	Total Training Cost
40.	1	$ 850	$ 500	$ 50	$1,400
41.	2	1,650	800	60	$5,020.00
42.	5	3,250	350	75	$18,375.00
43.	1	660	1,000	100	$1,760
44.	3	1,040	320	45	$4,215.00
45.	1	325	185	30	$540

REINFORCEMENT

Section 13-7
1. Jergen Pharmaceuticals is sending 7 technicians to a 2-day conference. Five of the technicians earn $186.00 per day while the other 2 earn $138.80 per day. Registration costs $128.00 per person. What is the total training cost? **$3,311.20**

Alternative Assessment

Count Me In: *How You'll Use Math*

Where You'll Want to Be   Before you can figure out what you want to do with your life, you'll need to get a little introspective. In order to find the job for you, try to analyze yourself, assess the job market, and develop a personal package, such as a résumé and application.

To determine your career goals, ask yourself: Where do I want to be five years from now? The five-year career plan is the standard life-planning strategy. So, how about some strategies?

46. Get yourself ready by putting together a personal portfolio. This helps you think and talk about your skills to a future employer. On a separate sheet of paper, use these basic categories to write down your ideas of what to include in your portfolio. **Answers will vary.**

   • Foundation Skills: List your achievements in reading, writing, mathematics, speaking, and/or listening. What subjects do you enjoy most?

   • Thinking Skills: Assess situations or times when you used critical thinking, creative thinking, decision making, problem solving, and/or reasoning.

   • Personal Qualities: Describe experiences when you demonstrated responsibility, self-esteem, dependability, social ability, integrity, and/or self-management.

   • Resource Management: Illustrate your achievements in management of time, money, space and facilities, and human resources.

   • Information Management: Show how you've acquired, organized, maintained, and evaluated information, and used computers to process this information.

   • Technology: Highlight your analytical skills by including documentation that reflects how you select, apply, and/or maintain current technology.

47. In order to find your ideal job, answer the questions below on a separate piece of paper. **Answers will vary.**

   • Which products or services are you interested in?

   • Which position do you want?

   • Do you want a career opportunity that offers training, educational opportunities, promotions, and perks?

   • You want to live and work in what city or geographical area?

   • How much do you want to make?

Thinking Critically

Generally, there are four ways to find a job: hidden job market, want ads, employment agencies, and other methods. Sixty-three percent of jobs are found and filled through word-of-mouth. Does it take more effort to find a job in a hidden job market (i.e., positions not publicly listed) than through other resources? Defend your answer.

Cumulative Test Prep

Aligned and verified by
The Princeton Review

Test-Taking Tip
As part of your preparation for a standardized test, review basic definitions and formulas. For example, the taxable wage base for unemployment tax is calculated on the first $7,000 paid in wages. Do not calculate the unemployment tax on the entire yearly salary. You can write definitions and formulas on index cards to use in review.

SECTION ONE: MULTIPLE CHOICE

This section contains eight multiple-choice questions. After working each problem, write the letter of the correct answer on your paper.

1. Russell Kirby is employed by Dental Associates. The annual premium for a comprehensive medical insurance program is $3,160. His employer pays 70 percent of the cost. How much does Kirby pay? **A**

   (A) $948   (B) $1,050
   (C) $1,108   (D) $2,212

2. Nancy King has her health insurance with a health maintenance organization. She has a $10 co-pay for each physician visit, a $15 co-pay for each physical therapy visit, and an annual deductible of $300. Last year she had 12 physician visits and 20 physical therapy visits. What is the total amount she paid? **D**

   (A) $120   (B) $300
   (C) $420   (D) $720

3. Monte Onstenk purchases a $60,000 5-year term life insurance policy. The annual base premium is $14.10 per $1,000. What is his annual premium? **B**

   (A) $659   (B) $846
   (C) $1,430.95   (D) $2,350

4. The Hi-Tech Corporation hired Albert Jent for a new administrative assistant position at an annual salary of $23,500. The hiring costs included advertising, $315; interview costs, $140; and office agency fee, 20 percent of first year's salary. What was the total cost of hiring Jent? **C**

   (A) $455   (B) $565
   (C) $5,155   (D) $11,450

5. Tonia Irwin is a statistician for Heritage Insurance Company. She earns $36,500 annually. Irwin receives a 4.1 percent cost-of-living increase and a 3.4 percent merit increase. What is her new salary? **C**

   (A) $37,741.00   (B) $37,996.55
   (C) $39,237.50   (D) $41,387.55

6. Vic Iagulli had worked at Eastern State University for 16 years when he suffered a stroke and became permanently disabled. Iagulli was 49 years of age and had planned to retire at age 60. His final average salary was $42,417.80. Eastern's rate of benefits is 2.1 percent. What is Iagulli's annual disability benefit? **B**

   (A) $23,856.02   (B) $24,050.89
   (C) $25,193.22   (D) $30,380.31

7. Linda Pitts owns 170 shares of Romez International for which she paid $28.88 per share. If the company pays dividends of $1.45 per share, what is the annual yield? **B**

   (A) 4.35%   (B) 5.02%
   (C) 6.43%   (D) 7.75%

8. Rick Reilly owns 70 shares of stock for which he paid a total of $4,472. He sold the stock for $84 per share and paid a sales commission of $50. What was his profit or loss on the investment? **A**

   (A) $1,358 profit (B) $1,358 loss
   (C) $1,458 profit (D) $1,458 loss

SECTION TWO: FREE RESPONSE

This section contains four questions for which you will supply short answers. Write your answers on your paper.

Use the table below for Problems 9 and 10.

Amount per $1 Invested, Compounded Quarterly		
Annual Rate	Interest Period	
	1 year	4 years
10.00%	1.103813	1.484506
10.25%	1.106508	1.499055
10.50%	1.109207	1.513738

9. Kelly Calderon invested $8,000 in a one-year CD. The CD earns interest at a rate of 10 percent compounded quarterly. How much interest will she earn on the date of maturity? **$830.50**

10. Joe Ponderoza invested $4,500 in a certificate of deposit that earns interest at a rate of 10.5 percent and matures after one year. Interest is compounded quarterly. What is the effective yield?
10.9207% = 10.92%

11. Leah O'Grady purchased 300 shares of stock at $44.38 per share. She was charged a $30.00 commission. What was the total amount that she paid for the purchase? **$13,344**

12. Martha Hiller works for the General Gravel Corporation. She earns $28,620 per year. The corporation provides benefits for Hiller. To the nearest percent, what is the rate of benefits?
Vacation:	2 weeks
Holidays:	8 days
Compensation insurance:	3.7%
Unemployment insurance:	4.7%
Social Security:	6.20%
Medicare:	1.45%
	23%

SECTION THREE: OPEN-ENDED

This section contains four open-ended questions. Demonstrate your knowledge by giving a clear, concise solution to each problem. Your score on these problems will depend on how well you do the following:

- Explain your reasoning.
- Show your understanding of mathematics in an organized manner.
- Use charts, graphs, and diagrams in your explanation.
- Show the solution in more than one way or relate it to other situations.
- Investigate beyond the requirements of the problem.

13. Explain why health benefits are important to an employee.

14. Discuss the various types of life insurance, including term, whole life, limited-payment life, and universal life.

13–16. Answers will vary. Use rubric to evaluate.

15. Some places of employment never offer merit increases in pay. How would you feel if you knew that you would get the same cost-of-living raise as everyone else in the organization whether they worked as hard as you or not? Would you still work just as hard? Explain.

16. Respond to this statement: "I don't need disability insurance; I am young. When I turn 50, then maybe I will think about purchasing some."

Mathematics Online

To learn more about calculating the costs of personnel, visit the *Mathematics with Business Applications* Web site at www.busmath.glencoe.com.

National Standards for Business Education

Section Objectives	1. Mathematical Foundations	2. Number Relationships and Operations	3. Patterns, Functions, and Algebra	4. Measurements	5. Statistics and Probability	6. Problem-Solving Applications	
14-1 Manufacturing (pp. 458–460) Compute the prime cost of manufacturing an item.	X	X				X	
14-2 Break-Even Analysis (pp. 461–462) Calculate the break-even point in the number of manufactured units.	X	X				X	
14-3 Quality Control (pp. 463–465) Compute the percent of defective goods and determine if the process is in or out of control.	X	X				X	
14-4 Time Study—Number of Units (pp. 466–468) Use time-study results to compute how many units can be produced.	X	X					
14-5 Time Study—Percent of Time (pp. 469–471) Use the time-study results to compute the percent of time spent on each task.	X	X					
14-6 Packaging (pp. 472–475) Figure out the dimensions of packaging cartons.	X	X				X	

(Source: Reprinted with permission from the National Standards for Business Education, copyright © 2001 by National Business Education Association, 1914 Association Drive, Reston, Virginia 21901-1596)

SCANS Correlation

Foundation Skills

Basic Skills	Reading	Writing	Math	Listening	Speaking	
Thinking Skills	Creative Thinking	Decision Making	Problem Solving	Seeing Things in the Mind's Eye	Knowing How to Learn	Reasoning
Personal Qualities	Responsibility	Self-Esteem	Sociability	Self-Management	Integrity/Honesty	

This chapter's highlighted blocks indicate the chapter's content coverage in the Student Edition and the Teacher Wraparound Edition.

1. Numbers & Operations	2. Algebra	3. Geometry	4. Measurement	5. Data Analysis & Probability	6. Problem Solving	7. Reasoning & Proof	8. Communication	9. Connections	10. Representations
X			X		X		X		
X					X		X		
X			X				X		
X					X		X		
X					X		X		
X		X			X		X		

SCANS Correlation

Workplace Competencies

Resources	Allocating Time	Allocating Money	Allocating Material and Facility Resources	Allocating Human Resources		
Information	Acquiring and Evaluating Information	Organizing and Maintaining Information	Interpreting and Communicating Information	Using Computers to Process Information		
Interpersonal Skills	Participating as a Member of a Team	Teaching Others	Serving Clients/Customers	Exercising Leadership	Negotiating to Arrive at a Decision	Working with Cultural Diversity
Systems	Understanding Systems	Monitoring and Correcting Performance	Improving and Designing Systems			
Technology	Selecting Technology	Applying Technology to Task	Maintaining and Troubleshooting Technology			

CHAPTER 14

Production

What You'll Learn

Tell students that in this chapter on production you'll focus on how much it costs to produce goods and how to find the break-even point. Other topics include how to monitor quality control and to figure out how much room you'll need to store the packaged goods.

Why It's Important

Products are manufactured all over the world based on the resources available in a given area. These resources might include raw materials, supplies from other manufacturers, or labor. The quality of goods is important as lives can be endangered as a result of faulty manufacturing. Consider the effect of a defect in an airplane engine versus a defect in the size that a machine cuts a piece of candy.

Key Word Review

Guess and Check

Attempt to write your own definition for each key word. Then check your definition with the definition in the Glossary. If the definitions are not alike, copy the Glossary definition.

What You'll Learn

Section 14-1 Compute the prime cost of manufacturing an item.

Section 14-2 Calculate the break-even point in the number of manufactured units.

Section 14-3 Compute the percent of defective goods and determine if the process is in or out of control.

Section 14-4 Use time-study results to compute how many units can be produced.

Section 14-5 Use time-study results to compute the percent of time spent on each task.

Section 14-6 Figure out the dimensions of packaging cartons.

When Will You Ever Use This?

Can you tell how much time is needed to complete something? In business it's essential you know this, since time is money! Whenever you're producing something, the production's variables are weighed against time and money.

Key Words to Know

- manufactures
- direct material cost
- direct labor cost
- prime cost
- break-even analysis
- break-even point
- profit
- fixed costs
- variable costs
- quality control
- defective
- quality control chart
- time study
- packaging

Mathematics Online

To learn more about mathematics associated with production issues, visit the *Mathematics with Business Applications* Web site at www.busmath.glencoe.com.

CLASSROOM RESOURCES

Application and Enrichment
- 🖉 *Teacher Wraparound Edition*
- 🖉 *Teacher Resource Binder, Blackline Masters*
- 💿 *Interactive Lesson Planner* CD-ROM
- 💿 *PowerPoint® Presentations* CD-ROM

Review and Enforcement
- Mathematics Online
  www.busmath.glencoe.com
- 🖉 *Teacher Resource Binder, Internet Resources*

- 🖉 *Student Activity Workbook*
- 🖉 *Student Activity Workbook, Teacher Annotated Edition*
- 🖉 *School-to-Home Activity Workbook*

Assessment and Evaluation
- 🖉 *Assessment Binder, Reproducible Tests*
- 🖉 *Assessment Binder, Alternative Assessment Strategies*
- 💿 **Exam**View® *Pro Test Generator* CD-ROM

For the Teacher
- 🖉 *Student Activity Workbook, Teacher Annotated Edition*
- 🖉 *Assessment Binder*
- 💿 *Interactive Lesson Planner* CD-ROM
- 🖉 *Teacher Resource Binder*
- 🖥 Mathematics Online
  www.busmath.glencoe.com

For the Student
- 🖉 *Student Activity Workbook*
- 🖉 *School-to-Home Activity Workbook*

Living in the Real World

Tracking Tractors

Alicia Foster is an accounting manager for a farm equipment manufacturer, Thor Tractors. Later this week, she is meeting with industrial engineer Antoine Luther to determine if Thor needs to improve its speed and quality of production. Before the meeting, Foster is gathering data to calculate the company's productivity.

Read on. Go to . . .

457

Living in the Real World

Story's Summary

Alicia Foster, accounting manager for a farm equipment manufacturer, is meeting with an industrial engineer to see if the company can improve its speed and quality of production. Students follow Foster's process as she calculates the company's productivity—examining prime cost, break-even analysis, quality control, time studies, and packaging.

Did You Know...

Many years ago, baseballs produced for American League teams were stitched using red and blue thread, while National League baseballs were made with red and black thread. Inventory balancing problems led manufacturers to make a switch, stitching all balls with only red thread, as you see them today.

Think about This

What would happen if large manufacturing plants stopped regulating quality control?

LOCAL STANDARDS

National Standards for Business Education

Standard 1	Mathematical Foundations
Standard 2	Number Relationships and Operations
Standard 6	Problem-Solving Applications

National Council of Teachers of Mathematics Standards

Standard 1	Numbers and Operations
Standard 4	Measurement
Standard 6	Problem Solving
Standard 8	Communication

1 FOCUS

Show students an item, such as a plastic bookmark. Ask students how they think the item is manufactured. Mention that the bookmark is most likely created by a machine that cuts multiple bookmarks from a large sheet of plastic.

In-Class Examples

Work through these exercises with students before having them do the Self-Check. Round answers to the nearest tenth of a cent.

1. $0.98 ÷ 9 **$0.109**
2. ($0.50 ÷ 18) + ($8.75 ÷ 105)
   $0.027 + $0.083 = $0.111 = $0.11
3. How many seconds are in 1 hour? **3,600**

SECTION 14-1 Manufacturing

○ **Section Objective**

Compute the prime cost of manufacturing an item.

The production department of your business makes, or **manufactures**, and packages the products you sell. The cost of manufacturing an item depends, in part, on the **direct material cost** and the **direct labor cost.** The direct material cost is the cost of the goods that you use to produce the item. The direct labor cost includes the wages paid to the employees who make the item. The **prime cost** is the total of the direct material cost and the direct labor cost. The prime cost is frequently expressed on a per-unit basis. It looks like this:

$$\text{Prime Cost per Item} = \text{Direct Material Cost per Item} + \text{Direct Labor Cost per Item}$$

Living in the Real World

Tracking Tractors

Getting Down to the Basics Foster begins by finding out some of Thor's basic costs. By examining last year's annual report, she discovers the prime cost to manufacture each tractor model. She includes this figure in the introduction to her report and explains its significance.

Draw Conclusions Why is it important for Thor to know the prime cost?

Continued on page 461

Example 1

Electric Supply, Inc., produces aluminum circuit housings. The machine operator stamps 20 housings from each strip of aluminum. Each strip costs $1.80. The operator can stamp 720 housings per hour. The direct labor charge is $19.50 per hour. To the nearest tenth of a cent, what is the prime cost of manufacturing a circuit housing?

STEP 1: Find the direct material cost per item.

$$\frac{\$1.80}{20} = \$0.09$$

STEP 2: Find the direct labor cost per item.

$$\frac{\$19.50}{720} = \$0.027 \text{ direct labor cost}$$

STEP 3: Find the prime cost per item.

$$\text{Direct Material Cost per Item} + \text{Direct Labor Cost per Item}$$
$$\$0.09 + \$0.027$$
$$= \textbf{\$0.117 cost per housing}$$

BUSINESS NOTES

Ethical Manufacturing

Kodak is committed to reducing emissions, cutting waste, and preserving natural resources. Ask students what kind of natural resources Kodak might need, and why they think the company is careful about environmental management. **Energy usage, wager usage, and chemicals such as mercury and lead. It wants to protect the health and safety of employees and communities near its plants, and for future generations.**

Living in the Real World

If a company is able to reduce its costs for material and labor, it may be able to increase the profit per unit or decrease the selling price.

CONCEPT CHECK

Complete the problems, then check your answers at the end of the chapter.

1. Forty brackets are made from a strip of metal costing $0.80. What is the direct material cost per item? **$0.80 ÷ 40.00 = $0.02**

2. The direct material cost per item is $0.04. The direct labor cost per item is $0.18. Find the prime cost per item. **$0.04 + $0.18 = $0.22**

SECTION 14-1 PRACTICE

Round answers to the nearest tenth of a cent.

	Cost per Strip	Pieces per Strip	Direct Material Cost per Piece	Labor Cost per Hour	Pieces per Hour	Direct Labor Cost per Piece	Prime Cost
3.	$0.80	10	$0.080	$11.70	1,000	$0.012	a. $0.092
4.	0.75	25	a. $0.03	13.50	1,200	b. $0.011	c. $0.041
5.	0.70	50	a. $0.014	17.45	80	b. $0.022	c. $0.036

Round answers to the nearest tenth of a cent.

6. Thirty-six boxes per sheet of cardboard.
   Cost: $3.60 per sheet.
   Direct labor charge: $12.60 per hour.
   Two hundred boxes cut per hour.
   What is the prime cost per box? **$0.163**

7. Four thousand two hundred washers per steel strip.
   Cost: $8.75 per strip.
   Direct labor charge: $17.65 per hour.
   Thirteen thousand five hundred washers punched per hour.
   What is the prime cost per washer? **$0.003**

8. The Donnely Manufacturing Company manufactures plastic tablecloths. Each roll of printed plastic yields 120 tablecloths. Each roll costs $21.70. The direct labor charge is $19.20 per hour. The machine operator can cut and fold 90 tablecloths per hour. What is the prime cost of manufacturing each tablecloth? **$0.394**

9. The Northern Aluminum Company manufactures aluminum products. One of the company's machines stamps housings for smoke alarms from strips of aluminum. Each strip of aluminum costs $1.20. The machine stamps 40 housings from each strip. The machine operator produces 10 housings per minute. The direct labor cost is $16.76 per hour. What is the prime cost of manufacturing each housing? **$0.058**

Continued on next page

COOPERATIVE LEARNING

Costs
Students bring an ordinary product to class, such as a can of soup or a candy bar. The product should have a product label. Students work in groups to check the contents of one of the products and see how many different materials went into making the product. Discuss in class the elements that might have contributed to the production costs. **Elements might include the cost of ingredients from the vendors or producers, the costs of packaging, as well as the labor involved in manufacturing.**

② TEACH

Ask students to discuss the costs involved in manufacturing an item. Mention that the costs not only include the material required to make the item, but the labor involved. Manufacturing often necessitates the use of machines and people to operate the machines. Point out that to determine the prime cost per item, you need to know the direct material cost per item and the direct labor cost per item.

Motivating the Lesson
Have students work in groups. Each group needs a sheet of paper, scissors, pencil, and an item to trace. Have students trace their item on the paper as many times as it will fit. Then tell students that they are manufacturing die cut shapes. Have one group member cut out the shapes and another group member keep track of the time it takes. Give students a cost for the piece of paper and the labor. Then ask students if they can figure out how much the material and the labor costs per item. **Answers will vary.**

In-Class Examples
1. Fifteen belts are made from a piece of leather costing $9.20. What is the direct material cost per item? **$0.613**
2. The direct material cost per item is $0.07. The direct labor cost per item is $0.12. Find the prime cost per item. **$0.19**
3. Glazco Manufacturing makes windowpanes. From each sheet of glass, a machine operator can cut 12 windowpanes. Each sheet of glass costs $46.84. The operator can cut 240 windowpanes per hour. The direct labor charge is $20.35 per hour. What is the prime cost of manufacturing windowpanes? **$3.99**

3 ASSESS

Error Analysis

Students need to know how to convert units of measure. Review how to convert from seconds to hours. Give students some conversions to practice. Rounding to the nearest tenth of a cent may be unfamiliar to students. Students may confuse rounding to the nearest tenth of a cent with rounding a decimal to the nearest tenth. Have students first round some costs to the nearest cent. Then have students round the same costs to the nearest tenth of a cent. Point out that since the unit is cents, the decimal place to the right of the unit place is tenths of a cent.

4 CLOSE

Closing Activity

1. ($2.20 ÷ 15) + ($11.75 ÷ 123) **$0.242**

2. ($4.36 ÷ 108) + ($16.95 ÷ 900) **$0.059**

3. A piece of metal makes 243 mailbox flags. Each piece of metal costs $11.13. The direct labor cost is $19.55 per hour. Each hour 2056 flags are made. What is the prime cost of manufacturing each mailbox flag? **$0.055**

4. Harry Cooke operates an engraving machine at Noonan Metals. From one sheet of metal, 120 nameplates can be made. Each sheet costs $24.75. He can engrave one every 3 seconds. The direct labor cost is $18.50 per hour. What is the prime cost of engraving one nameplate? **$0.222**

10. Sue Clark is a machine operator at Modern Plastics. She molds 65 buckets from one container of molding plastic. Each container costs $2.98. Clark's machine molds 1 bucket every 4 seconds. The direct labor cost is $13.65 per hour. What is the prime cost of manufacturing one bucket? **$0.061**

11. A strip of heavy gauge tin makes 115 switch plates. The cost per strip is $1.46. The direct labor cost is $21.67 per hour. Every hour 1,060 plates are stamped. What is the prime cost of manufacturing each switch plate? **$0.033**

12. A strip of aluminum makes 20 fan blades. The aluminum costs $1.82 per strip. The direct labor cost is $15.65 per hour. One blade is stamped every 5 seconds. What is the prime cost of manufacturing each fan blade? **$0.113**

13. Eduardo Diaz is a molding machine operator at US Accessories, Inc. He molds 130 tinted license plate holders from one container of molding plastic. Each container costs $5.85. Eduardo is able to mold 1 holder every 3 seconds. The direct labor cost is $18.95 per hour. What is the prime cost of manufacturing 1 tinted license plate holder? **$0.061**

14. Suppose Eduardo Diaz, in Problem 13, finds a way to mold 140 license plate holders per container and each container costs $5.85. US Accessories gives him a pay raise to $19.10 per hour. What is the prime cost of manufacturing 1 tinted license plate holder?

    Prime cost per holder: $0.042 + $0.016 = $0.058 or $0.04178 + $0.01591 = $0.577

MAINTAINING YOUR SKILLS

> **Need Help? Go to...**
> ► Skill 2: **Rounding Numbers,** page 729
> ► Skill 11: **Dividing Decimals,** page 738

Round answers to the nearest tenth of a cent.

15. $0.21486 **$0.215**   16. $0.05512 **$0.055**

17. $0.00707 **$0.007**   18. $0.3419 **$0.342**

19. $0.07241 **$0.072**   20. $0.01987 **$0.020**

Divide. Round answers to the nearest tenth of a cent.

21. $0.90 ÷ 18 **$0.05**   22. $0.95 ÷ 5 **$0.19**

23. $0.92 ÷ 12 **$0.077**   24. $0.85 ÷ 12 **$0.071**

25. $1.47 ÷ 10 **$0.147**   26. $1.76 ÷ 5 **$0.352**

27. $17.85 ÷ 470 **$0.038**   28. $9.65 ÷ 330 **$0.029**

29. $17.90 ÷ 435 **$0.041**   30. $7.15 ÷ 120 **$0.056**

31. $11.72 ÷ 510 **$0.023**   32. $21.93 ÷ 1,475 **$0.015**

WRAP-UP

Go over any problem for which a wrong answer is given.

Assignment Guide

Basic: 3–5
Average: 6–9

20 min.

SECTION 14-2 Break-Even Analysis

Section Objective

Calculate the break-even point in the number of manufactured units.

Before you start pouring money into a product, you need to know your expenses. Your business can prepare a **break-even analysis**. This determines how many units of a product must be made and sold to cover production expenses. On a break-even analysis chart, you might see the **break-even point.** This shows you the point where income from sales equals the cost of production. Units sold after that point will result in a **profit** for your business. Profit is the primary goal for any business (except for not-for-profit organizations).

To calculate the break-even point, you must know the total **fixed costs**, the **variable costs** per unit, and the selling price per unit. Fixed costs include rent, salaries, and other costs that are not changed by the number of units produced. Variable costs include the cost of raw materials, the cost of packaging, and any other costs that vary directly with the number of units produced. Remember that:

$$\text{Break-Even Point in Units} = \frac{\text{Total Fixed Costs}}{\text{Selling Price per Unit} - \text{Variable Costs per Unit}}$$

Living in the Real World

Tracking Tractors

Time and Money Foster knows that engineer Luther will be very interested in her break-even analysis, which indicates the point at which income from the sale of tractors is equal to the cost to produce them. This figure will give Luther an idea of how many tractors must be manufactured and sold to cover production costs. And, of course, if more tractors are sold, the company will do better than break even—it will make a profit.

Draw Conclusions What formula do you use in order to find the break-even point?

Continued on page 463

Example 1

Token Metal Products manufactures can openers. They plan to manufacture 750,000 hand-held can openers to be sold at $0.44 each. The fixed costs are estimated to be $142,570. Variable costs are $0.19 per unit. How many can openers must be sold for Token Metal Products to break even?

STEP: Find the break-even point in units.

Total Fixed Costs	÷	(Selling Price per Unit	−	Variable Costs per Unit)	
$142,570.00	÷	($0.44	−	$0.19)	−
$142,570.00	÷		$0.25		= **570,280 sold**

.44 − .19 = 0.25 M+ 142570 ÷ RM = 570280

ALTERNATIVE ASSESSMENT

Students with Problems Reading
Students with problems reading or organizing material can benefit from recognizing the kinds of organization used in their textbooks. Have students rewrite the section headings in the chapter as questions—each on a separate page. For example: "What's the formula used in manufacturing?" "How do I do a break-even analysis?" Then ask students to write the solution to the Self-Check problems under their questions.

Living in the Real World

The total fixed costs divided by the selling price per unit minus the variable costs per unit.

National Standards for Business Education

Standard 1	Mathematical Foundations
Standard 2	Number Relationships and Operations
Standard 6	Problem-Solving Applications

National Council of Teachers of Mathematics Standards

Standard 1	Numbers and Operations
Standard 6	Problem Solving
Standard 8	Communication

1 FOCUS

A break-even analysis can help a company determine how many goods must be produced and sold before a profit is realized. Have students discuss types of costs that may be involved in producing a product.

In-Class Examples
Work through these exercises with students before having them do the Self-Check. Round answers to the nearest whole number.
1. $16,245 \div (0.98 - 0.42)$ **29,009**
2. $128,468 \div (1.97 - 0.89)$ **118,952**
3. $283,977.80 \div (12.82 - 7.90)$ **57,719**
4. $568,323.55 \div (31.97 - 20.06)$ **47,718**

2 TEACH

Discuss fixed and variable costs as they apply to a family. Some fixed costs are a mortgage or rent payment and homeowners or rental insurance. Some variable costs are utility bills and groceries.

TEACH (cont'd)

In-Class Examples

Find the break-even point in units.

1. Selling price: $8.59.
   Variable cost per unit: $3.64.
   Total fixed costs: $185,298.
   37,434

2. Selling price: $0.89.
   Variable cost per unit: $0.25.
   Total fixed costs: $206,397.
   322,495

ASSESS

Error Analysis

Students may mistakenly divide the total fixed costs by the selling price per unit and then subtract the variable costs per unit. Remind students to use parentheses when they write the equations. They should perform the subtraction first and then perform the division. You may want to give students some simpler problems to try first. For example, compare the answers to these two problems: $\frac{20}{5} - 3$ and $\frac{20}{(5-3)}$. This should help them to understand the importance of the use of parentheses and performing the operations in the correct order.

CLOSE

Closing Activity

Find the break-even point in units.

1. Selling price: $0.49.
   Variable cost per unit: $0.24.
   Total fixed costs: $29,563.
   118,252

2. Solo Circuits manufactures calculators. They plan to manufacture scientific calculators to be sold at $10.99 each. The fixed costs are estimated to be $605,225. Variable costs are $8.89 per unit. How many calculators must be sold for Solo Circuits to break even? **288,202**

SELF-CHECK ✓

1. 87,500.00 ÷ ($0.79 − $0.29) = 87,500.00 ÷ $0.50 = 175,000.00

2. 124,500.00 ÷ ($1.49 − $0.74) = 124,500.00 ÷ $0.75 = 166,000.00

CONCEPT CHECK

Complete the problems, then check your answers at the end of the chapter.
Find the break-even point in units.

1. Selling price is $0.79.
   Variable cost per unit is $0.29.
   Total fixed costs are $87,500.00.

2. Selling price is $1.49.
   Variable cost per unit is $0.74.
   Total fixed costs are $124,500.00.

SECTION 14-2 PRACTICE

Find the break-even point in units.

	Total Fixed Costs	÷	(Selling Price per Unit	−	Variable Costs per Unit)	=	Break-Even Point in Units
3.	$ 95,000.00	÷	($ 1.79	−	$ 0.79)	=	95,000
4.	148,000.00	÷	(0.59	−	0.34)	=	592,000
5.	225,000.00	÷	(2.29	−	1.79)	=	450,000
6.	478,400.00	÷	(3.49	−	2.69)	=	598,000
7.	1,470,000.00	÷	(174.99	−	98.75)	=	19,281
8.	12,476,500.00	÷	(417.79	−	279.81)	=	90,423

9. TenCo junior tennis rackets.
   Fixed costs: $740,000.00.
   Selling price per racket: $74.29.
   Variable cost per racket: $48.76.
   What is the break-even point in units? **28,986**

10. Farm Supply rural mailboxes.
    Fixed costs: $192,800.00.
    Selling price per mailbox: $39.99.
    Variable cost per mailbox: $21.43.
    What is the break-even point in units? **10,388**

11. Today's Music produces classical CDs. The fixed costs total $2,417,950.00. The selling price per disc is $19.95. The variable cost per disc is $9.48. What is the break-even point in number of discs? **230,941**

12. Superior Custom Homes builds a limited number of custom homes. The fixed costs of the operation total $2,157,750. The base selling price per custom home is $479,500. The base variable cost per custom home is $431,550. What is the break-even point in number of custom homes? **45**

13. True Bounce basketballs are manufactured by General Sports. They have total fixed costs of $3,110,400.00. The variable cost per basketball is $18.47. The selling price per basketball is $24.95. What is the break-even point in number of basketballs? **480,000**

14. The Alumni Association plans to produce and market monogrammed sweatshirts. They anticipate selling each sweatshirt for $39.95. Their variable costs per sweatshirt include $18.19 for supplies and $9.47 per shirt for direct labor. The fixed costs of the operation total $7,450.00. How many monogrammed sweatshirts does The Alumni Association need to sell to break even? **606**

MAINTAINING YOUR SKILLS

Need Help? Go to...
➤ Skill 6: Subtracting Decimals, page 733
➤ Skill 11: Dividing Decimals, page 738

Subtract.

15. $14.79 − $9.43 **$5.36** 16. $1.89 − $0.97 **$0.92** 17. $14.49 − $7.74 **$6.75**

18. $7.19 − $5.54 **$1.65** 19. $147.47 − $109.88 **$37.59** 20. $8,129.00 − $6,417.48 **$1,711.52**

Divide. Round answers to the nearest whole number.

21. $47,500.00 ÷ $0.25 **190,000** 22. $163,540.00 ÷ $0.20 **817,700** 23. $216,491.00 ÷ $0.79 **274,039**

COMMUNICATION SKILLS

Investigate and Report

The Band Boosters might be operating a concession stand at the games or the Spirit Club might be selling sweatshirts. In these examples, there are fixed and variable costs to consider when you're establishing the selling price and the break-even point. Students write proposals for these activities identifying cost, selling price, and break-even point.

LS , P

WRAP-UP

Go over any problem for which a wrong answer is given.

Assignment Guide
Basic: 3–8
Average: 9–10

20 min.

SECTION 14-3 Quality Control

○ **Section Objective**

Compute the percent of defective goods and determine if the process is in or out of control.

If your business deals with mass production, you need a **quality control** inspector to check the items that are manufactured. The inspector may examine a specified number of items. If the size of the item is incorrect or if the item is broken or damaged, it is classified as **defective**.

The inspector computes the percent of the sample that is defective and plots the percent on a **quality control chart**. The quality control chart shows the percent of defective products that is allowable. If the actual percent of defective items is greater than the percent allowable, the process is said to be "out of control." Production must then be stopped and corrected.

$$\text{Percent Defective} = \frac{\text{Number Defective}}{\text{Total Number Checked}}$$

Living in the Real World

Tracking Tractors

What to Do about Defects Foster finds the quality control information she was after. The quality control chart shows the percent of defective products that the company tolerates. Just like people, companies are not perfect. Therefore, they tolerate a certain number of defective units as a normal part of production.

Draw Conclusions At Thor Tractors, who might be interested in how effective the production process is?

Continued on page 466

Example 1

Bob Atkinson is a quality control inspector for Material Plating. At 9 A.M., he checked 25 stamped brackets produced during the previous hour and found 2 defective brackets. The process is in control if 5 percent or less of the sample is defective. Is the process in control or out of control? Plot the percent defective on a quality control chart.

STEP 1: Find the percent defective.

$$\frac{\text{Number Defective}}{\text{Total Number Checked}}$$

$$\frac{2}{25} = 0.08 \text{ or } 8\% \text{ (Process is out of control.)}$$

Continued on next page

National Standards for Business Education

Standard 1	Mathematical Foundations
Standard 2	Number Relationships and Operations
Standard 6	Problem-Solving Applications

National Council of Teachers of Mathematics Standards

Standard 1	Numbers and Operations
Standard 6	Problem Solving
Standard 8	Communication

① FOCUS

Ask students what is meant by *quality control*. Discuss why companies would want to maintain a high level of quality control.

In-Class Examples
Work through these exercises with students before having them do the Self-Check.
1. 2 ÷ 25 **0.08**
2. 4 ÷ 100 **0.04**
3. 14 ÷ 280 **0.05**
4. Five is what percent of 50? **10%**
5. Three is what percent of 25? **12%**

RETEACH / ENRICHMENT

"Out of Control"
The process of manufacturing a product is "out of control" if more than 5 percent of the samples are defective. Some companies would set the percent lower than 5 percent. Discuss with the class how important is quality to a company? **Recalling the product, repairing or replacing the product, lost business due to bad publicity, hiring a public relations firm to restore the company's reputation, and lawsuits.**

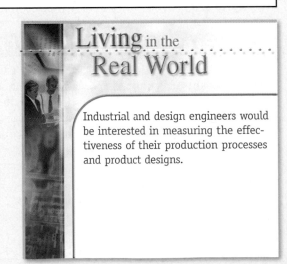

Living in the Real World

Industrial and design engineers would be interested in measuring the effectiveness of their production processes and product designs.

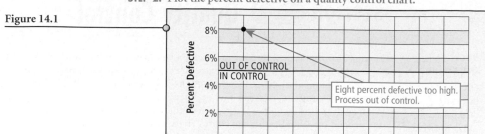

STEP 2: Plot the percent defective on a quality control chart.

Figure 14.1

Eight percent defective too high. Process out of control.

---

② TEACH

Students may not realize that some defective items can still be manufactured even if there is a high level of quality control. Since only a sample of the items being manufactured is checked, some items that are defective will still be produced. The manufacturing process is only stopped when it is out of control. Whether it is out of control depends on the percent defective and the percent allowable. Different companies will have different allowable percents. Discuss why there will be fewer defective items if the percent allowable is smaller.

Point out the benefits of using a quality control chart. By looking at a quality control chart, you can quickly see how often a process was in control and how often it was out of control.

Motivating the Lesson
A manufacturing process is out of control if the percent defective is greater than 4 percent. Tell whether the following are in or out of control.

6/100 **out of control**
2/80 **in control**
5/250 **in control**
10/200 **out of control**

In-Class Examples
Find the percent defective.
1. Number defective: 3.
   Number checked: 60. **5%**
2. Number defective: 5.
   Number checked: 125. **4%**
3. A quality control inspector checked a sample of 50 items. Two of the items were defective. If more than 5 percent of the sample is defective, the process is out of control. What percent of the sample is defective? **(4%)** Is the process in or out of control? **in control**

CONCEPT CHECK

SELF-CHECK ✓

Complete the problems, then check your answers at the end of the chapter.

1. Number defective is 5.
   Number checked is 200.
   What is the percent defective?
   5 ÷ 200 = 0.025 = 2.5%

2. Number defective is 3.
   Number checked is 50.
   What is the percent defective?
   3 ÷ 50 = 0.06 = 6%

SECTION 14-3 PRACTICE

As you solve these problems, if more than 5 percent of the sample is defective, the process is out of control.

	Number Defective	÷	Number Checked	=		Percent Defective		In or Out of Control?
3.	2	÷	50	=	a.	4%	b.	In
4.	1	÷	50	=	a.	2%	b.	In
5.	4	÷	50	=	a.	8%	b.	Out
6.	0	÷	80	=	a.	0%	b.	In
7.	3	÷	60	=	a.	5%	b.	In
8.	5	÷	40	=	a.	12.5%	b.	Out

9. Wetherley Woolen Works packages imported sweaters. One hundred in sample. Five defective. In control if 6 percent or less is defective. Is the process in or out of control? **(5%); In**

10. US Products manufactures plastic flashlights. Twenty-five in sample. One defective. In control if 5 percent or less is defective. Is the process in or out of control? **(4%); In**

11. Alice McHenry is a quality control inspector for Nu-Age Cassettes. The process is in control if 6 percent or less of each sample is defective. McHenry checked a sample of 50 cassettes and found 4 defective cassettes. What percent of the sample is defective? Is the process in or out of control? **8%; Out**

12. Tucker Jensen, a quality control inspector for Office Products, checked a sample of 250 ballpoint pens. Fourteen of the pens were defective. If more than 6 percent of the sample is defective, the process is out of control. What percent of the sample is defective? Is the process in or out of control? **5.6%; In**

GLOBAL PERSPECTIVE

Check the Tag
Have students check the tags or labels of items such as backpacks, calculators, shoes, clothing, and other things in the classroom. Record the names of the items on the board and the countries in which they were manufactured. How many of the goods are imported? What's the percent of the total recorded? Are similar items manufactured in both the United States and in other countries? Discuss with students their impressions of imported goods. Are they more expensive? Less expensive? How do the goods compare in quality?

LS , CL

For Problems 13–16, draw a quality control chart, compute the percent defective in each sample, and plot the percents on the chart.

Check students' charts for Problems 13–17.

13. Every 2 hours, Guadalupe Mendez checks samples from a punch press. Each sample contains 50 pieces. The operation is in control if 5 percent or less of each sample is defective. Mendez found the following:

Figure 14.2

Punch Press Samples

Time	9 A.M.	11 A.M.	1 P.M.	3 P.M.	5 P.M.
Number Defective	1	0	3	2	2

9 A.M. 2%; 11 A.M. 0%; 1 P.M. 6%; 3 P.M. 4%; 5 P.M. 4%; Out of control at 1 P.M.

14. Every hour 10 digital video disc (DVD) players are taken off the production line at Modern Technologies and checked to see if they are defective. If more than 10 percent are defective, production is out of control. The number of defective players for the 9 A.M. to 5 P.M. checks are as follows:

Figure 14.3

14. 9 A.M. 0%; 10 A.M. 10%; 11 A.M. 0%; 12 noon 20%; 1 P.M. 10%; 2 P.M. 0%; 3 P.M. 10%; 4 P.M. 0%; 5 P.M. 20%; Out of control at 12 noon and 5 P.M.

DVD Players

Time	9 A.M.	10 A.M.	11 A.M.	12 P.M.	1 P.M.	2 P.M.	3 P.M.	4 P.M.	5 P.M.
Number Defective	0	1	0	2	1	0	1	0	2

15. Tien-Yu Lee randomly checks 75 transistors 10 times a day. If more than 4 percent are defective, the production is stopped and corrections are made. Complete the table and draw a quality control chart.

Figure 14.4

15. 1.3%; 2.7%; 1.3%; 0%; 2.7%; 1.3%; 4%; 5.3%; 1.3%; 0%; Out of control at checkpoint 7.

Transistors

Checkpoint No.	1	2	3	4	5	6	7	8	9	10
Number Defective	1	2	1	0	2	1	3	4	1	0
Percent Defective										

16. Alberto Burris checks circuit board production at different times during the day. He will check a different number each time. If more than 5 percent are defective, he will close down production and have corrections made. The circuit boards are checked electronically. Complete the table and draw a quality control chart.

Figure 14.5

Circuit Boards

Time	9:40 A.M.	10:15 A.M.	11:50 A.M.	1:30 P.M.	3:30 P.M.	4:30 P.M.
Number Checked	60	50	80	100	40	50
Number Defective	3	2	3	4	2	2
Percent Defective						

5%; 4%; 3.75%; 4%; 5%; 4%; In control at all times.

MAINTAINING YOUR SKILLS

Find the rate. Round answers to the nearest tenth of a percent.

Need Help? Go to...
➤ Skill 31: Finding the Rate, page 758
➤ Skill 1: Numbers, page 727

17. Two is what percent of 50? **4%**   **18.** Six is what percent of 100? **6%**

19. Four is what percent of 25? **16%**   **20.** Two is what percent of 60? **3.3%**

Which number is greater?

21. 5.3% or 5%   **22.** 6% or 5.2%   **23.** 3% or 4%   **24.** 6% or 6.7%
     5.3%   **6%**   **4%**   **6.7%**

Section 14-3 Quality Control ▶ **465**

WRAP-UP

Go over any problem for which a wrong answer is given.

Assignment Guide
Basic: 3–8
Average: 9–10

20 min.

ASSESS

Error Analysis
Students may need practice with inequalities. Review what it means to be greater than, less than, greater than or equal to, and less than or equal to. If the allowable percent defective is less than 5 percent, that means 5 percent is out of control. If the allowable percent defective is 6 percent or less, then 6 percent is in control.

When performing a division to find the percent defective, such as $\frac{2}{50}$, students may think that the quotient, 0.04, is the percent. Remind students that they need to write the decimal as a percent.

4 **CLOSE**

Closing Activity
Find the percent defective.
1. Number defective: 2. Number checked: 20. **10%**
2. Number defective: 4. Number checked: 100. **4%**
3. A quality control inspector checked 50 items. Three of the items were defective. If more than 6 percent of the sample is defective, the process is out of control. What percent of the sample is defective? **(6%)** Is the process in or out of control? **in control**
4. Every 3 hours Janet Goode checks 10 items from a stamping machine. The process is in control if 5 percent or less of the items are defective. Goode made the following quality control chart. When was the process in and out of control? **10 A.M. and 4 P.M.**

Percent Defective	7 A.M.	10 A.M.	1 P.M.	4 P.M.
6%		*		*
4%			*	
2%	*			
0%				

465

○ **Section Objective**

Use time-study results to compute how many units can be produced.

Your business may conduct a **time study** to determine how long a particular job should take. A time study involves watching a typical employee complete a job, recording the time required for each task, and calculating the average time for each task. You can use the averages to determine how many units a worker can produce in a fixed period of time.

$$\text{Number of Units} = \frac{\text{Actual Time Worked}}{\text{Average Time Required per Unit}}$$

Living in the Real World

Tracking Tractors

Measuring Time   Foster and Luther are discussing several time studies that his department has conducted. The studies show the amount of time spent on various parts of the production process. The first time study focuses on the number of tractors produced per hour. In addition, various parts of the production process also are broken down into production-per-hour figures.

Draw Conclusions   Why would a time study be important to Thor?

Continued on page 469

National Standards for Business Education

Standard 1	Mathematical Foundations
Standard 2	Number Relationships and Operations

National Council of Teachers of Mathematics Standards

Standard 1	Numbers and Operations
Standard 6	Problem Solving
Standard 8	Communication

1 FOCUS

The focus of this section is on using a time study to find the number of units produced in a certain period of time. Give students an example of a situation in real life where you would be producing a number of units, such as when sending invitations. For each invitation, it takes time to write it, put it in an envelope, address it, and stick a stamp on it.

In-Class Examples

Work through these exercises with students before having them do the Self-Check. Round to the nearest whole number.

1. $(55 \times 60) \div 33$ **100**
2. $(46 \times 60) \div 39.7$ **70**
3. $(58 \times 60) \div 28.5$ **122**
4. $(34 \times 60) \div 28.2$ **72**

Example 1

General Lamps did a time study of Beth Peters's job as a carton packer. Her times were recorded. The averages were calculated. If Peters gets a 10-minute break each hour, how many cartons can she fill per hour?

Figure 14.6

Task	Observations in Seconds					Average Time
	#1	#2	#3	#4	#5	
Pick up carton	3.9	5.4	3.9	4.4	3.9	4.3 sec.
Fill carton	12.0	13.0	14.5	12.5	11.0	12.6 sec.
Apply glue	14.5	12.5	13.0	13.5	13.5	13.4 sec.
Close carton	5.1	4.4	4.6	4.3	5.1	4.7 sec.
Remove filled carton	5.5	5.5	5.5	5.5	5.5	5.5 sec.

Sum of Times
Number of Observations

STEP 1: Find the average time required per unit.
$$4.3 + 12.6 + 13.4 + 4.7 + 5.5 = 40.5 \text{ seconds}$$

STEP 2: Find the actual time worked per hour.
$$(60 - 10) \text{ minutes} \times 60 \text{ seconds} = 3,000 \text{ seconds}$$

Living in the Real World

Information gathered from time studies would help industrial engineers determine if they can produce tractors more efficiently while still maintaining high standards and a safe work environment.

STEP 3: Find the number of units per hour.

$$\frac{\text{Actual Time Worked}}{\text{Average Time Required per Unit}}$$

$$\frac{3,000 \text{ seconds}}{40.5 \text{ seconds per unit}}$$

$$= 74.07 \text{ or } 74 \text{ units per hour}$$

4.3 $+$ 12.6 $+$ 13.4 $+$ 4.7 $+$ 5.5 $=$ 40.5 $M+$

60 $-$ 10 $=$ 50 $\times$ 60 $=$ 3000 $\div$ RM $=$ 74.074

CONCEPT CHECK

Complete the problems, then check your answers at the end of the chapter. Find the number of units per hour.

1. Average time is 6 minutes per unit. 48 minutes worked per hour.
48 ÷ 6 = 8

2. Average time is 15 minutes per unit. 55 minutes worked per hour.
55 ÷ 15 = 3.7

Example 2

Santana Woods is a circuit board tester for Meta's Electronics. Woods works 8 hours per day less a 10-minute break every 2 hours. He spends 5 minutes per board in the testing process. How many boards per day should Woods be able to test?

STEP 1: Find the actual time worked.
(A 10-minute break every 2 hours is the same "time wise" as 5 minutes per hour.)
$(60 - 5) \times 8 = 440$ minutes

STEP 2: Find the number of units.
$$\frac{440 \text{ minutes}}{5 \text{ minutes per board}} = 88 \text{ boards}$$

CONCEPT CHECK

Complete the problem, then check your answer at the end of the chapter.

3. Owen Acker's assembly line task is to weld a bracket on support beams for manufactured homes. He works 8.5 hours a day with a 15-minute break at 10 A.M., a 30-minute lunch break at noon, and a 20-minute break at 3 P.M. It takes him 12 minutes to weld each bracket. How many brackets a day should he be expected to weld? **[(8.5 × 60) − (15 + 30 + 20)] ÷ 12 = [510 − 65] ÷ 12 = 445 ÷ 12 = 37**

SECTION 14-4 PRACTICE

	Actual Time Worked	÷	Average Time per Unit	=	Number of Units
4.	40 minutes (× 60)	÷	43.5 seconds	=	66.2 = 66
5.	50 minutes (× 60)	÷	39.7 seconds	=	75.5 = 76
6.	55 minutes (× 60)	÷	65.6 seconds	=	50.3 = 50
7.	45 minutes (× 60)	÷	5.5 seconds	=	490.9 = 491

Continued on next page

TECHNOLOGY POWER

In March 1999, Hyundai dominated the car market in Korea, but in crucial overseas markets, it had a reputation for poor quality—doors that didn't fit properly, frames that rattled, engines that delivered puny acceleration—and it was losing money. When CEO Chung Mong Koo looked under the hood of a Sonata sedan and saw loose wires, tangled hoses, bolts painted different colors, he instructed the plant chief to paint all bolts and screws black and not to release any car unless all was orderly. Today, due to improved quality and design, sales increased 8 percent in 2001.

SECTION 14-4

② TEACH

Have students discuss why a company would want to perform a time study. **(Time is money and excess time spent to produce something is money wasted.)** A time study can not only help a company project how much future production costs will be to manufacture an item, it can help a company determine if the time spent could be shortened.

A company may perform several time studies if the company has several employees doing the same job. This would give the company a more accurate idea of the average number of units produced.

Motivating the Lesson

Ask students to record how much time they spend getting ready for school each day for one week. Have students record the amount of time for each task. For example, students can record the time it takes to shower, get dressed, brush their teeth, and eat breakfast. Have students use their weekly record to find the average amount of time spent each day on each task. **Answers will vary**

In-Class Examples

Find the number of units per hour.

1. Actual time worked: 3000 seconds. Average time per unit: 15 seconds. **200**

2. Actual time worked: 45 minutes per hour. Average time per unit: 90 seconds. **30**

3. Actual time worked: 50 minutes per hour. Average time per unit: 25.2 seconds. **119**

3 ASSESS

Error Analysis

In some of the exercises in this section, the number of units will refer to items manufactured and in others the number of units will refer to people. Discuss with students why it doesn't make sense for the number of units to be a fraction since you are dealing with people. Remind students how to round to the nearest whole number. Also, discuss why in this section it is more appropriate to round down since the whole number represents the number of units completed.

4 CLOSE

Closing Activity

Find the number of units per hour.

1. Actual time worked: 2,700 seconds. Average time per unit: 30 seconds. **90**

2. Actual time worked: 50 minutes per hour. Average time per unit: 15 seconds. **200**

3. Janice Quinoa greets customers at Jasper Amusements. Her average time per customer is 10 seconds. She works 40 minutes per hour. How many customers can be greeted per hour? **240**

4. General Appliance did a time study of Phil Jacobs' job as a metal fabricator. Jacobs' times per item, in seconds, were recorded as follows: 42.5, 44.1, 42.8, 45.9, 45.6, and 43.7. If he gets a ten-minute break each hour, how many items can he make per hour? **11**

---

8. Addison McLane bags groceries for Giant Value Super Store and she carries out the bags for customers when requested.
Average time per customer is 3 minutes.
Fifty minutes worked per hour.
How many customers can be served per hour? **16.6 = 17**

9. Coretta Cole sells theatre tickets at Hollywood Cinemas.
Average time is 21.4 seconds per customer.
Fifty minutes worked per hour.
How many customers can be served per hour? **140.1 = 140**

10. Ben Krieger prepared a time study to determine the average time required to make a cash withdrawal at the 24-hour automatic teller machine (ATM).

Figure 14.7

Task	Time in Seconds				
	#1	#2	#3	#4	#5
Insert card in machine	1.0	2.0	1.5	2.5	1.5
Type in code	17.0	11.5	16.0	15.5	14.5
Specify amount wanted	7.4	6.9	7.1	7.0	7.1
Remove cash	1.5	1.0	2.0	1.5	1.5
Remove card	1.2	1.4	1.0	1.1	1.3

10. a. Insert card 1.7 sec; Type code 14.9 sec; Specify amt 7.1 sec; Remove cash 1.5 sec; Remove card 1.2 sec
b. 26.4 sec
c. 136.3 = 136

a. What is the average time required for each task?
b. What is the average time required to make a cash withdrawal?
c. How many cash withdrawals can be made at a machine in 1 hour?

11. American Pump Company prepared a time study of Shirley Monroe's job as an assembler. How many units can she complete in 1 hour if she takes one 10-minute break during the hour? **115**

Figure 14.8

Task	Time in Seconds				
	#1	#2	#3	#4	#5
Move water pump to filter	3.7	4.2	3.9	3.8	3.7
Insert filter coil	5.1	5.2	4.9	5.2	5.1
Affix gasket	4.8	4.4	4.7	4.6	4.8
Hand thread bolts	6.1	6.3	6.3	6.2	6.4
Machine tighten bolts	6.1	6.0	6.2	6.3	6.2

MAINTAINING YOUR SKILLS

Need Help? Go to...
▶ Skill 5: **Adding Decimals**, page 732
▶ Skill 11: **Dividing Decimals**, page 738

Add.

12. $3.6 + 3.8 + 3.7 + 3.6 + 3.7$ **18.4**
13. $14.2 + 14.1 + 13.8 + 14.0 + 13.9$ **70**
14. $7.2 + 7.4 + 7.1 + 6.8 + 7.2$ **35.7**
15. $1.1 + 0.9 + 0.8 + 1.2 + 1.0$ **5**

Divide. Round answers to the nearest whole number.

16. $3,600 \div 4.5$ **800**
17. $3,000 \div 2.4$ **1,250**
18. $3,300 \div 15.2$ **217**
19. $8 \div 0.12$ **67**

WRAP-UP

Go over any problem for which a wrong answer is given.

Assignment Guide
Basic: 4–7
Average: 8–9

20 min.

Time Study— Percent of Time

Section Objective

Use time-study results to compute the percent of time spent on each task.

What are your employees doing? How long does it take them to perform a series of tasks in a week? To schedule workload and deadlines, you might need them to perform a time study. You can use a time study to determine what percent of an employee's time is spent on various activities during a workday. Remember that:

$$\text{Percent of Time Spent on Activity} = \frac{\text{Time Spent on Activity}}{\text{Total Time}}$$

Living in the Real World

Tracking Tractors

Improving Work   As an industrial engineer, Luther examines the production process of Thor Tractors to see where production can be improved. He has given Foster a summary of time studies he has conducted on the Thor Tractors production line.

Draw Conclusions   True or false: Analyzing various jobs on the production line can influence the bottom line.

Continued on page 472

Example 1

Mike Reese works in the mailroom of a large office. A time study showed that he spent his time on the following activities. What percent of his time does Reese spend picking up and delivering mail?

Activity	Hours
Sorting mail	2.5
Picking up and delivering mail	3.0
Talking with employees	0.5
Taking coffee breaks	0.5
Making special deliveries	1.5
Total	8.0

STEP: Find the percent of time spent on activity.

$$\frac{\text{Time Spent on Activity}}{\text{Total Time}}$$

$\frac{3.0}{8.0} = 0.375$ or 37.5 percent of time spent on picking up and delivering mail

---

National Standards for Business Education

Standard 1	Mathematical Foundations
Standard 2	Number Relationships and Operations

National Council of Teachers of Mathematics Standards

Standard 1	Numbers and Operations
Standard 6	Problem Solving
Standard 8	Communication

(1) FOCUS

Often employees are responsible for completing more than one task during a workday. This section focuses on the percent of time spent doing these different tasks.

In-Class Examples
Work through these exercises with students before having them do the Self-Check. Round answers to the nearest hundredth.
1. 2.5 ÷ 8 **0.31**
2. 5 ÷ 7.5 **0.67**
3. 3 ÷ 8 **0.38**
4. Write 0.065 as a percent. **6.5%**
5. Write 0.2 as a percent. **20%**

Living in the Real World

True. This would mean not only producing better tractors faster, but also improving work conditions for production line employees.

COMMUNICATION SKILLS

Research and Present
Students research safety or labor laws relating to jobs involving dangerous or loud activity. Have students find data on restrictions, including time restrictions, for activities. Students give a short presentation including the source of their data. The Occupational Safety and Health Administration (OSHA) is a reliable source.

2 TEACH

Have students discuss a particular job. Have them name some tasks that an employee with this job would perform daily. Then have students predict how much time would be spent on the different tasks. For example, a customer service representative at a store may spend time answering calls on the phone and helping customers in the store.

In Example 1 on page 469, some of Reese's time is spent taking breaks. Point out that a time study takes into consideration the time spent on breaks and not just the time spent on performing tasks for the job.

In-Class Examples

Find the percent of time spent. Round to the nearest hundredth of a percent.

1. Time spent: 1.5.
   Total time: 6. **25%**
2. Time spent: 3.
   Total time: 7.5. **40%**
3. Nelson Chaves works 8 hours each day at Fields Nursery. He spends 3 hours of his workday watering plants. What percent of his workday is spent watering plants? **37.5%**

CONCEPT CHECK

SELF-CHECK ✓ Complete the problems, then check your answers at the end of the chapter.

1. In Example 1, what percent of his time does Reese spend sorting mail?
   2.5 ÷ 8 = 0.3125 = 31.25%
2. In Example 1, what percent of his time does Reese spend making special deliveries? **1.5 ÷ 8 = 0.1875 = 18.75%**

Example 2

What percent of the time does Mike Reese (see Example 1) spend talking with employees and taking coffee breaks?

   STEP: Find the percent of time spent on activity.

$$(0.5 + 0.5) \div 8.0$$
$$= \quad 1 \quad \div \quad 8$$
$$= 0.125 \text{ or } 12.5\%$$

CONCEPT CHECK

SELF-CHECK ✓ Complete the problems, then check your answers at the end of the chapter. In Example 1, what percent of time does Reese spend:

3. Sorting mail, picking up mail, and delivering mail? **(2.5 + 3.0) ÷ 8.0 = 0.6875 or 68.75%**
4. Sorting mail, picking up mail, delivering mail, and making special deliveries? **(2.5 + 3.0 + 1.5) ÷ 8.0 = 0.875 or 87.5%**

SECTION 14-5 PRACTICE

Round answers to the nearest hundredth of a percent.

	Activity	Hours	÷	Total Time	=	Percent of Time
5.	Loading furniture	3.00	÷	8	=	0.375 = 37.5%
6.	Delivering furniture	4.50	÷	8	=	0.5625 = 56.25%
7.	Lunch	1.00	÷	8	=	0.125 = 12.5%
8.	Returning truck	0.50	÷	8	=	0.0625 = 6.25%

9. Chandra Lane, a carton packer for Grandma's Jams.
   Fills cartons 2.5 hours per day.
   Works 8 total hours per day.
   What percent of her day is spent filling cartons? **0.3125 = 31.25%**

10. Amy North, a realtor in Florida.
    Answers the phone 1 hour per day.
    Works 8 total hours per day.
    What percent of her day is spent answering the phone? **0.125 = 12.5%**

11. Tomas Lopez, a property manager for Triangle Management Company.
    Meets with property owners 2.8 hours per day.
    Works 7.5 total hours per day.
    What percent of his day is spent meeting with property owners? **0.37333 = 37.33%**

ALTERNATIVE ASSESSMENT STRATEGIES

Self-Esteem and Confidence

At school, on the job, and in life, self-confidence and a high self-esteem are assets. Here are some tips to build self-esteem and confidence:

- Focus on your strengths and positive qualities, and find ways to boost them.
- Be yourself, and don't compare yourself with others.
- Look upon mistakes or limitations as a chance to learn. Don't dwell on them, accept them and move on.
- Replace negative thoughts and images with positive ones.
- Take responsibility for your life instead of blaming others. Decide what you *can* do.
- Control your own thoughts, emotions, words, and actions.

12. Paul Hong, a professor of accounting at Central State University.
Is in the classroom 3 hours per day.
Works 8.5 total hours per day.
What percent of his day is spent in the classroom? **0.35294 = 35.29%**

13. Ben Dornan is a maintenance programmer for Ace Corporation. He works
7.5 hours per day. He spends about 2.25 hours each day testing programs
on which he has made changes. What percent of his day is spent testing these
programs? **0.3 = 30%**

14. Ruth Loeb is a clerk at Violet's Dress Shoppe. She works 8 hours each day.
A time study recorded her activities. What percent of the 8 hours does she
spend on each activity? What percent of her day is spent restocking and
pricing? (See Figure 14.9.)

Figure 14.9

14. Assisting customers 0.525 = 52.5%;
Processing sales 0.1375 = 13.75%;
Restocking racks 0.1125 = 11.25%;
Pricing merchandising 0.1 = 10%;
Break and miscellaneous 0.125 =
12.5%; 21.25% spent restocking and
pricing

Activity	Hours
Assisting customers	4.2
Processing sales	1.1
Restocking racks	0.9
Pricing merchandise	0.8
Break and miscellaneous	1.0
Total	**8.0**

15. Kwame Lucas delivers bread for City Bakery Company. He works 9 hours
each day. A time study showed the following figures. What percent of his
workday is spent on each of the activities? What percent of the day does
Lucas spend loading, driving, and delivering? (See Figure 14.10.)

Figure 14.10

15. Loading truck 0.14444 = 14.44%;
Driving truck 0.34444 = 34.44%;
Delivering bread 0.24444 = 24.44%;
Recording sale 0.05555 = 5.56%;
Checking out 0.03333 = 3.33%;
Break and miscellaneous 0.06666 =
6.67%; Lunch 0.11111 = 11.11%;
73.32% spent loading, driving, and
delivering

Activity	Hours
Loading truck	1.3
Driving truck	3.1
Delivering bread	2.2
Recording sale	0.5
Checking out	0.3
Break and miscellaneous	0.6
Lunch	1.0
Total	**9.0**

MAINTAINING YOUR SKILLS

Need Help? Go to...
► Skill 5: **Adding Decimals,** page 732
► Skill 31: **Finding the Rate,** page 758
► Workshop 1: **Writing and Reading Numbers,** page 4

Add.

16. $1.7 + 2.4 + 3.1 + 0.8$ **8**

17. $2.1 + 1.8 + 3.3 + 0.9 + 1.9$ **10**

Find the rate. Round answers to the nearest hundredth of a percent.

18. One and six tenths is what percent of 7.5? **0.21333 = 21.33%**

19. Two and one tenth is what percent of 9? **0.23333 = 23.33%**

 **ASSESS**

Error Analysis
Remind students how to find percents. In this section, students need to be able to find what percent one number is of another. Sometimes students confuse the two numbers when they divide. When they find the percent of time spent on an activity, remind students that they are finding what percent of the total time is spent on that activity. Therefore, you always divide the time spent on the activity by the total time.

4 CLOSE

Closing Activity
Find the percent of time spent. Round to the nearest hundredth of a percent.

1. Time spent: 2.
   Total time: 8. **25%**
2. Time spent: 3.
   Total time: 6.5. **46.15%**
3. Time spent: 3.5.
   Total time: 7.5. **46.67%**
4. Frank Gomes spends 5 hours of each 7.5-hour workday answering email. What percent of his workday is spent answering e-mail? **66.67%**
5. Christine Glass works 8 hours each day at Silver Computing. She spends 3 hours of her workday giving technical assistance. What percent of her workday is giving technical assistance? **37.5%**

WRAP-UP

Go over any problem for which a wrong answer is given.

Assignment Guide
   Basic: 5–8
Average: 9–12

20 min.

National Standards for Business Education

Standard 1	Mathematical Foundations
Standard 2	Number Relationships and Operations
Standard 6	Problem-Solving Applications

National Council of Teachers of Mathematics Standards

Standard 1	Numbers and Operations
Standard 6	Problem Solving
Standard 8	Communication

1 FOCUS

Ask students to describe some items that are sold in cartons with multiple items in the carton. Have students describe how the cartons are packaged.

In-Class Examples

Work through these exercises with students before having them do the Self-Check.

1. 3×0.5 **1.5**
2. 6×0.75 **4.5**
3. $8 \times \frac{5}{8}$ **5**
4. $(3 \times 7) + (2 \times 0.25)$ **21.50**
5. $(12 \times \frac{1}{4}) + (5 \times \frac{1}{2})$ **$5\frac{1}{2}$**

SECTION 14-6 Packaging

○ **Section Objective**

Figure out the dimensions of packaging cartons.

How do you get customers? One way is through smart packaging. Depending on your product, people are often lured by colorful or creative **packaging**. The production of your company's merchandise ends with packaging, placing the product in a container for shipment. The container eases handling and prevents breaking. The package may also identify the product and show it attractively. The size of the package depends on the size of the finished product. Remember that:

Dimensions: Length, Width, Height

Living in the Real World

Tracking Tractors

Big Delivery Foster knows that the cost of production doesn't end when a tractor rolls off the production line. Farm equipment still must reach the farm and that's where the packaging and shipping department come into the picture.

Draw Conclusions Before the tractors are delivered, are there any other packaging needs Thor might have to take into consideration?

Continued on page 477

(Example 1)

Cleaning Genie Company manufactures a cleaning solution that is sold in bottles with a diameter of 7 centimeters and a height of 20 centimeters. The company plans to package 12 bottles to a carton for shipping. The carton is made of 0.5-centimeter-thick corrugated cardboard with 0.3-centimeter cardboard partitions. What are the dimensions of the package that Cleaning Genie Company needs?

Figure 14.11

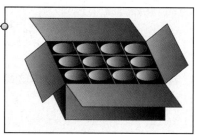

STEP 1: Find the length.

4 bottles × 7 cm in diameter	28.0 cm
3 partitions × 0.3 cm wide	0.9 cm
2 ends × 0.5 cm wide	1.0 cm
Length:	**29.9 cm**

Living in the Real World

Some parts of Thor tractors are packaged for protection; seats are covered with heavy-duty plastic; and wheel hubs are covered with heavy cardboard. Windshields also require a protective cover for long-haul shipping.

USING CALCULATORS

Entering fractional (rational) numbers in a calculator is as simple as entering one number divided by another number. Mixed numbers require the whole number portion in addition to the fractional part. For example $3\frac{3}{5}$ is entered as $3 \boxed{+} 3 \boxed{\div} 5 \boxed{=} 3.6$.

STEP 2: Find the width.

3 bottles × 7 cm in diameter	21.0 cm
2 partitions × 0.3 cm	0.6 cm
2 ends × 0.5 m	1.0 cm
Width:	**22.6 cm**

STEP 3: Find the height.

1 bottle × 20	20.0 cm
2 top flaps × 0.5 cm	1.0 cm
2 bottom flaps × 0.5 cm	1.0 cm
Height:	**22.0 cm**

STEP 4: Find the dimensions.

Length: 29.9 cm; Width: 22.6 cm; Height: 22.0 cm

Point out that there are several factors involved when deciding how to package a product. Not only does a package need to look attractive, it also has to keep its contents safe during shipment. Since the shipping process could damage items that are not adequately protected, companies need to be careful how they package items. Companies are also concerned with the costs involved in packaging. Excess material that is not absolutely necessary means excess costs. The size, shape, and type of item being packaged will determine the material used for packaging.

Motivating the Lesson

A carton is 21 inches long. It contains 4 packages that are of equal length. Each end of the carton is $\frac{1}{2}$-inch cardboard. How long is each package? **5 inches**

CONCEPT CHECK

Complete the problems, then check your answers at the end of the chapter.

1. There are 4 packages, each 5 inches wide, next to each other in a carton. Each end of the carton is 0.25-inch cardboard. How wide is the carton?
   5 + 5 + 5 + 5 + 0.25 + 0.25 = 20.5 inches
2. There are 6 packages, each 12 cm long, next to each other in a carton. Each end of the carton is 0.5-cm cardboard. How long is the carton?
   (12 × 6) + 0.5 + 0.5 = 73 cm

(Example 2)

Cleaning Genie Company from Example 1 decides to experiment with a longer, narrower packaging scheme. It wants to try arranging the bottles in 2 rows with 6 bottles in each row. What are the dimensions of the package that Cleaning Genie Company needs?

STEP 1: Find the length.

(6 bottles × 7 cm) + (5 partitions × 0.3 cm) + (2 ends × 0.5 cm)
    42.0 cm   +   1.5 cm   +   1.0 cm
= **44.5 cm length**

STEP 2: Find the width.

(2 bottles × 7 cm) + (1 partition × 0.3 cm) + (2 ends × 0.5 cm)
    14.0 cm   +   0.3 cm   +   1.0 cm
= **15.3 cm width**

STEP 3: Find the height.

(1 bottle × 20 cm) + (2 top flaps × 0.5 cm) + (2 bottom flaps × 0.5 cm)
    20.0 cm   +   1.0 cm   +   1.0 cm
= **22.0 cm height**

STEP 4: Find the dimensions.

Dimensions: Length of 44.5 cm; Width of 15.3 cm; Height of 22.0 cm

Section 14-6 Packaging ▶ **473**

THINKING CRITICALLY

Packaging Dimensions

Here is a good way to demonstrate the physical reality of this section. Students bring in shipping cartons with partitions still in them from grocery stores, department stores, drug stores, and so on. Students choose a carton and measure a partition, then calculate the overall package dimensions. The students check their answer by measuring the actual carton. Students repeat the process to measure three or four cartons. **LS** , **CL**

2 TEACH (cont'd)

In-Class Examples

1. A carton contains 6 packages, each 10 inches wide next to each other. Each end is $\frac{3}{4}$-inch cardboard. How wide is the carton? **$61\frac{1}{2}$ inches**

2. A carton contains 8 packages, each 6 inches long next to each other. Each end is 0.25 inch cardboard. How long is the carton? **48.5 inches**

3. A carton contains 24 bottles of juice. Each bottle is 8 inches in diameter and 11 inches high. The carton is 0.75 inches thick and has 0.25 inch-thick partitions positioned between the bottles.

   a. What are the dimensions of the carton if the bottles are packaged in 4 rows with 6 bottles in the row? **12.5 in. H × 50.75 in. L × 34.25 in. W**

   b. What are the dimensions of the carton if the bottles are packaged in 3 rows with 8 bottles in the row? **12.5 in. H × 67.25 in. L × 26 in. W**

3 ASSESS

Error Analysis

Some of the problems in this section contain fractional measurements. Review how to add and multiply fractions. Give students some exercises to practice. Be sure to include some fraction addition exercises that involve finding the least common denominator. Make sure students know how to write fractions in lowest terms.

SELF-CHECK ✓

3. Length:
   (6 × 9) +
   (5 × 0.2) +
   (2 × 0.5) =
   54 + 1 + 1 =
   56 cm
   Width:
   (2 × 9) +
   (1 × 0.2) +
   (2 × 0.5) =
   18 + 0.2 + 1 =
   19.2 cm
   Height: (1 × 12) +
   (2 × 0.5) + (2 ×
   0.5) = 12 + 1 + 1
   = 14 cm

Figure 14.12

17. WITHOUT Top and Bottom flap: 21 × 20.25 × 19.75
    Width (3 across):
    0.375 + 6.25 + 0.75 + 6.25 + 0.75 + 6.25 + 0.375 = 21.0
    Length: 0.375 + 19.5 + 0.375 = 20.25
    Height (Without flaps): 0.375 + 19.0 + 0.375 = 19.75
    WITH Top and Bottom flap: 21 × 20.25 × 20.50
    Height (With top/bot flap): 0.375 + 0.375 + 19.0 + 0.375 + 0.375 = 20.50

CONCEPT CHECK

Complete the problems, then check your answers at the end of the chapter.

Canned Food Company packages 12 cans of mixed vegetables to a package. Each can is 9 centimeters in diameter and 12 centimeters high. The carton is 0.5-centimeter thick, with 0.2-centimeter-thick partitions positioned between the cans. (**Don't forget to include the top and bottom flaps.**)

3. What are the dimensions of the carton if the cans are packaged in 2 rows with 6 cans in the row?

4. What are the dimensions of the carton if the cans are arranged in 3 rows with 4 cans in each row?
   Length: (4 × 9) + (3 × 0.2) + (2 × 0.5) = 36 + 0.6 + 1 = 37.6 cm
   Width: (3 × 9) + (2 × 0.2) + (2 × 0.5) = 27 + 0.4 + 1 = 28.4 cm
   Height: (1 × 12) + (2 × 0.5) + (2 × 0.5) = 12 + 1 + 1 = 14 cm

SECTION 14-6 PRACTICE

Find the dimensions of the carton.

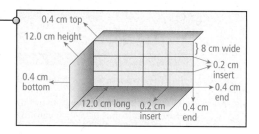

Height:

5. Top and bottom of 0.4 cm each **0.8 cm**

6. Height of each package **12.0 cm**

7. Total height **12.8 cm**

Width:

8. 3 packages, each 8 cm wide **24.0 cm**

9. 2 inserts, each 0.2 cm **0.4 cm**

10. 2 ends, each 0.4 cm **0.8 cm**

11. Total width **25.2 cm**

Length:

12. 4 packages, each 12 cm long **48.0 cm**

13. 3 inserts, each 0.2 cm **0.6 cm**

14. 2 ends, each 0.4 cm **0.8 cm**

15. Total length **49.4 cm**

16. Dimensions **12.8 cm (H) by 25.2 cm (W) by 49.4 cm (L)**

Draw a sketch for each carton in Exercises 17–20.

17. Clean Air Corporation packages 3 humidifiers per carton. The humidifiers are 19 inches tall, 19.5 inches long, and 6.25 inches wide. The humidifiers are placed next to each other with a 0.75-inch-thick piece of Styrofoam between them. The carton is made of 0.375-inch-thick corrugated cardboard. What are the dimensions of the carton in which the humidifiers are packed?

COOPERATIVE LEARNING

Assign small groups the task of solving Problems 17 and 18. Ask a representative from several groups to present their solutions to the class.

18. Marine Radio Corporation packages 6 of their weather alert radios in 1 carton. The carton is made of $\frac{3}{8}$-inch-thick corrugated cardboard. Partitions between the radios are $\frac{1}{4}$-inch-thick. **(Picture not drawn to scale.)**

Figure 14.13

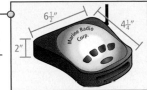

20. WITHOUT Top and Bottom flap: 28.6 × 9.6 × 14.6; Width (4 across): 0.3 + 7 + 7 + 7 + 7 + 0.3 = 28.6; Length (6 across): 0.3 + 1.5 + 1.5 + 1.5 + 1.5 + 1.5 + 1.5 + 0.3 = 9.6; Height (Without flaps): 0.3 + 14 + 0.3 = 14.6;
WITH Top and Bottom flap: 28.6 × 9.6 × 15.2; Height (With top/bot flap): 0.3 + 0.3 + 14 + 0.3 + 0.3 = 15.2; **19.** Answers will vary: If arranged 3 × 8, dimensions are 21.6 × 12.6 × 14.6

a. What are the dimensions of the carton if the radios are arranged in 2 rows of 3, with each radio on its side? $7\frac{1}{4}$ in (H); $7\frac{1}{4}$ in (L); $9\frac{1}{2}$ in (W)

b. What are the dimensions of the carton if the radios are arranged in 1 row of 6, with each radio on its side?

19. These 100-capacity tackle boxes are packaged 12 to a carton. The box is 10.75 inches long, 6 inches wide, and 6.5 inches high. The carton is constructed of 0.25-inch-thick cardboard. Styrofoam spacers, 0.125 inches thick, are positioned between the boxes and the layers. What are the dimensions of the carton if the boxes are arranged in 2 layers, with each layer consisting of 2 rows of 3 boxes?

Figure 14.14

Height = $13\frac{5}{8}$ in;
Length = $22\frac{1}{8}$ in;
Width = $18\frac{3}{4}$ in

20. Boxed hand warmers are packaged 24 to a carton. One boxed hand warmer is 14 centimeters tall, 7 centimeters long, and $1\frac{1}{2}$ centimeters wide. The carton is made of 0.3 centimeter cardboard. There are no partitions.
a. What are the dimensions of the carton if the boxes are arranged standing up in 4 rows of 6 hand warmers each?
b. What other arrangements could be used to package the hand warmers? Draw sketches and give the dimensions of the cartons.

MAINTAINING YOUR SKILLS

Need Help? Go to...
→ Skill 16: Adding Fractions, Unlike Denominators, page 743
→ Skill 20: Multiplying Fractions/Mixed Numbers, page 747

Add.

21. $\frac{1}{2} + \frac{1}{8}$ $\frac{5}{8}$

22. $\frac{1}{8} + \frac{3}{16}$ $\frac{5}{16}$

23. $\frac{1}{4} + \frac{3}{16}$ $\frac{7}{16}$

24. $\frac{1}{8} + \frac{7}{16}$ $\frac{9}{16}$

25. $\frac{1}{2} + \frac{1}{4}$ $\frac{3}{4}$

26. $\frac{3}{4} + \frac{9}{16}$ $1\frac{5}{16}$

Multiply.

27. $6 \times \frac{1}{2}$ 3

28. $4 \times \frac{1}{8}$ $\frac{1}{2}$

29. $5 \times \frac{1}{16}$ $\frac{5}{16}$

30. $4 \times \frac{3}{8}$ $1\frac{1}{2}$

31. $6 \times \frac{3}{4}$ $4\frac{1}{2}$

32. $6 \times \frac{5}{8}$ $3\frac{3}{4}$

Section 14-6 Packaging ▶ **475**

WRAP-UP

Go over any problem for which a wrong answer is given.

Assignment Guide
   Basic: 5–16
   Average: 17–18

20 min.

---

18. a. WITHOUT Top and Bottom flap: $7\frac{1}{4}$ × 5 × 14
Width: (3 across) $\frac{3}{8} + 2 + \frac{1}{4} + 2 + \frac{1}{4} + 2 + \frac{3}{8} = 7\frac{1}{4}$
Length: $\frac{3}{8} + 4\frac{1}{4} + \frac{3}{8} = 5$
Height: (Without flaps & 2 high) $\frac{3}{8} + 6\frac{1}{2} + \frac{1}{4} + 6\frac{1}{2} + \frac{3}{8} = 14$
WITH Top and Bottom flap: $7\frac{1}{4}$ × 5 × $14\frac{3}{4}$
Height: (With top/bot flap) $\frac{3}{8} + \frac{3}{8} + 6\frac{1}{2} + \frac{1}{4} + 6\frac{1}{2} + \frac{3}{8} + \frac{3}{8} = 14\frac{3}{4}$

b. WITHOUT Top and Bottom flap: 5 × 14 × $7\frac{1}{4}$
Width: $\frac{3}{8} + 4\frac{1}{4} + \frac{3}{8} = 5$
Length: (6 across) $\frac{3}{8} + 2 + \frac{1}{4} + 2 + \frac{1}{4} + 2 + \frac{1}{4} + 2 + \frac{1}{4} + 2 + \frac{1}{4} + 2 + \frac{3}{8} = 14$
Height: (Without flaps) $\frac{3}{8} + 6\frac{1}{2} + \frac{3}{8} = 7\frac{1}{4}$
WITH Top and Bottom flap: 5 × 14 × 8
Height: (With top/bot flap) $\frac{3}{8} + \frac{3}{8} + 6\frac{1}{2} + \frac{3}{8} + \frac{3}{8} = 8$

4 CLOSE

Closing Activity

1. A carton contains 12 packages, each 5 inches wide next to each other. Each end is $\frac{1}{4}$-inch cardboard. How wide is the carton? $60\frac{1}{2}$ **inches**

2. The Noya Camera Company produces digital cameras that are 5 inches long by $1\frac{3}{4}$ inches wide by 3 inches tall. The company packages 8 of their cameras in 1 carton. The carton is made of $\frac{3}{8}$-inch cardboard. Partitions between the cameras are $\frac{1}{4}$-inch-thick.
   a. What are the dimensions of the carton if the cameras are arranged in 2 rows of 4? $3\frac{3}{4}$ **in. H ×** $21\frac{1}{2}$ **in. L ×** $4\frac{1}{2}$ **in. W**
   b. What are the dimensions of the carton if the cameras are arranged in 1 row of 8? $3\frac{3}{4}$ **in. H ×** $42\frac{1}{2}$ **in. L ×** $2\frac{1}{2}$ **in. W**

CHAPTER 14 REVIEW

Quick Quiz

1. Ten wallets are made from one piece of leather costing $38.90. What is the direct material cost per item? **$3.89**
2. Find the break-even point in units if the selling price of an item is $2.49, the variable cost per unit is $1.80, and the total fixed costs are $19,645. **28,471**
3. A quality control inspector checked 50 items. Two of the items were defective. If more than 5 percent of the sample is defective, the process is out of control. What percent of the sample is defective? **(4%)** Is the process in or out of control? **in control**
4. Gerry Pry spends 2 hours of each 8-hour workday reading reports. What percent of his workday is spent reading reports? **25%**

SECTION 14-1 CONCEPT CHECK (p. 459)
1. $0.80 \div 40.00 =$ **$0.02**
2. $0.04 + $0.18 =$ **$0.22**

SECTION 14-2 CONCEPT CHECK (p. 462)
1. $87,500.00 \div (\$0.79 - \$0.29) = 87,500.00 \div \$0.50 =$ **175,000.00**
2. $124,500.00 \div (\$1.49 - \$0.74) = 124,500.00 \div \$0.75 =$ **166,000.00**

SECTION 14-3 CONCEPT CHECK (p. 464)
1. $5 \div 200 = 0.025 =$ **2.5%**
2. $3 \div 50 = 0.06 =$ **6%**

SECTION 14-4 CONCEPT CHECK (p. 467)
1. $48 \div 6 =$ **8**
2. $55 \div 15 =$ **3.7**
3. $[(8.5 \times 60) - (15 + 30 + 20)] \div 12 =$
   $[510 - 65] \div 12 =$
   $445 \div 12 =$ **37**

SECTION 14-5 CONCEPT CHECK (p. 470)
1. $2.5 \div 8 = 0.3125 =$ **31.25%**
2. $1.5 \div 8 = 0.1875 =$ **18.75%**
3. $(2.5 + 3.0) \div 8.0 =$ **0.6875 or 68.75%**
4. $(2.5 + 3.0 + 1.5) \div 8.0 =$ **0.875 or 87.5%**

SECTION 14-6 CONCEPT CHECK (p. 473, 474)
1. $5 + 5 + 5 + 5 + 0.25 + 0.25 =$ **20.5 inches**
2. $(12 \times 6) + 0.5 + 0.5 =$ **73 cm**
3. Length: $(6 \times 9) + (5 \times 0.2) + (2 \times 0.5) = 54 + 1 + 1 =$ **56 cm**
   Width: $(2 \times 9) + (1 \times 0.2) + (2 \times 0.5) = 18 + 0.2 + 1 =$ **19.2 cm**
   Height: $(1 \times 12) + (2 \times 0.5) + (2 \times 0.5) = 12 + 1 + 1 =$ **14 cm**
4. Length: $(4 \times 9) + (3 \times 0.2) + (2 \times 0.5) = 36 + 0.6 + 1 =$ **37.6 cm**
   Width: $(3 \times 9) + (2 \times 0.2) + (2 \times 0.5) = 27 + 0.4 + 1 =$ **28.4 cm**
   Height: $(1 \times 12) + (2 \times 0.5) + (2 \times 0.5) = 12 + 1 + 1 =$ **14 cm**

Living in the Real World

Tracking Tractors

Assessment Foster and Luther work together to analyze and evaluate the productivity of Thor Tractors. In order to get a global picture of the entire company, they ask the mail-order parts department to gather information about its tasks. To evaluate the data, they use statistical measures, such as averages. They suggest the department show how it arranges, labels, and locates goods so that shippers can find them more easily and orders are processed more quickly.

The mail-order parts department prepared a survey for Foster and Luther a few weeks ago. Each employee was timed over a five-week period in order to complete each task; the times were averaged. The results are shown in the table and chart below.

Time Spent on Processing an Order	
Process	**Time**
Gather goods ordered	0.75 hours
Package the goods	0.25 hours
Prepare the invoice	0.33 hours
Ship the order	0.25 hours

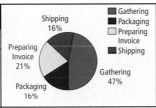

Shipping 16%
Preparing Invoice 21%
Packaging 16%
Gathering 47%

Legend: Gathering, Packaging, Preparing Invoice, Shipping

1. Which tasks take the same amount of time to complete?

2. True or false: The time needed to gather the goods is about half of all the time it takes to process an order.

3. Some employees recommended using small carts to get around the inventory area. If managers agree to this, do you think the 47.47 percent slice of the pie will get smaller?

4. A new computer system will reduce the time needed to prepare an invoice of 0.1 hours. What percent of the new total time is this? Will the preparing an invoice portion of the pie be smaller?

Living in the Real World

1. Packaging shipping
2. True
3. Yes
4. 9%; Yes

REVIEW OF KEY WORDS

manufactures (p. 458)
direct material cost (p. 458)
direct labor cost (p. 458)
prime cost (p. 458)
break-even analysis (p. 461)

break-even point (p. 461)
profit (p. 461)
fixed costs (p. 461)
variable costs (p. 461)
quality control (p. 463)

defective (p. 463)
quality control chart (p. 463)
time study (p. 466)
packaging (p. 472)

For Problems 1–14, write the definition of each key word in your own words. Then compare your version of the words to those found in the glossary.

1–14. Answers will vary depending on students' understanding. Make sure they understand the fundamental concept behind each key word.

Skills and Concepts

SECTION OBJECTIVE 14-1 AND EXAMPLES

Compute the prime cost of manufacturing an item.

Clear Choice produces plastic CD cases. The machine operator presses 30 cases from each piece of plastic. Each piece costs $4.50. The operator can press 250 cases per hour. The direct labor charge is $20.25 per hour. To the nearest tenth of a cent, what is the prime cost of manufacturing a CD case?

STEP 1: Find the direct material cost per item.
$4.50 ÷ 30 = $0.150 direct material cost per item

STEP 2: Find the direct labor cost per item.
$20.25 ÷ 250 = $0.081 direct labor cost per item

STEP 3: Find the prime cost per item.

Direct Material Cost per Item + Direct Labor Cost per Item

$0.150 + $0.081 = $0.231 prime cost per CD case

REVIEW EXERCISES

	Cost per Item	Pieces per Item	Direct Material Cost per Piece	Labor Cost per Hour	Pieces per Hour	Direct Labor Cost per Piece	Prime Cost	
15.	$0.75	20	a. $0.03750	$12.50	1,000	b.	c. $0.05	b. $0.01250
16.	0.90	50	a. $0.01800	15.00	1,200	b.	c. $0.03	b. $0.01250
17.	0.65	30	a. $0.02167	17.95	500	b.	c. $0.06	b. $0.03590
18.	0.95	25	a. $0.03800	20.00	1,800	b.	c. $0.05	b. $0.01111
19.	1.10	10	a. $0.11000	13.25	700	b.	c. $0.13	b. $0.01893
20.	0.55	15	a. $0.03667	15.25	650	b.	c. $0.06	b. $0.02346

SECTION OBJECTIVE 14-2 AND EXAMPLES

Calculate the break-even point in the number of manufactured units.

Fa Talai manufactures cell phone cases. It plans to manufacture 1,200,000 cases to be sold at $8.55 each. The fixed costs are estimated to be $300,249. Variable costs are $3.83 per unit. How many cases must be sold for Fa Talai to break even?

STEP: Find the break-even point in units.

Total Fixed Costs ÷ (Selling Price per Unit − Variable Costs per Unit)

$300,249 ÷ ($8.55 − $3.83) = 63,612.076 or 63,612 cases sold to break even

REINFORCEMENT

Section 14-1

1. Jenna Fields is a die cut machine operator. She makes 105 shoe soles from one piece of rubber. Each sheet of rubber costs $3.95. Fields is able to make 1 every 5 seconds. The direct labor cost is $17.50 per hour. What is the prime cost of manufacturing one shoe sole? **$0.062**

REVIEW EXERCISES

	Total Fixed Costs	÷	Selling Price per Unit	−	Variable Costs per Unit	=	Break-Even Point in Units
21.	$ 75,000	÷	($ 1.55	−	$ 0.55)	=	75,000
22.	98,000	÷	(0.86	−	0.29)	=	171,930
23.	127,000	÷	(2.35	−	1.58)	=	164,935
24.	456,000	÷	(4.59	−	2.43)	=	211,111
25.	1,230,000	÷	(203.00	−	135.56)	=	18,238
26.	2,987,000	÷	(513.34	−	303.50)	=	14,235

SECTION OBJECTIVE 14-3 AND EXAMPLES

Compute the percent of defective goods and determine if the process is in or out of control.

Marcy Jenkins is a quality control inspector for T1, Inc. At 8 A.M. she checked 30 stamped casings produced during the previous hour and found 2 defective casings. The process is in control if 3 percent or less of the sample is defective. Is the process in control or out of control? Plot the percent defective on a quality control chart.

STEP 1: Find the percent defective.
Number Defective ÷ Total Number Checked
      2   ÷   30
= 0.666 or 7% defective (Process is out of control.)

STEP 2: Plot the percent defective on a quality control chart.

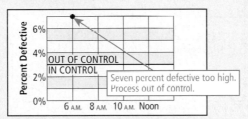

REVIEW EXERCISES

In the problems below, if more than 4 percent of the sample is defective, then the process is out of control.

	Number Defective	÷	Number Checked	=	Percent Defective	In Control or Out of Control?
27.	3	÷	45	=	a. 6.67%	b. Out
28.	5	÷	45	=	a. 11.11%	b. Out
29.	1	÷	45	=	a. 2.22%	b. In
30.	4	÷	45	=	a. 8.89%	b. Out
31.	2	÷	45	=	a. 4.44%	b. Out

Study Guide and Assessment ▶ **479**

REINFORCEMENT

Section 14-2
1. Yell Textiles manufactures rugs. They plan to manufacture small rugs to be sold at $22.99 each. The fixed costs are estimated to be $265,490. Variable costs are $16.82 per unit. How many rugs must be sold for Yell Textiles to break even? **43,029**

Section 14-3
1. Harry Jones works in the quality control department of Haskell Manufacturing. Every 4 hours, he checks 50 umbrellas. If more than 6 percent of the umbrellas are defective, production is out of control. Determine whether the process is in or out of control at each check.

    8:00 A.M.—2 defective **in control**
    12 P.M.—5 defective **out of control**
    4 P.M.—1 defective **in control**

SECTION OBJECTIVE 14-4 AND EXAMPLES

Use time-study results to compute how many units can be produced.

FRS Task Analysis did a time study of Peter Newsome's job as a cook. Newsome's times were recorded. The averages were calculated. If Newsome gets a 10-minute break each hour, how many salads can he make in an hour?

Task	Time in Seconds					Average
	#1	#2	#3	#4	#5	
Gather vegetables	45	33	30	40	51	39.8
Wash vegetables	95	98	101	89	90	94.6
Cut up vegetables	199	120	134	210	156	163.8
Fill bowls	56	66	68	71	83	68.8

STEP 1: Find the average time required per unit.
$39.8 + 94.6 + 163.8 + 68.8 = 367.0$ seconds

STEP 2: Find the actual time worked per hour.
$60 - 10 = 50$ minutes $\times$ 60 seconds $= 3,000$ seconds

STEP 3: Find the number of units per hour.
$$\frac{\text{Actual Time Worked}}{\text{Average Time Required per Unit}} = \frac{3,000}{367} = 8.17 \text{ or } 8 \text{ units per hour}$$

REVIEW EXERCISES

	Actual Time Worked	÷	Average Time per Unit	=	Number of Units
32.	49 minutes	÷	40.1 seconds	=	73
33.	57 minutes	÷	59.7 seconds	=	57
34.	48 minutes	÷	36.5 seconds	=	79
35.	58 minutes	÷	45.2 seconds	=	77
36.	66 minutes	÷	51.3 seconds	=	77
37.	38 minutes	÷	29.9 seconds	=	76

SECTION OBJECTIVE 14-5 AND EXAMPLES

Use time-study results to compute the percent of time spent on each task.

Nguyen Trong works as a first grade teacher. A time study shows that he spent his time on these activities. What percent of his time does he spend grading papers?

Activity	Hours
Teaching	3.75
Playground duty	0.50
Lesson planning	1.50
Grading papers	1.50
Cleaning classroom	0.75
Total	**8.00**

REINFORCEMENT

Section 14-4

1. Greg Collette serves customers at Sunshine Lemonade. His average time per customer is 4 minutes. He works 45 minutes per hour. How many customers can be served per hour? **11**

STEP: Find the percent of time spent on activity.

$$\frac{\text{Time Spent on Activity}}{\text{Total Time}}$$

$$1.5 \div 8 \qquad = 18.75\% \text{ of time spent grading papers}$$

REVIEW EXERCISES

	Activity	Hours	Total Time	Percent of Time
38.	Answers e-mail	1.00	8	12.5%
39.	Word processes documents	2.00	8	25%
40.	Answers phone	1.50	8	18.75%
41.	Files	1.25	8	15.63%
42.	Run copies	0.50	8	6.25%
43.	Send faxes	1.75	8	21.88%

SECTION OBJECTIVE 14-6 AND EXAMPLES

Figure out the dimensions of packaging cartons.

A pottery company manufactures bowls that have a diameter of 9 centimeters and a height of 15 centimeters. The company plans to package 12 bowls to a carton in 3 rows of 4 bowls each for shipping. The carton is made of 0.6-centimeter-thick corrugated cardboard with 0.4-centimeter cardboard partitions. What are the dimensions of the package that the pottery company needs?

STEP 1: Find the length.

4 bowls × 9 cm in diameter	36.0 cm
3 partitions × 0.4 cm wide	1.2 cm
2 ends × 0.6 cm	1.2 cm
Length	**38.4 cm**

STEP 2: Find the width.

3 bowls × 9 cm in diameter	27.0 cm
2 partitions × 0.4 cm wide	0.8 cm
2 ends × 0.6 cm	1.2 cm
Width	**29.0 cm**

STEP 3: Find the height.

1 bowl × 15 cm	15.0 cm
2 top flaps × 0.6 cm	1.2 cm
2 bottom flaps × 0.6 cm	1.2 cm
Height	**17.4 cm**

STEP 4: Find the dimensions.

Length: 38.4 cm
Width: 29.0 cm
Height: 17.4 cm

44. **Top and bottom of 0.3 cm: 0.6**
47. **28 cm**
51. **28 cm**

REVIEW EXERCISES
Find the dimensions of the carton.

Height:
44. Top and bottom of 0.3 cm:
45. Height: **15.6 cm**
46. Total height: **16.2 cm**
Width:
47. 4 packages, each 7 cm wide: **28 cm**
48. 3 inserts, each 0.1 cm: **0.3 cm**
49. 2 ends, each 0.4 cm: **0.8 cm**
50. Total width: **29.1 cm**
Length:
51. 4 packages, each 7 cm long: **28 cm**
52. 3 inserts, each 0.1 cm: **0.3 cm**
53. 2 ends, each 0.4 cm: **0.8 cm**
54. Total length: **39.1 cm**

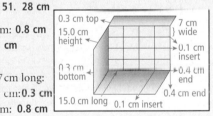

0.3 cm top
15.0 cm height
0.3 cm bottom
15.0 cm long
0.1 cm insert
7 cm wide
0.1 cm insert
0.4 cm end
0.4 cm end

REINFORCEMENT

Section 14-5
Find the percent of time spent. Round to the nearest hundredth of a percent.
1. Time spent: 6.5.
   Total time: 8. **81.25%**
2. Paula Day spends 4 hours of each 8-hour workday answering calls. What percent of her workday is spent answering calls? **50%**

Section 14-6
1. A carton contains 18 packages, each 6 inches wide next to each other. Each end is $\frac{1}{2}$-inch cardboard. How wide is the carton? **109 inches**

A Creative Lab

① FOCUS

Math Studio Overview

Students become the owner of a successful catering company that has signed on to provide food for a political rally. Through the exercise and interviews with caterers in their area, they will learn the important connections between quality, economy, efficiency, and profit.

Bell Ringer Activity

Ask students to name 10 mass-produced items in the classroom. Record their answers on the board. Speculate how manufacturing of the items (i.e., made by machine, produced by hand, or both?) affects efficiency. Lead a discussion on the creation and delivery of products.

② TEACH

Cooperative Learning

Break students into groups of three or four and ask each group to research any product produced in your area. (Suggestions: local bakery, local manufacturing plant.) Ask each group to interview a person in charge of production of their particular product and have each group prepare an oral presentation of its findings. Each presentation should mention the product, its importance to the community, and any details on production, packaging and delivery, and associated costs.

Preparing for a Big Bash

You started a catering business from your home. This week you have signed a contract to provide food for a political rally. You'll devote most of today to planning the production of the event to ensure that you'll make a profit.

Purpose

This exercise can help you understand the important connections between quality, economy, efficiency, and profit. If you produce goods or services for a client or customer, you must be able to produce for less than you sell while also maintaining high standards of quality. In this way you'll keep your customers satisfied and returning for more business and you'll remain in business. In addition, you might even be able to grow your business.

Supplies Needed

- Pen
- Paper
- A kitchen, basic cooking supplies, and kitchen tools
- A stopwatch
- A telephone and possibly access to the Internet

Your Activity

Step 1: In this project, you want to understand and experience some of the issues a caterer faces when planning for a large event. Begin by talking with several local caterers. Contact them on the telephone or find a catering

business's Web site and e-mail the owner several questions. Your list of questions might include:

- How do you as a caterer calculate quantities of food for large groups?
- What kinds of food are appropriate or inappropriate for a political rally where people stand around and chat?

(In all cases, explain that you are gathering information for a school assignment.)

Step 2: Set up a plan of action for your own event.

A. Begin by mapping out the various elements of production. Decide on one simple food item that you would like to include on the menu for the political rally. (Perhaps it's a morning event and you'll want to include muffins.)

B. Assume (for this example) that the political rally will be a morning event and you'll provide muffins. Using a muffin mix or starting from scratch, you're going to prepare a "test case" of muffins in your kitchen.
   Before you begin, however, you're going to start gathering important financial and production data that

---

NEWSWORTHY TREND

Software-Directed Packaging: Part 1

Technology plays an increasingly larger role in packaging these days, as advances give machinery greater capability for completing tasks that are more complex. According to *Modern Materials Handling* magazine, Medtronic, Inc., a California distribution center, is utilizing a software-directed packaging kit that bundles medical instruments with the exactness of a skilled surgeon. The company manufactures and ships 50 different pre-sterilized kits and ships these to hospitals and medical facilities nationwide.

After sterilization, the disposable tools are packaged and sent to the distribution center, where they remain until a hospital places an order. Once the requests are received, line workers pull and package the appropriate instruments.

will tell you how to make sure you make money with that item.

Keep a log about the purchase, preparation, and presentation of the muffins you bake.

- Compute the prime cost of producing the muffins.

- How can you factor these into the price you'll charge for your muffins to make sure you don't lose money or just break even?

- How will you figure labor costs?

- What is the break-even point for muffins for 100 people? Why is this important to know?

- Once you have the cost of ingredients for a dozen muffins, decide how many muffins you'll need to serve 100 people. Then calculate the total cost of muffins for the political rally.

- Calculate the cost of damaged muffins. Have you burned your muffins?

- How many muffins can you make in an hour? How much time does it take you from start to finish (opening the box to putting away all your washed utensils) to make a dozen muffins?

Step 3: Break down the production process into its component parts. List them on a piece of paper. Include preparation time (gathering utensils and ingredients) as well as time to read the instructions, mix each ingredient, grease the pan, and pour the mix into the pan. While you're making the muffins, use a stopwatch to help you determine how much time you spend on each task. Can certain tasks be made more efficient? For instance, are the mixing bowls, measuring spoons, and other cooking tools efficiently organized in your kitchen, or scattered in hard-to-find places?

Step 4: Finally, decide how you'll transport and present your muffins. How much will this packaging cost?

Step 5: Now that you have analyzed the costs of production, calculate how much you must charge per muffin to make a reasonable profit. How much will the total bill be for muffins for the 100 attendees at the political rally?

Step 6: Design a fun letterhead incorporating your company's name and a logo. Write an attractive and informative invoice showing the price of the muffins you'll give to the customer.

Critique It

Based on what you know about production, what conclusion might you make about a company that manufactures thousands of items a minute? If the production process slowed down due to a faulty piece of equipment, how does that cause a ripple effect?

ASSESS

Enrichment
Ask students to write a paragraph starting with the sentence, "It is important for manufacturing plants to institute quality control programs because...."

CLOSE

Critique It

Equipment problems ripple through other plant departments. Some companies plan for such emergencies with back-up machinery and other time-saving tools so that production is not slowed and customers do not experience a change in product quality or availability.

NEWSWORTHY TREND

Software-Directed Packaging: Part 2

Before implementing the software, Medtronic kept packaging instructions for the large variety of kit combinations in an antiquated card filing system. Whenever a kit was required, workers researched the required instruments and pulled them from storage.

Now, a display screen tells the line worker which type of carton to use for packing the kit and a picture of the correct instruments also appear on the screen. The simple to follow formula even illustrates the best arrangement within the carton. A machine then generates the precise amount of padded shipping material and the display screen shows the worker the ideal way to wrap the tools.

Training time is reduced and packing speed is increased. The computer process eliminated the paperwork.

Section Objectives	National Standards for Business Education					
	1. Mathematical Foundations	2. Number Relationships and Operations	3. Patterns, Functions, and Algebra	4. Measurements	5. Statistics and Probability	6. Problem-Solving Applications
15-1 Trade Discounts (pp. 486–488) Compute the trade discount and the net price.	X	X				
15-2 Trade Discount—Complement Method (pp. 489–491) Calculate the net price using the complement method.	X	X				
15-3 Trade-Discount Rate (pp. 492–494) Figure out the trade-discount rate.	X	X				
15-4 Chain Discounts (pp. 495–497) Determine the final net price after a chain of discounts.	X	X				
15-5 Chain Discounts—Complement Method (pp. 498–501) Prove the final net price using the complement method.	X	X				
15-6 Cash Discounts—Ordinary Dating (pp. 502–504) Compute the cash price when the discount is based on ordinary dating.	X	X				
15-7 Cash Discounts—EOM Dating (pp. 505–507) Calculate the cash price when the discount is based on end-of-month dating.	X	X				

(Source: Reprinted with permission from the National Standards for Business Education, copyright © 2001 by National Business Education Association, 1914 Association Drive, Reston, Virginia 21901-1596)

SCANS Correlation

Foundation Skills

Basic Skills	Reading	Writing	Math	Listening	Speaking	
Thinking Skills	Creative Thinking	Decision Making	Problem Solving	Seeing Things in the Mind's Eye	Knowing How to Learn	Reasoning
Personal Qualities	Responsibility	Self-Esteem	Sociability	Self-Management	Integrity/Honesty	

This chapter's highlighted blocks indicate the chapter's content coverage in the Student Edition and the Teacher Wraparound Edition.

1. Numbers & Operations	2. Algebra	3. Geometry	4. Measurement	5. Data Analysis & Probability	6. Problem Solving	7. Reasoning & Proof	8. Communication	9. Connections	10. Representations
X					X		X		
X					X		X		
X					X		X		
X					X		X		
X					X		X		
X					X		X		
X					X		X		

SCANS Correlation

Workplace Competencies

Resources	Allocating Time	Allocating Money	Allocating Material and Facility Resources	Allocating Human Resources		
Information	Acquiring and Evaluating Information	Organizing and Maintaining Information	Interpreting and Communicating Information	Using Computers to Process Information		
Interpersonal Skills	Participating as a Member of a Team	Teaching Others	Serving Clients/Customers	Exercising Leadership	Negotiating to Arrive at a Decision	Working with Cultural Diversity
Systems	Understanding Systems	Monitoring and Correcting Performance	Improving and Designing Systems			
Technology	Selecting Technology	Applying Technology to Task	Maintaining and Troubleshooting Technology			

What You'll Learn

Tell students that when companies order supplies they often receive trade discounts. In this chapter you'll focus on finding the best trade discounts.

Why It's Important

Taking advantage of discounts offered by vendors allows a company to increase cash flow. There are tradeoffs in that the money might be better off invested for a short period of time versus paying a bill early to receive a smaller discount. Discounts are also available by purchasing bulk quantities of goods and again, there are tradeoffs between carrying inventory and receiving a discount.

Key Word Review
Motivation

Pair students up and have them take turns motivating each other in learning and understanding the key words for this chapter. You can suggest tricks and techniques such as mnemonics, index cards, "beating the clock," and so on.

`LS` , `CL`

CHAPTER (15)

Purchasing

What You'll Learn

Section 15-1 Compute the trade discount and the net price.

Section 15-2 Calculate the net price using the complement method.

Section 15-3 Figure out the trade-discount rate.

Section 15-4 Determine the final net price after a chain of discounts.

Section 15-5 Compute the final net price using the complement method.

Section 15-6 Compute the cash price when the discount is based on ordinary dating.

Section 15-7 Calculate the cash price when the discount is based on end-of-month dating.

When Will You Ever Use This?

At some point in your career, you might need to order supplies from the purchasing department. You might buy merchandise for your business from suppliers, such as distributors, wholesalers, or manufacturers.

Key Words to Know

- list price
- trade discount
- trade-discount rate
- net price
- complement method
- chain discounts
- net-price rate
- single equivalent discount
- invoice
- cash discount
- ordinary dating
- end-of-month dating

Mathematics Online

To learn more about the mathematics of purchasing, visit the *Mathematics with Business Applications* Web site at www.busmath.glencoe.com.

CLASSROOM RESOURCES

Application and Enrichment
- 🖝 *Teacher Wraparound Edition*
- 🖝 *Teacher Resource Binder, Blackline Masters*
- ◉ *Interactive Lesson Planner* CD-ROM
- ◉ *PowerPoint® Presentations* CD-ROM

Review and Enforcement
Mathematics Online
www.busmath.glencoe.com
- 🖝 *Teacher Resource Binder, Internet Resources*

- 🖝 *Student Activity Workbook*
- 🖝 *Student Activity Workbook, Teacher Annotated Edition*
- 🖝 *School-to-Home Activity Workbook*

Assessment and Evaluation
- 🖝 *Assessment Binder, Reproducible Tests*
- 🖝 *Assessment Binder, Alternative Assessment Strategies*
- ◉ **Exam***View*® *Pro Test Generator* CD-ROM

For the Teacher
- 🖝 *Student Activity Workbook, Teacher Annotated Edition*
- 🖝 *Assessment Binder*
- ◉ *Interactive Lesson Planner* CD-ROM
- 🖝 *Teacher Resource Binder*
- 🖥 Mathematics Online
www.busmath.glencoe.com

For the Student
- 🖝 *Student Activity Workbook*
- 🖝 *School-to-Home Activity Workbook*

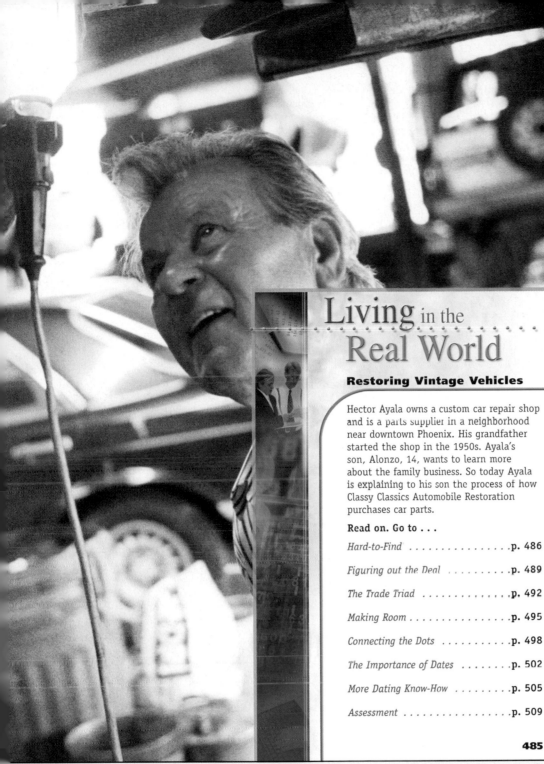

Living in the Real World

Restoring Vintage Vehicles

Hector Ayala owns a custom car repair shop and is a parts supplier in a neighborhood near downtown Phoenix. His grandfather started the shop in the 1950s. Ayala's son, Alonzo, 14, wants to learn more about the family business. So today Ayala is explaining to his son the process of how Classy Classics Automobile Restoration purchases car parts.

Read on. Go to . . .

485

Living in the Real World

Story's Summary

Hector Ayala owns a custom car repair shop and parts business that was established by his grandfather in the 1950s. Hector's 14-year-old son, Alonzo, is interested in learning the business, so his father begins by explaining the ins and outs of purchasing car parts for the shop's inventory. Along the way, Alonzo learns about trade, chain and cash discounts.

Did You Know...

Generally, *purchasers* buy goods and services for a company, while *buyers* normally procure items for resale by the same company.

Think about This

Why is it important for a purchasing manager or buyer to keep abreast of market conditions and price trends?

LOCAL STANDARDS

National Standards for Business Education

Standard 1	Mathematical Foundations
Standard 2	Number Relationships and Operations

National Council of Teachers of Mathematics Standards

Standard 1	Numbers and Operations
Standard 6	Problem Solving
Standard 8	Communication

1 FOCUS

Discuss with students the path a product follows to get to the consumer. Mention that the path begins at the manufacturer and then usually travels next to a wholesaler. The wholesaler sells to retailers who then sell to consumers.

In-Class Examples

Work through these exercises with students before having them do the Self-Check. Round answers to the nearest cent.
1. $16.50 × 5% **$0.83**
2. $27.89 × 10% **$2.79**
3. $22.59 − $0.90 **$21.69**

○ Section Objective

Compute the trade discount and the net price.

Most suppliers provide a catalog from which your business can buy items. The catalog includes a description and the **list price** (or catalog price) of each item that the supplier sells. The list price is generally the price at which you may sell the item. You usually purchase the item at a **trade discount**, which is a discount from the list price. The **trade-discount rate** is the amount of the discount expressed as a percent. The **net price** is the price you actually pay for the item. Remember that:

$$\text{Trade Discount} = \text{List Price} \times \text{Trade-Discount Rate}$$

$$\text{Net Price} = \text{List Price} - \text{Trade Discount}$$

Living in the Real World

Restoring Vintage Vehicles

Hard-to-Find Classy Classics not only restores antique and vintage cars for customers but also sells parts, paint, and tools for individuals restoring their own vehicles. The shop provides a wide array of hard-to-find items that antique automobile fans want. Ayala shows his son the description of the ornament and its list, or catalog price. The company gives dealers a deal, which is called the trade discount. After the discount is taken off the list price, the price the dealer pays is the net price.

Draw Conclusions Who gets a cut of the money from an item, such as a hood ornament?

Continued on page 489

Example 1

Johnson Auto Repair Shop is purchasing an electronic ignition module for a sport coupe that is six years old. The list price in the wholesaler's catalogue is $845. Johnson receives a 40 percent trade discount. What is the net price of the module?

STEP 1: Find the trade discount.

List Price × Trade-Discount Rate
$845.00 × 40% = $338.00 trade discount

STEP 2: Find the net price.

List Price − Trade Discount
$845.00 − $338.00 = **$507.00 net price**

845 [M+] [×] 40 [%] 338. [RM] [−] 338 [=] 507

Living in the Real World

The dealers get a portion of each sale in order to cover expenses, such as wages, utilities, and so on.

BUSINESS NOTES

Interview

Mom-and-Pop corner groceries and five-and-dime variety stores are quickly becoming relics. Have students interview older relatives or acquaintances to find out how consumer buying habits have changed over the years. Have students write a 150-word summary of the interview. **LS**, **P**

CONCEPT CHECK

Complete the problems, then check your answers at the end of the chapter.

1. List price of paint: $24.00.
   Trade-discount rate: 30 percent.
   a. Find the trade discount.   **Trade discount = $24.00 × 0.30 = $7.20;**
   b. Find the net price.   **Net price = $24.00 − $7.20 = $16.80**

2. List price of glue: $34.60.
   Trade-discount rate: 25 percent.
   a. Find the trade discount.   **Trade discount = $34.60 × 0.25 = $8.65;**
   b. Find the net price.   **Net price = $34.60 − $8.65 = $25.95**

SECTION 15-1 PRACTICE

Round answers to the nearest cent.

	List Price	Trade-Discount Rate	Trade Discount	Net Price
3.	$140.00	25%	$35.00	a. $105
4.	240.00	10%	a. $24.00	b. $216.00
5.	400.00	35%	a. $140.00	b. $260.00
6.	360.00	15%	a. $54.00	b. $306.00
7.	174.00	32%	a. $55.68	b. $118.32
8.	216.80	27%	a. $58.54	b. $158.26
9.	94.75	9%	a. $8.53	b. $86.22

10. List price for a spark plug: $3.15.
    Trade-discount rate: 35 percent.
    What is the net price? **$2.05**

11. List price for a compact disc player: $219.
    Trade-discount rate: 42 percent.
    What is the net price? **$127.02**

12. A furnace gas regulator carries a catalog price of $139.75. Its competitor offers a 30 percent trade-discount rate. What is the net price? **$97.83**

13. Harry's Hardware purchases the items shown from the wholesalers. Find the trade discount and net price for each item.

	Item	List	Trade-Discount Rate
$4.53; $8.42 a.	Paint thinner	$12.95	35%
$0.90; $8.09 b.	Lawn fertilizer	8.99	10%
$8.84; $50.11 c.	B&D electric saw	58.95	15%

Continued on next page

2 TEACH

Have students discuss why trade discounts are offered to wholesalers and retailers. Both wholesalers and retailers depend on trade discounts in order to make a profit on the sale of merchandise. The manufacturer depends on sales to the wholesaler. The wholesaler depends on sales to the retailer. The retailer depends on sales to the customer.

Point out that the list price is also known as the suggested retail price. This list price is the price a customer pays to the retailer for an item. The net price is the price the retailer pays for an item.

Motivating the Lesson
Officeworld purchases pens from a wholesaler at a discounted rate of 20 percent. The list prices are shown below. What is the net price of each pen?
Medium gel $1.19 **$0.95**
Fine ballpoint $1.29 **$1.03**
Extra fine felt tip $1.59 **$1.27**

In-Class Examples
Find the trade discount and the net price.
1. List price: $14.89
   Trade-discount rate: 20%
   $2.98; $11.91
2. List price: $41.50
   Trade-discount rate: 15%
   $6.23; $35.27
3. Murray Plumbing receives an 18 percent trade discount from their wholesale supply company. The list price on an item that Murray needs to purchase is $145.79. What is the net price? **$119.55**

COOPERATIVE LEARNING

Visit a Business
Students work in pairs to visit or call a local business they frequent, such as a video store, music store, or clothing store. Students talk with the manager and find out where the store gets its goods. Does the store get goods from a distributor or directly from a manufacturer? Do they get any special discounts, such as a trade or cash discount? How often do they get new supplies? Have students share their findings. **LS** , **CL**

PROBLEM SOLVING

Rounding
Some students have difficulties when working with percents and decimals. Provide practice in using percents and decimals. Tell students that if there are a number of steps in a calculation, such as in Section 15-5, not to round until the final step in the problem.

3 ASSESS

Error Analysis

Remind students to round to the nearest cent when they find the trade discounts. In Chapter 14 students rounded to the nearest tenth of a cent, so they may think that is what they should do in this section.

Students may confuse finding the trade discount with finding the net price since they are both dollar amounts. Point out that finding the trade discount involves using the trade-discount rate. Students may assume that the trade discount will always be less than the net price. Give students an example of why this is not true. For instance, use a trade-discount rate of 55 percent.

4 CLOSE

Closing Activity

Find the trade discount and the net price.
1. List price: $10.59. Trade-discount rate: 12 percent. **$1.27; $9.32**
2. List price: $22.60. Trade-discount rate: 25 percent. **$5.65; $16.95**
3. List price: $125.99. Trade-discount rate: 30 percent. **$37.80; $88.19**
4. Dayco Cabinets offers their dealers a 30 percent trade discount. The list price on a cabinet is $168.99. What is the net price? **$118.29**

14. Hero, Inc., manufactures automobile parts and accessories. A portion of its parts and accessories price list for auto dealers is shown. Hero offers the trade discounts listed to its dealers. Find the dealer price for each item.

Class	Part Number	Suggested List Price	Trade-Discount Rate
A	D2UZ 8200-B	$89.60	42%
HX	D27Z 82-A	57.20	38%
CQ	CPYT 8A178	2.90	45%
D	C7ZZ 8B90	7.80	30%

$51.97; $35.46; $1.59 ($1.60 with complement method); $5.46

15. Alvin Sales Agency receives a 33 percent trade-discount rate on farm equipment replacement parts from Land Wholesale Supply. What is the net price for each order?

Quantity	Stock Item	Description	Unit Price
6	$\frac{3}{4} \times 6$	Heavy bolts	$ 2.95
4	$\frac{3}{4}$	Star-lock washer	0.40
2	24" HOB	Chopper blades	25.45
6	#7271	Tune-up kit	49.99
4	#5051	PTO guard	39.90
12	$\frac{5}{8} \times 24$	Threaded rod	8.90

$11.86; $1.07; $34.10; $200.96; $106.93; $71.56

MAINTAINING YOUR SKILLS

Need Help? Go to...
▸ **Skill 30: Finding the Percentage,** page 757
▸ **Skill 6: Subtracting Decimals,** page 733

Find the percentage. Round answers to the nearest cent.

16. $47.80 × 10% **$4.78**
17. $91.40 × 18% **$16.45**
18. $416.60 × 20% **$83.32**
19. $27.79 × 35% **$9.73**
20. $279.49 × 50% **$139.75**
21. $2,178.99 × 42% **$915.18**

Subtract.

22. $47.80 − $4.78 **$43.02**
23. $416.60 − $83.32 **$333.28**
24. $279.49 − $139.75 **$139.74**

WRAP-UP

Go over any problem for which a wrong answer is given.

Assignment Guide
Basic: 3–9
Average: 10–12

20 min.

SECTION 15-2 Trade Discount— Complement Method

Section Objective

Calculate the net price using the complement method.

The **complement method** is another method of finding the net price. When you receive a trade discount, you subtract the discount rate from 100 percent. This gives you the complement of the trade-discount rate, sometimes called the *net-price rate*. You can multiply the list price by the complement to find the net price. Remember that:

Net Price = List Price × Complement of Trade-Discount Rate

Living in the Real World

Restoring Vintage Vehicles

Figuring out the Deal   While his father waits on a customer, Alonzo looks through several other catalogs and notices that some companies use a slightly different method to figure the net price for dealers. One catalog supplier, for instance, indicates that it offers shops a 35 percent trade discount. The company doesn't list the net price for each item; rather, when Ayala buys from this company, he calculates 65 percent of each price to determine his cost.

"So if we wanted to buy chrome repair supplies, we would subtract 35 percent from 100 percent. That would mean we would be paying 65 percent of the list price. So to figure out our net price, we would multiply the list price times 0.65," says Alonzo.

Draw Conclusions   What is the complement of 35 percent?

Continued on page 492

Example 1

The list price of an electronic ignition module in the wholesaler's catalog is $845. Repair shops receive a 40 percent trade discount. What is the net price of the module?

STEP 1: Find the complement of trade-discount rate.
100% − 40% = 60% complement of trade-discount rate

STEP 2: Find the net price.
List Price × Complement of Trade-Discount Rate
$845.00 ×   60%   = $507 net price

100 − 40 = 60 M+ 845 × RM 60 % 507

National Standards for Business Education

Standard 1	Mathematical Foundations
Standard 2	Number Relationships and Operations

National Council of Teachers of Mathematics Standards

Standard 1	Numbers and Operations
Standard 6	Problem Solving
Standard 8	Communication

① FOCUS

Ask students what the word complement means. Discuss how to find the complement of a percent. Have students find the complement of several percents.

In-Class Examples
Work through these exercises with students before having them do the Self-Check.
1. 100% − 20% **80%**
2. 100% − 24% **76%**
3. $99.50 × 80% **$79.60**

ALTERNATIVE ASSESSMENT

Students with Weak Study Skills
Ask students to time themselves doing homework and keep a record for a week. Suggest that students calculate the total time they need to complete homework. Ask students to think of the time block they're most happy with for studying: $\frac{1}{2}$ hour, 45 minutes, an hour, or $1\frac{1}{2}$ hours. Have students make a chart, or mark a calendar or planner and block out the time slots for homework. LS , CL

Living in the Real World

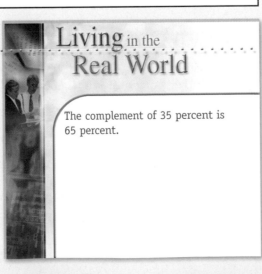

The complement of 35 percent is 65 percent.

489

② TEACH

Show students how the complement method can be used to find a net price. Give students a price, say $40, and a discount rate, say 25 percent. Have students find the net price using the method they learned in Section 15-1. Students should determine that the net price is $30. Tell students that $40 represents 100 percent of the price. Ask students what $30 represents. Show students that the net price can be found using 75 percent. **(Point out that when you get 25 percent off, you pay 75 percent.)**

After reviewing Example 1 on page 489 in this section, go back to Example 1 on page 486 in Section 15-1. Have students use the complement method to find the net price.

Motivating the Lesson

A retailer receives a 30 percent trade discount. What is the net price of an item that has a list price of $2.50? **$1.75**

In-Class Examples

Find the net price.
1. List price: $15.67.
   Trade-discount rate: 15 percent.
   $13.32
2. List price: $47.55.
   Trade-discount rate: 20 percent.
   $38.04
3. Partyland receives a 23 percent trade discount. What will Partyland pay for the following items?
   Paper plates: $1.57 **$1.21**
   Plastic cups: $1.09 **$0.84**
   Plastic cutlery: $0.99 **$0.76**

CONCEPT CHECK

 SELF-CHECK✓

Complete the problems, then check your answers at the end of the chapter. Find the complement and the net price.

1. List price of paint: $24.
   Trade-discount rate: 30 percent.
2. List price of glue: $34.50.
   Trade-discount rate: 25 percent.

1. 100% − 30% =
   70% complement of
   trade-discount rate
   $24.00 × 70% =
   $16.80 net price
2. 100% − 25% =
   75% complement of
   trade-discount rate
   $34.50 × 75% =
   $25.88 net price

You can think of the complement of the discount rate as the *percent paid*. It is another way to calculate the net price using the complement method:

$$\text{Net Price} = \text{List Price} \times \text{Percent Paid}$$

This formula looks almost the same as the one used in Example 1 except here you're to focus on the percent paid. (Example 1 focused on the complement of trade-discount rate.) You need to figure out the percent paid before you can find the net price. The list price should be given. To find the percent paid, take 100 and subtract the percent off. For example, if you get 30 percent off, then you pay 70 percent (or 100% − 30% = 70%).

◆ Example 2 ◆

Shelita Reeves runs Affiliated Lumber and buys paint from Dap Corporation. Dap grants a 40 percent trade-discount rate to all retail outlets. How much does Reeves pay for a case of white ceiling paint if it retails for $132?

STEP: Find the net price.

List Price × Percent Paid
$132.00 × (100% − 40%) =
$132.00 × 60% = **$79.20 net price**

CONCEPT CHECK

SELF-CHECK✓

Complete the problems, then check your answers at the end of the chapter. Find the percent paid and the net price.

3. Commercial truck tire: $460.
   Twenty percent trade-discount rate.
4. Beauty supplies: $16.50.
   Forty percent trade-discount rate.

3. a. 100% − 20% =
      80%
   b. $460 × 80% =
      $368
4. a. 100% − 40% =
      60%
   b. $16.50 × 60% =
      $9.90

SECTION 15-2 PRACTICE

For Problems 5–11, use the complement method to solve each problem. Round to the nearest cent.

	List Price	Trade-Discount Rate		Complement		Net Price
5.	$120.00	25%		75%	a.	$90.00
6.	85.00	20%	a.	80%	b.	$68.00
7.	317.48	35%	a.	65%	b.	$206.36
8.	74.99	15%	a.	85%	b.	$63.74
9.	317.95	24%	a.	76%	b.	$241.64
10.	4.79	50%	a.	50%	b.	$2.40
11.	417.89	60%	a.	40%	b.	$167.16

For Problems 12 and 13, find the net price.

12. List price for a sprinkler: $48.77.
    Trade-discount rate: 30 percent.
    $34.14
13. List price for computer: $2,178.90.
    Trade-discount rate: 27 percent.
    $1,590.60

COMMUNICATION SKILLS

Sales Force

Among other functions, wholesalers provide a sales force for manufacturers. Some sales personnel are called factory representatives. Ask students why this is advantageous to a manufacturer of pencils. **(The cost of employing enough salespeople to sell its product to all the potential retailers would be enormous.)**

14. Hakola Sales Agency receives a 27 percent trade-discount rate on these items. What will Hakola pay for the total order? **$488.84**

Quantity	Stock No.	Description	Unit Price	Total List
2	84-D	DAXCO cutter-complete	$316.45	$632.90
5	84-06	Blades	7.35	36.75

15. Gosik Automotive Group receives a 41 percent trade-discount rate on these auto parts. What is the total list price and the net price for each part?

	Stock No.	Description	Quantity	List	Total List	Net Price
a.	ED-1	Water pump	2	$ 95.99	**$191.98**	**$113.27**
b.	HL-4	Headlight	4	23.50	**$94.00**	**$55.46**
c.	10S	Shock absorber	8	29.95	**$239.60**	**$141.36**
d.	PF-91	Sound module	3	256.50	**$769.50**	**$454.01**

16. Tabitha Charles receives a 54 percent trade-discount rate from Commercial Clothes Company. Find the total and the net price for each item listed.

	Item	Style No.	No. of Units	List Price	Total List	Net Price
a.	Blazer	87024	24	$179.45	**$4,306.80**	**$1,981.13**
b.	Jacket	87026	24	98.75	**$2,370.00**	**$1,090.20**
c.	White shirt	87233	48	29.79	**$1,429.92**	**$657.76**
d.	Blue shirt	87234	36	24.49	**$881.64**	**$405.55**
e.	Tan shirt	87235	24	19.99	**$479.76**	**$220.69**

17. True Hardware receives various discounts from its supplier. Find the net price for each amount on the invoice.

	Stock No.	Description	Quantity	List Price	Discount	Net per Item	Total Net
a.	PT-WG	White paint	36	$18.25	38%	**$11.32**	**$407.52**
b.	NA-10	Nails	25	3.69	33%	**$2.47**	**$61.75**
c.	HW-132	Paring knife	6	4.95	15%	**$4.21**	**$25.26**
d.	HAM-16	Hammer	6	15.95	20%	**$12.76**	**$76.56**

18. Suppose a catalytic converter is manufactured and sold to a jobber, who sells it to a wholesaler, who sells it to a retailer. The retailer receives a 40 percent trade discount from the wholesaler. The wholesaler receives a 33 percent trade discount from the jobber. The jobber receives a 25 percent trade discount from the manufacturer. What did each one pay for a converter that retails for $480? **$144.72**

Need Help? Go to...
▶ Application L: The Complement of a Number, page 767
▶ Skill 30: Finding the Percentage, page 757

MAINTAINING YOUR SKILLS

Find the complement.

19. 50% **50%**

20. 40% **60%**

21. 22% **78%**

Find the percentage. Round to nearest cent.

22. $43.80 × 60% **$26.28**

23. $149.45 × 78% **$116.57**

24. $91.79 × 81% **$74.35**

25. $9.89 × 74% **$7.32**

26. $4,171.84 × 63% **$2,628.26**

27. $191.99 × 50% **$96.00**

Section 15-2 Trade Discount—Complement Method ▶ **491**

3 ASSESS

Error Analysis
Students may get confused between the total and the net price. The total refers to the quantity times the list price. Students should apply the trade discount to the total in order to find the net price. Point out that in these problems, the net price is the price of the quantity being purchased instead of the price of one item.

4 CLOSE

Closing Activity
Find the net price.

1. List price: $5.75. Trade-discount rate: 12 percent. **$5.06**

2. List price: $30.45. Trade-discount rate: 24 percent. **$23.14**

3. List price: $115.59. Trade-discount rate: 41 percent. **$68.20**

4. Sew More places the following order with their wholesaler. The store receives a 35 percent trade discount. What is the total price and net price for each item?

Description	Qty.	List Price	Total Price	Net Price
Scissors	5	$6.95	$34.75	$22.59
Thread	12	$1.99	$23.88	$15.52
Ribbon	23	$3.95	$90.85	$59.05

WRAP-UP

Go over any problem for which a wrong answer is given.

Assignment Guide
Basic: 5–11
Average: 12–13

20 min.

National Standards for Business Education

Standard 1	Mathematical Foundations
Standard 2	Number Relationships and Operations

National Council of Teachers of Mathematics Standards

Standard 1	Numbers and Operations
Standard 6	Problem Solving
Standard 8	Communication

1 FOCUS

Sometimes you do not know the trade-discount rate. Instead you are given only the list price and the net price. In this section, students will learn how to find the trade-discount rate given the list price and net price.

In-Class Examples

Work through these exercises with students before having them do the Self-Check.

1. $57.99 − $46.39 **$11.60**
2. $80.55 − $68.47 **$12.08**
3. $1.99 ÷ $9.89 **$0.201**

○ **Section Objective**

Figure out the trade-discount rate.

SECTION 15·3 Trade-Discount Rate

Some wholesalers and manufacturers publish only the list prices and net prices in their catalogs. If you know both of these prices, you can calculate the trade-discount rate.

$$\text{Trade Discount} = \text{List Price} - \text{Net Price}$$

$$\text{Trade-Discount Rate} = \frac{\text{Trade Discount}}{\text{List Price}}$$

Living in the Real World

Restoring Vintage Vehicles

The Trade Triad During a lull in business, Ayala shows his son yet another way of figuring the relationships between net price, list price, and trade-discount rate.

"Sometimes," Ayala says, "the catalog companies publish only the list and net prices. But if we want to see how much of a discount they're offering, we have to figure the trade-discount rate ourselves. That way, we can compare what kind of a deal they're offering compared to other companies."

Draw Conclusions How do you find the trade-discount rate?

Continued on page 495

Example 1

Auto Parts Manufacturing Company shows a $156 list price in its catalog for a water pump. The net price to the retailer is $117. What is the trade-discount rate?

STEP 1: Find the trade discount.

List Price − Net Price

$156   − $117   = $39 trade discount

STEP 2: Find the trade-discount rate.

$$\frac{\text{Trade Discount}}{\text{List Price}}$$

$$\frac{\$39}{\$156} = 0.25 \text{ or } 25\% \text{ trade-discount rate}$$

156 M+ − 117 = 39 ÷ RM 156 % 25

Living in the Real World

First, subtract the net price from the list price, which will determine the trade discount. Then take this number and divide it by the list price to reach the trade-discount rate.

RETEACH / ENRICHMENT

Percent Increase

Suppose a window manufacturer offers a 20 percent discount on a window with an $800 list price. Two weeks later the cost of production increases and the old list price becomes the new net price. What is the percent increase? **$800 × 80% = $640 and ($800 − $640) ÷ $640 = 25%**

CONCEPT CHECK

SELF-CHECK✓

Complete the problems, then check your answers at the end of the chapter.

1. List price for a window: $240.
   Net price: $168.
   a. Find the trade discount. **Trade discount = $240 − $168 = $72**
   b. Find the trade-discount rate. **Trade-discount rate = $72 ÷ $240 = 30%**

2. List price for a lawn mower: $420.
   Net price: $315.
   a. Find the trade discount. **Trade discount = $420 − $315 = $105**
   b. Find the trade-discount rate. **Trade-discount rate = $105 ÷ $420 = 25%**

SECTION 15-3 PRACTICE

Round the trade-discount rate to the nearest tenth of a percent.

	List Price	Net Price		Trade Discount		Trade-Discount Rate
3.	$ 5.00	$ 4.00		$1.00	a.	20%
4.	75.00	50.00	a.	$25	b.	33.3%
5.	60.00	42.00	a.	$18	b.	30.0%
6.	50.00	27.50	a.	$22.50	b.	45.0%
7.	112.60	27.50	a.	$85.10	b.	75.6%
8.	97.49	68.78	a.	$28.71	b.	29.4%
9.	5,147.58	4,258.69	a.	$888.89	b.	17.3%

10. List price for shoe dye: $9.00.
    Net price is $6.00.
    a. Find the trade discount. **$3.00**
    b. Compute the trade-discount rate. **Compute: $\frac{3}{9}$ = 33.3%**

11. List price for a computer: $2,000.
    Net price is $1,600.
    a. Find the trade discount. **$400**
    b. Compute the trade-discount rate. **Compute: $\frac{400}{2,000}$ = 20%**

12. Beauty Shop Wholesalers offers discounts on most items they sell. What is the trade-discount rate for each of the items listed?

		Beauty Shop Wholesalers	
	Item	List	Net
26% **a.**	Complexion brushes	$15.79	$11.68
26% **b.**	Lighted makeup mirror	59.99	44.39
26% **c.**	Cleansing brushes	9.79	7.24
26% **d.**	Makeup mirror	47.49	35.14

Continued on next page

▶FYI

The globalization of business has meant a demand for international packaging and shipping, which uses huge containers transported by large cargo ships. Cargo ships even carry entire railway cars, which are already loaded with cargo.

▶▶▶

2 TEACH

Have students discuss how they can use the complement method that they learned in the previous section to check their answers in this section. Use Example 1 on page 492 to illustrate how to perform a check. Multiply the list price by the complement of the trade-discount rate to check that the net price is the one given. Point out that sometimes the results can be slightly different because of rounding. For instance, given a list price of $5.99 and a net price of $4.59, you determine the trade-discount rate is 23 percent. If you multiply the list price, $5.99, by the complement of the trade-discount rate, 77 percent, you get $4.61 instead of $4.59.

Motivating the Lesson
The list price of an item is $128.95. The net price is $112.50. What is the trade discount? **$16.45**

In-Class Examples
Find the trade discount and the trade-discount rate.
1. List price: $20.00.
   Net price: $19.00. **$1.00; 5%**
2. List price: $87.99
   Net price: $65.99. **$22.00; 25%**
3. Mayo Electronics shows a $19.99 list price in its catalog for a surge protector. The net price to the retailer is $13.00. What is the trade-discount rate? **35%**

GLOBAL PERSPECTIVE

Cost of Housing
Students call or visit an import store that sells products made overseas. Students find out where the imported products come from, how they get there, what costs are involved, and whether the store gets any special discounts. **(Imports may have tariffs on them and go through a distribution center.)** Students draw or use a map to show where the imported goods come from. Students can work individually or in groups to give a short presentation. **LS**

3 ASSESS

Error Analysis

Students may confuse the list price and the trade discount when they perform the division to find the trade-discount rate. Stress that they always divide by the list price. Give students some problems and have them practice just setting up the division. Encourage students to write the formula first and then next to it write the formula with the numbers substituted in for the trade discount and list price.

4 CLOSE

Closing Activity

Find the trade discount and the trade-discount rate.

1. List price: $24.00.
   Net price: $18.00. **$6.00; 25%**

2. List price: $45.99.
   Net price: $31.73. **$14.26; 31%**

3. List price: $394.57.
   Net price: $256.57. **$138.00; 35%**

4. Find the trade-discount rate for each of the items listed.

Item	List	Net	Trade-Discount Rate
Bath towel	$7.99	$6.39	20%
Hand towel	$5.99	$4.49	25%
Washcloth	$3.99	$2.79	30%

13. Auto Paint Supply varies the rate of discount with the item purchased. Nu-Car Service received this invoice. What is the trade-discount rate for each gross amount? (**Round to the nearest whole percent.**)

Auto Paint Supply						
Use Invoice Number On All Correspondence						All Items Net Unless Otherwise Specified
Quantity Shipped	Quantity Ordered	Description	Unit Price	Gross Amount	Discount	Net Amount
4	4	001-WH	$3.98	$15.92	$5.57	$10.35
2	2	001 BL	3.98	7.96	1.99	5.97
2	2	001 AVO	4.98	9.96	3.32	6.64
4	4	001 GLD	4.98	19.92	3.98	15.94

WH: 35%; BL: 25%; AVO: 33%; GLD: 20%

14. Find the trade-discount rate for each gross amount listed on the invoice for the Wilson Paint Store. (**Round to the nearest whole percent.**)

		Quantity	Product	Price per Unit	Gross Amount	Net Amount
10.0%	a.	140	1" brush	$ 7.99	$1,118.60	$1,006.74
35.0%	b.	160	Wallpaper	19.67	3,147.20	2,045.68
50.3%	c.	110	Enamel paint	24.99	2,748.90	1,366.20
35.0%	d.	100	2-step ladder	36.99	3,699.00	2,404.35
33.0%	e.	200	Wall seize	14.99	2,998.00	2,003.30
30.0%	f.	24	Masking tape	8.95	214.80	150.36
33.3%	g.	48	Brush kit	6.29	301.92	201.40

Retail: 40% off—60% paid; Wholesaler: 33% off—67% paid

15. A catalytic converter is manufactured and sold to a jobber for $180.90, then sold to a wholesaler for $241.20, then sold to a retailer for $360.00, who places a retail price of $600.00 on the converter. Find the trade discount each time it is sold.
    40%; 33%; 25%

Need Help? Go to...
➤ Skill 6: Subtracting Decimals, page 733
➤ Skill 31: Finding the Rate, page 758

MAINTAINING YOUR SKILLS

Subtract.

16. $78.00 − $54.60 **$23.40**

17. $16.40 − $9.84 **$6.56**

18. $162.70 − $122.03 **$40.67**

19. $45.84 − $34.38 **$11.46**

20. $1,075.79 − $788.32 **$287.47**

21. $2,471.83 − $1,971.92 **$499.91**

Divide. Round answers to the nearest tenth.

22. $23.40 ÷ $78.00 **0.3**

23. $6.56 ÷ $16.40 **0.4**

24. $40.67 ÷ $162.70 **0.2**

25. $214.91 ÷ $1,073.78 **0.2**

26. $1,171.81 ÷ $11,721.49 **0.1**

27. $1.78 ÷ $3.54 **0.5**

WRAP-UP

Go over any problem for which a wrong answer is given.

Assignment Guide
Basic: 3–9
Average: 10–12

20 min.

SECTION (15-4) Chain Discounts

Section Objective
Determine the final net price after a chain of discounts.

A supplier may offer **chain discounts** to sell out a discontinued item or to encourage you to place a larger order. A chain discount is a series of trade discounts. For example:

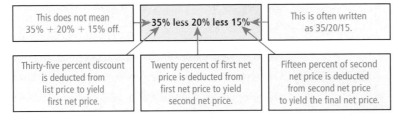

This does not mean 35% + 20% + 15% off.	→ 35% less 20% less 15% ←	This is often written as 35/20/15.
Thirty-five percent discount is deducted from list price to yield first net price.	Twenty percent of first net price is deducted from first net price to yield second net price.	Fifteen percent of second net price is deducted from second net price to yield the final net price.

Living in the Real World

Restoring Vintage Vehicles

Making Room One afternoon when Alonzo is in the shop, a catalog for custom car paint arrives in the mail. He remembers one customer who wants to restore his '69 convertible and is interested in applying several coats of top-quality paint. Some of the paint in the catalog has been discontinued, and it's clear that the company is trying to sell it quickly to provide space for new inventory.

Alonzo says, "This company is giving three different discounts—20, 15, and 10 percent."

Ayala looks at the catalog and then sits down with paper and pencil.

Draw Conclusions How do chain discounts work?

Continued on page 498

(Example 1)

Lawn Corporation produces a $4\frac{1}{2}$-horsepower lawn mower, which is priced at $695. A new model is ready for production, so the $4\frac{1}{2}$-horsepower model will be discontinued. Lawn Corporation is offering a chain discount of 20 percent less 10 percent, also written as 20/10. What is the final net price of the lawn mower?

STEP 1: Find the first discount.
List Price × Discount Rate
$695.00 × 20% = $139.00

STEP 2: Find the first net price.
List Price − Discount
$695.00 − $139.00 = $556.00

Continued on next page

National Standards for Business Education

Standard 1	Mathematical Foundations
Standard 2	Number Relationships and Operations

National Council of Teachers of Mathematics Standards

Standard 1	Numbers and Operations
Standard 6	Problem Solving
Standard 8	Communication

(1) FOCUS

Chain discounts are sometimes offered by wholesalers to encourage retailers to buy items. A chain discount is a series of discounts instead of just one discount on the list price.

In-Class Examples
Work through these exercises with students before having them do the Self-Check.
1. $210 − (20% × $210) **$168**
2. $85.79 − (10% × $85.79) **$77.21**
3. $251.85 − (30% × $251.85) **$176.29 if discount of $75.555 is rounded to $75.56**

Living in the Real World

A first discount is applied to the list price, resulting in a new net price; the next discount is applied to that figure, resulting in a second net price; and a third discount is applied to the second net price to find a third net price.

2 TEACH

Have students discuss why a supplier would offer additional discounts. Sometimes items are discontinued or overstocked and suppliers want to sell the items quickly. Sometimes suppliers want to entice their customers to purchase more items than usual. Sometimes suppliers just want to show their appreciation for someone's business.

Have students use the method for calculating trade discounts that they learned in the first section of this chapter. In the next section, students will learn to use the complement method with chain discounts.

Motivating the Lesson

Bring in an advertisement that shows a retailer offering an additional percent off an item already marked down. An ad might say, "Take another 10 percent off our 25 percent off sale on all garden tools." Have students calculate the price of items based on the ad. Point out that the two markdowns the retailer gives the customer are similar to the chain discounts the wholesaler gives to the retailer.

In-Class Examples

Find the net price.
1. List price: $34.99.
    Chain discount: 20 percent less 5 percent. **$26.59**
2. List price: $51.50.
    Chain discount: 25/10. **$34.76**
3. A wholesaler offers chain discounts of 25 percent less 10 percent to sell out a discontinued item. If the list price of the item is $25.49, what is the net price? **$17.21**

STEP 3: Find the second discount.
$556.00 × 10% = $55.60

STEP 4: Find the final net price.
$556.00 − $55.60 = **$500.40 final net price**

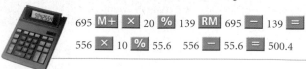

695 M+ × 20 % 139 RM 695 − 139 =

556 × 10 % 55.6 556 − 55.6 = 500.4

CONCEPT CHECK

SELF-CHECK✓

Complete the problems, then check your answers at the end of the chapter.

List price is $400. Chain discount is 30 percent less 25 percent.

1. Find the first net price.
First discount = $400 × $30% = $120;
First net price = $400 − $120 = $280

2. Find the final net price.
Second discount = $280 × 25% = $70;
Final net price = $280 − $70 = $210

SECTION 15-4 PRACTICE

	List Price	Chain Discount	First Discount	First Net Price	Second Discount	Final Net Price
3.	$ 500	30% less 20%	$150	$350	a. $70	b. $280
4.	780	25% less 15%	195	585	a. $87.75	b. $497.25
5.	1,240	20% less 15%	a. $248	b. $992	c. $148.80	d. $843.20
6.	475	40% less 30%	a. $190	b. $285	c. $85.50	d. $199.50
7.	2,170	40% less 25%	a. $868	b. $1,302	c. $325.50	d. $976.50

8. A clock radio has a list price of $74.95.
    Chain discount is 30/10.
    What is the net price?
    $47.22 using the complement method

9. A cordless phone has a list price of $125.50.
    Chain discount is 40/20.
    What is the net price? **$60.24**

10. Larson, Inc., offers Mark Stores chain discounts of 30/15. What is the net price for each item? **$117.69; $226.01; $110.37; $13.66; $7.44; $6.25**

Item	List Price
Storm door	$197.80
Replacement window	379.85
Basement window	185.50
Storm door closer	22.95
Replacement latch	12.50
Weather stripping	10.50

THINKING CRITICALLY

Chain Discount

Have students find the net price for an item with a list price of $100 and a chain discount of 30 percent less 20 percent less 10 percent. Write three choices for the answer on the board: (a) $40, (b) $63.40, and (c) $50.40. **Students who chose (a) added the discount rates (30% + 20% + 10%). Students who chose (b) did not subtract the discount amount from the list price ($100 × 30% = $30, $30 × 20% = $6, $6 × 10% = $0.60; $30 + $6 + $0.60 = $36.60; $100 − $36.60 = $63.40). Point out to students that in problems, such as this one, they might use the problem-solving strategy of estimation, or guess and check.** (See Workshops 32 and 35.)

11. General Saw Corporation offers trade discounts and additional discounts to encourage large orders. What is the net price per item if each invoice total is high enough to obtain the additional discount? **$46.93; $41.44; $35.02**

Item	List Price	Trade Discount	Additional Discount
Masonry drill	$98.80	50%	5% (if invoice total is over $250)
Raw-tip drill	76.75	40%	10% (if invoice total is over $500)
Hole saw	62.53	30%	20% (if invoice total is over $1,000)

12. Wholesale Supply Company offers chain discounts of 35 percent less 20 percent less 15 percent to sell out a discontinued item. Find the final net price for a $1,460 order. **$645.32**

13. What is the final net price for each of these overstocked items from the Everything Automotive Parts list? **$349.91; $100.77; $40.24; $5.36**

Part Number	Suggested List Price	Chain Discount
B7S	$914.80	40% less 25% less 15%
C37X	247.50	42% less 22% less 10%
173A	76.67	35% less 15% less 5%
B62Y	8.54	25% less 10% less 7%

MAINTAINING YOUR SKILLS

Need Help? Go to...
▶ Skill 2: **Rounding Numbers,** page 729
▶ Skill 6: **Subtracting Decimals,** page 733
▶ Skill 30: **Finding the Percentage,** page 757

Round to the place value indicated.

14. $17.71155 (nearest cent) **$17.71**

15. $113.7051 (nearest dollar) **$114**

16. 17.98% (nearest tenth of a percent) **18.0%**

17. $8,178.1449 (nearest cent) **$8,178.14**

18. 71.47% (nearest whole percent) **71%**

19. $51.476 (nearest whole number) **$51**

Subtract.

20. $17.60 − $5.28 **$12.32**

21. $94.35 − $37.74 **$56.61**

22. $214.80 − $21.48 **$193.32**

23. $567.88 − $141.97 **$425.91**

24. $1,774.86 − $591.62 **$1,183.24**

25. $24,599.99 − $11,069.55 **$13,530.44**

Find the percentage. Round to nearest cent.

26. $217.80 × 35% **$76.23**

27. $670.45 × 25% **$167.61**

28. $814.86 × 15% **$122.23**

29. $3,417.56 × 30% **$1,025.27**

30. $7,147.63 × 20% **$1,429.53**

31. $56,147.71 × 10% **$5,614.77**

WRAP-UP

Go over any problem for which a wrong answer is given.

Assignment Guide
   Basic: 3–7
   Average: 8–10

20 min.

3 **ASSESS**

Error Analysis

Make sure students understand that a chain discount of 30 percent less 10 percent less 5 percent does not mean the discount rate is 45 percent. Give students an example to show why this is not true.
Example: List price: $53.25.
Chain discount: 30/10/5.
First discount: 30 percent.
$53.25 − (30% × $53.25) = $37.28
Second discount: 10 percent.
$37.28 − (10% × $37.28) = $33.55
Third discount: 5 percent.
$33.55 − (5% × $33.55) = $31.87
A 45 percent discount would be:
$53.25 − (45% × $53.25) = $29.29
$31.87 does not equal $29.29

4 **CLOSE**

Closing Activity

Find the net price.
1. List price: $16.29.
   Chain discount: 10 percent less 5 percent. **$13.93**
2. List price: $32.78
   Chain discount: 20/15. **$22.29**
3. List price: $230.37.
   Chain discount: 30/10/5. **$137.87**
4. Allsworth Supply is discontinuing a shower valve and offering a chain discount of 20/15. The list price of the shower valve is $120.39. What is the net price? **$81.86**
5. A wholesaler offers chain discounts of 35 percent less 15 percent less 10 percent to sell out a discontinued item. If the list price of the item is $135.60, what is the net price? **$67.43**

National Standards for Business Education

Standard 1	Mathematical Foundations
Standard 2	Number Relationships and Operations

National Council of Teachers of Mathematics Standards

Standard 1	Numbers and Operations
Standard 6	Problem Solving
Standard 8	Communication

1 FOCUS

Have students discuss the method they used in the previous section to find chain discounts. Mention that it was a time-consuming method. Ask students how they could make it easier.

In-Class Examples

Work through these exercises with students before having them do the Self-Check.
Find the complement.
1. 25% **75%**
2. 34% **66%**
Find the product.
3. 40% × 22% **8.8%**
4. 25% × 15% × 10% **0.375%**

○ **Section Objective**

Compute the final net price using the complement method.

The complement method applied to trade discounts can also be applied to chain discounts. First subtract each discount from 100 percent to find the complements. Then multiply the complements to find the percent that you actually pay. This percent is called the **net-price rate**. To find the net price, multiply the net-price rate by the list price.

Net-Price Rate = Product of Complements of Chain-Discount Rates

Net Price = List Price × Net-Price Rate

Living in the Real World

Restoring Vintage Vehicles

Connecting the Dots Alonzo is starting to become familiar with the operation of his family's business.

"Remember when I thought the company's chain discounts of 20, 15, and 10 percent were going to add up to a 45 percent discount on paint? That would mean we would pay 55 percent net price. Actually, the net price is 61.2 percent—still it's a really good deal!"

Draw Conclusions How do you find the final net price using the complement method?

Continued on page 502

Example 1

Del's Garden Center manufactures a riding mower, which is priced at $1,450. A new model is ready for production, so the model will be discontinued. Del's Garden Center is offering a chain discount of 25 percent less 20 percent less 10 percent. What is the net price of the mower?

STEP 1: Find the complements.
Complement of 25 percent: 100% − 25% = 75%
Complement of 20 percent: 100% − 20% = 80%
Complement of 10 percent: 100% − 10% = 90%

STEP 2: Find the net-price rate.
Product of Complements of Chain-Discount Rates
75% × 80% × 90% = 54% net-price rate

STEP 3: Find the net price.
List Price × Net-Price Rate
$1,450 × 54% = **$783 net price**

Living in the Real World

Multiply the list price by the complement of the trade-discount rate.
Net Price = List Price × Complement of Trade-Discount Rate. A 20/15/10 discount implies you pay 80/85/90; 0.80 × 0.85 × 0.90 = 0.612.

CONCEPT CHECK

 SELF-CHECK✔

Complete the problems, then check your answers at the end of the chapter.

List price is $560. Chain discount is 30 percent less 10 percent.

1. Find the net-price rate.

2. Find the net price. **Net price = $560.00 × 0.63 = $352.80**

1. **Complement of 30% is 70%. Complement of 10% is 90%.**
   Net-price rate — 0.70 × 0.90 — 0.63 — 63%

FIND THE DOLLAR AMOUNT OF THE DISCOUNT You can also use the complement method to find the dollar amount of the discount. Find the complement of the net-price rate by subtracting it from 100 percent. That percent is called the **single equivalent discount** (SED). Multiply the SED by the list price to find the discount. You can check by subtracting the net price from the list price.

$$\text{SED} = \text{Complement of Net-Price Rate}$$

$$\text{Discount} = \text{List Price} \times \text{SED}$$

Example 2

In Example 1 the chain discount complements were 75 percent/80 percent/ 90 percent and the net-price rate was 54 percent. What is the SED? What is the discount?

STEP 1: Find the SED.
Complement of the Net-Price Rate
100% − 54% = **46% SED**
(Note that 54 percent paid implies 46 percent off.)

STEP 2: Find the discount.
List Price × SED
$1,450 × 46% = **$667 discount**

STEP 3: Check: List Price − Discount = Net Price
$1,450 − $667 = $783 (same as Example 1)

CONCEPT CHECK

 SELF-CHECK✔

Complete the problems, then check your answers at the end of the chapter.

List price is $560. Chain discount is 30 percent less 10 percent and net-price rate is 63 percent.

3. Find the SED. **The SED = 100% − 63% = 37%**

4. Find the discount. **Discount = $560.00 × 37% = $207.20**
   Check: $560.00 − $207.20 = $352.80
   (same as Self-Check Problem 2)

Section 15-5 Chain Discounts—Complement Method ▶ **499**

---

2 TEACH

In this section, students will multiply the list price by the single equivalent discount (SED) to find the discount. However, students can also use the method from 15-3. Remind students that in Section 15-3, they found the trade discount by subtracting the net price from the list price. Students can find the net-price rate and then use it to find the net price. Then subtract the net price from the list price to find the discount. You may want to offer this method as a check to verify that the discount obtain using the SED is correct. **(Point out that the net-price rate is also called the percent paid.)**

Motivating the Lesson
Find the complements of the chain-discount rate. Then find the product of the complements. 25/10/5 **75%, 90%, 95%; 64.125%** 40/35/20 **60%, 65%, 80%; 31.2%**

In-Class Examples
Find the net-price rate and the net price.
1. List price: $32.89.
   Chain discount: 20 percent less 10 percent.
   72%; $23.68
2. List price: $185.30.
   Chain discount: 30/20/10.
   50.4%; $93.39
Find the SED and the discount.
3. List price: $398.55.
   Chain discount: 40/25/15.
   61.75%; $246.10

TECHNOLOGY POWER

Singapore-based Neptune Orient Lines (NOL) is moving its paper-based shipping business onto the Internet. In 1995, it established the first Web site for NOL's American President Lines (APL), and has steadily transferred to the Web the transactions required to ship cargo via APL's 80-odd vessels. The company now uses electronic bills of lading, online versions of the letters of credit required for insurance, and real-time rate quotes for specialized cargoes. Today 38 percent of APL's customers conduct business via online transactions and 25 percent of APL's North American customers never see a paper bill of lading.

Error Analysis

Students may get confused when they multiply percents together. They may multiply 65 percent times 80 percent and get 5,200 percent. Remind students that 65 percent is equivalent to 0.65 or $\frac{65}{100}$ and 80 percent is equivalent to 0.8 or $\frac{80}{100}$. So, when they multiply 60 percent times 80 percent, they will get 52 percent.

As a short cut, students can multiply the number part of the percents together. However, they need to remember to divide their answer by 100 since percent means per hundred.

SECTION 15-5 PRACTICE

	List Price	Chain Discounts	Net-Price Rate	Net Price	SED	Discount
5.	$ 620.00	30%/20%	56%	$347.20	a. 44%	b. $272.80
6.	140.00	20%/15%	68%	95.20	a. 32%	b. $44.80
7.	436.00	40%/20%	a. 48%	b. $209.28	c. 52%	d. $226.72
8.	1,237.00	40%/30%	a. 42%	b. $519.54	c. 58%	d. $717.46
9.	147.80	30%/20%/10%	a. 50.4%	b. $74.49	c. 49.6%	d. $73.31
10.	96.46	20%/10%/5%	a. 68.4%	b. $65.98	c. 31.6%	d. $30.48

11. A personal computer has a list price of $2,150. The chain discount is 15/10.
  a. What is the net price? **$1,644.75**
  b. What is the discount? **$505.25**

12. A calculator has a list price of $74.85. The chain discount is 20/5.
  a. What is the net price? **$56.89**
  b. What is the discount? **$17.96**

13. Outfitters, Inc., offers Clark's Clothes Company chain discounts of 45/10. What is the net price for each item? What is the SED for each item?

		Item	List Price
$74.15; 50.50%	**a.**	Storm boots	$149.79
$108.65; 50.50%	**b.**	Storm coat	219.49
$14.85; 50.50%	**c.**	Storm gloves	29.99

14. The Globe Corporation offers trade discounts and additional discounts to encourage large orders. What is the net price per item and net discount if each invoice total is high enough to obtain the additional discount?

		Item Number	List Price	Trade Discount	Additional Discount
$64.40; $54.86	**a.**	14ZB	$119.25	40%	10% (if invoice total is over $500)
$54.25; $30.51	**b.**	11TC	84.76	20%	20% (if invoice total is over $1,000)
$34.03; $17.15	**c.**	93MR	51.18	30%	5% (if invoice total is over $250)

COMMUNICATION SKILLS

Single Equivalent Discount (SED)

Mention to students that the SED is used by buyers to select the supplier with the best deal. Have students solve the following problem. Three suppliers have the same list price. Chain discounts of 20/10 are offered by Supplier A and 10/10/10 by Supplier B. Supplier C offers a single discount of 27 percent. Ask students which supplier has the best price and why. Have student volunteers come to the board in turn to calculate the SEDs for Suppliers A, B, and C. **A: 28%, B: 27.1%, C: 27%.**

15. What is the net price and net discount for each of these overstocked items from the car catalog price list?

Item	Suggested List Price	Chain Discount
SHK #147	$ 78.45	40% less 25% less 10%
BPR #96	341.82	30% less 20% less 5%
Rim #421	58.37	25% less 15% less 5%
QT −#753	147.86	20% less 10% less 5%

$31.77; $46.68 **a.**
$181.85; $159.97 **b.**
$35.35; $23.02 **c.**
$101.14; $46.72 **d.**

16. Small Appliance Wholesalers offers a variety of discounts from the list price in its catalog. Jensen's Department Store ordered the following. Using the complement method determine the net prices.

Item	Number Ordered	List Price (each)	Amount	Discount	Complements	Net Price
Toaster	20	$ 21.50	$430.00	50/10/5	50/90/95	a.
Mixer	14	89.95	a.	40/20/10	b.	c.
Broiler	86	129.60	a.	50/10	b.	c.
Fan	25	36.00	a.	40	b.	c.
					Total	

Toaster: a. $183.83
Mixer: a. $1,259.30;
b. 60/80/90; c. $544.02
Broiler: a. $11,145.60;
b. 50/90; c. $5,015.52
Fan: a. $900.00; b.
60; c. $540.00
Total: $6,283.37

Need Help? Go to...
➤ Skill 2: **Rounding Numbers,** page 729
➤ Application L: **The Complement of a Number,** page 767
➤ Skill 31: **Finding the Rate,** page 758

MAINTAINING YOUR SKILLS

Round to the nearest cent.

17. $19.7171 **$19.72**

18. $114.555 **$114.56**

19. $912.4142 **$912.41**

20. $2,481.5764 **$2,481.58**

Find the complement.

21. 30% **70%**

22. 20% **80%**

23. 25% **75%**

24. 5% **95%**

25. 10% **90%**

26. 15% **85%**

Find the percentage.

27. $347.80 × 50.4% **$175.29**

28. $81.70 × 43.2% **$35.29**

SECTION 15-5

4 **CLOSE**

Closing Activity

Find the net-price rate, net price, SED, and discount.

1. List price: $12.59. Chain discount: 15 percent less 10 percent. **76.5%; $9.63, 23.5%; $2.96**

2. List price: $21.70. Chain discount: 25/20/5. **57%; $12.37; 43%; $9.33**

3. List price: $173.89. Chain discount: 35 percent less 20 percent less 10 percent. **46.8%; $81.38; 53.2%; $92.51**

4. Eagle Parts offers a chain discount of 35/20 on a discontinued part. The list price is $235.89. What is the net price of the part? **$122.66**

WRAP-UP

Go over any problem for which a wrong answer is given.

Assignment Guide
   Basic: 5–10
   Average: 11–13

20 min.

National Standards for Business Education

Standard 1	Mathematical Foundations
Standard 2	Number Relationships and Operations

National Council of Teachers of Mathematics Standards

Standard 1	Numbers and Operations
Standard 6	Problem Solving
Standard 8	Communication

1 FOCUS

Ask students to discuss ways that a supplier could use to get its customers to pay their invoices quickly. Mention that some suppliers offer cash discounts if payment is made within a specific time frame.

In-Class Examples

Work through these exercises with students before having them do the Self-Check.
1. $786 × 2% **$15.72**
2. $245.50 × 2% **$4.91**
3. $199.47 × 1% **$1.99**

○ **Section Objective**

Compute the cash price when the discount is based on ordinary dating.

SECTION 15-6 Cash Discounts— Ordinary Dating

You receive an **invoice** for each purchase you make from a supplier. The invoice lists the quantities and costs of the items purchased. To encourage prompt payment, the supplier may offer a **cash discount** if the bill is paid within a certain number of days. The exact terms of the discount are stated on the invoice. Many suppliers use **ordinary dating**. You might see suppliers write the ordinary dating one of two ways:

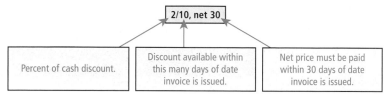

2/10, net 30		
Percent of cash discount.	Discount available within this many days of date invoice is issued.	Net price must be paid within 30 days of date invoice is issued.

You may also see the ordinary dating written like this: 2/10, n/30. It means the same thing as 2/10, net 30. Here's a quick guide to remembering how to figure out cash discounts:

Important Questions	What Formula Do I Use?
How do I calculate the **cash discount**?	Cash Discount = Net Price × Cash-Discount Rate
How do I calculate the **cash price**?	Cash Price = Net Price − Cash Discount
How do I use the **complement method** to find the cash price?	Cash Price = Net Price × Complement of Cash-Discount Rate

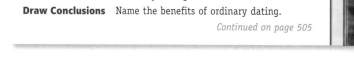

Living in the Real World

Restoring Vintage Vehicles

The Importance of Dates Ayala wants Alonzo to learn about the business's invoicing system.

Ayala says, "Each time we buy something from a supplier, we receive a written record of the purchase. The record includes important information about the items, quantities, and costs. Many of our suppliers offer cash discount if we pay within a few days of receiving the invoice. You'll sometimes hear people refer to that shorthand as 'ordinary dating.'"

Draw Conclusions Name the benefits of ordinary dating.

Continued on page 505

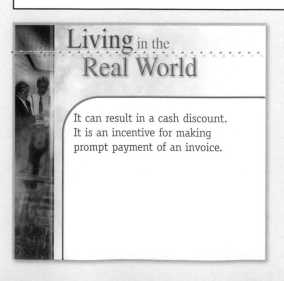

Living in the Real World

It can result in a cash discount. It is an incentive for making prompt payment of an invoice.

Example 1

This is part of an invoice that the Lighting Store received for a shipment of lamps. What is the last day the discount can be taken? What is the last day to pay the invoice? What is the cash discount? What is the cash price of the lamps if the bill is paid within ten days?

Oak Hill Lighting				
Ship To: The Lighting Store		Invoice No.: 4-3467		
Date: June 5, 20--	Order No.: Lh3019	Terms: 2/10, Net 30	Acct. No.: 712E 4	
Style	Color	Qty.	Price	Amount
A9407	BGE	8	$37.25	$ 298.00
A9841	GRN	6	42.15	252.90
J2113	NVY	10	26.40	264.00
J2114	GRN	8	26.40	211.20
			TOTAL	$1,026.10

STEP 1: Find the last day a discount can be taken.
Date of invoice: June 5
Terms: 2/10, net 30
Discount can be taken until June 15—10 days from date of invoice.

STEP 2: Find the last day to pay the invoice.
Terms: 2/10, net 30. The "net 30" means the invoice must be paid by: June 05 + 30 days = June 35 (which doesn't exist). Obviously you are into July, and because June has 30 days, you subtract 30 days: June 35 − 30 = **July 05**

STEP 3: Find the cash discount.
Net Price × Cash-Discount Rate
$1,026.10 × 2% = **$20.522 or $20.52 cash discount**

STEP 4: Find the cash price.
Net Price − Cash Discount
$1,026.10 − $20.52 = **$1,005.58 cash price**

1026.1 M+ × 2 % 20.522 RM
1026.1 − 20.52 − 1005.58

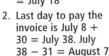
1. Last day a discount can be taken is July 8 + 10 days = July 18
2. Last day to pay the invoice is July 8 + 30 = July 38. July 38 − 31 = August 7

CONCEPT CHECK

SELF-CHECK✓

Complete the problems, then check your answers at the end of the chapter.

Date is July 8. Terms are 3/10, n/30. Net price is $640.

1. Find the last day to take the discount. 2. Find the last day to pay the invoice.

3. Find the cash discount.
Cash discount = $640.00 + 3%
= $19.20

4. Find the cash price.
Cash price = $640.00 − $19.20
= $620.80

Section 15-6 Cash Discounts—Ordinary Dating ▶ **503**

SECTION 15-6

2 TEACH

In this section students need to know how to determine the number of days between two dates. Review how many calendar days are in each month. Point out that a cash discount given if payment is made within ten days includes the tenth day.

Motivating the Lesson

An invoice dated August 3 requires payment within thirty days. A cash discount is given if payment is made within ten days. What is the last day to take the discount? **(August 13)** What is the last day to pay the invoice? **September 2**

In-Class Examples

For each of the following find:
a. The last day to take the discount.
b. The last day to pay the invoice.
c. The cash discount.
d. The cash price.
1. Invoice date: June 29.
Terms: 2/10, n/30.
Net price: $280. **a. July 9; b. July 29; c. $5.60; d. $274.40**
2. Invoice date: June 24.
Terms: 2/15, n/30.
Net price: $621.60. **a. July 9; b. July 24; c. $12.43; d. $609.17**

COOPERATIVE LEARNING

You're the Supplier
Students imagine they run a small business, such as designing video games or making jewelry and selling goods or services to a large company. Have students work in groups to look at the invoices used in the chapter. What is included in the invoice? **(Description of the items supplied, the quantity, the terms of the sale, total charges, and amount due.)** Groups draft an invoice of the sale by hand or using a computer. Inform students that they should always have at least two copies: one for the company they did business with and one for their own records. **LS , CL**

ASSESS

Error Analysis
Remind students that the complement method can be used to check the correct cash price. Alternately, if students have already used the complement method to find the cash price, then they can use the method presented in Example 1 on page 503 to check their results.

CLOSE

Closing Activity

1. An invoice is dated February 13 in a non-leap year. The terms of the invoice are 2/10, n/30. What is the last day to take the discount? **(February 23)** What is the last day to pay the invoice? **March 15**

2. An invoice in the amount of $410 is dated March 29. The terms of the invoice are 3/10, n/30. What is the cash discount? **$12.30**

3. An invoice in the amount of $1,590.75 is dated April 10. The terms of the invoice are 2/15, n/30. Use the complement method to find the cash price if the invoice is paid on April 22. **$1,558.94**

4. The net price of goods from Three Penny Nails to the General Store was $699.50. The invoice was paid on October 21. According to the terms on the invoice, what was the cash price? **$699.50; Oct. 21 is too late to qualify for a discount**

Date Shipped:	Terms:	Invoice Date:
10/11/––	2/10, n/30	10/09/––

5. Complement = (100% − 3%) = 97%; Cash Price = $640.00 × 0.97 = $620.80

SELF-CHECK ✓

7. a. $725.20
8. a. $15.49
   b. $500.91
9. c. 0 (no discount)
   d. $348.64
10. c. $292.49
    d. $3,885.96

Example 2

In Example 1 on page 503, the terms are 2/10, net 30 with an invoice amount of $1,026.10. What is the cash price using the complement of the cash-discount rate?

STEP 1: Find the complement of the cash-discount rate.
100% − 2% = 98%

STEP 2: Find the cash price.
Net Price × Complement of Cash-Discount Rate
$1,026.01 × 0.98
= **$1,005.578 or $1,005.58 cash price**

CONCEPT CHECK

Complete the problems, then check your answers at the end of the chapter.

Find the cash price using the complement method.

5. Terms are 3/10, n/30. Net price is $640.

6. Terms are 5/15, net 45. Net price is $8,994. **Complement = (100% − 5%) = 95%; Cash Price = $8,994.00 × 0.95 = $8,544.30**

SECTION 15-6 PRACTICE

Invoice Date	Terms	Last Date to Take Discount	Last Date to Pay Invoice	Date Paid	Net Price	Cash Discount	Cash Price
7.	04/09	2/10, n/30	04/19	05/09	04/12	$ 740.00	$14.80	a.
8.	05/06	3/10, n/30	05/16	06/05	05/13	516.40	a.	b.
9.	09/03	5/15, n/30	a. 09/18	b. 10/03	09/23	348.64	c.	d.
10.	11/22	7/10, n/30	a. 12/02	b. 12/22	12/01	4,178.45	c.	d.

11. Net price for hardware: $6,715.80. Terms are 4/10, n/30. Date of invoice is October 7. Date paid is October 14.
    a. What is the last date to take the cash discount? **10/17**
    b. What is the last date to pay the invoice? **11/06**
    c. What is the cash price? **$6,447.17**

12. Net price for auto parts: $614.85. Terms are 5/15, net 30. Date of invoice is December 11. Invoice is paid on December 23.
    a. What is the last date to take the cash discount? **12/26**
    b. What is the last date to pay the invoice? **01/10**
    c. What is the cash price? **$584.11**

MAINTAINING YOUR SKILLS

Need Help? Go to...
▶ Skill 6: Subtracting Decimals, page 733
▶ Skill 30: Finding the Percentage, page 757

Subtract.

13. $516.00 − $10.32 **$505.68**
14. $916.70 − $27.50 **$889.20**
15. $3,178.42 − $127.14 **$3,051.28**
16. $119.20 − $11.92 **$107.28**
17. $9,784.52 − $489.21 **$9,295.31**
18. $96.20 − $0.48 **$95.72**

Find the percentage. Round to nearest cent.

19. $415.00 × 2% **$8.30**
20. $147.84 × 3% **$4.44**
21. $916.74 × 92% **$843.40**

USING CALCULATORS

Students who use calculators may find their answer for the final net price to be different depending on their procedure. A one-cent difference may occur because the calculator will not round the discount if it is part of a large keystroke procedure.

WRAP-UP

Go over any problem for which a wrong answer is given.

Assignment Guide
Basic: 7–10
Average: 11–12

20 min.

SECTION 15-7 Cash Discounts— EOM Dating

○ **Section Objective**

Calculate the cash price when the discount is based on end-of-month dating.

Many wholesalers use **end-of-month dating** when granting cash discounts. With this method of dating, your business receives a cash discount if you pay for your merchandise within a certain number of days after the end of the month. For example:

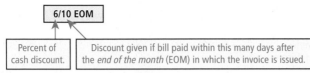

6/10 EOM

Percent of cash discount.

Discount given if bill paid within this many days after the *end of the month* (EOM) in which the invoice is issued.

Although it is not stated, it is implied that the full amount is due 20 days after the last day for taking the discount. Remember that:

Cash Discount = Net Price × Cash-Discount Rate

Cash Price = Net Price − Cash Discount

Living in the Real World

Restoring Vintage Vehicles

More Dating Know-How   Next, Ayala shows his son another invoice that indicates a different way to calculate cash discounts. This supplier figures a discount using the end-of-month approach.

Draw Conclusions   What does EOM stand for?

Continued on page 509

(**Example 1**)

Bob's Drugstore received this invoice from General Wholesalers. What is the last day that Bob's can take advantage of the 4 percent cash discount? What is the last day to pay the invoice? What is the cash discount? What is the cash price?

Date July 12	Invoice No. 213788-6	Acct. No. 208 712	Store No. 34	Terms 4/10 EOM	Vendor No. 1207
Salesperson 38L		Via UPS		Order Reg. No. 0547-6	
Customer Order No.	Style	Quantity	Price	Amount	
L3075	02673	10	$17.00	$170.00	
L3076	02677	15	24.17	362.55	
L3077	02681	25	7.46	186.50	
			TOTAL	$727.05	

Continued on next page

Living in the Real World

End of month. A 2/10 EOM means a 2 percent discount may be taken until the 10th of the next month.

SECTION 15-7

National Standards for Business Education

Standard 1	Mathematical Foundations
Standard 2	Number Relationships and Operations

National Council of Teachers of Mathematics Standards

Standard 1	Numbers and Operations
Standard 6	Problem Solving
Standard 8	Communication

1 **FOCUS**

Have students discuss why businesses may prefer to get invoices at the end of the month rather than throughout the month.

In-Class Examples

Work through these exercises with students before having them do the Self-Check.

1. $228 × 4% **$9.12**
2. $498.33 × 2% **$9.97**
3. $3,489.25 × 97% **$3,384.57**

② TEACH

Just like with chain discounts, cash discounts can also be calculated using the complement method. After reviewing Example 2 on page 506, have students find the cash discount without using the complement method. Discuss why the complement method saves time.

Have students use a dictionary to look up the word *proximo*. Point out that proximo, or prox, is sometimes used on invoices instead of end of month (EOM).

Motivating the Lesson

Give students the following invoice and have them identify the (1) invoice date, (2) terms, and (3) net price. **Jan. 16; 4/10 EOM; $95.58**

INVOICE			
Date Jan 16	**Customer** 436871	**Store** No 109	**Clerk** 30
Item	**Qty**	**Price**	**Amount**
A14-1035-H	1	$12.59	$12.59
A16-2087-Y	3	15.99	47.97
B12-1096-G	10	3.90	39.00
Terms: 4/10 EOM		**Total**	$99.56

In-Class Examples

Find the last day a discount can be taken and the last day to pay the invoice.

1. Date of invoice: September 5. Terms: 2/10 EOM. **October 10, October 30**
2. Date of invoice: June 12. Terms: 3/10 EOM. **July 10, July 30**
3. Find the cash price using the complement method.
   Net price: $1,280.95
   Terms: 3/10 EOM.
   Invoice date: August 11.
   Invoice paid: August 30.
   $1,242.52

STEP 1: Find the last day a discount can be taken.
Date of invoice: July 12.
Terms: 4/10 EOM.
Discount can be taken until August 10—10 days after the end of July.

STEP 2: Find the last day to pay the invoice.
Terms: 4/10 EOM.
The full amount is due 20 days after the discount date.
August 10 + 20 = **August 30 last day to pay invoice**

STEP 3: Find the cash discount.
Net Price × Cash-Discount Rate
$727.05 × 4% = $29.082 or $29.08 cash discount

STEP 4: Find the cash price.
Net Price − Cash Discount
$727.05 − $29.08 = **$697.97 cash price**

1. Last day a discount can be taken is 12/10—10 days after the end of November. The invoice must be paid by 12/10 + 20 = 12/30.

SELF-CHECK ✓

CONCEPT CHECK

Complete the problems, then check your answers at the end of the chapter.

An invoice dated November 7 has terms of 2/10 EOM. Net price is $7,100. The invoice is paid December 9.

1. Find the last day a discount can be taken and the last day to pay the invoice.
2. Find the cash price. **Discount = $7,100 × 2% = $142**
   Cash price = $7,100 − $142 = $6,958

END-OF-MONTH DATING When EOM dating is involved, it is common business practice to grant a one-month extension on invoices dated on or after the 26th of the month. An invoice dated June 28 with terms of 3/10 EOM is considered to be dated July 1, and the cash discount may be taken for 10 days after the end of July or until August 10.

(Example 2)

An invoice dated November 27 has terms of 2/10 EOM. Net price is $8,100. The invoice is paid January 9. What is the last day that the 2 percent cash discount can be taken and the last day to pay the invoice? Find the cash price using the complement method.

STEP 1: Find the last day a discount can be taken and the last date to pay the invoice.
Date of invoice: November 27, which is after the 26th, thus a 1-month extension is granted.
A 1-month extension means the discount can be taken until **January 10—10 days after the end of December.**
The invoice must be paid by 1/10 + 20 = 1/30.

STEP 2: Find the complement of the cash-discount rate.
100% − 2% = 98%

STEP 3: Find the cash price.
$8,100 × 98% = **$7,938 cash price**

ALTERNATIVE ASSESSMENT

Funny Sketches
Students with difficulty categorizing information will find it helpful to draw a chart comparing the different discounts and dating methods used in this chapter. Remind students that drawing simple freehand or funny sketches might help them remember each discount method.

LS , **CL**

TECHNOLOGY POWER

Emerson Electric Co. asks suppliers for quotes via the Web. They discuss design specs and quality issues online and sometimes use a video feed over the Internet for live chat sessions. Using the Web has cut the time it takes to negotiate a supply contract by as much as two-thirds. Many companies do their purchasing on the Internet, saving millions by having employees buy everything from computers to copier paper from approved vendors.

CONCEPT CHECK

 **SELF-CHECK ✓**

Complete the problems, then check your answers at the end of the chapter.

An invoice dated February 27 has terms of 3/10 EOM. The net price is $2,400.

3. Find the last day a discount can be taken and the last day to pay the invoice.

4. Find the cash price using the complement method.
Cash price = $2,400 × (100% − 3%) = $2,400 × 97% = $2,328

3. A 1-month extension is granted, thus the last day a discount can be taken is 10 days into April, or April 10. Last day to pay the invoice is 4/10 + 20 = 4/30

5. a. $602.70

6. b. $42.53
 c. $1,375.27

7. c. $287.39
 d. $6,897.34

8. b. 02/28 or 03/02
 c. $825.89
 d. $15,691.95

SECTION 15-7 PRACTICE

Invoice Date	Terms	Last Date to Take Discount	Last Date to Pay Invoice	Date Paid	Net Price	Cash Discount	Cash Price
5. Feb. 21	2/10 EOM	Mar. 10	Mar. 30	Mar. 6	$ 615.00	$12.30	a.
6. April 14	3/15 EOM	May 15	a. 05/30	May 12	1,417.80	b.	c.
7. Sept. 2	4/10 EOM	a. 10/10	b. 10/30	Oct. 9	7,184.73	c.	d.
8. Dec. 29	5/10 EOM	a. 02/10	b.	Feb. 8	16,517.84	c.	d.

9. Net price is $916.40.
Terms are 1/10 EOM.
Invoice date is September 20.
Invoice is paid on October 9.
 a. What is the last day to take the discount? **10/10**
 b. What is the last day to pay the invoice? **10/30**
 c. What is the cash price? **$907.24**

10. Net price is $7,641.60.
Terms are 6/10 EOM, n/30 EOM.
Invoice date is May 29.
Invoice is paid on July 29.
 a. What is the last day to take the discount? **07/10**
 b. What is the last day to pay the invoice? **07/30**
 c. What is the cash price? **$7,183.10**

11. An invoice from Gentlemen's Clothiers to Champion Tux Rentals shows a net price of $761.87. The terms are 5/15 EOM, n/30 EOM. The invoice is dated August 14. The invoice is paid September 15. What is the last day to take the discount? What is the last day to pay the invoice? How much is paid on September 15? **9/15; 9/30; $723.78**

12. An invoice from Krio Foods Corporation to Barr Wholesalers carries a net price of $26,715.81. The terms are 7/10 EOM. The invoice is dated Feb. 28. The invoice is paid April 7. What is the last day to take the discount? What is the last day to pay the invoice? What is the cash price? **4/10; 4/30; $24,845.70**

MAINTAINING YOUR SKILLS

Need Help? Go to...
► Skill 6: Subtracting Decimals, page 733
► Skill 30: Finding the Percentage, page 757

Find the percentage.

13. $821.00 × 2% **$16.42**

14. $8,614.50 × 3% **$258.44**

15. $12,643.17 × 8% **$1,011.45**

16. $821.00 × 98% **$804.58**

17. $8,614.50 × 97% **$8,356.07**

18. $1,417.80 × 99% **$1,403.62**

Section 15-7 Cash Discounts—EOM Dating ► **507**

③ ASSESS

Error Analysis

Students may confuse end-of-month dating with ordinary dating. When students see 3/10 EOM on an invoice dated May 5, they may mistakenly think that the last day a discount can be taken is May 15. Reinforce with students that whenever they see EOM, they should automatically think of the month that follows the invoice date. However, when an invoice date is the 26th of the month or after, it is considered to be dated the first of the following month. So, in this case, students should think of two months following the invoice date.

④ CLOSE

Closing Activity

Find the last day a discount can be taken and the last day to pay the invoice.

1. Date of invoice: October 2.
 Terms: 2/10 EOM.
 November 10, November 30
2. Date of invoice: July 18.
 Terms: 3/10 EOM.
 August 10, August 30
3. Date of invoice: April 27.
 Terms: 2/10 EOM. **June 10, June 30**

Find the cash price using the complement method.

4. Net price: $678.90.
 Terms: 2/10 EOM.
 Invoice date: May 26.
 Invoice paid: July 5. **$665.32**
5. Net price: $1995.29.
 Terms: 1/10 EOM.
 Invoice date: April 15.
 Invoice paid: April 30. **$1,975.34**

WRAP-UP

Go over any problem for which a wrong answer is given.

Assignment Guide
 Basic: 5–8
 Average: 9–10

20 min.

Quick Quiz

1. The list price of an item is $15.67. The trade-discount rate is 25 percent. What is the trade discount? **($3.92)** What is the net price? **$11.75**

2. Total Toys shows a $59.99 list price in its catalog for a game. The net price to the retailer is $43.19. What is the trade-discount rate? **28%**

3. Sun Plastics offers a chain discount of 35/20 on a discontinued part. The list price is $81.50. What is the net price of the part? **($42.38)** What is the SED? **(48%)** What is the discount? **$39.12**

4. An invoice in the amount of $1,250.65 is dated June 14. The terms of the invoice are 2/15, n/30. Use the complement method to find the cash price if the invoice is paid June 22. **$1,225.64**

5. An invoice is dated December 10. The net price is $78.50 with terms 3/10 EOM. What is the cash discount if the invoice is paid January 10? **$76.15**

SECTION 15-1 **CONCEPT CHECK** (p. 487)
1. Trade discount = $24.00 × 0.30 = **$7.20**; Net price = $24.00 − $7.20 = **$16.80**
2. Trade discount = $34.60 × 0.25 = **$8.65**; Net price = $34.60 − $8.65 = **$25.95**

SECTION 15-2 **CONCEPT CHECK** (p. 490)
1. 100% − 30% = **70% complement of trade-discount rate**
   $24.00 × 70% = **$16.80 net price**
2. 100% − 25% = **75% complement of trade-discount rate**
   $34.50 × 75% = **$25.88 net price**
3. **a.** 100% − 20% = **80%**   **b.** $460 × 80% = **$368**
4. **a.** 100% − 40% = **60%**   **b.** $16.50 × 60% = **$9.90**

SECTION 15-3 **CONCEPT CHECK** (p. 493)
1. **a.** Trade discount = $240 − $168 = **$72**
   b. Trade-discount rate = $72 ÷ $240 = **30%**
2. **a.** Trade discount = $420 − $315 = **$105**
   b. Trade-discount rate = $105 ÷ $420 = **25%**

SECTION 15-4 **CONCEPT CHECK** (p. 496)
1. First discount = $400 × $30% = $120; First net price = $400 − $120 = **$280**
2. Second discount = $280 × 25% = $70; Final net price = $280 − $70 = **$210**

SECTION 15-5 **CONCEPT CHECK** (p. 499)
1. Complement of 30% is 70%. Complement of 10% is 90%.
   Net-price rate = 0.70 × 0.90 = 0.63 = **63%**
2. Net price = $560.00 × 0.63 = **$352.80**
3. The SED = 100% − 63% = **37%**
4. Discount = $560.00 × 37% = **$207.20**
   Check: $560.00 − $207.20 = $352.80 (same as Self-Check Problem 2)

SECTION 15-6 **CONCEPT CHECK** (p. 503, 504)
1. Last day a discount can be taken is July 8 + 10 days = **July 18**
2. Last day to pay the invoice is July 8 + 30 = July 38. July 38 − 31 = **August 7**
3. Cash discount = $640.00 + 3% = **$19.20**
4. Cash price = $640.00 − $19.20 = **$620.80**
5. Complement = (100% − 3%) = 97%; Cash Price = $640.00 × 0.97 = **$620.80**
6. Complement = (100% − 5%) = 95%
   Cash Price = $8,994.00 × 0.95 = **$8,544.30**

SECTION 15-7 **CONCEPT CHECK** (p. 506, 507)
1. Last day a discount can be taken is **12/10—10 days after the end of November.**
   The invoice must be paid by 12/10 + 20 = **12/30**
2. Discount = $7,100 × 2% = $142
   Cash price = $7,100 − $142 = **$6,958**
3. A 1-month extension is granted, thus the last day a discount can be taken is **10 days into April, or April 10.** Last day to pay the invoice is 4/10 + 20 = **4/30**
4. Cash price = $2,400 × (100% − 3%) = $2,400 × 97% = **$2,328**

Living in the Real World

Restoring Vintage Vehicles

Assessment Ayala walked Alonzo through the ropes of owning a business. When it comes to owning a business, you need to know how each facet works in order to get the most *bang* for your buck. Businesses and their vendors work together to strike deals and continue their businesses successfully.

1. Ayala's shop purchases paint from American Establishment, Inc. The list price on one invoice was $714.86. Ayala received a 20 percent trade discount. What is the net price for that invoice?

2. Ayala's invoice from American Establishment, Inc. was dated March 15. The invoice carried terms of 2/10, net 30.
   A. What does the 2/10, net 30 mean?
   B. Using the net price you solved for in Problem 1, what was the cash price if it was paid on March 22?

3. General Fenders offers Ayala a 5/20 EOM. His invoice for $1,558 is dated March 31.
   A. What is the last day that Ayala can take advantage of the 5 percent discount?
   B. Find the cash discount.
   C. Find the cash price.

Living in the Real World

1. $571.89
2. **A.** 2 percent cash discount if paid within 10 days of date of invoice; Net price must be paid within 30 days of date of invoice.
   B. $560.45
3. **A.** May 20; Ayala gets a one month extension since the invoice is dated after the 26th.
   B. $77.90
   C. $1,480.10

REVIEW OF KEY WORDS

list price (p. 486)
trade discount (p. 486)
trade-discount rate (p. 486)
net price (p. 486)

complement method (p. 489)
chain discounts (p. 495)
net-price rate (p. 498)
single equivalent discount (p. 499)

invoice (p. 502)
cash discount (p. 502)
ordinary dating (p. 502)
end-of-month dating (p. 505)

Use each key word above in one of the sentences below.

1. _____ is an example of 3/5, net 30. **ordinary dating**

2. The _____ is a way to find the net price when a trade-discount rate is given.

3. A series of discounts on an item is called a **chain discount**

4. _____ is an example of 9/5 EOM.

5. Chain discounts are applied to the list price to get the **net price**.

6. A discount from the catalog price is called a **trade discount**

7. The catalog price is the **list price** .

2. **complement method**
4. **end-of-month dating**

8. A document that lists the quantities and costs of the items purchased is called an **invoice**

9. To determine the **net-price rate**, multiply the complements of the chain-discount rates.

10. To encourage prompt payment, a supplier may offer a _____ if the bill is paid within a certain period of time. **cash discount**

11. The _____ is the complement of the net-price rate. **single equivalent discount**

12. The _____ is the amount of a discount on an item expressed as a percent. **trade-discount rate**

CHAPTER 15   Study Guide and Assessment

Skills and Concepts

SECTION OBJECTIVE 15-1 AND EXAMPLES

Compute the trade discount and the net price.

Professional Home Interiors is purchasing a leather couch for a home it is decorating. The list price in the wholesaler's catalog is $2,950. Professional Home Interiors receives a 45 percent trade discount. What is the net price of the couch?

STEP 1: Find the trade discount.

List Price × Trade-Discount Rate

$2,950.00 × 45% = $1,327.50 trade discount

STEP 2: Find the net price.

List Price − Trade Discount

$2,950.00 − $1,327.50 = **$1,622.50 net price**

REVIEW EXERCISES

	List Price	Trade-Discount Rate	Trade Discount	Net Price
13.	$132.00	30.00%	a. $39.60	b. $92.40
14.	239.00	15.00%	a. $35.85	b. $203.15
15.	395.65	10.00%	a. $39.57	b. $356.08
16.	759.12	42.00%	a. $318.83	b. $440.29
17.	337.55	9.50%	a. $32.07	b. $305.48
18.	945.61	14.55%	a. $137.59	b. $808.02

SECTION OBJECTIVE 15-2 AND EXAMPLES

Calculate the net price using the complement method.

Professional Home Interiors is purchasing a leather couch for a home it is decorating. The list price in the wholesaler's catalog is $2,950. Professional Home Interiors receives a 45 percent trade discount. What is the net price of the couch?

STEP 1: Find the complement of trade-discount rate.

100% − 45% = 55% complement of trade-discount rate

REINFORCEMENT

Section 15-1

1. Find the trade discount and the net price. List price: $105.59 Trade-discount rate: 32% **$33.79; $71.80**

Section 15-2

1. Find the net price. List price: $295.79 Trade-discount rate: 32% **$201.14**

STEP 2: Find the net price.

List Price × Complement of Trade Discount

$2,950.00 × 55% = $1,622.50 net price

REVIEW EXERCISES

19. Junior Golf receives a 47 percent trade discount on these golf accessories. What is the total list price and the net price for each accessory?

Number	Description	Quantity	List Price	Total List	Net Price
JG-091	Nine iron club	9	$36.54		
JG-123	Golf bag	30	95.41		
JG-32A	Package of golf tees	100	2.99 per package		

	List Price	Trade-Discount Rate	Complement Rate		Net Price	
20.	$115.00	20.0%	a.	80%	b.	$92
21.	94.50	37.0%	a.	63%	b.	$59.54
22.	459.22	11.0%	a.	89%	b.	$408.71
23.	650.12	45.0%	a.	55%	b.	$357.57
24.	88.45	33.5%	a.	66.5%	b.	$58.82
25.	3.29	75.0%	a.	25%	b.	$0.82

19. 100% − 47% = 53% complement of trade-discount rate
9 × $36.54 = $328.86 total list; $328.86 × 53% = $174.30 net price;
30 × $95.41 = $2,862.30 total list; $2,862.30 × 53% = $1,517.02 net price;
100 × 2.99 = $299; $299 × 53% = $158.47 net price

SECTION OBJECTIVE 15-3 AND EXAMPLES

Figure out the trade-discount rate.

SYS Cooking Supply Company shows a $38.00 list price in its catalog for a stainless steel coffee bean grinder. The net price to the retailer is $29.50. What is the trade-discount rate?

STEP 1: Find the trade discount.

List Price − Net Price

$38.00 − $29.50 = $8.50 trade discount

STEP 2: Find the trade-discount rate.

Trade Discount ÷ List Price

$8.50 ÷ $38.00 = 0.22368 or 22.4% trade-discount rate

Continued on next page

REINFORCEMENT

Section 15-3

1. Find the trade discount and the trade-discount rate. List price: $239.50 Net price: $155.67 **$83.83; 35%**

REVIEW EXERCISES

Round the trade-discount rate to the nearest tenth of a percent.

	List Price	Net Price		Discount		Trade-Discount Rate
26.	$ 15.00	$ 12.00	a.	$3.00	b.	20%
27.	85.45	60.00	a.	$25.45	b.	29.8%
28.	95.65	48.00	a.	$47.65	b.	49.8%
29.	350.50	285.50	a.	$65.00	b.	18.5%
30.	7.59	4.95	a.	$2.64	b.	34.8%
31.	6,312.44	5,009.31	a.	$1,303.13	b.	20.6%

SECTION OBJECTIVE 15-4 AND EXAMPLES

Determine the final net price after a chain of discounts.

Running Shoe Company produces a low-impact aerobic tennis shoe called Run XX, which is priced at $99.00. Because a new line of shoes will be out shortly, Run XX will be discontinued. Running Shoe Company is offering a chain discount of 30 percent less 15 percent. This can also be written as 30/15. What is the final net price of the Run XX shoe?

STEP 1: Find the first discount.
List Price × Discount Rate
$99 × 30% = $29.70 first discount

STEP 2: Find the first net price.
List Price − Discount
$99.00 − $29.70 = $69.30 first net price

STEP 3: Find the second discount.
$69.30 × 15% = $10.395 second discount

STEP 4: Find the final net price.
$69.30 − $10.40 = **$58.90 final net price**

REVIEW EXERCISES

	List Price	Chain Discount	First Discount		First Net Price		Second Discount		Final Net Price	
32.	$ 800.00	30% less 15%	a.	$240	b.	$560	c.	$84	d.	$476
33.	640.00	25% less 10%	a.	$160	b.	$480	c.	$48	d.	$432
34.	3,250.00	40% less 25%	a.	$1,300	b.	$1,950	c.	$487.50	d.	$1,462.50
35.	3,545.00	40% less 15%	a.	$1,418	b.	$2,127	c.	$319.05	d.	$1,807.95
36.	85.00	35% less 25%	a.	$29.75	b.	$55.25	c.	$13.81	d.	$41.44
37.	2,955.00	20% less 15%	a.	$591	b.	$2,364	c.	$354.60	d.	$2,009.40

REINFORCEMENT

Section 15-4

1. Find the net price. List price: $109.48 Chain discount: 30/15/10 **$58.63**
2. Propco Marine is discontinuing a certain type of fishing pole and is offering a chain discount of 35/20/10. The list price of the fishing pole is $67.59. What is the net price? **$31.63**

SECTION OBJECTIVE 15-5 AND EXAMPLES

Compute the final net price using the complement method.

Running Shoe Company's low-impact aerobic tennis shoe, called Run XX, is priced at $99.00. Because the new line of shoes will be out shortly, Run XX will be discontinued. Running Shoe Company is offering a chain discount of 30 percent less 15 percent. Prove the final net price of the Run XX shoe using the complement method.

STEP 1: Find the complements.
Complement of 30 percent: 100% − 30% = 70%
Complement of 15 percent: 100% − 15% = 85%

STEP 2: Find the net-price rate.
Product of Complements of Chain-Discount Rates
70% × 85% = 59.5% net-price rate

STEP 3: Find the net price.
List Price × Net-Price Rate
$99.00 × 59.5% = **$58.905 or $58.91 net price**

In the example above, the chain discount complements were 70 percent/ 85 percent and the net-price rate was 59.5 percent. What is the SED? What is the discount?

STEP 1: Find the SED.
Complement of the Net-Price Rate
100.00% − 59.50% = **40.50% SED**
(Note that 59.50 percent paid implies 40.50 percent off.)

STEP 2: Find the discount.
List Price × SED
$99.00 × 40.50% = **$40.095 or $40.10 discount**

STEP 3: Check: List Price − Discount = Net Price
$99.00 − $40.10 = $58.90
(The two answers differ by $0.01 because of rounding)

REVIEW EXERCISES

	List Price	Chain Discounts	Net-Price Rate	Net Price	SED	Discount
38.	$ 560.00	30%/15%	a. 59.5%	b. $333.20	c. 40.5%	d. $226.80
39.	230.00	35%/25%	a. 48.75%	b. $112.13	c. 51.25%	d. $117.87
40.	1,250.00	40%/20%	a. 48%	b. $600	c. 52%	d. $650
41.	3,984.00	25%/15%	a. 63.75%	b.	c. 36.25%	d.
42.	237.60	30%/20%/10%	a. 50.4%	b. $119.75	c. 49.60%	d. $117.85
43.	15.45	25%/15%/10%	a. 57.38%	b. $8.86	c. 42.62%	d. $6.59

41. b. $2,539.80
    d. $1,444.20

REINFORCEMENT

Section 15-5

1. Find the SED and the discount. List price: $40.99 Chain discount: 30 percent less 15 percent. **40.5%; $16.60**

SECTION OBJECTIVE 15-6 AND EXAMPLES

Compute the cash price when the discount is based on ordinary dating.

This is part of an invoice that The Frame Shop received for a shipment of picture frames. What is the last day the discount can be taken? What is the last day to pay the invoice? What is the cash price of the frames if the bill is paid within 10 days?

Frames Unlimited, Inc.				
Ship To: The Frame Shop			**Invoice No.:** 3-112AG	
Date: May 16, 20--	**Order No.:** F02-44		**Terms:** 2/10, Net 30	**Acct. No.:** 1234565
Style	**Color**	**Qty.**	**Price**	**Amount**
Futuristic	Silver	15	$18.95	$ 284.25
Traditional	Brown	45	22.50	1,012.50
			TOTAL	**$1,296.75**

STEP 1: Find the last day a discount can be taken.
Date of invoice: May 16
Terms: 2/10, net 30
Discount can be taken until May 26—10 days from date of invoice.

STEP 2: Find the last day to pay the invoice.
Terms: 2/10, net 30.
May 16 + 30 days = May 46 (which doesn't exist). Because you are into June and because May has 31 days, you subtract 31 days.
May 46 − 31 = **June 15**

STEP 3: Find the cash discount.
Net Price × Cash-Discount Rate
$1,296.75 × 2% = $25.935 or $25.94 cash discount

STEP 4: Find the cash price.
Net Price − Cash Discount
$1,296.75 − $25.94 = **$1,270.81 cash price**

REVIEW EXERCISES

	Invoice Date	Terms	Last Date to Take Discount	Last Date to Pay Invoice	Date Paid	Net Price	Cash Discount	Cash Price
44.	05/25	2/10, n/30	a.	b.	05/30	$806.50	c.	d.
45.	06/27	3/10, n/30	a.	b.	07/03	135.60	c.	d.
46.	10/10	4/10, n/30	a.	b.	10/20	248.76	c.	d.
47.	03/13	6/10, n/30	a.	b.	03/24	941.22	c.	d.
48.	04/06	5/15, n/30	a.	b.	04/18	109.82	c.	d.
49.	05/26	2/15, n/30	a.	b.	06/08	365.44	c.	d.

44. a. June 4
b. June 24
c. $16.13
d. $790.37

45. a. July 7
b. July 27
c. $4.07
d. $131.53

46. a. Oct. 20
b. Nov. 9
c. $9.95
d. $238.81

47. a. March 23
b. April 12
c. $0
d. $941.22

48. a. April 21
b. May 6
c. $5.49
d. $104.33

49. a. June 10
b. June 25
c. $7.31
d. $358.13

REINFORCEMENT

Section 15-6

For each of the following find:
    a. The last day to take the discount.
    b. The last day to pay the invoice.
    c. The cash discount.
    d. The cash price.
1. Invoice date: October 4.
    Terms: 3/10, n/30.
    Net price: $599. **a. October 14; b. November 3; c. $17.97; d. $581.03**
2. Use the complement method to verify the cash price in part (d) of Problem 3.
    $599 × 97% = $581.03

SECTION OBJECTIVE 15-7 AND EXAMPLES

Calculate the cash price when the discount is based on end-of-month dating.

Kid's Stop received an invoice for $986.50 from General Toy Store. The terms of the sale are 3/10 EOM. The date of the invoice is October 19. What is the last day Kid's Stop can take advantage of the 3 percent discount? What is the last day to pay the invoice? What is the cash price?

STEP 1: Find the last day a discount can be taken.
Date of invoice: October 19
Terms: 3/10 EOM
Discount can be taken until November 10—10 days after the end of October.

STEP 2: Find the last day to pay the invoice.
The full amount is due 20 days after the discount date.
November 10 + 20 = **November 30**

STEP 3: Find the cash discount.
Net Price × Cash-Discount Rate
$986.50 × 3% = $29.595 or $29.60 cash discount

STEP 4: Find the cash price.
Net Price − Cash Discount
$986.50 − $29.60 = **$956.90 cash price**

REVIEW EXERCISES

	Invoice Date	Terms	Last Date to Take Discount	Last Date to Pay Invoice	Date Paid	Net Price	Cash Discount	Cash Price
50.	12/18	2/10 EOM	a.	b.	01/02	$ 194.50	c.	d.
51.	02/14	3/10 EOM	a.	b.	03/08	365.12	c.	d.
52.	04/15	3/15 EOM	a.	b.	05/06	875.44	c.	d.
53.	07/11	4/10 EOM	a.	b.	08/08	1,209.81	c.	d.
54.	09/30	5/10 EOM	a.	b.	10/10	3,291.02	c.	d.
55.	11/20	5/15 EOM	a.	b.	12/07	239.87	c.	d.

50. a. Jan. 10
   b. Jan. 30
   c. $3.89
   d. $190.61
51. a. March 10
   b. March 30
   c. $10.95
   d. $354.17
52. a. May 15
   b. May 30
   c. $26.26
   d. $849.18
53. a. Aug. 10
   b. Aug. 30
   c. $48.39
   d. $1,161.42
54. a. Nov. 10
   b. Nov. 30
   c. $164.55
   d. $3,126.47
55. a. Dec. 15
   b. Jan. 4
   c. $11.99
   d. $227.88

REINFORCEMENT

Section 15-7

1. Find the last day a discount can be taken and the last day to pay the invoice.
Date of invoice: May 26.
Terms: 2/10 EOM. **July 10, July 30**

2. Find the cash price using the complement method.
Net price: $1280.95.
Terms: 3/10 EOM.
Invoice date: August 11.
Invoice paid: August 30. **$1,242.52**

National Standards for Business Education

Section Objectives	1. Mathematical Foundations	2. Number Relationships and Operations	3. Patterns, Functions, and Algebra	4. Measurements	5. Statistics and Probability	6. Problem-Solving Applications	
16-1 Markup (pp. 518–519) Compute the markup in dollars.	X	X					
16-2 Markup Rate (pp. 520–521) Calculate the markup as a percent of the selling price.	X	X					
16-3 Net Profit (pp. 522–524) Figure out the net profit in dollars.	X	X					
16-4 Net-Profit Rate (pp. 525–527) Find the net profit as a percent of the selling price.	X	X					
16-5 Determining Selling Price—Markup Based on Selling Price (pp. 528–530) Calculate the selling price of an item based on cost and markup rate.	X	X					
16-6 Markup Rate Based on Cost (pp. 531–533) Solve the markup rate based on cost.	X	X					
16-7 Determining Selling Price—Markup Based on Cost (pp. 534–536) Compute the selling price based on cost and markup rate.	X	X					
16-8 Markdown (pp. 537–539) Calculate the markdown in dollars and as a percent of the regular selling price.	X	X					

(Source: Reprinted with permission from the National Standards for Business Education, copyright © 2001 by National Business Education Association, 1914 Association Drive, Reston, Virginia 21901-1596)

SCANS Correlation

Foundation Skills

Basic Skills	Reading	Writing	Math	Listening	Speaking	
Thinking Skills	Creative Thinking	Decision Making	Problem Solving	Seeing Things in the Mind's Eye	Knowing How to Learn	Reasoning
Personal Qualities	Responsibility	Self-Esteem	Sociability	Self-Management	Integrity/Honesty	

This chapter's highlighted blocks indicate the chapter's content coverage in the Student Edition and the Teacher Wraparound Edition.

National Council of Teachers of Mathematics Standards

1. Numbers & Operations	2. Algebra	3. Geometry	4. Measurement	5. Data Analysis & Probability	6. Problem Solving	7. Reasoning & Proof	8. Communication	9. Connections	10. Representations
X					X		X		
X					X		X		
X					X		X		
X					X		X		
X					X		X		
X					X		X		
X					X		X		
X					X		X		

SCANS Correlation

Workplace Competencies

Resources	Allocating Time	Allocating Money	Allocating Material and Facility Resources	Allocating Human Resources		
Information	Acquiring and Evaluating Information	Organizing and Maintaining Information	Interpreting and Communicating Information	Using Computers to Process Information		
Interpersonal Skills	Participating as a Member of a Team	Teaching Others	Serving Clients/Customers	Exercising Leadership	Negotiating to Arrive at a Decision	Working with Cultural Diversity
Systems	Understanding Systems	Monitoring and Correcting Performance	Improving and Designing Systems			
Technology	Selecting Technology	Applying Technology to Task	Maintaining and Troubleshooting Technology			

What You'll Learn

Tell students that in this chapter you'll focus on factors involved with sales, such as selling price, costs, markup, markdown, and net profit.

Why It's Important

It is important for a company to develop relationships with customers and understand what influences their buying decisions. Time is well spent developing a sales strategy that determines an appropriate selling price to maximize profits without turning customers away by high prices. The success of a business lies in selling customers what they want to buy.

Key Word Review

Sell Your Ideas

Form the class into 16 groups. Give each group one key word. Groups devise a strategy to "sell" the meaning of their word to their customers—the class.

LS , CL

CHAPTER 16

Sales

What You'll Learn

Section 16-1 Compute the markup in dollars.

Section 16-2 Calculate the markup as a percent of the selling price.

Section 16-3 Figure out the net profit in dollars.

Section 16-4 Find the net profit as a percent of the selling price.

Section 16-5 Calculate the selling price of an item based on cost and markup rate.

Section 16-6 Solve for the markup rate based on cost.

Section 16-7 Compute the selling price based on cost and markup rate.

Section 16-8 Calculate the markdown in dollars and as a percent of the regular selling price.

When Will You Ever Use This?

After your business has purchased goods, you must determine the price you're going to sell them for in order to make a profit. Profit helps you stay in business.

Key Words to Know
- cost
- selling price
- markup
- gross profit
- net profit
- markup rate
- operating expenses
- net-profit rate
- markdown
- markdown rate

Mathematics Online

To learn more about calculating business sales, visit the *Mathematics with Business Applications* Web site at www.busmath.glencoe.com.

CLASSROOM RESOURCES

Application and Enrichment
- *Teacher Wraparound Edition*
- *Teacher Resource Binder, Blackline Masters*
- *Interactive Lesson Planner* CD-ROM
- *PowerPoint® Presentations* CD-ROM

Review and Enforcement
- Mathematics Online
  www.busmath.glencoe.com
- *Teacher Resource Binder, Internet Resources*

- *Student Activity Workbook*
- *Student Activity Workbook, Teacher Annotated Edition*
- *School-to-Home Activity Workbook*

Assessment and Evaluation
- *Assessment Binder, Reproducible Tests*
- *Assessment Binder, Alternative Assessment Strategies*
- **Exam**View® *Pro Test Generator* CD-ROM

For the Teacher
- *Student Activity Workbook, Teacher Annotated Edition*
- *Assessment Binder*
- *Interactive Lesson Planner* CD-ROM
- *Teacher Resource Binder*
- Mathematics Online
  www.busmath.glencoe.com

For the Student
- *Student Activity Workbook*
- *School-to-Home Activity Workbook*

Living in the Real World
Markups at the Enchanted Forest

The Enchanted Forest is a small shop owned by master gardener, Sylvia Tallman. Since she was a little girl, Tallman has loved gardens. She has designed and planted gardens on abandoned city lots, on large farms, and in suburban back yards. Once she even hauled dozens of bags of soil, peat moss, and manure to the top of a 30-story apartment building to make a large vegetable patch right on the roof. Her shop sells small flowering potted plants and books, sculpture, and furniture for the garden. Her inventory changes often and hardly a day goes by without boxes arriving with some new treasure for the garden.

Read on. Go to . . .

517

Living in the Real World

Story's Summary
Sylvia Tallman owns a small garden shop called The Enchanted Forest. Like the proprietors of most specialty shops, Tallman must carefully consider prices and placement of goods to ensure profitability. Students follow Tallman through a typical day of determining mark-up, selling prices, and appropriate markdowns.

Did You Know...
The beginnings of sales skills, methods, techniques, and tricks as we know them today were first formed and documented in the early 1900s.

Think about This
How would the economy be different if there were no such thing as sale prices, if every item sold at every store always carried the same price tag?

LOCAL STANDARDS

National Standards for Business Education

Standard 1	Mathematical Foundations
Standard 2	Number Relationships and Operations

National Council of Teachers of Mathematics Standards

Standard 1	Numbers and Operations
Standard 6	Problem Solving
Standard 8	Communication

1 FOCUS

Bring in some sales flyers for retail stores. Point out some items that show the regular retail price and the sale price. Have students discuss why it is possible for a store to sell an item for less than its regular price.

In-Class Examples

Work through these exercises with students before having them do the Self-Check.

1. $10.49 − $6.00 **$4.49**
2. $24.99 − $15.19 **$9.80**
3. $152.78 − $127.35 **$25.43**

2 TEACH

Since retailers need to make a profit, they sell items at a higher price than what they pay for them. Point out that the difference between the price a retailer charges its customers for an item and the price a retailer pays for the item is called the markup. Gross profit and profit margin refer to the markup.

Have students discuss whether or not the entire markup is profit. Point out that business must pay for its operating expenses.

518

○ **Section Objective**

Compute the markup in dollars.

SECTION 16-1 Markup

You want to sell a product at a higher price than its **cost**, or the amount you paid for it. The cost includes expenses such as freight charges. The **selling price**, or retail price, is what a product actually sells for in the store. It is usually higher than the cost of the product. The difference between the cost and the selling price is your **markup**, or **gross profit**. When your markup is larger than your overhead or operating expenses, you make a **net profit**. Remember that:

Markup = Selling Price − Cost

Living in the Real World

Markups at the Enchanted Forest

Pricing Birdbaths   The delivery man leaves Tallman a few boxes. She opens a box and examines the invoice. The list price for the singing birdbath is $113.44 and shipping cost is $34.12. Tallman pulls out some scratch paper to figure her cost, which is $147.56. After looking and listening to the birdbath again, she decides to add $40.00 markup and attaches a tag with the selling price for $187.56.

Draw Conclusions   How do you calculate the markup of an item?

Continued on page 520

Example 1

Discount Electronics purchased TV/DVD sets for $187.83 each. Discount Electronics sells the TV/DVD sets for $299.99 each. What is the markup on each TV/DVD?

STEP: Find the markup.

Selling Price − Cost
$299.99 − $187.83 = **$112.16 markup**

299.99 [−] 187.83 [=] 112.16

CONCEPT CHECK

SELF-CHECK✓

Complete the problems, then check your answers at the end of the chapter. Find the markup.

1. Selling price is $19.49. Cost is $7.63. **$19.49 − $7.63 = $11.86**
2. Selling price is $545.45. Cost is $272.72. **$545.45 − $272.72 = $272.73**
3. Toy trains sell for $29.95. A case of 3 costs $47.85.
   $29.95 − ($47.85 ÷ 3) = $14.00
4. Peanut butter sells for $3.79. A case of 24 costs $68.16.
   $3.79 − ($68.16 ÷ 24) = $0.95

BUSINESS NOTES

The World of Business
Adine and Donzel Garcia consider buying Fun-for-All. The Garcia's have been given Fun-for-All's financial statements for the past 36 months. What should they be paying attention to on the financial statements? **(Has the company earned a net income? Has income increased, remained the same, or decreased? Have expenses increased or decreased?)** CL , LS

Living in the Real World

The markup of an item is the difference between the total cost (including any shipping charges or other expenses) and the selling price.

	Item	Selling Price	−	Cost	=	Markup
5.	Sedan	$20,070.00	−	$18,605.00	=	$1,465.00
6.	Cordless phone	149.79	−	97.84	=	$51.95
7.	Chronograph	297.87	−	132.98	=	$164.89
8.	Hardcover book	24.97	−	18.43	=	$6.54
9.	Chainsaw	297.79	−	235.84	=	$61.95
10.	Rosebush	9.97	−	6.68	=	$3.29
11.	Bicycle	219.79	−	148.93	=	$70.86
12.	Pencil eraser	0.35	−	0.27	=	$0.08

13. Walking shoes.
Cost is $51.48.
Selling price is $79.59.
What is the markup? **$28.11**

14. Grape jam.
Case of 12 costs $6.78.
Selling price is $0.89.
What is the markup per jar? **$0.32**

15. Basketball.
Cost is $12.78.
Selling price is $17.49.
What is the markup? **$4.71**

16. Digital camera.
Cost is $417.97.
Selling price is $649.79.
What is the markup? **$231.82**

17. Mostly Kitchens purchases paper towel holders at a cost of $7.14. Mostly Kitchens sells the paper towel holders for $10.99 each. What is the markup? **$3.85**

18. General Department Stores purchased bedroom curtains from The Linen Company for $6.19. General Department Stores sold the curtains for $9.79. What was the markup on the bedroom curtains? **$3.60**

19. Theresa Oakley operates a mini-engine repair shop. Recently she bought an older lawn mower for $20.00 at a local auction. She repaired the lawn mower at a cost of $9.17 in parts. She painted and polished the lawn mower at a cost of $6.43. When the lawn mower was finished, Oakley sold it for $75.00. What was the markup on the lawn mower? **$39.40**

20. Tasty Bakery Company sells chocolate éclairs for $15.48 a dozen. It costs Tasty Bakery $0.74 to produce each éclair.
a. What is the markup on a dozen éclairs? **$6.60**
b. What is the markup on each éclair? **$0.55**

MAINTAINING YOUR SKILLS

Need Help? Go to...
► Skill 6: Subtracting Decimals, page 733

Subtract.

21. $54.45 − $43.56 **$10.89**

22. $1.74 − $1.57 **$0.17**

23. $216.96 − $130.18 **$86.78**

24. $491.79 − $418.02 **$73.77**

25. $24.49 − $23.27 **$1.22**

26. $643.89 − $321.94 **$321.95**

27. $14.79 − $11.54 **$3.25**

28. $4,217.83 − $2,319.81 **$1,898.02**

29. $9,179.84 − $4,773.52 **$4,406.32**

COMMUNICATION SKILLS

Compulsive Shopping
As many as 15 million Americans may be compulsive shoppers. Researchers at the University of Minnesota classified compulsive shoppers into three categories: binge buyers, daily shoppers, and multiple buyers. They charge large amounts of goods to credit cards without having the funds available to pay their debts. Ask students to analyze their shopping behavior.

WRAP-UP

Go over any problem for which a wrong answer is given.

Assignment Guide
Basic: 5–12
Average: 13–16

20 min.

Motivating the Lesson
Sunshine Nursery sells potting soil for $3.99 per bag. The cost per bag is $0.99. What is the difference between the selling price and the cost? **$3.00**

In-Class Examples
Find the markup.
1. Selling price: $12.99.
Cost: $7.58. **$5.41**
2. Selling price: $23.50.
Cost: $16.20. **$7.30**
3. Jasper Furniture purchases desks for $499 and sells them for $799. What is the markup? **$300**

(3) ASSESS

Error Analysis
Students may subtract the selling price from the cost instead of the cost from the selling price. Point out to students that the cost should be less than the selling price. Therefore, they should be subtracting the cost from the selling price to find the markup. If students mistakenly subtract the selling price from the cost, they will get a negative answer. Since this is a lesson on markup, a negative answer should be an indication to students that they have subtracted incorrectly.

(4) CLOSE

Closing Activity
Find the markup.
1. Selling price: $7.99.
Cost: $3.59. **$4.40**
2. Selling price: $31.00.
Cost: $20.35. **$10.65**
3. Selling price: $256.88.
Cost: $198.32. **$58.56**

National Standards for Business Education

Standard 1	Mathematical Foundations
Standard 2	Number Relationships and Operations

National Council of Teachers of Mathematics Standards

Standard 1	Numbers and Operations
Standard 6	Problem Solving
Standard 8	Communication

FOCUS

Discuss with students that another way to express the markup is as a rate. Point out that this rate is a percent of the selling price.

In-Class Examples

Work through these exercises with students before having them do the Self-Check. Round answers to the nearest hundredth.

1. $4.25 \div 17.32$ **0.25**
2. $6.35 \div 21.95$ **0.30**
3. $(40.99 - 28.55) \div 40.99$ **0.30**

TEACH

Point out that businesses generally use a percent instead of dollar amounts when referring to markup. Mention that markup is usually expressed as a percent of cost rather than selling price for manufacturers and wholesalers. Retailers express markup as a percent of selling price rather than cost.

Point out that you can use the markup rate to find the markup in dollars. If the markup rate is given, multiply the rate by the selling price to get the markup.

520

Section Objective

Calculate the markup as a percent of the selling price.

Businesses have to make money; otherwise, they won't be in business very long. Businesses usually express the markup as a percent of the selling price. The **markup rate** is the markup expressed as a percent. It looks like this:

$$\text{Markup Rate} = \frac{\text{Markup}}{\text{Selling Price}}$$

Living in the Real World

Markups at the Enchanted Forest

A Normal Markup   After placing her new singing birdbath in the shop window, Tallman starts potting English primroses. As she works she thinks about the markup rate she has figured for the birdbath. She does some quick calculations and realizes she's only added a 27 percent markup, which is about half her normal 40 percent markup. Tallman goes to the store window, and changes the price to $203.60 for about a 38 percent markup.

Draw Conclusions   Had Tallman actually marked up the singing birdbath to 40 percent, how much would it sell for?

Continued on page 522

Example 1

Roy's Florist buys roses for $10.99 a dozen. It sells them for $18.95 a dozen. What is the markup rate based on the selling price?

STEP 1: Find the markup.

Selling Price — Cost
$18.95 — $10.99 = $7.96

STEP 2: Find the markup rate based on the selling price.

Markup ÷ Selling Price
$7.96 ÷ $18.95 = 0.420 or 42% markup rate

18.95 **M+** **—** 10.99 **=** 7.96 **÷** **RM** 18.95 **=** 0.42005277

CONCEPT CHECK

Complete the problems, then check your answers at the end of the chapter. Find the markup and the markup rate based on the selling price.

1. Selling price is $49.79.
   Cost is $34.85.
   $49.79 − $34.85 = $14.94;
   $14.94 ÷ $49.79 = 0.300 or 30%

2. Selling price is $249.19.
   Cost is $161.97.
   $249.19 − $161.97 = $87.22;
   $87.22 ÷ $249.19 = 0.3500 or 35%

Living in the Real World

$147.56 + (40\% \times \$147.56) =$
$147.56 + \$59.02 = \$206.58$

ALTERNATIVE ASSESSMENT

Students with Attention Difficulties
Students who have difficulty paying attention in class can benefit from being given a time limit for a task. Give students five-and-a-half minutes to do problems. Students record the number of problems they can finish correctly in the time limit. Time them again. Did they manage to do more problems? Check for correct solutions. Discuss with students the effect of a time limit on their ability to stay on task. **LS** , **CL**

Example 2

A $\frac{3}{8}$-inch drill kit sells for $59.99. The cost of the drill kit to the store is $29.00. Find the markup as a percent of the selling price.

STEP 1: Find the markup.
Selling Price — Cost
$59.99 — $29.00 = $30.99

STEP 2: Find the markup as a percent of the selling price.
Markup ÷ Selling Price
$30.99 ÷ $59.99 = 0.5165 or 51.2% markup

CONCEPT CHECK

Complete the problems, then check your answers at the end of the chapter. What is the markup rate based on the selling price?

3. A toy train selling price is $29.95. The cost is $15.95.
($29.95 − $15.95) ÷ $29.95 = 0.4674 or 46.7%
4. Peanut butter selling price is $3.79. The cost is $2.84.
($3.79 − $2.84) ÷ $3.79 = 0.2506 or 25.1%

SECTION 16-2 PRACTICE

Round answers to the nearest tenth of a percent.

5. Pete Kraemer is a buyer for a mattress store. He purchases twin-size box springs for $86.74 each. The Sleep Store sells them for $167.49 each. What is the markup for each box spring? What is the markup rate based on the selling price? **Markup $80.75; Markup rate 0.4821 = 48.2%**

6. Rodolfo's purchases silk shirts for $18.43 each. The selling price of each shirt is $42.50. What is the markup rate based on the selling price of each shirt?
0.5663 = 56.6%

7. A camera costs a department store $67.38. It sells the camera at a selling price of $119.99. What is the markup rate based on the selling price?
0.4384 = 43.8%

8. Convenient Carryout purchases pens for $0.90 a dozen. The selling price of them is $1.99 per dozen. What is the markup rate based on the selling price?
0.5477 = 54.8%

9. Office Mate buys an electronic organizer with a full-color display for $247.68. It sells for $399.99. What is the markup rate based on the selling price?
0.3807 = 38.1%

10. Video Rentals sells used DVDs for $7.95. The cost to Video Rentals is $4.86 per DVD. What is the markup rate based on the selling price?
0.3886 = 38.9%

11. A lawn tractor sells for $1,589 at Home and Lawn. Each tractor costs Home and Lawn $984.72. What is the markup rate based on the selling price?
0.3802 = 38.0%

MAINTAINING YOUR SKILLS

Need Help? Go to...
▶ Skill 6: Subtracting Decimals, page 733
▶ Skill 31: Finding the Rate, page 758

Subtract.

12. $25.40 − $19.32
$6.08
13. $79.49 − $63.59
$15.90
14. $119.29 − $83.50
$35.79

Find the rate. Round answers to the nearest tenth of a percent.

15. $6.13 ÷ $25.45
0.2408 = 24.1%
16. $35.79 ÷ $119.29
0.3000 = 30.0%
17. $1,309.22 ÷ $1,309.23
0.9999 = 100.0%

WRAP-UP

Go over any problem for which a wrong answer is given.

Assignment Guide
Basic: 5–7
Average: 8–9

20 min.

Motivating the Lesson
The selling price and cost are listed in the first two columns below. Write the markup in column C. Then divide column C by column A, and write the results in column D.

A Selling Price	B Cost	C Markup	D Markup Rate
$ 4.95	$ 2.00	$ 2.95	60%
12.50	9.99	2.51	20%
139.57	114.60	24.97	18%

In-Class Examples
Find the markup and the markup rate based on the selling price.
1. Selling price: $5.00.
   Cost: $3.00. **$2.00; 40%**
2. Selling price: $12.99.
   Cost: $7.49. **$5.50; 42%**
3. A bowl sells for $9.99. The cost of the bowl to a store is $5.99. Find the markup as a percent of the selling price. **40%**

Error Analysis
Students may confuse the selling price and the cost when they calculate the markup rate. Go over the formula for the markup rate. Point out that to find the markup rate, you divide the markup by the selling price, not by the cost. Have students practice writing the formula and filling in the values for different problems.

Closing Activity
Find the markup and the markup rate based on the selling price.
1. Selling price: $3.50.
   Cost: $1.00. **$2.50; 71%**
2. Selling price: $17.59.
   Cost: $11.39. **$6.20; 35%**
3. Selling price: $129.40.
   Cost: $89.99. **$39.41; 30%**

SECTION 16-3 Net Profit

National Standards for Business Education

Standard 1	Mathematical Foundations
Standard 2	Number Relationships and Operations

National Council of Teachers of Mathematics Standards

Standard 1	Numbers and Operations
Standard 6	Problem Solving
Standard 8	Communication

FOCUS

Remind students that in Chapter 14 they learned about costs involved in manufacturing an item. Just as there are costs in manufacturing an item, there are costs in selling an item.

In-Class Examples

Work through these exercises with students before having them do the Self-Check.
1. $39.50 − $28.65 **$10.85**
2. $42.25 − $31.59 **$10.66**
3. $129.99 × 30% **$39.00**

SECTION 16-3 Net Profit

○ Section Objective

Figure out the net profit in dollars.

The markup on the products you sell must cover your **operating expenses** or *overhead.* These expenses include wages and salaries of employees, rent, utility charges, and taxes. If you work at a small business, you will spend less on wages and salaries, rent, utilities, and other expenses than a firm with thousands of people in several large facilities.

The exact overhead expense on each item sold is difficult to determine accurately. You may approximate the overhead expense of each item. For example, if your total overhead expenses are 40 percent of total sales, you may estimate the overhead expense of each item sold to be 40 percent of its selling price. When the markup of an item is greater than its overhead expense, you make a net profit on the item.

Important Questions to Ask Yourself	What Formula Do I Use?
How do I calculate **overhead expenses?**	Overhead = Selling Price × Overhead Percent
How do I calculate the **net profit?**	Net Profit = Markup − Overhead

Living in the Real World

Markups at the Enchanted Forest

Calculating to Break Even A young man rings the wind chimes, and the store is filled with lilting melodies. As he considers which one to buy, Tallman continues to think about the markup for the singing birdbath. Her rent is about to go up, and she's thinking about hiring a part-time employee to help during the summer. In order to break even or make a profit, she must take into account these costs and other aspects of her overhead when setting prices.

Draw Conclusions What are some examples of overhead costs at a garden store?

Continued on page 525

Example 1

Sport Shop purchases water tubes for $44.98 each. It sells the tubes for $89.99 each. The owner estimates the overhead expenses to be 40 percent of the selling price of the merchandise. What is the net profit on each tube?

Living in the Real World

Employee wages, rent, utilities, insurance, maintenance, trash pick-up, advertising, and taxes.

STEP 1: Find the markup.
Selling Price − Cost
$89.99 − $44.98 = $45.01

STEP 2: Find the overhead.
Selling Price × Overhead Percent
$89.99 × 40% = $35.996 or $36.00

STEP 3: Find the net profit.
Markup − Overhead
$45.01 − $36.00 = **$9.01 net profit**

CONCEPT CHECK

Complete the problems, then check your answers at the end of the chapter.

Find the markup, overhead, and net profit.

1. Selling price is $140.
   Cost is $56.
   Overhead is 50 percent of
   the selling price.
   $140 − $56 = $84; $140 × 50%
   = $70; $84 − $70 = $14

2. Selling price is $964.
   Cost is $578.40.
   Overhead is 35 percent of
   the selling price.
   $964.00 − $578.40 = $385.60; $964.00
   × 35% = $337.40; $385.60 − $337.40
   = $48.20

(Example 2)

Anamarie's Shoppe buys chemises at a cost of $12.78. Anamarie's sells the chemises at a selling price of $24.49. Its management estimates the overhead expenses to be 34 percent of the selling price of the merchandise. What is the net profit on each chemise sold at $24.49?

STEP 1: Find the markup.
Selling Price − Cost
$24.49 − $12.78 = $11.71

STEP 2: Find the overhead.
Selling Price × Overhead Percent
$24.49 × 34% = $8.3266 or $8.33

STEP 3: Find the net profit.
Markup − Overhead
$11.71 − $8.33 = **$3.38 net profit**

CONCEPT CHECK

Complete the problems, then check your answers at the end of the chapter.

Find the markup, overhead, and net profit.

3. Toy train cars selling price is $29.95. The cost is $15.95. Overhead is 40 percent of the selling price. $29.95 − $15.95 = $14.00; $29.95 × 40% = $11.98; $14.00 − $11.98 = $2.02

4. Peanut butter selling price is $3.79. The cost is $2.84. Overhead is 24 percent of the selling price. $3.79 − $2.84 = $0.95; $3.79 × 24% = $0.9096 − $0.91; $0.95 − $0.91 = $0.04

THINKING CRITICALLY

Net Profit

Selling Price	Cost	Markup	Overhead Percent	Overhead Net	Profit
1) $ 79.79	$38.56	$41.23	25%	$19.95	$21.28
2) 119.95	68.47	$51.48	30%	$35.99	$15.49
3) 2.49	1.12	$ 1.37	18%	$ 0.45	$ 0.92

(2) TEACH

Have students discuss operating expenses that different businesses may have. These expenses include wages, security, cleaning, maintenance, rent, taxes, and insurance. Mention that some of these expenses are fixed and some vary from month to month. This is why an overhead percent is often used. Point out that a business does not realize a profit until all of its expenses are paid. Sometimes a business does not realize a profit and is forced to go out of business.

Motivating the Lesson

Carrie's Confections sells apple turnovers for $3.95 each. Carrie's cost to make one apple turnover is $0.89. What is the markup on one apple turnover? **($3.06)** If the operating expenses are estimated to be $0.79 per turnover, what is the net profit per turnover sold? **$2.27**

In-Class Examples

Find the markup, overhead, and net profit.

1. Selling price: $60.
   Cost: $40.
   Overhead: 50 percent of selling price. **$20; $30; $10**

2. Selling price: $124.99.
   Cost: $71.59.
   Overhead: 40 percent of selling price. **$53.40; $50.00; $3.40**

3. Sandals Design purchased some fabric at a cost of $15.99 per yard. The company charges its customers $24.99 per yard. Operating expenses are estimated to be about 25 percent of the selling price. What is the net profit per yard of fabric? **$2.75**

 **ASSESS**

Error Analysis

Finding the net profit takes several steps. First, students need to subtract the cost from the selling price to find the markup. Second, students need to multiply the selling price by the overhead percent to find the overhead. They may mistakenly multiply the cost by the overhead percent. Remind students that the overhead is a percent of the selling price and not the cost. Last, students need to subtract the overhead from the markup. Point out that the markup should always be more than the overhead if the business is to make a profit.

④ CLOSE

Closing Activity

Find the markup, overhead, and net profit.

1. Selling price: $16.50.
   Cost: $9.25.
   Overhead: 30 percent of selling price. **$7.25; $4.95; $2.30**

2. Selling price: $32.68.
   Cost: $19.57.
   Overhead: 36 percent of selling price. **$13.11; $11.76; $1.35**

3. Selling price: $230.82.
   Cost: $109.54.
   Overhead: 47 percent of selling price. **$121.28; $108.49; $12.79**

4. Haley Hardware purchases shovels at a cost of $5.99 each. The store charges its customers $12.99 each. The overhead for a shovel is estimated to be about 30 percent of the selling price. What is the net profit per shovel? **$3.10**

Need Help? Go to…
→ Skill 2: **Rounding Numbers**, page 729
→ Skill 6: **Subtracting Decimals**, page 733
→ Skill 30: **Finding the Percentage**, page 757

▶ FYI

Money really has no value except what society agrees to give it. It is essential to a way of life, however, because it makes possible the exchange of goods and services. Otherwise, you might exchange rocks for barley as a means of payment.

▶▶▶

Find the net profit.

	Markup	−	(Selling Price	×	Overhead Percent)	=	Net Profit
5.	$ 20	−	($ 40	×	30%)	=	$8
6.	108	−	(180	×	40%)	=	$36
7.	81	−	(270	×	20%)	=	$27

Compute the net profit based on the estimated overhead.

8. Hardware Company purchases door hardware sets for $29.86 each. It charges customers $49.99 for the hardware and installation. The labor and other overhead total $11.75 for each set installed. What is the net profit per set? **$8.38**

9. Storm King purchases private-label storm doors at a cost of $41.74 each. The selling price of an installed storm door is $119.50. The overhead for the storm door is estimated to be 40 percent of the selling price. What is the net profit? **$29.96**

10. Mary Callas is a buyer for Classic Shoes. She purchased some dress slip-ons for a cost of $13.89 a pair. Her store sells them for $29.99 a pair. Operating expenses are estimated to be 30 percent of the selling price. What is the net profit per pair of shoes? **$7.10**

11. Custom Comp, assemblers of customized professional central processing units, delivered a system to Universal Delivery for a selling price of $1,078,450. The cost of the unit to Custom Comp was $416,785. The system design, programming, installation, and other overhead expenses were estimated to be 38.5 percent of the selling price. What net profit did Custom Comp make on the sale? **$246,461.75**

12. Thomas Gibson has managed Craft Cave for over a decade. He buys trimming knives for $11.28 a dozen. He sells them for $3.38 a pair. The overhead is estimated to be 25 percent of the selling price. What is the net profit per pair? **$1.59, found by $3.38 − [($11.28/12) + (25% × $3.38)] = $3.38 − [$0.94 + $0.845] = $3.38 − $1.79 = $1.59**

Round answers to the nearest cent.

13. $1.111 **$1.11**   14. $4.545 **$4.55**   15. $0.4581 **$0.46**

Subtract.

16. $71.86 − $45.47 **$26.39**   17. $9.78 − $9.43 **$0.35**   18. $47.81 − $21.93 **$25.88**

Find the percentage. Round answers to the nearest cent.

19. $160 × 30% **$48.00**   20. $47.79 × 35% **$16.7265 = $16.73**   21. $178.88 × 25% **$44.72**

WRAP-UP

Go over any problem for which a wrong answer is given.

Assignment Guide
Basic: 5–7
Average: 8–10

20 min.

SECTION 16-4 Net-Profit Rate

○ **Section Objective**
Find the net profit as a percent of the selling price.

Businesses provide you with basic necessities such as food, clothing, books, newspapers, medical care, and transportation, as well as other goods and services that make your life easier. You may want to know the **net-profit rate** of an item your business sells. The net-profit rate is net profit expressed as a percent of the selling price of the item. Remember that:

$$\text{Net-Profit Rate} = \frac{\text{Net Profit}}{\text{Selling Price}}$$

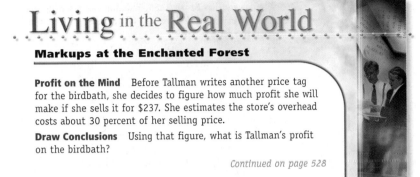

Living in the Real World

Markups at the Enchanted Forest

Profit on the Mind   Before Tallman writes another price tag for the birdbath, she decides to figure how much profit she will make if she sells it for $237. She estimates the store's overhead costs about 30 percent of her selling price.

Draw Conclusions   Using that figure, what is Tallman's profit on the birdbath?

Continued on page 528

National Standards for Business Education

Standard 1	Mathematical Foundations
Standard 2	Number Relationships and Operations

National Council of Teachers of Mathematics Standards

Standard 1	Numbers and Operations
Standard 6	Problem Solving
Standard 8	Communication

(1) FOCUS

Just as businesses often want to know the markup rate instead of the markup, businesses often want to know the net-profit rate instead of the net profit. Businesses can use the net-profit rate to compare how profitable different items are for the business.

In-Class Examples
Work through these exercises with students before having them do the Self-Check.
1. ($32.75 − $20.32) − ($32.75 × 30%) **$2.60**
2. ($51.68 − $40.99) − ($51.68 × 20%) **$0.35**
3. ($102.99 − $70.56) − ($102.99 × 25%) **$6.68**

(Example 1)

Giant Discounts sells a vacuum cleaner for $49.99. The cost of the vacuum cleaner to Giant Discounts is $23.74. Giant estimates the overhead expenses on the vacuum to be 30 percent of the selling price. What is the net-profit rate based on the selling price of the vacuum cleaner?

STEP 1: Find the net profit.

Markup	−	Overhead
($49.99 − $23.74)	−	($49.99 × 30%)
= $26.25	−	$15.00
= $11.25		

STEP 2: Find the net-profit rate.
Net Profit ÷ Selling Price
$11.25 ÷ $49.99
= 0.2250 or 22.5% net-profit rate

 49.99 M+ − 23.74 − RM

× 30 % = 11.253 ÷ RM = 0.225105021

Living in the Real World

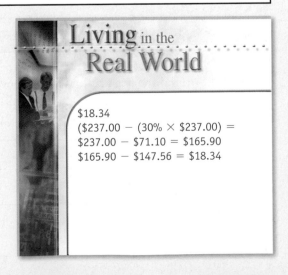

$18.34
($237.00 − (30% × $237.00) =
$237.00 − $71.10 = $165.90
$165.90 − $147.56 = $18.34

SECTION 16-4

② TEACH

Have students compare the formula for markup rate with the formula for net-profit rate. Point out that both the markup rate and the net-profit rate are percents of the selling price.

This lesson depends on almost all of the concepts learned so far in this chapter. Students need to remember how to find markup, overhead, and net profit. As you go over Examples 1 and 2 on pages 525 and 526, review each of these concepts.

Motivating the Lesson

The selling price of an item is $5.25. The cost of the item is $3.50. The overhead expense is 20 percent of the selling price. What is the net profit? **$0.70**

In-Class Examples

Find the markup, overhead, net profit, and net-profit rate.

1. Selling price: $20.55.
   Cost: $9.98.
   Overhead expense: 30 percent of selling price. **$10.57; $6.17; $4.40; 21%**

2. Selling price: $41.25.
   Cost: $23.25.
   Overhead expense: 25 percent of selling price. **$18; $10.31; $7.69; 19%**

3. Selling price: $459.45.
   Cost: $205.35.
   Overhead expense: 45 percent of selling price. **$254.10; $206.75; $47.35; 10%**

CONCEPT CHECK

SELF-CHECK ✓

Complete the problems, then check your answers at the end of the chapter. Find the markup, overhead, net profit, and net-profit rate.

1. Selling price is $119.50. **$119.50 − $44.78 = $74.72; $119.50 × 40% =**
   Cost is $44.78. **$47.80; $74.72 − $47.80 = $26.92; $26.92 ÷ $119.50**
   Overhead expense is 40 percent of the selling price. **= 0.2252 or 22.5%**

2. Selling price is $224.50. **$224.50 − $102.60 = $121.90; $224.50 × 35% =**
   Cost is $102.60. **$78.58; $121.90 − $78.58 = $43.32; $43.32 ÷**
   Overhead expense is 35 percent of the selling price. **$224.50 = 0.1929 or 19.3%**

Example 2

A doll costs the Toy Store $7.85. The doll has a selling price of $16.96. The store estimates overhead at 28 percent of the selling price. Find the net-profit rate based on the selling price.

STEP 1: Find the net profit.

$$\begin{array}{ccc} \text{Markup} & - & \text{Overhead} \\ (\$16.96 - \$7.85) & - & (\$16.96 \times 28\%) \\ = \quad \$9.11 & - & \$4.75 \\ = \$4.36 \end{array}$$

3. $29.95 ÷ $15.95 = $14.00; $29.95 × 40% = $11.98; $14.00 − $11.98 = $2.02; $2.02 ÷ $29.95 = 0.06744 or 6.7%

STEP 2: Find the net-profit rate.

$$\begin{array}{ccc} \text{Net Profit} & \div & \text{Selling Price} \\ \$4.36 & \div & \$16.96 \end{array}$$

= **0.2570 or 25.7% net-profit rate**

CONCEPT CHECK

SELF-CHECK ✓

Complete the problems, then check your answers at the end of the chapter. What is the net-profit rate?

3. Toy train cars cost $15.95. The selling price is $29.95. The overhead is 40 percent of the selling price.

4. Peanut butter costs $2.84. It has a selling price of $3.79. The overhead is 24 percent of the selling price.

4. $3.79 − $2.84 = $0.95; $3.79 × 24% = $0.9096 or $0.91; $0.95 − $0.91 = $0.04; $0.04 ÷ $3.79 = 0.01055 or 1.1%

SECTION 16-4 PRACTICE

Round answers to the nearest whole percent.

	Markup	−	(Selling Price	×	Overhead Percent)	=	Net Profit		Net-Profit Rate
5.	$ 40.00	−	($ 50.00	×	30%)	=	a. $25.00	b.	50%
6.	35.00	−	(70.00	×	25%)	=	a. $17.50	b.	25%
7.	81.47	−	(149.70	×	35%)	=	a. $29.07	b.	19%
8.	191.75	−	(449.49	×	20%)	=	a. $101.85	b.	23%
9.	7,366.90	−	(8,475.75	×	40%)	=	a. $3,976.60	b.	47%

THINKING CRITICALLY

Net-Profit Rate
Find the net-profit rate to the nearest tenth percent:

	Selling Price	Net Profit	Net Profit Rate
1.	$ 79.79	$21.28	26.7%
2.	119.95	15.49	12.9%
3.	2.49	0.92	36.9%

Round answers to the nearest tenth of a percent.

10. Court-Time is selling tennis rackets for $64.99. The cost to Court-Time is $37.48 per racket. Overhead is estimated to be 20 percent of the selling price. What is the net-profit rate? **22.3%**

11. Value Shop sells sweaters for $27.79 each. The markup on each sweater is $12.85. Overhead is estimated to be 30 percent of the selling price. What is the net-profit rate? **16.2%**

12. A deli purchases apple butter for $1.03 a jar. It sells the apple butter for $1.79 a jar. The deli estimates the overhead at 25 percent of the selling price. What is the net-profit rate on each jar of apple butter? **17.3%**

13. Latoya Luttrell manufactures hunting decoys. She pays $4.79 for the parts for each decoy. Luttrell assembles the decoys and sells them to sporting goods stores for $14.85. She estimates the overhead to be 37.5 percent of the selling price of the decoys. What is the net-profit rate per decoy? **30.2%**

14. The Sevas Shop purchases steel bars for $9.85 per bar. An automatic machine cuts and forms each bar into 30 steel pins. The 30 pins are packaged individually and marked to sell at $0.79 each. Overhead expenses are estimated to be 12.5 percent of the selling price per pin. What is the net-profit rate per pin? **45.6%**

15. Video Rentals buys video cassettes for $52.56 a carton. A carton contains 24 cassettes. Video Rentals sells the cassettes for $4.95 each or $109.99 per carton. Overhead is estimated to be 32 percent of the selling price.
    a. What is the net-profit rate on the sale of a single cassette? **23.8%**
    b. What is the net-profit rate when a carton of cassettes is sold? **20.2%**

16. Portable CD player costs $21.74. Selling price is $47.50. Overhead is 40 percent of the selling price. What is the net profit rate?

    14.2%, found by {$47.50 − [$21.74 + (40% × $47.50)]}/$47.50 = {$47.50 − [$21.74 + $19.00]}/$47.50 = {$47.50 − $40.74}/$47.50 = $6.76/$47.50 = 0.1423 or 14.2%

17. Cedar Mission swing costs $55.67. Selling price is $129.99. Overhead is 15 percent of the selling price. What is the net-profit rate?

    42.2%, found by {$129.99 − [$55.67 + (15% × $129.99)]}/$129.99 = {$129.99 − [$55.67 + $19.50]}/$129.99 = {$129.99 − $75.17}/$129.99 = $54.82/$129.99 = 0.4217 or 42.2%

MAINTAINING YOUR SKILLS

 Need Help? Go to...
► Skill 30: Finding the Percentage, page 757
► Skill 31: Finding the Rate, page 758

Find the percentage. Round answers to the nearest cent.

18. $49.49 × 30% **$14.85**   19. $9.78 × 20% **$1.96**   20. $134.49 × 25% **$33.62**

Find the rate. Round answers to the nearest tenth of a percent.

21. $5.86 ÷ $19.79 **29.6%**   22. $41.16 ÷ $99.49 **41.4%**   23. $67.50 ÷ $449.99 **15.0%**

Great Ideas from the Classroom Of...

Margaret Colvin
Southern Regional High School, Manahawkin, N.J.

Advertising
Students find six different types of ads from newspapers or magazines. Do the ads appeal to consumers by profit, convenience, health, social value, and so on? Work with fractals to show how mathematical models connect to the real world.

WRAP-UP

Go over any problem for which a wrong answer is given.

Assignment Guide
Basic: 5–9
Average: 10–13

20 min.

③ ASSESS

Error Analysis
Students may get confused in this section because finding the net-profit rate involves several calculations if given only the selling price, cost, and overhead percent. Encourage students to find each part of the formula separately and label each part. For instance, find the markup first. Next, find the overhead. Then, find the net profit. Finally, use the net profit to find the net-profit rate.

④ CLOSE

Closing Activity
Find the net-profit rate.
1. Selling price: $19.59. Cost: $10.78. Overhead expense: 30 percent of selling price. **15%**
2. Selling price: $34.89. Cost: $19.80. Overhead expense: 35 percent of selling price. **8%**
3. Selling price: $72.88. Cost: $52.99. Overhead expense: 25 percent of selling price. **2%**
4. Selling price: $277.50. Cost: $123.05. Overhead expense: 40 percent of selling price. **16%**
5. Price Rite sells boots for $42.88 each. The markup on each pair of boots is $18.25. Overhead is estimated to be 30 percent of the selling price. What is the net-profit rate? **13%**

527

National Standards for Business Education

Standard 1	Mathematical Foundations
Standard 2	Number Relationships and Operations

National Council of Teachers of Mathematics Standards

Standard 1	Numbers and Operations
Standard 6	Problem Solving
Standard 8	Communication

FOCUS

The selling price of an item is often determined by the markup rate needed to ensure a profit. Businesses often use past sales histories to determine the markup rate.

In-Class Examples

Work through these exercises with students before having them do the Self-Check.

1. $32.99 ÷ 40% **$82.48**
2. $87.57 ÷ 55% **$159.22**
3. Find the complement of 35 percent. **65%**

○ **Section Objective**

Calculate the selling price of an item based on cost and markup rate.

SECTION 16-5 Determining Selling Price—Markup Based on Selling Price

You can use records of past sales and expenses to plan the markup rate needed to cover overhead expenses and to yield a profit. You can use the cost of an item and the desired markup rate based on the selling price to figure the best selling price. Remember that:

$$\text{Selling Price} = \frac{\text{Cost}}{\text{Complement of Markup Rate}}$$

Living in the Real World

Markups at the Enchanted Forest

What the Records Tell Her Just to double-check her calculations, Tallman decides to figure the selling price a slightly different way. Based on financial records from her first year in business, she knows she will need a markup rate of around 38 percent to make a profit. If she decides to sell the singing birdbath for $210.80, the cost to her is 62 percent of the total selling price. If she divides the cost ($147.56) by 0.62, she gets $238.00—within a dollar of what she is charging.

Draw Conclusions Name some things you need to consider when determining the selling price of an item.

Continued on page 531

Example 1

VJ's Sporting Goods Store knows from past expense records (as shown below) that it must aim for a markup that is 40 percent of the selling price of its merchandise. The store received a shipment of running shoes at a cost of $38.99 per pair. What is the minimum selling price that the store should charge?

Sales for Month: $42,000		Percent of Total Sales
Cost of goods sold	25,200	60%
Overhead expenses	8,400	20%
Profit	8,400	20%
TOTAL	$42,000	100%

Living in the Real World

Cost of item, overhead costs, popularity of said item, comparable prices at other stores.

(Note: Markup plus cost equals selling price. If the markup is 40 percent of the selling price, then the cost must be 60 percent of the selling price. Sixty percent is the complement of 40 percent.)

STEP 1: Find the complement of the markup rate.
100% − 40% = 60% complement of markup rate

STEP 2: Find the selling price.
Cost ÷ Complement of Markup Rate
$38.99 ÷ 60%
= **$64.98 minimum selling price**

CONCEPT CHECK

Complete the problems, then check your answers at the end of the chapter. Find the selling price.

1. Cost is $345.
Markup is 25 percent of the selling price.
100% − 25% = 75%;
$345 ÷ 0.75 = $460

2. Cost is $1.40.
Markup is 30 percent of the selling price.
100% − 30% = 70%;
$1.40 ÷ 0.70 = $2.00

Example 2

Circuit Town purchased some digital cordless phones for $31.99. Its markup policy is 20 percent based on the selling price. What is the selling price of the phones?

STEP 1: Find the complement of the markup rate.
100% − 20% = 80% complement of markup rate

STEP 2: Find the selling price.
Cost ÷ Complement of Markup Rate
$31.99 ÷ 80% = **$39.99 selling price**

CONCEPT CHECK

Complete the problems, then check your answers at the end of the chapter. Find the selling price.

3. Toothpaste costs $1.49 and the markup is 25 percent of the selling price.
100% − 25% = 75%; $1.49 ÷ 0.75 = $1.9866 or $1.99
4. A pruning saw costs $49.95 and the markup is 20 percent of the selling price.
100% − 20% = 80%; $49.95 ÷ 0.80 = $62.4375 or $62.44

SECTION 16-5 PRACTICE

Complete the table.

	Cost	Markup Rate	Complement of Markup Rate		Selling Price (Nearest Cent)	
5.	$ 6.50	35.0%		65%	a.	$10.00
6.	120.00	20.0%	a.	80%	b.	$150.00
7.	86.74	50.0%	a.	50%	b.	$173.48
8.	420.00	45.0%	a.	55%	b.	$763.64
9.	47.84	37.5%	a.	62.5%	b.	$76.54
10.	212.60	12.5%	a.	87.5%	b.	$242.97

Continued on next page

(2) TEACH

Point out that in the past few sections the selling price was given. In this section, students will determine the selling price based on the cost and the complement of the markup rate. Review with students how to find complements.

Discuss with students why the method of markup presented in this section is used only after records of past sales and expenses have been studied. A business cannot randomly assign a markup rate. A pattern has to be established for sales and expenses.

Motivating the Lesson
Summer Grilling marks up charcoal 20 percent of the selling price. A bag of charcoal costs the store $4.79. What is the selling price? **$5.99**

In-Class Examples
Find the selling price.
1. Cost: $7.00.
   Markup: 20 percent of selling price. **$8.75**
2. Cost: $19.99.
   Markup: 25 percent of selling price. **$26.65**
3. Hillard Jewelers marks up necklaces 65 percent of the selling price. The cost of one necklace is $89.50. What is the selling price? **$255.71**

COMMUNICATION SKILLS

Write about a Sales Manager
Students research the career of a sales manager. Students find out what the job entails, the skills a sales manager should have, what education is required, and the salary range for an entry-level sales position. How much does the manager use math? Students write a one-page paper with their findings. **LS** , **P**

ASSESS

Error Analysis

Remind students that to find the complement of a percent, they need to subtract the percent from 100 percent. Students should be able to use mental math to find the complements. You may want to do some short verbal drills at the beginning of this section. Tell students a percent and have them say the complement as a class.

CLOSE

Closing Activity

Find the selling price.

1. Cost: $4.50.
   Markup: 25 percent of selling price. **$6.00**
2. Cost: $39.97.
   Markup: 30 percent of selling price. **$57.10**
3. Cost: $108.77.
   Markup: 45 percent of selling price. **$197.76**
4. Red Pottery marks up plant pots 25 percent of the selling price. The cost of one plant pot is $8.99. What is the selling price? **$11.99**
5. Oakhill Furniture purchases chairs and marks them up 55 percent of the selling price. A rocking chair costs Oakhill $179.49. What is the selling price? **$398.87**

---

11. Fashion watches.
    Cost is $7.48.
    Markup is 60 percent of the selling price.
    What is the selling price? **$18.70**

12. Toolbox.
    Cost is $5.16.
    Markup is 40 percent of the selling price.
    What is the selling price? **$8.60**

13. Paperback Paupers marks up paperback books 35 percent of the selling price. A paperback book costs Paupers $4.52. What is the selling price of the book? **$6.95**

14. Juan Charles, as assistant manager, prices items at BarBells, Inc. BarBells has a storewide policy to mark up each item 53 percent of the selling price. What selling price does Charles place on these items?

14. a. Weight set: $20.00
    b. Treadmill: $600.00
    c. Weight system: $400.00
    d. Cycle: $200.00
    e. Bench: $50.00
    f. Belt: $25.00

	Item	Cost
a.	Weight set	$ 9.40
b.	Treadmill	282.00
c.	Pro weight system	188.00
d.	Cycle	94.00
e.	Adjustable bench	23.50
f.	Weight belt	11.75

15. Hillary Lee manages the craft department of Super Craft. What selling price will she place on each of these items?

15. a. $1.21
    b. $0.21
    c. $0.71
    d. $0.37
    e. $0.42

	Line Item	Code	Description	Unit	Store Cost	Markup Rate
a.	14	063614	Tape masking	Roll	$0.545	55.0%
b.	15	071358	Protractor w/ruler pkg	Each	0.105	50.0%
c.	16	031615	Twine cotton	Each	0.302	57.5%
d.	17	062824	Chalk white	Pack	0.149	60.0%
e.	18	120057	Model cement plastic	Each	0.218	48.2%

16. Suppose Hillary Lee in Problem 15 decided to markup all the items 55 percent of the selling price. If you purchase one of each item, how much more or less do you pay?

Item	Selling Price	Pay more or less
14	$1.21	same
15	0.23	$0.02 more
16	0.67	$0.04 less
17	0.33	$0.04 less
18	0.48	$0.11 more

MAINTAINING YOUR SKILLS

Need Help? Go to...
▶ Application L: The Complement of a Number, page 767
▶ Skill 11: Dividing Decimals, page 738

Find the complement.

17. 35% **65%**   18. 20% **80%**   19. 50% **50%**

Divide. Round answers to the nearest cent.

20. $23.00 ÷ 65% **$35.38**   21. $48.00 ÷ 80% **$60.00**   22. $117.40 ÷ 50% **$234.80**

WRAP-UP

Go over any problem for which a wrong answer is given.

Assignment Guide
  Basic: 5–10
  Average: 11–13

20 min.

SECTION 16-6 Markup Rate Based on Cost

○ **Section Objective**

Solve for the markup rate based on cost.

Your business may use the cost of a product as the base for the markup rate. The markup rate in supermarkets is relatively low. For example, milk may be marked up 5 percent of the cost and other dairy products 20 percent to 30 percent of the cost. The markup of clothing may be from 80 percent to 140 percent of the cost. The markup of jewelry may be 100 percent or more of the cost. Remember that:

$$\text{Markup Rate} = \frac{\text{Markup}}{\text{Cost}}$$

Living in the Real World

Markups at the Enchanted Forest

Competitive Pricing   Tallman takes a break from her calculations as the young man places a wind chime on the counter. She'll sell it for $14.26.

"Wow, I saw the same thing in a catalog," the man says, "and your price is a lot better."

"I try to keep my markup reasonable," Tallman says as she wraps the wind chime in tissue paper. "And, of course, we don't charge shipping and handling."

Draw Conclusions   Can the markup on an item be even more than twice the cost it takes to manufacture it?

Continued on page 534

Example 1

The Table Co. purchases a dinette set for $180 from the manufacturer. It sells the set for $288. What is the markup rate based on cost?

STEP 1: Find the markup.
  Selling Price —   Cost
   $288.00   —   180.00
  = $108.00

STEP 2: Find the markup rate based on cost.
  Markup ÷   Cost
  $108.00 ÷ $180.00 — 0.6 or 60% markup rate

288 [−] 180 [=] 108 [÷] 180 [=] 0.6

Section 16-6 Markup Rate Based on Cost ▶ **531**

Living in the Real World

Yes, but sometimes these items won't sell as well as items with less of a markup.

COOPERATIVE LEARNING

"Team Teaching"
Have students do this activity part way through this chapter, or at the end of the chapter. Divide the class into teams and have individual members each write a note explaining what they understand about the chapter so far. They should also write a question about a concept that is not clear to them. Team members should trade notes with each other and write answers to other team member's questions. LS , CL , P

National Standards for Business Education

Standard 1	Mathematical Foundations
Standard 2	Number Relationships and Operations

National Council of Teachers of Mathematics Standards

Standard 1	Numbers and Operations
Standard 6	Problem Solving
Standard 8	Communication

① FOCUS

Point out that this section is very similar to Section 16-2 where students found the markup rate based on the selling price. Another way that the markup rate can be determined is based on cost.

In-Class Examples
Work through these exercises with students before having them do the Self-Check.
1. 6.50 ÷ 12.70 **0.51**
2. 10.25 ÷ 22.95 **0.45**
3. (53.49 − 31.59) ÷ 53.49 **0.41**

② TEACH

Have students write the formula for determining the markup rate based on the selling price. Then have students write the formula for determining the markup rate based on the cost. Compare the two formulas. Point out that the only difference is the divisor.

Discuss why manufacturers are more likely to use the markup rate presented in this section. Point out that manufacturers know how much it costs to produce an item. Then they can determine what the markup rate should be to reach a certain profit.

Motivating the Lesson

Able Sporting Goods buys two-person tents for $89.99. The store sells the tents for $129.99. What is the markup? **($40)** Divide the markup by the cost to find the markup rate on the cost. **44%**

In-Class Examples

Find the markup rate based on cost.

1. Selling price: $29.50.
   Cost: $18.50. **59%**
2. Selling price: $57.95.
   Cost: $38.25. **52%**
3. Silver Gifts buys picture frames for $9.75 each. They mark up each picture frame $5.25. What is the markup rate based on the cost? **54%**

CONCEPT CHECK

 SELF-CHECK✔

Complete the problems, then check your answers at the end of the chapter. Find the markup rate based on cost.

1. Selling price is $97.50.
   Cost is $58.50.
   $97.50 − $58.50 = $39.00; $39.00 ÷ $58.50 = 0.6666 or 66.7%

2. Selling price is $148.
   Cost is $74.
   $148 − $74 = $74; $74 ÷ $74 = 1.00 or 100%

Example 2

Corner Drugs buys 16-oz fruity tea for $0.70 and sells it on sale for $0.77. Find the markup rate based on cost.

STEP 1: Find the markup.

Selling Price	−	Cost	
$0.77	−	$0.70	= $0.07

STEP 2: Find the markup rate based on cost.

Markup	÷	Cost	
$0.07	÷	$0.70	= 0.1 or 10% markup rate

CONCEPT CHECK

 SELF-CHECK✔

Complete the problems, then check your answers at the end of the chapter. Find the markup rate based on cost.

3. Toy trains sell for $29.95. The cost is $15.95.
   $29.95 − $15.95 = $14.00; $14.00 ÷ $15.95 = 0.8777 or 87.8%
4. Peanut butter sells for $3.79. The cost is $2.84.
   $3.79 − $2.84 = $0.95; $0.95 ÷ $2.84 = 0.3345 or 33.5%

SECTION 16-6 PRACTICE

Round answers to the nearest tenth of a percent.

	Selling Price	−	Cost	=	Markup)	÷	Cost	=	Markup Rate Based on Cost
5.	($ 1.75	−	$ 1.25	=	a. $0.50)	÷	$ 1.25	=	b. 40.0%
6.	(50.00	−	20.00	=	a. $30.00)	÷	20.00	=	b. 150.0%
7.	(85.50	−	47.50	=	a. $38.00)	÷	47.50	=	b. 80.0%
8.	(791.00	−	316.40	=	a.$474.60)	÷	316.40	=	b. 150.0%
9.	(1.04	−	0.13	=	a. $0.91)	÷	0.13	=	b. 700.0%

10. Selling price is $226.64.
    Cost is $141.65.
    What is the markup rate based on cost? **60.0%**

11. Selling price is $18.65 each.
    Cost is $7.46 each.
    What is the markup rate based on cost? **150.0%**

12. The Jeans Company buys men's carpenter jeans at $8.68 per pair. It marks up each pair $7.31. What is the markup rate based on cost? **84.2%**

USING CALCULATORS

A calculator does not give answers as percents, instead it gives percent answers as decimals. Multiplying a decimal by 100 will give you the percent. For example, 15.80 ÷ 95.99 = 0.165 × 100 = 16.5 which is 16.5 percent.

13. Quentin Clark, a salesperson at Doolittle's Department Store, sold a pair of golf shoes for $84.95. The shoes cost Doolittle's $27.84 a pair. What is the markup rate based on cost? **205.1%**

14. Trudi Alvarez is a buyer for the Small Tots Shoppe. She purchased an assortment of sun suits for $2.74 each. They were marked to sell for $5.48 each. What is the markup rate based on cost? **100.0%**

15. Craig Nielson works at his parents' outdoor market. He sells tomatoes for $1.99 a pound. The tomatoes cost $0.89 a pound. What is the markup rate based on cost? **123.6%**

16. Amani Tucker is in charge of newspapers and magazines at Cramer's News. What is the markup rate based on cost for each item?

16. a. 66.7%
    b. 150.0%
    c. 160.0%
    d. 120.0%

	Item	Cost	Selling Price
a.	Local Sunday paper	$1.50	$2.50
b.	Map of city	0.50	1.25
c.	Out-of-state Sunday paper	2.50	6.50
d.	Antique magazine	1.25	2.75

17. Discount Electronics sells quality stereo components. The following list shows the cost and selling price of various components. Find the markup rate based on cost for each item.

17. a. 150.0%
    b. 66.7%
    c. 100.0%
    d. 185.7%
    e. 144.7%
    f. 68.4%
    g. 68.1%
    h. 83.7%
    i. 12.9%

	Item	Cost	Selling Price
a.	P636 Receiver	$167.96	$419.89
b.	P552 CD player	224.69	374.49
c.	P9191 Cassette deck	199.99	399.99
d.	P88A Speakers (pair)	286.72	819.19
e.	P793 DVD player	134.86	329.99
f.	P799 DVD/cassette player	195.90	329.99
g.	H201 Deluxe headset	56.50	94.99
h.	R045 Universal remote	24.49	44.99
i.	YZ23 Speaker stand	88.59	99.99

MAINTAINING YOUR SKILLS

Need Help? Go to...
▶ Skill 6: **Subtracting Decimals**, page 733
▶ Skill 31: **Finding the Rate**, page 758

Subtract.

18. $74.80 − $37.40
    $37.40

19. $149.49 − $59.80
    $89.69

20. $19.19 − $12.38
    $6.81

Find the rate. Round answers to the nearest tenth of a percent.

21. $89.69 ÷ $59.80
    150.0%

22. $109.80 ÷ $164.69
    66.7%

23. $5,157.90 ÷ $20,631.59
    25.0%

Section 16-6 Markup Rate Based on Cost ▶ **533**

Error Analysis

Remind students that to find the markup they need to subtract the cost from the selling price. Review the markup rate formula. Point out that if the markup is given, students do not need to know the selling price.

Closing Activity

Find the markup rate based on cost.
1. Selling price: $3.20. Cost: $2.80. **14%**
2. Selling price: $32.55. Cost: $27.25. **19%**
3. Selling price: $298.18. Cost: $194.87. **53%**
4. Plaid Clothing buys T-shirts for $4.59 each. They mark up each T-shirt $3.30. What is the markup rate based on the cost? **72%**
5. Shapes Toy Factory sells teddy bears for $14.99 each. The cost of each teddy bear is $8.99. What is the markup rate based on the cost? **67%**

WRAP-UP

Go over any problem for which a wrong answer is given.

Assignment Guide
  Basic: 5–9
  Average: 10–13

20 min.

SECTION 16·7

National Standards for Business Education

Standard 1	Mathematical Foundations
Standard 2	Number Relationships and Operations

National Council of Teachers of Mathematics Standards

Standard 1	Numbers and Operations
Standard 6	Problem Solving
Standard 8	Communication

 **FOCUS**

In Section 16-5, students learned how to determine the selling price by using the markup based on the selling price. In this section, students will learn how to determine the selling price by using the markup based on the cost.

In-Class Examples
Work through these exercises with students before having them do the Self-Check.
1. $6.99 × 80% **$5.59**
2. $18.50 × 110% **$20.35**
3. $61.25 × 142% **$86.98**

○ **Section Objective**
Compute the selling price based on cost and markup rate.

SECTION Determining Selling Price—Markup Based on Cost

You can use the cost of an item and the desired markup rate based on cost to compute the selling price of an item.

Important Questions to Ask Yourself	What Formula Do I Use?
How do I calculate the **markup**?	Markup = Cost × Markup Rate
How do I calculate the **selling price**?	Selling Price = Cost + Markup

Living in the Real World

Markups at the Enchanted Forest

A Good Pricing Strategy Tallman prides herself on not overpricing herself right out of business. The higher the price above the realistic value, the fewer customers you'll have. Higher priced goods take longer to sell than those fairly priced.

Draw Conclusions How would Tallman know if she were selling her goods at a competitive price?

Continued on page 537

Example 1

Wholesale Jewelers sells electronic digital watches to jewelry stores for $18.45 each. Wholesale Jewelers calculates the suggested retail price and attaches it to each watch. The retail price is computed by marking up the cost to the jewelry store by 160 percent of the cost. What is the suggested retail selling price?

STEP 1: Find the markup.
$$\text{Cost} \times \text{Markup Rate}$$
$$\$18.45 \times 160\% = \$29.52$$

STEP 2: Find the selling price.
$$\text{Cost} + \text{Markup}$$
$$\$18.45 + \$29.52 = \textbf{\$47.97 retail selling price}$$

18.45 ⊠ 160 % = 25.92 ⊞ 18.45 = 47.97

Living in the Real World

Sales would be steady and comparable to competing stores in the area.

SELF-CHECK✔

Complete the problems, then check your answers at the end of the chapter.
Find the markup and the selling price.

1. Cost is $50.
Markup is 70 percent of cost.
Markup: $50 × 70% = $35;
Selling price: $50 + $35 = $85

2. Cost is $140.
Markup is 150 percent of cost.
Markup: $140 × 150% = $210;
Selling price: $140 + $210 = $350

Example 2

Florida Nursery Stock sells flowering hanging baskets to retail outlets at a cost of $2.58. Most of the outlets mark up hanging baskets at 150 percent of cost. What selling price do most outlets put on the hanging baskets?

STEP 1: Find the markup.
Cost × Markup Rate
$2.58 ×   150%   = $3.87

STEP 2: Find the selling price.
Cost + Markup
$2.58 + $3.87 = **$6.45 selling price**

CONCEPT CHECK

SELF-CHECK✔

Complete the problems, then check your answers at the end of the chapter.
Find the selling price.

3. Milk costs $2.60. The markup is 5 percent of cost.
Markup: $2.60 × 5% = $0.13; Selling price: $2.60 + $0.13 = $2.73
4. A file cabinet costs $64.00. The markup is 50 percent of cost.
Markup: 50% × $64 = $32.00; Selling price: $64 + $32 = $96

SECTION 16-7 PRACTICE

Complete the table below.

	Cost	Markup Rate Based on Cost	Markup		Selling Price	
5.	$ 45.00	80.0%	$36.00	a.	$81.00	
6.	96.49	100.0%	96.49	a.	$192.98	
7.	86.40	150.0%	a. $129.60	b.	$216.00	
8.	16.40	225.0%	a. $36.90	b.	$53.30	
9.	751.80	87.5%	a. $657.83	b.	$1,409.63	
10.	14.24	400.0%	a. $56.96	b.	$71.20	

11. Trimmer.
Cost is $111.87.
Markup rate is 60 percent of cost.
What is the selling price? **$178.99**

12. Digital camera.
Cost is $177.75.
Markup rate is 125 percent of cost.
What is the selling price? **$399.94**

Continued on next page

In this section, students will encounter markup rates that are greater than 100 percent. As you review Examples 1 and 2 and pages 534 and 535, point out that the markup rates are greater than 100 percent. Review what it means to have a percent greater than 100 percent. Have students practice calculating some large percents. Begin with 100 percent of a number. Then, increase the percent to 105 percent or 110 percent of the number. Continue increasing the percent several times so that students see the pattern.

Motivating the Lesson
Write the markup based on cost for each of the following.

Cost	Markup Rate	Markup
$ 0.45	75%	$ 0.34
2.29	112%	2.56
98.32	273%	268.41

In-Class Examples
Find the markup and the selling price.

1. Cost: $40.
Markup: 75 percent of cost.
$30; $70

2. Cost: $100.
Markup: 120 percent of cost.
$120; $220

3. Cost: $309.05.
Markup: 125 percent of cost.
$386.31; $695.36

RETEACH / ENRICHMENT

Speedy Summary
Ask students to take part in a speedy summary. To prepare ask students to write down three or four main points they learned as part of this chapter. These main points may include definitions, memorized facts, or points the student felt were most meaningful to his or her own life. As you rapidly and randomly call on students in the class, each student tells a point.

 **ASSESS**

Error Analysis

Since this section contains percents greater than 100 percent, students need to remember how to deal with them. Remind students how to write percents greater than 100 percent as decimals. Give students some percents to write as practice. A common mistake for students is to put the decimal point in the wrong place. For instance, some students mistakenly write 125 percent as the decimal 0.125. Even if students use the percent key on their calculators, it is important that students know how to write percents as decimals.

4 CLOSE

Closing Activity

Find the markup and the selling price.

1. Cost: $21.50.
   Markup: 65 percent of cost.
   $13.98; $35.48

2. Cost: $145.75.
   Markup: 100 percent of cost.
   $145.75; $291.50

3. Cost: $276.31.
   Markup: 128 percent of cost.
   $353.68; $629.99

4. Cut-Rite Lawns buys a lawn-mower blade from a manufacturer for $6.15 each. Cut-Rite Lawns marks up each lawn-mower blade 160 percent of cost. What is the selling price?
   $15.99

5. The Aquasense Company manufacturers bottled water. Cost per gross (144 items) is $57.60. The bottled water is sold at a markup of 198 percent based on cost. What is the selling price for one bottle of water? **$1.19**

13. The Sports Wholesale Company purchases weight racks directly from the manufacturer for $10.80 each. The weight racks are marked up 210 percent of cost and sold to retail sporting goods stores. What is the selling price of each weight rack? **$33.48**

14. The Door Company produces truck dock door seals. Its 9′ × 10′ seal costs $280 to produce. The markup rate is 75 percent of cost. What is the selling price? **$490.00**

15. XYZ Appliances buys Circle Clean washers from a distributor for $147.85 each. The markup is 100 percent of cost. What is the selling price? **$295.70**

16. Surface Combustion, Inc., calculates the cost of manufacturing a particular open-pit furnace as $1,214.78. Surface marks up each furnace 120 percent based on cost. What is the selling price? **$2,672.52**

17. The Pet Company buys dog collars from a manufacturer for $0.18 each. It marks up each collar 356 percent of cost. What is the selling price? **$0.82**

18. The Glass Company manufactures stemware. The cost per gross (144 items) is $66.24. The stemware is sold at a markup of 115 percent based on cost.
    a. What is the selling price for one dozen stemware? **$11.87**
    b. What is the selling price for a single piece of stemware? **$0.99**

19. Cook-n-Serve carries fancy oven mitts that cost $0.86 a pair. Cook-n-Serve operates on a markup rate of 166 percent of cost.
    a. What is the selling price? **$2.29**
    b. What is the markup rate as a percent of the selling price? **62.4%**

20. Alvin Exports buys engine gaskets for $13.32 a dozen from a U.S. manufacturer. Alvin marks up the gaskets 100 percent based on cost. The overhead is estimated to be 30 percent of the selling price.
    a. What is the selling price per gasket? **$2.22**
    b. What is the markup rate as a percent of the selling price? **50%**
    c. What is the net profit? **$0.44**
    d. What is the net profit as a percent of the selling price? **19.9%**

MAINTAINING YOUR SKILLS

(Need Help? Go to...)
▶ **Skill 5: Adding Decimals,** page 732
▶ **Skill 30: Finding the Percentage,** page 757

Add.

21. $85.00 + $44.00 **$129.00**

22. $144.47 + $185.52 **$329.99**

23. $1,474.87 + $444.62 **$1,919.49**

Find the percentage. Round answers to the nearest cent.

24. $60.00 × 30% **$18.00**

25. $240.00 × 75% **$180.00**

26. $179.49 × 100% **$179.49**

WRAP-UP

Go over any problem for which a wrong answer is given.

Assignment Guide
Basic: 5–10
Average: 11–14

20 min.

SECTION 16-8 Markdown

Section Objective

Calculate the markdown in dollars and as a percent of the regular selling price.

Your business may sell some merchandise at sale prices to attract customers or to make room for new merchandise. The **markdown,** or discount, is the difference between the regular selling price of an item and its sale price. The **markdown rate** is the markdown expressed as a percent of the regular selling price of the item.

Important Questions to Ask Yourself	What Formula Do I Use?
How do I calculate the markdown?	Markdown = Regular Selling Price − Sale Price
How do I calculate the markdown rate?	Markdown Rate = $\dfrac{\text{Markdown}}{\text{Regular Selling Price}}$

Living in the Real World

Markups at the Enchanted Forest

The Sale Table After the customer leaves, Tallman decides to look over her inventory to see what items have been in the shop for more than two months. She will calculate a markdown rate for those items and put a "sale" sign on each one. As Tallman works, an attractive gray-haired woman enters the store. She's looking for a birdbath.

Draw Conclusions Where should Tallman place the "sale" items in the garden store? Does placement have much to do with how merchandise is sold?

Continued on page 541

Example 1

Ski's Sport Shop sells cross-country skis at a regular selling price of $98.49. For one week only, Ski's has marked down the price to $68.94. What is the markdown rate?

STEP 1: Find the markdown.
Regular Selling Price − Sale Price
$98.49 − $68.94 = $29.55

STEP 2: Find the markdown rate.
Markdown ÷ Regular Selling Price
$29.55 ÷ $98.49 = 0.3000 or 30%

98.49 − 68.94 = 29.55 ÷ 98.49 = 0.300030459

Living in the Real World

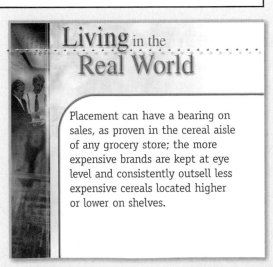

Placement can have a bearing on sales, as proven in the cereal aisle of any grocery store; the more expensive brands are kept at eye level and consistently outsell less expensive cereals located higher or lower on shelves.

National Standards for Business Education

Standard 1	Mathematical Foundations
Standard 2	Number Relationships and Operations

National Council of Teachers of Mathematics Standards

Standard 1	Numbers and Operations
Standard 6	Problem Solving
Standard 8	Communication

1 FOCUS

Bring in some newspaper ads from retail stores. Have students discuss what it means to buy something on sale. The focus of this section is on markdowns. Students will find the amount of a markdown and the markdown rate.

In-Class Examples

Work through these exercises with students before having them do the Self-Check. Round answers to the nearest thousandth.

1. $(26 - 15) \div 26$ **0.423**
2. $(31.99 - 24.99) \div 31.99$ **0.219**
3. $(50.47 - 46.79) \div 50.47$ **0.073**
4. $(100.75 - 85.57) \div 100.75$ **0.151**
5. $(265.78 - 239.88) \div 265.78$ **0.097**

 2 TEACH

Discuss with students why businesses markdown items and have sales. Point out that businesses must get rid of overstocked or outdated items. Some businesses sell seasonal items. So, these businesses often have sales at the beginning of a season to encourage purchases and then markdown items at the end of the season to get rid of merchandise.

Motivating the Lesson

Friendly Grocer has apple juice for $2.29. After a 30-cent store coupon is used, what is the markdown rate? **12%**

In-Class Examples

Find the markdown and markdown rate.

1. Regular selling price: $20. Sale price: $15. **$5; 25%**
2. Regular selling price: $39.99. Sale price: $31.99. **$8.00; 20%**
3. Regular selling price: $137.88. Sale price: $130.58. **$7.30; 5%**
4. George's Seafood has shrimp on sale for $7.99 per pound. The regular price is $9.99 per pound. What is the markdown rate? **20%**
5. Sturdy Plastics has trash barrels on sale for $19.99, a savings of $15.00 over its regular price. Find the markdown rate. **43%**

CONCEPT CHECK

SELF-CHECK ✓

Complete the problems, then check your answers at the end of the chapter. Find the markdown and the markdown rate.

1. Regular selling price is $80. Sale price is $60. **$80 − $60 = $20; $20 ÷ $80 = 0.25 or 25%**

2. Regular selling price is $174.79. Sale price is $104.87. **$174.79 − $104.87 = $69.92; $69.92 ÷ $174.79 = 0.400 or 40%**

Example 2

Diamond Connection has marked down diamond heart necklaces from $49.99 to $39.99. What is the markdown and the markdown rate?

STEP 1: Find the markdown.

Regular Selling Price	−	Sale Price	
$49.99	−	$39.99	= **$10.00 markdown**

STEP 2: Find the markdown rate.

Markdown	÷	Regular Selling Price	
$10.00	÷	$49.99	= **0.2000 or 20% markdown rate**

CONCEPT CHECK

SELF-CHECK ✓

Complete the problems, then check your answers at the end of the chapter. Find the markdown and the markdown rate.

3. A chain saw at regular price is $349.95. The sale price is $319.95. **$349.95 − $319.95 = $30.00; $30.00 ÷ $349.95 = 0.08572 or 8.6%**

4. An office desk at regular price is $359.99. The sale price is $249.95. **$359.99 − $249.95 = $110.04; $110.04 ÷ $359.99 = 0.3056 or 30.6%**

SECTION 16-8 PRACTICE

Round answers to the nearest tenth of a percent.

	Regular Price	−	Sale Price	=	Markdown	÷	Regular Price	=	Markdown Rate
5.	($25.00	−	$20.00	=	a. $5.00)	÷	$25.00	=	b. 20.0%
6.	(99.99	−	64.99	=	a. $35.00)	÷	99.99	=	b. 35.0%
7.	(247.87	−	149.99	=	a. $97.88)	÷	247.87	=	b. 39.5%
8.	(8,674.50	−	4,337.25	=	a. $4,337.25	) ÷	8,674.50	=	b. 50.0%

9. Gum has a regular price of $0.99. Sale price is $0.59. What is the markdown rate? **40.4%**

10. A digital still camera has a regular price of $799.99. Sale price is $699.99. What is the markdown rate? **12.5%**

11. Design Center has a palm tree on sale for $179. The regular price is $209. What is the markdown rate? **14.4%**

GLOBAL PERSPECTIVE

Discounter Doing Well

Fifty percent of Dollar Tree Stores merchandise comes from overseas, where materials, production, and labor costs are cheaper. Dollar Tree, with sales of well over $1 billion, has the buying power to offer bargain prices. Can students suggest any problems the company might have with its global trade? **Quality of goods and receiving goods on time can be a problem. The company needs to deal with human-rights issues for workers overseas.**

TECHNOLOGY POWER

In March of 2002, Continental, Delta, and American Airlines cut commissions on domestic tickets sold by travel agents to zero. The Internet has allowed them to do this. According to one study, a ticket sold over the Web costs an airline $3 in overhead while a ticket sold through a travel agent costs $35. Approximately 63 percent of Americans who book travel this year will do so online.

12. Office Center has marked down a computer from a regular price of $1,179.97 to a sale price of $979.97. What is the markdown rate? **16.9%**

13. At Food Safe a dozen eggs can be purchased for $0.59 with a coupon, $0.79 without. What is the markdown rate if the coupon is used? **25.3%**

14. a. Videocassette 50.3%; Jell-O 57.6%; Candy hearts 33.9%; Camera 6.3%; Socks 63.3%; Toothbrush 12.5%

14. Discount Store's Sunday flyer had these sale items listed:

Item	Regular Price	Sale Price
Videocassette	$ 1.99	$ 0.99
Jell-O	0.59	0.25
Candy hearts	0.59	0.39
Camera	79.99	74.99
Socks	0.79	0.29
Sonic toothbrush	79.99	69.99

a. Find the markdown rate for each item.
b. Which item has the greatest markdown rate? **Socks at 63.3%**
c. Which item has the greatest dollar markdown? **Toothbrush at $10.00 off**

15. A reciprocating saw is on sale for $59.99, a savings of $30.00 over the regular price. Find the markdown rate. **33.3%**

16. T-Mart is participating in a national promotion of vacuum cleaners. The supreme vacuum is marked down $9.98 to a sale price of $59.99. The widepath vacuum is marked down from $139.99 to $129.99. The top-of-the-line ultra vacuum is marked down $31.02 from the regular price of $329.99. What is the markdown rate for each? **Runabout Supreme: 14.3%; Widepath: 7.1%; Ultra: 9.4%**

MAINTAINING YOUR SKILLS

Need Help? Go to...
➤ Skill 6: **Subtracting Decimals**, page 733
➤ Skill 31: **Finding the Rate**, page 758

Subtract.

17. $74.99 − $14.99 **$60.00**   **18.** $7.25 − $2.15 **$5.10**

Find the rate. (Round to nearest tenth percent.)

19. $15.00 ÷ $50.00 **30.0%**   **20.** $4.99 ÷ $24.99 **20.0%**

21. $5.25 ÷ $25.99 **20.2%**   **22.** $71.79 ÷ $179.79 **39.9%**

23. $15.52 ÷ $44.49 **34.9%**   **24.** $9.00 ÷ $19.99 **45.0%**

25. $124.50 ÷ $829.29 **15.0%**   **26.** $269.50 ÷ $489.49 **55.1%**

27. $5.78 ÷ $17.35 **33.3%**   **28.** $16.50 ÷ $329.39 **5.0%**

29. $186.88 ÷ $747.50 **25.0%**   **30.** $8,818.33 ÷ $26,455.00 **33.3%**

3 ASSESS

Error Analysis
Students can get confused when calculating the markdown rate. Sometimes students mistakenly divide the markdown by the sale price instead of dividing the markdown by the regular selling price. Review the formula with students. Have students use the complement of the markdown rate to verify that they have calculated the correct rate.

4 CLOSE

Closing Activity
Find the markdown and markdown rate.
1. Regular selling price: $10. Sale price: $6. **$4; 40%**
2. Regular selling price: $0.99. Sale price: $0.79. **$0.20; 20%**
3. Regular selling price: $245.95. Sale price: $224.50. **$21.45; 9%**
4. Galaxy Sports has hiking boots on sale for $89.97. The regular price is $129.97. What is the markdown rate? **31%**
5. Corner Convenience has milk on sale for $2.69, which is $0.30 off their regular price. Find the markdown rate. **10%**

TECHNOLOGY POWER

Digital technology opens up the threat of uncontrolled piracy when creative works can be converted to bits that are copied endlessly and distributed globally. However, the music labels agree that their future is on the Internet, where distribution costs are low. At the same time the industry is trying to stop Net piracy, it's also trying to cash in on music sales via the Internet.

WRAP-UP

Go over any problem for which a wrong answer is given.

Assignment Guide
 Basic: 5–8
 Average: 9–12

20 min.

539

Quick Quiz

1. Find the markup and the markup rate based on a selling price of $4.99. The cost is $2.50. **$2.49; 50%**

2. Design Time purchased some art pieces at a cost of $125 each. The company charges its customers $204.99 each. Operating expenses are estimated to be about 25 percent of the selling price. What is the net profit per art piece? **$28.74**

3. Find the selling price of an item that has a cost of $5.00 and a markup that is 20 percent of the selling price. **$6.25**

4. Find the markup rate based on cost of an item that has a selling price of $24.99 and a cost of $18.59. **34%**

5. Sam's Surplus has birdseed on sale for $4.99 per bag. The regular price is $6.99 per bag. What is the markdown rate? **29%**

SECTION 16-1   **CONCEPT CHECK** (p. 518)
1. $19.49 − $7.63 = **$11.86**
2. $545.45 − $272.72 = **$272.73**
3. $29.95 − ($47.85 ÷ 3) = **$14.00**
4. $3.79 − ($68.16 ÷ 24) = **$0.95**

SECTION 16-2   **CONCEPT CHECK** (p. 520, 521)
1. $49.79 − $34.85 = **$14.94**; $14.94 ÷ $49.79 = **0.300 or 30%**
2. $249.19 − $161.97 = **$87.22**; $87.22 ÷ $249.19 = **0.3500 or 35%**
3. ($29.95 − $15.95) ÷ $29.95 = **0.4674 or 46.7%**
4. ($3.79 − $2.84) ÷ $3.79 = **0.2506 or 25.1%**

SECTION 16-3   **CONCEPT CHECK** (p. 523)
1. $140 − $56 = **$84**; $140 × 50% = **$70**; $84 − $70 = **$14**
2. $964.00 − $578.40 = **$385.60**; $964.00 × 35% = **$337.40**; $385.60 − $337.40 = **$48.20**
3. $29.95 − $15.95 = **$14.00**; $29.95 × 40% = **$11.98**; $14.00 − $11.98 = **$2.02**
4. $3.79 − $2.84 = **$0.95**; $3.79 × 24% = $0.9096 = **$0.91**; $0.95 − $0.91 = **$0.04**

SECTION 16-4   **CONCEPT CHECK** (p. 526)
1. $119.50 − $44.78 = **$74.72**; $119.50 × 40% = **$47.80**; $74.72 − $47.80 = **$26.92**; $26.92 ÷ $119.50 = **0.2252 or 22.5%**
2. $224.50 − $102.60 = **$121.90**; $224.50 × 35% = **$78.58**; $121.90 − $78.58 = **$43.32**; $43.32 ÷ $224.50 = **0.1929 or 19.3%**
3. $29.95 ÷ $15.95 = $14.00; $29.95 × 40% = $11.98; $14.00 − $11.98 = $2.02; $2.02 ÷ $29.95 = **0.06744 or 6.7%**
4. $3.79 − $2.84 = $0.95; $3.79 × 24% = $0.9096 or $0.91; $0.95 − $0.91 = $0.04; $0.04 ÷ $3.79 = **0.01055 or 1.1%**

SECTION 16-5   **CONCEPT CHECK** (p. 529)
1. 100% − 25% = 75%; $345 ÷ 0.75 = **$460**
2. 100% − 30% = 70%; $1.40 ÷ 0.70 = **$2.00**
3. 100% − 25% = 75%; $1.49 ÷ 0.75 = **$1.9866 or $1.99**
4. 100% − 20% = 80%; $49.95 ÷ 0.80 = **$62.4375 or $62.44**

SECTION 16-6   **CONCEPT CHECK** (p. 532)
1. $97.50 − $58.50 = $39.00; $39.00 ÷ $58.50 = **0.6666 or 66.7%**
2. $148 − $74 = $74; $74 ÷ $74 = **1.00 or 100%**
3. $29.95 − $15.95 = $14.00; $14.00 ÷ $15.95 = **0.8777 or 87.8%**
4. $3.79 − $2.84 = $0.95; $0.95 ÷ $2.84 = **0.3345 or 33.5%**

SECTION 16-7   **CONCEPT CHECK** (p. 535)
1. Markup: $50 × 70% = **$35**; Selling price: $50 + $35 = **$85**
2. Markup: $140 × 150% = **$210**; Selling price: $140 + $210 = **$350**
3. Markup: $2.60 × 5% = **$0.13**; Selling price: $2.60 + $0.13 = **$2.73**
4. Markup: 50% × $64 = **$32.00**; Selling price: $64 + $32 = **$96**

SECTION 16-8   **CONCEPT CHECK** (p. 538)
1. $80 − $60 = **$20**; $20 ÷ $80 = **0.25 or 25%**
2. $174.79 − $104.87 = **$69.92**; $69.92 ÷ $174.79 = **0.400 or 40%**
3. $349.95 − $319.95 = **$30.00**; $30.00 ÷ $349.95 = **0.08572 or 8.6%**
4. $359.99 − $249.95 = **$110.04**; $110.04 ÷ $359.99 = **0.3056 or 30.6%**

Living in the Real World

Markups at the Enchanted Forest

Assessment   Tallman's shop is a typical specialty store found almost anywhere. You read how she determines the selling price and why she decides to markdown goods. Based upon the content you learned in this chapter (and using a little common sense), complete this quiz on a separate piece of paper. Discuss your answers with classmates.

Retail Success

1   T   F   With a busy retailing season, comes an overrun of marked down products (i.e., leftover, seasonal items).   **T**

2   T   F   Specialty stores don't have as big of overrun inventory as large department stores.   **T**

3   T   F   Specialty stores must sell goods at a faster rate than a large department store.   **T**

4   T   F   Color coding and price points are not given top consideration when determining the markdown of goods.   **F**

5   T   F   Customers relate faster to percent off than dollar amounts when buying goods.   **F**

REVIEW OF KEY WORDS

cost (p. 518)
selling price (p. 518)
markup (p. 518)
gross profit (p. 518)

net profit (p. 518)
markup rate (p. 520)
operating expenses (p. 522)

net-profit rate (p. 525)
markdown (p. 537)
markdown rate (p. 537)

Match one of the key words above with a definition below.

1. the difference between the regular selling price and the sale price of a product; also called discount. **markdown**

2. the net profit expressed as a percent of the selling price of a product. **net profit rate**

3. the difference between the markup and the overhead when the markup is greater than the overhead. **net profit**

4. the amount your business pays for a product. **cost**

5. the discount expressed as a percent of the regular selling price of a product. **markdown rate**

6. what a product actually sells for in a store.

7. expenses that include employee salaries, rent, utilities, and taxes; also called overhead.

8. is determined by subtracting the cost from the selling price. **markup**

9. the difference between the selling price and the cost; also called markup. **gross profit**

10. is determined by dividing the markup by the selling price. **markup rate**

    6. **selling price**
    7. **operating expenses**

CHAPTER **Study Guide and Assessment**

16

Skills and Concepts

SECTION OBJECTIVE 16-1 AND EXAMPLES

Compute the markup in dollars.

Wall-to-Wall purchased throw rugs for $79.95 each. Wall-to-Wall sells the rugs for $129.95 each. What is the markup on each rug?

STEP: Find the markup.

Selling Price — Cost
$129.95 — $79.95 = **$50.00**

REVIEW EXERCISES
Complete the table.

	Item	Selling Price	—	Cost	=	Markup
11.	Candy bar	$ 0.79	—	$ 0.50	=	**$0.29**
12.	Leather sofa	1,899.99	—	1,095.00	=	**$804.99**
13.	Tennis shoes	85.50	—	46.76	=	**$38.74**
14.	Color printer	299.97	—	205.00	=	**$94.97**
15.	Textbook	45.50	—	21.35	=	**$24.15**
16.	Router	365.25	—	210.27	=	**$154.98**

17. Tom's Nursery buys petunias by the pallet. Each pallet contains 36 petunia plants. The cost of each pallet to Tom's Nursery is $17.35. Tom sells the petunias for $1.99 per plant.
   a. What is the markup per plant? **$1.51**
   b. What is the markup per pallet? **$54.36**

SECTION OBJECTIVE 16-2 AND EXAMPLES

Calculate the markup as a percent of the selling price.

Lucky Charms buys silver charms for $10.99 each. It sells them for $19.95 each. What is the markup rate based on the selling price?

STEP 1: Find the markup.

Selling Price — Cost
$19.95 — $10.99 = $8.96 markup

STEP 2: Find the markup rate based on the selling price.

Markup ÷ Selling Price
$8.96 ÷ $19.95 = **.0449 or 45% markup rate based on the selling price**

REINFORCEMENT

Section 16-1

1. Green Foods purchases packages of noodles by the carton. Each carton contains 36 packages and costs $43.20. Green Foods sells the noodles for $2.29 per package. What is the markup per carton? **($39.24)** What is the markup per package? **$1.09**

Section 16-2

1. Find the markup and the mark-up rate based on the selling price.
   Selling price: $56.87. Cost: $39.99. **$16.88; 30%**

REVIEW EXERCISES
Find the markup and markup rate.

	Item	Selling Price	Cost	Markup	Markup Rate
18.	Golf shirt	$ 39.95	$ 25.50	a. $14.45	b. 36.2%
19.	Dog collar	12.59	6.45	a. $6.14	b. 48.8%
20.	DVD player	178.50	95.43	a. $83.07	b. 46.5%
21.	Motorcycle	1,299.97	899.50	a. $400.47	b. 30.8%
22.	Necklace	134.95	65.44	a. $69.51	b. 51.5%
23.	Wrench	25.95	15.50	a. $10.45	b. 40.3%

SECTION OBJECTIVE 16-3 AND EXAMPLES

Figure out the net profit in dollars.

Carl's Camera Shop purchases digital cameras for $356.98 each. Carl sells the cameras for $629.95. Carl estimates his overhead expenses to be 30 percent of the selling price of his merchandise. What is the net profit on each camera?

STEP 1: Find the markup.
Selling Price   −   Cost
   $629.95   − $356.98   = $272.97 markup

STEP 2: Find the overhead.
Selling Price   ×   Overhead Percent
   $629.95   ×   30%   = $188.99 overhead

STEP 3: Find the net profit.
Markup   −   Overhead
$272.97   − $188.99   = **$83.98 net profit**

REVIEW EXERCISES
Find the net profit.

	Markup	−	(Selling Price	×	Overhead Percent)	=	Net Profit
24.	$ 28.00	−	($ 55.00	×	30%)	=	$11.50
25.	103.00	−	(198.95	×	25%)	=	$53.26
26.	65.50	−	(133.50	×	45%)	=	$5.42
27.	88.35	−	(147.50	×	22%)	=	$55.90
28.	100.00	−	(185.00	×	36%)	=	$33.40

29. The buyer for Mango Mania purchases Key West-style hats for a cost of $14.50 each. Mango Mania sells them for $29.95 each. Operating expenses are estimated to be 25 percent of the selling price. What is the net profit per hat? **$7.96**

REINFORCEMENT

Section 16-3
Find the markup, overhead, and net profit.
1. Selling price: $60. Cost: $40.
   Overhead: 50 percent of selling price. **$20; $30; $10**
2. Selling price: $124.99. Cost: $71.59.
   Overhead: 40 percent of selling price. **$53.40; $50.00; $3.40**
3. Selling price: $189.50. Cost: $123.5.6.
   Overhead: 25 percent of selling price. **$65.94; $47.38; $18.56**

SECTION OBJECTIVE 16-4 AND EXAMPLES

Find the net profit as a percent of the selling price.

Gina Kamrey is a buyer for a vintage clothing shop. She purchased some vintage handkerchiefs for a cost of $3.28 each. Her store sells them for $9.25 each. Operating expenses are estimated to be 33 percent of the selling price. What is the net-profit rate based on the selling price of the handkerchief?

STEP 1: Find the net profit.

Markup — Overhead

($9.25 − $3.28) − ($9.25 × 33%)

= $5.97 − $3.05 = $2.92 net profit

STEP 2: Find the net-profit rate.

Net Profit ÷ Selling Price

$2.92 ÷ $9.25 = 0.3156 or 31.6% net-profit rate

REVIEW EXERCISES

Find the net profit and the net-profit rate.

	Markup	−	(Selling Price	×	Overhead Percent)	=	Net Profit		Net-Profit Rate	
30.	$ 106.00	−	($ 219.98	×	40%)	=	a. $18.01	b.	8.2%	
31.	48.00	−	(73.45	×	20%)	=	a. $33.31	b.	45.4%	
32.	132.95	−	(259.95	×	25%)	=	a. $67.96	b.	26.1%	
33.	60.75	−	(109.95	×	30%)	=	a. $27.76	b.	25.2%	
34.	239.56	−	(446.50	×	40%)	=	a. $60.96	b.	13.7%	
35.	1,135.50	−	(1,950.46	×	50%)	=	a. $160.27	b.	8.2%	

SECTION OBJECTIVE 16-5 AND EXAMPLES

Calculate the selling price of an item based on cost and markup rate.

Margie's Gifts purchased some leather book covers for $13.50. Its markup policy is 35 percent based on the selling price. Find the selling price of the book covers.

STEP 1: Find the complement of the markup rate.

100% − 35% = 65% complement of the markup rate

STEP 2: Find the selling price.

Cost ÷ Complement of Markup Rate

$13.50 ÷ 65%

= $20.769 or $20.77 selling price

REINFORCEMENT

Section 16-4

1. Find the markup, overhead, net profit, and net-profit rate.
   Selling price: $135.78. Cost: $67.30.
   Overhead expense: 40 percent of selling price. **$68.48; $54.31; $14.17; 10%**

REVIEW EXERCISES
Complete the table.

	Cost	Markup Rate	Complement of Markup Rate		Selling Price (Nearest Cent)	
36.	$ 12.00	35.0%	a.	65%	b.	$18.46
37.	105.50	22.0%	a.	78%	b.	$135.26
38.	129.95	45.0%	a.	55%	b.	$236.27
39.	83.23	32.0%	a.	68%	b.	$122.40
40.	35.91	41.5%	a.	58.5%	b.	$61.38
41.	1,009.15	18.5%	a.	81.5%	b.	$1,238.22

SECTION OBJECTIVE 16-6 AND EXAMPLES

Solve for the markup rate based on cost.

Boxes, Etc. purchases small wooden jewelry boxes for $31.20 from the manufacturer. Boxes, Etc. sells the boxes for $59.50. What is the markup rate based on cost?

STEP 1: Find the markup.

Selling Price   −   Cost
    $59.50   − $31.20
  = $28.30 markup

STEP 2: Find the markup rate based on cost.

Markup   ÷   Cost
 $28.30 ÷ $31.20
  = 0.907 or 90.7% markup rate based on cost

REVIEW EXERCISES
Find the markup and the markup rate based on cost.

	(Selling Price	−	Cost	=	Markup)	÷	Cost	=	Markup Rate Based on Cost
42.	($ 2.50	−	$ 1.75	=	a. $0.75)	÷	$ 1.75	=	b. 42.9%
43.	(29.95	−	18.53	=	a. $11.42)	÷	18.53	=	b. 61.6%
44.	(38.55	−	22.45	=	a. $16.10)	÷	22.45	=	b. 71.7%
45.	(109.95	−	79.95	=	a. $30.00)	÷	79.95	=	b. 37.5%
46.	(954.33	−	654.10	=	a.	÷	654.10	=	b. 45.9% a. $300.23
47.	(89.75	−	55.50	=	a. $34.25)	÷	55.50	=	b. 61.7%

REINFORCEMENT

Section 16-5
1. Find the complement: 20 percent. **80%**

Section 16-6
1. Find the selling price.
   Cost: $87.50.
   Markup: 40 percent of selling price. **$145.83**
2. Blue Crystal purchases glasses and marks them up 45 percent of the selling price. A juice glass costs Blue Crystal $4.89. What is the selling price? **$8.89**

SECTION OBJECTIVE 16-7 AND EXAMPLES

Compute the selling price based on cost and markup rate.

Wholesale Electronics sells speakers to electronics stores for $18.50 a pair. Wholesale Electronics calculates the suggested retail price and attaches it to each set of speakers. The retail price is computed by marking up the cost to the electronics store by 150 percent. What is the suggested retail selling price?

STEP 1: Find the markup.

    Cost × Markup Rate

    $18.50 ×   150%

    = $27.75 markup

STEP 2: Find the selling price.

    Cost + Markup

    $18.50 + $27.75

    = $46.25 selling price

REVIEW EXERCISES

Find the markup and the selling price (to the nearest cent).

	Cost	Markup Rate	Markup		Selling Price (Nearest Cent)	
48.	$ 32.00	75.00%	a.	$24	b.	$56
49.	185.50	100.00%	a.	$185.50	b.	$371
50.	229.55	125.00%	a.	$286.94	b.	$516.49
51.	63.15	200.00%	a.	$126.30	b.	$189.45
52.	7.66	75.50%	a.	$5.78	b.	$13.44
53.	841.02	90.25%	a.	$759.02	b.	$1,600.04

SECTION OBJECTIVE 16-8 AND EXAMPLES

Calculate the markdown in dollars and as a percent of the regular selling price.

Summer Fun sells a particular jet ski at a regular selling price of $2,995.50. For one week only, Summer Fun has marked down the price to $2,450.00. What is the markdown rate?

STEP 1: Find the markdown.

    Regular Selling Price — Sale Price

    $2,995.50   — $2,450.00 = $545.50 markdown

STEP 2: Find the markdown rate.

    Markdown ÷ Regular Selling Price

    $545.50 ÷ $2,995.50   = 0.1821 or 18.2% markdown rate

REVIEW EXERCISES

Find the markdown and the markdown rate.

	(Regular Price	—	Sale Price	=	Markdown)	÷	Regular Price	=	Markdown Rate	
54.	($ 25.00	—	$ 19.95	=	a. $5.05)	÷	$ 25.00	=	b.	20.2%
55.	(165.50	—	99.95	=	a. $65.55)	÷	165.50	=	b.	39.6%
56.	(79.99	—	65.50	=	a. $14.49)	÷	79.99	=	b.	18.1%
57.	(1,895.45	—	999.95	=	a. $895.50)	÷	1,895.45	=	b.	47.2%
58.	(1.29	—	0.79	=	a. $0.50)	÷	1.29	=	b.	38.8%
59.	(12.67	—	5.50	=	a. $7.17)	÷	12.67	=	b.	56.6%

546 ◀ Chapter 16 Sales

REINFORCEMENT

Section 16-7

Find the mark-up rate based on cost.

1. Selling price: $134.27. Cost: $93.39. **44%**
2. Peaceful Candles sells votives for $4.29 each. The cost of each candle is $2.99. What is the markup rate based on the cost? **43%**

Section 16-8

Find the markup and the selling price.

1. Cost: $285.90. Markup: 110 percent of cost. **$314.49; $600.39**
2. Noah's Toys buys pinwheels from a manufacturer for $0.45 each. Noah's Toys marks up each pinwheel 342 percent of cost. What is the selling price? **$1.99**

Alternative Assessment

Count Me In: *How You'll Use Math*

Where the Money Goes What goes into making a book? The authors, the paper, the publisher, the manufacturers, and so on all have to be considered in the formula of selling a book. Take a look at **Figure 16.1** before you answer the questions below.

Figure 16.1

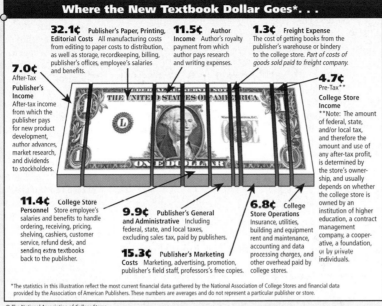

Where the New Textbook Dollar Goes*...

32.1¢ Publisher's Paper, Printing, Editorial Costs All manufacturing costs from editing to paper costs to distribution, as well as storage, recordkeeping, billing, publisher's offices, employee's salaries and benefits.

11.5¢ Author Income Author's royalty payment from which author pays research and writing expenses.

1.3¢ Freight Expense The cost of getting books from the publisher's warehouse or bindery to the college store. *Part of costs of goods sold paid to freight company.*

7.0¢ After-Tax Publisher's Income After-tax income from which the publisher pays for new product development, author advances, market research, and dividends to stockholders.

4.7¢ Pre-Tax** College Store Income **Note: The amount of federal, state, and/or local tax, and therefore the amount and use of any after-tax profit, is determined by the store's ownership, and usually depends on whether the college store is owned by an institution of higher education, a contract management company, a cooperative, a foundation, or by private individuals.

11.4¢ College Store Personnel Store employee's salaries and benefits to handle ordering, receiving, pricing, shelving, cashiers, customer service, refund desk, and sending extra textbooks back to the publisher.

9.9¢ Publisher's General and Administrative Including federal, state, and local taxes, excluding sales tax, paid by publishers.

6.8¢ College Store Operations Insurance, utilities, building and equipment rent and maintenance, accounting and data processing charges, and other overhead paid by college stores.

15.3¢ Publisher's Marketing Costs Marketing, advertising, promotion, publisher's field staff, professor's free copies.

*The statistics in this illustration reflect the most current financial data gathered by the National Association of College Stores and financial data provided by the Association of American Publishers. These numbers are averages and do not represent a particular publisher or store.

© The National Association of College Stores

60. Describe how a single dollar is split among the parties involved in making new books. **Answers will vary.**

61. Create a flowchart based upon how you think the publishing process works before a book ends up in your hands. **Answers will vary.**

62. Suppose Stephen King's latest book retails for $18.20 at the bookstore. Given the financial data in Figure 16.1, calculate how much each party earns per book. **$5.84; $2.09; $0.24; $0.86; $1.24; $2.78; $1.80; $2.07; $1.27**

Thinking Critically
- Why do you think booksellers charge their customers a markup?
- How might electronic books (or e-books) or online magazines affect the print publishing industry? Will print become obsolete and overrun by online content?

Portfolio
Select one of the assignments from this chapter that you found especially challenging and place it in your portfolio.

THINKING CRITICALLY

Why do you think booksellers charge their customers a markup? **In order to make a profit and remain in the business of producing books.** How might electronic books (or e-books) or online magazines effect the print publishing industry? Will print become obsolete and overrun by online content? **To date, e-books and online magazines haven't made much of a dent in the print publishing industry. Online magazines are proving more popular than e-books, but people are still purchasing traditional books and magazines in droves.**

Math Studio Overview

Students become image consultants for a local hospital that's not keeping up with the times in terms of services and its image. They will interview, analyze, and draw conclusions about public opinion. This Math Studio teaches them techniques for the informational interview, investigative practices, and writing public relations content. Intrapersonal and critical-thinking skills are tested.

Bell Ringer Activity

Students pick a common product and conduct research on the perception of it.
- Research the history of this particular product.
- How and where is it produced?

Students write a report on their findings and present it orally to the class.

2 TEACH

Cooperative Learning

Ask students to create a simple diagram, which outlines the responses to Step 3. Allow them to visualize their data. You might suggest they browse *USA Today* Snapshots online; it offers good examples of visual journalism.

A Creative Lab

Healing the Hospital

Health care in the United States is among the best and most accessible in the world. Vast scientific research, quality education, stringent regulations, and caring healthcare professionals mean most Americans have access to excellent medical facilities and treatment. On the other hand, some people dislike visiting the doctor, in part because they're afraid they might receive bad news. Some medical tests can be unpleasant and expensive. Often people want miracles from medicine and when their doctors can't oblige, patients want to blame someone.

Purpose

Some day you may be a consultant who's asked to fix a product that people enjoy using or believe is important to use, but that also frustrates or upsets them. You may need to figure out the problems with the product or its image and then propose a way to improve the design or marketing of the product, or both. The bottom line for the company, of course, is a matter of sales and profit.

Supplies Needed

- Pen
- Paper
- Or computer and word-processing program

Your Activity

You are an image consultant with a hypothetical company called Polished to Perfection. You have recently received an account with a large local hospital. The hospital board has concluded that it's not keeping up with the times in terms of its image or the services it offers its patients. It has called you to help convince people in the local community that the hospital's medical services are still the best.

Step 1: Interview several people who recently have been in a hospital to determine what they liked or disliked about the hospital. Include several people who were patients as well as people who visited patients. You'll need to prepare several questions ahead of time.

> ### QUICK TIPS FOR AN INTERVIEW
> **Before the Interview**
> - Appearance is everything. No loud colors, no gaudy jewelry, no cologne or aftershave, etc.
> - Dress conservatively and professionally.
> - Watch your personal grooming. Ensure that you have no body odor or bad breath.
> - Make sure hair, nails, and shoes are neat and clean.
>
> **During the Interview**
> - Be attentive and speak clearly.
> - Face the interviewer directly and speak to him or her.
> - Speak slowly and enunciate carefully.
> - Express confidence.
> - Relax and smile occasionally.
> - Take notes, but also try to maintain eye contact now and then.

NEWSWORTHY TREND

Healthy People Proclamation: Part 1

In January 2000, the Department of Health and Human Services started the campaign, Healthy People 2010. It outlined 467 objectives to classify the road to a healthy life. The purpose is twofold—to increase your life by leading a healthy one and to decrease health problems. Ask students to find the 28 focus areas that comprise this health agenda. Have them write in a journal about they meet the 28 areas.

Step 2: Begin the interviews by briefly explaining why you are asking the questions. (Reread the beginning of this Math Studio if you're still unclear of this assignment's purpose.)

Step 3: After the interview, reread your notes. Rewrite them by categorizing them. For example, are there certain patterns in the responses? Did people share the same concerns or talk about different ones? What do you think caused the concerns people have? Did the people you interviewed have suggestions for ways to improve the hospital's service or environment? What ideas do you have?

Step 4: Draw up a list of problems and suggested solutions. Is the expense of medical care one of the problems people complained about? If so, investigate the costs of several basic services offered by your own local hospital and at least one other. Ask about the cost of a basic room, parking, and supplies, such as tissues.

Step 5: Create a chart that compares the costs in the hospitals you have contacted. (Many urban hospitals are trying to make the environment for patients, family, and visitors more inviting. Comfortable lounges, art collections, even small museums are now available within hospital walls to help patients and visitors pass the hours and days more quickly and pleasantly.)

Step 6: As a consultant, you've been asked to prepare a brochure for patients that outlines some of the costs (including overhead) that the hospital must pay.

A. Write an introductory paragraph for such a brochure. Make sure it is friendly in tone and that it explains why the price of an item for patients must be higher than the cost to the hospital. (Remind readers that hospitals can only exist as profitable businesses.)

B. List ways in which the hospital uses its profits to benefit patients and the community.

Critique It

- Who do you think pays for these services?
- If you were a hospital administrator, would you simply increase the price of supplies, rooms, and service?
- What other ways could you acquire funds to cover these non-medical costs of running an appealing hospital?

Math Studio *Healing the Hospital* ▶ **549**

Enrichment
Becoming a good writer requires knowing how to edit and rewrite. Create groups for students to edit one another's brochure copy in Step 6. Suggestions and criticisms are handled diplomatically.

Critique It

Who do you think pays for these services? **Answers will vary.**

If you were a hospital administrator, would you simply increase the price of supplies, rooms, and services? **Answers will vary.**

What other ways could you acquire funds to cover these non-medical costs of running an appealing hospital? **Sponsoring community events, producing benefits/galas, private donations, etc.**

NEWSWORTHY TREND

Healthy People Proclamation: Part 2
Describe how Healthy People 2010 affects health agencies. Ask students to think about this agenda from a public policy and business perspectives. They might visit the Center for Disease Control Web site and the National Center for Health Statistics to track the nation's health. Have them write an expository paper. They must incorporate statistics into their analysis and position.

National Standards for Business Education

Section Objectives	1. Mathematical Foundations	2. Number Relationships and Operations	3. Patterns, Functions, and Algebra	4. Measurements	5. Statistics and Probability	6. Problem-Solving Applications	
17-1 Opinion Surveys (pp. 552–553) Compute the rate of a particular response in an opinion survey.	X	X					
17-2 Sales Potential (pp. 554–555) Figure out the annual sales potential of a new product.	X	X					
17-3 Marketing Share (pp. 556–557) Calculate the market share of a new product.	X	X					
17-4 Sales Projections (pp. 558–560) Use a graph to compute projected sales.	X	X					
17-5 Sales Projections—Factor Method (pp. 561–562) Use the factor method to compute projected sales.	X	X					
17-6 Newspaper Advertising Costs (pp. 563–564) Calculate the cost of advertising in a newspaper.	X	X					
17-7 Televisions Advertising Costs (pp. 565–567) Compute the cost of advertising on television.	X	X					
17-8 Pricing (pp. 568–569) Calculate the selling price that will result in the highest possible net profit.	X	X					

(Source: Reprinted with permission from the National Standards for Business Education, copyright © 2001 by National Business Education Association, 1914 Association Drive, Reston, Virginia 21901-1596)

SCANS Correlation

Foundation Skills

Basic Skills	Reading	Writing	Math	Listening	Speaking	
Thinking Skills	Creative Thinking	Decision Making	Problem Solving	Seeing Things in the Mind's Eye	Knowing How to Learn	Reasoning
Personal Qualities	Responsibility	Self-Esteem	Sociability	Self-Management	Integrity/Honesty	

This chapter's highlighted blocks indicate the chapter's content coverage in the Student Edition and the Teacher Wraparound Edition.

National Council of Teachers of Mathematics Standards

1. Numbers & Operations	2. Algebra	3. Geometry	4. Measurement	5. Data Analysis & Probability	6. Problem Solving	7. Reasoning & Proof	8. Communication	9. Connections	10. Representations
X					X		X		
X					X		X		
X					X		X		
X				X	X		X		X
X					X		X		
X					X		X		
X					X		X		
X					X		X		

SCANS Correlation

Workplace Competencies

Resources	Allocating Time	Allocating Money	Allocating Material and Facility Resources	Allocating Human Resources		
Information	Acquiring and Evaluating Information	Organizing and Maintaining Information	Interpreting and Communicating Information	Using Computers to Process Information		
Interpersonal Skills	Participating as a Member of a Team	Teaching Others	Serving Clients/Customers	Exercising Leadership	Negotiating to Arrive at a Decision	Working with Cultural Diversity
Systems	Understanding Systems	Monitoring and Correcting Performance	Improving and Designing Systems			
Technology	Selecting Technology	Applying Technology to Task	Maintaining and Troubleshooting Technology			

What You'll Learn
Tell students that a company's marketing department deals with many factors. In this chapter you'll focus on: surveys, sales potential, market share, sales projections, advertising costs, and pricing.

Why It's Important
The concept of marketing means making your company name and/or product recognizable. Companies successful in marketing can out perform another company with a superior product on name recognition alone. Some product names, such as Clorox is synonymous with bleach due to good marketing efforts. A trend began in the late 1970's of using obscure names for companies that do not describe the product or service the company offers. The Standard & Poor's 500 includes Agilent, Altera, Ameren, Exelon, Mirant, Synovus, Visteon and Xilinx. It's nearly impossible to tell by the name what any of these companies do.

Key Word Review
List and Name
Students list, in three minutes, company names from their favorite TV, billboard, or magazine ads. Decide if these are real words or created. **LS**

CHAPTER 17

Marketing

What You'll Learn
Section 17-1 Compute the rate of a particular response in an opinion survey.

Section 17-2 Figure out the annual sales potential of a new product.

Section 17-3 Calculate the market share of a new product.

Section 17-4 Use a graph to compute projected sales.

Section 17-5 Use the factor method to compute projected sales.

Section 17-6 Calculate the cost of advertising in a newspaper.

Section 17-7 Compute the cost of advertising on television.

Section 17-8 Calculate the selling price that will result in the highest possible net profit.

When Will You Ever Use This?
You could create the best product in the world, but if you don't market it, you're doomed. People need to know about your product or service, otherwise you won't sell it and you won't make any money. The goal of your business's marketing efforts, in the end, is to get your product out into consumers' hands and money in your pocket.

Key Words to Know
- product test
- opinion research firm
- opinion survey
- sales potential
- sample
- market
- market share
- sales projection
- factor method
- factor

Mathematics Online
To learn more about marketing, visit the *Mathematics with Business Applications* Web site at www.busmath.glencoe.com.

CLASSROOM RESOURCES

Application and Enrichment
- *Teacher Wraparound Edition*
- *Teacher Resource Binder, Blackline Masters*
- Interactive Lesson Planner CD-ROM
- PowerPoint® Presentations CD-ROM

Review and Enforcement
Mathematics Online
www.busmath.glencoe.com
- *Teacher Resource Binder, Internet Resources*

- *Student Activity Workbook*
- *Student Activity Workbook, Teacher Annotated Edition*
- *School-to-Home Activity Workbook*

Assessment and Evaluation
- *Assessment Binder, Reproducible Tests*
- *Assessment Binder, Alternative Assessment Strategies*
- **Exam***View*® *Pro Test Generator* CD-ROM

For the Teacher
- *Student Activity Workbook, Teacher Annotated Edition*
- *Assessment Binder*
- Interactive Lesson Planner CD-ROM
- *Teacher Resource Binder*
- Mathematics Online
  www.busmath.glencoe.com

For the Student
- *Student Activity Workbook*
- *School-to-Home Activity Workbook*

...

Living in the Real World

The Campaign for Dozie D'Oats

Sahir Patel is a market campaign director at Goldsmith & Lieberg (G & L), a marketing firm in Nebraska. G & L's clients include beef producers, cereal companies, and politicians. Because Patel has been with the company for five years, he often designs entire marketing campaigns for some of G & L's most important clients. Read to see how Patel works with a client to plan a cereal advertising campaign.

Read on. Go to . . .

551

Living in the Real World

Story's Summary

Students follow the story of Sahir Patel, a marketing campaign director for a cereal company in Nebraska. As he meets with his client to plan an advertising blitz for Dozie D'Oats cereal, students learn about the importance of opinion surveys, market share, sales projections, and advertising costs.

Did You Know...

An increasing number of Web sites deploy "cookies" on your personal computer to study the types of sites you visit in hopes that they can learn how to better tailor a marketing message to you or your demographic group.

Think about This

How would society be different if marketing did not exist?

LOCAL STANDARDS

National Standards for Business Education

Standard 1	Mathematical Foundations
Standard 2	Number Relationships and Operations

National Council of Teachers of Mathematics Standards

Standard 1	Numbers and Operations
Standard 6	Problem Solving
Standard 8	Communication

1 FOCUS

Give students this short survey. Present the results as a table.

1. How do you feel about the length of classes—too long/just right/too short?
2. How do you feel about the length of a school day—too long/just right/too short?
3. How do you feel about the length of the school year—too long/just right/too short?

This section focuses on opinion surveys. Point out that surveys, like this one, give information. In business, surveys tell whether a product is likely to sell.

In-Class Examples

Work through these exercises with students before having them do the Self-Check. Round answers to the nearest hundredth.

1. 20 ÷ 65 **0.31**
2. 150 ÷ 225 **0.67**
3. 1,148 ÷ 3,295 **0.35**

SECTION 17-1 Opinion Surveys

○ **Section Objective**

Compute the rate of a particular response in an opinion survey.

When you develop a new product, you'll want to know how likely it is to sell. You may conduct a **product test**. This is when you ask a group of people to try the product. You may hire an **opinion research firm** that specializes in product testing to conduct the test. Panels of volunteers try the product and respond to questions in an **opinion survey**. An opinion research firm tabulates the answers to the questions and submits tables of results to you. You'll use this formula when conducting opinion surveys:

$$\text{Percent of Particular Response} = \frac{\text{Number of Times Particular Response Occurs}}{\text{Total Number of Responses}}$$

Living in the Real World

The Campaign for Dozie D'Oats

Mapping the Plan   The purpose of the meeting is to map out a plan for an advertising campaign to promote Harvester's new cereal, Dozie D'Oats. Patel suggested that it start a campaign with an opinion survey in order to see if kids will go for Dozie D'Oats. The feedback on the product test will determine how fast it's produced.

Draw Conclusions   What is the purpose of an opinion survey?

Continued on page 554

Example 1

Countryside Cereal Company conducted an opinion survey of 2,600 people for its new Good Morning Cereal. This table shows the responses of the 2,600 surveyed.

Age Group				
Opinion	Under 18	18 to 40	40 or older	Total
Excellent	200	430	1,450	2,080
Good	25	108	215	348
Fair	10	12	99	121
Dislike	5	10	36	51
Total	240	560	1,800	2,600

What percent of the total responses rated the cereal "good"?

STEP: Compute the rate of the response.

$$\frac{\text{Number of Times Particular Response Occurs}}{\text{Total Number of Responses}}$$

348 ÷ 2,600 = **0.1338 or 13.4% of "good" responses**

348 ÷ 2600 = 0.133846153

BUSINESS NOTES

Bilingual Workers Are in Demand
Corporate America is hiring people who speak two languages, especially in their marketing, sales, and operations departments. Who's hiring bilingual professionals? **(Most of the Fortune 500 companies and some of the big-name companies like IBM, Texaco, Target, and American Express.)** Students find out which local companies are hiring bilingual professionals in which company department, and report to the class.

Living in the Real World

To collect the opinions of a representative sample of people, which will help a company best tailor its product or service.

CONCEPT CHECK

SELF-CHECK ✔

Complete the problems, then check your answers at the end of the chapter.

1. Eighteen hundred out of 2,000 people surveyed own computers. What percent of the total people surveyed own computers? **1,800 ÷ 2,000 = 90%**

2. Four hundred and sixty out of 500 people surveyed like Mintie toothpaste. What percent of the total people surveyed like it? **460 ÷ 500 = 92%**

SECTION 17-1 PRACTICE

Round answers to the nearest tenth of a percent.

	Product in Survey	Number of "Good" Responses	÷	Total Number of Responses	=	Percent of "Good" Responses
3.	Ice cream	320	÷	400	=	80.0%
4.	Soup	75	÷	200	=	37.5%
5.	Cleanser	600	÷	1,000	=	60.0%
6.	Movie	350	÷	1,250	=	28.0%
7.	Calculator	2,047	÷	2,300	=	89.0%

8. 12.3% moved away; 4.7% disliked quality; 31.7% charges too high; 36.7% crowded; 4.7% location; 10.0% other reason

8. Fisher Motors conducted a survey on its dealer service. The people surveyed were asked to choose one answer for this question: "If you DO NOT usually go to the dealer from whom you bought your car for service, why not?" The choices and number of responses received for each were the following:

   <u>37</u> Moved away from vicinity   <u>110</u> Crowded service department

   <u>14</u> Disliked quality of service   <u>14</u> Location not convenient

   <u>95</u> Service charges too high   <u>30</u> Some other reason

What is the percent of each response?

9. a. Definitely: 405; Probably: 602; Possibly: 451; No: 282

  b. Under 25: 306; 25–34: 527; 35–49: 513; 50 and over: 394

  c. 1,740

  d. Definitely: 23.3%; Probably: 34.6%; Possibly: 25.9%; No: 16.2%

  e. Under 25: 13.1%; 25–34: 37.3%; 35–49: 31.1%; 50 and over: 18.5%

  f. 25–34

  g. Under 25: 32.3%; 25–34: 20.2%; 35–49: 19.1%; 50 and over: 28.4%

  h. Under 25

9. Before beginning production of its new vacuum cleaner, the Devaney Company conducted an opinion survey of a group of people at the mall. When asked if they would purchase the product, the people gave these responses:

			Age Group		
Response	Under 25	25 to 34	35 to 49	50 and older	Total
Definitely	53	151	126	75	
Probably	75	184	203	140	
Possibly	87	135	130	99	
No	91	57	54	80	
Total					

a. Find the total for each response.
b. Find the total in each age group.
c. Find the total number of people in the survey.
d. Find the percent of the total for each response group.
e. What is the percent of "definitely" responses in each age group?
f. What age group is most likely to purchase the product?
g. What is the percent of "no" responses in each age group?
h. What age group is least likely to purchase the product?

Need Help? Go to...

▶ Skill 30: Finding the Percentage, page 757

MAINTAINING YOUR SKILLS

Find the percentage. Round to the nearest tenth.

10. 8% of 70 **5.6**   11. 70% of 80 **56**   12. 30% of 500 **150**

Section 17-1 Opinion Surveys ▶ **553**

WRAP-UP

Go over any problem for which a wrong answer is given.

Assignment Guide
  Basic: 3–7
Average: 8

20 min.

② TEACH

Have students discuss why a company would hire a research firm to conduct product tests for the company. **Point out that it is important that surveys are not biased. Surveys can be conducted on a few people or many people. Point out the importance of an adequate survey size. Opinion research firms often choose volunteers that meet certain criteria for a particular survey. For example, a research firm that is conducting a survey about dog food would want volunteers who own dogs.**

In-Class Example

1. A survey shows that 270 out of 500 people own bicycles. What percent of the total people surveyed own bicycles? **54%**

③ ASSESS

Error Analysis

When students calculate the percent of a particular response by dividing the number of times the particular response occurs by the total number of responses, they need to remember to write the decimal quotient as a percent. Remind students how to convert decimals to percents. You may want to give students a few decimals to practice.

④ CLOSE

Closing Activity

1. A survey concludes that 150 out of 230 people rent movies on a regular basis. What percent of the total people surveyed rent movies? **65.2%**

2. A survey concludes that 980 out of 3,535 people own minivans. What percent of the total people surveyed own minivans? **27.7%**

553

National Standards for Business Education

Standard 1	Mathematical Foundations
Standard 2	Number Relationships and Operations

National Council of Teachers of Mathematics Standards

Standard 1	Numbers and Operations
Standard 6	Problem Solving
Standard 8	Communication

1 FOCUS

Businesses try to only produce items that will sell and make a profit. Before an item is mass-produced, it is important to determine the sales potential. By testing how well the item is liked with a group of volunteers, a business can predict the sales potential.

In-Class Examples

Work through these exercises with students before having them do the Self-Check.

1. 9,000 × 2 × 50% **9,000**
2. 30,000 × 4 × 40% **48,000**
3. 50,000 × 5 × (1,400 ÷ 2,200) **159,090.91**

2 TEACH

Have students discuss what they learned about opinion surveys in Section 17-1. Point out that opinion surveys can be used to help predict sales potential. Manufacturers often produce a small number of a product and test it on a group of volunteers, or sample. If the results of the test are positive, then the manufacturer must determine

554

○ **Section Objective**

Figure out the annual sales potential of a new product.

SECTION 17-2 Sales Potential

Before your business produces a new product, you may try to determine the product's **sales potential.** The sales potential is an estimate of the sales volume of a product during a specified period of time. You may manufacture a small number of the product for a selected group of people to try. This group is called a **sample.**

The sales potential of your new product is based on: (1) the percent of people in the sample who would purchase your product, (2) an estimate of the size of the **market,** and (3) the average number of times that an individual might purchase this type of product during a specified period of time. The market is the total number of people who might purchase the product.

$$\begin{matrix} \text{Annual Sales} \\ \text{Potential} \end{matrix} = \begin{matrix} \text{Estimated} \\ \text{Market Size} \end{matrix} \times \begin{matrix} \text{Individual Rate} \\ \text{of Purchase} \end{matrix} \times \begin{matrix} \text{Percent of} \\ \text{Potential Purchasers} \end{matrix}$$

Living in the Real World

The Campaign for Dozie D'Oats

Surveying the Markets   Harvester doesn't have the time or money to survey an entire population so it selects a sample of the entire target population. The data shows that the cereal—crunchy, healthy (except for those chocolate-covered raisins)—is a big hit with children ages 5 to 12. Next Harvester wants to determine its market share.

Draw Conclusions   If you have a larger rather than smaller sample, would you get better data?

Continued on page 556

Example 1

The Ruston Corporation has developed a suntan cream called Lite Stuff. Ruston chose a sample of teenagers to try the new product. Of the 3,000 teenagers in the sample, 1,200 said they would purchase Lite Stuff. The Ruston Corporation estimates that there are 2,000,000 teenagers that buy suntan creams. Ruston's surveys indicate that each teenager purchases about three tubes of suntan cream per year. What is the sales potential for Lite Stuff for one year?

STEP 1: Find the percent of potential purchasers.
1,200 ÷ 3,000 = 0.40 or 40% potential purchasers

STEP 2: Find the annual sales potential.

$$\begin{matrix} \text{Estimated} \\ \text{Market Size} \end{matrix} \times \begin{matrix} \text{Individual Rate} \\ \text{of Purchase} \end{matrix} \times \begin{matrix} \text{Percent} \\ \text{of Potential} \\ \text{Purchasers} \end{matrix}$$

$$2{,}000{,}000 \quad \times \quad 3 \quad \times \quad 40\% \quad = \textbf{2,400,000 annual sales potential}$$

Living in the Real World

The larger a sample, the surer a company can be that answers truly reflect the population.

ALTERNATIVE ASSESSMENT

Students with Visual Impairments
Students with impairments to their vision face special risks and require special tools in order to participate in academic and workplace environments. Some students benefit from working with a peer "visual translator" who is able to verbally describe visual images, such as the photos and diagrams in the textbook. LS , CL , P

1. Percent potential = 80 ÷ 1,000 = 0.08 or 8%; Sales potential = 40,000 × 1 × 0.08 = 3,200

SELF-CHECK ✓

2. Percent potential = 320 ÷ 1,600 = 0.2 or 20%; Sales potential = 1,400,000 × 2 × 0.2 = 560,000

1200 ÷ 3000 = 0.40 M+

2000000 × 3 × RM = 2400000

CONCEPT CHECK

Complete the problems, then check your answers at the end of the chapter. Find the percent of potential users and the annual sales potential.

1. New pruning shears.
   Estimated market: 40,000.
   Eighty out of 1,000 would purchase.
   Rate of purchase: 1.

2. New face cream.
   Estimated market: 1,400,000.
   Three hundred twenty out of 1,600 would purchase.
   Rate of purchase: 2.

SECTION 17-2 PRACTICE

Complete the table.

	Number in Sample	Number of Potential Customers	Percent of Potential Customers	Estimated Market Size	Individual Rate of Purchase per Year	Annual Sales Potential
3.	400	100	25%	800,000	1 can	a. 200,000
4.	500	10	a. 2.0%	1,800,000	1 once	b. 36,000
5.	1,500	300	a. 20.0%	5,700,000	1 once	b. 1,140,000
6.	2,000	240	a. 12.0%	25,000,000	4 boxes	b. 12,000,000
7.	2,000	50	a. 2.5%	32,600,000	10 issues	b. 8,150,000

8. Child's car seat.
   People in the sample: 1,200.
   People who would purchase the car seat: 360.
   Market size is 3,000,000.
   Each family buys 1 once.
   What is the annual sales potential? **900,000**

9. New word-processing software.
   People in the sample: 8,700.
   People who would purchase the product: 870.
   Market size is 5,000,000.
   Each person buys 1 per year.
   What is the annual sales potential? **500,000**

10. Dishwashing detergent is tested by 1,000 people. Eighty-seven said they would buy it. The estimated market size is 4,500,000. The company estimates that each person would buy the detergent 12 times a year. What is the annual sales potential? **4,698,000**

11. The National Optometrics Company is marketing a new, softer, more pliable disposable contact lens. Out of a sample of 1,200 users, 150 preferred the new lenses. The estimated total market of disposal contact lens users is 1,500,000. The average disposable contact lens wearer would purchase 12 lenses per year. What is the sales potential for the new lenses for 1 year? **2,250,000**

MAINTAINING YOUR SKILLS

Need Help? Go to...
➤ Skill 30: Finding the Percentage, page 757

Find the percentage. Round answers to the nearest hundredth.

12. $4\frac{1}{4}$% of 96 **4.08**

13. $\frac{3}{8}$% of 120 **0.45**

14. 125% of $4,140 **$5,175.00**

COMMUNICATION SKILLS

Marketing Fast Facts
Working in a team, or individually, students find and read several articles on marketing, market research, or relationship marketing. Students create a one-minute news report titled, "Marketing Fast Facts" on topics from the articles. **LS** , **CL**

WRAP-UP

Go over any problem for which a wrong answer is given.

Assignment Guide
   Basic: 3–7
   Average: 8–9

20 min.

---

how often people would purchase the product. This could be determined by a survey. The manufacturer also must determine the total market size for the product. For instance, if the product is baby food, the total market would be the number of households that buy baby food. Often, statistical reports are used to estimate the total market.

In-Class Example
Find the annual sales potential.
1. Estimated market size: 500,000.
   Individual rate of purchase: 4.
   Potential purchasers: 20 percent. **400,000**

3 ASSESS

Error Analysis
Remind students that they can leave the percent of potential purchasers as a decimal when they use it to find the annual sales potential. Students are less likely to make mistakes if they don't convert it to a percent. This way, students will not have to remember to use the percent key on their calculators.

4 CLOSE

Closing Activity
Find the annual sales potential.
1. Number in sample: 820.
   Number of potential purchasers: 287.
   Estimated market size: 450,000.
   Individual rate of purchase: 2.
   315,000
2. Number in sample: 2,380.
   Number of potential purchasers: 952.
   Estimated market size: 35,980.
   Individual rate of purchase: 4.
   57,568

Standard 1	Mathematical Foundations
Standard 2	Number Relationships and Operations

National Council of Teachers of Mathematics Standards

Standard 1	Numbers and Operations
Standard 6	Problem Solving
Standard 8	Communication

① FOCUS

Compare your product to the competition. It is important to know how many people are purchasing your product instead of a competitor's product. The focus of this section is on finding a product's market share.

In-Class Examples

Work through these exercises with students before having them do the Self-Check.

1. 20,000 ÷ 100,000 **0.2**
2. 800,000 ÷ 1,000,000 **0.8**
3. 5,600,000 ÷ 10,000,000 **0.56**

② TEACH

Have students discuss the formula for market share. The market share formula can be used with either the number of units sold or the dollar value of the sales. Point out that if the total product sales is expressed as the number of units sold, then the total market sales must also be expressed as the number of units sold. If the total product sales is expressed as the dollar value of sales, then the total market sales must also be expressed as the dollar value of sales.

556

○ **Section Objective**

Calculate the market share of a new product.

SECTION 17-3 Market Share

To find out how well your product is selling in the marketplace, you may want to find your product's **market share.** Market share is the percent of the total market that purchases your product instead of a competitor's. You can calculate your percent of the total market share by using either the number of units sold or the dollar value of sales.

$$\text{Market Share} = \frac{\text{Total Product Sales}}{\text{Total Market Sales}}$$

Living in the Real World

The Campaign for Dozie D'Oats

Determining Market Share Patel decides researcher Louise Farina is the best person to determine the market share. Farina gathers the data and then calculates the percent of consumers in the total market who buy Dozie D'Oats rather than competitors' cereal. She'll use those figures to calculate other financial data, including predictions of future sales and profits or losses.

Draw Conclusions Market share is a company's percent of the total sales volume generated by all competitors in a given market. Mathematically, how do you calculate market share?

Continued on page 558

Example 1

Amdex, an air conditioner manufacturer, sold 1,200,000 air conditioners during the year. During the same period, a total of 8,000,000 air conditioners were purchased in the entire U.S. market. What was Amdex's market share for the year?

STEP: Find the market share.

Total Product Sales ÷ Total Market Sales

1,200,000 ÷ 8,000,000 = 0.15 or 15% market share

1200000 ÷ 8000000 = 0.15

CONCEPT CHECK

SELF-CHECK ✓

Complete the problems, then check your answers at the end of the chapter. Find the market share.

1. Product sales total $2,000,000. Market sales total $20,000,000.
2,000,000 ÷ 20,000,000 = 0.10 or 10%

2. Product sales total $4,000,000. Market sales total $180,000,000.
4,000,000 ÷ 180,000,000 = 0.0222 or 2.2%

Living in the Real World

Possibly. The range may be less skewed.

RETEACH / ENRICHMENT

Game Console Market

Students name the video game player(s) they have at home or would choose to purchase. How many students have each type of player? Students use these figures to create a circle graph showing what share each player has in their market. **(For example, Sony 57%, Nintendo 21%, Sega 21%, Other 1%.)**

SECTION 17-3 PRACTICE

Find the market share.

Company	Total Product Sales	÷	Total Market Sales	=	Market Share
3. Waida	$8,000,000	÷	$20,000,000	=	**40.0%**
4. Simross	700,000	÷	42,000,000	=	**1.67%**
5. Hershel	1,400,000	÷	5,000,000	=	**28.0%**
6. ComCo	9,000,000	÷	45,000,000	=	**20.0%**
7. MGI	1,200,000	÷	20,000,000	=	**6.0%**
8. Lawner	750,000	÷	5,000,000	=	**15.0%**
9. Forestal	8,000,000	÷	80,000,000	=	**10.0%**
10. Weaver	3,000,000	÷	90,000,000	=	**3.33%**

11. A tire company sells approximately 4,000,000 automobile tires per year. There are approximately 44,000,000 automobile tires sold per year in the entire market. What is the company's market share? **9.1%**

12. A book company sells approximately 9,000,000 paperback books per year. Sales for the entire paperback book market total approximately 30,000,000 books per year. What is the company's market share of paperbacks? **30.0%**

13. The Grill Company sells about $3,100,000 in outdoor grills annually. The total annual sales of outdoor grills in the entire market are about $8,500,000. What is Grill's market share for outdoor grills? **36.5%**

14. The Linen Sheet Company has sales totaling approximately $1,400,000 in fitted sheets. Total sales of fitted sheets by all companies are approximately $5,350,000. What is Linen's market share of fitted sheets? **26.2%**

15. Fast Shoes had sales totaling approximately $975,000 in basketball shoes last year. (All of last year's sales of all the basketball shoes totaled approximately $22,450,000.) What market share of basketball shoes did Fast Shoes have? **4.3%**

16. Last year there were total sales of approximately $8,500,000 in dining room furniture. Chair Company's sales of dining room furniture totaled approximately $900,000 last year. What was Chair Company's market share of dining room furniture? **10.6%**

17. Game Brothers, a company that manufactures games, sells an electronic video game. Last year's sales of the game totaled approximately $732,000. Total market sales for electronic video games were approximately $15,350,000. What market share did Game Brothers have? **4.8%**

18. Mountainside's local landscaping business totaled approximately $789,400 in sales for the year. The landscaping business for the area totaled about $1,340,000 for the year. What market share did Mountainside have? **58.9%**

19. Last year, the Computer Company sold $200,000,000 worth of its computer chips out of a total market of $1,428,000,000. What market share did it have in computer chips? **14.0%**

Need Help? Go to...
▶ Skill 31: Finding the Rate, page 758
▶ Skill 10: Dividing (Decimal Remainder), page 737

MAINTAINING YOUR SKILLS

Find the rate. Round answers to the nearest tenth of a percent.

20. $n\%$ of 84 = 21 **25.0%** **21.** $n\%$ of 50 = 35 **70.0%** **22.** $n\%$ of 45 = 50 **111.1%**

Divide. Round answers to the nearest tenth.

23. 920 ÷ 40 **23.0** **24.** 1,145 ÷ 85 **13.5** **25.** 868 ÷ 1,224 **0.7**

GLOBAL PERSPECTIVE

Worldwide Advertising

Give students the following figures for the *total* amount each country spends on advertising each year: United States, $450 billion; Egypt, $12.6 billion; Kenya, $1.5 billion; Russia, $9.6 billion; Singapore, $15.2 billion; Vietnam $1.4 billion. Students make a pictograph. Ask students why the United States spends so much on advertising. **Free market economy.**

WRAP-UP

Go over any problem for which a wrong answer is given.

Assignment Guide
Basic: 3–10
Average: 11–18

20 min.

SECTION 17-3

Motivating the Lesson

The Franconia Hat Company sells approximately 500,000 hats per year. Sales for the entire market total approximately 40,000,000 hats per year. Find Franconia's market share. **0.0125**

In-Class Example

Find the market share.
1. Total product sales: $700,000. Total market sales: $1,000,000. **70%**

 **ASSESS**

Error Analysis

Review the formula for market share. Have students pick out the total product sales and the total market sales from Example 1 on page 556. Point out that this is all the information needed for the market share formula.

4 CLOSE

Closing Activity

Find the market share.
1. Total product sales: $500,000. Total market sales: $2,500,000. **20%**
2. Total product sales: $1,200,000. Total market sales: $4,800,000. **25%**
3. Total units sold: 8,500,000. Total market: 17,000,000. **50%**
4. Cambridge Accessories sells approximately $800,000 in handbags per year. The total annual sales for handbags in the entire market are about $64,000,000. What is Cambridge's market share for handbags? **1.25%**
5. Last year, Jenning Pharmaceuticals sold about 1,400,000 packages of gauze. There were approximately 5,600,000 packages of gauze sold last year in the entire market. What is Jenning's market share for gauze? **25%**

Standard 1	Mathematical Foundations
Standard 2	Number Relationships and Operations

National Council of Teachers of Mathematics Standards

Standard 1	Numbers and Operations
Standard 5	Data Analysis and Probability
Standard 6	Problem Solving
Standard 8	Communication
Standard 10	Representations

1 FOCUS

Discuss with students why companies would want to project future sales. Point out that companies use sales projections to determine things, like how much product to make, how many supplies to purchase, and how many employees to hire for production.

SECTION **17-4** **Sales Projections**

○ **Section Objective**

Use a graph to compute projected sales.

A **sales projection** is an estimate of the dollar volume or unit sales that might occur during a future time period. A sales projection is usually based on past sales. You may use a sales projection to plan for production or purchasing. New products or changing economic conditions may result in sales figures that differ from the figures you projected.

You may use a graph to project a rough estimate of future sales:

1. Construct a graph of past sales.
2. Draw a straight line from the first year of data, approximately through the middle of the data, to the year for which the projection is being made.
3. Read the number, or dollar value, which is the sales projection.

Living in the Real World

The Campaign for Dozie D'Oats

Lesson on Capturing Attention Farina spends two months gathering and analyzing data to determine Harvester's market share for its Dozie D'Oats cereal. When she finishes writing her summary report, she and Patel meet to discuss the results. It looks like it has already captured 9 percent of the market in the areas where it's being sold. The sales projections include all 50 states. In two years, Dozie D'Oats should capture another 3 or 4 percent of the market.

Draw Conclusions Dozie D'Oats does well in areas where there are more children and families live. How might the cereal do in the Southwest?

Continued on page 561

(**Example 1**)

The marketing department of Stanley Store wants to project sales for the year 2017. The sales are:

Stanley Store's Sales							
Year	2003	2004	2005	2006	2007	2008	2009
Sales (in millions)	$2.5	$2.0	$3.0	$4.3	$3.3	$5.0	$4.5

Using a graph, what sales projection might the marketing department make for 2017?

STEP 1: Graph the sales from 2003 through 2009.

STEP 2: Starting from sales in 2003, draw a straight line through the middle of the data to 2017.

Living in the Real World

The population of the Southwest contains fewer children and families and more retirees, so Dozie D'Oats may not sell as well in that area of the country.

STEP 3: Read the sales projection for 2017.

Figure 17.1

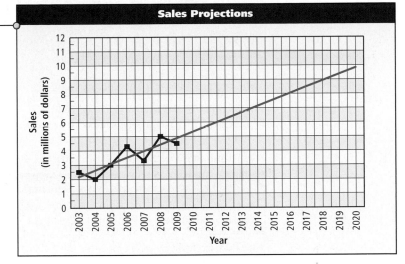

Sales Projections

Projected sales for 2017 are approximately **$8.5 million.**

CONCEPT CHECK

SELF-CHECK ✓

Complete the problem, then check your answer at the end of the chapter.

1. Refer to **Figure 17.1.** Read the approximate sales projections for 2010, 2012, and 2014. **2010: $5.3 million; 2012: $6.2 million; 2014: $7.0 million**

SECTION 17-4 PRACTICE

Use Figure 17.2 to estimate the sales projections for Problems 2–7.

Figure 17.2

Sales Projections

Continued on next page

② **TEACH**

This lesson depends on the ability to read a graph and use a table to construct a graph. As you review Example 1 on pages 588 and 589, remind students about the features of a graph. Point out the titles of the axes and the unit labels. Have students read out loud the sales for each year graphed in Example 1.

Once the past sales are plotted on a graph, the graph is used to predict future sales. Point out that no prediction can be 100 percent accurate, but some predictions are better than others. This method of prediction is most accurate when the graph is consistent, without major variations in sales from year to year.

Motivating the Lesson
Construct a line graph of the following.

Year	2000	2001	2002	2003
Sales (in millions)	$2	$4	$3	$4

In-Class Examples
Use the graph.

1. Estimate the sales projection for 2010. **$15 million**
2. Estimate the sales projection for 2015. **$16 million**
3. Estimate the sales projection for 2020. **$17 million**

Great Ideas from the Classroom Of...

**Loren Holthaus
Big Lake Middle School
Big Lake, Minn.**

Compare Graphs
Students work in cooperative groups to collect data and then use a protractor to construct a circle graph of their data. Then, we use a spreadsheet and statistical graphing computer software to enter the same data, and make a circle graph. Compare the graphs, and discuss.

③ ASSESS

Error Analysis

Remind students that the straight line that they draw on a sales projection graph should begin at the first year of data and extend through the middle of the data to the year being projected. Sometimes it is difficult to draw a line through the middle of the data because the sales are not consistent. Emphasize that for these types of graphs the projection is not very accurate.

④ CLOSE

Closing Activity

Sales records for Rhodes Framing show this data:

Year	1995	1997	1999	2001	2003
Sales (in thousands)	$32	$34	$28	$30	$27

1. Graph the sales from 1995 through 2003.
2. Project the sales for 2005. **$34,000**
3. Project the sales for 2008. **$34,750**
4. Project the sales for 2011. **$35,500**

	Year	Sales Projections
2.	2013	$31,000
3.	2014	$37,000
4.	2015	$40,000
5.	2016	$44,000
6.	2017	$46,000
7.	2018	$50,000

Construct a graph for each problem and draw a straight line through the middle of the data to project sales.

8. Sales records for Target Sporting Goods show this data:

Target Sporting Goods's Sales Records										
Year	2003	2004	2005	2006	2007	2008	2009	2010	2011	2012
Sales (in millions)	$4.4	$4.9	$5.0	$4.5	$5.1	$5.4	$5.0	$5.5	$5.7	$5.0

What sales might be projected for 2019? **$6.2 million**

9. The sales history of Bi-Lo Market shows:

Bi-Lo Market's Sales Records						
Year	1975	1980	1985	1990	1995	2000
Sales (in millions)	$12	$14	$11	$12	$15	$14

Project sales for 2005, 2010, and 2015. **2005: $15 million; 2010: $16 million; 2015: $17 million**

10. PDP manufactures mainframe computers. Production records for the first half of the year show this information for the Model XT720 computer.

PDP Production Records						
Month	Jan	Feb	Mar	Apr	May	June
Production (in thousands of units)	14	13	12	13	14	13

Project production quantities for July, August, and September. **All are 13.**

MAINTAINING YOUR SKILLS

Need Help? Go to...
➤ Skill 8: **Multiplying Decimals,** page 735
➤ Skill 1: **Numbers,** page 727

Multiply. Round answers to the nearest thousandth.

11.	$442.86	12.	$3,240.03	13.	0.044
	× 100.00		× 1,000.00		× 400.000
	$44,286.00		$3,240,030.00		17.600

Write each number in words.

14. 407
   Four hundred seven

15. 52
   Fifty-two

16. 0.6
   Six tenths

WRAP-UP

Go over any problem for which a wrong answer is given.

Assignment Guide
Basic: 2–7
Average: 8–9

20 min.

SECTION **17-5** Sales Projections— Factor Method

Section Objective

Use the factor method to compute projected sales.

In the last section you learned about sales projections. There's also another method used to project sales. It's called the **factor method**. The **factor** is your company's present market share. Your company may use federal government publications or other sources to find the total sales projected for the entire market for the coming year. Remember that:

Projected Sales = Projected Market Sales × Market-Share Factor

Living in the Real World

The Campaign for Dozie D'Oats

First Outlook   Farina and Patel talk about the graphs showing sales projections. The graph's positive outlook indicated by comparing the first graphs with another set of graphs is based on the factor method.

Draw Conclusions   If Harvester's factor (a.k.a. market share) also increases, will sales increase or decrease?

Continued on page 563

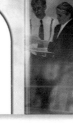

Example 1

Community Food Store has a 6 percent share of the market for food sales in the Chicago Heights area. Food sales in the Chicago Heights area for next year are estimated to be $38,400,000. What is the projected sales figure for Community Food Store in the Chicago Heights area for next year?

STEP: Find the projected sales.

Projected Market Sales	×	Market-Share Factor	
$38,400,000	×	6%	= **$2,304,000**
			projected sales

  38400000 × 6 % 2,304,000

CONCEPT CHECK

 SELF-CHECK ✔

Complete the problems, then check your answers at the end of the chapter. Find the projected sales.

1. Market-share factor: 8 percent.
   Projected market sales: $6,300,000.
   $6,300,000 × 8% = $504,000

2. Market-share factor: 14 percent.
   Projected market sales: $10,250,000.
   $10,250,000 × 14% = $1,435,000

Living in the Real World

Sales will increase as market share increases.

---

① FOCUS

Another way to make a sales projection is to use the factor method. Instead of using graphs to project sales, this method uses percents.

In-Class Examples

Work through these exercises with students before having them do the Self-Check.

1. $4,000,000 × 5% **$200,000**
2. $10,500,000 × 40% **$4,200,000**
3. $100,000,000 × 7.5% **$7,500,000**

② TEACH

The factor method to project sales uses a company's market share today to predict what will happen with sales in the future. For instance, the total product sales for a company this year are $2,000,000 and the total market sales are $4,000,000. So, the company's market share today is 50 percent. Suppose in five years the total market sales rose to $6,000,000. It is expected that the company will still have a 50 percent market share. Therefore, the total product sales can be projected at $3,000,000.

National Standards for Business Education

Standard 1	Mathematical Foundations
Standard 2	Number Relationships and Operations

National Council of Teachers of Mathematics Standards

Standard 1	Numbers and Operations
Standard 6	Problem Solving
Standard 8	Communication

(cont'd)

In addition to sales, the factor method can also be used to project future numbers of items or people. For example, the factor method can be used to predict future school enrollment.

In-Class Examples
Find the projected sales.
1. Market-share factor: 25 percent. Projected market sales: $5,000,000. **$1,250,000**
2. Market-share factor: 10.5 percent. Projected market sales: $1,275,000. **$133,875**

Error Analysis
Remind students to be careful with the numbers in this section. Many of the projected market sales figures and projected sales figures contain multiple zeros. Students can use reverse operations to check their answers in this section.

④ CLOSE

Closing Activity
Find the projected sales.
1. This year 56 percent of all preschool-aged children in Cisco County were enrolled at Fields Preschool. Next year there are expected to be 750 preschool-aged children in Cisco County. What enrollment can Fields expect next year? **420**
2. Bass Dairy now has 24 percent of the market for Oak County. The total estimated sales of the county for next year are $4,250,000. What sales volume should Bass project for next year? **$1,020,000**

Find the projected sales.

	Company	Projected Market Sales	×	Market-Share Factor	=	Projected Sales
3.	ABS	$10,000,000	×	4.0%	=	$400,000
4.	Webb	32,400,000	×	8.0%	=	$2,592,000
5.	Moore's	54,000,000	×	7.5%	=	$4,050,000
6.	Beck	70,000,000	×	3.2%	=	$2,240,000

7. Long-Life Lumber Distributors. Market share: 18 percent. Estimated market sales for next year: $1,800,000. What is Long-Life's sales projection for next year? **$324,000**

8. Quick Copy Machines. Market share: 15 percent. Estimated market sales for next year: $9,100,000. What is Quick Copy's sales projection for next year? **$1,365,000**

9. Bonaventura Bakery now has 13 percent of the market for Watson County. The total estimated sales in the county for next year are $4,750,000. What sales volume should Bonaventura Bakery project for next year? **$617,500**

10. Silver Oaks Bowling Lanes has traditionally had 15 percent of the bowling business in the East Delta area. The total estimated bowling business in this area for next year is $11,900,000. What bowling business can Silver Oaks project for next year? **$1,785,000**

11. Elliot's Auto Repair does 24 percent of the auto repair business in the town of Northport. The estimated auto repair business for next year is $542,600. What sales volume can Elliot's project for next year? **$130,224**

12. This year enrollment at Silverado Central University (SCU) accounted for 55 percent of all university students in the greater metropolitan area. Next year the total university enrollment in the greater metropolitan area is expected to be about 34,000 students. What enrollment figures can SCU project for next year? **18,700**

13. Based on past records, First National Savings Bank determined that it has a market share of 9.5 percent of all the savings accounts in Butler County. Estimated savings accounts in Butler County for next year are 470,000. Project the number of savings accounts First National Savings Bank will have next year. **44,650**

MAINTAINING YOUR SKILLS

Need Help? Go to...
▶ Skill 30: **Finding the Percentage,** page 757

Find the percentage. Round answers to the nearest hundredth.

14. 5.8% of 410 **23.78**

15. 9.81% of $32,500 **$3,188.25**

16. 4.1% of $420,000 **$17,220.00**

17. 145% of 700 **1,015.00**

18. $\frac{5}{8}$% of $800 **$5.00**

19. 0.8% of $60,000 **$480.00**

20. 2,000% of $120 **$2,400.00**

21. 1% of $85,000 **$850.00**

COMMUNICATION SKILLS

Potential Sales
Students use U.S. Department of Transportation Motor Vehicle Facts and Figures, or similar sources, to find the present market share of the major vehicle manufacturers in the United States. Using projections of the total sales of all vehicles for next year in the United States, students find the potential sales of each major manufacturer. Students communicate their findings in a brief "State of the Industry" report. `LS`, `CL`, `P`

WRAP-UP

Go over any problem for which a wrong answer is given.

Assignment Guide
Basic: 3–6
Average: 7–8

20 min.

Newspaper Advertising Costs

○ **Section Objective**

Calculate the cost of advertising in a newspaper.

To attract customers, you may advertise your products or services in a newspaper. The purpose is to increase your sales. The cost of the advertisement depends on several factors: the circulation of the newspaper; what day of the week you run the advertisement; whether the advertisement is in color or black and white; and the amount of space it uses. The amount of space is figured in column inches. Generally, newspapers charge a certain rate for each column inch. Some newspapers offer a reduced rate if you contract annually for a specified number of column inches or if you run the ad repeatedly. Remember that:

$$\text{Advertisement Cost} = \text{Number of Column Inches} \times \text{Rate per Column Inch}$$

Living in the Real World

The Campaign for Dozie D'Oats

A Well-Received Cereal Thanks to Farina's efforts, Patel has a marketing report that indicates Harvester's new cereal will be well-received in various markets across the country, it will increase total market sales, and Harvester's share of the market will rise.

During a lunch meeting, Patel presents the report and his recommendations to Harvester's vice president for sales, Marty O'Connell. O'Connell is impressed, and gives Patel the go-ahead to launch a creative and aggressive advertising campaign to promote Dozie D'Oats.

Draw Conclusions Name types of advertising. Which one do you think reaches more people?

Continued on page 565

 Example 1

Northshore Real Estate contracted with the *Daily News* for 5,000 inches of advertising per year. Northshore plans to advertise a new subdivision in the daily newspaper. The advertisement is the equivalent of 21 column inches. What is the cost of the advertisement?

STEP 1: Find the rate per column inch. (See Figure 17.3, The *Daily News* Advertising Rates table on page 564.)
The rate per column inch for 5,000 inches per year/daily is $26.13.

STEP 2: Find the advertisement cost.

Number of Column Inches × Rate per Column Inch
　　　21　　　×　　　$26.13
= **$548.73** advertisement cost

COOPERATIVE LEARNING

Cyber Ads
Companies advertise not only in print, radio, and TV, but also on the Internet. These are often referred to as cyber ads. Lead a discussion on the advantages of using cyber ads. **(Direct cyber delivery, direct order form, and look up a business from any link provided.)** Assign groups of students to find the cost of advertising on the Internet. `LS` , `CL`

Living in the Real World

Answers will vary but could include television, newspaper, magazine, radio, billboards, and Internet.

National Standards for Business Education

Standard 1	Mathematical Foundations
Standard 2	Number Relationships and Operations

National Council of Teachers of Mathematics Standards

Standard 1	Numbers and Operations
Standard 6	Problem Solving
Standard 8	Communication

 **1 FOCUS**

Businesses often place advertisements in newspapers to promote business. Not all advertisements cost the same. This section focuses on how to determine these costs.

In-Class Examples
Work through these exercises with students before having them do the Self-Check.
1. 6 × $42.99 **$257.94**
2. 13 × $35.79 **$465.27**
3. 50 × $29.15 **$1,457.50**

2 TEACH

Explore advertisements. You may want students to measure the advertisements in inches and identify the day of the week on which the newspaper was published. Point out that the cost for a newspaper advertisement often depends on the size of the ad, on what day the ad is published, and on whether or not the business has a contract with the newspaper. Have students identify which advertisements were probably the most expensive and which were probably the least expensive. Students should explain their reasoning.

TEACH (cont'd)

In-Class Examples
Find the advertisement cost.
1. Number of column inches: 12. Rate per column inch: $42.99. **$515.88**
2. Number of column inches: 133. Rate per column inch: $24.25. **$3,225.25**
3. The Seashell Grill contracts with *The Daily News* for 20,000 inches of advertising space per year. A 40-inch ad is run on Wednesday. Use the table given in **Figure 17.3** on page 564 to find the cost of the advertisement? **$949.60**

ASSESS

Error Analysis
When using the table given in **Figure 17.3**, students need to first decide whether to look at the contract rates or non-contract rates. If it is a contract bulk rate, students then need to find the row with the appropriate number of inches. In order to find the price per column inch, students then need to follow across the row to the appropriate rate column.

CLOSE

Closing Activity
Find the advertisement cost.
1. Number of column inches: 10. Rate per column inch: $32.99. **$329.90**
2. Number of column inches: 30. Rate per column inch: $39.50. **$1,185**
3. Number of column inches: 100. Rate per column inch: $24.75. **$2,475**

Figure 17.3

The *Daily News* Advertising Rates (per column inch)		Daily	Saturday	Sunday
Open Rate	No contract	$49.50	$50.40	$62.00
Flight Plan	50 inches per year	38.53	39.26	48.71
Bulk Rate	100 inches per year	29.31	29.86	37.52
	500 inches per year	29.04	29.59	37.26
	1,000 inches per year	28.73	29.27	36.89
	5,000 inches per year	26.13	26.62	33.44
	10,000 inches per year	25.71	26.19	32.33
	20,000 inches per year	23.74	24.19	30.42
	30,000 inches per year	22.05	22.46	28.25
	40,000 inches per year	20.99	21.38	26.66
	50,000 inches per year	19.45	19.82	24.01

CONCEPT CHECK

SELF-CHECK✔

Complete the problems, then check your answers at the end of the chapter. Use the advertising rates in Figure 17.3 to find the advertisement costs for The Carpet Store. The Carpet Store has contracted for 1,000 inches per year.

1. An advertisement in the Sunday paper is 12 column inches.
$36.89 × 12 = **$442.68**
2. An advertisement in the Saturday paper is 10 column inches.
$29.27 × 10 = **$292.70**

SECTION 17-6 PRACTICE

Use Figure 17.3 for the *Daily News* for Problems 3–9.

	Annual Contract (in inches)	Edition	Number of Column Inches	×	Rate per Column Inch	=	Advertisement Cost
3.	10,000	Daily	15	×	$25.71	=	a. $385.65
4.	5,000	Daily	40	×	a. $26.13	=	b. $1,045.20
5.	100	Sunday	10	×	a. $37.52	=	b. $375.20
6.	50,000	Saturday	120	×	a. $19.82	=	b. $2,378.40
7.	No contract	Daily	5	×	a. $49.50	=	b. $247.50

8. Super Supermarket has an annual contract for 30,000 inches of advertising. In the Wednesday paper, Super has an advertisement equivalent to 105 column inches. What is the cost of the advertisement? **$2,315.25**

9. The Aspen Ski Lodge does not have a contract for advertising. Sunday's paper will carry a 12-inch advertisement for the lodge. How much does the advertisement cost? **$744.00**

MAINTAINING YOUR SKILLS

Need Help? Go to...
➤ Skill 8: Multiplying Decimals, page 735

Multiply.

10. $50.40 × 40
$2,016.00

11. $29.31 × 120
$3,517.20

12. $37.26 × 50
$1,863.00

13. $29.27 × 133
$3,892.91

14. $26.13 × 80
$2,090.40

15. $32.33 × 75
$2,424.75

USING CALCULATORS

Some calculators including graphing calculators allow the user to set the number of decimal places in the output to a specific number. When doing calculations that involve money or result in a monetary answer, it is helpful to set the number of decimal places to two. Your calculator manual will instruct you on how to accomplish this.

WRAP-UP

Go over any problem for which a wrong answer is given.

Assignment Guide
 Basic: 3–7
 Average: 8–9

20 min.

SECTION (17-7) Television Advertising Costs

Section Objective

Compute the cost of advertising on television.

You may advertise your products or services on television. The cost of a television advertisement depends on the time of day, program ratings, and the length of the advertisement. Television commercials are generally 10, 30, or 60 seconds long. The cost of a 10-second advertisement is usually one-half the cost of a 30-second advertisement. The cost of a 60-second advertisement is usually twice the cost of a 30-second advertisement.

$$\text{Cost of 10-Second Ad} = \tfrac{1}{2} \times \text{Cost of 30-Second Ad}$$

$$\text{Cost of 60-Second Ad} = 2 \times \text{Cost of 30-Second Ad}$$

Living in the Real World

The Campaign for Dozie D'Oats

Getting the Product Out There   Patel knows that the cost of television advertising is very expensive. He doesn't think Harvester is willing to pay for expensive time slots. For instance, advertising during Monday Night Football would be extremely expensive. In addition, because the new cereal is targeted mostly toward children that time slot wouldn't reach its audience.

Draw Conclusions   What do you think are the best times for Harvester to advertise if it wants to reach its audience?

Continued on page 568

Example 1

The marketing department of the Mayberry Company plans to advertise several new cosmetics on network television. The advertising campaign calls for these commercials:

Number	Length	Time
3	30 seconds	Daytime
2	10 seconds	Daytime
2	30 seconds	Prime time
4	60 seconds	Prime time

The rates are $10,400 for a 30-second daytime commercial and $250,000 for a 30-second prime-time commercial. What is the total cost for this advertising campaign?

Continued on next page

Section 17-7 Television Advertising Costs ▶ **565**

Living in the Real World

Saturday morning would be a good time, as children are often watching cartoons. Daytime or after school, when a parent might be watching television would also be a good time for television advertising.

THINKING CRITICALLY

How Many Ads?
Students track the number of ads they see during a day. Students add up the number of ads they see and then multiply the number by 365 to give them an idea of how many ads they see in one year. What effect might this have? Students discuss their findings in class.

National Standards for Business Education

Standard 1	Mathematical Foundations
Standard 2	Number Relationships and Operations

National Council of Teachers of Mathematics Standards

Standard 1	Numbers and Operations
Standard 6	Problem Solving
Standard 8	Communication

① FOCUS

Ask students if they know the length of time a television commercial takes. Point out that television commercials are usually 10, 30, or 60 seconds. Mention that advertisers pay for commercials based on the length of time.

In-Class Examples
Work through these exercises with students before having them do the Self Check.
1. $\tfrac{1}{2} \times \$2,400$ **$1,200**
2. $\tfrac{1}{2} \times \$10,500$ **$5,250**
3. $2 \times (\tfrac{1}{2} \times \$18,000) + (2 \times \$18,000)$ **$54,000**

② TEACH

Discuss whether or not it matters when a television commercial is aired and on what channel. Point out that prime time is more expensive than daytime. Local channels may have a fewer number of viewers than major national networks. However, local channels reach a local audience. So, if a local business is trying to attract customers, it may be more beneficial to advertise on a local channel.

565

 **TEACH** (cont'd)

Have students suggest some businesses that would most likely advertise on local channels and some that would most likely advertise on national channels.

In-Class Examples

1. A 30-second ad costs $1,400. What is the cost of two 60-second ads? **$5,600**
2. A 30-second ad costs $15,000. What is the cost of three 10-second ads? **$22,500**
3. A 30-second ad costs $10,800. What is the cost of four 10-second ads and three 60-second ads? **$86,400**

3 ASSESS

Error Analysis

Encourage students to refer to the formulas when they calculate the cost of a 10-second ad or the cost of a 60-second ad. Students more easily remember the formula for the cost of a 60-second ad because the cost is twice the cost of a 30-second ad and 60 is twice 30. This logic may make some students think that a 10-second ad should be $\frac{1}{3}$ of a 30-second ad since 10 is $\frac{1}{3}$ of 30. Remind students that the cost of a 10-second ad is $\frac{1}{2}$ of the cost of a 30-second ad.

STEP 1: Find the cost of 30-second commercials.
Daytime: $10,400 × 3 = $31,200
Prime time: $250,000 × 2 = $500,000

STEP 2: Find the cost of 10-second commercials.
$\frac{1}{2}$ × Cost of 30-Second Ad
Daytime: ($\frac{1}{2}$ × $10,400) × 2 = $10,400

STEP 3: Find the cost of 60-second commercials.
2 × Cost of 30-Second Ad
Prime time: (2 × $250,000) × 4 = $2,000,000

STEP 4: Find the total cost.
$31,200 + $500,000 + $10,400 + $2,000,000 = **$2,541,600 total cost**

10400 ⊠ 3 ▭ 31200 M+ 250000 ⊠ 2 ▭ 500000 M+
0.5 ⊠ 10400 ⊠ 2 ▭ 10400 M+ 2 ⊠ 250000 ⊠ 4 ▭
2000000 M+ RM 2541600

CONCEPT CHECK

 Complete the problems, then check your answers at the end of the chapter.

1. A 30-second commercial costs $9,000.
   Find the total cost for four 60-second commercials.
   4 × (2 × $9,000) = 4 × $18,000 = $72,000
2. A 30-second commercial costs $35,000.
   Find the total cost for four 30-second commercials and five 10-second commercials.
   (4 × $35,000) + (5 × $\frac{1}{2}$ × $35,000) = $140,000 + $ 87,500 = $227,500

Example 2

A 30-second television commercial aired during the Super Bowl costs $2,000,000, the highest priced TV commercial. Electronics.com bought one 10-second commercial and one 60-second commercial during the Super Bowl. What did the two commercials cost Electronics.com?

STEP 1: Find the cost of the 10-second commercial.
0.5 × $2,000,000 × 1 = $1,000,000

STEP 2: Find the cost of the 60-second commercial.
2 × $2,000,000 × 1 = $4,000,000

STEP 3: Find the total cost.
$1,000,000 + $4,000,000 = **$5,000,000 total cost**

CONCEPT CHECK

Complete the problems, then check your answers at the end of the chapter.

What is the cost of the commercials for Electronics.com in Example 2 if it bought:

3. Two 30-second commercials? **2 × $2,000,000 = $4,000,000**
4. Four 10-second and three 60-second commercials?
   (4 × $\frac{1}{2}$ × $2,000,000) + (3 × 2 × $2,000,000) = $4,000,000 + $12,000,000 = $16,000,000

ALTERNATIVE ASSESSMENT

Design an Ad

Students design an ad for a local newspaper. Students choose the size of the ad and what they will advertise. Students should use the five key components for ad design: headline, copy, illustration, logo, and slogan. Provide students with the advertising rates for the local newspaper. Students calculate how much it would cost to place their ads.

LS , CL , P

Calculate the total cost.

	Rate per 30-Second Commercial	Number of 10-Second Commercials	Number of 30-Second Commercials	Number of 60-Second Commercials	Total Cost
5.	$10,000	4	3	3	$110,000
6.	500	3	4	0	$2,750
7.	30,000	5	5	2	$345,000
8.	96,500	0	4	3	$965,000

9. The manufacturers of Brighten mouthwash have planned an advertising campaign that includes these commercials:

Number	Length	Time
4	30 seconds	Daytime
3	10 seconds	Daytime
5	30 seconds	Prime time
6	60 seconds	Prime time

The rates are $4,500 for a 30-second daytime commercial and $225,500 for a 30-second prime-time commercial. What is the cost of the advertising campaign? **$3,858,250**

10. Pacific New Car Sales is interested in sponsoring the sports coverage on the local television station. The rate per 30-second commercial is $1,475. Pacific New Car Sales has contracts for ten 30-second advertisements, five 10-second advertisements, and five 60-second advertisements. What is the total cost for these advertisements? **$33,187.50**

11. Alamo Amusement Park has planned a special television campaign. It will use a daytime show for twenty 10-second ads and five 30-second ads. It will use a prime-time show for ten 30-second ads and five 60-second ads. The rates are $500 per 30-second daytime ad and $15,000 per 30-second prime-time ad. What is the cost of the television campaign? **$307,500**

CLOSE

Closing Activity

1. A 30-second ad costs $10,000. What is the cost of three 60-second ads? **$60,000**

2. A 30-second ad costs $12,000. What is the cost of six 10-second ads? **$36,000**

3. A 30-second ad costs $7,500. What is the cost of two 30-second ads and two 10-second ads? **$22,500**

4. A 30-second ad costs $9,750. What is the cost of three 10-second ads and five 60-second ads? **$112,125**

5. Century Fitness plans to advertise with five 10-second prime-time commercials and seven 60-second daytime commercials. The rates are $8,000 for a 30-second daytime commercial and $13,500 for a 30-second prime-time commercial. What is the cost of the advertising? **$145,750**

MAINTAINING YOUR SKILLS

Need Help? Go to...
▶ Skill 20.
Multiplying Fractions/ Mixed Numbers, page 747

Multiply. Express the answers in lowest terms.

12. $\frac{1}{3} \times \frac{3}{5}$ $\frac{1}{5}$

13. $\frac{3}{12} \times \frac{4}{8}$ $\frac{1}{8}$

14. $6 \times 8\frac{1}{7}$ $48\frac{6}{7}$

WRAP-UP

Go over any problem for which a wrong answer is given.

Assignment Guide
    Basic: 5–8
Average: 9–11

20 min.

National Standards for Business Education

| Standard 1 | Mathematical Foundations |
| Standard 2 | Number Relationships and Operations |

National Council of Teachers of Mathematics Standards

Standard 1	Numbers and Operations
Standard 6	Problem Solving
Standard 8	Communication

1 FOCUS

Businesses set the selling prices of their items high enough so that they will make a profit. However, if the selling price of an item is too high, customers will not want to purchase the item.

In-Class Examples

Work through these exercises with students before having them do the Self-Check.

1. ($8 − $6) × 5,000 **$10,000**
2. ($12.50 − $9.75) × 10,000 **$27,500**
3. ($34.55 − $22.39) × 400,000 **$4,864,000**

2 TEACH

Have students discuss how the selling price of an item affects their decision to purchase the item. Point out that setting a selling price is very important. A business needs to obtain the highest amount of profit possible, but not lose potential customers because the price is too high.

SECTION 17-8 Pricing

○ **Section Objective**

Calculate the selling price that will result in the highest possible net profit.

You must set the selling prices of your products high enough to cover expenses and to make a profit. You may determine the selling price of an item by estimating the net profit for each of several possible selling prices and then by choosing the selling price that will result in the highest profit. In manufacturing, the cost per item varies with the number manufactured and ultimately sold. Often, the higher the selling price of an item, the fewer the items that will be sold. Remember that:

$$\text{Possible Net Profit} = \left(\frac{\text{Selling Price}}{\text{per Unit}} - \frac{\text{Total Cost}}{\text{per Unit}}\right) \times \frac{\text{Estimated}}{\text{Unit Sales}}$$

Living in the Real World

The Campaign for Dozie D'Oats

Searching for the Right Media Outlet Like other costs, the cost of advertising takes a bite out of a producer's profit. Because of this, Patel is careful when recommending an advertising plan. He doesn't want the cost of advertising to be so high that it forces the company to raise the price of its new cereal. So when he presents his marketing recommendations to O'Connell, he suggests starting with newspaper ads and coupons and waiting for at least six months before investing in television advertising.

Draw Conclusions Why is price important to a company?

Continued on page 571

Example 1

Gamma Electronics manufactures preprinted circuit boards. Gamma has a fixed overhead of $120,000. The variable costs to produce the circuit boards are $1.50 per unit. To determine the best selling price, Gamma estimates the number of units that could be sold at various selling prices. What selling price will maximize Gamma's profits?

Selling Price per Unit	Estimated Unit Sales	Fixed Costs	Fixed Costs per Unit	Variable Costs per Unit	Total Cost per Unit
$ 8.00	20,000	$120,000	$ 6.00	$1.50	$ 7.50
11.00	15,000	120,000	8.00	1.50	9.50
15.00	10,000	120,000	12.00	1.50	13.50
22.00	6,000	120,000	20.00	1.50	21.50

STEP 1: Find the possible net profit for each selling price.

$$\left(\frac{\text{Selling Price}}{\text{per Unit}} - \frac{\text{Total Cost}}{\text{per Unit}}\right) \times \frac{\text{Estimated}}{\text{Unit Sales}}$$

($8.00	−	$7.50)	×	20,000	=	$10,000
($11.00	−	$9.50)	×	15,000	=	$22,500
($15.00	−	$13.50)	×	10,000	=	$15,000
($22.00	−	$21.50)	×	6,000	=	$ 3,000

Living in the Real World

Price establishes and maintains a firm's image, competitive edge, and profits.

GLOBAL PERSPECTIVE

Brand Names
Brand names that are successful in one country may not be when translated into another language. Here are some examples of original meanings being lost in translation. In Spanish-speaking countries, Ford's Fiera meant "ugly old woman" and General Motors' Nova meant "it doesn't go," if pronounced *no va*. Ask students if they have encountered any other such brand name blunders.

STEP 2: Find the greatest possible profit $22,500

STEP 3: Find the best selling price   **$11.00**

8 `−` 7.5 `=` 0.5 `×` 20000 `=` 10000   11 `−` 9.5 `=` 1.5

`×` 15000 `=` 22500   15 `−` 13.5 `=` 1.5 `×` 10000 `=`

15000   22 `−` 21.5 `=` 0.5 `×` 6000 `=` 3000

1. ($3.00 − $1.05) × 200,000 = $1.95 × 200,000 = $390,000; ($4.50 − $1.38) × 150,000 = $3.12 × 150,000 = $468,000

(SELF-CHECK ✓)

CONCEPT CHECK

Complete the problems, then check your answers at the end of the chapter.

Selling Price per Unit	Estimated Unit Sales	Fixed Costs	Fixed Costs per Unit	Variable Costs per Unit	Total Cost per Unit
$3.00	200,000	$200,000	$1.00	$0.05	$1.05
4.50	150,000	200,000	1.33	0.05	1.38

1. Find the possible net profit for each selling price.

2. Which selling price yields the greatest possible profit?
A $4.50 selling price yields the greatest possible profit.

---

3. a. $120,000
4. a. $236,000
5. a. $17.14
   b. $38.14
   c. $258,020
6. a. $20.00
   b. $41.00
   c. $264,000
7. Selling price of $3.75: $0.53; $1.58; $2,061,500; Selling price of $4.50: $0.71; $1.76; $1,918,000; Selling price of $8.50: $1.67; $2.72; $1,734,000; Selling price of $10.25: $2.00; $3.05; $1,800,000; Selling price of $3.75 yields greatest possible profit of $2,061,500. 950,000 units should be produced.

(Need Help? Go to...)
➤ **Skill 6: Subtracting Decimals, page 733**

SECTION 17-8 PRACTICE

Round answers to the nearest cent.

	Selling Price per Unit	Estimated Unit Sales	Fixed Costs	Fixed Costs per Unit	Variable Costs per Unit	Total Cost per Unit	Possible Net Profit
3.	$45.00	10,000	$120,000	$12.00	$21.00	$33.00	a.
4.	65.50	8,000	120,000	15.00	21.00	36.00	a.
5.	75.00	7,000	120,000	a.	21.00	b.	c.
6.	85.00	6,000	120,000	a.	21.00	b.	c.

7. Complete the table for the Wood Specialties Company. Which selling price yields the greatest possible profit? How many units should be produced?

Selling Price per Unit	Estimated Unit Sales	Fixed Costs	Fixed Costs per Unit	Variable Costs per Unit	Total Cost per Unit	Possible Net Profit
$ 3.75	950,000	$500,000		$1.05		
4.50	700,000	500,000		1.05		
8.50	300,000	500,000		1.05		
10.25	250,000	500,000		1.05		

MAINTAINING YOUR SKILLS

Subtract.

8. 649.91 − 73.89
     576.02

9. 12.9 − 1.023
     11.877

10. 78 − 32.8
     45.2

Section 17-8 Pricing ▶ **569**

In-Class Examples

Find the possible net profit.
1. Selling price per unit: $4.00. Total cost per unit: $2.75. Estimated unit sales: 5,000. **$6,250**
2. Selling price per unit: $8.99. Total cost per unit: $6.29. Estimated unit sales: 13,000. **$35,100**

(3) ASSESS

Error Analysis

Students may not realize how to find the fixed costs per unit given the fixed costs and estimated unit sales. In Example 1 on pages 568 and 569, point out in the first row that the fixed costs, $120,000, divide by the estimated unit sales, 20,000, is equal to the fixed costs per unit, $6.00.

(4) CLOSE

Closing Activity

Find the possible net profit.
1. Selling price per unit: $3.95. Total cost per unit: $1.50. Estimated unit sales: 12,000. **$29,400**
2. Selling price per unit: $14.50. Total cost per unit: $12.05. Estimated unit sales: 20,000. **$49,000**
3. Selling price per unit: $24.95. Fixed costs per unit: $16.75. Variable costs per unit: $3.25. Estimated unit sales: 50,000. **$247,500**
4. Complete the table for Haskin Paper. Which selling price yields the greatest possible profit? How many units should be produced? **$4.79; 40,00**

TECHNOLOGY POWER

Advertisers in the U.S. spent $8.2 billion online in 2000, up from zero as of 1994, according to Pricewaterhouse Coopers. Filmlets are a new form of Internet advertising. Filmlets are advertised in 30-second TV spots, in movie theaters, and magazines, but the only place you can watch them is online. Carmaker BMW spent tens of millions of dollars to develop several of these five-minute films.

WRAP-UP

Go over any problem for which a wrong answer is given.

Assignment Guide
   Basic: 3–6
   Average: 7

20 min.

Quick Quiz

1. A snack company conducted a survey for its new pretzels. Out of 455 total responses, 325 were positive. What is the percent of positive responses? **71.4%**

2. Sara's Candy sells approximately $150,000 in chocolates annually. The total annual sales of chocolates in the entire market is about $2,500,000. What is Sara's market share for chocolates? **6%**

3. Riverview Landscaping has a market share of 35 percent. The projected market sales are $10,000,000. What are the projected sales? **$3,500,000**

4. A newspaper ad consists of 18-column inches. The rate per column inch is $36.99. What is the cost of the advertisement? **$665.82**

5. A 30-second television commercial costs $2,800. What is the cost of two 60-second commercials and one 10-second commercial? **$12,600**

SECTION 17-1 **CONCEPT CHECK** (p. 553)

1. $1,800 \div 2,000 = $ **90%**
2. $460 \div 500 = $ **92%**

SECTION 17-2 **CONCEPT CHECK** (p. 555)

1. Percent potential = $80 \div 1,000 = $ **0.08 or 8%**
   Sales potential = $40,000 \times 1 \times 0.08 = $ **3,200**
2. Percent potential = $320 \div 1,600 = $ **0.20 or 20%**
   Sales potential = $1,400,000 \times 2 \times 0.20 = $ **560,000**

SECTION 17-3 **CONCEPT CHECK** (p. 556)

1. $2,000,000 \div 20,000,000 = $ **0.10 or 10%**
2. $4,000,000 \div 180,000,000 = $ **0.0222 or 2.2%**

SECTION 17-4 **CONCEPT CHECK** (p. 559)

1. 2010: **$5.3 million**
   2012: **$6.2 million**
   2014: **$7.0 million**

SECTION 17-5 **CONCEPT CHECK** (p. 561)

1. $\$6,300,000 \times 8\% = $ **$504,000**
2. $\$10,250,000 \times 14\% = $ **$1,435,000**

SECTION 17-6 **CONCEPT CHECK** (p. 564)

1. $\$36.89 \times 12 = $ **$442.68**
2. $\$29.27 \times 10 = $ **$292.70**

SECTION 17-7 **CONCEPT CHECK** (p. 566)

1. $4 \times (2 \times \$9,000) = 4 \times \$18,000 = $ **$72,000**
2. $(4 \times \$35,000) + (5 \times \frac{1}{2} \times \$35,000) = \$140,000 + \$87,500 = $ **$227,500**
3. $2 \times \$2,000,000 = $ **$4,000,000**
4. $(4 \times \frac{1}{2} \times \$2,000,000) + (3 \times 2 \times \$2,000,000) = $
   $\$4,000,000 + \$12,000,000 = $ **$16,000,000**

SECTION 17-8 **CONCEPT CHECK** (p. 569)

1. $(\$3.00 - \$1.05) \times 200,000 = \$1.95 \times 200,000 = $ **$390,000**
   $(\$4.50 - \$1.38) \times 150,000 = \$3.12 \times 150,000 = $ **$468,000**
2. **A $4.50 selling price yields the greatest possible profit.**

Living in the Real World

The Campaign for Dozie D'Oats

Assessment A morning sugar cereal might be your breakfast of choice, but how is it fueling your body? Remember: garbage in, garbage out. This means that if you're eating lots of sugar and fatty foods, then you're going to have less energy, weight gain, and health problems. Therefore, the five major food groups are represented on this chart, which shows you how much you should eat a day. Study the chart and then answer the questions below.

<table>
<tr><th colspan="2">What Constitutes a Serving?</th></tr>
<tr><td rowspan="4">Fruit Group</td><td>• 1 whole medium fruit (about 1 cup)</td></tr>
<tr><td>• $\frac{1}{4}$ cup dried fruit</td></tr>
<tr><td>• $\frac{1}{2}$ cup canned fruit</td></tr>
<tr><td>• $\frac{1}{2}$ to $\frac{3}{4}$ cup fruit juice</td></tr>
<tr><td rowspan="10">Bread & Cereal Group</td><td>• 1 slice bread</td></tr>
<tr><td>• 1 medium muffin</td></tr>
<tr><td>• $\frac{1}{2}$ hot dog bun or hamburger bun</td></tr>
<tr><td>• $\frac{1}{2}$ bagel or english muffin</td></tr>
<tr><td>• 4 small crackers</td></tr>
<tr><td>• 1 tortilla</td></tr>
<tr><td>• 1 cup cold cereal</td></tr>
<tr><td>• $\frac{1}{2}$ cup cooked cereal</td></tr>
<tr><td>• $\frac{1}{2}$ cup rice</td></tr>
<tr><td>• $\frac{1}{2}$ cup pasta</td></tr>
</table>

The Food Guide Pyramid

Number of Servings per Day

KEY
- Fat (naturally occurring and added)
- Sugars (added)
These symbols show fats and added sugars in foods.

Fats, Oils & Sweets
Use Sparingly

Milk, Yogurt & Cheese Group
2–3 Servings

Meat, Poultry, Fish, Dry Beans, Eggs & Nuts Group
2–3 Servings

Vegetable Group
3–5 Servings

Fruit Group
2–4 Servings

Bread, Cereal, Rice & Pasta Group
6–11 Servings

1 Reporting. How big is 1 serving of vegetables or grains? (See the sidebar for a sample of what constitutes a serving.) For one week, track what you eat—meals, snacks, liquids . . . everything. Start this log today.

2 Calculating. At the end of the week refer to your health report and add up the servings that you ate each day. How does your diet compare to the Food Guide Pyramid? What changes to your diet do you need to make to become a healthier person?

Living in the Real World

1. Make sure students are honest about their log. They need to include everything they consumed and their number of servings.
2. Answers will vary. Will the results affect students food intake?

REVIEW OF KEY WORDS

product test (p. 552)
opinion research firm (p. 552)
opinion survey (p. 552)
sales potential (p. 554)

sample (p. 554)
market (p. 554)
market share (p. 556)

sales projection (p. 550)
factor method (p. 561)
factor (p. 561)

For Problems 1–10, write your own definition for each key word. Students' definitions will vary. Make sure they use their own words and show an understanding of the definition.

CHAPTER Study Guide and Assessment

17

Skills and Concepts

SECTION OBJECTIVE 17-1 AND EXAMPLES

Compute the rate of a particular response in an opinion survey.

APP, a polling company, conducted an opinion survey of 3,500 people for an approval rating of the governor. The following table shows the responses of the 3,500 people in the survey. What percent of the total responses was for "outstanding"?

| | Age Group | | | | |
Opinion	18 to 25	26 to 35	36 to 45	45 or older	Total
Outstanding	35	100	15	30	180
Good	75	300	400	500	1,275
Fair	150	500	750	200	1,600
Poor	200	100	100	45	445
Total	460	1,000	1,265	775	3,500

STEP: Compute the rate of the response.

$$\frac{\text{Number of Times Particular Response Occurs}}{\text{Total Number of Responses}}$$

$180 \div 3,500 = $ **0.0514 or 5.1% rate of response**

REVIEW EXERCISES
Round the answers to the nearest tenth of a percent.

	Product in Survey	Number of "Poor" Responses	÷	Total Number of Responses	=	Percent of "Poor" Responses
11.	Face cream	11	÷	100	=	**11%**
12.	Candy bar	130	÷	600	=	**21.7%**
13.	Music video	612	÷	2,000	=	**30.6%**
14.	Perfume	98	÷	500	=	**19.6%**
15.	Hamburger	26	÷	125	=	**20.8%**
16.	Blue jeans	43	÷	500	=	**8.6%**

SECTION OBJECTIVE 17-2 AND EXAMPLES

Figure out the annual sales potential of a new product.

Stamper's Plus has developed a new line of stationery called Pacific Mist. Stamper's chose a sample of women between the ages of 18 and 25 to try the new product. Of the 500 women in the sample, 125 said they would buy the stationery. Stamper's Plus estimates that 1,200,000 women would buy stationery. Their surveys indicate that each woman purchases stationery once per year. What is the annual sales potential for Pacific Mist?

REINFORCEMENT

Section 17-1

1. In a survey, 1,050 out of 3,425 people preferred spearmint gum. What percent of the total people surveyed preferred spearmint gum? **30.7%**

2. In a survey for an educational toy, there were 76 negative responses out of 358 total responses. What is the percent of positive responses? **78.8%**

STEP 1: Find the percent of potential purchasers.

$125 \div 500 = 25\%$ potential purchasers

STEP 2: Find the annual sales potential.

Estimated Market Size	$\times$	Individual Rate of Purchase	$\times$	Percent of Potential Purchasers
1,200,000	$\times$	1	$\times$	25%

= **300,000 annual sales potential**

REVIEW EXERCISES
Complete the table.

	Number in Sample	Number of Potential Customers	Percent of Potential Customers	Estimated Market Size	Individual Rate of Purchases per Year	Annual Sales Potential
17.	300	100	a. **33.3%**	100,000	3 times	b. **99,900**
18.	600	250	a. **41.7%**	850,000	1 once	b. **354,450**
19.	1,000	500	a. **50%**	1,500,000	4 cans	b.**3,000,000**
20.	50	10	a. **20%**	600,500	10 boxes	b.**1,201,000**
21.	350	125	a. **35.7%**	25,000	5 issues	b. **44,625**
22.	1,500	300	a. **20%**	65,000	1 once	b. **13,000**

SECTION OBJECTIVE 17-3 AND EXAMPLES

Calculate the market share of a new product.

Alex Irrigation sold 35,000 sprinkler systems during the year. During the same period, 1,650,000 sprinkler systems were purchased in the entire U.S. market. What was Alex's market share for the year?

STEP: Find the market share.

$\dfrac{\text{Total Product Sales}}{\text{Total Market Sales}}$

$35,000 \div 1,650,000 = 0.0212$ or **2.1% market share**

REVIEW EXERCISES
Find the market share.

	Company	Total Product Sales	$\div$	Total Market Sales	=	Market Share
23.	Online Media	$9,500,000	$\div$	$19,000,000	=	**50%**
24.	Computer Surplus	3,200,000	$\div$	9,000,000	=	**35.6%**
25.	Office Inc.	900,000	$\div$	2,500,000	=	**36%**
26.	Printer Specialists	1,200,000	$\div$	5,000,000	=	**24%**
27.	Electronix	750,000	$\div$	10,000,000	=	**7.5%**
28.	New Media	5,400,000	$\div$	15,400,000	=	**35.1%**

REINFORCEMENT

Section 17-2

1. Find the annual sales potential.
   Number in sample: 700.
   Number of potential purchasers: 280.
   Estimated market size: 980,000.
   Individual rate of purchase: 2. **784,000**

2. Out of 14,000 college professors in a sample, 980 preferred a new grade book. The estimated market size is 950,000. Each professor uses about 2 grade books a year. What is the annual sales potential? **133,000**

CHAPTER Study Guide and Assessment

17

SECTION OBJECTIVE 17-4 AND EXAMPLES

Use a graph to compute projected sales.

The marketing department of Central Supply House wants to project sales for the year 2009. The chart below shows Central Supply House's sales history. Use a graph to figure out what sales projection the marketing department might make for 2009.

Central Supply House's Sales Projections						
Year	1998	1999	2000	2001	2002	2003
Sales (in millions)	$3.1	$3.6	$3.7	$3.3	$4.6	$3.4

STEP 1: Graph the sales from 1998 through 2003.

STEP 2: Starting from sales in 1998, draw a straight line through the middle of the data to 2009.

STEP 3: Read the sales projection for 2009. Projected sales for 2009 are approximately **$4.8 million.**

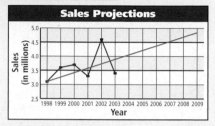

Sales Projections

REVIEW EXERCISES

Construct a graph for each problem and draw a straight line through the middle of the data to project sales.

29. The chart below shows the sales history of a particular television set. What sales might be projected for the year 2005? **Approximately $9.0 million.**

Sales Projections					
Year	1980	1985	1990	1995	2000
Sales (in millions)	$3.1	$4.6	$5.7	$6.3	$7.6

30. What are the projected sales for 2014? **Approximately $19.5 million.**

Sales Projections							
Year	2003	2004	2005	2006	2007	2008	2009
Sales (in millions)	$10	$11.3	$12.1	$14	$12.5	$13	$15

31. What are the projected sales for 2019? **Approximately $5.5 million.**

Sales Projections							
Year	2000	2002	2004	2006	2008	2010	2012
Sales (in millions)	$1.2	$2.2	$2.4	$2.5	$2.0	$3.5	$4

32. What is projected production for the following May? **Approximately 15.8 thousand units.**

Sales Projections						
Month	July	Aug.	Sept.	Oct.	Nov.	Dec.
Production (in thousands of units)	12	18	13	14	12	13

REINFORCEMENT

Section 17-3

1. Find the market share.
Total product sales: $800,000.
Total market sales: $10,000,000. **8%**

Section 17-4

1. The sales history for Star Floral shows:

Year	1999	2000	2001	2002	2003
Sales (in thousands)	$22	$24	$25	$23	$27

What sales might be projected for 2010? **$33,000**

SECTION OBJECTIVE 17-5 AND EXAMPLES

Use the factor method to compute projected sales.

Seminole Sun has an 11 percent market share for sunscreen in the Ft. Lauderdale area. Sunscreen sales in the Ft. Lauderdale area are estimated to be $3,200,000. What are the projected sales figures for Seminole Sun in the Ft. Lauderdale area for next year?

STEP: Find the projected sales.
Projected Market Sales × Market-Share Factor
$3,200,000   ×   11%   = $352,000 projected sales

REVIEW EXERCISES
Find the projected sales.

	Company	Projected Market Sales	×	Market Share	=	Projected Sales
33.	Blake's	$13,000,000	×	12.0%	=	$1,560,000
34.	ABC Toys	35,300,000	×	8.5%	=	$3,000,500
35.	Pencil Pushers	25,400,000	×	6.6%	=	$1,676,400
36.	Cathy's Club	50,000,000	×	11.0%	=	$5,500,000
37.	Furniture Fun	75,000,000	×	22.0%	=	$16,500,000
38.	Sally's Supplies	18,500,000	×	35.0%	=	$6,475,000

SECTION OBJECTIVE 17-6 AND EXAMPLES

Calculate the cost of advertising in a newspaper.

Southwest Trucking Company contracted with the *Daily News* for 10,000 inches of advertising per year. Southwest plans to advertise a new service in the daily newspaper. The advertisement is the equivalent of 15 column inches. What is the cost of the advertisement?

STEP 1: Find the rate per column for 10,000 inches per year/daily. (Use Figure 17.3, The *Daily News* Advertising Rates table on page 564 for this section.) It is $25.71.

STEP 2: Find the advertisement cost.
Number of Column Inches × Rate per Column Inch
15 column inches × $25.71   = **$385.65 advertisement cost**

Continued on next page

REINFORCEMENT

Section 17-5
1. Find the projected sales.
   Market-share factor: 32 percent.
   Projected market sales: $50,000,000. **$16,000,000**

Section 17-6
1. Find the advertisement cost.
   Number of column inches: 36.
   Rate per column inch: $37.50. **$1,350**

REVIEW EXERCISES

Use Figure 17.3, The *Daily News* Advertising Rates table on page 564 for the following problems.

	Annual Contract (in inches)	Edition	Number of Column Inches	×	Rate per Column Inch	=	Advertisement Cost
39.	5,000	Daily	30	×	a. $26.13	=	b. $783.90
40.	40,000	Sunday	45	×	a. $26.66	=	b. $1,199.70
41.	No contract	Saturday	15	×	a. $50.40	=	b. $756.00
42.	1,000	Daily	10	×	a. $28.73	=	b. $287.30
43.	50,000	Daily	100	×	a. $19.45	=	b. $1,945
44.	30,000	Sunday	600	×	a. $28.25	=	b. $16,950

SECTION OBJECTIVE 17-7 AND EXAMPLES

Compute the cost of advertising on television.

Tony's Crab Shack plans to advertise its shrimp and crab platter on local television this weekend. The rates are $1,200 for a 30-second daytime commercial and $2,400 for a 30-second prime-time commercial. If Tony's runs six 10-second daytime ads and five 60-second prime-time ads, what is the total cost of the advertising campaign?

STEP 1: Find the cost of the 10-second daytime ads.

$\frac{1}{2}$ × Cost of 30-Second Ad

($\frac{1}{2}$ × $1,200)   × 6 = $3,600 cost of the 10-second daytime ads

STEP 2: Find the cost of the 60-second prime-time ads.

2 × Cost of 30-Second Ad

(2 × $2,400)   × 5 = $24,000 cost of the 60-second prime-time ads

STEP 3: Find the total cost.

$3,600 + $24,000 = **$27,600 total cost**

REVIEW EXERCISES

Find the total cost.

	Rate per 30-Second Commercial	Number of 10-Second Commercials	Number of 30-Second Commercials	Number of 60-Second Commercials	Total Cost
45.	$ 18,000	4	2	2	$144,000
46.	1,000	3	4	3	$11,500
47.	25,000	10	6	1	$325,000
48.	1,000,000	3	8	2	$13,500,000
49.	2,500	5	1	5	$33,750
50.	8,000	6	3	3	$96,000

REINFORCEMENT

Section 17-7

1. A 30-second ad costs $9,500. What is the cost of five 30-second ads and two 10-second ads? **$57,000**

2. Cobalt Motors plans to advertise with two 10-second prime-time commercials and five 30-second daytime commercials. The rates are $6,800 for a 30-second daytime commercial and $14,900 for a 30 second prime-time commercial. What is the cost of the advertising? **$48,900**

SECTION OBJECTIVE 17-8 AND EXAMPLES

Calculate the selling price that will result in the highest possible net profit.

The Yum Yum Shop manufactures ice cream. Yum Yum has a fixed overhead of $210,000. The variable costs to produce vanilla ice cream are $1.05 per 10-gallon tub. To determine the best selling price, Yum Yum estimates the number of tubs that could be sold at various prices. What selling price will maximize Yum Yum's profits?

Selling Price per Unit	Estimated Unit Sales	Fixed Costs	Fixed Costs per Unit	Variable Costs per Unit	Total Cost per Unit
$10.00	30,000	$210,000	$ 7.00	$1.05	$ 8.05
12.00	25,000	210,000	8.40	1.05	9.45
15.00	20,000	210,000	10.50	1.05	11.55
18.00	15,000	210,000	14.00	1.05	15.05

STEP 1: Find the possible net profit for each selling price.

$$\left(\begin{array}{c}\text{Selling Price}\\\text{per Unit}\end{array} - \begin{array}{c}\text{Total Cost}\\\text{per Unit}\end{array}\right) \times \begin{array}{c}\text{Estimated}\\\text{Unit Sales}\end{array}$$

($10	−	$8.05)	× 30,000	= $58,500
($12	−	$9.45)	× 25,000	− $63,750
($15	−	$11.55)	× 20,000	= $69,000
($18	−	$15.05)	× 15,000	= $44,250

STEP 2: Find the greatest possible profit $69,000

STEP 3: Find the best selling price $15.00

51. $12.50 selling price results in net profit of $76,250, found by {$12.50 − $9.45} × 25,000 = $3.05 × 25,000 = $76,250; $16.00 selling price results in net profit of $89,000, found by {$16.00 − $11.55} × 20,000 = $4.45 × 20,000 = $89,000; $22.00 selling price results in net profit of $104,250, found by {$22.00 − $15.05} × 15,000 = $6.95 × 15,000 = $104,250; $26.00 selling price results in net profit of $39,500, found by {$26.00 − $22.05} × 10,000 = $3.95 × 10,000 = $39,500

REVIEW EXERCISES

Revised data for the Yum Yum Shop is shown. Use the table to solve Problems 51 and 52.

Selling Price per Unit	Estimated Unit Sales	Fixed Costs	Fixed Costs per Unit	Variable Costs per Unit	Total Cost per Unit
$12.50	25,000	$210,000	$ 8.40	$1.05	$ 9.45
16.00	20,000	210,000	10.50	1.05	11.55
22.00	15,000	210,000	14.00	1.05	15.05
26.00	10,000	210,000	21.00	1.05	22.05

51. Find the possible net profit for each selling price.

52. What selling price will maximize Yum Yum's profits? **$22.00**

Complete the table.

	Selling Price per Unit	Estimated Unit Sales	Fixed Costs	Fixed Costs per Unit	Variable Costs per Unit	Total Cost per Unit	Possible Net Profit	
53.	$ 54.00	8,000	$200,000	a. $25	$18.00	b. $43	c.	c. $88,000
54.	68.00	10,500	200,000	a. $19.05	18.00	b. $37.05	c.	c. $324,975
55.	101.50	200,000	200,000	a. $1.00	18.00	b. $19.00	c.	c. $16,500,000
56.	200.00	35,000	200,000	a. $5.71	18.00	b. $23.71	c.	c. $6,170,150

REINFORCEMENT

Section 17-8

1. Complete the table for Circle Toys. Which selling price yields the greatest possible profit? **($11.50)** How many units should be produced? **5,000**

Selling Price per Unit	$8.99	$11.50
Estimated Unit Sales	6,000	5,000
Fixed Costs	$30,000	$30,000
Fixed Costs per Unit	$5.00	$6.00
Variable Costs per Unit	$1.25	$1.25
Total Costs per Unit	$6.25	$7.25
Possible Net Profit	$16,440	$21,250

Aligned and verified by
The Princeton Review

Cumulative Test Prep

Test-Taking Tip
You can solve many problems without much calculation if you understand the basic mathematical concepts. Always carefully consider what is asked and look for answers that make sense.

SECTION ONE: MULTIPLE CHOICE

This section contains seven multiple-choice questions. After working each problem, write the letter of the correct answer on your paper.

1. The Dockmasters Company buys an outdoor light fixture for $27.87. The company sells the fixture for $67.89. What is the markup? **A**
   - (A) $40.02
   - (B) $40.20
   - (C) $95.67
   - (D) $95.76

2. Central Publishing Company plans to produce do-it-yourself books to be sold at $14.95 each. The fixed costs are estimated at $180,800. The variable costs are $10.43 per book. What is the estimated break-even point in units? **B**
   - (A) 30,000
   - (B) 40,000
   - (C) 50,000
   - (D) 150,000

3. Pipe Outfitters, an oil equipment wholesaler, purchases piping for $217.85 a length. It sells the lengths for $447.50. Pipe Outfitters estimates the overhead expenses for each length to be 30 percent of the selling price. What is the estimated net profit on each length? **A**
   - (A) $95.40
   - (B) $134.25
   - (C) $229.65
   - (D) $363.90

4. Secure-It sells a dead bolt lock for $79.49. It costs Secure-It $41.67 to purchase the lock. The overhead is estimated to be 20 percent of the selling price of the lock. What is the estimated net-profit rate based on the selling price? **A**
   - (A) 27.6%
   - (B) 29.9%
   - (C) 31.2%
   - (D) 36.5%

5. Penn Skate purchases Ambassador roller skates that have a list price of $129.79 a pair. Penn Skate receives a trade-discount rate of 25 percent. What is the discount that Penn Skate receives for each pair of skates? **A**
   - (A) $32.45
   - (B) $35.66
   - (C) $97.34
   - (D) $100.79

6. Of the sample of 800 swimming pool owners, 60 said they would buy Leisure Living's new chemical for swimming pools. There is a market of about 8,000,000 potential users. Each user would purchase the chemical twice per year. What is the sales potential for the chemical for one year? **B**
   - (A) 900,000
   - (B) 1,200,000
   - (C) 1,500,000
   - (D) 2,500,000

7. The Fitness Company manufacturers an all-purpose exercise set that is priced at $947.50. When it introduced its newest model, The Fitness Company offered a chain discount of 30 percent less than 20 percent off the old model. What is the final net price of the all-purpose exercise set? **C**
   - (A) $132.65
   - (B) $473.75
   - (C) $530.60
   - (D) $663.25

SECTION TWO: FREE RESPONSE

This section contains eight questions for which you will supply short answers. Write your answer on your paper.

8. Air-Hi produces a sports shoe that is priced at $114.49. When the new model was introduced, the $114.49 shoe was discounted at 15 percent less 5 percent. What is the net price of the old model using the complement method? **$92.45**

9. Tia's, a shoe boutique, sells Italian-made shoes for $164.49. Tia's purchases the shoes for $97.88. To the nearest tenth of a percent, what is the markup rate based on cost? **68.1%**

10. During the winter, Sun Grown buys oranges from overseas growers. Sun Grown determines the retail selling price of the oranges by marking up the oranges 125 percent of the cost. The fruit company bought its first shipment of winter oranges for $1.48 per dozen. What is the retail selling price per dozen of this shipment? **$1.85/day**

11. Northside Auto Supply, an automobile supply shop, buys its products from Federal Auto Parts. Because of a downturn in sales, Federal has decided to reduce the price of its rebuilt generator. The regular selling price is $47.38. The generator's new selling price is $37.90. To the nearest tenth of a percent, what is the markdown rate? **20%**

12. Use a graph to project Suntyme's sales for 2006 based on this sales history.

Suntyme's Sales Projections				
Year	2000	2001	2002	2003
Sales (in millions)	$3.0	$4.0	$3.1	$4.9

$6 million

13. The Capital Theater received an invoice dated September 13 from Theater Supply.

The invoice carried terms of 2/10, net 30. The net price of the invoices was $561.87. What was the cash price of the invoice if it was paid on September 20? **$550.63**

14. Samson's Music Studio has a contract for 64-column inches of advertising in the *Herald* this week. What is the cost of a 40-inch advertisement on Sunday? **$1,728**

Per Column Inch		
Contract Rates (in inches)	Daily	Sunday
16	$35.80	$45.80
64	35.00	43.20
126	34.00	42.70

15. Countryside Cereal plans to advertise on television. Costs for 30-second commercials are $1,000 for daytime and $8,000 for prime time. What is the estimated cost of the advertising campaign? **$66,500**

Number	Length of Commercial	Time
5	10-second	Daytime
4	30-second	Prime time
2	60-second	Prime time

SECTION THREE: OPEN-ENDED

This section contains four open-ended questions. Demonstrate your knowledge by giving a clear, concise solution to each problem. Your score on these problems will depend on how well you do on the following:

- Explain your reasoning.
- Show your understanding of mathematics in an organized manner.
- Use charts, graphs, and diagrams in your explanation.
- Show the solution in more than one way or relate it to other situations.
- Investigate beyond the requirements of the problem.

16. Explain why you think it is important for a business to understand its break-even point.

17. Why do manufacturers hire quality control inspectors? Wouldn't it be less **Answers may vary. Defective items could result in loss of customers.**

expensive to just let a few defective items pass through the process?

18. Describe the difference between cash discounts with ordinary dating and cash discounts with end-of-month dating.

19. Why do you think businesses offer discounts if the invoice is paid early? Do you think it is always to the purchaser's advantage to pay early?

Mathematics Online

To learn more about marketing, visit the *Mathematics with Business Applications* Web site at www.busmath.glencoe.com.

Cumulative Test Prep ▶ **579**

16. Answers may vary, but might include that they know how many stems need to be sold and how much to charge.

18. Cash discounts with ordinary dating are based on the date of sale. Cash discounts with end-of-month dating are based on a fixed number of days from the end of the month.

19. It can be hard to collect money. Offering cash discounts is an incentive to pay. It is not always advantageous to pay early if the money is invested somewhere making more money than the discount.

National Standards for Business Education

Section Objectives	1. Mathematical Foundations	2. Number Relationships and Operations	3. Patterns, Functions, and Algebra	4. Measurements	5. Statistics and Probability	6. Problem-Solving Applications	
18-1 Storage Space (pp. 582–584) Compute the total storage space.	X	X		X			
18-2 Taking an Inventory (pp. 585–588) Calculate the total inventory.	X	X					
18-3 Valuing an Inventory (pp. 589–593) Use the average-cost method to compute the inventory value.	X	X					
18-4 Carrying an Inventory (pp. 594–595) Calculate the annual cost of carrying an inventory.	X	X					
18-5 Door-to-Door Transportation Cost (pp. 596–598) Work out the total door-to-door shipping costs.	X	X					
18-6 Transportation by Truck (pp. 599–601) Calculate the total shipping cost by truck.	X	X					

(Source: Reprinted with permission from the National Standards for Business Education, copyright © 2001 by National Business Education Association, 1914 Association Drive, Reston, Virginia 21901-1596)

SCANS Correlation

Foundation Skills

Basic Skills	Reading	Writing	Math	Listening	Speaking	
Thinking Skills	Creative Thinking	Decision Making	Problem Solving	Seeing Things in the Mind's Eye	Knowing How to Learn	Reasoning
Personal Qualities	Responsibility	Self-Esteem	Sociability	Self-Management	Integrity/Honesty	

This chapter's highlighted blocks indicate the chapter's content coverage in the Student Edition and the Teacher Wraparound Edition.

National Council of Teachers of Mathematics Standards

1. Numbers & Operations	2. Algebra	3. Geometry	4. Measurement	5. Data Analysis & Probability	6. Problem Solving	7. Reasoning & Proof	8. Communication	9. Connections	10. Representations
X		X			X		X		
X					X		X		
X					X		X		
X					X		X		
X					X		X		
X					X		X		

SCANS Correlation

Workplace Competencies

Resources	Allocating Time	Allocating Money	Allocating Material and Facility Resources	Allocating Human Resources		
Information	Acquiring and Evaluating Information	Organizing and Maintaining Information	Interpreting and Communicating Information	Using Computers to Process Information		
Interpersonal Skills	Participating as a Member of a Team	Teaching Others	Serving Clients/Customers	Exercising Leadership	Negotiating to Arrive at a Decision	Working with Cultural Diversity
Systems	Understanding Systems	Monitoring and Correcting Performance	Improving and Designing Systems			
Technology	Selecting Technology	Applying Technology to Task	Maintaining and Troubleshooting Technology			

What You'll Learn

Tell students that in this chapter you'll focus on the responsibilities of a warehousing and distribution department, such as inventory, product storage, and shipping the product by air or by truck.

Why It's Important

Proper management of inventory helps businesses to more efficiently and accurately plan, coordinate, and execute the delivery of goods. Profits are maximized by the increased cash flow of efficient inventory delivery systems and optimized inventory levels due to minimizing the storage and transportation of goods.

Key Word Review

Be Resourceful

Being resourceful on the job includes allocating time to complete tasks. You can practice this skill by dividing this chapter into learning tasks. Include the tasks of learning and reviewing the key terms. Mark the tasks in time slots on your planner. CL , LS

CHAPTER 18

Warehousing and Distributing

What You'll Learn

Section 18-1 Compute the total storage space.

Section 18-2 Calculate the total inventory.

Section 18-3 Use the average-cost method to compute the inventory value.

Section 18-4 Calculate the annual cost of carrying an inventory.

Section 18-5 Work out the total door-to-door shipping costs.

Section 18-6 Calculate the total shipping cost by truck.

When Will You Ever Use This?

The warehousing and distribution department keeps a record of all merchandise, and it ships your product. Your inventory must be large enough to meet your sales needs. The size and value of your inventory will affect your insurance, taxes, and the worth of your business.

Key Words to Know

- warehouse
- inventory
- inventory card
- average-cost method
- first in, first out
- last in, first out

Mathematics Online

To learn more about warehousing and distributing, visit the *Mathematics with Business Applications* Web site at www.busmath.glencoe.com.

CLASSROOM RESOURCES

Application and Enrichment

- *Teacher Wraparound Edition*
- *Teacher Resource Binder, Blackline Masters*
- Interactive Lesson Planner CD-ROM
- PowerPoint® Presentations CD-ROM

Review and Enforcement

- Mathematics Online
  www.busmath.glencoe.com
- *Teacher Resource Binder, Internet Resources*

- *Student Activity Workbook*
- *Student Activity Workbook, Teacher Annotated Edition*
- *School-to-Home Activity Workbook*

Assessment and Evaluation

- *Assessment Binder, Reproducible Tests*
- *Assessment Binder, Alternative Assessment Strategies*
- **ExamView®** Pro Test Generator CD-ROM

For the Teacher

- *Student Activity Workbook, Teacher Annotated Edition*
- *Assessment Binder*
- Interactive Lesson Planner CD-ROM
- *Teacher Resource Binder*
- Mathematics Online
  www.busmath.glencoe.com

For the Student

- *Student Activity Workbook*
- *School-to-Home Activity Workbook*

Living in the Real World

Story's Summary

The Nauwaf father and son team own a trio of successful auto parts stores. In this chapter, they weigh the pros and cons of how their company deals with warehousing and distribution. Maybe it's time to close the warehouse in the suburbs and simply ship inventory directly to their three stores in the city limits.

Living in the Real World

Auto Do It Right

It's Friday morning and Armin Nauwaf is opening the auto parts store he owns with his father. Auto Do It Right has been in business for 21 years, and Armin and his father own and operate three stores in town. Even when the economy is slow, business is good. In fact, the auto parts business often booms in an economic downturn because people start working on their own cars more. In this chapter, read about this father-and-son business's approach to warehousing and distributing.

Read on. Go to . . .

581

Did You Know...

Many mail-order and Internet companies store their inventory in warehouses, rather than on-site. For instance, if you order an item from Amazon.com, located in Seattle, Washington, the product you purchase could be sent from any of a number of warehouses the company owns and operates across the country.

Think about This

This is a time where most any item is available quickly and easily—via warehouse stores, the Internet, and such. What do you think it was like to shop in nineteenth century America? How would inventory in a general store differ from that in today's grocery store?

LOCAL STANDARDS

SECTION (18-1) **Storage Space**

National Standards for Business Education

Standard 1	Mathematical Foundations
Standard 2	Number Relationships and Operations
Standard 4	Measurements

National Council of Teachers of Mathematics Standards

Standard 1	Numbers and Operations
Standard 3	Geometry
Standard 6	Problem Solving
Standard 8	Communication

 **FOCUS**

Ask students to name some storage spaces that can be found at school and at home. **(Pantries, garages, attics, and school lockers are some examples of storage spaces.)** Point out that businesses often use warehouses to store items.

In-Class Examples

Work through these exercises with students before having them do the Self-Check.

1. 2 in × 3 in × 3 in **18 in³**
2. 4 ft × 2.5 ft × 3 ft **30 ft³**
3. 5,184 ÷ 1,728 **3**

SECTION (18-1) **Storage Space**

○ **Section Objective**

Compute the total storage space.

Your business needs a **warehouse**, or storage space. This is a place to keep materials or products until you are ready to use them, sell them, or ship them. You may need space in a large warehouse or in a small stockroom. As a retailer you may need shelving space or aisle space. Your space requirements depend on the size and quantity of the items you are storing. To figure out how much storage space you need for your product, you'll need to do some math. Here's how:

$$\text{Volume} = \text{Length} \times \text{Width} \times \text{Height}$$

$$\text{Storage Space} = \text{Volume per Item} \times \text{Number of Items}$$

Living in the Real World

Auto Do It Right

Location, Location, Location Armin and his father, Rasheed, own a warehouse in a suburb that is convenient to all three stores. They direct shipments of new inventory there and when the stores need to fill orders or stock their shelves, the store managers contact the warehouse manager.

Draw Conclusions How does a business find out how much storage space it needs?

Continued on page 585

Example 1

The Andersons' store has a display of various brands of twenty-four 12-ounce cans per case of soft drinks. Each case measures 16 inches by 10.75 inches by 5 inches. How many cubic inches of space are required for 480 cases?

STEP 1: Find the volume per item.
Length × Width × Height
16 inches × 10.75 inches × 5 inches = 860 cubic inches volume per item

STEP 2: Find the storage space.
Volume per Item × Number of Items
860 cubic inches × 480 cases = **412,800 cubic inches**

16 × 10.75 × 5 = 860 × 480 = 412800

BUSINESS NOTES

Discuss the reasons why a business must know the quantity of each item that is in stock. **(If the stock is low, the manager might decide to reorder immediately. If the stock is high, it might indicate an item is not selling well and needs to be promoted or priced lower.)** Emphasize that the number of items "in stock" is the same as the number of items "on hand." These terms refer to the total number of a particular item that a business has for sale.

Living in the Real World

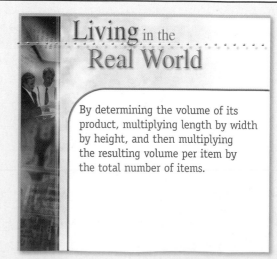

By determining the volume of its product, multiplying length by width by height, and then multiplying the resulting volume per item by the total number of items.

CONCEPT CHECK

 SELF-CHECK ✓

Complete the problems, then check your answers at the end of the chapter. **Find the storage space needed.**

1. Six-pack case of one-gallon bottles of chainsaw oil.
   Dimensions of case: 12 in × 12 in × 18 in.
   Twenty cases. **Volume per item = 12 in × 12 in × 18 in = 2,592 cubic in**
   Storage space = 2,592 cubic in × 20 = 51,840 cubic in
2. Dimensions of a case of cereal: 13.25 in × 16 in × 10 in.
   Thirty-six cases.
   Volume per item = 13.25 in × 16 in × 10 in = 2,120 cubic in
   Storage space = 2,120 cubic in × 36 = 76,320 cubic in

 ▶ **F Y I**

According to *Warehousing Management,* 35 percent of merchandise sold through catalogs is returned.

▶ ▶ ▶

MEASURING IN CUBIC FEET The majority of storage space is measured in cubic feet, but most small items found in grocery stores are measured in inches. Because a cubic foot is 12 inches by 12 inches by 12 inches equals 1,728 cubic inches, you change cubic inches to cubic feet by dividing by 1,728.

Example 2

In Example 1 on page 582, 480 cases of soft drinks took up 412,800 cubic inches of space. Change the cubic inches to cubic feet.

STEP: Change cubic inches to cubic feet.
  Cubic Inches   ÷   1,728
  412,800 cubic inches ÷   1,728 = **238.9 or 239 cubic feet of space**

CONCEPT CHECK

SELF-CHECK ✓

Complete the problems, then check your answers at the end of the chapter. **Find the storage space needed.**

3. Change the cubic inches in Problem 1 to cubic feet.
   51,840 ÷ 1,728 = 30 cubic feet
4. Change the cubic inches in Problem 2 to cubic feet.
   76,320 ÷ 1,728 = 44.16 cubic feet = 44 cubic feet

SECTION 18-1 PRACTICE

5. Washstand cupboard.
   Carton is 3 feet by 1.75 feet by 2.5 feet.
   One hundred cartons to be stored.
   How much storage space is required? **1,313 cu ft**

6. Table lamp.
   Carton is 0.75 meters by 0.6 meters by 0.8 meters.
   Seven hundred cartons to be stored.
   How much storage space is required? **252 cu meters**

Continued on next page

THINKING CRITICALLY

Warehouse Space
Imagine the classroom is a warehouse used to store teachers' desks. Have the students work in pairs to calculate the storage capacity of the room in cubic feet. Then have them calculate how many cubic feet your desk takes up. **(You can give them the dimensions if you like or have them measure the desk themselves.)** Then have them calculate the number of teachers' desks their classroom could store.

GLOBAL PERSPECTIVE

Storage Overseas
Many countries outside the United States use the metric system. If you're an American businessperson who wants to know how many units of something you can store in a warehouse in Europe, for example, you need to tell them the size in meters. Students imagine they want to ship 500 school desks to a warehouse in Paris. Have them measure the size of their desks and then calculate how much space they'll need in cubic meters.

2 TEACH

In this section, students need to understand the concept of volume. Give students some real-world examples of volume as they relate to storage spaces. For instance, ask students to think about the volume of the classroom. Have them visualize the classroom filled with cartons. Remind students that volume has three dimensions and is therefore measured in cubic units. Give students some examples like 2 ft × 3 ft × 5 ft = 30 ft³ to practice writing cubic units.

Motivating the Lesson
Have students work in groups. Give each group a different sized cardboard box. Have students measure the length, width, and height of the box and then use their measurements to find the volume. Then have each group present their results to the class. **Answers will vary.**

In-Class Examples
Find the storage space needed.
1. Carton dimensions:
   3 in × 2 in × 1 in.
   Number of cartons: 100.
   600 in³
2. Carton dimensions:
   1 ft × 1 ft × 3.5 ft.
   Number of cartons: 350.
   1,225 ft³
3. Crane Silver manufactures teapots. Each teapot is packaged in a carton measuring 12.8 inches long, 15 inches wide, and 18 inches high. How many cubic feet of space does Crane need to store 300 teapots? **600 ft³**

3 ASSESS

Error Analysis

In Example 2 on page 583, students learn to convert from cubic inches to cubic feet. Remind students that they need to read each problem carefully to determine in what unit of measurement the answer should be written. If the units are given in cubic inches and the problem asks for the storage space in cubic feet, then students need to remember to divide by 1,728.

4 CLOSE

Closing Activity

Find the storage space needed.

1. Carton dimensions:
   4 ft × 3 ft × 2 ft.
   Number of cartons: 500.
   12,000 ft³

2. Carton dimensions:
   2.6 m × 3.4 m × 4.8 m.
   Number of cartons: 100.
   4,243.2 m³

3. Carton dimensions:
   6.25 in. × 4.5 in × 8.25 in.
   Number of cartons: 1,400.
   324,843.75 in³

4. Stools are packed in cartons measuring 2.5 feet long, 2.5 feet wide, and 4.5 feet high. Kitchen Corner has ordered 420 stools. How much storage space is needed? **11,812.5 ft³**

5. Century Electronics manufactures laptop computers. Each computer is packaged in a carton measuring 18 inches long, 16 inches wide, and 5 inches high. How many cubic feet of space does Century need to store 1,500 laptop computers? **1,250 ft³**

---

7. a. 4
   b. 80 cu ft
8. a. 30.25
   b. 726 cu ft
9. a. 20
   b. 240 cu ft
10. a. 6.59
    b. 237.3 or 237 cu ft
11. a. 2,056.25
    b. 17.8 or 18 cu ft
12. a. 1,859
    b. 32 cu ft

Find the volume and storage space.

	Boxed Item	Unit of Measure	Carton Dimensions (Length × Width × Height = Volume)					Number of Items	= Storage Space
7.	Computer	feet	(1.000 ×	2.000 ×	2.000 =	a.) ×		20	= b.
8.	Washing machine	feet	(2.750 ×	2.750 ×	4.000 =	a.) ×		24	= b.
9.	Hot water tank	feet	(2.000 ×	2.000 ×	5.000 =	a.) ×		12	= b.
10.	Color television	feet	(1.875 ×	1.875 ×	1.875 =	a.) ×		36	= b.
11.	Oranges— $\frac{4}{5}$ bushel	inches	(17.500 ×	10.000 ×	11.750 =	a.) ×		15	= b.
12.	Milk crates	inches	(13.000 ×	13.000 ×	11.000 =	a.) ×		30	= b.

13. A company manufactures personal computer monitors. Each monitor is packaged in a carton measuring 24 inches by 18 inches by 24 inches high. How many cubic feet of space does the company need to store 800 monitors? **4,800 cu ft**

14. Study lamps are packed 2 in a carton. The dimensions of the carton are 2.5 feet by 1.25 feet by 1.75 feet. The Supply Store wants to order 200 pairs of lamps. How much storage space will the Supply Store need to store the lamps? **1,094 cu ft**

15. Kitchen World has ordered 48 dishes with carrying cases in cartons. Each carton measures $16\frac{1}{4}$ inches by 13 inches by $4\frac{1}{4}$ inches. How many cubic feet of storage space are required? **25 cu ft**

16. Television sets are packaged in cartons measuring 4 feet long, 2.5 feet wide, and 3 feet high. How much storage space is required for 150 television sets? **4,500 cu ft**

17. Tables are packed in cartons measuring 1.75 meters long, 0.8 meters wide, and 1.2 meters high. Empire Importing has ordered 500 tables. How much storage space is needed? **840 cu meters**

18. Bananas are delivered to grocery stores in crates measuring 1 yard by 1.5 feet by 12 inches. How many cubic feet of storage space are required for 25 crates of bananas? **112.5 cu ft**

19. Twenty-four clock radios are packed in a carton measuring 36 inches long, 30 inches wide, and 21 inches high. How much storage space is required for 200 of the cartons? How many cubic feet of storage space is required. **4,536,000 cubic inches; 2,625 cubic feet**

MAINTAINING YOUR SKILLS

> Need Help? Go to...
> → Skill 8: Multiplying Decimals, page 735

Multiply.

20. 2 ft × 3 ft × 5 ft **30 cu ft**
21. 1.4 m × 1.0 m × 0.8 m **1.12 cu meters**
22. 8 in × 6 in × 4 in **192 cu in**
23. 18 mm × 15 mm × 9 mm **2,430 cu meters**
24. 9.7 cm × 7.5 cm × 6.8 cm **494.7 cu meters**
25. 2.1 yd × 0.75 yd × 1.5 yd **2.3625 cu yd**

WRAP-UP

Go over any problem for which a wrong answer is given.

Assignment Guide
Basic: 5–6
Average: 7–12

20 min.

SECTION (18-2) Taking an Inventory

An **inventory** shows the number of each item that your business has in stock. An **inventory card** may be kept on either a computer or on a card to keep a record of the items on hand. The number of incoming items, called receipts, is added to the previous inventory. The number of outgoing items, called issues, is subtracted from the previous inventory. This is frequently done on a computer using Universal Pricing Code (UPC labels). Remember that:

Inventory = Previous Inventory + Receipts − Issues

Living in the Real World

Auto Do It Right

Time vs. Money Regarding inventory, Armin explains to his father that he's wondering whether it would be more cost effective to close the warehouse and then simply direct shipments to each store.

Draw Conclusions What are the benefits to a company for having an effective inventory system?

Continued on page 589

Example 1

Office Town has 40 file cabinets in stock on January 1. During January it received 20 and sold 45. Find the total inventory on February 1.

STEP: Calculate the total inventory.

Previous Inventory + Receipts − Issues

$$40 \quad + \quad 20 \quad - \quad 45 \quad = 15 \text{ total inventory}$$

CONCEPT CHECK

Complete the problems, then check your answers at the end of the chapter. Find the total inventory.

1. Four-drawer files.
   Previous inventory 82, receipts 15, issues 65. **82 + 15 − 65 = 32**

2. Five-ream case of paper.
   Previous inventory 220, receipts 70, issues 180. **220 + 70 − 180 = 110**

National Standards for Business Education

Standard 1	Mathematical Foundations
Standard 2	Number Relationships and Operations

National Council of Teachers of Mathematics Standards

Standard 1	Numbers and Operations
Standard 6	Problem Solving
Standard 8	Communication

(1) FOCUS

Ask students if they know how stores keep track of the number of items that they have on hand. **Point out that businesses keep track of their stock by taking an inventory.**

In-Class Examples

Work through these exercises with students before having them do the Self-Check.

1. 150 − 25 − 40 **85**
2. 245 + 80 + 64 **389**
3. 1,502 + 365 − 217 **1,650**

Living in the Real World

It's important for a company to know how many existing items it can sell; an effective inventory system helps assure customer satisfaction by always having products available to satisfy demand.

585

② TEACH

Computers are used to keep track of inventories. Often in retail stores, computerized cash registers keep track of items that are purchased. Computers are also used to keep track of new items received by the stores. Although computers do a good job at keeping track of inventory, it is not possible to have a perfect record. Some items are stolen from stores, and therefore, unaccountable by a computer. So, businesses often take a physical inventory at least once per year.

Motivating the Lesson

A store had 400 greeting cards in stock. The store received 100 and sold 200. How many greeting cards are in stock? **300**

In-Class Examples

Find the inventory.

1. Previous inventory: 200.
   Receipts: 80.
   Issues: 50. **230**

2. Previous inventory: 325.
   Receipts: 115.
   Issues: 125. **315**

3. At the beginning of the week, Nathan's Art Supplies had 1,200 paintbrushes in stock. The store received 260 on Wednesday and issued 200 during the week. How many paintbrushes were in stock at the end of the week? **1,260**

3. $300 + 120 - 150 = 270$
4. $270 + 80 - 140 = 210$
5. a. March = 210 from end of February
   b. $210 + 120 - 100 = 230$
6. a. April = 230 from end of March
   b. $230 + 0 - 80 = 150$

(SELF-CHECK ✔)

Example 2

The inventory record for Wholesale Paint Supply shows that 80 gallons of white latex paint, stock number WL-9, were in inventory on February 1. Each week the inventory record is updated. How many gallons were on hand March 1?

Item: Latex paint, white			Stock Number: WL-9	
Week of	Opening Balance	Units Receipts (Qty. In)	Issues (Qty. Out)	Inventory at End of Week
Feb. 1	80	40	62	58
Feb. 8	58	0	25	33
Feb. 15	33	80	28	85
Feb. 22	85	40	37	88
Mar. 1	88			

Inventory at beginning of week   Number on hand

STEP: Calculate the inventory on hand.

	Opening Balance	Units +Receipts (Qty. In)	Issues − (Qty. Out)	=	Number on Hand
Week of February 1:	80	+ 40	− 62	=	58
Week of February 8:	58	+ 0	− 25	=	33
Week of February 15:	33	+ 80	− 28	=	85
Week of February 22:	85	+ 40	− 37	=	88 on hand March 1

CONCEPT CHECK

Complete the problems, then check your answers at the end of the chapter. The inventory record for the Affiliated Lumber Company shows the status of 4 by 8 sheets of wallboard. Complete the inventory record.

	Month	Opening Balance	+	Units Receipts (Qty. In)	−	Issues (Qty. Out)	=	Number on Hand
3.	January	300	+	120	−	150	=	a.
4.	February	270	+	80	−	140	=	a.
5.	March	a.	+	120	−	100	=	b.
6.	April	a.	+	0	−	80	=	b.

SECTION 18-2 PRACTICE

7. The Key Auto Supply Company takes an inventory on a monthly basis. What is the balance on hand for each item?

Item Number	Description	Beginning Balance	+	Units Receipts (Qty. In)	−	Issues (Qty. Out)	=	Number on Hand
X 23	10W-30 oil quarts	147	+	50	−	78	=	a. 119
W 15	Washer solvent	91	+	36	−	45	=	b. 82
C 5	5-gal. oil	17	+	12	−	23	=	c. 6
TR-90	Transmission fluid	18	+	16	−	28	=	d. 6

COOPERATIVE LEARNING

Go Team!

Divide the class into seven teams. Give each team a topic from this chapter. Have each team prepare a short lesson on their topic. Their lesson must utilize the four-step teaching plan, modeled in the chapters in this textbook: *Focus, Teach, Assess,* and *Close.* In *Focus,* the group must ask a motivating question and stress the importance of their topic. In *Teach,* the group must give instruction, and then provide a short class activity. In *Assess,* the group must give a short evaluation quiz. In *Close,* the group must give the class a short study-aid activity to wrap up their presentation. In 25 minutes or less, have each team present its lesson. LS , CL , P

8. How many of each item does the math department office supplies cabinet contain at the end of the month?

Stock No.	Description	Opening Balance	+	Units Receipts	−	Issues	=	Number on Hand
11398	STPLR-RS153	4	+	0	−	3	=	a. 1
11402	BOX STPLS-RT11	12	+	0	−	3	=	b. 9
11610	BOX PA CLPS-L3	18	+	36	−	21	=	c. 33
11682	Marking Pens PR-7	4	+	36	−	19	=	d. 21

9. How many dictionaries does the bookstore have in stock on each date?

Last Action Date	Units Receipts	Issues	Number on Hand
09/03	225	0	225
09/10		97	a. 128
09/17		54	b. 74
09/24		40	c. 34
10/01	144	20	d. 158
10/08		43	e. 115

10. The Stock Status Summary for the distribution center for the lumber store is available on the computer. How many of each item is in stock?

Date 8/28						Stock Status Summary
Material Class	Stock No.	Description	Opening Balance	Transactions Receipts	Issued	Number on Hand
174	146301	Plywood $\frac{1}{2} \times 4 \times 8$	2,400		1,500	a. 900
174	146334	2×4×8 pallet load 128	64	24	60	b. 28
175	25121	25-yr. fib gl roof	987	144	547	c. 584
175	526841	Notebook	1,413	72	465	d. 1,020

11. Whitewater Supply Company carries this inventory record on inflatable vests. Find the balance for each date.

Item History	Date	Units Receipts	Issues	Balance
Part No. IV-17	6/01	76		76
Description:	6/12		36	a. 40
Inflatable vest	6/18	144		b. 184
Location: 24	6/26		58	c. 126

Continued on next page

3 **ASSESS**

Error Analysis

Remind students that the number of items that a business receives is called the receipts, and the number of outgoing items is called the issues. Receipts are added to the beginning balance, and the issues are subtracted from the beginning balance. Students may confuse the two numbers by adding the issues and subtracting the receipts. Have students discuss the words *receipt* and *issue* so they know that one represents a quantity coming in, and the other represents a quantity going out.

COMMUNICATION SKILLS

Inventory Spreadsheet

Have students imagine they're about to move into their own apartment. Have them take an inventory of all their personal belongings. They don't need to list every item they own, but can use categorizes, such as books, clothing, and CDs. Encourage students to list their belongings in a spreadsheet. In addition, you could ask students to estimate how much space their belongings will take up to determine what size moving truck they might need or how many trips they'd need to make using the family car.

15.

Date	Receipts	Shipments	Balance
8/1			47
8/6		24	23
8/16	40		63
8/27		36	27
8/31	50		77

16.

Date	Receipts	Shipments	Balance
7/1			74
7/17		24	50
7/20	30		80
8/22		40	40
9/20	24		64
9/30		36	28

4 CLOSE

Closing Activity

Find the inventory.

1. Previous inventory: 500.
   Receipts: 250.
   Issues: 150. **600**

2. Previous inventory: 608.
   Receipts: 0.
   Issues: 212. **396**

3. Previous inventory: 2,375.
   Receipts: 349.
   Issues: 415. **2,309**

4. Print Bookstore takes inventory on a weekly basis. How many of each item are in stock?

Item	Opening Balance	Received	Issued	Inventory
A450-32	52	10	6	**56**
S310-02	36	15	18	**33**
B135-24	46	29	31	**44**

12. Complete this hardware supply inventory record for a deadbolt lock set.

Date	Units Receipts	Shipments	Balance
09/01			110
09/09	100		a. **210**
10/12		75	b. **135**
10/30		100	c. **35**
11/15	200		d. **235**
12/11		95	e. **140**

13. An inventory record for Sunrise Wholesale Pool Supply shows a receipt of 100 folding canvas lounge chairs on April 1. Another shipment of 125 arrived on April 15. On May 10, 110 chairs were shipped out. On June 2, 50 arrived and on June 17, 75 were shipped out. Find the balance as of June 17. **90**

14. On January 1 Sport Wholesalers started with an inventory of 175 soccer balls. Shipments of 45, 76, and 25 were sent out on January 13, February 18, and March 11, respectively. Receipts of 36, 144, and 72 were received on January 20, February 25, and March 15, respectively. Find the balance as of March 15. **281**

15. The Car Care Company started on August 1 with a balance of 47 cases of car wax. On August 6, 24 cases were shipped out. On August 16, 40 cases were received. On August 27, 36 cases were shipped out, and on August 31, 50 cases were received. Prepare an inventory card showing the balance after each transaction.

16. The Wholesale Hardware Supply Company began July 1 with a balance of 74 chain saws. It received shipments of 30 and 24 chain saws on July 20 and September 20, respectively. It made shipments of 24, 40, and 36 chain saws on July 17, August 22, and September 30, respectively. Prepare an inventory card showing the balance after each transaction.

MAINTAINING YOUR SKILLS

Need Help? Go to...
➤ Skill 3: **Adding Whole Numbers,** page 730
➤ Skill 4: **Subtracting Whole Numbers,** page 731

Add.

17. 125 + 45 + 25 **195**

18. 144 + 72 + 36 **252**

Subtract.

19. 144 − 50 **94**

20. 72 − 48 **24**

21. 286 − 144 **142**

22. 7,146 − 5,268 **1,878**

23. 9,178 − 493 **8,685**

24. 14,147 − 9,749 **4,398**

WRAP-UP

Go over any problem for which a wrong answer is given.

Assignment Guide
   Basic: 7–9
Average: 10–12

20 min.

SECTION (18-3) Valuing an Inventory

Section Objective

Use the average-cost method to compute the inventory value.

You must calculate the value of your inventory when you purchase insurance, pay taxes, or compute the worth of your business. The **average-cost method** is one way of calculating the value of an inventory. Because the cost of incoming items may change, you calculate the value of the inventory based on the average cost of the goods you received. Remember that:

$$\text{Inventory Value} = \text{Average Cost per Unit} \times \text{Number on Hand}$$

Living in the Real World

Auto Do It Right

Value What You've Got   Before deciding whether to keep their warehouse, the Nauwafs decide to calculate the value of their inventory. It's important to know the value of an inventory so that the amount of insurance will fully cover any losses.

Draw Conclusions   What inventory valuation method do most businesses use?

Continued on page 594

Example 1

Wholesale Paint Supply is valuing its inventory of white latex paint. On March 1, Wholesale Paint Supply had 88 gallons of white latex paint on hand. What is the value of the inventory on March 1?

Item: Latex paint, white		Stock Number: WL-9-gallons	
Week of	**Units Received**	**Unit Cost**	**Total Cost**
Feb. 1	80	$2.15	$172.00
Feb. 8	40	2.25	90.00
Feb. 15	80	2.30	184.00
Feb. 22	40	2.40	96.00
Total	240		$542.00

Number on hand at beginning of week   Average cost in January

STEP 1: Find the average cost per unit.

Total Cost of Units ÷ Number Received

$542.00   ÷   240   = $2.2583 or $2.26 average cost per unit

STEP 2: Find the inventory value.

Average Cost per Unit × Number on Hand

$2.26   ×   88   = **$198.88 inventory value**

542 ÷ 240 = 2.2583333   2.26 × 88 = 198.88

National Standards for Business Education

Standard 1	Mathematical Foundations
Standard 2	Number Relationships and Operations

National Council of Teachers of Mathematics Standards

Standard 1	Numbers and Operations
Standard 6	Problem Solving
Standard 8	Communication

1 FOCUS

Businesses must calculate the value of their inventory if they want to know what their business is worth. Since a business purchases products at different times, there are often different costs. To find the value of an inventory, a business can use the average cost method.

In-Class Examples

Work through these exercises with students before having them do the Self-Check.

1. $3.25 × 90 **$292.50**
2. $8.99 × 570 **$5,124.30**
3. $537.50 ÷ 250 **$2.15**

Living in the Real World

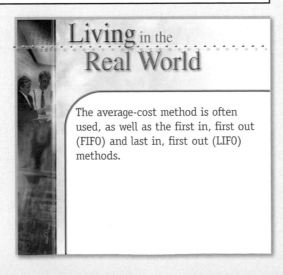

The average-cost method is often used, as well as the first in, first out (FIFO) and last in, first out (LIFO) methods.

2 TEACH

Have students discuss what it means to find an average. Give students some costs and ask them to find the average cost. For example, find the average costs of $2.25, $3.10, $2.50, $2.70, and $2.95. **($2.70)**

Since businesses receive the same products on different dates, the costs may be different. In Example 1 on page 589, point out the unit cost on each date. Since some costs are higher and some are lower, an average is used to determine the value of the inventory. You may want to give students a similar situation to think about. Ask students to describe something that they or their parents buy on a regular basis that has a variable price. For instance, the price of milk can vary over time. If you wanted to know the average cost of a gallon of milk during one month, you would find the total amount you spent on milk and divide by the number of gallons you purchased.

CONCEPT CHECK

SELF-CHECK ✓

Complete the problems, then check your answers at the end of the chapter.

Two items are purchased: 100 packs of felt pens at $4.00 each and 60 packs of felt pens at $3.80 each. (A pack is comprised of 12 felt pens.)

1. Find the average cost per pack.

2. Find the inventory value if 50 packs were on hand. **50 × $3.93 = $196.50**

1. [(100 × $4) + (60 × $3.80)] ÷ (100 + 60) = [$400 + $228] ÷ 160 = $628 ÷ 160 = $3.925 or $3.93

INVENTORY VALUATION METHODS For most businesses the physical flow of inventory is "the first item purchased is the first item sold." The **first in, first out** (FIFO) method assumes that the oldest merchandise is sold first. Therefore, the first item purchased is the first item transferred out. For example, milk sold at the supermarket is stocked as first in, first out. As milk is sold, later purchases of milk are added to the back of the shelves.

Example 2

For Wholesale Paint Supply in Example 1 on page 589, find the cost of goods and the value of the inventory using the FIFO method.

STEP 1: Find the cost of goods sold using the FIFO method. Find the items purchased. (Note: This assumes the first items purchased are the items sold first.)

a. Read the table accompanying Example 1; you'll see that 240 units were received. Then, refer to Step 2 in Example 1 on page 589; there were 88 items on hand.
240 − 88 = 152 units sold

b. Under the FIFO method, the 152 units sold were assumed as follows:

Week of	Units Received	Unit Cost	Total Cost
Feb. 1 (Beginning Inventory)	80	$2.15	$172.00
Feb. 8	40	2.25	90.00
Feb. 15	32*	2.30	73.60

*152 (units sold) − 80 − 40 = 32

c. Add the total cost of the units received.
$172.00 + $90.00 + $73.60 = **$335.60 cost of items sold using FIFO**
(Note: You do not include in this step the units received on Feb. 22, because those units will help you calculate the value of the inventory, as you'll see next in Step 2.)

STEP 2: Find the value of the inventory using FIFO. (Note: There are 88 units on hand—refer to Step 2 in Example 1.)

a. The items remaining were:

Week of	Units Received	Unit Cost	Total Cost
Feb. 15	48**	$2.30	$110.40
Feb. 22	40	2.40	96.00

590 ◄ Chapter 18 Warehousing and Distributing

PROBLEM SOLVING

FIFO and LIFO

Point out that with average cost you must round off the average cost per unit to the nearest cent before continuing. Find the value of the inventory on the 30th using the average cost, FIFO, and LIFO methods. **Avg. Cost = $7 × 65 = $455. FIFO = ($8 × 30) + ($7.50 × 35) = highest $502.50. LIFO = ($6 × 50) + ($7.50 × 15) = lowest $412.50**

Date	Unit Cost	In	Out	Bal.
1	$6.00	50		50
8			30	20
14	$7.50	40		60
22			25	35
30	$8.00	30		65

** If you go back to Example 1 on page 589, you'll notice that originally on Feb. 15, 80 units were received. But out of that 80 on Feb. 15, only 32 were purchased. Therefore, 80 − 32 = 48. (There are 48 items remaining in inventory.)

    b. Find the value of the ending inventory. (Note: The cost of the ending inventory is computed by using the cost of the most recent units received.)

      $110.40 + $96.00 = **$206.40 value of inventory**

Some businesses might use the **last in, first out** (LIFO) method. This assumes that the most recently purchased merchandise is sold first. The LIFO method assumes that units purchased first are still on hand at the end of the period. The physical flow of a stone and gravel company is last in, first out. When new gravel is purchased, it's placed on top of the old gravel at the bottom of the pile.

(Example 3)

For Wholesale Paint Supply in Example 1 on page 589, find the cost of goods and the value of the inventory using the LIFO method.

STEP 1: Find the items purchased.

    a. Read the table accompanying Example 1; you'll see that 240 units were received. Then, refer to Step 2 in Example 1 on page 589; there were 88 items on hand.

      240 − 88 = 152 units sold

    b. Under the LIFO method, the 152 units received were as follows:

Week of	Units Received	Unit Cost	Total Cost
Feb. 22	40	$2.40	$ 96.00
Feb. 15	80	2.30	184.00
Feb. 8	32*	2.25	72.00

    *152 (units sold) − 80 − 40 = 32 (units received)

    c. Add the total cost of the units received.

      $96.00 + 184.00 + 72.00 = **$352.00 cost of units sold using LIFO**

STEP 2: Find the value of the inventory using LIFO. (Note: There are 88 units on hand—refer to Step 2 in Example 1 on page 589.)

    a. The items remaining were:

Week of	Units Received	Unit Cost	Total Cost
Feb. 1	80	$2.15	$172.00
Feb. 8	8**	2.25	18.00

    ** If you go back to Example 1, Step 2 on page 589, you'll notice that 88 units were on hand. Of that 88 on hand, on Feb. 1, 80 units were sold. Therefore, 88 − 80 = 8 (units received).

    b. Find the value of the ending inventory.

      $172.00 + $18.00 = **$190.00 value of inventory using LIFO**

Motivating the Lesson

Complete the table.

Date	Receipts	Unit Cost	Total Cost
2/3	34	$4.05	$137.70
2/18	42	4.12	173.04
2/27	39	4.15	161.85
Total 115		Total	$472.59

What is the average cost? **$4.11**

In-Class Examples

Find the average cost per unit and the inventory value.

1. Total cost of units: $425.
   Number received: 100.
   Number on hand: 75.
   $4.25; $318.75
2. Total cost of units: $509.78.
   Number received: 142.
   Number on hand: 86.
   $3.59; $308.74
3. Total cost of units: $1,316.79.
   Number received: 187.
   Number on hand: 123.
   $7.04; $865.92

ALTERNATIVE ASSESSMENT STRATEGIES

Students with Hearing Impairments

Students with hearing impairments can and do participate in a wide range of classroom activities. To encourage their maximum participation, look toward these students when you speak. Do this even if the student talks with the assistance of an interpreter. This allows the student with hearing impairments the option of viewing you and your lip movements directly. If class materials involve technical terminology, supply a list of these words in advance to the student and his or her interpreter. Unfamiliar words can be difficult to lip-read or sign without prior exposure.

ASSESS

Error Analysis

Remind students to round the average cost per unit to the nearest cent before they use the figure in the inventory value formula. If students do not round first, the inventory values may differ slightly from the correct answers. You may want to give students an example to point out the importance of rounding. For instance, suppose the total cost of units is $215.67 and the number of units received is 42. The number of units on hand is 39. So, the average cost per unit is $215.67 ÷ 42 = $5.135, or $5.14, and the inventory value is $5.14 × 39 = $200.46. If $5.135 was used instead of $5.14, the inventory value would be $5.135 × 39 = $200.265, or $200.27.

SELF-CHECK✓

3. (100 × $4.00) +
(10 × $3.80) =
$400.00 + $38.00
= $438.00;
50 × $3.80 =
$190.00

CONCEPT CHECK

Complete the problems, then check your answers at the end of the chapter.

Assume the 100 packs of felt pens purchased at $4.00 each in Self-Check Problem 1 were purchased first before the 60 packs of felt pens purchased at $3.80 each. There were 50 packs left.

3. Find the cost of goods sold and value of the inventory using FIFO.

4. Find the cost of goods sold and value of the inventory using LIFO.
(60 × $3.80) + (50 × $4.00) = $228.00 + $200.00 = $428.00;
50 × $4.00 = $200.00

SECTION 18-3 PRACTICE

5. Kitchen World is valuing its inventory of popcorn poppers. On June 1 Kitchen World had 23 poppers on hand.
   a. What is the average cost per popper? **$22.15**
   b. What is the value of the inventory of poppers on June 1? **$509.45**

Week of	Units Received	Unit Cost	Total Cost
May 1	40	$22.10	$ 884.00
May 8	36	22.15	797.40
May 15	24	22.20	532.80
May 22	36	22.15	797.40
May 29	12	22.25	267.00
Total	148	—	$3,278.60

6. Office Town is valuing its inventory of laser printer toner cartridges. On April 1 it had 53 cartridges on hand.
   a. What is the average cost per cartridge? **$66.05**
   b. What is the value of the inventory of cartridges on April 1? **$3,500.65**

Date	Units Received	Unit Cost	Total Cost
01/12	50	$66.30	$ 3,315.00
02/11	65	66.10	4,296.50
03/21	80	65.85	5,268.00
Total	195	—	$12,879.50

For Problems 7 and 8, complete the tables and answer the questions.

7. Sealing tape.
Number on hand on April 30 is 260.
   a. What is the average cost per unit? **$0.91**
   b. What is the value of the inventory? **$236.60**

Date	Units Received	Unit Cost	Total Cost
3/10	1,152	$0.89	$1,025.28
4/22	936	0.94	$879.84
Total	2,088	—	$1,905.12

8. Coffee packets—case of 36.
Number on hand on February 8 is 20.
   a. What is the average cost per case? **$18.77**
   b. What is the value of the inventory? **$375.40**

Date	Units Received	Unit Cost	Total Cost
12/18	50	$17.99	$899.50
01/10	50	19.79	$989.50
02/06	40	18.48	$739.20
Total	140	—	$2,628.20

9. Records for Chief Super Market show this opening balance and these receipts for soup in November. At the end of the month, 31 cans were on hand. What is the value of the inventory using the average-cost method? **$40.61**

Date	Units Received	Unit Cost
11/01 (Opening bal.)	94	$1.32
11/10	72	1.30
11/17	36	1.32
11/24	48	1.31

10. At the end of the month, 79 packages of windshield wipers were on hand. Find the value of the inventory using the average-cost method. **$752.08**

Date	Units Received	Unit Cost
5/01	96	$9.43
5/19	72	9.56
5/31	48	9.63

11. The Leisure Company, a swimming pool supply company, uses the FIFO method of valuing inventory. As of May 20 the Leisure Company had sold 160 of the tubs of chlorine.

Date	Units Received	Unit Cost	Total Cost
5/01	100	$9.65	$965.00
5/08	65	9.75	$633.75
5/19	145	9.90	$1,435.50
Total	310		$3,034.25

 a. Complete the records for units received of tubs of chlorine.
 b. Use the FIFO method to calculate the cost of the 160 tubs sold. **$1,550**
 c. Use the FIFO method to calculate the value of the 150 tubs in stock. **$1,484.25**

100 at $9.65	=	$965
60 at $9.75	=	$585
160 Total		**$1,550**

Of the 65 received on 5/8

5 at $9.75	=	$48.75
145 at $9.90	=	$1,435.50
150 Total		**$1,484.25**

12. a. (100 × $9.65) + (50 × $9.75) = $965.00 + $487.50 = $1,452.50

12. The Leisure Company switches to the LIFO method of valuing inventory.
 a. Use the LIFO method to calculate the value of the Leisure Company's 150 tubs in stock in Problem 11 above.
 b. Use the average-cost method to calculate the value of the Leisure Company's 150 tubs in stock in Problem 11 above.
 Avg. = ($3,034.25 ÷ 310) = $9.79; 150 × $9.79 = $1,468.50

MAINTAINING YOUR SKILLS

Need Help? Go to...
→ Skill 8: Multiplying Decimals, page 735
→ Skill 11: Dividing Decimals, page 738

Multiply.

13. 50 × $8.40 **$420**　**14.** 100 × $17.85 **$1,785**　**15.** 72 × $36.90 **$2,656.80**

16. 144 × $141.73 **$20,409.12**　**17.** 36 × $0.87 **$31.32**　**18.** 119 × $47.87 **$5,696.53**

Divide. Round answers to the nearest cent.

19. $1,046.25 ÷ 125 **$8.37**　**20.** $438.70 ÷ 28 **$15.67**　**21.** $314.91 ÷ 92 **$3.42**

22. $30,613.74 ÷ 216 **$141.73**　**23.** $357.81 ÷ 410 **$0.87**　**24.** $9,012.31 ÷ 187 **$48.19**

Closing Activity

Find the average cost per unit and the inventory value.

1. Total cost of units: $350. Number received: 125. Number on hand: 100. **$2.80; $280**

2. Total cost of units: $644.36. Number received: 178. Number on hand: 152. **$3.62; $550.24**

3. Total cost of units: $1,205.37. Number received: 227. Number on hand: 216. **$5.31; $1,146.96**

4. Celestial Carpets is valuing its inventory of area rugs. At the end of the month, 52 area rugs were on hand. What is the value of the inventory? **$1,990.04**

Date	Receipts	Unit Cost
10/4	56	$38.99
10/18	60	37.59
10/31	54	38.29

WRAP-UP

Go over any problem for which a wrong answer is given.

Assignment Guide
　Basic: 5–6
　Average: 7–9

20 min.

National Standards for Business Education

Standard 1	Mathematical Foundations
Standard 2	Number Relationships and Operations

National Council of Teachers of Mathematics Standards

Standard 1	Numbers and Operations
Standard 6	Problem Solving
Standard 8	Communication

1 FOCUS

Have students discuss why businesses carry an inventory. Point out that it is important for businesses to have enough products on hand to meet the needs of customers. If a business does not have a product that a customer needs, then that means the loss of a sale for the business.

In-Class Examples

Work through these exercises with students before having them do the Self-Check.
1. $850 × 20% **$170**
2. $1,890 × 30% **$567**
3. $1,200.70 × 22% **$264.15**

2 TEACH

Discuss with students the factors involved with carrying an inventory. Have students describe some different businesses and the costs that may be involved with carrying an inventory for the business. **(Point out that a business does not want to carry too much inventory since it costs the business money.)** It's unwise to keep products in inventory if they don't sell in a timely fashion.

594

SECTION (18-4) Carrying an Inventory

Section Objective

Calculate the annual cost of carrying an inventory.

Your business must keep a sufficient inventory of goods to meet production or sales needs. Based on past records, you may estimate the annual cost of maintaining (or carrying) the inventory at a certain level for the coming year. The annual cost is often expressed as a percent of the value of the inventory. The annual cost of carrying the inventory includes taxes, insurance, storage fees, handling charges, and so on. You'll need to remember that:

Annual Cost of Carrying Inventory = Inventory Value × Percent

Living in the Real World

Auto Do It Right

Analyze Your Goods   By looking through the records for the past three years, the cost of insurance, taxes, and storage for the inventory in the warehouse is pretty high, Armin decides. They have to pay twice for handling—once when items are delivered to the warehouse, and then again when they transport them from the warehouse to the stores.

Draw Conclusions   Companies estimate that the cost of maintaining inventory to be around what percent?

Continued on page 596

Example 1

Steel Facilitators estimates the annual cost of maintaining the inventory to be 25 percent of the value of the inventory. This year the company plans to maintain an inventory totaling $500,000 in value. What amount should be set as the estimated cost of carrying the inventory for the year?

STEP: Find the annual cost of carrying inventory.

Inventory Value × Percent

$500,000   ×   25%   = **$125,000 annual cost of carrying inventory**

500000 ⊠ 25 % 125000

CONCEPT CHECK

SELF-CHECK ✓

Complete the problems, then check your answers at the end of the chapter. Find the annual cost of carrying an inventory.

1. Inventory value is $200,000. Estimated annual cost is 30 percent of value. **$200,000 × 0.30 = $60,000**

2. Inventory value is $85,000. Estimated annual cost is 20 percent of value. **$85,000 × 0.20 = $17,000**

Living in the Real World

Answers will vary from company to company, as the cost of maintaining inventory is usually calculated as a percent of the value of the inventory.

TECHNOLOGY POWER

With the adoption of the Universal Product Code (UPC) as the standard for retail grocery stores in the late 70's, the use of bar coding has grown dramatically. Bar codes increase the efficiency and accuracy of data entry by reducing the employee time required to input data. Handheld bar code readers that transmit on radio frequencies use lasers to scan the UPC codes on items received into inventory and immediately update the inventory tracking system.

SECTION 18-4 PRACTICE

Find the annual cost of carrying an inventory.

	Value of Inventory	Percent	Annual Cost of Carrying Inventory
3.	$ 960	25.0%	$240
4.	14,000	35.0%	$4,900
5.	7,800	15.0%	$1,170
6.	41,840	22.0%	$9,204.80
7.	134,786	28.5%	$38,414.01
8.	514,795	32.5%	$167,308.38

9. Central Drug Stores estimates the cost of carrying its inventory of goods to be 18 percent of the value of the merchandise. About how much does it cost Central Drug Stores annually to carry a $181,560 inventory? **$32,680.80**

10. Iron and Steel carries a $564,800 inventory. The company estimates the annual cost of carrying the inventory at 27 percent of the value of the inventory. What is the approximate annual cost of carrying the inventory?
$152,496

11. Red Hardware estimates the annual cost of carrying its inventory at 25 percent of the value of the inventory. The 25 percent is broken down as follows:

11. a.
		Type of Expense	Percent
4.0%	$15,200	Spoilage and physical deterioration	4.0%
8.0%	$30,400	Interest	8.0%
10.0%	$38,000	Handling	10.0%
2.0%	$ 7,600	Storage facilities	2.0%
0.5%	$ 1,900	Taxes	0.5%
0.5%	$ 1,900	Insurance	0.5%
25.0%	$95,000	Total	25.0%

   a. Red Hardware generally carries an inventory valued at $380,000. What is the approximate annual cost for each expense of carrying the inventory?

   b. With the advent of on-time shipping, Red Hardware was able to reduce its inventory to three-fourths of its value and still meet customer orders. About how much did Red Hardware save on the total cost of carrying its inventory? **$23,750**

12.
4.0%	$11,400
8.0%	$22,800
10.0%	$28,500
2.0%	$ 5,700
0.5%	$ 1,425
0.5%	$ 1,425
25.0%	$71,250

12. In Problem 11, if Red Hardware carried an inventory valued at $285,000, what would be the approximate annual cost for each expense of carrying the inventory?

Need Help? Go to...
> Skill 30: Finding the Percentage, page 757

MAINTAINING YOUR SKILLS

Multiply.

13. $120,000 × 20% **$24,000**

14. $96,400 × 25% **$24,100**

15. $146,500 × 30% **$43,990**

16. $196,750 × 15% **$29,512.50**

17. $71,630 × 35% **$25,070.50**

18. $347,840 × 28% **$97,395.20**

Section 18-4 Carrying an Inventory ▶ **595**

In-Class Example

1. ABC Retail Goods estimates the cost of carrying its inventory to be 24 percent of the value of the merchandise. About how much does is cost ABC annually to carry a $34,750 inventory? **$8,340**

3 ASSESS

Error Analysis

For students who must find the cost of each expense involved with carrying an inventory, have them check their results. If students do not get the same figure, then they will know that some of their calculations are incorrect.

4 CLOSE

Closing Activity

Find the annual cost of carrying an inventory.

1. Inventory value: $980. Percent: 20%. **$196**

2. Inventory value: $1,250.65. Percent: 27%. **$337.68**

3. Inventory value: $2,549.89. Percent: 18.5%. **$471.73**

4. Ace Metals estimates the cost of carrying its inventory to be 26 percent of the value of the merchandise. About how much does it cost Ace annually to carry a $145,250 inventory? **$37,765**

WRAP-UP

Go over any problem for which a wrong answer is given.

Assignment Guide
   Basic: 3–8
   Average: 9–10

20 min.

National Standards for Business Education

Standard 1	Mathematical Foundations
Standard 2	Number Relationships and Operations

National Council of Teachers of Mathematics Standards

Standard 1	Numbers and Operations
Standard 6	Problem Solving
Standard 8	Communication

FOCUS

Ask students if they know how products are shipped. Have students estimate how much they think it would cost to ship a carton that weighs 650 pounds from Chicago to Detroit. In Example 1 on page 596, students will find out whether their estimates are reasonable.

In-Class Examples

Work through these exercises with students before having them do the Self-Check.

1. $31.45 + $199.50 + $60.75 + $23.67 **$315.37**
2. $4.95 × (800 ÷ 100) **$39.60**
3. $632.57 × 5% **$31.63**

○ **Section Objective**

Work out the total door-to-door shipping costs.

SECTION 18-5 Door-to-Door Transportation Cost

There are a number of ways to ship goods, such as barge, train, truck, airplane, or a combination of these. Many shippers transport items door-to-door. Door-to-door means the shipper picks up the item and delivers it to its destination. The shipping cost may include air freight costs as well as trucking costs.

The cost of shipping depends on the weight of the item and the speed of the delivery. Next-day delivery costs more than second-day delivery. Remember that:

$$\text{Shipping Costs} = \text{Weight} \times \text{Base Rate}$$

Living in the Real World

Auto Do It Right

Formula for a Speedy Delivery Rasheed and Armin continue to discuss the best solution to maintaining profits, inventory, and customers.

"Since the cost of shipment depends on weight, not distance," Armin says, "it will not cost us anything extra to have our suppliers deliver directly to the stores in the city rather than to the warehouse in the suburbs."

Draw Conclusions Why should they consider getting rid of the warehouse in lieu of a door-to-door shipment method?

Continued on page 599

Example 1

The Innovative Auto Company is shipping 650 pounds of automotive equipment from Chicago to Detroit. The shipment will be sent Guaranteed Overnight. What is the total cost of shipping the equipment? (Use Figure 18.1 on page 597 to solve the problem.)

STEP 1: Find the shipping charge per 100 pounds sent Guaranteed Overnight. It is $155.85 per 100 pounds.

STEP 2: Find the shipping costs.

$$\frac{\text{Weight}}{100 \text{ lbs.}} \times \text{Base Rate}$$

$$\frac{650}{100} \times \$155.85 = \$1,013.025 \text{ or } \$1,013.03 \text{ shipping costs}$$

650 ÷ 100 × 155.85 = 1013.025

Living in the Real World

In this case, it won't cost the company any more to have suppliers deliver directly to the stores in the city; no longer using the warehouse will prove more cost effective.

Figure 18.1

Door-to-Door Shipping Cost per 100 lbs. for Selected Routes							
City	City	Guaranteed First Arrival	Guaranteed Overnight	Standard Overnight	Guaranteed Second Day	Standard Second Day	BAX Saver
Atlanta	Dallas/ Ft Worth	$196.00	$186.25	$145.30	$127.75	$108.25	$46.00
Boston	Miami	196.00	186.25	145.30	127.75	108.25	46.00
Chicago	Detroit	164.00	155.85	121.62	106.95	90.65	46.00
Denver	Sacramento	196.00	186.25	145.30	127.75	108.25	46.00
Los Angeles	Asheville, NC	266.00	252.75	197.10	173.25	146.75	62.00
Tampa	Syracuse	196.00	186.25	145.30	127.75	108.25	46.00
Memphis	Miami	164.00	155.85	121.62	106.95	90.65	46.00
Syracuse	New Orleans	216.00	205.25	160.10	140.75	119.25	62.00
San Diego	Portland, OR	164.00	155.85	121.62	106.95	90.65	46.00
Toledo, OH	Missoula, MT	241.00	230.25	185.10	165.75	144.25	87.00
St. Louis	Cedar Rapids, IA	164.00	155.85	121.62	106.95	90.65	46.00
Salt Lake City	Fairbanks, AK			310.90		237.75	

CONCEPT CHECK

Complete the problems, then check your answers at the end of the chapter. Find the shipping costs if the auto parts in Example 1 on page 596 were shipped:

1. Standard Overnight.
   $121.62; $121.62 × (650 ÷ 100) = $790.53

2. BAX Saver.
   $46.00; $46.00 × (650 ÷ 100) = $299.00

— **Example 2** —

Jarvis Boyers is the shipping clerk for Computer Design, Inc. Boyers needs to ship 330 pounds of computers from the factory in Los Angeles to a dealer in Asheville, North Carolina. Find the difference in shipping cost between the BAX Saver rate and the Guaranteed First Arrival rate.

STEP 1: Find the shipping charge for 100 pounds of Guaranteed First Arrival. It is $266.00 per 100 pounds.

STEP 2: Find the shipping charge for 100 pounds of BAX Saver. It is $62.00 per 100 pounds.

STEP 3: Find the shipping costs.

$$\text{Weight} \times \text{Base Rate}$$
$$(330 \div 100) \times (\$266.00 - \$62.00) =$$
$$3.30 \times \$204.00 = \$673.20 \text{ difference in shipping costs}$$

USING CALCULATORS

You will most likely use the calculator for all math classes that you take now and in the future. The more features a calculator has, the more versatile the calculator is. Having a store key, as well as parenthesis, and several other functions will make your calculator more user friendly. It is suggested that you purchase a scientific calculator as opposed to a basic four-function calculator.

② TEACH

Point out that there are several major companies that will ship items for you. You may want to get a list of some of the rates to show students. Many companies post their rates online. Point out that some companies even have online tracking so you can check the status of your shipment at any given time. The United States Postal Service ships items for businesses, as well. The rates can also be found online.

In addition to cost based on weight, cost may also be based on package size. Sometimes if a package exceeds allotted dimensions, there is an additional charge.

Motivating the Lesson

Use **Figure 18.1** to find the door-to-door shipping cost per 100 pounds for each route.

1. Memphis to Miami, Standard Overnight **$121.62**
2. Syracuse to New Orleans, BAX Saver **$62.00**
3. Los Angeles to Asheville, N.C., Guaranteed First Arrival **$266.00**

In-Class Examples

Use **Figure 18.1** on page 597 to find the total shipping cost.

1. From Boston to Miami. 200 pounds. Guaranteed Overnight. **$372.50**
2. From Toledo to Missoula. 340 pounds. Guaranteed First Arrival. **$819.40**
3. Dine Time Tables is shipping a package that weighs 165 pounds from Chicago to Detroit. What is the difference in shipping cost between the Guaranteed Second Day and the Standard Second Day? **$26.90**

597

SECTION 18-5

Error Analysis

Remind students that **Figure 18.1** on page 597 gives the shipping costs per 100 pounds. Students may mistakenly use the figure given in the table and multiply it by the weight of the item being shipped. This would result in extremely large shipping costs. Encourage students to always look at their answers and check whether they seem reasonable.

4 CLOSE

Closing Activity

Use **Figure 18.1** on page 597 to find the total shipping cost.

1. From St. Louis to Cedar Rapids
    500 pounds
    Standard Overnight **$608.10**

2. From Tampa to Syracuse
    497 pounds
    Guaranteed Overnight
    $925.66

3. From Atlanta to Dallas/Ft. Worth
    1,050 pounds BAX Saver
    $483.00

4. A crate of pottery that weighs 237 pounds is shipped from Boston to Miami. The shipment is sent Standard Overnight. What is the total shipping cost? **$344.36**

5. Galaxy Appliances plans to ship a stove that weighs 175 pounds from San Diego to Portland, Oregon. What is the difference in shipping cost between the Standard Second Day and the BAX Saver? **$78.14**

SELF-CHECK ✓

3. $252.75; $62.00;
   ($252.75 − $62.00)
   × (330 ÷ 100) =
   $629.475 or
   $629.48

CONCEPT CHECK

Complete the problems, then check your answers at the end of the chapter. Find the difference in shipping costs for the computers in Example 2 if the computers are shipped. Use Figure 18.1 on page 597 for Problems 3 and 4.

3. Guaranteed Overnight versus BAX Saver.

4. Standard Overnight versus Standard Second Day.
    $197.10; $146.75; ($197.10 − $146.75) × (330 ÷ 100) = $166.155 or $166.16

SECTION 18-5 PRACTICE

Find the shipping costs. Use Figure 18.1 on page 597 for Problems 5–11.

	From	To	Arrival	Weight (in lbs.)	Cost per 100 lbs.	Total
5.	Atlanta	Dallas/ Fort Worth	Guaranteed First	600	a. $196.00	b. $1,176.00
6.	Tampa	Syracuse	Standard Second Day	350	a. $108.25	b. $378.88
7.	Syracuse	New Orleans	Standard Overnight	759	a. $160.10	b. $1,215.16
8.	Toledo, OH	Missoula, MT	BAX Saver	1,230	a. $87.00	b. $1,070.10

9. A crate of musical instruments that weighs 470 pounds is shipped from Memphis to Miami. The shipment will be sent Guaranteed First Arrival. What is the total shipping cost? How much less is it to ship by BAX Saver?
    $770.80; $554.60

10. A crate of prototype Global Positioning System instruments that weighs 225 pounds is shipped from Tampa to Syracuse. The shipment will be sent Guaranteed First Arrival. What is the total shipping cost? How much less is it to ship by Guaranteed Overnight? **$441.00; $21.94**

11. AB Consultants in San Diego is shipping a special radio antenna for a fishing vessel docked in Portland, Oregon. Because the antenna exceeds 174 inches in length, it is subject to an oversize surcharge of 30 percent of the freight cost.
    a. If the crate weighs 190 pounds and is shipped Guaranteed Overnight, how much are the shipping costs? **$384.95**
    b. How much is saved if the antenna is shipped BAX Saver? **$271.33**

Need Help? Go to...
▶ Skill 30: **Finding the Percentage,** page 757
▶ Skill 5: **Adding Decimals,** page 732

MAINTAINING YOUR SKILLS

Find the percentage. Round answers to the nearest cent.

12. $417.80 × 5% **$20.89**   13. $1,216.90 × 6% **$73.01**

14. $641.85 × 5½% **$35.30**   15. $347.84 × 6½% **$22.61**

Add.

16. $54.50 + $317.80 + $41.70 + $15.89 **$429.89**

17. $31.75 + $743.86 + $71.80 + $44.63 **$892.04**

WRAP-UP

Go over any problem for which a wrong answer is given.

Assignment Guide
  Basic: 5–8
Average: 9–10

20 min.

SECTION 18·6 Transportation by Truck

Section Objective

Calculate the total shipping cost by truck.

Your business may use expedited door-to-door direct trucking to ship products. Expedited shipping means that your shipment is given exclusive use of a driver and a truck to move your shipment as quickly as possible.

The basic rates differ according to the weight of the goods and the distance they are being shipped. Most companies charge only for the actual distance the goods are being shipped. Remember that:

$$\text{Shipping Cost} = \text{Number of Miles} \times \text{Rate per Mile}$$

Living in the Real World

Auto Do It Right

Forming a Partnership The Nauwafs decide to close their warehouse and start shipping inventory directly to their three auto parts stores. They'll use overnight shipping for certain orders. For other orders, they'll be able to convince a local trucking company to use expedited shipping.

Draw Conclusions Since the Nauwafs and the trucking company struck a deal, how might they help each other from a business perspective?

Continued on page 603

Example 1

The King Spark Plug Company is shipping 4,470 pounds of spark plugs via Motor Express. Motor Express will pick up the spark plugs at the manufacturing plant and deliver them to an automobile parts distributor. The distance is 325 miles. What is the total shipping cost? (Use Figure 18.2 to solve the problem.)

Figure 18.2

Expedited Door-to-Door Motor Freight Rates in Cost per Mile					
Weight Group (in lbs.)	Minimum Charge	1–99 Miles	100–199 Miles	200–299 Miles	300-plus Miles
0–500	$118.00	$1.74	$1.59	$1.52	$1.48
501–3,000	127.00	1.95	1.83	1.75	1.73
3,001–5,000	169.00	2.97	2.73	2.42	2.21
5,001–13,000	225.00	3.32	2.99	2.69	2.39
13,001–15,000	500.00	5.25	4.30	3.64	3.11

Continued on next page

Living in the Real World

The trucking company could give the Nauwafs a price break on shipments, if they in turn supply needed truck parts when the company's trucks need repair.

National Standards for Business Education

Standard 1	Mathematical Foundations
Standard 2	Number Relationships and Operations

National Council of Teachers of Mathematics Standards

Standard 1	Numbers and Operations
Standard 6	Problem Solving
Standard 8	Communication

1 FOCUS

Have students discuss some items that may be shipped by truck. Have them point out the possible benefits to shipping the items by truck.

In-Class Examples

Work through these exercises with students before having them do the Self-Check.
1. 125 × $1.85 **$231.25**
2. 180 × $1.93 **$347.40**
3. $50 + $50 + $125 + $125 **$350**

STEP 1: Find the basic rate.
    Weight group: 3,001–5,000 pounds
    Distance: 300 plus miles
    $2.21 rate per mile

STEP 2: Find the total shipping cost.
    Number of Miles × Rate per Mile
         325   × $2.21   = **$718.25 total shipping cost**

    325 ☒ 2.21 ▣ 718.25

CONCEPT CHECK

SELF-CHECK✓

Complete the problems, then check your answers at the end of the chapter. Use **Figure 18.2** on page 599 to find the basic rate and then the shipping cost.

1. Ship 420 pounds, 125 miles.
   $1.59; $1.59 × 125 = $198.75

2. Ship 3,250 pounds, 310 miles.
   $2.21; $2.21 × 310 = $685.10

ACCESSORIAL CHARGES You may have accessorial charges such as those shown in **Figure 18.3.** Accessorial charges apply to special services beyond just moving the goods from one location to another. If the driver is detained at the unloading dock, you'll be charged an extra hourly fee.

Figure 18.3

Accessorial Charges	
Collect-on-Delivery (COD)—Fee	$ 50.00
Detention Time after 2 Hours—Hourly Rate	50.00
Hand Loading or Unloading—Hourly Rate	35.00
Hazardous Materials	75.00
Lift Gate Required on Truck	125.00
Pickup/Delivery—Holidays	125.00
Second Person—Hourly Rate	50.00
Stop Off—Multiple Drops—Each	50.00

(Example 2)

The King Spark Plug Company is shipping 2,400 pounds of spark plugs via Motor Express. Motor Express will pick up the spark plugs at the manufacturing plant and deliver them to two automobile parts distributors. The total distance is 248 miles and requires a truck with a lift gate, an hour of unloading by hand, and the second stop requires a COD collection. What is the total shipping cost?

STEP 1: Find the shipping cost.
    Number of Miles × Rate per Mile
         248   × $1.75   = $434.00 shipping cost

② TEACH

In Section 18-1, students learned about volume as it relates to storage space. Remind students about the section. Point out that volume must be taken into consideration when transporting products by truck. A limited amount of space is available on each truck. Some other considerations when transporting by truck are weight, type of product, distance involved, and cost.

Sometimes there are additional costs. **Figure 18.3** on page 600 lists some costs that businesses may have when using truck transportation. These accessorial charges can sometimes add a significant additional expense to the cost of transportation.

Motivating the Lesson

Have students work in groups. Each group should write a problem that consists of a specific type of item being shipped, the weight of the shipment, and the distance. Each group should present their problem to the class. At the end of the section, students can solve the problems. **Answers will vary.**

In-Class Examples

Use **Figures 18.2** (on page 599) and **18.3** to find the total shipping cost.
1. Weight: 450 pounds.
   Distance: 126 miles. **$200.34**
2. Weight: 10,782 pounds.
   Distance: 410 miles.
   Accessorial charges: hazardous materials. **$1,054.90**
3. Weight: 23,980 pounds.
   Distance: 123 miles.
   Accessorial charges: hand loading for 2 hours, holiday. **$723.90**

GLOBAL PERSPECTIVE

Airfreight
Students pick three cities in different countries outside the United States. They have 3 boxes of books that weigh 50 lbs. each. Have them check on the Internet or call an airfreight company, such as Federal Express, UPS, Emery, or so on, and find out how much it would cost to ship the books to each of the cities they chose. Then have them draw a map showing the route from their hometown to each of the cities and then clearly label the cost of shipment.

COOPERATIVE LEARNING

Ten Questions
Students work in groups of four to develop a ten-question quiz for this chapter. Direct groups to include questions on storage space, taking inventory, valuing an inventory, costs of carrying inventory, transportation by air, and transportation by truck. Groups work together to write, check, and correct an answer sheet. **LS** , **CL**

STEP 2: Find the accessorial charges.

Stop Off + Lift Gate + Unloading by Hand + COD

$50   + $125   + $35   + $50 = $260

STEP 3: Find the total shipping cost.

$434 + $260 = **$694 total shipping cost**

CONCEPT CHECK

Complete the problems, then check your answers at the end of the chapter. Find the total shipping cost.

3. Ship: 800 pounds of shoes, 90 miles, holiday delivery, hand loading and unloading for 2.5 hours. ($1.95 × 90) + ($35 × 2.5) + $125 = $175.50 + $212.50 = **$388.00**

4. Ship: 900 pounds of chemicals, 120 miles, hazardous materials, lift gate, detained 3 hours. ($1.83 × 120) + [$75 + $125 + ($50 × 1)] = $219.60 + $250 = **$469.60**

SECTION 18-6 PRACTICE

Use Figures 18.2 (page 599) and 18.3 (page 600) to find the basic rates.

	Weight (in lbs.)	Distance (in miles)	Basic Rate	Shipping Cost	COD	Lift Gate	Second Person	Total Costs
5.	170	95	$1.74	a.	No	No	No	b.
6.	620	154	1.83	a.	Yes	Yes	No	b.
7.	1,476	86	a.	b.	No	Yes	3 hrs	c.
8.	5,719	212	a.	b.	No	No	5 hrs	c.
9.	33,381	391	a.	b.	No	No	No	c.
10.	3,147	274	a.	b.	Yes	Yes	No	c.

Answers (left margin):

5. a. $165.30
   b. $165.30
6. a. $281.82
   b. $456.82
7. a. $1.95
   b. $167.70
   c. $442.70
8. a. $2.69
   b. $570.28
   c. $820.28
9. a. $3.11
   b. $1,216.01
   c. $1,216.01
10. a. $2.42
    b. $663.08
    c. $838.08

11. A shipment of ski jackets weighing 384 pounds is transported by truck from the Outback Clothing plant to its Waterside warehouse. The distance is 278 miles. It is a COD delivery on a holiday and requires 1 hour of hand unloading. What is the total shipping cost? **$632.56**

12. A shipment of brooms and brushes is sent by truck from Green Bay, Wisconsin, to St. Louis, Missouri. The distance is 445 miles. The brooms and brushes weigh 2,447 pounds. A lift gate is required and the driver was detained 3.5 hours. What is the total shipping cost? **$969.85**

13. A 641-pound shipment of seat covers is transported from The Cover Factory to the national distribution center in Chicago. The distance is 124 miles. Hand loading and unloading took 2.5 hours, with 1 stop off. What is the shipping charge? **$364.42**

MAINTAINING YOUR SKILLS

Multiply. Round answers to nearest cent.

14. 4.70 × $32.13 $151.01

15. 11.60 × $20.40 $236.64

16. 41.73 × $15.30 $638.47

17. 14.84 × $31.02 $460.34

18. 5.72 × $12.84 $73.44

19. 17.13 × $12.66 $216.87

20. 7.56 × $27.81 $210.24

21. 20.72 × $17.64 $365.50

22. 81.48 × $10.25 $835.17

SELF-CHECK✓

Need Help? Go to...
▶ **Skill 8: Multiplying Decimals,** page 735

SECTION 18-6

③ ASSESS

Error Analysis

Students sometimes have trouble reading charts and tables. Have students practice reading the rate table. Give students a specific rate to find. For instance, find the rate for shipping 300 pounds a distance of 150 miles. In Example 1 on page 599, change either the weight or the distance and have students recalculate the problem. For example, you could have students find the total shipping cost if the distance is only 200 miles instead of 325 miles.

④ CLOSE

Closing Activity

Use **Figures 18.2** and **18.3** (on pages 599 and 600, respectively) to find the total shipping cost.

1. Weight: 280 pounds. Distance: 112 miles. **$178.08**
2. Weight: 5,045 pounds. Distance: 78 miles. **$258.96**
3. Weight: 7,824 pounds. Distance: 315 miles. Accessorial charges: COD fee, holiday. **$927.85**
4. Weight: 23,000 pounds. Distance: 400 miles. Accessorial charges: unloading for 1 hour, lift gate, 3 drops. **$1,554**
5. A shipment of birdbaths weighing 458 pounds is transported by truck. The distance is 206 miles. It is a COD delivery and requires 1.5 hours of hand unloading. What is the total shipping cost? **$415.62**

ALTERNATIVE ASSESSMENT

Write it Down

A student, Ronnie Purnell, has a hint for others: For a particularly difficult formula that you can't remember, review your index cards or study aid to read the formula right before a test is handed out, and then immediately write the formula down somewhere on the answer sheet. More hints like this are available online at www.introbus.glencoe.com. Choose the Student Site, then click on *Homework Hints*.

WRAP-UP

Go over any problem for which a wrong answer is given.

Assignment Guide
  Basic: 5–10
  Average: 11–12

20 min.

Quick Quiz

1. A carton has dimensions 2 ft × 3 ft × 2 ft. Find the storage space needed for 60 cartons. **720 ft³**

2. Home Paint had 150 pints of black satin paint in inventory at the beginning of the month. The store had 50 receipts and 45 issues of the paint during the month. Find the inventory at the end of the month. **155**

3. Find the average cost per unit if 50 items are purchased at $5.00 each and 20 items are purchased at $4.50 each. **$4.86**

4. Home for You estimates the cost of carrying its inventory to be 28 percent of the value of the merchandise. About how much does it cost the store annually to carry a $120,000 inventory? **$33,600**

5. Use **Figure 18.2** on page 599 to find the basic rate and total shipping cost for a weight of 600 pounds and a distance of 390 miles. **$1.73; $674.70**

CHAPTER **18**

Self-Check Answers

SECTION 18-1 **CONCEPT CHECK** (p. 583)

1. Volume per item = 12 in × 12 in × 18 in = 2,592 cubic in
   Storage space = 2,592 cubic in × 20 = **51,840 cubic in**

2. Volume per item = 13.25 in × 16 in × 10 in = 2,120 cubic in
   Storage space = 2,120 cubic in × 36 = **76,320 cubic in**

3. 51,840 ÷ 1,728 = **30 cubic feet**

4. 76,320 ÷ 1,728 = 44.16 cubic feet = **44 cubic feet**

SECTION 18-2 **CONCEPT CHECK** (p. 585, 586)

1. 82 + 15 − 65 = **32**   2. 220 + 70 − 180 = **110**
3. 300 + 120 − 150 = **270**   4. 270 + 80 − 140 = **210**
5. a. March = **210 from end of February**   b. 210 + 120 − 100 = **230**
6. a. April = **230 from end of March**   b. 230 + 0 − 80 = **150**

SECTION 18-3 **CONCEPT CHECK** (p. 590, 592)

1. [(100 × $4) + (60 × $3.80)] ÷ (100 + 60) = [$400 + $228] ÷ 160 =
   $628 ÷ 160 = **$3.925 or $3.93**

2. 50 × $3.93 = **$196.50**

3. (100 × $4.00) + (10 × $3.80) = $400.00 + $38.00 = **$438.00;**
   50 × $3.80 = **$190.00**

4. (60 × $3.80) + (50 × $4.00) = $228.00 + $200.00 = **$428.00;**
   50 × $4.00 = **$200.00**

SECTION 18-4 **CONCEPT CHECK** (p. 594)

1. $200,000 × 0.30 = **$60,000**   2. $85,000 × 0.20 = **$17,000**

SECTION 18-5 **CONCEPT CHECK** (p. 597, 598)

1. $121.62; $121.62 × (650 ÷ 100) = **$790.53**

2. $46.00; $46.00 × (650 ÷ 100) = **$299.00**

3. $252.75; $62.00; ($252.75 − $62.00) × (330 ÷ 100) = **$629.475 or $629.48**

4. $197.10; $146.75; ($197.10 − $146.75) × (330 ÷ 100) = **$166.155 or $166.16**

SECTION 18-6 **CONCEPT CHECK** (p. 600, 601)

1. $1.59; $1.59 × 125 = **$198.75**

2. $2.21; $2.21 × 310 = **$685.10**

3. ($1.95 × 90) + ($35 × 2.5) + $125 = $175.50 + $212.50 = **$388.00**

4. ($1.83 × 120) + [$75 + $125 + ($50 × 1)] = $219.60 + $250 = **$469.60**

602 ◄ Chapter 18 **Warehousing and Distributing**

Living in the Real World

Auto Do It Right

Assessment   For a business, the physical handling and movement of products in warehousing and transportation vary depending on the product characteristics. The procedures a business implements on handling goods increase the efficiency of a warehouse and improve customer service.

Physical distribution includes the process of moving products from producers to customers (e.g., inventory control, transportation, warehousing, and materials handling). Without logistics of how the physical distribution works, a business is left with inadequate service and maximum costs.

In the chain of delivery from manufacturer to consumer, returns are a fact of life. To succeed in today's marketplace, businesses must develop a strategy to handle returned merchandise. They must plan an efficient way to receive, inspect, and record the returns, as well as transform returns into profits.

❶ Creative Thinking. You are in charge of managing returns for a new catalog company that specializes in items for the home. What issues will you have to deal with in terms of merchandise and customers?

❷ Analyze. Business today boils down to one word: trust. How does a customer's trust in a company relate to the issue of returns?

Living in the Real World

1. Damaged goods, how to account for damaged goods, where to place returned goods—discard or place on sale, and so on.
2. good return policy, happy customer service representative.

REVIEW OF KEY WORDS

warehouse (p. 582)
inventory (p. 585)
inventory card (p. 585)

average-cost method (p. 589)
first in, first out (p. 590)
last in, first out (p. 591)

Match one of the key words above with a definition below.

1. a way of calculating an inventory's value.
2. the number of each item you have in stock. **inventory**
3. a place in which to keep products until they are needed. **warehouse**

4. used to keep a record of the items on hand.
5. assumes the oldest merchandise is sold first. **first in, first out**
6. assumes the most recently purchased merchandise is sold first. **last in, first out**

4. inventory card

1. average-cost method

Skills and Concepts

SECTION OBJECTIVE 18-1 AND EXAMPLES

Compute the total storage space.

MMX Marketing has to store boxes of key chains. Each box measures 15 inches by 12.5 inches by 6 inches. How much space is needed for 1,000 boxes?

STEP 1: Find the volume per item.

Length × Width × Height
15 inches × 12.5 inches × 6 inches
= 1,125 cubic inches per item

STEP 2: Find the storage space.

Volume per Item × Number of Items
1,125 cubic inches × 1,000 boxes
= **1,125,000 cubic inches storage space**

REVIEW EXERCISES

Find the storage space.

	Boxed Item	Unit of Measure	Carton Dimensions (Length × Width × Height)			×	Number of Items	=	Storage Space	
7.	Air compressor	Feet	(2.0 ×	2.0 ×	3.0)	×	30	=	360	cubic ft
8.	Tomatoes—1 bushel	Inches	(16.0 ×	12.0 ×	10.5)	×	15	=	30,240	cubic in
9.	Kitchen sink	Feet	(1.5 ×	2.0 ×	1.0)	×	35	=	105	cubic ft
10.	Eggs—1 case	Inches	(22.0 ×	24.0 ×	10.0)	×	100	=	528,000	cubic in
11.	Lawn mower	Feet	(5.0 ×	3.0 ×	4.0)	×	22	=	1,320	cubic ft
12.	Dictionary	Inches	(8.0 ×	5.0 ×	2.0)	×	25	=	2,000	cubic in

SECTION OBJECTIVE 18-2 AND EXAMPLES

Calculate the total inventory.

Office Store has 135 electric pencil sharpeners in stock on December 1. During December it received 100 and sold 120. How many are in stock on January 1?

STEP: Calculate the total inventory.

Previous Inventory + Receipts − Issues
135 + 100 − 120 = **115 in total inventory**

REVIEW EXERCISES

Find the opening balance and number on hand.

	Month	Opening Balance	+	Units Receipts (Qty. In)	−	Issues (Qty. Out)	=	Number on Hand
13.	April	543	+	106	−	50	=	a. 599
14.	May	a. 599	+	30	−	90	=	b. 539
15.	June	a. 539	+	100	−	175	=	b. 464
16.	July	a. 464	+	45	−	75	=	b. 434
17.	August	a. 434	+	125	−	56	=	b. 503
18.	September	a. 503	+	39	−	87	=	b. 455

REINFORCEMENT

Section 18-1

1. Carton dimensions: 3 m × 6 m × 4 m.
   Number of cartons: 60. **4,320 m³**
2. Carton dimensions: 9.5 in × 8.5 in × 5 in.
   Number of cartons: 1,500. **605,625 in³**

Section 18-2

1. Previous inventory: 1,030.
   Receipts: 0.
   Issues: 406.
   624

SECTION OBJECTIVE 18-3 AND EXAMPLES

Use the average-cost method to compute the inventory value.

On May 1, the discount store had 103 cards on hand. What is the value of the inventory on May 1?

Date	Units Received	Unit Cost	Total Cost
March 10	52	$0.50	$26.00
April 2	101	0.45	45.45
April 21	35	0.65	22.75
Total	188		$94.20

STEP 1: Find the average cost per unit.
Total Cost of Units ÷ Number Received
$94.20 ÷ 188 = $0.5010 or $0.50 average cost per unit

STEP 2: Find the inventory value.
Average Cost per Unit × Number on Hand
$0.50 × 103 = $51.50 inventory value

To review the LIFO and FIFO methods for valuing inventory, review Examples 2 and 3 on pages 590–591 before you complete Problem 21 below.

REVIEW EXERCISES

19. Records for Maxine's Beauty Supply show this opening balance and these units received for Ruby Red fingernail polish in December. At the end of the month, 12 bottles were on hand. What is the value of the inventory using the average-cost method?
$733.88 ÷ 510 = $1.44 average cost per unit
$1.44 × 12 = $17.28 inventory value

Date	Units Received	Unit Cost	Total Cost
Dec. 3 (Beginning Inventory)	43	$1.49	$ 64.07
Dec. 10	267	1.43	381.81
Dec. 20	200	1.44	288.00
Total	510		$733.88

20. Shirley's Bridal Shop's inventory records for short bridal veils show this information. At the end of the month, 15 veils were on hand. Find the value of the inventory using the average-cost method.

Date	Units Received	Unit Cost
July 3	36	$45.62
July 15	21	48.99
July 30	75	36.50

21. The Peach Pit, a trendy clothing store, uses the FIFO method of valuing inventory. Complete the Peach Pit's records for units received of black belts. As of April 25, the Peach Pit has sold 145 belts. Use the FIFO method to calculate the cost of the 145 belts sold. Use the LIFO method to calculate the value of the 15 belts in stock.
FIFO: $2,717.50; LIFO: $277.50

Date	Units Received	Unit Cost	Total Cost
4/02	120	$18.50	
4/13	30	19.90	
4/22	10	21.50	

20. 36 × $45.62 = $1,642.32
21 × $48.99 = $1,028.79
75 × $36.50 = $2,737.50
$1,642.32 + $1,028.79 + $2,737.50 = $5,408.61 total cost of inventory
36 + 21 + 75 = 132 total receipts
$5,408.61 ÷ 132 = $40.97 average cost per unit
$40.97 × 15 = $614.55 inventory value

REINFORCEMENT

Section 18-3

1. Flash Lighting Inc. is valuing its inventory of lamps. At the end of the month, 67 lamps were on hand. What is the value of the inventory? **$847.55**

Date	Receipts	Unit Cost
7/1	70	$12.59
7/14	71	12.65
7/29	68	12.70

SECTION OBJECTIVE 18-4 AND EXAMPLES

Calculate the annual cost of carrying an inventory.

Cidermill Games estimates the annual cost of maintaining the inventory to be 28 percent of the value of the inventory. This year Cidermill plans to maintain an inventory totaling $310,000. What amount should be set as the estimated cost of carrying inventory for the year?

STEP: Find the annual cost of carrying inventory.

Inventory Value $\times$ Percent
$310,000 $\times$ 28%
= **$86,800 annual cost of carrying inventory**

REVIEW EXERCISES
Find the annual cost of carrying inventory.

	Value of Inventory	Percent	Annual Cost of Carrying Inventory
22.	$ 1,200	26.0%	$312
23.	12,300	29.5%	$3,628.50
24.	985	33.0%	$325.05
25.	10,500	34.0%	$3,570
26.	123,400	34.5%	$42,573
27.	595,000	37.5%	$223,125

SECTION OBJECTIVE 18-5 AND EXAMPLES

Work out the total door-to-door shipping costs.

The Clean Machine is shipping 845 pounds of cleaning supplies from Memphis to Miami. The shipment will be sent Guaranteed First Arrival. What is the total cost of shipping the cleaning supplies? (Use Figure 18.1 on page 597 to find the solution to the examples in this section.)

STEP 1: Find the charge per pound for guaranteed first arrival.
It is $164.00.

STEP 2: Find the shipping cost.
$164.00 $\times$ (845 $\div$ 100) = **$1,385.80 shipping cost**

REINFORCEMENT

Section 18-4

1. Find the annual cost of carrying an inventory. Inventory value: $2,345.67. Percent: 26.5% **$621.60**

2. Ark Marine estimates the annual cost of carrying its inventory at 22.6 percent of the value of the inventory. The 22.6 percent is broken down as shown. What is the approximate annual cost for each expense of carrying a $120,000 inventory?

Type of Expense	Percent	Amount
Spoilage and physical deterioration	2.0%	$ 2,400
Interest	6.0%	7,200
Handling	12.0%	14,400
Storage facilities	1.5%	1,800
Taxes	0.6%	720
Insurance	0.5%	600
Total	22.6%	$27,120

REVIEW EXERCISES
Use Figure 18.1 on page 597 to find the shipping costs for Problems 28–33.

	From	To	Arrival	Weight (in lbs.)	Cost per 100 lbs.	Total
28.	Boston	Miami	Standard Overnight	500	a. $145.30	b. $726.50
29.	Denver	Sacramento	Guaranteed Second Day	1,000	a. $127.75	b. $1,277.50
30.	St. Louis	Cedar Rapids, IA	Guaranteed First Arrival	329	a. $164	b. $539.56
31.	Memphis	Miami	BAX Saver	1,200	a. $46	b. $552
32.	Toledo, OH	Missoula, MT	Guaranteed Overnight	498	a. $230.25	b. $1,146.65
33.	Los Angeles	Asheville, NC	Standard Second Day	902	a. $146.75	b. $1,323.69

SECTION OBJECTIVE 18-6 AND EXAMPLES

Calculate the total shipping cost by truck.

Ramona's Restaurant Supply is shipping 1,490 pounds of table linens to Cathy's Catering. The distance is 762 miles. What is the total shipping charge? (Use Figure 18.2 on page 599 to solve this problem.)

STEP 1: Find the basic rate.
 Weight Group: 501–3,000 pounds
 Distance: 300-plus miles
 Rate: $1.73 per mile

STEP 2: Find the total shipping cost.
 Mile × Rate per Mile
 762 × $1.73 = $1,318.26 total shipping cost

REVIEW EXERCISES
Refer to Figures 18.2 on page 599 and 18.3 on page 600 to solve the problems below.

	Weight (in lbs.)	Distance (in miles)	Basic Rate	Shipping Cost	COD	Lift Gate	Second Person	Total Costs
34.	220	56	a.	b.	No	Yes	No	c.
35.	760	99	a.	b.	No	No	1 hr	c.
36.	1,564	540	a.	b.	Yes	Yes	2 hrs	c.
37.	8,751	278	a.	b.	No	Yes	4 hrs	c.
38.	13,000	301	a.	b.	Yes	Yes	No	c.
39.	42,691	165	a.	b.	No	No	5 hrs	c.
40.	1,871	431	a.	b.	Yes	No	No	c.

34. a. $1.74
 b. $97.44
 c. $222.44
35. a. $1.95
 b. $193.05
 c. $243.05
36. a. $1.73
 b. $934.20
 c. $1,209.20
37. a. $2.69
 b. $742.44
 c. $1,067.44
38. a. $2.39
 b. $719.39
 c. $894.39
39. a. $4.30
 b. $709.50
 c. $959.50
40. a. $1.73
 b. $745.63
 c. $795.63

REINFORCEMENT

Section 18-5
Use **Figure 18.1** on page 597 to find the total shipping cost.
1. From Memphis to Miami.
 568 pounds.
 BAX Saver. **$261.28**
2. From Denver to Sacramento.
 451 pounds.
 Standard Second Day. **$488.21**

Section 18-6
Use **Figures 18.2** and **18.3** (on pages 599 and 600, respectively) to find the total shipping cost.
1. Weight: 3,378 pounds.
 Distance: 57 miles. **$169.29**
2. Weight: 4,998 pounds.
 Distance: 239 miles.
 Accessorial charges: COD fee, lift gate.
 $753.38

National Standards for Business Education

Section Objectives	1. Mathematical Foundations	2. Number Relationships and Operations	3. Patterns, Functions, and Algebra	4. Measurements	5. Statistics and Probability	6. Problem-Solving Applications
19-1 Building Rental (pp. 610–611) Compute the monthly rental charge.	X	X				
19-2 Maintenance and Improvement (pp. 612–613) Calculate the total building maintenance charge.	X	X				
19-3 Equipment Rental (pp. 614–615) Figure out the total equipment rental cost.	X	X				
19-4 Utilities Costs—Telephone (pp. 616–618) Work out the monthly telephone cost.	X	X				
19-5 Utilities Costs—Electricity (pp. 619–620) Compute the monthly cost for electricity.	X	X				
19-6 Professional Service (pp. 621–623) Calculate the total cost of professional services.	X	X				

(Source: Reprinted with permission from the National Standards for Business Education, copyright © 2001 by National Business Education Association, 1914 Association Drive, Reston, Virginia 21901-1596)

SCANS Correlation

Foundation Skills

Basic Skills	Reading	Writing	Math	Listening	Speaking	
Thinking Skills	Creative Thinking	Decision Making	Problem Solving	Seeing Things in the Mind's Eye	Knowing How to Learn	Reasoning
Personal Qualities	Responsibility	Self-Esteem	Sociability	Self-Management	Integrity/Honesty	

This chapter's highlighted blocks indicate the chapter's content coverage in the Student Edition and the Teacher Wraparound Edition.

National Council of Teachers of Mathematics Standards

1. Numbers & Operations	2. Algebra	3. Geometry	4. Measurement	5. Data Analysis & Probability	6. Problem Solving	7. Reasoning & Proof	8. Communication	9. Connections	10. Representations
X		X			X		X		
X		X			X		X		
X					X		X		
X					X		X		
X					X		X		
X					X		X		

SCANS Correlation

Workplace Competencies

Resources	Allocating Time	Allocating Money	Allocating Material and Facility Resources	Allocating Human Resources		
Information	Acquiring and Evaluating Information	Organizing and Maintaining Information	Interpreting and Communicating Information	Using Computers to Process Information		
Interpersonal Skills	Participating as a Member of a Team	Teaching Others	Serving Clients/Customers	Exercising Leadership	Negotiating to Arrive at a Decision	Working with Cultural Diversity
Systems	Understanding Systems	Monitoring and Correcting Performance	Improving and Designing Systems			
Technology	Selecting Technology	Applying Technology to Task	Maintaining and Troubleshooting Technology			

CHAPTER 19

Services

What You'll Learn

Tell students that in this chapter you'll focus on services that businesses use. Businesses often hire service companies for maintenance and repair to buildings and equipment. Other services include building rental, utilities, and professional consultants.

Why It's Important

The cost of components required to run a business all have an effect on profits. Soaring electricity rates in the state of California have a ripple effect on consumers. A 15 percent increase in the electricity bill is passed on to customers. Rising prices for food, computer components, and other products manufactured in California are all results of an increase in electricity costs.

Key Word Review

Serving Customers

Assign half the class to be consultants and half the class to be customers. Have the customers go to a consultant. The consultant should smile and say, "How can I help you?" The customers need to find out the meaning of a key word and take notes. The consultant looks up the definition of the key word in the Glossary and helps the customer understand the meaning of the key word. The customer should smile, say "Thank you" and move on to a different consultant for each key word. LS , CL

What You'll Learn

Section 19-1 Compute the monthly rental charge.

Section 19-2 Calculate the total building maintenance charge.

Section 19-3 Determine the total equipment rental cost.

Section 19-4 Work out the monthly telephone cost.

Section 19-5 Compute the monthly cost for electricity.

Section 19-6 Calculate the total cost of professional services.

When Will You Ever Use This?

Need a place to work? Whether it's your own business or if you work for someone, you'll need to allot money for office space, maintenance costs, and costs of utilities.

Key Words to Know

- rent
- lease
- labor charge
- utilities
- monthly service charge
- demand charge
- energy charge
- peak load
- kilowatts
- fuel adjustment charge
- consultants
- consultant's fee

Mathematics Online

To learn more about the math behind a business's services, visit the *Mathematics with Business Applications* Web site at www.busmath.glencoe.com.

608 ◀ Chapter 19 Services

CLASSROOM RESOURCES

Application and Enrichment
- *Teacher Wraparound Edition*
- *Teacher Resource Binder, Blackline Masters*
- *Interactive Lesson Planner* CD-ROM
- *PowerPoint® Presentations* CD-ROM

Review and Enforcement
Mathematics Online
www.busmath.glencoe.com
- *Teacher Resource Binder, Internet Resources*

- *Student Activity Workbook*
- *Student Activity Workbook, Teacher Annotated Edition*
- *School-to-Home Activity Workbook*

Assessment and Evaluation
- *Assessment Binder, Reproducible Tests*
- *Assessment Binder, Alternative Assessment Strategies*
- **Exam***View*® *Pro Test Generator* CD-ROM

For the Teacher
- *Student Activity Workbook, Teacher Annotated Edition*
- *Assessment Binder*
- *Interactive Lesson Planner* CD-ROM
- *Teacher Resource Binder*
- Mathematics Online
www.busmath.glencoe.com

For the Student
- *Student Activity Workbook*
- *School-to-Home Activity Workbook*

Living in the Real World

Just the Write Thing

When she opened her writing service three months ago, Ariel Field rented a small office in a retail strip mall. Field's business, Just the Write Thing (JTWT), provides custom-written wedding toasts for tongue-tied best men. Field, who worked as a political speech writer prior to opening JTWT, interviews her clients about the bride and groom and then writes a wedding toast that the best man reads or memorizes. In this chapter, read about how her service has become so popular, she has had to expand just to keep up with business.

Read on. Go to . . .

609

Living in the Real World

Story's Summary

Ariel Field opened Just the Write Thing three months ago and has watched her business thrive. Now that her venture has proven successful, she's ready to plan for the future, which means buying furniture rather than renting, extending her office space lease agreement, reducing professional service costs, and utilizing the Internet as a marketing tool.

Did You Know...

Federal legislation created over 400 tax-law modifications in 2001. How many small business owners have the time to study and understand so many rule changes? This is just one of the many reasons hiring the services of an accountant can be crucial.

Think about This

Buying a building that seems perfect at the get-go can seem mighty attractive to a new business owner. But what would you do if your business—and space requirement—grew exponentially over the next few years?

LOCAL STANDARDS

SECTION **19-1** **Building Rental**

National Standards for Business Education

Standard 1	Mathematical Foundations
Standard 2	Number Relationships and Operations

National Council of Teachers of Mathematics Standards

Standard 1	Numbers and Operations
Standard 3	Geometry
Standard 6	Problem Solving
Standard 8	Communication

1 FOCUS

Read students some commercial real estate listings from a newspaper. Point out that the cost of rent for commercial space is usually based on the dimensions of the space.

In-Class Examples

Work through these exercises with students before having them do the Self-Check.
1. 20 ft × 100 ft **2,000 ft²**
2. 50 ft × 75 ft **3,750 ft²**
3. ($7.50 × 2,400) ÷ 12 **$1,500**

2 TEACH

Have students discuss why a business would rent space instead of owning space. **Point out that some businesses cannot afford to buy space. Some space, such as space in shopping malls, is not available for purchase so the only option is to rent. Also, there is more risk involved with owning a space. Suppose, for instance, that a business purchases a building. The business has to maintain the building and handle the maintenance of the property. What would**

610

SECTION 19-1 Building Rental

○ Section Objective

Compute the monthly rental charge.

Your business may **rent** or **lease** a building or a portion of a building, usually on an annual basis. This is the amount of money you pay to occupy the given space. The building owner may charge a certain rate per square foot per year. Your total monthly rental charge depends on the number of square feet that your business occupies. Remember that:

$$\text{Monthly Rental Charge} = \frac{\text{Annual Rate} \times \text{Number of Square Feet}}{12}$$

Living in the Real World

Just the Write Thing

A Place to Rent   When she opened JTWT, Field signed a six-month rental contract. Because she wasn't sure whether the business would take off, she was happy to find a reasonably priced corporate space that she could rent for only six months. Now that the company is succeeding beyond her dreams, she is hoping to change the arrangement to a one-year lease.

Draw Conclusions   What are the pros and cons of renting versus owning a space?

Continued on page 612

Example 1

Ajax Assemblers rents a portion of a building owned by The Gray Company. The floor space of Ajax's portion of the building measures 80 feet by 60 feet. The Gray Company charges an annual rate of $7.00 per square foot. To the nearest dollar, what is Ajax's monthly rental charge?

STEP 1: Find the number of square feet.
  Length × Width
  80 feet × 60 feet
  = 4,800 square feet

STEP 2: Find the monthly rental charge.
  $$\frac{\text{Annual Rate} \times \text{Number of Square Feet}}{12}$$
  ($7.00 × 4,800) ÷ 12
  = $33,600 ÷ 12
  = **$2,800 monthly rental charge**

80 ✕ 60 🟰 4800 ✕ 7 🟰 33600 ➗ 12 🟰 2800

BUSINESS NOTES

Business Consultants
Ask students to name different types of business consultants and list them on the board. (**Accountants, builders, lawyers.**) Role-play: Break students into groups. Each group is going to set up its own consulting business. Each group creates an advertisement for its consulting business. **Will they specialize in one type of service or offer several? Will they charge lower rates to compete or charge exorbitant fees?** LS , CL

Living in the Real World

Answers will vary. Owning a space is often a sound investment, although renting is convenient when a company is just starting and can't be sure it will succeed. There is some risk involved in renting, as a business may be forced to relocate when its lease expires.

SELF-CHECK ✓

1. Sq. Ft. = 100
   × 50 = 5,000
   Monthly
   Rent: ($8 × 5,000)
   ÷ 12 = $40,000 ÷
   12 = $3,333.33
2. Sq. Ft. = 125 × 45
   = 5,625
   Monthly Rent:
   ($9.50 × 5,625) ÷
   12 = $53,437.50 ÷
   12 = $4,453.13

CONCEPT CHECK

Complete the problems, then check your answers at the end of the chapter. Find the number of square feet and the monthly rental charge.

1. The store measures 100 feet × 50 feet at $8.00 per square foot annually.
2. The store measures 125 feet × 45 feet at $9.50 per square foot annually.

SECTION 19-1 PRACTICE

Find the number of square feet and monthly rental charge to the nearest dollar.

	Dimensions	=	(Number of Square Feet	×	Annual Rate per Square Foot)	÷ 12 =	Monthly Rental Charge
3.	15 ft × 30 ft	=	(a. 450 sq ft	×	$ 8.00)	÷ 12 =	b. $300
4.	40 ft × 20 ft	=	(a. 800 sq ft	×	7.50)	÷ 12 =	b. $500
5.	25 ft × 60 ft	=	(a. 1,500 sq ft	×	10.00)	÷ 12 =	b. $1,250

6. Westside Herald warehouse. Dimensions are 45 feet by 50 feet. Annual rental charge is $5.40 per square foot. What is the monthly rental charge? **$1,013**

7. Earring Tree kiosk in the City Center Mall. Dimensions are 15 feet by 20 feet. Annual rental charge is $12.75 per square foot. What is the monthly rental charge? **$319**

8. The Miller Manufacturing Company is considering the rental of additional manufacturing space at $4.80 per square foot per year. The space Miller wants to rent measures 80 feet by 120 feet. What monthly rent will Miller pay for the additional space? **$3,840**

9. The Cave has rented additional mall space to expand its arcade operation. The space measures 30 feet by 40 feet and rents for $15.60 per square foot per year. What monthly rent does the Cave pay for the additional space? **$1,560**

10. The Flower Shoppe is opening a store in the warehouse district. The rent is $8.75 per square foot per year plus 5 percent of the store's gross sales. The area of the store is 2,000 square feet. If The Flower Shoppe had $180,000 in gross sales the first year, what monthly rent will it pay? **$2,208.33**

11. The Luncheonette rents a 30-foot by 50-foot area at the Nottingham Mall. The Luncheonette pays $9.20 per square foot per year plus 2 percent of gross sales. Last year The Luncheonette had $225,000 in gross sales. What was its monthly rent? **$1,525**

12. Some businesses rent office space for 2 or 3 years at a time. Often the lease for the office space includes a rent escalation clause. The rent escalation clause states that the rent may increase by a certain percent after a certain period of time. The C and S Legal Clinic rents a suburban office space for $12.60 per square foot per year. The dimensions of the office are 35 feet by 40 feet. The clinic signed a 2-year lease with a 6 percent rent escalation clause. The rent will increase by 6 percent for the second year of the lease. What is the monthly rental charge for each year of the lease?
    1st year: $1,470; 2nd year: $1,558.20

Need Help? Go to...
➤ Skill 10: Dividing (Decimal Remainder), page 737

MAINTAINING YOUR SKILLS

Divide. Round answers to the nearest dollar.

13. $25,800 ÷ 12 **$2,150** 14. $14,949 ÷ 12 **$1,246** 15. $9,070 ÷ 12 **$756**

Section 19-1 Building Rental ▶ **611**

COOPERATIVE LEARNING

Warehouse Space
Students imagine that the classroom is a warehouse that rents storage space to businesses. The amount to rent the entire warehouse is $10,000 per month. Students work in groups to measure the dimensions of the classroom. Groups calculate how much it costs to rent space in the warehouse by the square foot and by the square meter. **LS** , **CL** , **P**

WRAP-UP

Go over any problem for which a wrong answer is given.

Assignment Guide
  Basic: 3–5
  Average: 6–9

20 min.

---

happen if it turned out to be a poor location for the business? The business would have to sell and possibly suffer a loss. There are many expenses involved with owning space that are not present with renting.

In-Class Examples
Find the number of square feet and the monthly rental charge.

1. Dimensions: 30 ft × 40 ft. Annual rate per square foot: $10.00. **1,200 ft², $1,000**

2. Dimensions: 26 ft × 38 ft. Annual rate per square foot: $11.75. **988 ft², $967.42**

3. Rugged Outerwear is opening a store downtown. The rent is $15.90 per square foot per year. The area of the store is 1,400 square feet. How much is the rent per month? **$1,855**

③ ASSESS

Error Analysis
Some students may not understand the idea of measuring in square feet. Point out that the room is made up of many square feet. You may want to use tape to mark out some squares that measure one foot by one foot. This way students will see what one square foot looks like.

④ CLOSE

Closing Activity
Find the monthly rental charge.

1. Al's Diner rents a 40 ft × 25 ft space. The rent is $14.85 per square foot per year. What is the monthly rent? **$1,237.50**

2. Glow Inc. plans to rent space in a new mall. The rent is $18.95 per square foot per year plus 4 percent of the store's gross sales. The area of the space is 1,200 square feet. If the gross sales for the first year are $90,000, what is the monthly rent? **$2,195**

SECTION **19-2** **Maintenance and Improvement**

National Standards for Business Education

Standard 1	Mathematical Foundations
Standard 2	Number Relationships and Operations

National Council of Teachers of Mathematics Standards

Standard 1	Numbers and Operations
Standard 3	Geometry
Standard 6	Problem Solving
Standard 8	Communication

1 FOCUS

Ask students to name some types of maintenance that a commercial building may need. Ask students to name some types of improvements that a business may want to make to its building. Point out that the cost for maintenance and improvement is often based on labor and materials.

In-Class Examples

Work through these exercises with students before having them do the Self-Check.
1. 31 × 18.75 **581.25**
2. 30 × 38 × 4 **4,560**
3. (20 × 1.5) × 12 × 6 **2,160**

2 TEACH

Students need to find the labor charge by multiplying the hourly rate by the number of hours worked by the number of workers. Remind students that they learned about hourly pay in Section 1-1. In this case when someone works time and a half the hourly rate needs to be multiplied by 1.5 to calculate time and a half.

612

○ **Section Objective**

Calculate the total building maintenance charge.

SECTION 19-2 Maintenance and Improvement

If your business owns a building, you'll need people to clean and maintain the building. You may have your own maintenance department, or you may hire a service firm. The total cost of a particular maintenance job generally includes a **labor charge.** The labor charge is the cost of paying the people who do the job. It is calculated on an hourly basis for each service person. In some cases the cleaning and maintenance charge is based on square footage. Remember that:

Total Charge = Labor Charge + Materials Charge

Living in the Real World

Just the Write Thing

Renegotiating a Lease Field calls the office building's landlord, Hal Linhardt. She wants to renegotiate the lease that she signed; she wants to sign on for one more year. He informs her that the cost of maintenance has gone up. (The company that cleans the units, plows the snow from the parking lot, and does odd jobs has raised its rates considerably.)

Draw Conclusions If Linhardt's costs go up, will this affect Field's monthly rent charge?

Continued on page 614

Example 1

Central Law Offices hired Commercial Painting Service to paint its offices. Four painters worked 23 hours each to complete the job. The regular hourly rate for each painter is $29.00. All work was done on weekends, so the painters were paid time and a half. The painters used 42 gallons of paint, for which they charged $19.75 per gallon. What was the total charge for painting the offices?

STEP 1: Find the labor charge.
($29.00 × 1.5) × 23 hours × 4 = $4,002.00 labor charge

STEP 2: Find the materials charge.
42 × $19.75 = $829.50 materials charge

STEP 3: Find the total charge.
Labor Charge + Materials Charge
$4,002.00 + $829.50
= **$4,831.50 total charge**

29 × 1.5 × 23 × 4 = 4002 M+
42 × 19.75 = 829.5 M+ RM 4831.5

Living in the Real World

He will raise it for sure. Linhardt will raise Field's rent to compensate for his higher costs.

CONCEPT CHECK

SELF-CHECK✓

Complete the problems, then check your answers at the end of the chapter.

1. Find the total charge.
   Three people worked 6 hours each at $8.50 per hour.
   Nine gallons of paint at $24.85 per gallon.

2. What is the monthly charge for cleaning a 40 foot by 50 foot room at $4.50 per square foot per year?
   Monthly Charge: 40 × 50 × $4.50 = $9,000; $9,000 ÷ 12 = $750

SECTION 19-2 PRACTICE

1. Labor Charge:
   3 × 6 × $8.50 =
   $153.00
   Materials Charge:
   9 × $24.85 =
   $223.65
   Total: $153.00 +
   $223.65 = $376.65

3. a. $168.00
   b. $593.00

4. a. $279.00
   b. $279.00

5. a. $196.00
   b. $1,143.56

(Time Required	×	Number of Employees	×	Hourly Rate	=	Labor Charge)	+	Materials Charge	=	Total
3.	(8 hours	×	2	×	$10.50	=	a.	) +	$425.00	=	b.
4.	(3 hours	×	12	×	7.75	=	a.	) +	0.00	=	b.
5.	(4 hours	×	5	×	9.80	=	a.	) +	947.56	=	b.

6. A janitorial service cleans and maintains an office area measuring 30 feet by 40 feet. The contract calls for $5.50 per square foot annually. What is the monthly charge? **$550.00**

7. Dr. Alice Desmond is moving from her present office to another office in the same building. It takes 4 people 3 hours to complete the move. The hourly rate per person is $12.80. What is the total charge? **$153.60**

8. City Cleaners hired 2 carpenters to remodel its store. The carpenters earned $18.95 each per hour. Each carpenter worked 21 hours. The materials charge was $1,617.48. Find the total charge. **$2,413.38**

9. The National Freight Company used 6 loads of crushed stone on a terminal lot at $112.75 a load. Ten people were each paid $7.15 an hour to spread the stone. It took 4 hours. What was the total charge? **$962.50**

10. Scott's Supermarket hired 5 people to refinish its floor. The regular hourly rate for each person was $7.25. Because the floor was refinished on Sunday, each worker was paid double time. The job took 5 hours to complete. The materials charge was $571.85. What was the total charge? **$934.35**

11. General Janitorial Service cleans the Second National Bank daily from Monday through Saturday. Second National Bank's contract specifies $3.50 per square foot annually for its 45 foot by 50 foot bank area. One General employee works at the bank for 3 hours each day, based on 25 days per month. General keeps 25 percent of the amount paid by Second National for overhead. What is the hourly rate (to the nearest cent) earned by the General employee? **$6.56**

MAINTAINING YOUR SKILLS

Need Help? Go to...
→ Skill 8: Multiplying Decimals, page 735

Multiply.

12. $3.85 × 5 × 4 **$77.00**

13. $9.75 × 5 × 3 **$146.25**

14. $7.43 × 2.5 × 4 **$74.30**

15. $8.45 × 2¼ × 5 **$95.06**

COMMUNICATION SKILLS

Explain on the Board

Teaching others is a great way for someone to learn. After students have completed Problems 3 to 11, ask volunteers to work through the solution to the problems on the board. Each volunteer explains the solution to one problem.

WRAP-UP

Go over any problem for which a wrong answer is given.

Assignment Guide
   Basic: 3–5
   Average: 6–8

20 min.

In-Class Examples

Find the labor charge and the total charge.

1. Time required: 7 hours.
   Number of employees: 4.
   Hourly rate: $14.85.
   Materials charge: $568.20.
   $415.80; $984.00

2. Time required: 12 hours.
   Number of employees: 3.
   Hourly rate: $21.00.
   Materials charge: $1,097.50.
   $756.00; $1,853.50

③ ASSESS

Error Analysis

Remind students that the labor charge often involves the labor of more than one worker. Students need to read each problem carefully and determine how many workers did the job described. Students should take the number of workers and multiply it by the hourly rate and by total number of hours worked. If the workers are paid time and a half or double time, then students also need to multiply the hourly rate by 1.5 or 2, respectively.

④ CLOSE

Closing Activity

Find the total charge.

1. Hour Photo hires a service to clean and maintain its store. The store area is 1,800 square feet and the service charges $4.95 per square foot annually. What is the monthly charge? **$742.50**

2. The Garden Restaurant used 12 flats of annual flowers at $12.99 a flat. Five people were each paid $7.80 an hour to plant the flowers. It took 3 hours. What was the total charge? **$272.88**

613

National Standards for Business Education

Standard 1	Mathematical Foundations
Standard 2	Number Relationships and Operations

National Council of Teachers of Mathematics Standards

Standard 1	Numbers and Operations
Standard 6	Problem Solving
Standard 8	Communication

1 FOCUS

Ask students to name some items that people often rent instead of buy. **(These items may include movies, video games, cars, and rug cleaners.)** Have students discuss the benefit of renting these things instead of purchasing them.

In-Class Examples

Work through these exercises with students before having them do the Self-Check.

1. ($10.25 × 3) + $1.85 **$32.60**
2. ($89.95 × 6) + $29.68 **$569.38**
3. ($1,064.20 × 2) + $101.10 **$2,229.50**

2 TEACH

Unlike some of the items for rent that students are familiar with, the rental charge for equipment is based on a percent of an item's value. In Example 1 on page 614, the rental charge is 10 percent of the item's list price. Unlike movies that you can usually rent for the same set price, different types of equipment have different rental prices.

614

Section Objective

Determine the total equipment rental cost.

In your business it may be more economical to rent than to buy certain equipment or furniture. Generally, the total cost of renting items is determined by the length of time for which you rent them. Some states charge a usage tax on items that are rented. Remember that:

$$\text{Total Rental Cost} = (\text{Rental Charge} \times \text{Time}) + \text{Usage Tax}$$

Living in the Real World

Just the Write Thing

Rent or Own? Field just started her business three months ago. Now that the business is succeeding, she has signed a year-long office lease, and she's ready to invest in her own office furniture and take back the rented desks and filing cabinets.

Draw Conclusions Is it more cost efficient to own or rent office furniture?

Continued on page 616

Example 1

Tax-Aide is renting new furniture for a small, temporary office. Office Rental Company charges 10 percent of the list price of new furniture per month. The list prices of the pieces that Tax-Aide is renting are as follows:

Item	List Price
Desk, 60 inch × 30 inch	$299.99
File cabinet, 4-drawer	149.99
Swivel armchair	179.99
2 guest chairs ($99.99 each)	199.98
Total	$829.95

In addition to the rental charge, there is a 6 percent usage tax. What is the total cost of renting the furniture for 4 months?

STEP 1: Find the rental charge per month.
Ten percent of the list price total.
$829.95 × 10% = $82.995 or $83.00

STEP 2: Find the usage tax.
($83.00 × 4) × 6% =
$332.00 × 6% = $19.92

STEP 3: Find the total rental cost.
(Rental Charge × Time) + Usage Tax
($83.00 × 4) + $19.92 =
$332.00 + $19.92 = **$351.92 total rental cost**

829.95 ⊠ 10 % 82.995 83 ⊠ 4 ⊟ 332 M+

⊠ 6 % 19.92 + RM 332 ⊟ 351.92

Living in the Real World

It depends on a business's particular situation, but if it plans to use the furniture for a long time, it's more cost efficient to own rather than lease.

RETEACH / ENRICHMENT

Rental Costs

Students use the Internet or call local rental companies to find the costs and terms of renting various types of equipment. Students could also ask the type of equipment that's in highest demand.

CONCEPT CHECK

SELF-CHECK✓

Complete the problems, then check your answers at the end of the chapter. Find the total rental cost.

1. Rental Charge:
$640 × 10%
= $64
Tax: $64 × 3 × 6%
= $11.52
Total: ($64.00 × 3)
+ $11.52 =
$192.00 + $11.52
= $203.52

2. Rental Charge:
$1,470 × 8% =
$117.60
Tax: $117.60 × 5 ×
5.5% = $32.34
Total: ($117.60 ×
5) + $32.34 =
$588.00 + $32.34
= $620.34

1. Rental charge: 10 percent of $640.
Tax rate: 6 percent.
Time: 3 months.

2. Rental charge: 8 percent of $1,470.
Tax rate: 5.5 percent.
Time: 5 months.

SECTION 19-3 PRACTICE

Complete the table.

	Item	List Price	Rental Rate	Monthly Charge	Number of Months	Usage Tax	Total Rental Cost
3.	Computer	$ 947.80	10% of list	a. $94.78	4	4.00%	b. $394.28
4.	File cabinet	97.45	11% of list	a. $10.72	8	6.00%	b. $90.90
5.	Fax machine	1,141.80	9% of list	a. $102.76	6	6.25%	b. $655.11

6. Backhoe rented for 3 weeks.
Rental charge is $1,475 per week.
Usage tax is 5 percent.
What is the total rental cost? **$4,646.25**

7. Jackhammer rented for 7 days.
Rental charge is $175.95 per day.
No usage tax.
What is the total rental cost? **$1,231.65**

8. The list price of a personal computer system is $2,248. The monthly rental charge is 10 percent of the list price. There is a 5 percent usage tax. What is the total rental charge for 1 year? **$2,832.48**

9. The Strong Cement Company plans to rent a bulldozer for 2 days. The rental charge is $212.45 per day plus a flat fee of $45.00 for delivery and pickup. There is no tax. What is the total rental cost? **$469.90**

10. The Legal Clinic is renting additional furniture for 6 months. The monthly rental charge is 9.5 percent of the list price. There is an 8 percent usage tax. What is the total rental cost of the following: **$1,474.24**

Item	List Price
3 desks with chairs	$329.95 (each)
10 guest chairs	69.25 (each)
1 computer	712.45

11. Net Discount Brokers rents an office telecommunications system for 12 months. There is a 10 percent discount for a 12-month rental. The rental charge is 12.5 percent of the list price. The list price of the system is $12,680. There is a 7 percent usage tax on the discounted amount.
a. What will it cost Net Discount Brokers to rent the telecommunications system for 12 months? **$18,316.26**
b. What would you advise if it needed the system for only 11 months? **Rent for 12 months, $18,316.26 for 12 months vs. $18,655.45 for 11 months (no discount). Rent for 12 months and save.**

MAINTAINING YOUR SKILLS

Need Help? Go to...
➤ Skill 30: Finding the Percentage, page 757

Find the percentage. Round answers to the nearest cent.

12. 5% of $516 **$25.80**   **13.** 6% of $48.40 **$2.90**   **14.** 5% of $146.30 **$7.32**

Section 19-3 Equipment Rental ▶ **615**

In-Class Example

1. Plants Etc. rents a forklift for 12 months. There is a 15 percent discount for a 12-month rental. The rental charge is 10 percent per month of the list price. The list price is $36,000. There is a 6 percent usage tax on the discounted amount. What is the total annual rental cost? **$38,923.20**

3 ASSESS

Error Analysis

Remind students that when they find the tax, they should multiply the tax rate by the product of the monthly rental charge and the number of months rented. Students may mistakenly multiply the tax rate just by the rental charge. This would result in too little tax, and therefore, an incorrect amount for the total rental cost.

4 CLOSE

Closing Activity

Find the total rental cost.
1. Rental charge: 8 percent of $875.
Tax rate: 6 percent.
Time: 3 months. **$222.60**

2. Rental charge: 12.5 percent of $1,570.
Tax rate: 6.25 percent.
Time: 8 months. **$1,688.13**

3. Direct Pro rents video conferencing equipment for five months. The rental charge is 12 percent of the list price. There is a 7.75 percent use tax. What is the total rental cost if the list price of the equipment is $10,750? **$6,949.88**

THINKING CRITICALLY

Fixed and Variable Expenses

When you're running a business, it's important to know the difference between fixed and variable expenses. Students ask their parents, a businessperson, or other adult about the different kinds of expenses they have and whether they're fixed or variable. Students create a spreadsheet differentiating fixed expenses and variable expenses. **LS** , **CL**

WRAP-UP

Go over any problem for which a wrong answer is given.

Assignment Guide
Basic: 3–5
Average: 6–8

20 min.

National Standards for Business Education

Standard 1	Mathematical Foundations
Standard 2	Number Relationships and Operations

National Council of Teachers of Mathematics Standards

Standard 1	Numbers and Operations
Standard 6	Problem Solving
Standard 8	Communication

1 FOCUS

Ask students if they know how their home phone bill is calculated. Show students a telephone bill. Several calling plans are usually available for customers to choose from. These plans address the different needs of customers.

In-Class Examples

Work through these exercises with students before having them do the Self-Check.

1. $(410 - 400) \times \$0.25$ **2.50**
2. $(\$52.99 + \$16.50) \times 3\%$ **2.08**
3. $(\$124.50 + \$12.30) \times 3.5\%$ **$4.788 = \$4.79$**

Section Objective

Work out the monthly telephone cost.

To operate your business, you'll need several **utilities.** Utilities are public services, such as telephone, electricity, water, and gas. Each utility uses a different cost structure for charging its customers. For example, the **monthly service charge** for your telephone service depends on the total minutes per month, the number of phone lines, the type of equipment, and the type of service and features you have. If you use more minutes than the number included in your monthly service charge, you must pay an additional amount per minute. A federal excise tax is also added to your telephone charge each month.

$$\begin{array}{c} \text{Total Cost} \\ \text{for the} \\ \text{Month} \end{array} = \begin{array}{c} \text{Monthly} \\ \text{Service} \\ \text{Charge} \end{array} + \begin{array}{c} \text{Cost of} \\ \text{Additional} \\ \text{Minutes} \end{array} + \begin{array}{c} \text{Cost of} \\ \text{Additional} \\ \text{Lines} \end{array} + \begin{array}{c} \text{Federal} \\ \text{Excise} \\ \text{Tax} \end{array}$$

►FYI

MessageLabs estimates that it processes 4.5 million messages per day. With e-mail use on the rise, most companies can expect to pay at least twice what they do now to manage that volume of communication.

►►►

Living in the Real World

Just the Write Thing

E-mail or Call? Like many households, Field's business maintains two phone lines—one to send and receive phone calls and one to access the Internet. The cost of these lines is reflected on her monthly phone bill along with the cost of long-distance calls.

Draw Conclusions How do you think the use of e-mail has affected long-distance calling services?

Continued on page 619

Example 1

Andy's Laundry has 2 telephone lines and uses the $59.99 plan from the Flexible Advantage Calling Plan (see Figure 19.1). Andy's uses 550 minutes. A 3 percent federal excise tax is added to the bill. What is the total cost of its telephone service for the month?

Figure 19.1

Flexible Advantage Calling Plan (for Two Lines of Service)					
Monthly Service Plan	Included Minutes	Additional Lines per Month	Additional Airtime per Minute	Domestic Wireless Long Distance	Roaming (per Minute across the U.S. and Canada)
$ 59.99	up to 500	$19.99	$0.35	$0.15 per minute	$0.60
89.99	up to 1,000	19.99	0.35	no charge	0.60
119.99	up to 1,500	19.99	0.35	no charge	0.60

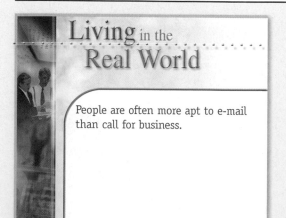

Living in the Real World

People are often more apt to e-mail than call for business.

COOPERATIVE LEARNING

Internet Service

The Internet has changed the way business is done. Invite a local business owner whose business uses the Internet to visit the class and answer students' questions about the choices and costs of Internet services. Have students work in pairs to prepare questions ahead of time. Students may also ask questions about how the owner uses the Internet in his or her business.

STEP 1: Find the cost of additional minutes.
$$(550 - 500) \times \$0.35$$
$$= \$17.50$$
No additional lines.

STEP 2: Find the federal excise tax.
$$(\$59.99 + \$17.50) \times 3\%$$
$$= \quad \$77.49 \quad \times 3\%$$
$$= \$2.3247 \text{ or } \$2.32$$

STEP 3: Find the total cost for the month.

Monthly Service Charge	+	Cost of Additional Minutes	+	Cost of Additional Lines	+	Federal Excise Tax
$59.99	+	$17.50	+	$0	+	$2.32

$$= \$79.81 \text{ total cost for the month}$$

550 − 500 = 50 × .35 = 17.5 + 59.99 = 77.49

M+ × .03 = 2.3247 + RM 77.49 = 79.8147

CONCEPT CHECK

Complete the problems, then check your answers at the end of the chapter. Find the total cost for the month. Use Figure 19.1 on page 616.

1. Monthly service plan is $89.99. Three lines and 1,200 minutes. Three percent federal tax.

2. Monthly service plan is $59.99. Two lines and 487 minutes. Five percent federal tax.

1. Additional line: ($19.99 × 1.00) = $19.99
Additional minutes: (1,200 − 1,000) × $0.35 = $70.00
Fed Tax: ($89.99 + $19.99 + $70.00) × 3% = $179.98 × 0.03 = $5.40
Total: $179.98 + $5.40 = $185.38

2. No additional minutes
Fed Tax: $59.99 × 5% = $2.9995 or $3.00
Total: $59.99 + $3.00 = $62.99

SECTION 19-4 PRACTICE

Use Figure 19.1, Flexible Advantage Calling Plan, for Problems 3–9.

	Monthly Plan	Number of Minutes Used	Number of Lines	Federal Excise Tax Rate	Total Cost for the Month
3.	$ 59.99	600	2	3%	$97.84
4.	89.99	1,250	3	4%	$205.38
5.	119.99	1,436	2	3%	$123.59
6.	89.99	970	4	5%	$136.47

For Problems 7–8, add a 3 percent federal excise tax to find the total cost for the month.

7. Spotlight Discount has 2 telephone lines. Monthly service plan is $119.99. Used 1,430 minutes. What is the total cost for the month? **$123.59**

Continued on next page

(2) TEACH

Have students discuss some of the telephone needs that a business might have. Point out that in addition to several telephone lines, a business might also need a cellular service plan. Some businesses use cellular service provided by the telephone company and the charge for the service is included in the calling plan. Other businesses use one company for its main telephone service and another company for its cellular service.

In Example 1 on pages 616 and 617, point out that the federal excise tax is based on the monthly service charge plus the cost of additional minutes and additional lines. The higher these charges are, the more federal excise tax is required to be paid.

Motivating the Lesson
Have students work in groups. Give each group a telephone bill that you have prepared ahead of time. Have students pick out different pieces of information, such as the type of calling plan, the charge per minute for calls exceeding the calling plan, and the total monthly cost. When students are finished, review the answers out loud. **Answers will vary.**

In-Class Examples
Use **Figure 19.1** on pages 616 and 617 to find the total cost for the month.

1. Monthly service plan: $89.99. Number of lines: 2. Number of minutes: 980. Federal excise tax: 3 percent. **$92.69**

2. Monthly service plan: $59.99. Number of lines: 3. Number of minutes: 508. Federal excise tax: 4 percent. **$86.09**

3. Monthly service plan: $119.99. Number of lines: 5. Number of minutes: 1298. Federal excise tax: 3.5 percent. **$186.26**

617

③ ASSESS

Error Analysis

Emphasize that the Flexible Advantage Calling Plan shown in Example 1 on page 616 is for two lines of service. Since this example is using this same plan, two of the lines are already included.

④ CLOSE

Closing Activity

Use **Figure 19.1** on page 616 to find the total cost for the month.

1. Monthly service plan: $119.99.
   Number of lines: 2.
   Number of minutes: 1,476.
   Federal excise tax: 4 percent.
   $124.79

2. Monthly service plan: $59.99.
   Number of lines: 3.
   Number of minutes: 532.
   Number of domestic wireless long distance minutes: 28.
   Federal excise tax: 3 percent.
   $98.24

3. Monthly service plan: $89.99.
   Number of lines: 4.
   Number of minutes: 1,098.
   Number of roaming minutes: 31.
   Federal excise tax: 3.5 percent.
   $189.27

4. Horizon Foods has 6 telephone lines and uses the $119.99 Flexible Advantage Calling Plan. This month the company used 1,730 minutes. The federal excise tax rate is 3 percent. What is the total cost for the month? **$288.86**

5. Green Books uses the $59.99 Flexible Advantage Calling Plan. Green Books has 4 telephone lines. This month they used 529 minutes and 23 minutes of domestic wireless long distance. The federal excise tax is 3.5 percent. What is the total cost for the month? **$117.54**

8. Public Pharmacy has 3 telephone lines.
   Monthly service plan is $89.99.
   Used 1,080 minutes.
   What is the total cost for the month? **$142.12**

9. The Brown Medical Clinic has 5 telephone lines. The clinic signed up for the $59.99 Flexible Advantage Calling Plan, used 530 minutes this past month, and used an additional 36 minutes of domestic wireless long distance. The federal excise tax rate is 4 percent. Find the total cost for the month. **$141.29**

For Problems 10–11, use the Expressions Telephone Plan.

Expressions Telephone Plan

	(4 lines, each additional line is $16.99/month)					Extras: (per month)	
Monthly plan	$19.99	$29.99	$69.99	$149.99	$249.99	Call waiting:	$0.99
Each additional minute	0.45	0.40	0.35	0.30	0.15	Caller ID:	0.99
Included minutes	50	250	1,000	2,000	3,750	Voice mail:	1.99

10. Ahmed Young, a broker for stocks and bonds, has 5 telephone lines on the $69.99 Expressions Telephone Plan. Young used 1,176 minutes this past month. He has call waiting, voice mail, and caller ID. The federal excise tax rate is 3 percent. What is the total cost for the month? **$157.13**

11. The Rodriquez Realty Company has 4 telephone lines. It signed up for the $149.99 Expressions Telephone Plan and used 1,987 minutes this past month. The company has call waiting and voice mail. The federal excise tax rate is 5 percent. What is the total cost for the month? **$160.62**

MAINTAINING YOUR SKILLS

> **Need Help? Go to...**
> ➤ Skill 5: **Adding Decimals,** page 732
> ➤ Skill 6: **Subtracting Decimals,** page 733
> ➤ Skill 8: **Multiplying Decimals,** page 735
> ➤ Skill 30: **Finding the Percentage,** page 757

Add.

12. $249.99 + $33.98 + [(3,900 − 3,750) × $0.15] + $9.19 **$315.66**

13. $19.99 + (2 × $16.99) + [(68 − 50) × $0.45] + $1.86 **$63.93**

14. $26.15 + $1.60 + $0.83 **$28.58**

15. $32.95 + $2.79 + $1.07 **$36.81**

16. $26.15 + [(103 − 73) × $0.08] **$28.55**

17. $37.45 + $2.45 + $3.25 + (3% of $43.15) **$44.44**

WRAP-UP

Go over any problem for which a wrong answer is given.

Assignment Guide
 Basic: 3–6
Average: 7–9

20 min.

SECTION 19-5 Utilities Costs— Electricity

Section Objective

Compute the monthly cost for electricity.

The monthly cost of electricity for your business depends on the **demand charge** and the **energy charge**. The demand charge is based on the **peak load** during the month. The peak load is the greatest number of **kilowatts** your business uses at one time during the month. The energy charge is based on the total number of kilowatt hours (kWh) that your business uses during the month. Meters installed at your business record the kilowatt demand and the number of kilowatt hours. The electric company may add a **fuel adjustment charge** to your monthly bill to help cover increases in the cost of fuel needed to produce your electricity. Remember that:

$$\text{Total Cost for the Month} = \text{Demand Charge} + \text{Energy Charge} + \text{Fuel Adjustment Charge}$$

Living in the Real World

Just the Write Thing

Powerful Topic   When JTWT opened last winter, the weather was unusually mild. Field's heating bill, therefore, has been relatively low. It looks like summer is coming in with a vengeance, however, so she already has turned on the air conditioning. Field considers installing ceiling fans for better air circulation and to reduce the amount of the utility bill.

Draw Conclusions   About 25 states will deregulate their electricity market. This move will stop utility companies from passing on rate hikes to their consumers. How does a state's electricity market affect businesses?

Continued on page 621

Example 1

The Acme Manufacturing Company had a peak load of 100 kilowatts of electricity during April. The demand charge is $6.54 per kilowatt. Acme used a total of 30,000 kilowatt hours of electricity during the month. The energy charge for the first 1,000 kilowatt hours is $0.076 per kilowatt hour. The cost of the remaining kilowatt hours is $0.058 per kilowatt hour. The fuel adjustment charge for April is $0.0155 per kilowatt hour. What is the total cost of the electricity that Acme used in April?

STEP 1: Find the demand charge.

100 kW × $6.54 = $654.00 demand charge

Continued on next page

Section 19-5 Utilities Costs—Electricity ▶ **619**

National Standards for Business Education

Standard 1	Mathematical Foundations
Standard 2	Number Relationships and Operations

National Council of Teachers of Mathematics Standards

Standard 1	Numbers and Operations
Standard 6	Problem Solving
Standard 8	Communication

FOCUS

In addition to the cost for using telephone service, another utility cost that businesses must pay is the cost for using electricity. Electricity is measured in kilowatt hours (kWh). In addition to the actual electricity used, there are several other charges that are part of an electric bill.

TEACH

Students may not be familiar with how electric meters are used. Electric meters record the amount of electricity used. Older electric meters require a manual reading. This means a technician from the electric company providing the utility service must go to the meter location and record the meter reading. When a technician is not able to read the meter, the electric bill gives an estimated usage instead of the actual amount of electricity used. The next actual reading compensates for any differences in the estimation. Newer meters are read automatically through telephone lines.

TECHNOLOGY POWER

The beaches in southwestern Delaware along the Atlantic coastline are a significant tourist attraction for the state. However, where you find tourists you will usually find traffic and a lot of it. With traffic problems, there are usually air quality problems. To preserve the tourist-friendly nature of the beach corridor, the State of Delaware is sponsoring a program to introduce low-speed electric vehicles into fleets at strategic locations along the beach.

Living in the Real World

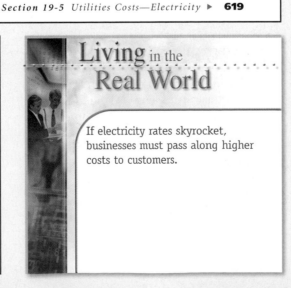

If electricity rates skyrocket, businesses must pass along higher costs to customers.

2 TEACH (cont'd)

In-Class Example

1. Find the total cost for the month.
   Usage: 8,000 kWh.
   Peak load: 90 kW.
   Demand charge: $5.95 per kW.
   Energy charge: $0.065 per kWh.
   Fuel adjustment: $0.015 per kWh. **$1,175.50**

3 ASSESS

Error Analysis

The section requires that students perform several steps before arriving at a final solution. Not only are there several steps to finding the total cost, some of the steps have sub-steps. To find the energy charge in Example 1 on page 619, you must first determine the charge for the first 1,000 kilowatt hours. Then you must subtract 1,000 from the total kilowatt hours used and finally multiply the difference by the charge for the remaining kilowatt hours used. Encourage students to clearly label their calculations so they can keep track of the different charges.

4 CLOSE

Closing Activity

1. Blackstone Valley Tires used 31,785 kilowatt hours of electricity in November. The peak load during the month was 205 kilowatts. The demand charge is $7.59 per kilowatt. The energy charge per kilowatt hour is $0.075 for the first 10,000 kilowatt hours and $0.063 per kilowatt hour for the remaining kilowatt hours. There fuel adjustment charge is $0.02 per kilowatt hour. What is the total cost of electricity for November? **$4,314.11**

STEP 2: Find the energy charge.
First 1,000 kilowatt hours: 1,000 kWh × $0.076 = $76.00
Remaining kilowatt hours: (30,000 − 1,000) kWh × $0.058 = $1,682.00
$76.00 + $1,682.00 = $1,758.00 energy charge

STEP 3: Find the fuel adjustment charge.
30,000 kWh × $0.0155 = $465.00 fuel adjustment charge

STEP 4: Find the total cost for the month.

Demand Charge	+	Energy Charge	+	Fuel Adjustment Charge
$654.00	+	$1,758.00	+	$465.00

= **$2,877.00 total cost for the month**

100 [×] 6.54 [=] 654 [M+] 1000 [×] .076 [=] 76 [M+]

30000 [−] 1000 [=] 29000 [×] .058 [=] 1682 [+] 76 [=]

1758 [M+] 30000 [×] .0155 [=] 465 [M+] [RM] 2877

CONCEPT CHECK

(SELF-CHECK ✓)

1. (100 × $6.60) + [(1,000 × $0.098) + (9,000 × $0.067)] + (10,000 × $0.016) = $660 + $98 + $603 + $160 = **$1,521**

Complete the problem, then check your answer at the end of the chapter. Find the total cost for the month.

1. (100 × $6.60) + [(1,000 × $0.098) + (9,000 × $0.067)] + (10,000 × $0.016)

SECTION 19-5 PRACTICE

2. Central City Deli used 8,700 kilowatt hours of electricity with a peak load of 100 kilowatts in June. The demand charge is $7.25 per kilowatt. The energy charge is $0.08 per kilowatt hour for the first 1,000 kilowatt hours and $0.06 per kilowatt hour for more than 1,000 kilowatt hours. The fuel adjustment charge is $0.03 per kilowatt hour. What is the total cost of electricity for City Deli for June? **$1,528.00**

3. The Pantry Supermarket used 21,400 kilowatt hours of electricity last month. The peak load for the month was 120 kilowatts. The demand charge is $5.91 per kilowatt. The energy charge per kilowatt hour is $0.0675 for the first 10,000 kilowatt hours and $0.0455 per kilowatt hour for more than 10,000 kilowatt hours. The fuel adjustment charge is $0.015 per kilowatt hour. What is the total cost of electricity for Pantry Supermarket for last month? **$2,223.90**

4. The City Centre Post used 12,417 kilowatt hours of electricity in August. The peak load during the month was 78 kilowatts. The demand charge is $6.96 per kilowatt. The energy charge per kilowatt hour is $0.0872 for the first 10,000 kilowatt hours and $0.0685 per kilowatt hour for more than 10,000 kilowatt hours. There is no fuel adjustment charge. What is the total cost of electricity for The City Centre Post in August? **$1,580.44**

MAINTAINING YOUR SKILLS

(Need Help? Go to...)
Skill 8: **Multiplying Decimals,** page 735

Multiply.

5. 100 × $6.47 **$647.00**

6. 1,000 × $0.087 **$87.00**

7. 8,700 × $0.063 **$548.10**

8. 9,700 × $0.015 **$145.50**

COMMUNICATION SKILLS

Conserving Resources
Small groups of students use the Internet or contact the local utility companies for information on how to conserve that particular company's resource, such as electricity, natural gas, or water. Groups prepare a short feature for a public service TV station, and present it to the class. **LS**, **CL**

WRAP-UP

Go over any problem for which a wrong answer is given.

Assignment Guide
   Basic: 2
Average: 3

20 min.

SECTION (19·6) Professional Services

Section Objective

Calculate the total cost of professional services.

You may hire professional **consultants**. They advise your business on a particular problem. The method of determining each **consultant's fee** may vary. Some consultants charge a flat fee, some charge a percent of the cost of the project, and some charge by the hour. Remember that:

Total Cost = Sum of Consultant's Fees

Living in the Real World

Just the Write Thing

The Importance of Accounting In addition to worrying about the various monthly expenses related to running her business, Field also wonders if she can reduce the cost of professional services, such as the cost of tax preparation and accounting. She talks to her accountant, who gives her tips on how to streamline her recordkeeping. That will reduce the amount of hours the accountant has to devote to the JTWT account.

Draw Conclusions Why is it important not to skimp on the budget by ignoring a professional service, like an accountant?

Continued on page 625

Example 1

Appleton Wholesale Grocers plans to construct a new building at a cost of $1,375,000. Appleton wants to hire an architect, a systems analyst, and a computer programmer. The architect charges 7 percent of the total cost of the building. The systems analyst charges a flat fee of $9,000. The computer programmer charges $30 an hour and works 150 hours. What is the total cost of the professional services?

STEP: Find the sum of consultant's fees.

Architect: $1,375,000 × 7%	$ 96,250
Systems analyst: flat fee	9,000
Computer programmer: $30 × 150	4,500
	$109,750 sum of consultant's fees

1375000 ☒ 7 ⅐ M+ 9000 M+

30 ☒ 150 ⊜ 4500 M+ RM 109750

National Standards for Business Education

Standard 1	Mathematical Foundations
Standard 2	Number Relationships and Operations

National Council of Teachers of Mathematics Standards

Standard 1	Numbers and Operations
Standard 6	Problem Solving
Standard 8	Communication

(1) FOCUS

Consultants advise people and businesses about certain situations or problems. Have students suggest some types of consultants. **For example, realtors, lawyers, architects, and accountants can be considered consultants because they provide advice or services for a fee.**

In-Class Examples

Work through these exercises with students before having them do the Self-Check.

1. $500,000 × 8% **$40,000**
2. (30 × $75.00) + ($400,000 × 20%) **$82,250**
3. (42 × $65.00) + (1,000,000 × 18%) **$182,730**

Living in the Real World

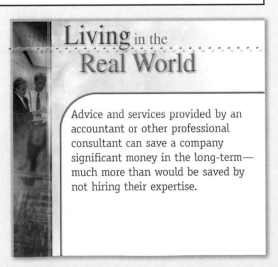

Advice and services provided by an accountant or other professional consultant can save a company significant money in the long-term—much more than would be saved by not hiring their expertise.

SECTION 19-6

② TEACH

Have students discuss why different types of consultants have different fee structures. Refer to Example 1 on page 621 to point out the differences between the consultants' fees. **Mention that some consultants charge by the hour while others charge by the scale of the job. Some lawyers charge by the hour since they do not know up front how much work will be required in a case. Other lawyers just charge a percent of the settlement. If there is no settlement, then there is no payment. However, these lawyers do not generally take on cases unless they are confident that there will be a settlement.**

Motivating the Lesson
Find the fee for each of the following consultants.
Lawyer: 24 hours at $125 per hour. **$3,000**
Engineer: 30 hours at $55 per hour. **$1,650**
Real estate broker: 6 percent of $435,000. **$26,100**

In-Class Examples
Find the total cost.
1. Lawyer: 23 hours at $80 per hour.
   Accountant: $2,400 flat fee.
   Stockbroker: 2 percent of $500,000. **$14,240**
2. Software designer: 35 hours at $60 per hour.
   Education consultant: $5,000. flat fee art consultant: 4 percent of $45,000. **$8,900**
3. Simex Real Estate sells a piece of commercial property for Choice Instruments. The selling price is $690,000. Simex receives 5.75 percent of the selling price. What does it cost Choice to have Simex handle the transaction? **$39,675**

SELF-CHECK✔

Complete the problems, then check your answers at the end of the chapter. Find the total cost.

1. Architect: 8 percent of $450,000.
   Lawyer: 20 hours at $75 per hour.
   Surveyor: $3,500 flat fee.
   Total Cost: (450,000 × 8%) + (20 × $75) + $3,500 = $36,000 + $1,500 + $3,500 = **$41,000**

2. Engineer: 25 hours at $42.50 per hour.
   Computer programmer: $5,000 flat fee.
   Computer time: $2,450 flat fee.
   Total Cost: (25 × $42.50) + $5,000 + $2,450 = $1,062.50 + $5,000 + $2,450 = **$8,512.50**

Example 2

Alice Mayfield hired attorney Julia Gallo to represent her as the plaintiff in an injury claim. Gallo charged $65 per hour plus 20 percent of the settlement. Including litigation, Gallo spent 48 hours on the case. Mayfield was awarded a settlement of $500,000. What did it cost Mayfield to employ Gallo? What did Mayfield receive (net) as a result of the injury claim?

STEP 1: Find the total consultant's fees.
(48 × $65.00) + ($500,000 × 20%)
= $3,120 + $100,000
= **$103,120 cost Mayfield to employ Gallo**

STEP 2: Find the net amount Mayfield received.
$500,000 − $103,120 = **$396,880 net to Mayfield**

3. Total Cost: (80 × $150) + (20% × $200,000) = $12,000 + $40,000 = $52,000
   Net = $200,000 − $52,000 = $148,000

SELF-CHECK✔

Complete the problems, then check your answers at the end of the chapter.

3. Yoko Nagasawa hired attorney. Attorney fee charges:
   • $150 per hour.
   • 20% of settlement.
   Worked 80 hours.
   Settlement of $200,000.
   Find the total fee.
   What was the net to Nagasawa?

4. Sherman Brewer. Hiring consultant charges:
   • $40 per hour.
   • 15% of first year salary.
   Worked 75 hours.
   First year salary of $80,000.
   Find the total fee.
   What was the net to Brewer?

4. Total Cost: (75 × $40) + (15% × $80,000) = $3,000 + $12,000 = $15,000
   Net = $80,000 − $15,000 = $65,000

SECTION 19-6 PRACTICE

Find the total fee.

	Professional Service	Fee Structure	Project Information	Total Fee
5.	Patent attorney	$75.00 per hour	Worked 20 hours	$1,500.00
6.	Industrial nurse	$21.25 per hour	Worked 40 hours	$850.00
7.	Design consultant	$5,000 flat fee	Worked 25 hours	$5,000.00

GLOBAL PERSPECTIVE

At 1500 … or 3:00?

Many American companies contract services from other countries, for example information technology services from India. It's important to figure out the local time, say in India, to avoid problems in scheduling conference calls, and so on. Aside from the different time zones to be familiar with, different countries use different methods of telling time.

What is known in the United States as "military time" is just plain time for our global partners in Europe. The trick? Add 12 to the P.M. hours. For example, 3:00 P.M. is 12 plus 3, which is 1500 hours. Many Europeans drop the "hours" and say that you can call them at 1500. Call out different times on the 12-hour clock (both A.M. and P.M.) in a lightning round with students calling out the time on the 24-hour clock.

8. Bond broker for J. Piermont Financial Services. Paid 2 percent of total bonds sold. Ten million dollars in bonds sold. What is the total fee? **$200,000.00**

9. Real estate broker sold a piece of property. Paid 3 percent of total sale. Sale totals $615,500. What is the total fee? **$18,465.00**

10. The June Company hired Maletus Brown, a staff development specialist, to conduct a workshop for 83 of its employees. Brown was paid $110 per person. What was the total cost of Brown's services? **$9,130.00**

11. Lakeside Hospital hired an industrial engineering firm to conduct a work sampling on the average nurse's day. Time Study did the work sampling and charged $67.50 per hour. It took Time Study 32 hours to complete the task. What did the work sampling cost Lakeside Hospital? **$2,160.00**

12. The Central Farmers Co-op plans to issue $20,000,000 in bonds to pay for an extensive expansion. One bond broker will sell the bonds for a fee of 3.25 percent of the $20,000,000 face value of the bonds. What will the broker's services cost Central? What is the net amount to Central?
$650,000.00; $19,350,000.00

13. Modern Service Stations plans to sell a large piece of commercial property. The selling price of the property is $975,000. Marcus Trent will handle the entire transaction for 6.5 percent of the selling price. What will it cost Modern Service Stations to have Trent handle the transaction? What is the net amount?
$63,375.00; $911,625.00

14. Liberty Bank and Trust plans to build a new branch office. Liberty hired Ed Baker, an architect, to design the new branch office. Baker's fee is 7 percent of the cost of the project. Liberty hired Tina Pike as project engineer for the new branch. Pike's fee is 4.5 percent of the cost of the project. Liberty hired attorney Sara Charles to handle the legal aspects of the project. She charges $75 per hour. It took her 10.5 hours to prepare the legal documents. The cost of the branch office is estimated to be $4,575,000. What amount should Liberty plan to pay for the 3 professional services? **$526,912.50**

15. Super Food Mart has installed automated checkout equipment in its six stores. It hired Robert Case to consult on its installation. Case charged 6 percent of the installation cost. It also hired Marilyn Lee to instruct its employees on the use of the equipment. Lee conducted six 4-hour sessions at $125 per session. The cost of the installation totaled $68,970. What was the total cost for professional services? **$4,888.20**

MAINTAINING YOUR SKILLS

Need Help? Go to...
► Skill 5: Adding Decimals, page 732
► Skill 8: Multiplying Decimals, page 735
► Skill 30: Finding the Percentage, page 757

Solve.

16. $175.00 + $493.75 + $216.80 **$885.55**

17. $14,150.00 + $7,185.90 + $417.95 **$21,753.85**

18. (5% of $1,750,000.00) + $14,750.00 **$102,250.00**

19. (7.5% of $863,900.00) + (25 × $9.50) **$65,030.00**

20. ($85.00 × 24.50) + $5,000 + (2% of $2,500,000) **$57,082.50**

21. (6% of $3,500,000) + ($75 × 6.5) + $1,475 **$211,962.50**

USING CALCULATORS

Have students determine what the following key-stroke sequence will give as a result: 650000 [×] 6 [%] 39000 [M+] 4000 [M+] 45 [×] 100 [=] 4500 [M+] 3000 [M+] [RM] 50500

You might suggest that the students attempt this by hand before entering it into a calculator.

WRAP-UP

Go over any problem for which a wrong answer is given.

Assignment Guide
  Basic: 5–7
  Average: 8–11

20 min.

(3) ASSESS

Error Analysis
Remind students to figure the fee for each consultant separately before attempting to combine any of the figures. Encourage students to first list each consultant, second calculate their fee, and last add the fees to find the total cost. Refer students to the organization of the steps in Example 1.

   In Example 2, emphasize that the settlement amount is not the amount that Mayfield receives. Point out that the lawyer's fees must be subtracted from the settlement amount.

(4) CLOSE

Closing Activity
Find the total cost.
1. Landscape architect: 21 hours at $57 per hour.
   Architect: 7 percent of $680,000.
   Surveyor: $3,500 flat fee.
   $52,297

2. Lawyer: 36 hours at $75 per hour.
   Tax specialist: $4,560 flat fee.
   Public relations consultant: 27 hours at $48 per hour.
   $8,556

3. Marketing consultant: 33 hours at $62 per hour.
   Product testing specialist: $9750 flat fee.
   Creative designer: 4 percent of $52,900. **$13,912**

4. Hanskin Company hired a professional development specialist to conduct a workshop for 150 employees. The specialist was paid $75 per person. What was the total cost? **$11,250**

Quick Quiz

1. Jones Cleaners rents a space that is 25 feet by 30 feet. The annual rent is $14 per square foot. Find the number of square feet and the monthly rental charge. **750 ft²; $875**

2. Uxbridge Enterprises cleans and maintains an office area that is 60 feet by 65 feet. The contract calls for $6.25 per square foot annually. What is the monthly charge? **$2,031.25**

3. The Wellrite Company rents office furniture for three months. The rental charge is 12 percent of the list price. The list price is $2,490 and the tax rate is 6 percent. What is the total rental cost? **$950.18**

4. Find the total electricity cost for the month.
Usage: 15,000 kWh.
Peak load: 100 kW.
Demand charge: $6.95 per kW.
Energy charge: $0.067 per kWh.
Fuel adjustment: $0.018 per kWh. **$1,970**

5. Gray Industries hired the following consultants to assist them with a project. Find the total cost.
Landscape architect: 26 hours at $50 per hour.
Architect: 6 percent of $750,000.
Surveyor: $2,500 flat fee.
$48,800

SECTION 19-1 CONCEPT CHECK (p. 611)

1. Sq. Ft. = 100 × 50 = **5,000**
   Monthly Rent: ($8 × 5,000) ÷ 12 = $40,000 ÷ 12 = **$3,333.33**
2. Sq. Ft. = 125 × 45 = **5,625**
   Monthly Rent: ($9.50 × 5,625) ÷ 12 = $53,437.50 ÷ 12 = **$4,453.13**

SECTION 19-2 CONCEPT CHECK (p. 613)

1. Labor Charge: 3 × 6 × $8.50 = $153.00
   Materials Charge: 9 × $24.85 = $223.65
   Total: $153.00 + $223.65 = **$376.65**
2. Monthly Charge: 40 × 50 × $4.50 = $9,000; $9,000 ÷ 12 = **$750**

SECTION 19-3 CONCEPT CHECK (p. 615)

1. Rental Charge: $640 × 10% = $64
   Tax: $64 × 3 × 6% = $11.52
   Total: ($64.00 × 3) + $11.52 = $192.00 + $11.52 = **$203.52**
2. Rental Charge: $1,470 × 8% = $117.60
   Tax: $117.60 × 5 × 5.5% = $32.34
   Total: ($117.60 × 5) + $32.34 = $588.00 + $32.34 = **$620.34**

SECTION 19-4 CONCEPT CHECK (p. 617)

1. Additional line: ($19.99 × 1.00) = $19.99
   Additional minutes: (1,200 − 1,000) × $0.35 = $70.00
   Fed Tax: ($89.99 + $19.99 + $70.00) × 3% = $179.98 × 0.03 = $5.40
   Total: $179.98 + $5.40 = **$185.38**
2. No additional minutes
   Fed Tax: $59.99 × 5% = $2.9995 or $3.00
   Total: $59.99 + $3.00 = **$62.99**

SECTION 19-5 CONCEPT CHECK (p. 620)

1. (100 × $6.60) + [(1,000 × $0.098) + (9,000 × $0.067)] + (10,000 × $0.016)
      $660   + $98   + $603   + $160
   = **$1,521**

SECTION 19-6 CONCEPT CHECK (p. 622)

1. Total Cost: (450,000 × 8%) + (20 × $75) + $3,500 =
      $36,000   + $1,500   + $3,500 = **$41,000**
2. Total Cost: (25 × $42.50) + $5,000 + $2,450 =
      $1,062.50   + $5,000 + $2,450 = **$8,512.50**
3. Total Cost: (80 × $150) + (20% × $200,000) =
      $12,000   + $40,000   = **$52,000**
   Net = $200,000 − $52,000 = **$148,000**
4. Total Cost: (75 × $40) + (15% × $80,000) =
      $3,000   + $12,000   = **$15,000**
   Net = $80,000 − $15,000 = **$65,000**

Living in the Real World

Just the Write Thing

Thinking Critically JTWT looks to use the Internet as a powerful tool to advertise its products and services. While the Internet can be useful to customers, it can also be looked upon as an annoyance, when mass e-mails or *spam* (junk e-mail) is sent. The Federal Trade Commission (FTC) has amassed a database of 8 million spam messages, with 10,000 new ones arriving daily. The FTC and state governments are attempting to stop the tidal wave of spam that threatens the Internet. On the other hand, the Direct Marketers' Association opposes limits on marketers' abilities to conduct blanket advertising through e-mail addresses.

1 **Debate.** Why would the Direct Marketers' Association oppose such limits on e-mail advertising?

2 **Critical Thinking.** Although other people find spam annoying, Direct Marketers' Association opposes limits as an infringement on Free Speech. List several arguments on both sides of this issue.

3 **Decision Making.** Field needs to compare the various types of unsolicited advertising, such as through U.S. mail, telemarketers, and online advertisers.
   A. How do you feel as the recipient of such advertising?
   B. Have you ever bought something advertised in any of these ways? Is one form more intrusive and annoying than others?
   C. Should the federal government regulate any of them? Why or why not?

Living in the Real World

1. What or who censors the mail; one person's spam is another person's treasure.
2. Censorship issues. First Amendment rights. Invasion of privacy. Tracking Internet site habits.
3. **A.** Answers will vary.
   B. Answers will vary.
   C. Answers will vary. Discuss censorship issues.

REVIEW OF KEY WORDS

rent (p. 610)	monthly service charge (p. 616)	kilowatts (p. 619)
lease (p. 610)	demand charge (p. 619)	fuel adjustment charge (p. 619)
labor charge (p. 612)	energy charge (p. 619)	consultants (p. 621)
utilities (p. 616)	peak load (p. 619)	consultant's fee (p. 621)

For Problems 1–12, write a definition for each key word in your own words. Then compare your version with the one in the Glossary.

1–12. Definitions will vary. Evaluate based on the students' understanding of the term and their ability to put the definition into their own words.

Skills and Concepts

SECTION OBJECTIVE 19-1 AND EXAMPLES

Compute the monthly rental charge.

Web Dot Com rents a small office. The floor space measures 12 feet by 20 feet. It pays an annual rate of $8.25 per square foot. Rounding to the nearest dollar, what is Web Dot Com's monthly rental charge?

STEP 1: Find the number of square feet.
Length × Width
12 feet × 20 feet = 240 square feet

STEP 2: Find the monthly rental charge.
(Annual Rate × Number of Square Feet) ÷ 12
($8.25 × 240) ÷ 12 = $165 monthly rental charge

REVIEW EXERCISES
Complete the table.

	Dimensions	=	(Number of Square Feet	×	Annual Rate per Square Foot)	÷ 12 =		Monthly Rental Charge
13.	10.0 ft × 20.0 ft	=	(a. 200	×	$ 9.00)	÷ 12 =	b.	$150
14.	30.0 ft × 15.0 ft	=	(a. 450	×	8.50)	÷ 12 =	b.	$318.75
15.	35.0 ft × 25.0 ft	=	(a. 875	×	10.50)	÷ 12 =	b.	$765.63
16.	40.5 ft × 12.0 ft	=	(a. 486	×	7.50)	÷ 12 =	b.	$303.75
17.	30.0 ft × 18.0 ft	=	(a. 540	×	6.25)	÷ 12 =	b.	$281.25
18.	45.0 ft × 22.0 ft	=	(a. 990	×	8.27)	÷ 12 =	b.	$682.28

SECTION OBJECTIVE 19-2 AND EXAMPLES

Calculate the total building maintenance charge.

Northern Office Supply hired Universal Roofers to repair the roof on its office building. Two roofers worked 17 hours each to complete the job. The regular hourly rate for each roofer was $11.25. The roofers used $653.20 in materials. What was the total charge for fixing the roof?

STEP 1: Find the labor charge.
($11.25 × 17) × 2 = $382.50 labor charge

STEP 2: Find the materials charge.
$653.20 materials charge

STEP 3: Find the total charge.
Labor Charge + Materials Charge
$382.50 + $653.20 = $1,035.70 total charge

REINFORCEMENT

Section 19-1
1. Dimensions: 50 ft × 55 ft
Annual rate per square foot: $9.85 **2,750 ft²; $2,257.29**
2. Dimensions: 24 ft × 26 ft
Annual rate per square foot: $14.60 **624 ft²; $759.20**

Study Guide and Assessment

REVIEW EXERCISES
Complete the table.

	$\begin{pmatrix} \text{Time} \\ \text{Required} \end{pmatrix}$	×	Number of Employees	×	Hourly Rate	=	$\begin{pmatrix} \text{Labor} \\ \text{Charge} \end{pmatrix}$	+	Materials Charge	=	Total
19.	(7.0 hours	×	3	×	$11.25	=	a.)	+	$321.98	=	b.
20.	(6.5 hours	×	2	×	10.50	=	a.)	+	193.58	=	b.
21.	(4.0 hours	×	4	×	9.90	=	a.)	+	621.90	=	b.
22.	(12.2 hours	×	8	×	13.50	=	a.)	+	239.66	=	b.
23.	(3.0 hours	×	2	×	9.80	=	a.)	+	712.90	=	b.
24.	(5.5 hours	×	9	×	12.75	=	a.)	+	239.76	=	b.

19. a. $236.25
    b. $558.23
20. a. $136.50
    b. $330.08
21. a. $158.40
    b. $780.30
22. a. $1,317.60
    b. $1,557.26
23. a. $58.80
    b. $771.70
24. a. $631.13
    b. $870.89

SECTION OBJECTIVE 19-3 AND EXAMPLES

Determine the total equipment rental cost.

The list price of a large canopy is $3,200. The monthly rental charge is 5 percent of the list price. There is a 6.5 percent usage tax. What is the total rent charge for 1 year?

STEP 1: Find the rental charge per month.
$3,200 × 5% = $160 rental charge per month

STEP 2: Find the tax.
($160 × 12) × 6.5% = $124.80 tax

STEP 3: Find the total rental cost.
(Rental Charge × Time) + Usage Tax
($160 × 12) + $124.80 =
$1,920 + $124.80 – $2,044.80 total rental cost

REVIEW EXERCISES
Complete the table.

	Item	List Price	Rental Rate	Monthly Charge	Number of Months	Usage Tax	Total Rental
25.	Copy machine	$ 5,210.85	12.0% of list	a.	6	6.5%	b.
26.	Tent	1,900.00	9.0% of list	a.	2	4.5%	b.
27.	Computer	1,390.55	11.0% of list	a.	4	8.5%	b.
28.	Phone system	10,511.83	8.5% of list	a.	9	7.0%	b.
29.	Color printer	5,408.45	15.0% of list	a.	12	6.0%	b.
30.	Forklift	35,000.00	9.5% of list	a.	5	5.5%	b.

25. a. $625.30
    b. $3,995.68
26. a. $171
    b. $357.39
27. a. $152.96
    b. $663.85
28. a. $893.51
    b. $8,604.46
29. a. $811.27
    b. $10,319.35
30. a. $3,325
    b. $17,539.38

REINFORCEMENT

Section 19-2
1. Find the labor charge and the total charge.
   Time required: 4 hours.
   Number of employees: 6.
   Hourly rate: $10.75.
   Materials charge: $389.00. **$647.00**

Section 19-3
1. Find the total rental cost.
   Rental charge: 12 percent of $1,450.
   Tax rate: 7.25 percent.
   Time: 5 months. **$933.08**

SECTION OBJECTIVE 19-4 AND EXAMPLES

Work out the monthly telephone cost.

Redwater Video Rental has 3 telephone lines. It signs up for the $89.99 plan from the Flexible Advantage Calling Plan (see Figure 19.1 on page 616). Redwater uses 1,201 minutes. A 2 percent federal excise tax is added to the bill. What is the total cost of Redwater's telephone service for the month?

STEP 1: Find the cost of additional minutes.
$(1,201 - 1,000) \times \$0.35 = \$70.35$ cost of additional minutes

STEP 2: Find the cost of an additional line.
$19.99 cost of an additional line

STEP 3: Find the federal excise tax.
$(\$89.99 + \$70.35 + \$19.99) \times 2\% = \$3.6066$ or $3.61 federal excise tax

STEP 4: Find the total cost for the month.

Monthly Service Charge		Cost of Additional Minutes		Cost of Additional Lines		Federal Excise Tax		
$89.99	+	$70.35	+	$19.99	+	$3.61	=	**$183.94 total cost for the month**

REVIEW EXERCISES

Use Figure 19.1, Flexible Advantage Calling Plan, on page 616 for Problems 31–36.

	Monthly Plan	Number of Minutes Used	Number of Lines	Federal Excise Tax Rate	Total Cost for the Month
31.	$ 59.99	750	2	4.0%	**$153.39**
32.	119.99	1,376	3	3.0%	**$144.18**
33.	119.99	1,522	4	3.5%	**$173.54**
34.	89.99	955	2	5.0%	**$94.49**
35.	59.99	515	3	4.0%	**$88.64**
36.	89.99	1,050	2	3.3%	**$111.04**

SECTION OBJECTIVE 19-5 AND EXAMPLES

Compute the monthly cost for electricity.

Destina Land Company had a peak load of 120 kilowatts of electricity during May. The demand charge is $5.98 per kilowatt. Destina used a total of 35,000 kilowatt hours of electricity during the month. The energy charge for the first 1,000 kilowatt hours is $0.061 per kilowatt hour. The cost of the remaining kilowatt hours is $0.055 per kilowatt hour. The fuel adjustment charge for May is $0.0165 per kilowatt hour. What is the total cost of the electricity that Destina Land Company used in May?

STEP 1: Find the demand charge.
$120 \text{ kWh} \times \$5.98 = \$717.60$ demand charge

REINFORCEMENT

Section 19-4

Use **Figure 19.1** in Example 1 on page 616. Century Homes has 4 telephone lines and uses the $89.99 Flexible Advantage Calling Plan. This month the company used 1,203 minutes, 20 minutes of domestic wireless long distance, and 15 minutes of roaming. The federal excise tax rate is 3 percent. What is the total cost for the month? **$195.73**

STEP 2: Find the energy charge.

First 1,000 kilowatt hours: 1,000 kWh × $0.061 = $61.00

Remaining kilowatt hours: (35,000 − 1,000) kWh × $0.055 = $1,870

$61 + $1,870 = $1,931 energy charge

STEP 3: Find the fuel adjustment charge.

35,000 kWh × $0.0165 = $577.50 fuel adjustment charge

STEP 4: Find the total cost for the month.

Demand Charge + Energy Charge + Fuel Adjustment Charge

$717.60   + $1,931   + $577.50   = **$3,226.10 total cost for the month**

REVIEW EXERCISES
Complete the table.

	Company	kWh Used	Peak Load (kWh)	Demand Charge per kWh	Energy Charge per kWh	Fuel Adjustment Charge per kWh	Total Cost for the Month
37.	Amarillo Rentals	18,500	100	$4.50	$0.090	$0.020	**$2,485**
38.	Battle, Inc.	16,000	110	5.85	0.110	0.008	**$2,531.50**
39.	Northwest Insurance	21,000	85	6.10	0.070	0.015	**$2,303.50**
40.	Hair Styles, Inc.	15,000	90	5.78	0.080	0.010	**$1,870.20**
41.	Max's Restaurant	30,000	150	4.96	0.095	0.030	**$4,494.00**
42.	Harry's Boots	17,250	110	5.05	0.081	0.035	**$2,556.60**

SECTION OBJECTIVE 19-6 AND EXAMPLES

Calculate the total cost of professional services.

Appleton Elementary School hired Michele Gaglione, a consultant, to conduct a reading workshop for its 25 teachers. Gaglione was paid $26 per teacher. What was the total cost of Gaglione's services?

STEP: Find the sum of the consultant's fees. $26 × 25 = **$650 consultant's fee**

REVIEW EXERCISES
Find the total fee.

	Professional Service	Fee Structure	Project Information	Total Fee
43.	Research Consultant	$125 per hour	Worked 15 hours	**$1,875**
44.	Private Investigator	$35 per hour	Worked 35 hours	**$1,225**
45.	Engineering Services	$75 per hour	Worked 12.5 hours	**$937.50**
46.	Landscape Design	$3,000 flat fee	Not applicable	**$3,000**
47.	Sales Consultant	6.5% of sales contract	Sales Contract—$490,000	**$31,850**
48.	Image Consultant	$125 per hour	Worked 2.25 hours	**$281.25**

REINFORCEMENT

Section 19-5

Find the total cost for the month.

1. Usage: 10,000 kWh .
   Peak load: 100 kW.
   Demand charge: $7.50 per kW.
   Energy charge: $0.07 per kWh.
   Fuel adjustment: $0.016 per kWh.
   $1,610.00

2. Usage: 21,000 kWh.
   Peak load: 200 kW.
   Demand charge: $7.25 per kW.
   Energy charge: $0.075 per kWh.
   Fuel adjustment: $0.02 per kWh.
   $3,445.00

Section 19-6

1. Find the total cost.
   Engineer: 25 hours at $50 per hour.
   Architect: 7 percent of $680,000.
   Surveyor: $3,750 flat fee. **$52,600**

Aligned and verified by

The Princeton Review

Cumulative Test Prep

Test-Taking Tip
Most standardized tests have a time limit, so budget your time carefully. If you cannot answer a question within a few minutes, mark your best guess and go on to the next question. If there is still time left when you get to the end of the section, go back to the questions that you were unsure of.

SECTION ONE: MULTIPLE CHOICE

This section contains eight multiple-choice questions. After working each problem, write the letter of the correct answer on your paper.

1. The Data-Base Equipment Company manufactures laser printers. Each printer is stored in a box measuring 2 feet high, 1.5 feet wide, and 2.5 feet deep. How many cubic feet of space does Data-Base need to store 744 printers? **B**

    Ⓐ 1,860   Ⓑ 5,580
    Ⓒ 6,320   Ⓓ 8,560

2. How many StraightAway models does Luxury Motor Coach have on its lot on October 1? **B**

Item: StraightAway			Stock Number: JR 2201F	
Month of	Opening Balance	Units Received	Issues	Inventory at End of Month
August	42	5	12	
September		6	18	
October				

    Ⓐ 12   Ⓑ 23
    Ⓒ 60   Ⓓ 83

3. Jimmy's Jewels maintains an inventory valued at $89,500 and estimates it costs 33 percent to carry the inventory. What is the approximate annual cost of carrying the inventory? **D**

    Ⓐ $28,432   Ⓑ $28,650
    Ⓒ $29,310   Ⓓ $29,535

4. The Barstow Company is shipping 846 pounds of automotive equipment. Commercial Trucking will handle the shipment. The distance is 180 miles. The rate is $1.83 per mile. What is the total shipping cost? **C**

    Ⓐ $15.48   Ⓑ $32.94
    Ⓒ $329.40   Ⓓ $1,548.18

5. Moore's Nursery rents warehouse space at an annual rate of $4.50 per square foot. Moore's warehouse measures 60 feet by 150 feet. What is the monthly rental charge? **D**

    Ⓐ $2,500   Ⓑ $3,000
    Ⓒ $3,150   Ⓓ $3,375

6. Town Mall hired 4 high school students to clean the grounds. Each student worked for 2.5 hours at an hourly rate of $8.25. The materials charge was $46.75. What was the total charge for this service? **C**

    Ⓐ $46.75   Ⓑ $82.50
    Ⓒ $129.25   Ⓓ $131.75

7. Mary Taylor is opening a branch tax office for 3 months. She plans to rent furniture at a monthly charge of 10 percent of the list price. What is the monthly cost for the furniture? **B**

Item	List Price
2 desks	$279.79 (each)
2 desk chairs	97.50 (each)
4 guest chairs	74.75 (each)
1 file cabinet	112.45
1 bookcase	147.50

    Ⓐ $125.82   Ⓑ $131.35
    Ⓒ $139.23   Ⓓ $417.70

8. The Greco Import Store pays a basic monthly charge of $36.15 for telephone service. The charge includes 73 outgoing local calls. Each additional outgoing local call costs $0.18. Last month a total of 95 outgoing local calls were made from Greco's. A 3 percent federal excise tax was added to the bill for the month. What was the total cost of telephone service for the month? **B**

    Ⓐ $37.23   Ⓑ $41.31
    Ⓒ $52.54   Ⓓ $53.12

SECTION TWO: FREE RESPONSE

This section contains eight questions for which you will supply short answers. Write your answer on your paper.

9. Explain the difference between units received and issues. **Receipts are incoming items; issues are outgoing items**

10. Describe the assumptions made when using the FIFO and LIFO methods of valuing inventory.

11. City Cleaners maintains a soap inventory valued at $14,700. The cost of maintaining the inventory is approximately 20 percent of the value of the inventory. What is the approximate annual cost of carrying this inventory? **$2,940**

12. Marker Graphics is shipping a 850-pound display for a trade show from Syracuse to New Orleans. The shipment needs to arrive "guaranteed first arrival." The rate is $216 per hundred pounds. What is the cost of shipping the display? **$1,836**

13. Describe the difference between demand charge and energy charge.

14. Name three ways a consultant may charge for services.

15. The Norris Company used 11,650 kilowatt hours of electricity with a peak load of 120 kilowatts in April. The demand charge is $6.54 per kilowatt. The energy charge per kilowatt hour is $0.076 for the first 10,000 kilowatt hours and $0.058 per kilowatt hour for more than 10,000 kilowatt hours. The fuel adjustment charge is $0.0165 per kilowatt hour. What is the total cost of electricity for The Norris Company for April? **$1,832.73**

16. Innovative Automotive hired a consultant from Engineering Consortium to help develop a new engine. The consultant's fee was 7.3 percent of the cost of the project. The project cost $843,500. What was the total cost of the consultant's services? **$61,575.50**

SECTION THREE: OPEN-ENDED

This section contains four open-ended questions. Demonstrate your knowledge by giving a clear, concise solution to each problem. Your score on these problems will depend on how well you do on the following:

- Explain your reasoning.
- Show your understanding of mathematics in an organized manner.
- Use charts, graphs, and diagrams in your explanation.
- Show the solution in more than one way or relate it to other situations.
- Investigate beyond the requirements of the problem.

17. Describe why it is important for a business to know how much inventory it has on hand at all times.

18. Explain why it costs money to carry inventory. What type of inventory might cost more than other types to carry? Why?

It costs to store the inventory in the form of rent or mortgage as well as utilities (it may cost a lot to refrigerate inventory).

19. Describe when it would be more economical for a business to rent rather than purchase equipment or furniture. Would there ever be a situation where—even if it costs more—a business would rent rather than purchase?

20. Explain the advantages and disadvantages for hiring consultants.

Mathematics Online

To learn more about the math behind a business's services, visit the *Mathematics with Business Applications* Web site at www.busmath.glencoe.com.

Cumulative Test Prep ▶ **631**

---

10. FIFO assumes that the first items received are the first items sold. LIFO assumes that the last items received are the first items shipped.

13. Demand charge is based on the peak load during the month; energy charge is based on the total number of kilowatt-hours that the business uses during the month.

14. (1) Flat fee, (2) a percent of the cost of the project, and (3) by the hour.

17. It is important so that a business can meet sales demands while not keeping excessive quantities.

19. If they only need the furniture for a short time.

20. Consultants are trained to analyze the situation. They may be able to save your business some money. Consultants are sometimes very expensive.

National Standards for Business Education

Section Objectives	1. Mathematical Foundations	2. Number Relationships and Operations	3. Patterns, Functions, and Algebra	4. Measurements	5. Statistics and Probability	6. Problem-Solving Applications	
20-1 Payroll Register (pp. 634–637) Complete a payroll register.	X	X					
20-2 Business Expenses (pp. 638–639) Calculate the percent that a particular business expense is of the total expenses.	X	X					
20-3 Apportioning (pp. 640–641) Figure out a department's share of the total business expense.	X	X					
20-4 Depreciation—Straight-Line Method (pp. 642–643) Utilize the straight-line method to compute the annual depreciation of an item.	X	X					
20-5 Depreciation—Book Value (pp. 644–646) Apply the straight-line method to compute the book value of an item.	X	X					
20-6 Modified Accelerated (MACRS) (pp. 647–649) Use the modified accelerated cost recovery system to compute the annual depreciation and book value.	X	X					

(Source: Reprinted with permission from the National Standards for Business Education, copyright © 2001 by National Business Education Association, 1914 Association Drive, Reston, Virginia 21901-1596)

SCANS Correlation

Foundation Skills

Basic Skills	Reading	Writing	Math	Listening	Speaking	
Thinking Skills	Creative Thinking	Decision Making	Problem Solving	Seeing Things in the Mind's Eye	Knowing How to Learn	Reasoning
Personal Qualities	Responsibility	Self-Esteem	Sociability	Self-Management	Integrity/Honesty	

This chapter's highlighted blocks indicate the chapter's content coverage in the Student Edition and the Teacher Wraparound Edition.

1. Numbers & Operations	2. Algebra	3. Geometry	4. Measurement	5. Data Analysis & Probability	6. Problem Solving	7. Reasoning & Proof	8. Communication	9. Connections	10. Representations
X					X		X		
X					X		X		
X		X			X		X		
X					X		X		
X					X		X		
X					X		X		

SCANS Correlation

Workplace Competencies

Resources	Allocating Time	Allocating Money	Allocating Material and Facility Resources	Allocating Human Resources		
Information	Acquiring and Evaluating Information	Organizing and Maintaining Information	Interpreting and Communicating Information	Using Computers to Process Information		
Interpersonal Skills	Participating as a Member of a Team	Teaching Others	Serving Clients/Customers	Exercising Leadership	Negotiating to Arrive at a Decision	Working with Cultural Diversity
Systems	Understanding Systems	Monitoring and Correcting Performance	Improving and Designing Systems			
Technology	Selecting Technology	Applying Technology to Task	Maintaining and Troubleshooting Technology			

What You'll Learn

In this chapter you'll focus on how companies account for their employees, equipment, and other business expenses. You'll look at payroll costs and the cost of depreciation of items, such as furniture and vehicles.

Why It's Important

The rapid development of global financial markets has created a need for international consistency in accounting standards and auditing approaches. The United States has a very detailed framework of generally accepted accounting principles (US GAAP). This is based on accounting standards and guidance of the Financial Accounting Standards Board. The world's economies are facing a future in which cash flows across borders will grow. Accounting and financial reporting is an important element of this evolving market and can support or undermine the efficiency of markets.

Key Word Review

Self-Esteem

Part of building self-esteem is being confident in your abilities. You can be more confident about your ability to learn this chapter when you prepare by recording the meaning of the key words. List the words and definitions in your journal.

CHAPTER 20

Accounting

What You'll Learn

Section 20-1 Complete a payroll register.

Section 20-2 Calculate the percent that a particular business expense is of the total expenses.

Section 20-3 Figure out a department's share of the total business expense.

Section 20-4 Utilize the straight-line method to compute the annual depreciation of an item.

Section 20-5 Apply the straight-line method to compute the book value of an item.

Section 20-6 Use the modified accelerated cost recovery system to compute the annual depreciation and book value.

When Will You Ever Use This?

At the core of any business is the success of its accounting department. It records not only all transactions that come and go in a business, but also the value of your equipment.

Key Words to Know

- payroll register
- apportion
- depreciation
- straight-line method
- estimated life
- salvage value
- book value
- accumulated depreciation
- modified accelerated cost recovery system

Mathematics Online

To learn more about accounting, visit the *Mathematics with Business Applications* Web site at www.busmath.glencoe.com.

CLASSROOM RESOURCES

Application and Enrichment
- Teacher Wraparound Edition
- Teacher Resource Binder, Blackline Masters
- Interactive Lesson Planner CD-ROM
- PowerPoint® Presentations CD-ROM

Review and Enforcement
Mathematics Online
   www.busmath.glencoe.com
- Teacher Resource Binder, Internet Resources

- Student Activity Workbook
- Student Activity Workbook, Teacher Annotated Edition
- School-to-Home Activity Workbook

Assessment and Evaluation
- Assessment Binder, Reproducible Tests
- Assessment Binder, Alternative Assessment Strategies
- **Exam*View*® Pro Test Generator** CD-ROM

For the Teacher
- Student Activity Workbook, Teacher Annotated Edition
- Assessment Binder
- Interactive Lesson Planner CD-ROM
- Teacher Resource Binder
- Mathematics Online
   www.busmath.glencoe.com

For the Student
- Student Activity Workbook
- School-to-Home Activity Workbook

Living in the Real World

A Well-Sprung Business

Dr. Borris Greywolf opened Wellspring Medical Clinic, a private practice. After a few years, he had so many patients, he decided to expand and take on two business partners. In this chapter, read about how the clinic's accounting firm handles its payroll, tax preparation, and general accounting.

Read on. Go to . . .

633

Living in the Real World

Story's Summary

Dr. Borris Greywolf opened a practice, Wellspring Medical Clinic, several years ago. He's watched his staff grow to three doctors, three nurses, and several support staff members, as well as an outside accountant. Tax time is approaching, and Dr. Greywolf's accountant gathers information to prepare the tax return for the clinic, looking at business expenses, other tax deductions, and equipment depreciation.

Did You Know...

The number of accountants in the United States has more than doubled every decade since the 1950s.

Think about This

The cost of taking a client out for dinner and drinks used to be 100 percent tax deductible; now businesses can claim just 50 percent of these costs. Why would many businesses like to see it reversed?

LOCAL STANDARDS

National Standards for Business Education

Standard 1	Mathematical Foundations
Standard 2	Number Relationships and Operations

National Council of Teachers of Mathematics Standards

Standard 1	Numbers and Operations
Standard 6	Problem Solving
Standard 8	Communication

 **FOCUS**

In Chapter 13 students learned about personnel issues, such as wages, salaries, and employee benefits. Payroll deductions, such as federal income tax, Social Security, Medicare, and health insurance should be familiar to them. Businesses maintain a payroll register to keep track of the income and deductions of their employees.

In-Class Examples

Work through these exercises with students before having them do the Self-Check.

1. $450 − [(0.0145 × $450) + (0.062 × $450)]$ **$415.58**
2. $342.50 − [(0.0145 × $342.50) + (0.062 × $342.50)]$ **$316.30**
3. $461.20 − [(0.0145 × $461.20) + (0.062 × $461.20)]$ **$425.92**

○ **Section Objective**

Complete a payroll register.

SECTION 20-1 Payroll Register

To keep track of how your company's money is being spent, you'll need a **payroll register**. This is a record of the gross income, deductions, and net income of your company's employees. You may use a computer to prepare your payroll register. If you prepare the register by hand, you'll probably refer to tables to determine the amount of income tax to withhold from each employee's pay.

Living in the Real World

A Well-Sprung Business

Paying Employees Greywolf's clinic pays its three doctors and three nurses as well as an office manager, two secretaries, a receptionist, and an insurance specialist every week. The office staff keeps careful records of the clinic's income, costs, insurance payments, and other financial matters. Joe Smalley, the accountant from an outside accounting firm, organizes its payroll system, including direct deposit, which is a deposit of funds in employee bank accounts.

Draw Conclusions Why do you think companies might prefer using direct deposit?

Continued on page 638

(**Example 1**)

Natural Foods Center pays its employees weekly. Mary Clark prepares the payroll register for the center's five employees from the following information.

Name	Regular Pay	Overtime Pay	Income Tax Information	Health Insurance Coverage
D.R. Benavides	$ 8.50/hour	Time and a half	Married, 2 allowances	Family
J.A. Babatunde	6.45/hour	Time and a half	Single, 1 allowance	Single
H.L. Chew	325.00/week	—	Single, 2 allowances	Single
N.J. Nystrand	435.00/week	—	Married, 3 allowances	Family
W.K. Fine	280.00/week plus 5% commission	—	Married, 4 allowances	Family

---

BUSINESS NOTES

Payroll Software

Students visit local computer stores to see what payroll software programs are available. Students note the model of computer for which the software is available and the cost. Students might ask a salesclerk for a sample printout of the payroll spreadsheet to bring to class.

`LS` , `CL`

Living in the Real World

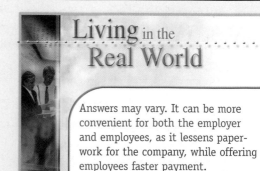

Answers may vary. It can be more convenient for both the employer and employees, as it lessens paperwork for the company, while offering employees faster payment.

Clark has prepared the payroll register for the week of March 2.

STEP: Find the net pay for the week.

From federal withholding tables   6.2% of gross pay   1.45% of gross pay

Payroll Register for Week of March 2, 20--

Name	Hours Worked Reg	OT	Hourly Rate	Gross Pay	FIT	Social Security	Medicare	Hosp. Ins.	Total Deductions	Net Pay
D.R. Benavides	40	3	$8.50	$ 378.25	$14.00	$ 23.45	$ 5.48	$ 41.54	$ 84.47	$ 293.78
J.A. Babatunde	40	—	6.45	258.00	16.00	16.00	3.74	20.77	56.61	201.49
H.L. Chew	—	—		325.00	18.00	20.15	4.71	20.77	63.63	261.37
N.J. Nystrand	—	—		435.00	14.00	26.97	6.31	41.54	88.82	346.18
W.K. Fine	—	—		373.00	2.00	23.13	5.41	41.54	72.08	300.92
			Total	$1,769.25	$64.00	$109.70	$25.65	$166.16	$365.51	$1,403.74

$280 plus 5% of $1,860 in sales

 14 ➕ 23.45 ➕ 5.48 ➕ 41.54 ➕ 84.47 [M+]

378.25 ➖ [RM] 84.47 🟰 293.78

CONCEPT CHECK

 Complete the problem, then check your answer at the end of the chapter.

1. Use this information to find the net pay: gross weekly pay, $396; FIT, $29; Social Security, $24.55; Medicare, $5.74; health insurance, $42.75.
$396.00 − ($29.00 + $24.55 + $5.74 + $42.75) = $396.00 − $102.04 = $293.96

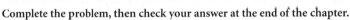
Example 2

Ajani Samuel is a printer employed by Kwik Copy. He is single and claims no allowances. Samuel is verifying his paycheck to ensure that the deductions are correct. Determine his net pay for a week when his gross pay was $285. Medicare is 1.45 percent of gross, Social Security is 6.2 percent of gross, city tax is 1.5 percent of gross, and federal income tax is obtained from tables on pages 788–791.

STEP: Find the net pay.
- Medicare: (0.0145 × $285) = $ 4.13
- Social Security: (0.062 × $285) = $17.67
- City tax: (0.015 × $285) = $ 4.28
- FIT: $29.00
- Net Pay = $285.00 − ($4.13 + $17.67 + $4.28 + $29.00)
- = $285.00 − $55.08
- = **$229.92 net pay**

2. Medicare: (0.0145 × $735.00) = $10.66; Social Security: (0.062 × $735.00) = $45.57; city tax: (0.02 × $735.00) = $14.70; FIT: $63.00; net pay = $735.00 − ($10.66 + $45.57 + $14.70 + $63.00) = $735.00 − $133.93 = $601.07

CONCEPT CHECK

 Complete the problem, then check your answer at the end of the chapter.

2. Dorsey Williams is married and claims 2 allowances. Her gross pay for the week was $735. Besides Medicare, Social Security, and federal income tax deductions, she pays a city tax that's 2 percent of gross pay. Find her net pay.

USING CALCULATORS

Some students will make mistakes and come up with an incorrect result if they are using an unfamiliar calculator. If students expect to use a calculator on a test or quiz, they should become comfortable with that particular calculator by using it in class and on homework. It is not a good idea to borrow a calculator on the day of a test.

COOPERATIVE LEARNING

Widget Factory Payroll
Imagine that the classroom is a widget factory and they all make widgets. Their pay is $8 per hour and they work 40 hours a week. Ten percent of that is deducted for taxes and $20 per week is deducted for health insurance. Have the class calculate what the payroll for the factory is in both gross pay and net pay. [LS] , [CL]

② TEACH

Discuss with students why companies keep a payroll register. **(Point out those businesses must file taxes. Since the payroll register contains information about the income and deductions of a company's employees, it is used in filing the taxes. It is also looked at if a business is audited.)**

In Example 1 on page 634, each employee has different income tax information and health insurance coverage. Review the income tax information with students. **Point out that employees choose how many allowances to take. This decision is usually based on whether the employee is married and has any children. Remind students that health insurance is an employee benefit. Often employees can choose whether they want an individual plan or a family plan. The costs are generally different for each plan.**

Motivating the Lesson
Have students work in groups. Give each group a payroll register that you have prepared. The payroll register should not have totals. Have students find the total gross pay, total deductions, and total net pay. **Answers will vary.**

In-Class Examples
Find the total net pay.
1. Total gross pay: $16,000. Total deductions: $3,500. **$12,500**
2. Gross pay: $410. Federal income tax: $23. State income tax: $7.38. Social Security: $25.42. Medicare: $5.95. **$348.25**
3. Gross pay: $399.70. Federal income tax: $10. State income tax: $6.40. Social Security: 6.2 percent. Medicare: 1.45 percent. Health insurance: $65. **$287.72**

635

3 ASSESS

Error Analysis

Remind students that an employee's federal income tax is based on the amount of wages earned and the number of withholdings that the employee claims. Even though two people may earn the same amount that does not necessarily mean that the federal income tax will be the same or that they will take home the same pay.

---

11. Banks: a. 180.00;
    b. 7.00; c. 11.16;
    d. 2.61; e. 23.29;
    f. 156.71
    Drake: a. 255.00;
    b. 25.00; c. 15.81;
    d. 3.70; e. 48.08;
    f. 206.92
    Faust: a. 270.00;
    b. 19.00; c. 16.74;
    d. 3.92; e. 43.44;
    f. 226.56
    Harakis: a. 285.00;
    b. 29.00; c. 17.67;
    d. 4.13; e. 54.79;
    f. 230.21
    Kendrick: a. 270.00;
    b. 28.00; c. 16.74;
    d. 3.92; e. 52.44;
    f. 217.56
    Reese: a. 285.00;
    b. 21.00; c. 17.67;
    d. 4.13; e. 46.79;
    f. 238.21
    Segura: a. 225.00;
    b. 20.00; c. 13.95;
    d. 3.26; e. 40.36;
    f. 184.64
    TOTAL: a. 1,770.00;
    b. 149.00; c. 109.74;
    d. 25.67; e. 309.19;
    f. 1,460.81

12. Calderon: a. 35.00;
    b. 37.20; c. 8.70;
    d. 150.65; e. 449.35
    Dobbs: a. 40.00;
    b. 36.27; c. 8.48;
    d. 151.25; e. 433.75
    Haddad: a. 40.00;
    b. 25.73; c. 6.02;
    d. 112.07; e. 302.93
    Harling: a. 46.00;
    b. 35.02; c. 8.19;
    d. 155.27; e. 409.53
    Hermeyesva:
    a. 50.00; b. 33.33;
    c. 7.79; d. 138.18;
    e. 399.32
    Presser: a. 27.00;
    b. 38.39; c. 8.98;
    d. 151.18; e. 468.02
    Wilberforce: a. 62.00;
    b. 37.97; c. 8.88;
    d. 160.03; e. 452.41
    TOTAL: a. 300.00;
    b. 243.91; c. 57.04;
    d. 1,018.63;
    e. 2,915.31

For Problems 3–6, find the total deductions and net pay.

	Employee	Gross Pay	FIT	Social Security	Medicare	Total Ded.	Net Pay
3.	Abbot	$485.00	$ 43.00	$30.07	$ 7.03	$80.10	a.404.90
4.	Escobedo	136.00	3.00	8.43	1.97	a. 13.40	b.122.60
5.	Jackson	795.00	117.00	49.29	11.53	a.177.82	b.617.18
6.	Lewton	975.00	166.00	60.45	14.14	a.240.59	b.734.41
7.	Murakami	643.00	67.00	39.87	9.32	a.116.19	b.526.81
8.	Zamora	519.00	47.00	32.18	7.53	a. 86.71	b.432.29

9. Pre-Fab Manufacturing Company.
   Payroll for week.
   Total gross pay: $16,478.43.
   Total deductions: $3,914.75.
   What is the total net pay? **$12,563.68**

10. Lou's Variety Store.
    Payroll for week.
    Total gross pay: $416.74.
    Total deductions: $97.82.
    What is the total net pay? **$318.92**

Use the tables on pages 788–791 for federal income tax (FIT). For Problems 11–14, use the Social Security tax rate of 6.2 percent and the Medicare tax rate of 1.45 percent.

11. The Goldstone Swimming Complex employs students in the summer. Goldstone pays a standard hourly rate of $7.50. The only deductions are federal withholding, Social Security, Medicare, and city income tax (CIT). Complete the payroll register for the week.

Payroll Register for Goldstone Swimming Complex								**Date: June 8**	
Employee	FIT Information	Hours Worked	Gross Pay	FIT	Social Security	Medicare	CIT	Total Ded.	Net Pay
Banks, C.	Single, 1 allowance	24	a.	b.	c.	d.	$2.52	e.	f.
Drake, H.	Single, 0 allowances	34	a.	b.	c.	d.	3.57	e.	f.
Faust, H.	Single, 1 allowance	36	a.	b.	c.	d.	3.78	e.	f.
Harakis, P.	Single, 0 allowances	38	a.	b.	c.	d.	3.99	e.	f.
Kendrick, P.	Single, 0 allowances	36	a.	b.	c.	d.	3.78	e.	f.
Reese, T.	Single, 1 allowance	38	a.	b.	c.	d.	3.99	e.	f.
Segura, M.	Single, 0 allowances	30	a.	b.	c.	d.	3.15	e.	f.
Total			a.	b.	c.	d.	24.78	e.	f.

12. The Consortium, a general warehouse and distributor of building supplies, pays its employees weekly salaries. Deductions include state income tax (SIT) and city income tax. Complete the payroll register for the week.

The Consortium										
Employee	Gross Pay	FIT Information	FIT	Social Security	Medicare	CIT	SIT	Hosp. Ins.	Total Ded.	Net Pay
Calderon	$ 600.00	Married, 3 allowances	a.	b.	c.	$ 10.50	$ 16.50	$ 42.75	d.	e.
Dobbs	585.00	Married, 2 allowances	a.	b.	c.	15.75	15.75	35.00	d.	e.
Haddad	415.00	Single, 1 allowance	a.	b.	c.	11.41	11.41	17.50	d.	e.
Harling	564.80	Married, 1 allowance	a.	b.	c.	15.53	15.53	35.00	d.	e.
Hermeyesva	537.50	Single, 2 allowances	a.	b.	c.	14.78	14.78	17.50	d.	e.
Presser	619.20	Married, 4 allowances	a.	b.	c.	17.03	17.03	42.75	d.	e.
Wilberforce	612.44	Married, 0 allowances	a.	b.	c.	16.84	16.84	17.50	d.	e.
Total	$3,933.94		a.	b.	c.	$101.84	$107.84	$208.00	d.	e.

PROBLEM SOLVING

Ranking Employees See Problem 13 on page 637. Silver Wholesale wanted to give bonuses to each salesperson, ranging from $5 for the least productive person to $35 for the most productive person. Have students rank the employees from lowest to highest productivity (total sales divided by hours worked) to determine the distribution of the bonuses. **Ranked by total sales divided by hours worked; ranking from lowest: Quinn ($57.20), Xerxes ($92.53), Grant ($92.87), Iskersky ($107.36), Melendez ($112.40), Valdez ($129.60), Aquilar ($140.00).**

13. Aguilar: a. 454.50;
  b. 46.00; c. 28.18;
  d. 6.59; e. 84.77;
  f. 369.73
  Grant: a. 369.66;
  b. 41.00; c. 22.92;
  d. 5.36; e. 73.28;
  f. 296.38
  Iskersky:
  a. 474.90;
  b. 24.00; c. 29.44;
  d. 6.89; e. 64.33;
  f. 410.57
  Melendez:
  a. 540.00;
  b. 60.00; c. 33.48;
  d. 7.83; e. 105.31;
  f. 436.69
  Quinn: a. 254.55;
  b. 25.00; c. 15.78;
  d. 3.69; e. 48.47;
  f. 206.08
  Valdez: a. 581.04;
  b. 32.00; c. 36.02;
  d. 8.43; e. 80.45;
  f. 500.59
  Xerxes: a. 418.26;
  b. 40.00; c. 25.93;
  d. 6.06; e. 75.99;
  f. 342.27
  TOTAL:
  a. 3,092.91;
  b. 268.00;
  c. 191.75;
  d. 44.85;
  e. 532.60;
  f. 2,560.31

14. Delgado:
  a. 505.50;
  b. 28.00; c. 31.34;
  d. 7.33; e. 5.06;
  f. 91.95; g. 413.55
  Lightner:
  a. 536.40;
  b. 58.00; c. 33.26;
  d. 7.78; e. 5.36;
  f. 125.86;
  g. 410.54

13. The Silver Wholesale Clothes Company hires extra sales personnel during its warehouse sale. The extra help earns $6.75 an hour plus 6 percent commission on all sales. Deductions include $4.00 per week for temporary help union dues. Complete the payroll register.

Silver Wholesale Clothes Company

Name	FIT Information	Hours Worked	Sales	Gross Pay	Deductions FIT	Deductions Social Security	Deductions Medicare	Union Dues	Total Ded.	Net Pay
Aguilar	Single, 1 allowance	30	$ 4,200.00	a.	b.	c.	d.	$ 4.00	e.	f.
Grant	Single, 0 allowances	30	2,786.00	a.	b.	c.	d.	4.00	e.	f.
Iskersky	Married, 2 allowances	36	3,865.00	a.	b.	c.	d.	4.00	e.	f.
Melendez	Single, 1 allowance	40	4,500.00	a.	b.	c.	d.	4.00	e.	f.
Quinn	Single, 0 allowances	25	1,430.00	a.	b.	c.	d.	4.00	e.	f.
Valdez	Married, 3 allowances	40	5,184.00	a.	b.	c.	d.	4.00	e.	f.
Xerxes	Single, 1 allowance	34	3,146.00	a.	b.	c.	d.	4.00	e.	f.
Total			$25,111.00	a.	b.	c.	d.	$28.00	e.	f.

14. King Sporting Goods pays its employees weekly. Deductions include federal withholding, state income tax, Social Security (6.2 percent), Medicare (1.45 percent), and 1 percent of gross pay for city income tax (CIT). Use this information to prepare the payroll for the week of November 30.

Name	FIT Information	Position	Pay Plan	Total Sales or Hours Worked
Delgado	Married, 2 allowances	Sales	7½% straight commission	$6,740
Lightner	Single, 1 allowance	Sales Manager	7½% straight commission	$7,152
Ramirez	Married, 3 allowances	Sales Manager	$420 + 6% commission	$3,298
Ulrich	Single, 0 allowances	Sales Trainee	5% straight commission	$4,165
Goode	Married, 1 allowance	Maintenance	$6.10 per hour	44 hours

King Sporting Goods — Payroll Register — Week of: November 30, 20--

Name	Gross Pay	FIT	SIT	Social Security	Medicare	CIT	Total Ded.	Net Pay
Delgado	a.	b.	$20.22	c.	d.	e.	f.	g.
Lightner	a.	b.	21.46	c.	d.	e.	f.	g.
Ramirez	a.	b.	32.59	c.	d.	e.	f.	g.
Ulrich	a.	b.	8.33	c.	d.	e.	f.	g.
Goode	a.	b.	10.47	c.	d.	e.	f.	g.
Total	a.	b.	93.07	c.	d.	e.	f.	g.1,711.56

14. Ramirez: a. 617.88; b. 36.00; c. 38.31; d. 8.96; e. 6.18; f. 122.04; g. 495.84
Ulrich: a. 208.25; b. 17.00; c. 12.91; d. 3.02; e. 2.08; f. 43.34; g. 164.91
Goode: a. 268.40; b. 8.00; c. 16.64; d. 3.89; e. 2.68; f. 41.68; g. 226.72
TOTAL: a. 2,136.43; b. 147.00; c. 132.46; d. 30.98; e. 21.36; f. 474.87

MAINTAINING YOUR SKILLS

Need Help? Go to...
→ Skill 5: Adding Decimals, page 732
→ Skill 6: Subtracting Decimals, page 733

Add.

15. $17.96 + $8.44
$26.40

16. $149.74 + $97.89
$247.63

17. $212.47 + $197.83
$410.30

Subtract.

18. $412.76 − $26.40
$386.36

19. $676.83 − $212.91
$463.92

20. $1,864.75 − $417.93
$1,446.82

CLOSE

Closing Activity
Find the net pay.
1. Gross pay: $480.
  Federal income tax: $34.
  State income tax: $12.
  Social Security: $29.76.
  Medicare: $6.96. **$397.28**
2. Gross pay: $525.50.
  Federal income tax: $31.
  State income tax: $12.61.
  Social Security: 6.2 percent.
  Medicare: 1.45 percent. **$441.69**
3. Gross pay: $602.41.
  Federal income tax: $52.
  State income tax: $10.84.
  Social Security: 6.2 percent.
  Medicare: 1.45 percent. **$493.49**
4. Gross pay: $343.06.
  Federal income tax: $22.
  State income tax: $5.15.
  Social Security: 6.2 percent.
  Medicare: 1.45 percent.
  Health insurance: $30.75.
  $258.92

ALTERNATIVE ASSESSMENT

Create a Model
As an alternate to the Cooperative Learning activity on page 635, have students create a model and imagine they work in a model-making factory instead of a widget factory. Students choose the material they wish to use to make a small model that they think will "sell" well for the company. To assess this project, see the illustration or model rubric in the *Assessment Binder, Alternative Assessment Strategies.* CL , LS , P

WRAP-UP

Go over any problem for which a wrong answer is given.

Assignment Guide
  Basic: 3–8
  Average: 9–10

20 min.

Standard 1	Mathematical Foundations
Standard 2	Number Relationships and Operations

National Council of Teachers of Mathematics Standards

Standard 1	Numbers and Operations
Standard 6	Problem Solving
Standard 8	Communication

1 FOCUS

Have students suggest some expenses that businesses have. Students are already familiar with some expenses, such as rental space and advertising. Point out that businesses must keep track of their expenses. Just like the payroll register, the record of expenses is needed when a business files its taxes.

In-Class Examples

Work through these exercises with students before having them do the Self-Check.

1. $65 + $318 + $6,214 + $2,986 **$9,583**
2. $8,104 is what percent of $50,650? **16%**
3. $78,480 is what percent of $654,000? **12%**

2 TEACH

Bring in a copy of an annual report from a company. Show students the report and point out the list of company expenses. Mention that companies provide annual reports to give shareholders and the public a record of the company's finances for the year.

638

SECTION 20-2 Business Expenses

○ **Section Objective**

Calculate the percent that a particular business expense is of the total expenses.

Your business must keep accurate records of all its expenses. You will use the information when you prepare income tax forms and when you calculate your company's profits. You may determine your total expenses monthly, quarterly, or annually. To plan for future spending, you may calculate the percent that each expense is of the total. Remember that:

$$\text{Percent of Total} = \frac{\text{Particular Expense}}{\text{Total Expenses}}$$

Living in the Real World

A Well-Sprung Business

A New System Although the accountant helps the Wellspring Clinic complete its taxes, it's up to the physicians to provide complete financial statements. Wellspring has hired someone just to complete the bookkeeping. Dr. Greywolf looks to Smalley to help him streamline the accounting system.

Draw Conclusions What are some ways of streamlining an accounting system for Wellspring Clinic?

Continued on page 640

Example 1

Molded Plastic Products manufactures plastic buckets, containers, and other products. Records of Molded Plastic's expenses for the first quarter of the year show the following:

What percent of total expenses did Molded Plastic spend on advertising during the quarter?

Payroll	$422,171.84
Advertising	8,557.65
Raw materials	122,417.83
Factory/showroom rent	18,500.00
Office supplies	2,216.90
Insurance	8,917.85
Utilities	26,417.93
Total	**$609,200.00**

STEP: Find the percent of the total.

Particular Expense ÷ Total Expenses

$8,557.65 ÷ $609,200.00 = **0.01404 or 1.40% of total expenses spent on advertising**

8557.65 ÷ 609200 = 0.014047

CONCEPT CHECK

SELF-CHECK✓

Complete the problems, then check your answers at the end of the chapter. Use the information in Example 1 to find what percent the following are of the total expenses:

1. Utilities $26,417.93 ÷ $609,200 =
   0.04336 or 4.3%
2. Payroll $422,171.84 ÷ $609,200
   = 0.692994 or 69.3%

Living in the Real World

Answer will vary, but Smalley might suggest that Wellspring Clinic use a computer program to manage its finances, which the accountant can in turn use to process payroll, prepare taxes, and accomplish other accounting tasks.

COMMUNICATION SKILLS

How Many Times?
Students work in pairs to give each other problems. For example: If your company determines expenses quarterly, how many times does your company calculate total expenses over a period of five years? **5 years × 4 occurrences per year = 20**

The U.S. government is accountable for its collection and spending of funds. The General Accounting Office (GAO) is designed to uphold the Constitution by ensuring the executive branch is responsible to Congress and the government is held responsible to the public.

3. Particular expenses: rent, $300; data processing, $5,200; payroll, $4,500. Rent is what percent of the total? **3%**

4. Particular expenses: telephone, $175; electricity, $450; natural gas, $375; water, $200. Water is what percent of the total? **16.7%**

For Problems 5–10, find what percent (nearest tenth) each item is of the total.

	Manufacturer's Cost and Profit		
5.	Fabrics and accessories	$ 81.10	31.5%
6.	Design and factory operations	49.10	19.1%
7.	Production wages and benefits	68.60	26.6%
8.	Administrative and sales salaries	39.70	15.4%
9.	Taxes	9.80	3.8%
10.	Profit from sale to retailer	9.20	3.6%
	Total (wholesale price to retailer)	$257.50	

11. Trapper Financial Consultants. Expenses total $72,650 for the quarter. Payroll for the quarter is $48,435. Payroll expense is what percent of the total? **66.7%**

12. Madison Motel. Annual expenses total $514,500. Annual utilities cost $98,400. Utility cost is what percent of the total? **19.1%**

13. a. 47.9%
b. 2%
c. 17.1%
d. 22.3%
e. 4%
f. 2.1%
g. 4.6%
h. $301,705

14. a. 4.7%
b. 4.0%
c. 75.5%
d. 3.5%
e. 2.2%
f. 3.1%
g. 6.9%
h. $206,000

13. The Clear Pool Company had these expenses last year. Determine what percent each item is of the total.

a.	Payroll	$144,565
b.	Advertising	6,000
c.	Equipment	51,496
d.	Supplies	67,194
e.	Insurance	12,000
f.	Utilities	6,450
g.	Rent	14,000
h.	**Total**	$

14. Parson's Traditional Clothiers had these business expenses last month. Determine what percent each item is of the total.

a.	Payroll	$ 9,646
b.	Advertising	8,325
c.	Cost of Goods Sold	155,525
d.	Rent	7,244
e.	Supplies	4,560
f.	Insurance	6,450
g.	Utilities	14,250
h.	**Total**	$

Need Help? Go to...
► Skill 5: Adding Decimals, page 732
► Skill 31: Finding the Rate, page 758

MAINTAINING YOUR SKILLS

Add.

15.
$114,570.00
31,720.00
+   56,493.00
$202,783

16.
$2,171.89
419.43
+   114.65
$2,705.97

Find the rate. Round answers to the nearest tenth of a percent.

17. What percent of $140,000 is $35,000? **25.0%**

18. What percent of $1,060 is $212? **20.0%**

WRAP-UP

Go over any problem for which a wrong answer is given.

Assignment Guide
Basic: 3–4
Average: 5–10

20 min.

SECTION 20-2

For additional practice, have students find the percent of the total expenses for each of the other expenses listed in Example 1 on page 638. Point out that the sum of the percents should equal 100, but due to rounding it may not.

In-Class Examples

1. Particular expenses: electricity, $190; water, $34; natural gas, $245; telephone, $218 Telephone is what percent of the total expenses? **31.7%**

2. Particular expenses: Particular expenses: electricity, $150; water, $80; natural gas, $208; telephone, $212. Water is what percent of the total expenses? **12.3%**

3 ASSESS

Error Analysis
Remind students that the sum of the percents should equal 100 percent. However, due to rounding, sometimes this is not the case. Have students find the sum of the percents for some of the problems. Have them tell whether or not the sum is equal to 100 percent.

4 CLOSE

Closing Activity
Find what percent each expense is of the total.

Payroll	$120,130	58%
Rent	10,500	5.1%
Utilities	5,639	2.7%
Advertising	2,008	1.0%
Storage	2,674	1.3%
Insurance	7,000	3.4%
Maintenance	640	0.3%
Supplies	58,409	28.2%
Total	$207,700	

National Standards for Business Education

Standard 1	Mathematical Foundations
Standard 2	Number Relationships and Operations

National Council of Teachers of Mathematics Standards

Standard 1	Numbers and Operations
Standard 3	Geometry
Standard 6	Problem Solving
Standard 8	Communication

1 FOCUS

Ask students to think about security at a shopping mall. If the stores are different sizes with some being very large and some being very small, should all of the stores pay the same amount for security? Similarly, businesses often have several departments that are different sizes. Each department may have different expenses.

In-Class Examples

Work through these exercises with students before having them do the Self-Check.

1. $(20,000 \div 100,000) \times \$19,000$
   $3,800
2. $(65,000 \div 295,000) \times \$67,500$
   $14,872.88
3. $(205,795 \div 1,900,000) \times$
   $132,600 **$14,362.32**

2 TEACH

Have students find the definition of apportion in a dictionary. Have students discuss what apportion means in terms of the expenses of a business. **(To apportion expenses is to distribute the expenses by**

640

○ **Section Objective**

Figure out a department's share of the total business expense.

SECTION 20-3 Apportioning Expenses

Your business may **apportion**, or distribute, certain expenses among its departments. Each department is charged a certain amount of the particular expense. Often the amount that each department is charged depends on the space that it occupies. Remember that:

$$\text{Amount Paid} = \frac{\text{Square Feet Occupied}}{\text{Total Square Footage}} \times \text{Total Expense}$$

Living in the Real World

A Well-Sprung Business

Calculations behind Extra Space   Wellspring's accountant Joseph Levi reads the local newsletter and is informed that the office building's complex is expanding. Since the owner of the building is adding more units, Wellspring's percent of the total square footage being occupied will actually decrease.

Draw Conclusions   In accounting, this is known as doing what to your expenses?

Continued on page 642

Example 1

Weston Outlet Mall contains 200,000 square feet of store space. The Socks Galore store occupies an area that measures 60 feet by 150 feet. The annual cost of security for the entire mall is $88,400. Weston apportions the cost based on square feet occupied. What annual amount for security does Weston charge to the Socks Galore store?

STEP 1: Find the square feet occupied.
60 feet $\times$ 150 feet = 9,000 square feet occupied

STEP 2: Find the annual amount paid.
$$\frac{\text{Square Feet Occupied}}{\text{Total Square Footage}} \times \text{Total Expense}$$
$(9,000 \div 200,000)$
0.045 $\times$ $\$88,400$ = **$3,978 annual amount paid**

60 × 150 = 9000 ÷ 200000 =

0.045 × 88400 = 3978

Living in the Real World

Apportioning the cost.

GLOBAL PERSPECTIVE

International Office Rental Costs
Give students the following figures for the cost of office space per square foot, per month, in U.S. dollars: London $118, Tokyo $93, Paris $63, Buenos Aires $51, New York $49. Ask students why they think some cities cost so much more than others. **More expensive cities might have a booming economy and limited space; less expensive cities might have more space available and want to attract business to build its economy.**

CONCEPT CHECK

SELF-CHECK ✓

Complete the problems, then check your answers at the end of the chapter.

1. The Boliton Law Office occupies 40 feet by 50 feet in a building with 50,000 square feet. Annual cost of the building's maintenance service is $96,000. What does The Boliton Law Office pay?

2. The Athlete's Foot shoe store occupies 50 feet by 100 feet in a mall with 40,000 square feet. Monthly security expenses for the mall are $22,500. What does the shoe store pay?

SECTION 20-3 PRACTICE

Find the amount paid.

(Square Feet Occupied	÷	Total Square Footage)	×	Total Expense	=	Amount Paid
3. (3,200	÷	160,000)	×	$62,500	=	**$1,250**
4. (15,000	÷	160,000)	×	62,500	=	**$5,859.38**
5. (50,000	÷	160,000)	×	62,500	=	**$19,531.25**

Round the intermediate answers to the nearest thousandth and the final answers to the nearest cent.

6. Building area: 980,000 square feet. Annual maintenance cost: $235,000. Billing department is 40 feet by 60 feet.
   What does the billing department pay annually for maintenance? **$575.51**

7. Building area: 450,000 square feet. Annual insurance charge: $155,000. Sales department is 80 feet by 80 feet.
   What does the sales department pay annually for insurance? **$2,204.44**

8. Tubular Assemblies pays a total of $2,960,000 per year to rent its building. The total area of the building is 480,000 square feet. Tubular Assemblies apportions the rental charge among its departments. How much does each of these departments pay for rent?
   a. Research and development 450 feet by 100 feet **$277,500**
   b. Shipping 300 feet by 320 feet **592,000**

9. Barteli Mini Mall apportions costs among the tenants on the basis of square footage. How much does each tenant pay for each annual expense?

Barteli Mini Mall

Tenant	Dimensions			Square Footage	Base Rent	Sec.	Taxes	Insur.	Maint.	Assoc. Fee	Total
					$13.00	$0.75	$1.35	$0.36	$3.45	$0.75	a.
Ken's Carry Out	40	×	100	a.	b.	c.	d.	e.	f.	g.	h.
The Jean Place	30	×	100	a.	b.	c.	d.	e.	f.	g.	h.
Pan's Pizza	25	×	100	a.	b.	c.	d.	e.	f.	g.	h.
World Travel	30	×	100	a.	b.	c.	d.	e.	f.	g.	h.
Fine Jewelers	25	×	100	a.	b.	c.	d.	e.	f.	g.	h.
			Total	a.	b.	c.	d.	e.	f.	g.	h.

MAINTAINING YOUR SKILLS

Divide. Round answers to the nearest thousandth.

10. 900 ÷ 12,450 **0.072**

11. 2,000 ÷ 96,500 **0.021**

12. 1,200 ÷ 50,000 **0.024**

13. 2,475 ÷ 475,000 **0.005**

Section 20-3 Apportioning Expenses ▶ **641**

Left margin answers:

1. Square feet occupied = 40 × 50 = 2,000
   Amount paid = (2,000 ÷ 50,000) × $96,000 = 0.04 × $96,000 = $3,840

2. Square feet occupied = 50 × 100 = 5,000
   Amount paid = (5,000 ÷ 40,000) × $22,500 = 0.125 × $22,500.00 = $2,812.50

9. a. 19.66 Ken's Carry Out: a. 4,000; b. 52,000; c. 3,000; d. 5,400; e. 1,440; f. 13,800; g. 3,000; h. 78,640
   The Jean Place: a. 3,000; b. 39,000; c. 2,250; d. 4,050; e. 1,080; f. 10,350; g. 2,250; h. 58,980
   Pan's Pizza: a. 2,500; b. 32,500; c. 1,875; d. 3,375; e. 900; f. 8,625; g. 1,875; h. 49,150
   World Travel: a. 3,000; b. 39,000; c. 2,250; d. 4,050; e. 1,080; f. 10,350; g. 2,250; h. 58,980
   Fine Jewelers: a. 2,500; b. 32,500; c. 1,875; d. 3,375; e. 900; f. 8,625; g. 1,875; h. 49,150
   Total: a. 15,000; b. 195,000; c. 11,250; d. 20,250; e. 5,400; f. 51,750; g. 11,250; h. 294,900

Need Help? Go to...
→ Skill 10: Dividing (Decimal Remainder), page 737

THINKING CRITICALLY

Departmental Expenses
The classroom is a business with monthly operating expenses of $100,000. Measure the dimensions of the classroom. Break students into groups representing different departments within the space. Have each group measure the size of its department and determine what portion of the operating expenses it's responsible for (they can provide estimates).

WRAP-UP

Go over any problem for which a wrong answer is given.

Assignment Guide
Basic: 3–5
Average: 6–8

20 min.

SECTION 20-3

some method.) In Example 1 on page 640, the expenses are apportioned by using the square footage that the Socks Galore store occupies. Sometimes businesses apportion expenses according to the gross sales of each department. Have students suggest other ways that a business may apportion expenses.

In-Class Example
Find the amount paid.
1. Square feet occupied: 15,000. Total square footage: 300,000. Total expense: $50,000. **$2,500**

3 ASSESS

Error Analysis
Students should already be familiar with determining area from the previous chapter when they learned about rental space. Remind students that to find the area of a space they need to multiply the dimensions of the space and write the answer in square feet. You may want to give students some simple area problems to practice.

4 CLOSE

Closing Activity
1. Candies & More occupies 50 feet by 78 feet in a mall with 45,000 square feet. The monthly security expenses are $18,500. The mall apportions this cost based on the square footage of its stores. What does Candies & More pay for security? **$1,603.33**

2. Slate Textiles apportions the annual cost of utilities among its departments on the basis of gross sales. The annual cost of utilities is $39,500. The total gross sales of Slate Textiles is $558,265. The bedding department had gross sales of $126,000. What does the bedding department pay for utilities? **$8,915.12**

641

National Standards for Business Education

Standard 1	Mathematical Foundations
Standard 2	Number Relationships and Operations

National Council of Teachers of Mathematics Standards

Standard 1	Numbers and Operations
Standard 6	Problem Solving
Standard 8	Communication

1 FOCUS

Discuss with students what it means for an item to depreciate. Give students an example of an item that loses its value soon after it is purchased, such as a vehicle. Businesses are able to deduct the depreciation of some items that they own on their taxes.

In-Class Examples

Work through these exercises with students before having them do the Self-Check.
1. ($300 − $25) ÷ 5 **$55**
2. ($1,050 − $100) ÷ 10 **$95**
3. ($10,490 − $2,000) ÷ 3 **$2,830**

2 TEACH

This section focuses on one method of depreciation: the straight-line method. In the next two sections, students will learn additional methods of depreciation. (**Point out that the straight-line method determines the depreciation of an item by assuming that the depreciation is the same each year.**)

Explain what it means for an item to have a salvage value.

642

○ **Section Objective**

Utilize the straight-line method to compute the annual depreciation of an item.

SECTION 20-4 Depreciation— Straight-Line Method

For tax purposes, the Internal Revenue Service (IRS) allows you to recognize the **depreciation** of many of the items that your business owns. Depreciation is a decrease in the value of an item because of its age or condition.

The **straight-line method** is one way of determining the annual depreciation of an item. This method assumes that the depreciation is the same from year to year. To calculate the depreciation, you must know the original cost, the **estimated life**, and the **salvage value** of the item. The estimated life of an item is the length of time, usually in years, it is expected to last. The salvage value is the estimated trade-in, resale, or scrap value at the end of the item's expected life. Remember that:

$$\text{Annual Depreciation} = \frac{\text{Original Cost} - \text{Salvage Value}}{\text{Estimated Life}}$$

Living in the Real World

A Well-Sprung Business

Preparing for Tax Time   Levi is starting to put together information about the previous year in preparation for tax time. Throughout the year, he has kept files of information about expenses and income so that the accountant can prepare Wellspring's tax forms. Today, Levi is calling Smalley, the clinic's tax preparer, to see whether new office equipment can be used as a tax deduction.

Draw Conclusions   Give examples of business items that are tax deductions.

Continued on page 644

Example 1

The law firm of Charles A. Adams purchased a new copier that cost $1,745. The life of the copier is estimated to be 5 years. The total salvage value after 5 years of use is estimated to be $245. Using the straight-line method, find the annual depreciation of the copier.

STEP: Find the annual depreciation.
(Original Cost − Salvage Value) ÷ Estimated Life
($1,745   − $245)
$1,500   ÷   5   = $300 annual depreciation

1745 ⊟ 245 ⊟ 1500 ⊟ 5 ⊟ 300

Living in the Real World

Office equipment and furnishings, advertising costs, travel expenses for work-related events, wages, utilities, insurance, and so on.

13.

	Cost	Salvage Value	Cost-Salvage Value	Annual Depreciation
Cut-Off Saw	$8,325	$500	$7,825	$1,565.00
Planner	5,675	500	5,175	1,035.00
Sander	368	75	293	58.60
Sander	368	75	293	58.60

CONCEPT CHECK

SELF-CHECK✓

Complete the problems, then check your answers at the end of the chapter.
Find the annual depreciation.

1. Original cost of telephone equipment: $6,000.
Estimated life: 10 years.
Salvage value: $200.

2. Original cost of tractor-trailer unit: $145,000.
Estimated life: 3 years.
Salvage value: $25,000.

1. Annual depreciation
= ($6,000 − $200)
÷ 10 = $5,800 ÷
10 = $580

2. Annual depreciation
= ($145,000 −
$25,000) ÷ 3 =
$120,000 ÷ 3 =
$40,000

SECTION 20-4 PRACTICE

Find the annual depreciation.

	Item	(Original Cost	−	Resale Value)	÷	Estimated Life	=	Annual Depreciation
3.	Rental furniture	($ 12,435	−	$ 435)	÷	3.0 years	=	$4,000
4.	Taxi	(19,186	−	3,186)	÷	5.0 years	=	$3,200
5.	Tractor	(14,750	−	2,000)	÷	10.0 years	=	$1,275
6.	Rental duplex	(145,500	−	10,000)	÷	27.5 years	=	$4,927.27

7. Fiber optic cable.
Cost is $975,000.
Estimated life is 20 years.
Salvage value estimated at $5,000.
What is the annual depreciation? **$48,500**

8. Luxury car.
Cost is $46,250.
Estimated life is 3 years.
Salvage value estimated at $7,250.
What is the annual depreciation? **$13,000**

9. Central Dental Clinic recently purchased a new computer system for a total cost of $64,735. The estimated life of the system is 5 years. The trade-in value of the system after 5 years is estimated to be $1,000. What is the annual depreciation? **$12,747**

10. Tina Cole is a certified financial advisor. She purchased equipment for her office for $7,843. The trade-in value of the equipment is estimated to be $500 after 7 years of use. What is the annual depreciation? **$1,049**

11. The Star Trucking Company purchased a new tractor unit for $155,000. After 3 years of useful life, the estimated salvage value is $10,000. What is the annual depreciation? **$48,333.33**

12. Third National Bank recently purchased 6 new laptop computers. Each computer cost $2,245. The estimated life of each computer is 5 years. The trade-in value of each computer is expected to be $125 at the end of the 5 years. What is the annual depreciation for all six computers? **$2,544**

13. Amish-Made Furniture recently purchased a new cut-off saw at a cost of $8,325, a new planer at a cost of $5,675, and two new sanders at a cost of $368 each. The salvage value of the cut-off saw and the planer is expected to be $500 each after 7 years of use. The salvage value of the sanders is expected to be $75 each after 5 years of use. What is the total annual depreciation for the first year? **$1,974.37**

Need Help? Go to...
- ▶ Skill 10: Dividing (Decimal Remainder), page 737
- ▶ Skill 8: Multiplying Decimals, page 735

MAINTAINING YOUR SKILLS

Divide. Round answers to the nearest cent.

14. $14,718 ÷ 20 **$735.90**

15. $9,171.45 ÷ 15 **$611.43**

Multiply.

16. $1,470.00 × 0.055 **$80.85**

17. $963.49 × 0.05 **$48.1745**

TECHNOLOGY POWER

San Francisco investment bank Putnam Lovell Securities estimates it will save $500,000 a year on printing and mail costs by distributing the company's reports via e-mail. The new process utilizes a number of Web sites that match the topic of the report with information about the interests of Putnam's clients that it draws from yet another Web site and automatically dispatches the reports.

WRAP-UP

Go over any problem for which a wrong answer is given.

Assignment Guide
Basic: 3–6
Average: 7–11

20 min.

(Point out that most items have some value even after they have exceeded their usefulness for a business. Some items are still in good working condition when a business replaces them.) Discuss with students some examples of items that businesses purchase and later salvage.

In-Class Examples
Find the annual depreciation.
1. Original cost: $500.
Salvage value: $100.
Estimated life (years): 5. **$80**
2. Original cost: $19,000.
Salvage value: $4,500.
Estimated life (years): 12.
$1,208.33

 **ASSESS**

Error Analysis
Encourage students to use parentheses when they are writing the annual depreciation formula. Students must subtract the salvage value from the original cost before dividing by the estimated life. If students do not use parentheses, then they may follow an incorrect order of operations. This will result in a wrong answer for the annual depreciation.

 **CLOSE**

Closing Activity
Find the annual depreciation.
1. Joanna Gold purchased a van for her business for $45,000. The trade-in value is estimated to be $25,000 after 10 years of use. What is the annual depreciation? **$2,000**
2. Spring Street Bakery purchased some new equipment for $24,750. The salvage value is estimated to be $6,300 after 5 years of use. What is the annual depreciation? **$3,690**

643

National Standards for Business Education

Standard 1	Mathematical Foundations
Standard 2	Number Relationships and Operations

National Council of Teachers of Mathematics Standards

Standard 1	Numbers and Operations
Standard 6	Problem Solving
Standard 8	Communication

1 FOCUS

When someone trades in a car toward the purchase of a new car, the person is usually given the book value of the car. Ask students if they have ever heard of the phrase "book value." In addition to cars, other items that depreciate also have a book value.

In-Class Examples

Work through these exercises with students before having them do the Self-Check.
1. $600 × 5 **$3,000**
2. $5,000 × 8 **$40,000**
3. $3,995.75 × 8 **$31,966**

2 TEACH

Explain to students that the book value of an item is the value of the item at a given time. The book value of an item that is ten years old will not be the same as the book value of the same item that is only five years old.

○ **Section Objective**

Apply the straight-line method to compute the book value of an item.

Book value is the approximate value of an item after you have owned it and depreciated it for a period of time. The book value is the original cost minus the **accumulated depreciation**. The accumulated depreciation is the total depreciation to date. At the end of an item's life, its book value and salvage value should be equal.

Important Questions to Ask Yourself	What Formula Do I Use?
How do I find the **accumulated depreciation?**	Accumulated Depreciation = Previous Year's Accumulated Depreciation + Current Year's Depreciation
How do I find the **book value?**	Book Value = Original Cost − Accumulated Depreciation

Living in the Real World

A Well-Sprung Business

The Book Value of Machines   When Levi discovers Wellspring is about to get a new X-ray machine, he decides it's time to use the book value of the old machine to help reduce the clinic's taxes.

Draw Conclusions   At the end of the life of an item, like an X-ray machine, why would you apply the book value to this asset?

Continued on page 647

Example 1

The law firm of Charles A. Adams purchased a new copier for $1,745. The total resale value after 5 years is estimated to be $245. Using the straight-line method, Charles A. Adams determined that the copier would depreciate $300 per year. What is the book value at the end of each year of depreciation?

STEP 1: Find the accumulated depreciation.

	Previous Year's Accumulated Depreciation	+	Current Year's Depreciation		
First year:	$ 0	+	$300	=	$ 300
Second year:	300	+	300	=	600
Third year:	600	+	300	=	900
Fourth year:	900	+	300	=	1,200
Fifth year:	1,200	+	300	=	1,500

644 ◄ Chapter 20 Accounting

Living in the Real World

It helps you determine the item's remaining worth and how much of its value is tax deductible.

COOPERATIVE LEARNING

Salvage or Scrap Value

Ask students to work in groups to show—by using the straight-line method—that the book value after the estimated life of an item equals its salvage or scrap value. **LS** , **CL**

STEP 2: Find the book value.

	Original Cost	−	Accumulated Depreciation		
First year:	$1,745	−	$ 300	=	**$1,445**
Second year:	1,745	−	600	=	1,145
Third year:	1,745	−	900	=	845
Fourth year:	1,745	−	1,200	=	545
Fifth year:	1,745	−	1,500	=	245

Note: The book value of the last year always equals the salvage value.

1. a. $16,000; b. $32,000 + $16,000 = $48,000; c. $90,000 − $48,000 = $42,000

2. a. $16,000; b. $48,000 + $16,000 = $64,000; c. $90,000 − $64,000 = $26,000

3. a. $16,000; b. $64,000 + $16,000 = $80,000; c. $90,000 − $80,000 = $10,000

SELF-CHECK ✔

Depreciation Schedule for Copier

End of Year	Original Cost	Annual Depreciation	Accumulated Depreciation	Book Value	
1	$1,745	$300	$ 300	$1,445 ◄	$1,745 − $ 300
2	1,745	300	600	1,145 ◄	$1,745 − $ 600
3	1,745	300	900	845 ◄	$1,745 − $ 900
4	1,745	300	1,200	545 ◄	$1,745 − $1,200
5	1,745	300	1,500	245 ◄	$1,745 − $1,500

Note: The book value at the end of the fifth year equals the salvage value.

CONCEPT CHECK

Complete the problems, then check your answers at the end of the chapter.
Calculate the depreciation schedule for a commercial bus that costs $90,000. Its estimated life is 5 years and the salvage value is $10,000.

End of Year	Original Cost	Annual Depreciation	Accumulated Depreciation	Book Value
1	$90,000	$16,000	$16,000	$74,000
2	90,000	16,000	32,000	58,000
1. 3	90,000	a.	b.	c.
2. 4	90,000	a.	b.	c.
3. 5	90,000	a.	b.	c.

SECTION 20-5 PRACTICE

For Problems 4–6, complete the depreciation schedule for new appliances in a residential rental complex. The appliances cost $5,000, have an estimated life of 5 years, and have a salvage value of $1,000.

End of Year	Original Cost	Annual Depreciation	Accumulated Depreciation	Book Value
1	$5,000	$800	$ 800	$4,200
2	5,000	800	1,600	3,400
4. 3	5,000	a. $800	b. $2,400	c. $2,600
5. 4	5,000	a. $800	b. $3,200	c. $1,800
6. 5	5,000	a. $800	b. $4,000	c. $1,000

Continued on next page

USING CALCULATORS

A calculator is meant to assist in the problem solving process. Possession of a calculator is not a substitute for studying. It is helpful to write out the steps and procedures and use the calculator to perform the calculations. This is especially important for problems involving multiple formulas.

After you review Example 1 on pages 644 and 645, ask students how they could determine the accumulated depreciation for the fifth year without adding the previous year's accumulation to the current year's depreciation. Ask students to look for a pattern in the list of equations given in the example. Point out that the accumulated depreciation for the second year is twice the current year's depreciation. Students should theorize that the fifth year would be five times the current year's depreciation.

Motivating the Lesson

Write the book value after each year by subtracting the accumulated depreciation from the original cost.

End of Year	Original Cost	Annual Depreciation	Accumulated Depreciation	Book Value
1	$2500	$150	$150	$2,350
2	2500	150	300	2,200
3	2500	150	450	2,050
4	2500	150	600	1,900

In-Class Example

John Tedeschi purchased a new machine for his business. The machine costs $5,000, has an estimated life of 10 years, and has a salvage value of $550. Calculate the straight-line depreciation and the book value after each year of use.

End of Year	Original Cost	Annual Depreciation	Accumulated Depreciation	Book Value
1	$5,000	$445	$ 445	$4,555
2	5,000	445	890	4,110
3	5,000	445	1,335	3,665
4	5,000	445	1,780	3,220
5	5,000	445	2,225	2,775
6	5,000	445	2,670	2,330
7	5,000	445	3,115	1,885
8	5,000	445	3,560	1,440
9	5,000	445	4,005	995
10	5,000	445	4,450	550

 **ASSESS**

Error Analysis

Remind students that the book value for the last year should always equal the salvage value. If these two values are not equal, then students will know that they have made a mistake. They can go back and check their calculations to find their mistake.

④ CLOSE

Closing Activity

Jenna Sears purchased a new truck for her business. The truck costs $52,745, has an estimated life of 8 years, and has a salvage value of $5,945. Calculate the straight-line depreciation and the book value after each year of use.

End of Year	Annual Depreciation	Accumulated Depreciation	Book Value
1	$5,850	$ 5,850	$46,895
2	5,850	11,700	41,045
3	5,850	17,550	35,195
4	5,850	23,400	29,345
5	5,850	29,250	23,495
6	5,850	35,100	17,645
7	5,850	40,950	11,795
8	5,850	46,800	5,945

For Problems 7–11, complete the depreciation schedule for new office furniture. The furniture cost $15,000, has an estimated life of 7 years, and has a salvage value of $1,000.

	End of Year	Original Cost	Annual Depreciation	Accumulated Depreciation	Book Value
	1	$15,000	$2,000	$2,000	$13,000
	2	15,000	2,000	4,000	11,000
7.	3	15,000	a. $2,000	b. $6,000	c. $9,000
8.	4	15,000	a. $2,000	b. $8,000	c. $7,000
9.	5	15,000	a. $2,000	b. $10,000	c. $5,000
10.	6	15,000	a. $2,000	b. $12,000	c. $3,000
11.	7	15,000	a. $2,000	b. $14,000	c. $1,000

For Problems 12–14, complete the depreciation schedule for computer software for Marker Graphics. The software cost $12,990, has an estimated life of 3 years, and has no salvage value.

	End of Year	Original Cost	Annual Depreciation	Accumulated Depreciation	Book Value
12.	1	$12,990	a. $4,330	b. $4,330	c. $8,660
13.	2	12,990	a. $4,330	b. $8,660	c. $4,330
14.	3	12,990	a. $4,330	b. $12,990	c. $0

15. Yolanda Davenport purchased a commercial mixer for her bakery. The mixer cost $1,880, has an estimated life of 7 years, and has a salvage value of $200. Calculate the straight-line depreciation and the book value after each year of use.

End of Year	Original Cost	Annual Depreciation	Accumulated Depreciation	Book Value
1	a. $1,880	b. $240	c. $ 240	d. $1,640
2	a. 1,880	b. 240	c. 480	d. 1,400
3	a. 1,880	b. 240	c. 720	d. 1,160
4	a. 1,880	b. 240	c. 960	d. 920
5	a. 1,880	b. 240	c. 1,200	d. 680
6	a. 1,880	b. 240	c. 1,440	d. 440
7	a. 1,880	b. 240	c. 1,680	d. 200

MAINTAINING YOUR SKILLS

Need Help? Go to...
► Skill 7: Multiplying Whole Numbers, page 734
► Skill 8: Multiplying Decimals, page 735

Multiply.

16. $550 × 3 **$1,650**   **17.** $1,240 × 5 **$6,200**   **18.** $17.60 × 4 **$70.40**

19. $2,500 × 7 **$17,500**   **20.** $11,400 × 9 **$102,600**   **21.** $8,175 × 6 **$49,050**

WRAP-UP

Go over any problem for which a wrong answer is given.

Assignment Guide
  Basic: 4–5
Average: 7–11

20 min.

SECTION 20-6 Modified Accelerated Cost Recovery System (MACRS)

Section Objective

Use the modified accelerated cost recovery system to compute the annual depreciation and book value.

The **modified accelerated cost recovery system** (MACRS) is another method of computing depreciation. Introduced by the Tax Reform Act of 1986 and further modified by the Tax Bill of 1989, MACRS allows businesses to depreciate assets fully over a set period of time. This method encourages businesses to replace equipment earlier than they would if they used other depreciation methods. Under MACRS, assets can be depreciated fully over recovery periods of 4, 6, 8, 11, 16, or 21 years, according to fixed percents. When working to solve MACRS, be mindful that book value is the approximate value of an item after you have owned it and depreciated it for a period of time.

Important Questions to Ask Yourself	What Formula Do I Use?
How do I find the **accumulated depreciation**?	$\text{Accumulated Depreciation} = \text{Previous Year's Accumulated Depreciation} + \text{Current Year's Depreciation}$
How do I calculate the **book value**?	$\text{Book Value} = \text{Original Cost} - \text{Accumulated Depreciation}$
How do I figure out the **annual depreciation**?	$\text{Annual Depreciation} = \text{Original Cost} \times \text{Fixed Percent}$

Living in the Real World

A Well-Sprung Business

Appreciating Depreciation Smalley, the independent tax preparer, mentions that there's another method for calculating depreciation on business equipment that encourages businesses to depreciate fully over a set period of time. It was designed by the federal government to encourage businesses to purchase new equipment sooner than they might have otherwise.

Draw Conclusions In your own words, what is MACRS?

Continued on page 651

Example 1

Prince Pizza purchased a new delivery van for $20,000 to use in delivering pizzas. MACRS allows delivery vans to be depreciated fully in 6 years according to six fixed percents: 20 percent the first year, 32 percent the second year, 19.2 percent the third year, 11.52 percent the fourth and fifth years, and 5.76 percent the sixth year. What is the annual depreciation?

Continued on next page

Section 20-6 Modified Accelerated Cost Recovery System (MACRS) ▶ **647**

Living in the Real World

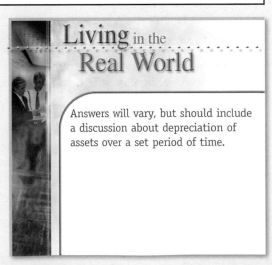

Answers will vary, but should include a discussion about depreciation of assets over a set period of time.

National Standards for Business Education

Standard 1	Mathematical Foundations
Standard 2	Number Relationships and Operations

National Council of Teachers of Mathematics Standards

Standard 1	Numbers and Operations
Standard 6	Problem Solving
Standard 8	Communication

 **1 FOCUS**

Instead of depreciating an item by the same fixed amount each year, there is another method of depreciation. This method enables businesses to depreciate the full cost of an item over a set period of time. It is called the modified accelerated cost recovery system (MACRS).

In-Class Examples

Work through these exercises with students before having them do the Self-Check.
1. 35% of $50,000 **$17,500**
2. 14% of $68,000 **$9,520**
3. 5.75% of $60,352 **$3,470.24**

 **2 TEACH**

This method of depreciation is used for tax purposes. Have students discuss why a business would be encouraged to use MACRS instead of the straight-line method of depreciation. Point out that items can be depreciated over less time with MACRS. As a result, businesses replace items sooner. This stimulates the economy.

647

② TEACH (cont'd)

In Example 1 on pages 647 and 648 point out that the sum of the fixed percents is equal to 100. Also, the sum of the annual depreciations is equal to the original cost of the item.

Motivating the Lesson
Find the annual depreciation for an item that costs $10,000.
40% **$4,000**
25% **$2,500**
22.5% **$2,250**
10.35% **$1,035**
2.15% **$215**

In-Class Examples
1. *The Sun Times* purchased a machine for $50,000. The machine is fully depreciated in 4 years. Fixed percents are 42 percent, 30 percent, 18 percent, and 10 percent. What is the depreciation for each year?

Year	Depreciation
1	$21,000
2	15,000
3	9,000
4	5,000

2. Plumbpro purchased some equipment for $21,750. The equipment is fully depreciated in 6 years. Fixed percents are 30 percent, 25.4 percent, 19.5 percent, 14.5 percent, 7 percent, and 3.6 percent. What is the depreciation for each year?

Year	Depreciation
1	$6,525.00
2	5,524.50
3	4,241.25
4	3,153.75
5	1,522.50
6	783.00

STEP: Find the annual depreciation.

Year	Original Cost	×	Fixed Percent	=	Annual Depreciation
1	$20,000.00	×	20.00%	=	$ 4,000.00
2	20,000.00	×	32.00%	=	6,400.00
3	20,000.00	×	19.20%	=	3,840.00
4	20,000.00	×	11.52%	=	2,304.00
5	20,000.00	×	11.52%	=	2,304.00
6	20,000.00	×	5.76%	=	1,152.00
	Total		100.00%		$20,000.00

20000 M+ × 20 % 4000 RM 20000 × 32 %
6400 RM 20000 × 19.2 % 3840 RM 20000 ×
11.52 % 2304 RM 20000 × 5.76 % 1152

CONCEPT CHECK

SELF-CHECK ✔

Complete the problem, then check your answers at the end of the chapter.

1. MACRS depreciates automobiles in 6 years according to the same six percents used for a delivery van in Example 1. Find the annual depreciation for each of the 6 years for an automobile costing $30,000.

Example 2

Find the book value for the van in Example 1.

STEP 1: Determine the annual depreciation.
It is the same as that determined for Example 1.

STEP 2: Determine the accumulated depreciation.
For year 1 it is $0 + $4,000 = $4,000
For year 2 it is $4,000 + $6,400 = $10,400
Same process for remaining years.

STEP 3: Determine the book value.
For year 1 it is $20,000 − $4,000 = $16,000
For year 2 it is $20,000 − $10,400 = $9,600
Same process for remaining years.

Year	Original Cost	Annual Depreciation	Accumulated Depreciation	Book Value
1	$20,000.00	$ 4,000.00	$ 4,000.00	$16,000.00
2	20,000.00	6,400.00	10,400.00	9,600.00
3	20,000.00	3,840.00	14,240.00	5,760.00
4	20,000.00	2,304.00	16,544.00	3,456.00
5	20,000.00	2,304.00	18,848.00	1,152.00
6	20,000.00	1,152.00	20,000.00	0.00
	$20,000.00			

CONCEPT CHECK

SELF-CHECK ✔

Complete the problem, then check your answers at the end of the chapter.

2. Find the book value for the automobile in Self-Check Problem 1.

648 ◄ Chapter 20 Accounting

ALTERNATIVE ASSESSMENT STRATEGIES

Students with Orthopedic Impairments

When you have students with orthopedic impairments in your class, you have the opportunity to educate other students and adults about people with physical impairments. Speak with your students who have orthopedic impairments ahead of time, discuss any issues you feel uncertain about. Read various educational journals about ways in which students with physical impairments are succeeding in the world. You can learn a great deal and overcome any doubts you may have about the capabilities of these individuals. Be aware that the way you treat students with physical impairments will be imitated. Use the opportunity to increase students' respectfulness and awareness.

3. **Taxi:**
   a. $3,200.00;
   b. $5,120.00;
   c. $3,072.00;
   d. $1,843.20;
   e. $1,843.20;
   f. $921.60

4. **Truck:**
   a. 4,940.00;
   b. 7,904.00;
   c. 4,742.40;
   d. 2,845.44;
   e. 2,845.44;
   f. 1,422.72

5. **Computers:**
   a. 6,960.00;
   b. 11,136.00;
   c. 6,681.60;
   d. 4,008.96;
   e. 4,008.96;
   f. 2,004.48

6. **Furniture:**
   a. 24,000.00;
   b. 38,400.00;
   c. 23,040.00;
   d. 13,824.00;
   e. 13,824.00;
   f. 6,912.00

SECTION 20-6 PRACTICE

Use the MACRS to find the annual depreciation. Round answers to the nearest cent.

	Item	Cost	Percent	1 20.00%	2 32.00%	3 19.20%	4 11.52%	5 11.52%	6 5.76%
3.	Taxi	$ 16,000	Annual Deprec.	a.	b.	c.	d.	e.	f.
4.	Truck	24,700	Annual Deprec.	a.	b.	c.	d.	e.	f.
5.	Computers	34,800	Annual Deprec.	a.	b.	c.	d.	e.	f.
6.	Furniture	120,000	Annual Deprec.	a.	b.	c.	d.	e.	f.

7. Three-year-old racehorse. Original cost is $164,500. Fully depreciated in 4 years. Fixed percents are 33.33 percent, 44.45 percent, 14.81 percent, and 7.41 percent. What is the depreciation for each of the 4 years?

8. Office furniture. Original cost is $47,600. Fully depreciated in 8 years. Fixed percents are 14.29 percent, 24.49 percent, 17.49 percent, 12.49 percent, 8.93 percent, 8.92 percent, 8.93 percent, and 4.46 percent. What is the depreciation for each of the 8 years?

9. The Extended Care Center purchased a van for $48,260 to transport residents to and from a shopping center. The van is fully depreciated in 6 years. Fixed percents are 20 percent, 32 percent, 19.20 percent, 11.52 percent, 11.52 percent, and 5.76 percent. Find the depreciation and book value for each year.

Year	Percent	Cost	Deprec.	Accumulated Deprec.	Book Value
1	20.00%	a.	b.	c.	d.
2	32.00%	a.	b.	c.	d.
3	19.20%	a.	b.	c.	d.
4	11.52%	a.	b.	c.	d.
5	11.52%	a.	b.	c.	d.
6	5.76%	a.	b.	c.	d.

10. Wastewater treatment plants are depreciated fully in 16 years. Complete the depreciation table for a plant costing $1,400,000.

Year	Percent	Cost	Deprec.	Accum. Deprec.	Book Value	Year	Percent	Cost	Deprec.	Accum. Deprec.	Book Value
1	5.00%	a.	b.	c.	d.	9	5.91%	a.	b.	c.	d.
2	9.50%	a.	b.	c.	d.	10	5.90%	a.	b.	c.	d.
3	8.55%	a.	b.	c.	d.	11	5.91%	a.	b.	c.	d.
4	7.70%	a.	b.	c.	d.	12	5.90%	a.	b.	c.	d.
5	6.93%	a.	b.	c.	d.	13	5.91%	a.	b.	c.	d.
6	6.23%	a.	b.	c.	d.	14	5.90%	a.	b.	c.	d.
7	5.90%	a.	b.	c.	d.	15	5.91%	a.	b.	c.	d.
8	5.90%	a.	b.	c.	d.	16	2.95%	a.	b.	c.	d.

MAINTAINING YOUR SKILLS

Need Help? Go to...
▶ Skill 30: Finding the Percentage, page 757

Find the percentage. Round answers to the nearest dollar.

11. 38% of $74,500 **$28,310**

12. 22% of $18,500 **$4,070**

13. 8% of $1,475 **$118**

14. 12% of $840 **$101**

Section 20-6 Modified Accelerated Cost Recovery System (MACRS) ▶ **649**

7.

Year	Original Cost	Fixed Percent	Annual Depreciation
1	$164,500.00	33.33%	$ 54,827.85
2	164,500.00	44.45%	73,120.25
3	164,500.00	14.81%	24,362.45
4	164,500.00	7.41%	12,189.45
		100.00%	164,500.00

See pages 650 to 651 for answers to Problems 8–10.

WRAP-UP

Go over any problem for which a wrong answer is given.

Assignment Guide
   Basic: 3–6
   Average: 7–8

20 min.

SECTION 20-6

3 ASSESS

Error Analysis

In Example 2 on page 648, students need to recall what they learned in the previous section about finding the book value of an item. Point out how the accumulated depreciation is still the previous year's accumulation, plus the current year's depreciation. However, unlike the previous section, you cannot just multiply the annual depreciation by the number of years, since the annual depreciation is not the same amount each year.

4 CLOSE

Closing Activity

1. Hatco purchased a car for $30,000. The car is fully depreciated 5 years. Fixed percents are: 35 percent, 32 percent, 12 percent, 13 percent, and 8 percent. What is the depreciation for each year?

Year	Depreciation
1	$10,500
2	9,600
3	3,600
4	3,900
5	2,400

2. Rosewood Inc. purchased some equipment for $35,900. The equipment is fully depreciated in 4 years. Fixed percents are: 31.5 percent, 26.3 percent, and 21.7 percent, and 20.5 percent. What is the depreciation for each year?

Year	Depreciation
1	$11,308.50
2	9,441.70
3	7,790.30
4	7,359.50

649

Quick Quiz

1. Wearco Manufacturing's total gross pay for one week is $18,000 with total deductions of $4,000. What is the total net pay? **$14,000**

2. A company's particular expenses include: rent, $1,500; utilities, $500; advertising, $305; and merchandise, $3,750. What percent of the total expenses is advertising? **5%**

3. The Stanley store occupies 50 feet by 70 feet in a mall with 80,000 square feet. The monthly security expenses are $25,000. The mall apportions this cost based on the square footage of its stores. What does the Stanley store pay for security? **$1,093.75**

4. Sara Price purchased equipment for her business for $24,000. The salvage value is estimated to be $5,000 after 5 years of use. What is the annual depreciation? **$3,800**

5. Louis Santana purchased a new machine for his business. The machine costs $25,000, has an estimated life of 4 years, and has a salvage value of $5,000. Calculate the book value after each year of use. **Year 1: $20,000; Year 2: $15,000; Year 3: $10,000; Year 4: $5,000**

SECTION 20-1 — CONCEPT CHECK (p. 635)

1. $396.00 − ($29.00 + $24.55 + $5.74 + $42.75) = $396.00 − $102.04 = **$293.96**

2. Medicare: $(0.0145 \times \$735.00) = \$10.66$; Social Security: $(0.062 \times \$735.00) = \$45.57$; city tax: $(0.02 \times \$735.00) = \$14.70$; FIT: $63.00; net pay: $735.00 − ($10.66 + $45.57 + $14.70 + $63.00) = $735.00 − $133.93 = **$601.07**

SECTION 20-2 — CONCEPT CHECK (p. 638)

1. $26,417.93 ÷ $609,200 = **0.04336 or 4.3%**

2. $422,171.84 ÷ $609,200 = **0.692994 or 69.3%**

SECTION 20-3 — CONCEPT CHECK (p. 641)

1. Square feet occupied = $40 \times 50 = 2,000$
Amount paid = $(2,000 ÷ 50,000) \times \$96,000 = 0.04 \times \$96,000 = **\$3,840**$

2. Square feet occupied = $50 \times 100 = 5,000$
Amount paid = $(5,000 ÷ 40,000) \times \$22,500 = 0.125 \times \$22,500.00 = **\$2,812.50**$

SECTION 20-4 — CONCEPT CHECK (p. 643)

1. Annual depreciation = ($6,000 − $200) ÷ 10 = $5,800 ÷ 10 = **$580**

2. Annual depreciation = ($145,000 − $25,000) ÷ 3 = $120,000 ÷ 3 = **$40,000**

SECTION 20-5 — CONCEPT CHECK (p. 645)

1. a. $16,000; b. $32,000 + $16,000 = **$48,000**; c. $90,000 − $48,000 = **$42,000**

2. a. $16,000; b. $48,000 + $16,000 = **$64,000**; c. $90,000 − $64,000 = **$26,000**

3. a. $16,000; b. $64,000 + $16,000 = **$80,000**; c. $90,000 − $80,000 = **$10,000**

SECTION 20-6 — CONCEPT CHECK (p. 648)

1.

Year	Original Cost	×	Fixed Percent	=	Annual Depreciation
1	$30,000.00	×	20.00%	=	$ 6,000.00
2	30,000.00	×	32.00%	=	9,600.00
3	30,000.00	×	19.20%	=	5,760.00
4	30,000.00	×	11.52%	=	3,456.00
5	30,000.00	×	11.52%	=	3,456.00
6	30,000.00	×	5.76%	=	1,728.00
	Total		100.00%		$30,000.00

2.

Year	Original Cost	Annual Depreciation	Accumulated Depreciation	Book Value
1	$30,000.00	$ 6,000.00	$ 6,000.00	$24,000.00
2	30,000.00	9,600.00	15,600.00	14,400.00
3	30,000.00	5,760.00	21,360.00	8,640.00
4	30,000.00	3,456.00	24,816.00	5,184.00
5	30,000.00	3,456.00	28,272.00	1,728.00
6	30,000.00	1,728.00	30,000.00	0.00
		$30,000.00		

Section 20–6 Problem

8.

Year	Original	Fixed Percent	Annual Depreciation
1	$47,600.00	14.29%	$ 6,802.04
2	47,600.00	24.49%	11,657.24
3	47,600.00	17.49%	8,325.24
4	47,600.00	12.49%	5,945.24
5	47,600.00	8.93%	4,250.68
6	47,600.00	8.92%	4,245.92
7	47,600.00	8.93%	4,250.68
8	47,600.00	4.46%	2,122.96
		100.00%	47,600.00

Section 20–6 Problem

9.

Year	Original Cost	Fixed Percent	Annual Depreciation	Accumulated Depreciation	Book Value
1	$48,260.00	20.00%	$ 9,652.00	$ 9,652.00	$38,608.00
2	48,260.00	32.00%	15,443.20	25,095.20	23,164.80
3	48,260.00	19.20%	9,265.92	34,361.12	13,898.88
4	48,260.00	11.52%	5,559.55	39,920.67	8,339.33
5	48,260.00	11.52%	5,559.55	45,480.22	2,779.78
6	48,260.00	5.76%	2,779.78	48,260.00	0
		100.00%	48,260.00		

Living in the Real World

A Well-Sprung Business

Critical Thinking At Wellspring, Greywolf places its accountant, Levi, in control of its accounting and finances. Having one person in control of the finances is an issue of trust. Unfortunately, not everyone with this access to money and financial knowledge can be trusted. Recently in the real world, mega-corporations have been penalized for "creative accounting" where upper management didn't act ethically in relation to corporations' finances. What followed after the whistle blowing was a distressed stock market and distraught company employees.

Take a look at the table to the left before answering the questions.

Cooking the Books		
	The Right Way	The Wrong Way
Revenues	$100 million	$100 million
Expenses	− 50 million	25 million
Earnings	$ 50 million	$ 75 million
Interest	5 million	5 million
Taxes	5 million	5 million
Depreciation	5 million	5 million
Amortization	5 million	10 million
Net Income	$ 30 million	$ 50 million

Source: MSNBC Research

❶ Defining the Term. Revenue is known as the "top line" of an income statement. What information does it provide? How might a company falsify this amount?

❷ Thinking Critically. Amortization is another category where companies have illegally falsified accounting information. To *amortize* is to spread out the costs of expenses over the long-term so you're only paying a fraction of the cost each quarter. How might a company falsify this line on an income statement?

❸ Creative Thinking. The net income is the "bottom line" of an income statement. It tells any analyst that it represents a company's "cash" earnings—after interest, taxes, depreciation and amortization have been subtracted. How might a company unethically hide monies on this line?

REVIEW OF KEY WORDS

payroll register (p. 634)
apportion (p. 640)
depreciation (p. 642)
straight-line method (p. 642)

estimated life (p. 642)
salvage value (p. 642)
book value (p. 644)

accumulated depreciation (p. 644)
modified accelerated cost
recovery system (p. 647)

For Problems 1–9, write the definition to each key word in your own words. Then compare your version to the one in the Glossary.

1–9. Definitions will vary. Evaluate based on the students' understanding of the term and their ability to put the definition into their own words.

Study Guide and Assessment ▶ **651**

Section 20–6 Problem 10.

Year	Original Cost	Fixed Percent	Annual Depreciation	Accumulated Depreciation	Book Value
1	$1,400,000	5.00%	$ 70,000	$ 70,000	$1,330,000
2	1,400,000	9.50%	133,000	203,000	1,197,000
3	1,400,000	8.55%	119,700	322,700	1,077,300
4	1,400,000	7.70%	107,800	430,500	969,500
5	1,400,000	6.93%	97,020	527,520	872,480
6	1,400,000	6.23%	87,220	614,740	785,260
7	1,400,000	5.90%	82,600	697,340	702,660
8	1,400,000	5.90%	82,600	779,940	620,060
9	1,400,000	5.91%	82,740	862,680	537,320
10	1,400,000	5.90%	82,600	945,280	454,720
11	1,400,000	5.91%	82,740	1,028,020	371,980
12	1,400,000	5.90%	82,600	1,110,620	289,380
13	1,400,000	5.91%	82,740	1,193,360	206,640
14	1,400,000	5.90%	82,600	1,275,960	124,040
15	1,400,000	5.91%	82,740	1,358,700	41,300
16	1,400,000	2.95%	41,300	1,400,000	0
		100.00%	1,400,000		

6. Century Tile purchased machinery for $78,000. The machinery is fully depreciated in 5 years. Fixed percents are: 40.2 percent, 22.3 percent, 14.1 percent, 12.2 percent, and 11.2 percent. What is the depreciation and book value for each year?

Year	Depreciation	Book Value
1	$31,356	$46,644
2	17,394	29,250
3	10,998	18,252
4	9,516	8,736
5	8,736	0

Living in the Real World

1. Revenues generally represent a company's sales. If the sales amount is inflated and expenses are not raised accordingly, then the earnings will be inflated.

2. By doing just what is stated. Instead of taking the expenses in the year they occur, the company artificially spreads the costs over several years to make the income appear high in the current year.

3. If interest, tax depreciation, or amortization are represented using false information, then the net income will be misstated.

CHAPTER Study Guide and Assessment

20

Skills and Concepts

SECTION OBJECTIVE 20-1 AND EXAMPLES

Complete a payroll register.

Lorenzo's Italian Eatery has a total weekly gross payroll of $9,432.02. Deductions totaled $5,410.65. What is the total net pay?

STEP: Find the net pay.

Gross Pay − Deductions

$9,432.02 − $5,410.65 = $4,021.37 total net pay

REVIEW EXERCISES

Use the Social Security tax rate of 6.2 percent and the Medicare tax rate of 1.45 percent.

	Employee	Gross Pay	FIT	Social Security	Medicare	Total Deductions	Net Pay
10.	Acevedo	$ 395.00	$ 37.00	a. $24.49	b. $5.73	c. $67.22	d. $327.78
11.	Bacci	561.25	62.00	a. $34.80	b. $8.14	c. $104.94	d. $456.31
12.	Cook	898.45	145.00	a. $55.70	b. $13.03	c. $213.73	d. $684.72
13.	Graham	311.00	25.00	a. $19.28	b. $4.51	c. $48.79	d. $262.21
14.	Grajales	432.00	43.00	a. $26.78	b. $6.26	c. $76.04	d. $355.96
15.	Lyons	1,090.50	197.00	a. $67.61	b. $15.81	c. $280.42	d. $810.08

16. Central Grocery Store's gross payroll for the week was $32,906.56. The total deductions were $12,458.93. What is the total net pay? **$20,447.63**

Use the tables on pages 788–791 for federal withholding. Use the Social Security tax rate of 6.2 percent and the Medicare tax rate of 1.45 percent.

17. Jeremy Scharfetter works for Rhodes Electronics and earns $13.50 per hour. He is single and claims 1 allowance. He is paid weekly. Last week, he worked 38 hours. What is his net pay? **$418.75**

SECTION OBJECTIVE 20-2 AND EXAMPLES

Calculate the percent that a particular business expense is of the total expenses.

Osvaldo Electronics manufactures pacemakers. Its monthly payroll expenses are $9,321 and total monthly expenses are $54,210. Payroll is what percent of the total expenses?

STEP: Find the percent of the total.

Particular Expense ÷ Total Expenses

$9,321 ÷ $54,210

= 0.1719 or 17.2% of total expenses

REINFORCEMENT

Section 20-1

1. Total gross pay: $24,600.
Total deductions: $9,930. **$14,670**
Find the net pay.

Section 20-2

1. Particular expenses: maintenance, $189; trash removal, $87; rent, $900; electricity, $119.
Rent is what percent of the total expenses? **69.5%**

REVIEW EXERCISES

For Problems 18–23, find out what percent (nearest tenth) each item is of the total?

	Retailer's Cost and Profit		
18.	Digital camera from manufacturer	$ 550.00	52.4%
19.	Advertising, other sales expenses	99.00	9.4%
20.	Store operations	150.00	14.3%
21.	Payroll	85.50	8.1%
22.	Taxes	25.50	2.4%
23.	Profit from sale to retail customer	140.00	13.3%
	Total (selling price to customer)	$1,050.00	

24. a. 2,975
b. $37,188
c. $2,529
d. $4,611
e. $193
f. $6,248
g. $2,678
h. $53,447

25. a. 3,400
b. $42,500
c. $2,890
d. $5,270
e. $221
f. $7,140
g. $3,060
h. $61,081

SECTION OBJECTIVE 20-3 AND EXAMPLES

Figure out a department's share of the total business expense.

Giant is a grocery store comprising 65,000 square feet of store space. Within Giant, Flower Mart occupies an area that measures 25 feet by 45 feet. The annual cost of maintenance for the entire grocery store is $125,000. Giant apportions the cost based on square feet occupied. What annual amount for maintenance does Giant charge Flower Mart?

STEP 1: Find the square feet occupied.
25 feet × 45 feet = 1,125 square feet occupied

STEP 2: Find the amount paid.
$\dfrac{\text{Square Feet Occupied}}{\text{Total Square Footage}} \times \text{Total Expense}$

$(1,125 \div 65,000)$

$0.017307692 \quad \times \quad \$125,000 \quad = \$2,163.46$ amount paid

26. a. 5,000
b. $62,500
c. $4,250
d. $7,750
e. $325
f. $10,500
g. $4,500
h. $89,825

27. a. 2,100
b. $26,250
c. $1,785
d. $3,255
e. $137
f. $4,410
g. $1,890
h. $37,727

28. a. 5,625
b. $70,313
c. $4,781
d. $8,719
e. $366
f. $11,813
g. $5,063
h. $101,055

REVIEW EXERCISES

For Problems 24–28, complete the chart.

The Expo Building apportions costs among the tenants on the basis of square footage. How much does each tenant pay for each annual expense?

	Expo Building									
	Tenant	Dimensions	Sq. Ft.	Base Rent	Sec.	Taxes	Insur.	Maint.	Assoc. Fee	Total
				$12.50	$0.85	$1.55	$.065	$2.10	$0.90	
24.	Kwok Insurance	35 × 85	a.	b.	c.	d.	e.	f.	g.	h.
25.	Lyons & Associates	40 × 05	a.	b.	c.	d.	e.	f.	g.	h.
26.	Go Travel	50 × 100	a.	b.	c.	d.	e.	f.	g.	h.
27.	Community Bank	30 × 70	a.	b.	c.	d.	e.	f.	g.	h.
28.	Computer Associates	75 × 75	a.	b.	c.	d.	e.	f.	g.	h.

REINFORCEMENT

Section 20-3
1. Find the amount paid.
   Square feet occupied: 40 ft × 55 ft.
   Total square footage: 425,000.
   Total expense: $106,500. **$551.29**
2. The Campnow sporting goods store occupies 40 feet by 80 feet in a mall with 64,000 square feet. The monthly security expenses are $26,000. The mall apportions this cost based on the square footage of its stores. What does Campnow pay for security?
   $1,300

SECTION OBJECTIVE 20-4 AND EXAMPLES

Utilize the straight-line method to compute the annual depreciation of an item.

An advertising agency purchased a color laser printer that cost $4,210. The life of the printer is estimated to be 4 years. The total salvage value after 4 years of use is estimated to be $610. Using the straight-line method, find the annual depreciation of the laser printer.

STEP: Find the annual depreciation.

(Original Cost − Salvage Value) ÷ Estimated Life

($4,210 − $610) ÷ 4 = **$900 annual depreciation**

REVIEW EXERCISES

Find the annual depreciation.

	Item	(Original Cost −	Salvage Value)	÷	Estimated Life	=	Annual Depreciation
29.	Server	($ 8,500 −	$ 900)	÷	2 years	=	**$3,800**
30.	Copy machine	(25,400 −	2,800)	÷	6 years	=	**$3,766.67**
31.	Tour bus	(170,000 −	18,000)	÷	10 years	=	**$15,200**
32.	Furniture	(4,310 −	257)	÷	3 years	=	**$1,351**
33.	Front end loader	(35,000 −	1,000)	÷	8 years	=	**$4,250**
34.	Fork lift	(18,750 −	750)	÷	9 years	=	**$2,000**

SECTION OBJECTIVE 20-5 AND EXAMPLES

Apply the straight-line method to compute the book value of an item.

An advertising agency purchased a color laser printer that cost $4,210. The life of the printer is estimated to be 4 years. The total salvage value after 4 years of use is estimated to be $610. Using the straight-line method, the agency determined that the printer would depreciate $900 per year. What is the book value at the end of each year of depreciation?

STEP 1: Find the accumulated depreciation.

Previous Year's Accumulated Depreciation + Current Year's Depreciation

First year:	$ 0	+	$900	= $ 900
Second year:	900	+	900	= 1,800
Third year:	1,800	+	900	= 2,700
Fourth year:	2,700	+	900	= 3,600

STEP 2: Find the book value.

Original Cost − Accumulated Depreciation

First year:	$4,210	−	$ 900	= **$3,310**
Second year:	4,210	−	1,800	= **2,410**
Third year:	4,210	−	2,700	= **1,510**
Fourth year:	4,210	−	3,600	= **610**

REINFORCEMENT

Section 20-4

Find the annual depreciation.
1. Original cost: $12,750.
   Salvage value: $3,675.
   Estimated life (years): 7. **$1,296.43**
2. Original cost: $150,000.
   Salvage value: $30,000.
   Estimated life (years): 12. **$10,000**

Section 20-5

1. Complete the straight line depreciation schedule for a pickup truck that cost $23,000, has a useful life of 5 years, and a salvage value of $3000.

Year	Original Cost	Annual Depreciation	Accumulated Depreciation	Book Value
1	$23,000	a. $4,000	b. $ 4,000	c. $19,000
2	23,000	a. 4,000	b. 8,000	c. 15,000
3	23,000	a. 4,000	b. 12,000	c. 11,000
4	23,000	a. 4,000	b. 16,000	c. 7,000
5	23,000	a. 4,000	b. 20,000	c. 3,000

REVIEW EXERCISES

Eileen Arthur purchased an underwater camera for her diving students to use. The camera cost $5,290, has a useful life of 8 years, and has a salvage value of $890. Calculate the straight-line depreciation and the book value after each year of use.

	End of Year	Original Cost	Annual Depreciation	Accumulated Depreciation	Book Value
35.	1	a. $5,290	b. $550	c. $550	d. $5,290
36.	2	a. $5,290	b. $550	c. $1,100	d. $5,290
37.	3	a. $5,290	b. $550	c. $1,650	d. $5,290
38.	4	a. $5,290	b. $550	c. $2,200	d. $5,290
39.	5	a. $5,290	b. $550	c. $2,750	d. $5,290
40.	6	a. $5,290	b. $550	c. $3,330	d. $5,290
41.	7	a. $5,290	b. $550	c. $3,850	d. $5,290
42.	8	a. $5,290	b. $550	c. $4,400	d. $5,290

SECTION OBJECTIVE 20-6 AND EXAMPLES

Use the modified accelerated cost recovery system to compute the annual depreciation and book value.

Case Digital Design Company purchased an equipment van for $15,000. MACRS allows equipment vans to be depreciated fully in 6 years according to six fixed percents: 20 percent the first year, 32 percent the second year, 19.2 percent the third year, 11.52 percent the fourth and fifth years, and 5.76 percent the sixth year. What is the annual depreciation?

STEP: Find the annual depreciation.

Year	Original Cost	×	Fixed Percent	=	Annual Depreciation
1	$15,000.00	×	20.00%	=	$ 3,000.00
2	15,000.00	×	32.00%	=	4,800.00
3	15,000.00	×	19.20%	=	2,880.00
4	15,000.00	×	11.52%	=	1,728.00
5	15,000.00	×	11.52%	=	1,728.00
6	15,000.00	×	5.76%	=	864.00
		Total	100.00%		$15,000.00

REVIEW EXERCISES

A laser engraving machine is fully depreciated in 8 years. Complete the depreciation table for a laser engraving machine costing $86,500.

	Year	Percent	Original Cost	Annual Depreciation	Accumulated Depreciation	Book Value
43.	1	20.00%	a. $86,500	b. $17,300	c. $17,300	d. $69,200
44.	2	16.80%	a. $86,500	b. $14,532	c. $31,832	d. $54,668
45.	3	14.20%	a. $86,500	b. $12,283	c. $44,115	d. $42,385
46.	4	12.20%	a. $86,500	b. $10,553	c. $54,668	d. $31,832
47.	5	9.85%	a. $86,500	b. $8,520.25	c.	d. $23,311.75	c. $63,188.25
48.	6	9.15%	a. $86,500	b. $7,914.75	c. $71,103	d. $15,397
49.	7	9.02%	a. $86,500	b. $7,802.30	c.	d. $7,594.70	c. $78,905.30
50.	8	8.78%	a. $86,500	b. $7,594.70	c. $86,500	d. 0

REINFORCEMENT

Section 20-6

1. Blake's Nursery purchased a truck for $40,000. The truck is fully depreciated in 6 years. Fixed percents are 32 percent, 20 percent, 19.20 percent, 11.52 percent, 11.52 percent, and 5.76 percent. What is the depreciation and book value for each year?

Year	Depreciation	Book Value
1	$12,800	$27,200
2	8,000	19,200
3	7,680	11,520
4	4,608	6,912
5	4,608	2,304
6	2,304	0

National Standards for Business Education

Section Objectives	1. Mathematical Foundations	2. Number Relationships and Operations	3. Patterns, Functions, and Algebra	4. Measurements	5. Statistics and Probability	6. Problem-Solving Applications	
21-1 Assets, Liabilities, and Equity (pp. 658–659) Compute the total assets, liabilities, and owner's equity.	X	X			X		
21-2 Balance Sheet (pp. 660–662) Calculate a balance sheet.	X	X			X		
21-3 Cost of Goods Sold (pp. 663–665) Figure out the cost of goods sold.	X	X			X		
21-4 Income Statement (pp. 666–668) Complete an income statement.	X	X			X		
21-5 Vertical Analysis (pp. 669–671) Analyze balance sheets and income statements.	X	X			X		
21-6 Horizontal Analysis (pp. 672–673) Compare two income statements using horizontal analysis, and compute the percent change.	X	X			X		

(Source: Reprinted with permission from the National Standards for Business Education, copyright © 2001 by National Business Education Association, 1914 Association Drive, Reston, Virginia 21901-1596)

SCANS Correlation

Foundation Skills

Basic Skills	Reading	Writing	Math	Listening	Speaking	
Thinking Skills	Creative Thinking	Decision Making	Problem Solving	Seeing Things in the Mind's Eye	Knowing How to Learn	Reasoning
Personal Qualities	Responsibility	Self-Esteem	Sociability	Self-Management	Integrity/Honesty	

This chapter's highlighted blocks indicate the chapter's content coverage in the Student Edition and the Teacher Wraparound Edition.

National Council of Teachers of Mathematics Standards

1. Numbers & Operations	2. Algebra	3. Geometry	4. Measurement	5. Data Analysis & Probability	6. Problem Solving	7. Reasoning & Proof	8. Communication	9. Connections	10. Representations
X					X		X		
X					X		X		
X					X		X		
X					X		X		
X					X		X		
X					X		X		

SCANS Correlation

Workplace Competencies

Resources	Allocating Time	Allocating Money	Allocating Material and Facility Resources	Allocating Human Resources		
Information	Acquiring and Evaluating Information	Organizing and Maintaining Information	Interpreting and Communicating Information	Using Computers to Process Information		
Interpersonal Skills	Participating as a Member of a Team	Teaching Others	Serving Clients/Customers	Exercising Leadership	Negotiating to Arrive at a Decision	Working with Cultural Diversity
Systems	Understanding Systems	Monitoring and Correcting Performance	Improving and Designing Systems			
Technology	Selecting Technology	Applying Technology to Task	Maintaining and Troubleshooting Technology			

What You'll Learn

Tell students that in this chapter you'll focus on records managed by the accounting department—the balance sheet and the income statement.

Why It's Important

Reporting financial information on the Internet is becoming common, giving investors from any country ready access to the financial information of other companies. This globalization of capital markets and the developments in telecommunications and the Internet bring a need for comparable and transparent financial reporting across companies, investors, creditors, and auditors about what financial information companies should publish and how best to communicate it.

Key Word Review

Teaching Others

Pair students. Each pair splits the key word list in half. Instruct students to find the definition of their words in the Glossary and then take turns to teach each other. For example, read the definition of the key word, and then ask the other student to write how a journalist might use the key word in a sentence. LS , CL , P

CHAPTER 21
Accounting Records

What You'll Learn

Section 21-1 Compute the total assets, liabilities, and owner's equity.

Section 21-2 Calculate a balance sheet.

Section 21-3 Figure out the cost of goods sold.

Section 21-4 Complete an income statement.

Section 21-5 Analyze balance sheets and income statements.

Section 21-6 Compare two income statements using horizontal analysis, and compute the percent change.

When Will You Ever Use This?

The accounting department also keeps other records that show the income, expenses, and value of your business. Get to know a business by learning how to analyze its important documents, such as a balance sheet.

Key Words to Know

- assets
- liabilities
- owner's equity
- net worth
- capital
- balance sheet
- cost of goods sold
- income statement
- profit-and-loss statement
- net income
- net profit
- current ratio
- quick ratio
- horizontal analysis
- base figure
- amount of change

Mathematics Online

To learn more about accounting records, visit the *Mathematics with Business Applications* Web site at www.busmath.glencoe.com.

CLASSROOM RESOURCES

Application and Enrichment
- Teacher Wraparound Edition
- Teacher Resource Binder, Blackline Masters
- Interactive Lesson Planner CD-ROM
- PowerPoint® Presentations CD-ROM

Review and Enforcement
Mathematics Online
www.busmath.glencoe.com
- Teacher Resource Binder, Internet Resources

- Student Activity Workbook
- Student Activity Workbook, Teacher Annotated Edition
- School-to-Home Activity Workbook

Assessment and Evaluation
- Assessment Binder, Reproducible Tests
- Assessment Binder, Alternative Assessment Strategies
- **ExamView®** Pro Test Generator CD-ROM

For the Teacher
- Student Activity Workbook, Teacher Annotated Edition
- Assessment Binder
- Interactive Lesson Planner CD-ROM
- Teacher Resource Binder
- Mathematics Online www.busmath.glencoe.com

For the Student
- Student Activity Workbook
- School-to-Home Activity Workbook

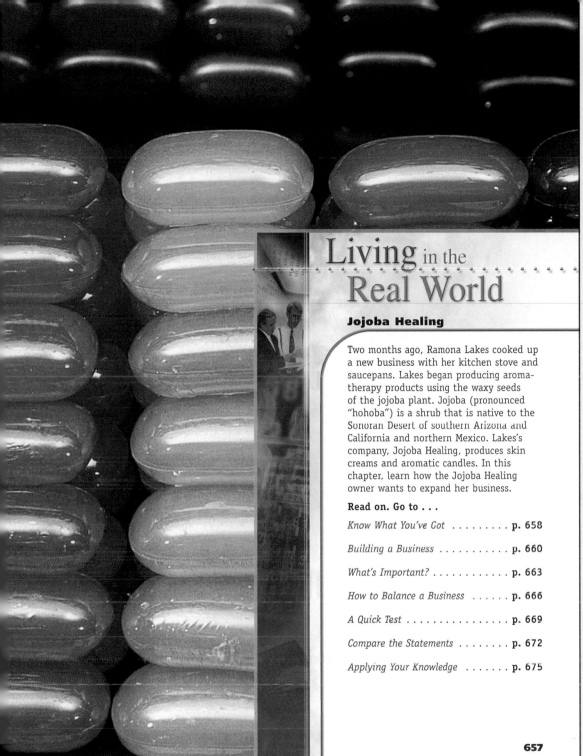

Living in the Real World

Jojoba Healing

Two months ago, Ramona Lakes cooked up a new business with her kitchen stove and saucepans. Lakes began producing aroma-therapy products using the waxy seeds of the jojoba plant. Jojoba (pronounced "hohoba") is a shrub that is native to the Sonoran Desert of southern Arizona and California and northern Mexico. Lakes's company, Jojoba Healing, produces skin creams and aromatic candles. In this chapter, learn how the Jojoba Healing owner wants to expand her business.

Read on. Go to . . .

657

Living in the Real World

Story's Summary

Ramona Lakes's new skin cream and candle company is burning bright, and she's always been careful to keep accurate business records. Now she's ready to expand and is looking at securing a commercial loan to buy property and build a new production facility. This chapter follows her through the loan application process, as she gathers together balance sheets, a list of goods sold, profit and loss statements, income statements, and more.

Did You Know...

Commercial lending in the United States grew 11.4 percent per year over a three year period according to the Mortgage Bankers Association of America. Its commercial mortgage members originated $73.8 billion in commercial loans in one year.

Think about This

Without the ability to borrow funds, the vast majority of businesses would never open their doors to the public. In what ways would society be different if all business owners had to save up large sums of money before setting up shop?

LOCAL STANDARDS

Standard 1	Mathematical Foundations
Standard 2	Number Relationships and Operations
Standard 5	Problem-Solving Applications

National Council of Teachers of Mathematics Standards

Standard 1	Numbers and Operations
Standard 6	Problem Solving
Standard 8	Communication

1 FOCUS

Have students discuss the steps involved with starting a business. Point out that in addition to deciding what type of business to start and whether or not there is a market for the business, a potential business owner needs to find the money to fund the business.

In-Class Examples

Work through these exercises with students before having them do the Self-Check.

1. $35,000 - ($5,000 + $3,000) **$27,000**
2. ($30,000 + $15,000) + $120,000 - ($15,500 + $50,000) **$99,500**
3. ($187,980 + $39,625) + $86,290 - ($12,456 + $74,255) **$227,184**

2 TEACH

Assets are the business' cash, merchandise, and supplies. Even though the $8,000 in merchandise has not yet been paid for, it is still considered an asset. Sometimes an asset is also a liability.

○ **Section Objective**

Compute the total assets, liabilities, and owner's equity.

SECTION 21-1 Assets, Liabilities, and Equity

When you start a business, you'll need to buy either merchandise to sell or materials with which to make your products. You may need to purchase office supplies, equipment, buildings, or land. In addition, you must have cash to make change, pay bills, and meet other expenses. **Assets** are the total of your cash, the items that you have purchased, and any money that your customers owe you.

You may borrow money to start your business, or you may purchase merchandise on credit. **Liabilities** are the total amount of money that you owe to creditors. **Owner's equity**, **net worth**, or **capital** is the total value of assets that you own minus total liabilities. Owner's equity plus liabilities equal assets. Remember that:

Important Questions to Ask Yourself	What Formula Do I Use?
How do I find the total value of a business's **assets**?	Assets = Liabilities + Owner's Equity
How do I calculate a business's **owner's equity**?	Owner's Equity = Assets − Liabilities
How do I find the total value of a business's total **liabilities**?	Liabilities = Assets − Owner's Equity

Living in the Real World

Jojoba Healing

Know What You've Got   You've got to have an accounting system in place in order to become a business. Lakes is producing aromatherapy products such as wax and fragrances. When Lakes totals her assets, she also includes the company's cash and the money in its bank accounts.

Draw Conclusions   If Jojoba Healing has outstanding vendor invoices, does Lakes consider this part of the company's assets?

Continued on page 660

Example 1

Tina and John Agee recently opened The Clothing Store. They used $60,000 of their own money and took out a bank loan of $25,000. From the $85,000, the Agees paid $15,000 for merchandise and $10,000 for supplies. This left a cash balance of $60,000. They received another shipment of $8,000 worth of merchandise. They did not pay for this merchandise immediately. What was their owner's equity?

BUSINESS NOTES

Assets and Liabilities
Have students ask the following questions of some people they know who work: What are some items that could be considered assets in your workplace? What are some items that could be considered liabilities in your workplace? Have students compare their lists for similarities and differences. Is an item ever considered to be an asset by one company and a liability by another? LS , CL

Living in the Real World

Yes, assets are defined as a business's total cash, purchased items, and any money owed by customers.

STEP 1: Find the assets.

Cash: $85,000 − ($15,000 + $10,000) = $60,000
Merchandise: $15,000 + $8,000 =   23,000
Supplies   + 10,000
                  Total Assets $93,000

STEP 2: Find the liabilities.

Bank loan $25,000
Unpaid merchandise   + 8,000
                  Total Liabilities $33,000

STEP 3: Find the owner's equity.

Assets − Liabilities $93,000
                                  − 33,000
                  Owner's Equity $60,000

CONCEPT CHECK

SELF-CHECK✓

Complete the problems, then check your answers at the end of the chapter.

1. Find the assets.
   Liabilities: $82,000.
   Owner's equity: $50,000.
   $82,000 + $50,000 = $132,000

2. Find the liabilities.
   Assets: $18,000 cash, $49,000 merchandise.
   Owner's equity: $25,000.
   2. ($18,000 + $49,000) − $25,000 = $42,000

SECTION 21-1 PRACTICE

Complete this table for Problems 3–8.

	Liabilities	+	Owner's Equity	=	Assets
3.	$27,000	+	$ 50,000	=	**$77,000**
4.	14,750	+	37,500	=	**$52,250**
5.	38,750	+	**$36,250**	=	$ 75,000
6.	54,690	+	**$88,960**	=	143,650
7.	**$17,450**	+	25,000	=	42,450
8.	**$327,530**	+	147,470	=	475,000

9. Family Pharmacy has these assets and liabilities.

   Cash: $4,187   Supplies: $7,185   Unpaid merchandise: $11,410
   Inventory: $17,450   Building: $125,000   Taxes owed: $847
   Equipment: $36,475   Land: $31,500   Real estate loan: $130,000

   What are the total assets? What are the total liabilities? What is the owner's equity? **Assets: $221,797; Liabilities: $142,257; Owner's equity: $79,540**

MAINTAINING YOUR SKILLS

Need Help? Go to...
➤ Skill 5: **Adding Decimals**, page 732
➤ Skill 6: **Subtracting Decimals**, page 733

Add.

10. $31,475.00
     10,719.50
     + 563.85
     $42,758.35

11. $9,187.40
     7,341.85
     + 1,174.97
     $17,704.22

Subtract.

12. $74,850.00
     − 35,798.00
     $39,052.00

13. $147,875.00
     − 74,917.00
     $72,958.00

PROBLEM SOLVING

What's Your Net Worth?
Anything of value that you own is an asset. Make a list of your assets, such as savings, electronic equipment, a bicycle, and so on. Assign each item a realistic market value, keeping in mind that even a new item loses value once it's taken out of the store. Total your assets to estimate your net worth. Create a spreadsheet with this information. `LS` , `CL`

WRAP-UP

Go over any problem for which a wrong answer is given.

Assignment Guide
   Basic: 3–8
   Average: 9

20 min.

In-Class Examples

1. Find the assets.
   Liabilities: $50,000.
   Owner's equity: $90,000.
   $140,000

2. Find the liabilities.
   Assets: $189,000.
   Owner's equity: $107,500.
   $81,500

(3) ASSESS

Error Analysis

Students may confuse assets and liabilities. Make sure students understand that assets are your cash, the items that you own, and any money owed to you. Liabilities are the amount of money you owe to your creditors. For practice, have students label each of the following as an asset or liability:

- $10,000 in supplies
- $125,000 in cash
- $50,000 business loan
- $30,000 in equipment
- $25,000 in taxes

(4) CLOSE

Closing Activity

Find the assets.
1. Liabilities: $150,000.
   Owner's equity: $200,000.
   $350,000
Find the liabilities.
2. Assets: $98,300.
   Owner's equity: $76,000.
   $22,300

National Standards for Business Education

Standard 1	Mathematical Foundations
Standard 2	Number Relationships and Operations
Standard 5	Problem-Solving Applications

National Council of Teachers of Mathematics Standards

Standard 1	Numbers and Operations
Standard 6	Problem Solving
Standard 8	Communication

1 FOCUS

To keep a record of the total assets, liabilities, and owner's equity, businesses use a balance sheet. As in the previous section, the total assets should equal the sum of the liabilities and owner's equity.

In-Class Examples

Work through these exercises with students before having them do the Self-Check.

1. $78,000 + $14,000 + $10,000 + $20,000 **$122,000**
2. $129,570 + $102,680 + $14,245 + $233,650 **$480,145**
3. $329,383.78 + $344,577.50 + $19,906.25 **$693,867.53**

Section Objective

Calculate a balance sheet.

A **balance sheet** shows the financial position of your company on a certain date. It is like a snapshot of your company's financial position. You may prepare a balance sheet monthly, quarterly, or annually. The balance sheet shows your total assets, total liabilities, and owner's equity. The balance sheet is designed so that the assets appear on the left. The liabilities and owner's equity appear on the right. The sum of the assets must equal the sum of the liabilities and owner's equity. Remember from the last section that:

$$\text{Assets} = \text{Liabilities} + \text{Owner's Equity}$$

By examining the numbers and percents, you can see changes that have taken place. The balance sheet is an important financial statement, but to make wise decisions you should compare the financial data to a previous balance sheet. Remember, the financial statements provide the information, but you must analyze and interpret them and make recommendations based on that information.

Living in the Real World

Jojoba Healing

Building a Business The more Lakes thinks about buying land and building a facility for her company, the more she thinks it's a good idea. But before she can apply for a loan to buy and build, she must prepare a balance sheet that shows her company's financial position. She tries to do this anyway (at least once every two months), so the information she has is always fairly up-to-date.

Draw Conclusions Jojoba Healing's most recent balance sheet shows the company owns assets of $123,589, has liabilities of $24,095, and equity of $99,494. Does this show the company is in good standing or not?

Continued on page 663

Example 1

The Agees (from Example 1, Section 21-1) used $60,000 of their own money plus a $25,000 loan to start their clothing store. They received two shipments of merchandise. They paid cash for the $15,000 shipment. They did not pay immediately for the $8,000 shipment. They bought supplies for $10,000. The Agees have $60,000 left in cash. What does their balance sheet show?

660 ◄ Chapter 21 Accounting Records

Living in the Real World

Yes, these numbers show that Jojoba Healings has a very healthy ratio of assets to liabilities.

ALTERNATIVE ASSESSMENT

Word-Processed Document
A balance sheet shows the financial condition of a company on a given day—it's like a snapshot. Ask each student to obtain a company's annual report. Have students analyze the balance sheet with respect to assets, liabilities, and owner's equity. Ask students to prepare a word-processed document explaining their findings. To assess this project, see the Word-Processed Document rubric in the *Assessment Binder, Alternative Assessment Strategies.*

STEP: Figure out the balance sheet.

Figure 21.1

3. a. $33,000
   b. $12,300
   c. $20,700
4. a. $312,100
   b. $208,800
   c. $103,300
5. a. $52,500
   b. $22,500
   c. $27,500
6. a. $334,900
   c. $9,900
   d. $184,900

Balance Sheet

The Clothing Store   Owed to bank   May 21

Assets		Liabilities	
Cash	$60,000	Notes payable	$25,000
Merchandise inventory	23,000	Accounts payable	8,000
Supplies	10,000	Total liabilities	$33,000

Owed for merchandise   Cash they invested

Shipments valued at $15,000 and $8,000

		Owner's Equity	
		Capital	60,000
Total assets	$93,000	Total liabilities and owner's equity	$93,000

Totals must equal. Note double lines under totals.

$$60000 + 23000 + 10000 = 93000$$

$$25000 + 8000 = 33000 + 60000 = 93000$$

CONCEPT CHECK

SELF-CHECK ✔

Complete the problems, then check your answers at the end of the chapter.

Assets		Liabilities	
Cash	$25,000	Notes payable	$10,000
Inventory	30,000	Accounts payable	7,000
Supplies	12,000	Owner's equity	50,000

1. What are the total assets? **Sum of assets is $67,000.**

2. What are the total liabilities and owner's equity? **Sum of total liabilities and owner's equity is $67,000.**

SECTION 21-2 PRACTICE

Complete the table.

7. a. $99,800
   b. $65,000
   c. $34,800
8. a. $19,620
   b. $10,000
   c. $9,620

	Cash	Inventory	Supplies	Total Assets	Bank Loan	Taxes Owed	Total Liabilities	Owner's Equity
3.	$ 18,000	$ 11,500	$ 3,500	a.	$ 10,500	$1,800	b.	c.
4.	45,000	255,700	11,400	a.	200,000	8,800	b.	c.
5.	10,500	41,200	800	a.	b.	5,000	c.	$ 25,000
6.	125,400	196,700	12,800	a.	175,000	b.	c.	150,000

7. Cash: $25,000
   Merchandise: $74,800
   Owed to bank: $65,000
   a. What are the total assets?
   b. What are the total liabilities?
   c. What is the owner's equity?

8. Cash: $8,450
   Equipment: $11,170
   Owed to bank: $10,000
   a. What are the total assets?
   b. What are the total liabilities?
   c. What is the owner's equity?

Continued on next page

Section 21-2 Balance Sheet ▶ **661**

GLOBAL PERSPECTIVE

International Accounting Standards

United States businesses entering joint ventures with businesses in the former Soviet Union have had to deal with vast differences between United States and Russian accounting standards. As the global market grows, the need for international accounting standards increases. The International Accounting Standards Committee has been charged with the task of developing accounting standards that can be used by businesses having operations in several countries and in various types of economies. Ask students to speculate on why international accounting standards are necessary.

SECTION 21-2

2 TEACH

Remind students that they learned about business expenses in Section 20-2. Just as business expenses are often reported to stockholders, balance sheets are also usually part of the financial report that is given to stockholders. Balance sheets may be prepared monthly, quarterly, or annually.

In Example 1 on pages 660 and 661, point out the double lines under the totals. The double lines are often used in accounting to emphasize equal amounts. They also indicate that nothing can be added or subtracted from these amounts.

Motivating the Lesson

What are the total assets?
- $35,000 in cash
- $600,000 building
- $175,000 land
- $210,000 in merchandise
  $1,020,000

In-Class Examples

Find the total assets, total liabilities, and owner's equity.

1. Cash: $75,000.
   Merchandise: $250,000.
   Bank loan: $90,000. **$325,000; $90,000; $235,000**

2. Cash: $90,035.
   Merchandise: $359,352.
   Bank loan: $109,000.
   Taxes owed: $45,982.
   $449,387; $154,982; $294,405

3. Cash: $150,000.
   Merchandise: $498,450.75.
   Building: $500,000.
   Bank loan: $148,984.40.
   Taxes owed: $14,672.21.
   Accounts payable: $290,000.
   $1,148,450.75; $453,656.61; $694,794.14

3 ASSESS

Error Analysis

Students may not remember what it means to write a number in terms of a number of dollars. Before you assign Problem 12, point out that large dollar amounts can be expressed as decimals of a given unit. For example, $2,500,000 can be written as $2.5 million dollars. Point out the convenience of using this format. Have students practice writing some large dollar amounts.

4 CLOSE

Closing Activity

Find the total assets, total liabilities, and owner's equity.

1. Cash: $45,000.
   Inventory: $150,000.
   Accounts payable: $23,000.
   $195,000; $23,000; $172,000

2. Prepare a balance sheet for a business with these assets and liabilities.
   - Cash: $110,000
   - Bank loan: $85,000
   - Inventory: $220,000
   - Accounts payable: $125,000
   - Building: $449,000
   - Mortgage loan: $200,000

Balance Sheet	Assets	Liabilities
Cash:	$110,000	
Bank loan:		$85,000
Inventory:	$220,000	
Accts. Payable:		$125,000
Building:	$449,000	
Mortg. Loan:		$200,000
Total:	$779,000	$410,000
Owner's Equity		
Capital:		$369,000
Total Liabilities		
& Total Assets:	$779,000	
Owner's Equity:	$779,000	

9. Complete the balance sheet for Howard's Jewelers.

Figure 21.2

Balance Sheet

Howard's Jewelers — June 30

Assets		Liabilities	
Cash on hand	3 4 1 7 00	Bank loan	1 2 2 1 4 00
Accts. receivable	6 2 1 4 00	Accts. payable	6 4 7 0 00
Inventory	1 3 4 1 9 00	Taxes owed	7 1 4 85
Supplies	4 1 7 50	Wages owed	2 7 4 35
Store fixtures	1 2 5 0 00	Mortgage loan	3 1 3 4 0 00
Building	3 5 7 5 0 00	Total liabilities	5 1 0 1 3 20
Land	2 0 0 0 0 00		
		Owner's Equity	
		Capital	2 9 4 5 4 30
Total assets	8 0 4 6 7 50	Total liabilities and owner's equity	8 0 4 6 7 50

10. Complete the balance sheet for Pet Supplies, Inc.

Figure 21.3

Balance Sheet

Pet Supplies, Inc. — Dec. 31

Assets		Liabilities	
Cash on hand	3 1 2 8 00	Bank loan	1 1 7 1 5 00
Accts. receivable	2 1 4 85	Accts. payable	4 7 4 84
Inventory	8 4 2 6 00	Taxes owed	4 6 1 72
Supplies	5 6 1 7 40	Wages owed	2 3 4 85
Store fixtures	2 4 0 5 75	Mortgage loan	5 4 1 7 5 00
Building	4 3 4 5 0 00	Total liabilities	6 7 0 6 1 41
Land	2 4 5 0 0 00		
		Owner's Equity	
		Capital	2 0 6 8 0 59
Total assets	8 7 7 4 2 00	Total liabilities and owner's equity	8 7 7 4 2 00

For Problems 11 and 12, prepare a balance sheet for each business.

11. Total Assets: $199,504,200; Total Liabilities: $142,599,410; Owner's Equity: $56,904,790; Total Liabilities and Owner's Equity: $199,504,200

11. Wholesale Grocer Supply Company had these assets and liabilities on December 31:

Assets		Liabilities	
Cash	$ 2,417,600	Accounts payable	$84,640,000
Accounts receivable	53,591,500	Notes payable	56,119,400
Inventory	48,478,600	Income taxes	975,450
Property	75,750,000	Other liabilities	864,560
Investments	475,000		
Other assets	18,791,500		

12. Total Assets: $47.5; Total Liabilities: $34.8; Owner's Equity: $12.7; Total Liabilities and Owner's Equity: $47.5

12. Metal Abrasives shows these assets and liabilities as of June 30:

Assets (in millions)		Liabilities (in millions)	
Cash	$ 1.1	Notes payable	$14.9
Accounts receivable	9.8	Accounts payable	4.3
Inventories	11.4	Income taxes	1.2
Property	19.7	Stock	10.3
Foreign investments	1.3	Other liabilities	4.1
Other assets	4.2		

Need Help? Go to...
→ Skill 3: Adding Whole Numbers, page 730

MAINTAINING YOUR SKILLS

Add.

13. $14,780 + $13,190 **$27,970**

14. $147,560 + $93,480 **$241,040**

15. $4,175,000 + $897,400 **$5,072,400**

16. $416,750 + $318,430 + $84,970 **$820,150**

WRAP-UP

Go over any problem for which a wrong answer is given.

Assignment Guide
Basic: 3–6
Average: 7–8

20 min.

SECTION 21-3 Cost of Goods Sold

Section Objective

Figure out the cost of goods sold.

The balance sheet shows your total assets, total liabilities, and owner's equity at a given point in time. You also need to know whether the company is operating at a profit or loss. To determine if you are making money or losing money, you must know sales figures, expenses, and the **cost of goods sold**. The cost of goods sold is equal to the value of the beginning inventory plus the cost of any goods received (receipts) minus the value of the ending inventory. Remember that:

Cost of Goods Sold = (Beginning Inventory + Receipts) − Ending Inventory

Living in the Real World

Jojoba Healing

What's Important? Lakes spends several afternoons talking with commercial loan officers at various banks in town. She hopes one of them will give her a loan to buy property and build a new production facility for her candle making and bath and body products.

Draw Conclusions Do you think a loan officer is more impressed with a steady balance sheet or future forecasts?

Continued on page 666

National Standards for Business Education

Standard 1	Mathematical Foundations
Standard 2	Number Relationships and Operations
Standard 5	Problem-Solving Applications

National Council of Teachers of Mathematics Standards

Standard 1	Numbers and Operations
Standard 6	Problem Solving
Standard 8	Communication

1 FOCUS

In order to determine if a business is making a profit or suffering a loss, it is necessary to know the cost of goods sold. The cost of goods sold takes into account the value of the inventory at the beginning of a period, any goods received during the period, and the value of the inventory at the end of the period.

Example 1

The Clothing Store began the quarter with an inventory valued at $14,750.00. During the quarter, it received 100 belts that cost $6.49 each, 50 scarves at $8.24 each, 25 sweaters at $19.72 each, and 144 plastic raincoats at $2.50 each. The ending inventory was valued at $12,847.00. What was the cost of goods sold?

STEP 1: Find the receipts.

100 belts	×	$ 6.49 each =	$ 649.00
50 scarves	×	$ 8.24 each =	412.00
25 sweaters	×	$19.72 each =	493.00
144 raincoats	×	$ 2.50 each =	360.00
Total Receipts			$1,914.00

STEP 2: Find the cost of goods sold.

(Beginning Inventory + Receipts) − Ending Inventory
($14,750.00 + $1,914.00) − $12,847.00
= **$3,817.00 cost of goods sold**

100 × 6.49 = 649 M+ 50 × 8.24 = 412 M+

25 × 19.72 = 493 M+ 144 × 2.5 = 360 M+ RM

1914 + 14750 − 12847 = 3817

FYI

Companies try to measure their "soft assets," such as the knowledge and experience of their employees and the intellectual property owned by the company in the form of patents, publications, and logos and other designs.

▶▶▶

Section 21-3 Cost of Goods Sold ▶ **663**

In-Class Examples

Work through these exercises with students before having them do the Self-Check.

1. ($8,000 + $3,000) − $9,000 **$2,000**
2. ($41,889 + $18,452) − $42,875 **$17,466**
3. (24 × $3.78) + (30 × $5.95) + (16 × $18.39) **$563.46**

Living in the Real World

A steady balance sheet would be more impressive, as it shows historical fact, while future forecasts may or may not pan out as projected.

RETEACH / ENRICHMENT

Cost of Goods Sold

Complete this table with your students. Refer to Workshop 36 on page 74 to solve.

	Beginning Inventory	Receipts	Ending Inventory	Cost of Goods Sold
1)	$546,980	$52,850	$497,690	**$102,140**
2)	72,750	14,750	68,498	**$ 19,002**
3)	158,000	61,900	**174,800**	**$ 45,100**

② TEACH

Point out that the cost of goods sold usually refers to the cost to the retailer. In Example 1 on page 663 point out that the costs given for the clothing are what the Clothing Store pays for the clothing. Emphasize that you must multiply the number of items by the cost per item in order to find the total receipts. Mention that these multiplications are referred to as extensions when they appear on an invoice.

Motivating the Lesson

Hanskin Jewelry received the following goods during a quarter. What are the total receipts for the quarter?
- 15 necklaces at $175 each
- 8 bracelets at $109 each
- 20 watches at $150 each
  $6,497

In-Class Examples

Find the cost of goods sold.
1. Beginning inventory: $25,000.
   Receipts: $9,000.
   Ending inventory: $20,000.
   $14,000
2. Beginning inventory: $42,500.
   Receipts: $10,750.
   Ending inventory: $39,000.
   $14,250
3. Beginning inventory:
   $238,554.
   Receipts: $24,998.
   Ending inventory: $234,996.
   $28,556

CONCEPT CHECK

SELF-CHECK ✓ Complete the problems, then check your answers at the end of the chapter. Find the cost of goods sold.

	Beginning Inventory	Receipts	Ending Inventory	Cost of Goods Sold
1.	$156,470	$21,960	$161,510	
2.	43,656	11,712	42,964	

1. $156,470 + $21,960 − $161,510 = $16,920
2. $43,656 + $11,712 − $42,964 = $12,404

SECTION 21-3 PRACTICE

3. Beginning inventory: $417,600.
   Receipts: $75,800.
   Ending inventory: $396,800.
   Find the cost of goods sold. **$96,600**

4. Beginning inventory: $125,400.
   Receipts: $31,200.
   Ending inventory: $131,400.
   Find the cost of goods sold. **$25,200**

5. Beginning inventory: $75,470.
   Receipts: $14,650.
   Ending inventory: $72,170.
   Find the cost of goods sold. **$17,950**

6. Beginning inventory: $19,560.
   Receipts: $3,780.
   Ending inventory: $20,450.
   Find the cost of goods sold. **$2,890**

7. Beginning inventory: $112,475.
   Receipts: $42,164.
   Ending inventory: $96,512.
   Find the cost of goods sold. **$58,127**

8. Beginning inventory: $11,186.
   Receipts: $2,871.
   Ending inventory: $12,074.
   Find the cost of goods sold. **$1,983**

9. Miller Music Land had a beginning inventory valued at $48,748.75. During the quarter, it had receipts of $9,164.86. The value of the ending inventory was $50,041.93. Find the cost of goods sold. **$7,871.68**

10. The Popcorn Castle had a beginning inventory valued at $2,146.73. During the quarter, receipts totaled $516.65. The value of the ending inventory was $1,989.83. Find the cost of goods sold. **$673.55**

GLOBAL PERSPECTIVE

Tourism
Many countries have tourism as a business. In a recent year, the United States had tourist receipts of about $75 billion. Have students use an almanac (such as *The World Almanac and Book of Facts*) or other source to find the amount of tourist receipts for three other countries.

11. Alicia's Dress Shop began the quarter with an inventory valued at $21,647. During the quarter, four shipments received were valued at $2,248.60, $1,874.55, $2,516.43, and $2,050.74. The ending inventory for the quarter was valued at $20,416. What was the cost of goods sold? **$9,921.32**

12. Central Auto Parts began the month with an inventory valued at $34,767.80. During the month, Central received 5 shipments valued at $1,274.74, $4,756.44, $983.45, $2,465.39, and $416.93. Central's month-end inventory was valued at $36,193.48. Find the cost of goods sold. **$8,471.27**

13. The Shoehorn Repair Shop started the quarter with an inventory valued at $5,178.43. During the quarter, it received 5 boxes of replacement heels at $7.35 a box, 3 boxes of replacement soles at $16.15 a box, 4 cards of shoelaces at $7.65 a card, 6 spools of nylon thread at $12.13 a spool, and 2 large bottles of industrial-strength adhesive at $19.87 a bottle. The ending inventory for the quarter was valued at $4,241.83. Find the cost of goods sold. **$1,164.92**

14. Leather Limited started the month with an inventory valued at $18,719.45. During the month, it received 9 men's jackets at $47.53 each, 15 belts at $2.79 each, 4 ladies' long coats at $84.37 each, 5 men's hats at $8.71 each, and 5 ladies' jackets at $38.84 each. The month-end inventory was valued at $16,478.54. Find the cost of goods sold. **$3,285.76**

15. Bits & Bytes, Inc., started the month with an inventory of computer hardware and software valued at $68,395.65. During the month, Bits & Bytes bought 16 scanners at a cost of $47.84 each, 24 CD burners at a cost of $37.75 each, and 48 software programs at a cost of $14.95 each. Bits & Bytes's ending inventory of computer hardware and software was valued at $52,936.89. What was the cost of the goods sold? **$17,847.80**

16. Battery Market began the quarter with an inventory valued at $12,550. Receipts included: 220 auto batteries at $35 each, 100 marine batteries at $60 each, 150 phone batteries at $15 each, and 60 portable tool batteries at $30 each. The ending inventory was valued at $8,400. Determine the total receipts and the cost of goods sold.
a. **$17,750;** b. **$21,900**

MAINTAINING YOUR SKILLS

Need Help? Go to...
➤ Skill 5: Adding Decimals, page 732
➤ Skill 6: Subtracting Decimals, page 733
➤ Skill 8: Multiplying Decimals, page 735

Add.

17. $14,178.90 + $2,417.36
$16,596.26

18. $8,174.32 + $2,461.89 **$10,636.21**

Subtract.

19. $16,596.80 − $13,743.34
$2,853.46

20. $9,771.83 − $5,421.95 **$4,349.88**

Multiply.

21. 12 × $7.98 **$95.76**

22. 5 × $46.73 **$233.65**

WRAP-UP

Go over any problem for which a wrong answer is given.

Assignment Guide
Basic: 3–8
Average: 9–10

20 min.

 **ASSESS**

Error Analysis
Remind students to find the total receipts before using the cost of goods sold formula. Students need to multiply the number of each item received by its cost. Some students may forget to multiply and instead just add the cost of one item. In Example 1 on page 663, stress the importance of the multiplication.

4 CLOSE

Closing Activity
Find the cost of goods sold.
1. Beginning inventory: $67,000. Receipts: $15,000. Ending inventory: $65,000. **$17,000**

2. Beginning inventory: $124,900. Receipts: $43,800. Ending inventory: $131,800. **$36,900**

3. Beginning inventory: $213,879. Receipts: $43,988. Ending inventory: $212,870. **$44,997**

4. Beginning inventory: $298,564.50. Receipts: $7,265.75. Ending inventory: $296,780.23. **$9,050.02**

5. Prince Lighting began the month with an inventory valued at $56,945.50. During the month, Prince received four shipments valued at $1,455.75, $3,256.49, $2,246.90, and $998.47. Prince's month-end inventory was valued at $54,689.20. Find the cost of goods sold. **$10,213.91**

Standard 1	Mathematical Foundations
Standard 2	Number Relationships and Operations
Standard 5	Problem-Solving Applications

National Council of Teachers of Mathematics Standards

Standard 1	Numbers and Operations
Standard 6	Problem Solving
Standard 8	Communication

 **1 FOCUS**

In Section 21-2 students learned that a balance sheet is a record of assets, liabilities, and owner's equity. In this section students will learn about income statements. An income statement shows the income and operating expenses of a business and whether or not the business is making or losing money.

In-Class Examples
Work through these exercises with students before having them do the Self-Check.
1. $14,500 − $9,325 **$5,175**
2. $78,876 − $16,981 **$61,895**
3. $26,450 + $2,000 + $790 + $422 + $1,700 **$31,362**

SECTION 21-4 Income Statement

○ **Section Objective**

Complete an income statement.

At the end of an accounting period, you want to know how much money your business made or lost. You also want to know how much money you took in from sales and where the money went. The information is reported on your income statement. An **income statement**, or **profit-and-loss statement**, shows in detail your income and operating expenses. If your gross profit is greater than your total operating expenses, your income statement will show a **net income**, or **net profit**.

Important Questions to Ask Yourself	What Formula Do I Use?
How do I find a company's **gross profit**?	Gross Profit = Net Sales − Cost of Goods Sold
How do I find a company's **net income**?	Net Income = Gross Profit − Total Operating Expenses

Living in the Real World

Jojoba Healing

How to Balance a Business After telling Lakes she needs to bring her balance sheet, cost of goods sold, and other financial information into the bank, the loan officer says that he also needs to see her profit-and-loss statement for the last two quarters.

Draw Conclusions Why is it important for the bank to see how her business is doing over several quarters?

Continued on page 669

Example 1

Three months after opening The Clothing Store, Tina and John Agee (from Example 1, Section 21-2) prepare an income statement. Sales for the first three months totaled $12,174. Merchandise totaling $173 was returned to them. The Agees' inventory records show that the goods they sold cost them $3,817. Records show that their operating expenses totaled $8,047. What is the net income?

Living in the Real World

It can help to identify trends that may predict future company growth or loss.

STEP: Find the net income.

Figure 21.4

Income Statement

The Clothing Store		For the Quarter Ended June 30, 20--	
Income:	Sales	$12,174	
	Less: Sales returns and allowances	173	
	Net sales		$12,001
Cost of goods sold	_Total Sales − Returns_		3,817
Gross profit on sales			$ 8,184
	Net Sales − Cost of Goods Sold		
Operating expenses:	Salaries and wages	$6,400	
	Delivery expenses	100	
	Rent	900	
	Advertising	75	
	Utilities	120	
	Supplies	50	
	Depreciation	150	
	Insurance	210	
	Miscellaneous	42	
	Total operating expenses		$ 8,047
	Gross Profit − Total Operating Expenses		
Net income			$ 137

12174 − 173 = 12001 − 3817 = 8184 6400 + 100

+ 900 + 75 + 120 + 50 + 150 + 210 + 42 =

8047 M+ 8184 − RM 8047 = 137

1. a. ($95,000 −
$3,500) −
$30,000 =
$61,500
b. $61,500 −
$34,700 =
$26,800

2. a. ($475,000 −
$7,500) −
$178,500 =
$289,000
b. $289,000 −
$105,400 =
$183,600

(SELF-CHECK✔)

CONCEPT CHECK

Complete the problems, then check your answers at the end of the chapter.

1. Sales: $95,000.
   Returned merchandise: $3,500.
   Cost of goods sold: $30,000.
   Total operating expenses: $34,700.
   a. Find the gross profit on sales.
   b. Find the net income.

2. Sales: $475,000.
   Returned merchandise: $7,500.
   Cost of goods sold: $178,500.
   Total operating expenses: $105,400.
   a. Find the gross profit on sales.
   b. Find the net income.

3. a. $4,685

4. a. $34,780
   b. $23,605
   c. $4,705

5. a. $3,675
   b. $1,935
   c. $1,107

6. a. $174,945
   b. $118,195
   c. $76,002

7. a. $673,642
   b. $255,726
   c. $159,307

SECTION 21-4 PRACTICE

Complete the table.

	Total Sales	Returns	Net Sales	Cost of Goods Sold	Gross Profit	Operating Expenses	Net Income
3.	$ 14,700	$ 540	$14,160	$ 8,750	$5,410	$ 725	a.
4.	38,900	4,120	a.	11,175	b.	18,900	c.
5.	3,750	75	a.	1,740	b.	828	c.
6.	174,945	0	d.	56,750	b.	42,193	c.
7.	674,916	1,274	a.	417,916	b.	96,419	c.

Continued on next page

THINKING CRITICALLY

Use the income statement to answer the questions.

1. How much did Gravity X pay for the bikes it sold? **$109,614**
2. How much was the gross profit for the year? **$102,401**
4. How much were total operating expenses? **$42,166**
5. Which operating expense was the most costly? **Salaries**
6. How much net income was earned during the year? **$60,235**

Income Statement for the Year Ended

Income:	
Net Sales	$212,015
Cost of Goods Sold	109,614
Gross Profit	$?
Operating Expenses:	
Salaries	$ 24,019
Rent	11,211
Utilities	4,514
Advertising	2,422
Total Operating Expenses	$_____
Net Income from Operations	$_____

(2) **TEACH**

Students should already be familiar with sales, markup, and net profit from Chapter 16. You may want to review these terms. Remind students that businesses sell items for more than they purchase them in order to make a profit. In Example 1 on pages 666 and 667 point out that the sales totaled $12,174, but they only paid $3,817 for the merchandise.

Sometimes customers return merchandise. Any returns during a period must be subtracted from the total sales. Ask students if they have ever returned something to a store. **Point out that when an item is returned, the store has already recorded the sale. Now the store must record the return by subtracting, the price paid for the item from its total sales.**

Motivating the Lesson
Have students work in groups. Give each group an income statement that you have prepared or one from an annual report of a business. Ask students to find the net sales, cost of goods sold, gross profit, total operating expenses, and net income. **Answers will vary.**

In-Class Examples
Find the gross profit on sales and the net income.

1. Sales: $6,000.
   Returned merchandise: $80.
   Cost of goods sold: $1,600.
   Total operating expenses: $950. **$4,320; $3,370**
2. Sales: $14,500.
   Returned merchandise: $560.
   Cost of goods sold: $4,850.
   Total operating expenses: $2,075. **$9,090; $7,015**
3. Sales: $145,718.
   Returned merchandise: $1,567.
   Cost of goods sold: $60,461.
   Total operating expenses: $5,092. **$83,690; $78,598**

667

 ASSESS

Error Analysis

Remind students that gross profit does not necessarily mean that a company is making money. The gross profit is determined by subtracting the cost of goods sold from the net sales. To determine if a business is making money, the operating expenses of a business cannot exceed the gross profit. Students should already be familiar with some types of operating expenses from Chapter 19.

4 CLOSE

Closing Activity

Find the gross profit on sales and the net income.

1. Sales: $12,000.
   Returned merchandise: $450.
   Cost of goods sold: $4,500.
   Total operating expenses:
   $895. **$7,050; $6,155**

2. Sunrise Windows prepares a monthly income statement. For this past month, the company made $35,750 with installations of windows that cost the company $5,950. It had $280 in allowances for jobs that had to be redone. Wages totaled $5,500, supplies were $910, and other operating expenses totaled $230. Prepare an income statement for the month.

Sunrise Windows Income Statement

Income:	
Sales...........................	$35,750
Less: allowances	280
Net sales	$35,470
Cost of goods sold	5,950
Gross profit on sales....	$29,520
Operating expenses:	
Wages.......................	$5,500
Supplies	910
Other expenses	230
Total operating expenses:	6,640
Net income:................	$22,880

668

Complete the income statements.

8. Income:

Sales		$47,890
Less: Sales returns and allowances		976
Net sales	a.	**$46,914**
Cost of goods sold		21,742
Gross profit on sales	b.	**$25,172**
Operating expenses: Salaries and wages		8,500
Taxes		497
Utilities		235
Depreciation		975
Total operating expenses	c.	**$10,207**
Net income	d.	**$14,965**

9. Income:

Sales		$463,575
Less: Sales returns and allowances		75,450
Net sales	a.	**$388,125**
Cost of goods sold		231,000
Gross profit on sales	b.	**$157,125**
Operating expenses: Total operating expenses		71,916
Net income	c.	**$ 85,209**

Prepare an income statement for each business in Problems 10–13.

10. **Net sales: $8,876; Gross profit: $3,259; Net income: $2,541**

10. Last month Clarita's Costume Jewelry kiosk at the mall had total sales of $8,961. Merchandise totaling $85 was returned. The goods that were sold cost Clarita's $5,617. Operating expenses for the month were $718.

11. **Net sales: $3,080; Gross profit: $3,080; Total operating expenses: $2,209; Net income: $871**

11. Advantage Housekeeping Service prepares a monthly income statement. For this past month, it collected $3,150 from homeowners for services provided (sales). It had $70 in allowances for jobs that had to be redone. Salaries and wages totaled $1,800, supplies cost $315 and other operating expenses totaled $94.

12. **Net sales: $27,198; Gross profit: $18,005; Total operating expenses: $4,320; Net income: $13,685**

12. During the past quarter, Henri's Clothes Company had total sales of $27,418 and returns of $220. The cost of goods sold amounted to $9,193. Operating expenses for the quarter included salaries and wages of $2,000, a real estate loan payment of $1,210, advertising at $190, utilities and supplies of $195, a bank loan payment of $350, and other operating expenses of $375.

13. **Gross profit: $58.3 million; Total operating expenses: $38.7 million; Net income: $19.6 million**

13. Hi-Tech Aluminum Company prepares an annual income statement for distribution to its stockholders. This past year net sales totaled $121.4 million. Cost of goods sold totaled $63.1 million. Operating expenses included wages and salaries of $23.4 million, depreciation and amortization of $3.3 million, general taxes of $1.1 million, interest paid totaling $1.0 million, income taxes of $8.7 million, and miscellaneous operating expenses of $1.2 million.

MAINTAINING YOUR SKILLS

Need Help? Go to...
- Skill 5: Adding Decimals, page 732
- Skill 6: Subtracting Decimals, page 733

Add.

14.	$567.56		15.	$ 18,516.50
	74.92			8,743.91
	+ 123.74			+ 191,434.84
	$766.22			$218,695.25

Subtract.

16.	$174.93		17.	$746.90
	− 84.79			− 291.84
	$90.14			$455.06

WRAP-UP

Go over any problem for which a wrong answer is given.

Assignment Guide
Basic: 3–7
Average: 8–9

20 min.

SECTION 21-5 Vertical Analysis

○ **Section Objective**

Analyze balance sheets and income statements.

Your business may analyze its income statement by finding what percent any given item is of the net sales. Your business may analyze its balance sheet by finding certain defined ratios. The **current ratio** is the ratio of total assets to total liabilities. The **quick ratio**, sometimes called the *acid-test ratio*, is the ratio of total assets minus inventory to total liabilities. Remember that:

Important Questions to Ask Yourself	What Formula Do I Use?
How do I find the **percent of net sales?**	$\text{Percent of Net Sales} = \dfrac{\text{Amount for Item}}{\text{Net Sales}}$
How do I compute the **current ratio?**	$\text{Current Ratio} = \dfrac{\text{Total Assets}}{\text{Total Liabilities}}$
How do I find the **quick ratio?**	$\text{Quick Ratio} = \dfrac{\text{Total Assets} - \text{Inventory}}{\text{Total Liabilities}}$

Living in the Real World

Jojoba Healing

A Quick Test   Lakes sits down to analyze her latest balance sheet. She first applies the current ratio, which tells her the ratio of total assets to total liabilities. The figure shows a good fiscal position. Lakes then decides to apply the quick ratio, or "acid test ratio," which indicates her liquid fiscal position.

Draw Conclusions   What is the formula for the "acid test ratio"?

Continued on page 672

(**Example 1**)

Tina and John Agee, from Example 1 in Section 21-4, analyze their income statement for the quarter. The statement shows:

Income:	Sales	$12,174
	Less: Sales returns and allowances	173
	Net sales	$12,001
Cost of goods sold		3,817
Gross profit on sales		$ 8,184

To the nearest tenth percent, what is the gross profit as a percent of net sales?

STEP: Find the percent of net sales.

Gross Profit ÷ Net Sales

$8,184   ÷ $12,001   − **0.6819 or 68.2% of net sales**

8184 ÷ 12001 = 0.681943171

Section 21-5 Vertical Analysis ▶ **669**

Living in the Real World

The ratio of total assets minus inventory to total liabilities.

COOPERATIVE LEARNING

Percent of Net Sales
Students work in pairs to answer the following questions: In Example 1, suppose that the Agees found that their "returns and allowances" were 40 percent of net sales. What conclusions could they reach about their merchandise? What course of action would you recommend? **Possible answers: Merchandise is defective, or otherwise unsatisfactory. Check merchandise before putting it out for sale or find another supplier.**

National Standards for Business Education

Standard 1	Mathematical Foundations
Standard 2	Number Relationships and Operations
Standard 5	Problem-Solving Applications

National Council of Teachers of Mathematics Standards

Standard 1	Numbers and Operations
Standard 6	Problem Solving
Standard 8	Communication

① FOCUS

Businesses often analyze income statements. In this section students will learn three ways to analyze income statements.

In-Class Examples
Work through these exercises with students before having them do the Self-Check.
1. 20,000 ÷ 16,000 **1.25**
2. 246,456 ÷ 102,442 **2.41**
3. $56,750 is what percent of $609,450? **9.3%**

② TEACH

As you review the formula for finding the percent of net sales, point out that the items can be sales returns, the cost of goods sold, wages, or gross profit. Emphasize that a business wants to keep the sales returns and cost of goods sold as low as possible.

Motivating the Lesson
A company has total assets of $100,000, an inventory of $21,000, and total liabilities of $70,500. Find each of the following.

Total assets ÷ Total liabilities **1.4**
(Total assets − Inventory) ÷ Total liabilities **1.1**

In-Class Examples
1. What are the sales returns as a percent of net sales for a business that has sales returns of $590 and net sales of $10,650? **5.5%**
2. What is the cost of goods sold as a percent of net sales for a business with net sales of of $2,935 and cost of goods sold of $540? **18.4%**
3. What is the quick ratio for a business that has total assets of $128,000, inventory of $60,000, and total liabilities of $49,000? **1.4 : 1**

CONCEPT CHECK

 SELF-CHECK✓

Complete the problems, then check your answers at the end of the chapter.

1. Sales returns: $173.
   Net sales: $12,001.
   What are the sales returns as a percent of net sales?
   $173 ÷ $12,001 = 0.0144 or 1.4%

2. Cost of goods sold: $17,847.80.
   Net sales: $34,908.89.
   What is the cost of goods sold as a percent of net sales?
   $17,847.80 ÷ $34,908.89 = 0.5112 or 51.1%

Example 2

The Agees analyze their May 21 balance sheet. The balance sheet shows:

Assets		Liabilities	
Cash	$60,000	Notes payable	$25,000
Merchandise inventory	23,000	Accounts payable	18,000
Supplies	10,000	Total liabilities	$33,000
Total assets	$93,000		

		Owner's Equity	
		Capital	$60,000
		Total liabilities and owner's equity	$93,000

What are the current ratio and the quick ratio?

STEP 1: Find the current ratio.

Total Assets ÷ Total Liabilities
$93,000 ÷ $33,000
= **2.818 or 2.8 to 1 or 2.8:1 current ratio**

This means that the Agees' total assets are 2.8 times their total liabilities. This is a good fiscal position. A current ratio of at least 2 to 1 is considered good.

STEP 2: Find the quick ratio.

(Total Assets − Inventory) ÷ Total Liabilities
($93,000 − $23,000) ÷ $33,000
= **2.12 or 2.1 to 1 or 2.1:1 quick ratio**

This means that the Agees' quick assets (liquid or quickly converted to cash) are 2.1 times their total liabilities. This is a very good fiscal position. A quick ratio of at least 1 to 1 is considered good.

CONCEPT CHECK

 SELF-CHECK✓

Complete the problems, then check your answers at the end of the chapter.

3. Total assets: $50,000.
   Total liabilities: $30,000.
   Find the current ratio.
   $50,000 ÷ $30,000 = 1.6666 or 1.67:1

4. Total assets: $56,000.
   Inventory: $16,500.
   Total liabilities: $30,000.
   Find the quick ratio.
   ($56,000 ÷ $16,500) ÷ $30,000 = 1.3333 or 1.33:1

USING CALCULATORS

Many calculators, such as a graphing calculator, display the entire expression as it is being entered. Some symbols displayed are not the same as the symbol entered. Multiplication and division are examples of this. The ✗ will often display a ∗ and the ÷ will often display a / .

ALTERNATIVE ASSESSMENT

Learning by Questioning
For many people, asking questions is often the best way to learn. Students practice creating questions by writing the following prompts at the top of separate pieces of paper: what, where, when, how, why, and who. Groups generate as many questions as they can about the information in this section. Lead a class discussion to answer a sample of the questions. **LS** , **CL**

SECTION 21-5 PRACTICE

Round answers to the nearest tenth of a percent.

	Item	Amount for Item	÷	Net Sales	=	Percent of Net Sales
5.	Cost of goods sold	$20,000	÷	$40,000	=	**50.0%**
6.	Operating expenses	12,500	÷	40,000	=	**31.3%**
7.	Net income	17,800	÷	40,000	=	**44.5%**

Find the ratios to the nearest tenth.

	Total Assets	Inventory	Total Liabilities	Current Ratio	Quick Ratio
8.	$ 78,500	$ 37,250	$ 40,000	a. **2.0:1.0**	b. **1.0:1.0**
9.	325,800	134,600	163,200	a. **2.0:1.0**	b. **1.2:1.0**
10.	4,897	995	2,750	a. **1.8:1.0**	b. **1.4:1.0**

11. Manny's Clothiers' income statement for one month showed these figures:

    Net sales $7,690
    Cost of goods sold   4,137
    a. Gross profit on sales   **$3,553**
    b. What is the gross profit on sales as a percent of net sales? **46.2%**

12. The income statement for one quarter for Music & Video Land showed these figures:

    Net sales $27,196
    Cost of goods sold   13,100
    a. Gross profit on sales   **$14,096**
    Total operating expenses $12,195
    b. Net income   **$ 1,901**
    c. What is the cost of goods sold as a percent of net sales? **48.2%**
    d. What is the gross profit on sales as a percent of net sales? **51.8%**
    e. What are the total operating expenses as a percent of net sales? **44.8%**
    f. What is the net income as a percent of net sales? **7.0%**

13. Use the balance sheet for Howard's Jewelers, dated June 30, from Problem 9, Figure 21.2 in Section 21-2 on page 662.
    a. Find the current ratio. **1.6:1.0**
    b. Find the quick ratio. **1.3:1.0**

MAINTAINING YOUR SKILLS

Find the rate. Round answers to the nearest tenth of a percent.

14. $n\%$ of 495 = 45 **9.1%**   15. $n\%$ of 120 = 30 **25%**

Write as ratios with a denominator of 1. Round answers to the nearest tenth.

16. $174:$94 **1.9:1.0**   17. $74.90:$76.40 **1.0:1.0**

Need Help? Go to...
- Skill 31: Finding the Rate, page 758
- Skill 22: Writing Ratios, page 749

3 ASSESS

Error Analysis

Students may confuse the formulas for current ratio and quick ratio. Review the formulas thoroughly. **Point out that the quick ratio formula takes into account the inventory of a business. The quick ratio shows a business's quick assets as they relate to its total liabilities whereas a current ratio shows a business's total assets as they relate to its total liabilities.**

4 CLOSE

Closing Activity

1. What are the sales returns as a percent of net sales for a business that has sales returns of $1,270 and net sales of $38,960? **3.3%**

2. What is the cost of goods sold as a percent of net sales for a business with net sales of $56,420 and cost of goods sold of $14,876? **26.4%**

3. What is the current ratio for a business that has total assets of $135,338 and total liabilities of $91,067? **1.5 : 1**

4. What is the quick ratio for a business that has total assets of $282,500, inventory of $78,475, and total liabilities of $89,298? **2.3 : 1**

WRAP-UP

Go over any problem for which a wrong answer is given.

Assignment Guide
    Basic: 5–7
Average: 8–10

20 min.

SECTION (21-6) **Horizontal Analysis**

National Standards for Business Education

Standard 1	Mathematical Foundations
Standard 2	Number Relationships and Operations
Standard 5	Problem-Solving Applications

National Council of Teachers of Mathematics Standards

Standard 1	Numbers and Operations
Standard 6	Problem Solving
Standard 8	Communication

1 FOCUS

Since an income statement only gives the financial picture of a business for a specific accounting period, businesses have multiple income statements over time. These statements can be compared to see whether or not the business is improving.

In-Class Examples

Work through these exercises with students before having them do the Self-Check.

1. $74,000 − $68,500 **$5,500**
2. $245,672 − $245,587 **$85**
3. What percent of $108,355 is $110,522.10? **102%**

2 TEACH

Have students discuss why they think percents are used to represent change from one income statement to another. Point out that percents are helpful to compare when you are looking at several income statements.

○ **Section Objective**

Compare two income statements using horizontal analysis, and compute the percent change.

Horizontal analysis is the comparison of two or more income statements for different periods. The comparison is done by computing percent changes from one income statement to another. When computing percent change, the dollar amount on the earlier statement is the **base figure**. The **amount of change** is the difference between the base figure and the corresponding figure on the current statement. If the amount for an item decreases from one income statement to the next, both the amount of change and the percent change are negative. Remember that:

$$\text{Percent Change} = \frac{\text{Amount of Change}}{\text{Base Figure}}$$

Living in the Real World

Jojoba Healing

Compare the Statements   Finally, Lakes decides to calculate the difference between the income statements from the last two quarters. This will tell her the percent of change from the first to the second quarter. Since she showed a loss for the first quarter and a profit for the second, she knows the business is getting stronger.

Draw Conclusions   In order to determine how much Jojoba Healing has improved, what must Lakes analyze?

Continued on page 675

Example 1

The Agees prepare a second income statement and compare it to the one for the previous quarter. To the nearest tenth of a percent, what is the percent change for each item?

STEP: Find the percent change for each item. $\dfrac{\text{Amount of Change}}{\text{Base Figure}}$

Figure 21.5

1. ($15,000 − $12,000)
   $3,000 ÷ $12,000
   = 0.25 or 25.0%
2. ($50,000 − $70,000)
   −$20,000 ÷ $70,000 = −0.2857
   or −28.6%

	Last Quarter (Base)	This Quarter	Amount of Change	Percent Change
Net sales	$12,001	$13,174	$1,173	9.8%
Cost of goods sold	3,817	4,190	373	9.8%
Gross profit on sales	8,184	8,984	800	9.8%
Operating expenses	8,047	7,995	−52	−0.6%
Net income	137	989	852	621.9%

Current Figure − Base Figure

Operating expenses decreased. Change is negative.

The Agees' net income increased by 621.9%.

SELF-CHECK ✓

CONCEPT CHECK

Complete the problems, then check your answers at the end of the chapter. Find the percent change from last quarter to this quarter to the nearest tenth percent.

1. Last quarter: $12,000
   This quarter: $15,000
2. Last quarter: $70,000
   This quarter: $50,000

Living in the Real World

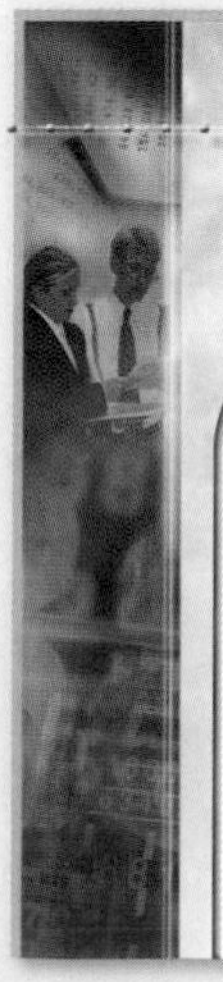

Comparing income statements from previous quarters will outline the growth of Jojoba Healing.

THINKING CRITICALLY

Percent Change
Find the percent change by completing this table.

	Before	After	Amount of Change	Percent Change
1.	$ 37,500	$ 39,480	$ 1,980	5.28%
2.	275,684	312,739	37,055	13.44%
3.	14.5 mil	15.3 mil	0.8 mil	5.52%

SECTION 21-6 PRACTICE

Round to the nearest tenth of a percent.

	Last Year (Base)	This Year	Amount of Change		Percent Change
3.	$720,000	$830,000	$110,000	**a.**	15.3%
4.	45,000	36,000	−9,000	**a.**	−20.0%
5.	114,750	137,840	**a.** $23,090	**b.**	20.1%

6. Last year net sales were $150,000. This year net sales are $210,000.
   a. What is the amount of change?
   b. What is the percent change?
   a. $60,000; b. 40.0%

7. Last week cost of goods sold was $4,650. This week cost of goods sold is $3,875.
   a. What is the amount of change?
   b. What is the percent change?
   a. −$775; b. −16.7%

8. Last year net sales were $400,000. This year net sales are $600,000.
   a. What is the amount of change?
   b. What is the percent change?
   a. $200,000; b. 50.0%

9. Last month net income was $42,476. This month net income is $51,419.
   a. What is the amount of change?
   b. What is the percent change?
   a. $8,943; b. 21.1%

10. Income statements for Clarita's Costume Jewelry kiosk at the mall showed these figures for March and April. Find the amount of change and the percent change.

		March	April	Amount of Change		Percent Change
a.	Net sales	$8,876	$9,172	**a.** $296	**b.**	3.3%
b.	Cost of goods sold	5,617	5,904	**a.** $287	**b.**	5.1%
c.	Gross profit on sales	3,259	3,268	**a.** $9	**b.**	0.3%
d.	Operating expenses	718	700	**a.** −$18	**b.**	−2.5%
e.	Net income	2,541	2,568	**a.** $27	**b.**	1.1%

11. Income statements for Wholesale Grocer Supply Company showed the following figures. Find the amount of change and the percent change.

		Last Year (thousands)	This Year (thousands)	Amount of Change (thousands)		Percent Change
a.	Net sales	$117.4	$109.9	**a.** −$7.5	**b.**	−6.4%
b.	Cost of goods sold	56.9	54.7	**a.** −$2.2	**b.**	−3.9%
c.	Gross profit on sales	60.5	55.2	**a.** −$5.3	**b.**	−8.8%
d.	Operating expenses	35.7	36.2	**a.** $0.5	**b.**	1.4%
e.	Net income	24.8	19.0	**a.** −$5.8	**b.**	−23.4%

MAINTAINING YOUR SKILLS

Need Help? Go to...
➤ **Skill 31: Finding the Rate,** page 758

Find the rate. Round answers to the nearest tenth of a percent.

12. $n\%$ of 95 = 19   **20.0%**

13. $n\%$ of 74 − 37   **50.0%**

14. $n\%$ of 1,450 = 974   **67.2%**

15. $n\%$ of $14,176 = $4,193   **29.6%**

Section 21-6 Horizontal Analysis ▶ **673**

COMMUNICATION SKILLS

List
Students compile a list of all the possible reasons they can find for why changes occur from one accounting period to another for each of these items: (1) net sales, (2) cost of goods sold, (3) operating expenses, and (4) net income. **Some reasons are inflation, seasonal sales, global influence on the market, change in utility bills, higher wages.**

WRAP-UP

Go over any problem for which a wrong answer is given.

Assignment Guide
  Basic: 3–5
  Average: 6–9

20 min.

To find the amount of change, students must subtract the earlier figure from the later figure. For example, if last year's figure is $50,000 and this year's figure is $55,000, students should subtract $50,000 from $55,000. The result is $5,000, which is an increase. Since some of the amounts of change in this section are negative, students may confuse the order of the subtraction and, in this case, get a result of −$5,000. Encourage students to identify whether the figure has increased or decreased by just looking at the figures first. If there is an increase, students will know the answer will be positive. If there is a decrease, students will know the answer will be negative.

In-Class Examples
Find the percentage change from last quarter to this quarter to the nearest tenth percent.
1. Last quarter: $8,000.
   This quarter: $9,000. **12.5%**
2. Last quarter: $79,342.
   This quarter: $67,993. **−14.3%**

3 **ASSESS**

Error Analysis
Remind students about negative numbers. Have students practice subtracting numbers whose difference is negative. Students may not be familiar with negative percents. Explain to students that if the amount of change is negative, then the percent change will also be negative. Give students some exercises to practice.

4 **CLOSE**

Closing Activity
1. Last year, the net sales for Holiday Express were $140,270. This year the net sales are $138,395. What is the amount of change? What is the percent change? **−$1,875; −1.3%**

673

Quick Quiz

1. Ren's Laundry has $8,000 in cash, $5,000 in supplies, and $50,000 in equipment. The business owes $8,000 in taxes. **($63,000)** What are the total assets? What are the total liabilities? **($8,000)** What is the owner's equity? **$55,000**

2. Eventime Electronics has $60,000 in cash and $145,000 in merchandise. They have a bank loan of $156,000. What is the owner's equity? **$49,000**

3. Find the cost of goods sold for a business that has a beginning inventory of $35,000, receipts of $13,000, and an ending inventory of $37,000. **$11,000**

4. Johnson Supply had sales of $14,000 returned merchandise of $380 during one month. The cost of goods sold was $3,000 and the operating expenses were $1,600. Find the gross profit on sales and the net income. **$10,620; $9,020**

5. What is the quick ratio for a business that has total assets of $256,000, inventory of $40,000, and total liabilities of $135,000? **1.6 : 1**

CHAPTER 21 Self-Check Answers

SECTION 21-1 CONCEPT CHECK (p. 659)

1. $82,000 + $50,000 = **$132,000**
2. ($18,000 + $49,000) − $25,000 = **$42,000**

SECTION 21-2 CONCEPT CHECK (p. 661)

1. Sum of assets is **$67,000.**
2. Sum of total liabilities and owner's equity is **$67,000.**

SECTION 21-3 CONCEPT CHECK (p. 664)

1. $156,470 + $21,960 − $161,510 = **$16,920**
2. $43,656 + $11,712 − $42,964 = **$12,404**

SECTION 21-4 CONCEPT CHECK (p. 667)

1. a. ($95,000 − $3,500) − $30,000 = **$61,500**
   b. $61,500 − $34,700 = **$26,800**
2. a. ($475,000 − $7,500) − $178,500 = **$289,000**
   b. $289,000 − $105,400 = **$183,600**

SECTION 21-5 CONCEPT CHECK (p. 670)

1. $173 ÷ $12,001 = **0.0144 or 1.4%**
2. $17,847.80 ÷ $34,908.89 = **0.5112 or 51.1%**
3. $50,000 ÷ $30,000 = **1.6666 or 1.67:1**
4. ($56,000 ÷ $16,500) ÷ $30,000 = **1.3333 or 1.33:1**

SECTION 21-6 CONCEPT CHECK (p. 672)

1. ($15,000 − $12,000)
   $3,000 ÷ $12,000 = **0.25 or 25.0%**
2. ($50,000 − $70,000)
   −$20,000 ÷ $70,000 = **−0.2857 or −28.6%**

Living in the Real World

Jojoba Healing

Applying Your Knowledge   As it turns out, Jojoba Healing has achieved an 11.7 percent increase in net profit during the last two quarters. Lakes feels satisfied that her young business is on the upswing and is confident that she can convince the bank to help her achieve her dreams of building a new facility.

1 **Investigate.** What type of job do you have now or want? Is it in the field you might continue to work in?

2 **Creative Thinking.** Imagine yourself in five years. What type of job do you want? Where are you living? What skills are you using?

3 **Observe.** Look at other people—your family, friends, co-workers, and so on. Do any of them have a career that you might enjoy? What skills would you need for this career? Do your dreams revolve around a career?

Living in the Real World

1. Students can go to the *Mathematics with Business Applications* Web site and click on Career City on the Student side. Ask students to take the Self-Assessment quizzes and inventories to get a better sense of their direction in life.
2. Answers will vary. Be sure to ask students, and make them answer this one question: What would you do in life if you knew you couldn't fail? Discuss their responses and dreams. Be incredibly encouraging.
3. Answers will vary. Encourage students to job shadow people with careers they might want to pursue.

REVIEW OF KEY WORDS

assets (p. 658)
liabilities (p. 658)
owner's equity (p. 658)
net worth (p. 658)
capital (p. 658)
balance sheet (p. 660)

cost of goods sold (p. 663)
income statement (p. 666)
profit-and-loss statement (p. 666)
net income (p. 666)
net profit (p. 666)

current ratio (p. 669)
quick ratio (p. 669)
horizontal analysis (p. 672)
base figure (p. 672)
amount of change (p. 672)

Match one of the key words above with a definition below.

1. shows your sales, operating expenses, and net profit or loss; also called profit-and-loss statement. **income statement**
2. the difference between your assets and liabilities; also called net worth or capital.
3. is negative if the amount decreases from one income statement to the next. **amount of change**
4. shows your assets, liabilities, and owner's equity. **balance sheet**
5. the total of your cash, the items that you have purchased, and any money that customers owe you. **assets**

6. the ratio of total assets to total liabilities.
7. the ratio of total assets minus inventory to total liabilities. **quick ratio**
8. the total amount of money you owe your creditors. **liabilities**
9. is the beginning inventory plus receipts minus the ending inventory.
10. a comparison of two or more income statements from different periods.
horizontal analysis

2. **owner's equity**

6. **current ratio**   9. **cost of goods sold**

Skills and Concepts

SECTION OBJECTIVE 21-1 AND EXAMPLES

Compute the total assets, liabilities, and owner's equity.

Philip Lawson starts Yellow Jackets by putting in $30,000 of his own money. Yellow Jackets is a retail outlet for outdoor hunting gear. Lawson obtains a bank loan of $100,000, of which $75,000 was used to purchase inventory. Store fixtures cost $10,000, which he did not pay for immediately. What was Lawson's owner's equity?

Assets:			Liabilities:		
Cash ($30,000 + $100,000) − $75,000	=	$ 55,000	Bank Loan	=	$100,000
Inventory	=	75,000	Unpaid Fixtures	=	10,000
Store Fixtures	=	10,000	Total Liabilities	=	**$110,000**
Total Assets:	=	**$140,000**			

Owner's Equity:

Total Assets − Total Liabilities

$140,000 − $110,000 = **$30,000**

REVIEW EXERCISES
Complete the table.

	Liabilities	+	Owner's Equity	=	Assets
11.	$17,844	+	$29,300	=	**$47,144**
12.	**$85,444**	+	36,500	=	$121,944
13.	9,230	+	**$32,870**	=	42,100
14.	**$18,692**	+	74,508	=	93,200
15.	32,190	+	64,310	=	**$96,500**
16.	21,390	+	**$4,108**	=	25,498

SECTION OBJECTIVE 21-2 AND EXAMPLES

Calculate a balance sheet.

Prepare a balance sheet for Yellow Jackets based on the information above.

STEP: Prepare a balance sheet.

Balance Sheet				
Yellow Jackets				March 15
Assets		**Liabilities**		
Cash	$ 55,000	Notes payable	$ 10,000	
Inventory	75,000	Bank loan	100,000	
Store fixtures	10,000	Total liabilities		$110,000
		Owner's Equity		
		Capital		30,000
Total assets	$140,000	Total liabilities and owner's equity		$140,000

REINFORCEMENT

Section 21-1

1. Find the assets.
   Liabilities: $128,500.
   Owner's equity: $205,750. **$334,250**
2. Find the liabilities.
   Assets: $235,895.
   Owner's equity: $104,563. **$131,332**

Section 21-2

1. Find the total assets, total liabilities, and owner's equity. Cash: $178,398.
   Merchandise: $987,200.
   Building: $675,230.
   Bank loan: $275,675.
   Taxes owed: $25,000. **$1,840,828; $300,675; $1,540,153**

17. a. $132,800; b. $113,400; c. $19,400
18. a. $50,232; b. $14,200; c. $36,032
19. a. $287,954; b. $5,600; c. $216,200

REVIEW EXERCISES
Complete the table.

20. a. $146,640; b. $11,030; c. $56,630
21. a. $113,192; b. $56,890; c. $68,390

	Cash	Inventory	Supplies	Total Assets	Bank Loan	Taxes Owed	Total Liabilities	Owner's Equity
17.	$ 11,500.00	$117,000.00	$ 4,300.00	a.	$100,000.00	$13,400.00	b.	c.
18.	32,400.00	9,432.00	8,400.00	a.	10,300.00	3,900.00	b.	c.
19.	109,864.00	156,790.00	21,300.00	a.	210,600.00	b.	c.	$71,754.00
20.	36,540.00	89,500.00	20,600.00	a.	45,600.00	b.	c.	90,010.00
21.	78,302.00	21,400.00	13,490.00	a.	b.	11,500.00	c.	44,802.00
22.	5,311.00	13,200.00	2,190.00	a.	b.	894.34	c.	9,806.68
23.	54,210.00	123,908.00	3,219.10	a.	b.	983.21	c.	99,853.21

22. a. $20,701; b. $9,999.98; c. $10,894.32
23. a. $181,337.10; b. $80,500.68; c. $81,483.89

SECTION OBJECTIVE 21-3 AND EXAMPLES

Figure out the cost of goods sold.

The Cat's Meow began the month with an inventory valued at $13,400. During the month it received merchandise valued at $3,200. The ending inventory was valued at $12,300. What was the cost of goods sold?

STEP: Find the cost of goods sold.

(Beginning Inventory + Receipts) − Ending Inventory
($13,400   + $3,200) − $12,300

= $4,300 cost of goods sold

REVIEW EXERCISES
Find the cost of goods sold.

	Beginning Inventory	Receipts	Ending Inventory	Cost of Goods Sold
24.	$183,204.00	$ 48,650.00	$ 90,431.00	**$141,423**
25.	104,588.00	132,005.00	100,459.00	**$136,134**
26.	85,430.32	34,509.56	100,231.96	**$19,707.92**
27.	73,210.11	3,490.65	32,985.66	**$43,715.10**
28.	5,490.86	21,390.86	3,490.35	**$23,391.37**
29.	45,796.23	61,209.58	21,890.91	**$85,114.90**

REINFORCEMENT

Section 21-3
1. Find the cost of goods sold.
   Beginning inventory: $126,997.
   Receipts: $67,340.
   Ending inventory: $131,805. **$62,532**

SECTION OBJECTIVE 21-4 AND EXAMPLES

Complete an income statement.

One month after Youssef Weston opened his music store, he prepared an income statement. Sales for the year totaled $67,540.32; merchandise totaling $1,200.00 was returned to him. Weston's inventory records show that the goods he sold cost him $29,304.86. Records show his operating expenses totaled $18,002.29. What is the net income?

STEP: Find the net income.

Gross Profit = Net Sales − Cost of Goods Sold
Net Income = Gross Profit − Total Operating Expenses

Income Statement

Youssef Weston's Music Store		For the Month Ending June 30	
Income:	Sales	$67,540.32	
	Less: Sales returns and allowances	1,200.00	
	Net sales		$66,340.32
Cost of goods sold			29,304.86
Gross profit on sales			$37,035.46
Operating expenses:	Total operating expenses		$18,002.29
Net income			$19,033.17

REVIEW EXERCISES
Complete the table.

	Total Sales	Returns	Net Sales	Cost of Goods Sold	Gross Profit	Operating Expenses	Net Income
30.	$ 21,905.00	$ 1,207.63	a.	$ 6,509.38	b.	$ 12,309.00	c.
31.	39,650.00	3,400.00	a.	8,540.20	b.	18,500.00	c.
32.	54,201.11	8,430.38	a.	18,409.43	b.	21,200.00	c.
33.	89,500.32	5,490.43	a.	15,900.34	b.	41,200.00	c.
34.	981,309.22	22,309.56	a.	431,098.99	b.	128,504.00	c.
35.	45,902.46	7,509.43	a.	21,209.31	b.	16,430.97	c.

30. a. $20,697.37
b. $14,187.99
c. $1,878.99

31. a. $36,250
b. $27,709.80
c. $9,209.80

32. a. $45,770.73
b. $27,361.30
c. $6,161.30

33. a. $84,009.89
b. $68,109.55
c. $26,909.55

34. a. $958,999.66
b. $527,900.67
c. $399,396.67

35. a. $38,393.03
b. $17,183.72
c. $752.75

REINFORCEMENT

Section 21-4
1. Find the gross profit on sales and the net income.
   Sales: $39,745.
   Returned merchandise: $1,025.
   Cost of goods sold: $19,046.
   Total operating expenses: $3,429. **$19,674; $16,245**

SECTION OBJECTIVE 21-5 AND EXAMPLES

Analyze balance sheets and income statements.

Look back at Youssef Weston's Music Shop's income statement in Section 21-4. To the nearest tenth percent, the total operating expenses are what percent of net sales?

STEP: Find the percent of net sales.

$$\frac{\text{Amount for Item}}{\text{Net Sales}} = \frac{\$18,002.29}{\$66,340.32} = 0.2713 \text{ or } 27.1\% \text{ net sales}$$

REVIEW EXERCISES

Find the current ratio and the quick ratio.

	Total Assets	Inventory	Total Liabilities	Current Ratio		Quick Ratio	
36.	$154,900.00	$32,900.00	$84,300.00	a.	1.8:1	b.	1.4:1
37.	75,400.00	11,900.00	43,400.00	a.	1.7:1	b.	1.5:1
38.	101,409.00	84,500.00	56,430.00	a.	1.8:1	b.	0.3:1
39.	219,549.33	39,843.29	98,459.44	a.	2.2:1	b.	1.8:1
40.	56,903.44	11,290.56	8,905.68	a.	6.4:1	b.	5.1:1

SECTION OBJECTIVE 21-6 AND EXAMPLES

Compare two income statements using horizontal analysis, and compute the percent change.

Last year's net sales were $129,569. This year's net sales are $199,540. What is the amount of change? What is the percent change?

STEP 1: Find the amount of change. $199,540 - \$129,569 = \$69,971$ amount of change

STEP 2: Find the percent change.

$$\frac{\text{Amount of Change}}{\text{Base Figure}} = \frac{\$69,971}{\$129,569} = 0.5400 \text{ or } 54\% \text{ change}$$

REVIEW EXERCISES

Find the amount of change and the percent of change.

	Last Year (Base)	This Year	Amount of Change		Percent Change	
41.	$ 560,900.00	$ 689,000.00	a.	$128,100	b.	22.8%
42.	465,030.00	398,400.00	a.	−$66,630	b.	−14.3%
43.	109,569.00	176,500.00	a.	$66,931	b.	61.1%
44.	156,905.00	200,560.00	a.	$43,655	b.	27.8%
45.	3,209,880.00	3,110,850.00	a.	−$99,030	b.	−3.1%
46.	96,320.00	110,540.00	a.	$14,220	b.	14.8%
47.	110,457.97	32,904.33	a.	−$77,553.64	b.	−70.2%

REINFORCEMENT

Section 21-5
1. What is the current ratio for a business that has total assets of $70,000 and total liabilities of $25,000? **2.8 : 1**

Section 21-6
Find the percent change from last quarter to this quarter to the nearest tenth percent.
1. Last quarter: $17,450.
   This quarter: $17,980. **3.0%**
2. Last quarter: $189,548.
   This quarter: $186,392. **−1.7%**

National Standards for Business Education

Section Objectives	1. Mathematical Foundations	2. Number Relationships and Operations	3. Patterns, Functions, and Algebra	4. Measurements	5. Statistics and Probability	6. Problem-Solving Applications	
22-1 Corporate Income Taxes (pp. 682–684) Compute the taxable income and the corporate income tax.	X	X					
22-2 Issuing Stocks and Bonds (pp. 685–687) Calculate the selling expenses and the net proceeds from an issue of stocks and bonds.	X	X					
22-3 Borrowing (pp. 688–690) Determine the maturity value of a commercial loan.	X	X					
22-4 Investments—Treasury Bills (pp. 691–692) Work out the cost and yield of a Treasury bill.	X	X					
22-5 Investments—Commercial Paper (pp. 693–694) Determine the cost and yield for commercial paper.	X	X					
22-6 Growth Expenses (pp. 695–697) Compute the total cost of expanding a business.	X	X					

(Source: Reprinted with permission from the National Standards for Business Education, copyright © 2001 by National Business Education Association, 1914 Association Drive, Reston, Virginia 21901-1596)

SCANS Correlation

Foundation Skills

Basic Skills	Reading	Writing	Math	Listening	Speaking	
Thinking Skills	Creative Thinking	Decision Making	Problem Solving	Seeing Things in the Mind's Eye	Knowing How to Learn	Reasoning
Personal Qualities	Responsibility	Self-Esteem	Sociability	Self-Management	Integrity/Honesty	

This chapter's highlighted blocks indicate the chapter's content coverage in the Student Edition and the Teacher Wraparound Edition.

National Council of Teachers of Mathematics Standards

1. Numbers & Operations	2. Algebra	3. Geometry	4. Measurement	5. Data Analysis & Probability	6. Problem Solving	7. Reasoning & Proof	8. Communication	9. Connections	10. Representations
X					X		X		
X					X		X		
X					X		X		
X					X		X		
X					X		X		
X					X		X		

SCANS Correlation

Workplace Competencies

Resources	Allocating Time	Allocating Money	Allocating Material and Facility Resources	Allocating Human Resources		
Information	Acquiring and Evaluating Information	Organizing and Maintaining Information	Interpreting and Communicating Information	Using Computers to Process Information		
Interpersonal Skills	Participating as a Member of a Team	Teaching Others	Serving Clients/Customers	Exercising Leadership	Negotiating to Arrive at a Decision	Working with Cultural Diversity
Systems	Understanding Systems	Monitoring and Correcting Performance	Improving and Designing Systems			
Technology	Selecting Technology	Applying Technology to Task	Maintaining and Troubleshooting Technology			

What You'll Learn

Tell students that in this chapter you'll focus on how companies make calculations to manage their taxes, investments, and loans.

Why It's Important

Developing a strong financial strategy is what grows a business. Home Depot stores adopted a strategy for growth by adding locations. The company must now convince investors that the company's growth is not restricted to the opening of fresh megastores in new markets. Wal-Mart was successful with this strategy in the mid-90's when it opened a line of Sam's Club and Wal-Mart Superstores.

Key Word Review

Guess and Check

Guess a definition for each key word. Check your definition against the Glossary definition. How did you do? Make any needed corrections. **LS**

CHAPTER 22

Financial Management

What You'll Learn

Section 22-1 Compute the taxable income and the corporate income tax.

Section 22-2 Calculate the selling expenses and the net proceeds from an issue of stocks and bonds.

Section 22-3 Determine the maturity value of a commercial loan.

Section 22-4 Work out the cost and yield of a Treasury bill.

Section 22-5 Determine the cost and yield for commercial paper.

Section 22-6 Compute the total cost of expanding a business.

When Will You Ever Use This?

To manage a business's finances, you need to know about its investments, loans, and taxes.

Key Words to Know

- corporations
- taxable income
- stocks
- bonds
- underwriting commission
- commercial loans
- maturity value
- prime rate
- Treasury bill
- discount
- face value
- yield
- commercial paper
- merge
- growth expenses

Mathematics Online

To learn more about financial management, visit the *Mathematics with Business Applications* Web site at www.busmath.glencoe.com.

CLASSROOM RESOURCES

Application and Enrichment
- *Teacher Wraparound Edition*
- *Teacher Resource Binder, Blackline Masters*
- *Interactive Lesson Planner* CD-ROM
- *PowerPoint® Presentations* CD-ROM

Review and Enforcement
  Mathematics Online
    www.busmath.glencoe.com
- *Teacher Resource Binder, Internet Resources*

- *Student Activity Workbook*
- *Student Activity Workbook, Teacher Annotated Edition*
- *School-to-Home Activity Workbook*

Assessment and Evaluation
- *Assessment Binder, Reproducible Tests*
- *Assessment Binder, Alternative Assessment Strategies*
- **Exam***View®* *Pro Test Generator* CD-ROM

For the Teacher
- *Student Activity Workbook, Teacher Annotated Edition*
- *Assessment Binder*
- *Interactive Lesson Planner* CD-ROM
- *Teacher Resource Binder*
- Mathematics Online
    www.busmath.glencoe.com

For the Student
- *Student Activity Workbook*
- *School-to-Home Activity Workbook*

Living in the Real World

Story's Summary

Students get a peek into the boardroom of Zenor Steel, as CEO Maria Rodriguez sits in on the annual board meeting. The company experienced modest growth last year, but a faltering economy has had a slowing affect. Important decisions must be made, such as issuing bonds, taking on a term loan to purchase new equipment, and investing profits.

Living in the Real World

Roundtable Discussion

Maria Rodriguez is president and CEO of a pipeline supply company. Zenor Steel, a large steel producer, is holding its annual board meeting in Pittsburgh, which she is attending. Since Rodriguez is not directly involved in steel manufacturing and doesn't work for Zenor, she's considered an "outside member" on the board. The Zenor board meets once a year to discuss corporate finances, vision, and organization. Today's discussions focus on the corporation's financial status and future.

Read on. Go to . . .

681

Did You Know...

Before the Stock Market Crash of 1929, few regulations were enforced. Investors were left unprotected from fraud, and individuals didn't know if companies' financial reports were reliable. The U.S. Securities and Exchange Commission was established after the Crash to impose laws and punish violators.

Think about This

Much has been made in recent years of corporate finance scandals. How might investors be affected when a company isn't truthful about its earnings or performance?

LOCAL STANDARDS

National Standards for Business Education

Standard 1	Mathematical Foundations
Standard 2	Number Relationships and Operations

National Council of Teachers of Mathematics Standards

Standard 1	Numbers and Operations
Standard 6	Problem Solving
Standard 8	Communication

1 FOCUS

Corporations must pay income taxes like individuals. Just as individuals are allowed to deduct certain expenses, corporations are also allowed to take deductions. These deductions are subtracted from the gross income. This determines the amount of taxable income.

In-Class Examples
Work through these exercises with students before having them do the Self-Check.
1. $7,050 + (0.25 × $10,000) **$9,550**
2. $22,250 + (0.39 × $50,235) **$41,841.65**
3. $3,400,000 + (0.35 × $518,378) **$3,581,432.30**

○ **Section Objective**
Compute the taxable income and the corporate income tax.

SECTION 22-1 Corporate Income Taxes

Your business must pay federal income taxes. The tax rates vary depending on the size and type of your business. **Corporations,** businesses owned by stockholders, are subject to federal tax rates ranging from 15 percent to 39 percent of **taxable income.** Taxable income is the portion of your company's gross income that remains after normal business expenses are deducted. Normal business expenses include wages, rent, utilities, interest (paid on loans), property taxes, depreciation, and so on. The structure for federal corporate income taxes is graduated.

Figure 22.1

Federal Corporate Income Tax			
Over—	But not over—	Tax is:	Of the amount over—
$ —	$ 50,000	15%	$ —
50,000	75,000	$ 7,500 + 25%	50,000
75,000	100,000	13,750 + 34%	75,000
100,000	335,000	22,250 + 39%	100,000
335,000	10,000,000	113,900 + 34%	335,000
10,000,000	15,000,000	3,400,000 + 35%	10,000,000
15,000,000	18,333,333	5,150,000 + 38%	15,000,000
18,333,333	—	5,150,000 + 38%	—

Remember that:

Taxable Income = Annual Gross Income − Deductions

Living in the Real World

Roundtable Discussion

Trying to Predict the Future Rodriguez sits in the boardroom to listen to Zenor's president, James Wu, discuss the year's performance thus far. Overall, the company did experience growth this year, but slower than usual. He expects the economy will be picking up in the third quarter, and its larger customers will be buying at a pretty good pace.

Draw Conclusions When the economy experiences a downturn, how does this affect businesses?

Continued on page 685

BUSINESS NOTES

Interview a Financial Manager
In groups of three or four, interview a business financial manager or accountant. Ask about:
- The long-range business plans for the company.
- How financial forecasting is used.
- The software used for the financial management of the company.
- The most common financial mistakes businesses make.

Write up the interview as a group. **LS**

Living in the Real World

An economic downturn usually equals a slowdown in consumer spending, which results in lower sales. A soft economy can also mean more layoffs and more businesses closing their doors.

Example 1

Dot-Software had a gross income of $558,145 for the year. It had these business expenses during the year:

Dot-Software Inc.	
Expenses	**Amount**
Accounting	$ 4,850
Business insurance	5,200
Depreciation	14,720
Health insurance	22,660
Interest	9,516
Office supplies	2,200
Rent	18,750
Utilities	11,219
Wages	375,500
Total	**$464,615**

What federal corporate income tax must Dot-Software pay?

STEP 1: Find the total deductions (expenses).
Total for the table is $464,615 in deductions.

STEP 2: Find the taxable income.
Annual Gross Income − Deductions
$558,145 − $464,615 = $93,530 taxable income

STEP 3: Find the federal corporate income tax. (Refer to Figure 22.1 on page 682.)
$13,750 + 34% of ($93,530 − $75,000) =
$13,750 + (0.34 × $18,530) =
$13,750 + $6,300.20 = **$20,050.20 federal corporate income tax**

93530  75000 = 18530 × 34 %

6300.20 + 13750 = 20050.20

CONCEPT CHECK

(SELF-CHECK✓)

Complete the problems, then check your answers at the end of the chapter. Use Figure 22.1 on page 682 to find the federal corporate income tax.

1. Gross income: $145,000.
Deductions: $60,000.
Taxable income:
$145,000 − $60,000 = $85,000
Tax: $13,750 + 34% of ($85,000 − $75,000) = $13,750 + (0.34 × $10,000) = $13,750 + $3,400 = $17,150 federal corporate income tax

2. Gross income: $219,000.
Deductions: $154,000.
Taxable income:
$219,000 − $154,000 = $65,000
Tax: $7,500 + 25% of ($65,000 − $50,000) = $7,500 + (0.25 × $15,000) = $7,500 + $3,750 = $11,250 federal corporate income tax

Section 22-1 Corporate Income Taxes ▶ **683**

COOPERATIVE LEARNING

Creditable Web Sites
Students work in groups to research on the Internet and create a list of ten Web sites that a financial manager might find valuable. Students check to make sure that the Web sites are reputable sources.
 LS , CL

GLOBAL PERSPECTIVE

Taxes Paid to a Foreign Government
U.S. corporations operate businesses in other parts of the world. They are taxed in the country in which they operate. However, a tax credit, or deduction, is allowed for taxes paid to a foreign government. The tax structure of a country can affect a corporation's decision as to whether or not to operate there. Have students report on the business tax structure of other countries.

---

② TEACH

Have students read **Figure 22.1** on page 682, the Federal Corporate Income Tax. Make sure that students understand how to find the amount of tax. You may want to give students some practice reading the table by asking them to find the amount of tax for different incomes.

Students may not understand the benefit of taking deductions. In Example 1 on page 683, have students find the amount of tax with no deductions taken. Have them compare this amount to the tax with the deductions taken. If businesses were taxed just on the annual gross income, then they would pay much more tax.

Motivating the Lesson
Find the total deductions.

Expenses	Amount
Accounting	$ 10,675
Insurance	32,699
Depreciation	19,934
Property taxes	28,449
Interest on a loan	8,387
Office supplies	5,870
Rent	82,138
Utilities	115,902
Wages	678,120
Total	**$982,174**

In-Class Examples
Use **Figure 22.1** on page 682 to find the federal corporate tax.
1. Gross income: $55,000. Deductions: $15,000. **$8,250**
2. Gross income: $128,560. Deductions: $31,076. **$21,394.56**
3. The Aqua Bell Company has an annual gross income of $530,985. Its deductions total $198,024. What is the federal corporate income tax? **$101,456.74**

SECTION 22-1

③ ASSESS

Error Analysis

Remind students that the number that they multiply the tax rate by is the amount of taxable income over the designated amount in the fourth column of **Figure 22.1**. Students may mistakenly multiply the percent by the total taxable income. Have students practice several problems in class to make certain that they understand how to calculate the federal corporate income tax using the tax table in **Figure 22.1** on page 682.

④ CLOSE

Closing Activity

Use **Figure 22.1** on page 682 to find the federal corporate tax.

1. Gross income: $85,000.
   Deductions: $37,000. **$12,750**

2. Gross income: $71,750.
   Deductions: $9,500.
   $10,562.50

3. Gross income: $697,280.
   Deductions: $197,765.
   $169,835.10

4. Gross income: $1,041,325.
   Deductions: $587,386.
   $154,339.26

5. Sands Manufacturing has an annual gross income of $1,640,029. Its deductions total $449,733. What is the federal corporate income tax? **$404,700.64**

To complete the table, refer to Figure 22.1 on page 682 for federal corporate income taxes.

	Annual Gross Income	−	Deductions	=	Taxable Income	Total Tax
3.	$ 74,918	−	$ 38,172	=	$36,746	a. $5,511.90
4.	212,971	−	125,539	=	a. $87,432	b. $17,976.88
5.	279,434	−	214,611	=	a. $64,823	b. $11,205.75
6.	720,338	−	621,913	=	a. $98,425	b. $21,714.50
7.	916,418	−	721,534	=	a. $194,884	b. $59,254.76

8. Johnson-Etna Manufacturing Corporation.
   Annual gross income is $316,921.
   Deductions total $234,847.
   What is the federal corporate income tax? **$16,155.16**

9. The Townnet Company.
   Annual gross income is $72,173.
   Deductions total $67,224.
   What is the federal corporate income tax? **$742.35**

10. The Magno-Met Company had these business expenses for the year:

Magno-Met Company	
Expenses	**Amount**
Accounting	$ 18,985
Insurance	145,632
Depreciation	26,916
Property taxes	45,495
Interest on a loan	15,465
Office supplies	8,422
Rent	62,580
Utilities	74,617
Wages	816,147
Total	$

The Magno-Met Company had a gross income of $1,516,749 for the year.
   a. What are the total business expenses? **$1,214,259**
   b. What is the taxable income? **$302,490**
   c. What is the federal corporate income tax for the year? **$101,221.10**

Find the percentage. Round answers to the nearest hundredth.

> Need Help? Go to...
> ➤ Skill 30: **Finding the Percentage,** page 757
> ➤ Skill 6: **Subtracting Decimals,** page 733

11. 6% of 74 **4.44**
12. 7.65% of 80.77 **6.18**
13. 7.8% of 160 **12.48**
14. 145% of 350 **507.50**
15. 35% of 4,700 **1,645**
16. 34% of 816 **277.44**

Subtract.

17. $87,434 − $75,000
    $12,434
18. $127,816 − $100,000
    $27,816
19. $74.718 − $16.634
    $58.084

WRAP-UP

Go over any problem for which a wrong answer is given.

Assignment Guide
   Basic: 3–7
Average: 8–9

20 min.

SECTION 22-2 Issuing Stocks and Bonds

Section Objective

○ **Section Objective**

Calculate the selling expenses and the net proceeds from an issue of stocks and bonds.

Your business may raise money by issuing **stocks** or **bonds**. When you issue stocks, the buyer becomes a part owner of your business. When you issue bonds, the buyer is lending money to your business.

When you issue stocks or bonds, you must pay certain expenses. One expense is an **underwriting commission**, a commission to the investment banker who helps you sell the stocks or bonds. Other expenses include accounting costs, legal fees, and printing costs. The amount your business actually receives from the sale of the stocks or bonds after paying these expenses is the *net proceeds*.

Important Questions to Ask Yourself	What Formulas Do I Use?
How do I find the **value** of stock issued?	Value of Issue = Price per Share × Number of Shares
How do I find the **underwriting commission**?	$\dfrac{\text{Underwriting}}{\text{Commission}} = \dfrac{\text{Value of}}{\text{Issue}} \times \dfrac{\text{Percent of Underwriting}}{\text{Commission}}$
How do I calculate the **net proceeds**?	Net Proceeds = Value of Issue − Total Selling Expenses

Living in the Real World

Roundtable Discussion

In Good Financial Shape Wu asks them to discuss the issue of bonds to help keep Zenor in good financial shape to expand.

"Stockholders are always an important source of funds" Rodriguez says, "but at the moment, we probably don't need any more owners in the company. But I think this is a good time to borrow money by issuing bonds. Of course, that always costs some money for the underwriting commission, accounting, legal fees, and printing costs. But those expenses can all be covered and then some by a significant sale of bonds."

Draw Conclusions List one way that companies can borrow money.

Continued on page 688

Example 1

The Landover Company is planning a major expansion program. To finance the program, Landover plans to sell an issue of 300,000 shares of stock at $41.50 per share. The underwriting commission will be 6.5 percent of the value of the stocks. Accounting fees, legal fees, printing costs, and other expenses are estimated to be $112,050. If all the shares of stock are sold, what net proceeds will Landover Company receive?

Continued on next page

Living in the Real World

Companies can borrow money by issuing bonds.

ALTERNATIVE ASSESSMENT

Classroom Climate

The classroom climate is important in promoting a positive learning environment for all students. Most students want to succeed and improve themselves. Students who are sensitive will benefit greatly by having an environment focused on cooperative learning. Try to emphasize class cooperation and success, as well as healthy competition. Competition between teams, as opposed to individuals, can be fun and create enthusiasm. **CL** , **LS**

National Standards for Business Education	
Standard 1	Mathematical Foundations
Standard 2	Number Relationships and Operations

National Council of Teachers of Mathematics Standards	
Standard 1	Numbers and Operations
Standard 6	Problem Solving
Standard 8	Communication

1 **FOCUS**

Ask students if they know what it means to own company stock. **(Sometimes businesses do not have enough money to get going.)** Discuss how businesses can offer stock in their company as a way to get the capital that they need.

In-Class Examples

Work through these exercises with students before having them do the Self-Check. Round answers to the nearest tenth of a cent.

1. $15,750,000 × 6% **$945,000**
2. $783,800 ÷ 420,000 **$1.866**
3. $2,098,795 ÷ 585,700 **$3.583**

2 **TEACH**

In addition to needing money to start a business, sometimes a business needs money to finance a specific project. For instance, a company that wants to build another manufacturing plant may issue stocks or bonds to finance the project. Make sure students understand the difference between stocks and bonds.

2 TEACH (cont'd)

You may want to bring in a company's prospectus to show students. **(Point out that you usually receive a company's prospectus when you purchase its stock.)** You may want to mention that some stocks can be purchased directly from a company while others must be purchased through a stockbroker. Companies that allow the direct purchase of their stock generally require that at least a certain set amount be purchased.

Motivating the Lesson

Find the commission for each stock value.

Value of Stock	Commission
$550,000	3% of the value
$16,500	
$1,000,000	4% of the value
$40,000	
$30,750,000	4.5% of the value
$1,383,750	

In-Class Examples

1. Find the net proceeds. Value of stock: $5,000,000. Commission: 4 percent of the value of the stock. Other selling expenses: $63,000. **$4,737,000**

2. Find the cost per share. Number of shares: 750,000. Total selling expenses: $1,250,000. **$1.667**

3. Times Two Inc. sold 850,000 shares of stock at $18.53 per share. The investment banker's commission was 4 percent of the value of the stock. The other expenses were 0.5 percent of the value of the stock. What net proceeds did Times Two receive? **$15,041,728** What is the selling expense per share? **$0.834**

STEP 1: Find the value of issue.

Price per Share × Number of Shares

| $41.50 | × | 300,000 | = $12,450,000 value of issue |

STEP 2a: Find the underwriting commission.

Value of Issue × Percent of Underwriting Commission

Underwriting commission:

| $12,450,000 | × | 6.5% | = $809,250 |

| Other expenses: | | | = $112,050 |

STEP 2b: Find the total selling expenses.

| $809,250 + $112,050 | | = $921,300 total selling expenses |

STEP 3: Find the net proceeds.

Value of Issue − Total Selling Expenses

| $12,450,000 | − | $921,300 | = **$11,528,700 net proceeds** |

41.5 [×] 300000 [=] 12450000 [M+] [×] 6.5 [%] 809250 [+]

112050 [=] 921300 [±] [+] [RM] 12450000 [=] 11528700

CONCEPT CHECK

SELF-CHECK✓

Complete the problems, then check your answers at the end of the chapter. Find the net proceeds.

Net proceeds: $8,000,000 − $432,000 = $7,568,000

1. Value of stock: $8,000,000.
   Commission: 5 percent of the value of the stock.
   Other selling expenses: 0.4 percent of the value of the stock.

2. Value of stock: $30,000,000.
   Underwriting commission: 4.5 percent of the value of the stock.
   Other selling expenses: 0.3 percent of the value of the stock.
   Net proceeds: $30,000,000 − $1,440,000 = $28,560,000

A PROSPECTUS A prospectus is a formal written document that gives the facts about a new offering of securities. The prospectus will indicate the underwriting expenses as cost per share. Remember that:

Cost per Share = Total Selling Expenses ÷ Total Number of Shares

Example 2

What is the cost per share for the Landover Company in Example 1?

STEP: Find the cost per share.

Total Selling Expenses ÷ Total Number of Shares

| $921,300 | ÷ | 300,000 | = **$3.071 cost per share** |

COMMUNICATION SKILLS

Discuss Pros and Cons

There are pros and cons for companies in issuing either stocks or bonds for long-term financing. Interest paid by a company on bonds is considered a debt and is deducted from gross profit, but stock dividends are issued after taxes have been paid. Ask students to suggest other reasons why a manager may prefer to raise money through bonds rather than through stocks. **Stockholders have some control over a company's management. A corporation shares its after-tax earnings with stockholders.**

CONCEPT CHECK

Complete the problems, then check your answers at the end of the chapter.
Find the cost per share. **3. Cost per share = $1,112,000 ÷ 1,000,000 = $1.112**

3. Number of shares: 1,000,000.
Total selling expenses: $1,112,000.

4. Number of shares: 900,000.
Total selling expenses: $1,200,000.

4. Cost per share = $1,200,000 ÷ 900,000 = $1.333

SECTION 22-2 PRACTICE

Complete the table.

- 5. a. $408,000
   b. $455,500
   c. $6,344,500
- 6. a. $85,500
   b. $112,000
   c. $838,000
- 7. a. $1,050,000
   b. $1,104,650
   c. $19,895,350
- 8. a. $3,202,500
   b. $3,297,050
   c. $42,452,950

	Value of Issue	Percent	Commission Expenses	Other Expenses	Total Selling Expenses	Net Proceeds	Number of Shares	Selling Cost per Share
5.	$ 6,800,000	6%	a.	$47,500	b.	c.	400,000	d. $1.14
6.	950,000	9%	a.	26,500	b.	c.	40,000	d. $2.80
7.	21,000,000	5%	a.	54,650	b.	c.	1,000,000	d. $1.10
8.	45,750,000	7%	a.	94,550	b.	c.	1,500,000	d. $2.20

9. Value of stocks is $750,000.
Underwriting commission is 10 percent.
Other expenses total $21,640.
What are the net proceeds? **$653,360**

10. Value of bonds is $7,435,750.
Underwriting commission is 5.5 percent.
Other expenses total $48,650.
What are the net proceeds? **$6,978,133.75**

11. Universal Waste Disposal sold 1,350,000 shares of stock at $24.625 per share.
The investment banker's commission was 5 percent of the value of the stock.
The other expenses were 1 percent of the value of the stock. What net proceeds
did Universal Waste Disposal receive? What is the selling expense per share?
$31,249,125; $1.48

12. The Mercury Electric Company issued 200,000 shares of stock at $62.50 per
share. Find the net proceeds and the selling expense per share after these
selling expenses are deducted. **$11,959,250; $2.70**

Underwriting Expenses

Commissions	4%
Legal fees	$15,000
Advertising	8,500
Miscellaneous	1,250
Printing costs	7,500
Accounting fees	8,500

MAINTAINING YOUR SKILLS

(Need Help? Go to...)
▶ Skill 30: Finding
the Percentage,
page 757

Find the percentage. Round answers to the nearest hundredth.

13. 6.5% of $980,000 **$63,700**

14. 5% of $3,150,000 **$157,500**

15. 6% of $743,000 **$44,580**

16. 5.5% of $1.5 million **$82,500**

Section 22-2 Issuing Stocks and Bonds ▶ **687**

WRAP-UP

Go over any problem for which a wrong
answer is given.

Assignment Guide
Basic: 5–8
Average: 9–10

20 min.

ASSESS

Error Analysis

In this section, some of the numbers are very large. Encourage
students to make sure that they
are using the correct amount of
zeros when they are writing the
numbers. Remind students to
always check their answers to see
whether or not they are reasonable.
An extremely large cost per share
or net proceeds that are more than
a stock's value might be indications
that an error has occurred somewhere in the computations.

4 CLOSE

Closing Activity

1. Value of stock: $4,900,000.
   Commission: 5 percent of the
   value of the stock.
   Other selling expenses:
   $45,000. Find the net
   proceeds. **$4,610,000**

2. Value of stock: $26,500,000.
   Commission: 3.5 percent of
   the value of the stock.
   Other selling expenses:
   0.8 percent of the value
   of the stock.
   Find the net proceeds.
   $25,360,500

3. Number of shares: 883,000.
   Total selling expenses:
   $1,780,000. Find the cost
   per share. **$2.016**

4. Number of shares: 279,540.
   Total selling expenses:
   $1,097,000. Find the cost
   per share. **$3.924**

5. Nelson & Co. sold 3,000,000
   shares of stock at $22.314 per
   share. The investment banker's
   commission was 5 percent of
   the value of the stock. The
   other expenses were 1.2 percent
   of the value of the stock. What
   net proceeds did Nelson & Co.
   receive? **$62,791,596** What is
   the selling expense per share?
   $1.383

National Standards for Business Education

Standard 1	Mathematical Foundations
Standard 2	Number Relationships and Operations

National Council of Teachers of Mathematics Standards

Standard 1	Numbers and Operations
Standard 6	Problem Solving
Standard 8	Communication

 **FOCUS**

Sometimes businesses must borrow money to buy materials or equipment. Discuss with students some things that companies may need to purchase, which would require borrowing money for a relatively short period of time.

In-Class Examples
Work through these exercises with students before having them do the Self-Check.

1. $50,000 × 7% × $\frac{60}{360}$ **$583.33**
2. $450,000 × 7.5% × $\frac{90}{360}$ **$8,437.50**
3. $275,000 × (2.00% + 5.25%) × $\frac{60}{360}$ **$3,322.92**

○ **Section Objective**
Determine the maturity value of a commercial loan.

Your business may borrow money to buy raw materials, products, or equipment. **Commercial loans**, or business loans, are similar to personal loans. The **maturity value** of your loan is the total amount you repay. The maturity value includes both the principal borrowed and the interest owed on the loan. Commercial loans usually charge *ordinary interest at exact time*. That is, the length of time of the loan is calculated by dividing the exact number of days of the loan by 360 days.

Important Questions to Ask Yourself	What Formula Do I Use?
How do I calculate **interest** on a loan?	Interest = Principal × Rate × Time Note: If you're to find the "ordinary" interest, then you'll need to divide the number of days of the loan by 360 days.
How do I find the **maturity value** on a loan?	Maturity Value = Principal + Interest Owed

Living in the Real World

Roundtable Discussion

Funding for Equipment Zenor has contemplated updating machinery and a few facilities around the country. As the board knows, short term loans are the most popular type of commercial loan available. They are used to purchase fixed assets, such as equipment.

Draw Conclusions Assuming a company pays back its term loan in regular installments, how soon must a short term loan be paid back?

Continued on page 691

○── (**Example 1**) ──────

Harm's Drugstore borrowed $80,000 from First National Bank to pay for remodeling costs. The bank lent the money at 9 percent ordinary interest for 60 days. What is the maturity value of the loan?

STEP 1: Find the interest owed.

Principal × Rate × Time
$80,000 × 9% × $\frac{60}{360}$ =
$432,000 ÷ 360 = $1,200 interest owed

STEP 2: Find the maturity value.

Principal + Interest Owed
$80,000 + $1,200 = **$81,200 maturity value**

80000 [M+] [×] 9 [%] [×] 60 [÷] 360 [=]

1200 [+] [RM] [=] 81200

Living in the Real World

A term loan is usually paid in equal periodic installments of principal and interest, but the time frame in which it must be repaid will vary.

RETEACH / ENRICHMENT

Commercial Loans
Have students call or visit a bank or go on the Internet to find out about commercial loans. What are the loans used for? How much will a bank lend? What are the conditions? Have students obtain a copy of a commercial loan application to bring to class. Go over the different parts with them in class and have them fill out the form as if they were applying for a loan to expand their business. **LS**

CONCEPT CHECK

Complete the problems, then check your answers at the end of the chapter. Find the maturity value of the loan.

1. One hundred thousand dollars borrowed at 10 percent ordinary interest for 100 days. **Interest = $100,000 × 0.10 × $\frac{100}{360}$ = $2,777.78**
   Maturity Value = $100,000.00 + $2,777.78 = $102,777.78
2. One hundred fifty thousand dollars borrowed at 9.5 percent ordinary interest for 140 days. **Interest = $150,000 × 0.095 × $\frac{140}{360}$ = $5,541.67**
   Maturity Value = $150,000.00 + $5,541.67 = $155,541.67

PRIME RATE ON A LOAN Commercial loans usually have interest rates that are one to two percentage points higher than the **prime rate.** The prime rate is the lowest rate of interest available to commercial customers at a given time.

Example 2

Keener Builders borrowed $180,000 from Farmers Bank to pay for materials and labor for a new building. Farmers Bank lent the money at 2 percent above the prime rate of 4.75 percent. The loan is ordinary interest for 90 days. What is the maturity value of the loan?

STEP 1: Find the interest owed.

Principal ×   Rate   × Time

$180,000 × (2.00% + 4.75%) × $\frac{90}{360}$ =

$180,000 ×   6.75%   × $\frac{90}{360}$ = $3,037.50 interest owed

STEP 2: Find the maturity value.

Principal   +   Interest Owed

$180,000   + $3,037.50   = **$183,037.50 maturity value**

CONCEPT CHECK

Complete the problems, then check your answers at the end of the chapter. Find the maturity value of the loan if the prime rate is 6.0 percent.

3. The amount of $120,000 is borrowed at 2.0 percent over prime, ordinary interest for 60 days. **Interest = $120,000 × (0.06 + 0.02) × $\frac{60}{360}$ = $1,600.00**
   Maturity Value = $120,000 + $1,600 = $121,600
4. The amount of $150,000 is borrowed at 2.5 percent over prime, ordinary interest for 150 days.

4. **Interest = $150,000 × (0.06 + 0.025) × $\frac{150}{360}$ = $5,312.50**
Maturity Value = $150,000.00 + $5,312.50 = $155,312.50

SECTION 22-3 PRACTICE

Use ordinary interest at exact time to solve.

	Principal	×	Rate	×	Time	=	Interest	Maturity Value
5.	$ 70,000	×	6.0%	×	$\frac{90}{360}$	=	a. $1,050	b. $71,050
6.	95,000	×	7.5%	×	$\frac{100}{360}$	=	a. $1,979.17	b. $96,979.17
7.	37,500	×	12.5%	×	$\frac{120}{360}$	=	a. $1,562.50	b. $39,062.50
8.	300,000	×	10.5%	×	$\frac{270}{360}$	=	a. $23,625	b. $323,625

Continued on next page

Section 22-3 Borrowing ▶ **689**

PROBLEM SOLVING

Trends in Prime Rate
Go over prime rate with students. **(The lowest rate of interest available to commercial customers at a given time. Commercial loans usually have interest rates that are one to two percentage points higher than the prime rate.)** Tell students that the prime rate can go up or down, depending on the state of the economy. Have students research changes in the prime rate over a period of time, say 1990 to the present. Then, have them make a line graph charting the changes. Have students describe the trends in the prime rate over the time graphed.

② TEACH

Explain to students that banks give personal loans to individuals and commercial loans to businesses. These loans are usually for a short period of time. Some banks offer commercial loans based on the prime rate. The prime rate is the lowest interest rate available at a given time. Banks often offer commercial loans at the prime rate plus another percent. Have students discuss why banks may offer one company a lower rate or higher rate than it offers another company. Point out that companies have credit histories just like individuals do. A poor credit history may result in a higher rate.

Motivating the Lesson
Richards Clothing borrowed $50,000 from Eastern Trust. The interest rate of the loan is 8 percent. The term of the loan is one year. How much interest will Richards Clothing pay? **$4,000**

In-Class Examples
Find the ordinary interest owed and the maturity value.
1. Borrowed $80,000 for 60 days. Interest rate: 7 percent. **$933.33; $80,933.33**
2. Borrowed $85,960 for 180 days. Interest rate: 2 percent over prime. Prime rate: 6 percent. **$3,438.40; $89,398.40**
3. Inverse, Inc., borrowed $70,000 from a bank that charged 3.45 percent interest over prime on the loan. The term of the loan was 90 days. The prime rate is 6.85 percent. What was the maturity value of the loan? **$71,802.50**

3 ASSESS

Error Analysis

Remind students that when they are figuring the interest owed on a loan that involves a prime rate, they must find the total rate. Students can both keep the prime rate and additional rate in percent form to add them or they can write both percents as decimals and then add them. Give students some examples of each method. For instance, find the interest owed on a $10,000 loan borrowed for 90 days at an interest rate of prime, 4.5 percent, plus 3 percent. So, the equation would be $10,000 $\times (4.5\% + 3\%) \times (\frac{90}{360})$ or $10,000 $\times (0.045 + 0.03) \times (\frac{90}{360})$.

4 CLOSE

Closing Activity

Find the ordinary interest owed and the maturity value.

1. Borrowed $55,000 for 60 days.
   Interest rate: 9.5 percent.
   $870.83; $55,870.83

2. Borrowed $238,000 for 270 days.
   Interest rate: 8.25 percent.
   $14,726.25; $252,726.25

3. Borrowed $135,990 for 90 days.
   Interest rate: 3 percent over prime.
   Prime rate: 5 percent.
   $2,719.80; $138,709.80

4. Borrowed $98,670 for 60 days.
   Interest rate: 2.29 percent over prime.
   Prime rate: 6.05 percent.
   $1,371.51; $100,041.51

5. Paintworks borrowed $113,000 from a bank that charged 2.91 percent interest over prime on the loan. The term of the loan was 180 days. The prime rate is 5.15 percent. What was the maturity value of the loan? **$117,553.90**

▶FYI

The New York Stock Exchange is the oldest and largest stock exchange in the United States. A group of brokers created it on May 17, 1792 when they signed the Buttonwood Tree Agreement beneath a tree of the same name at 68 Wall Street, New York City.

▶▶▶

9. Amount borrowed for 60 days: $64,000.
   Interest rate is 3 percent ordinary interest over prime.
   Prime rate is 7.0 percent.
   a. What is the interest owed?
   b. What is the maturity value?
   a. $1,066.67; b. $65,066.67

10. Amount borrowed for 180 days: $37,650.
    Interest rate is 1.75 percent ordinary interest over prime.
    Prime rate is 6.85 percent.
    a. What is the interest owed?
    b. What is the maturity value?
    a. $1,618.95; b. $39,268.95

11. Trust Bank lent $190,000 to Fernandez Home Builders. The term of the loan was 270 days. The interest rate was 3.5 percent ordinary interest over prime. What was the maturity value of the loan? (The prime rate is 5.25 percent.) **$202,468.75**

12. To take advantage of a bicycle manufacturer's closeout special on touring bikes, Wheels, Inc., borrowed $50,000 from Union Trust Company. Union Trust charged 3.21 percent ordinary interest over prime on the loan. The term of the loan was 175 days. The prime rate is 7.35 percent. What was the maturity value of the loan? **$52,566.67**

13. The Gibraltar Construction Manufacturing Company was granted a 1-year construction loan of $650,000 to finance the construction of an apartment complex. Gibraltar borrowed the money from Citizens Trust Company at an interest rate of 0.75 percent ordinary interest over prime. What was the maturity value of the loan if the prime rate is 9.75 percent? **$718,250**

14. The Solar Panel Manufacturing Company needs $1,450,000 for 270 days to help finance the production of an experimental solar hot water heater. The financial manager has arranged financing from three sources. Each loan charges ordinary interest at exact time. The prime is 7.15 percent.

Lending Institution	Amount of Loan	Time	Interest Rate
Swancreek Trust Company	$500,000	270 days	2.50% over prime
Universal Investment Company	450,000	270 days	2.45% over prime
Investment Bankers, Inc.	500,000	270 days	2.25% over prime

a. What is the total interest for the three loans?
b. What is the total maturity value?

	a. Interest	b. Maturity Value
STC	$ 36,187.50	$ 536,187.50
UIC	32,400.00	482,400.00
IBI	35,250.00	535,250.00
Total	103,837.50	1,553,837.50

MAINTAINING YOUR SKILLS

Need Help? Go to...
➤ Skill 28: Writing Percents as Decimals, page 755

Write the percents as decimals.

15. 12.7% **0.127**

16. 340% **3.40**

17. 0.6% **0.006**

18. $\frac{7}{10}$% **.007**

19. 0.05% **.0005**

20. 50% **0.50**

WRAP-UP

Go over any problem for which a wrong answer is given.

Assignment Guide
   Basic: 5–8
Average: 9–12

20 min.

SECTION (22-4) Investments— Treasury Bills

○ **Section Objective**

Work out the cost and yield of a Treasury bill.

Your business may invest surplus cash that is not needed for day-to-day operations. One way to invest your money is to purchase a U.S. **Treasury bill** (or T-bill). You may purchase the bills through a bank.

When you purchase a Treasury bill, you are actually lending money to the government. In return, you receive interest at the rate that is in effect at the time you purchase the bill. The interest is ordinary interest at exact time. Treasury bills are issued on a **discount** basis. That is, the interest is computed and then subtracted from the **face value** of the bill to determine the cost of the bill. The face value of the Treasury bill is the amount of money you will receive on the maturity date of the bill. Maturity dates for Treasury bills range from 30 days to a year.

You can calculate the **yield** on your Treasury bill by a formula. Yield is the rate of return (usually as a percent) earned by an investor who holds a bond for a certain period of time. Remember that:

Cost of a Treasury Bill = (Face Value of Bill − Interest) + Service Fee

Yield = Interest ÷ (Cost × Time)

Living in the Real World

Roundtable Discussion

Money to Invest The Zenor board of directors agrees that the slow national economy has affected sales. Nevertheless, last year's sales generated enough profit that the company has money to invest. A board member suggests T-bills, which are always a sound investment, and they don't have to commit to the investment for a long period of time.

Draw Conclusions When the economy turns around, what position might Zenor take on expanding or contracting manufacturing of steel products?

Continued on page 693

Example 1

The financial manager of the Osinski Manufacturing Company has decided to invest the company's surplus cash in a $100,000 U.S. Treasury bill for 120 days. The interest rate is 6 percent. The bank charges a service fee of $25 to obtain the Treasury bill. What is the cost of the Treasury bill? What is the yield for the Treasury bill?

STEP 1: Find the interest.

Principal	×	Rate	×	Time		
$100,000	×	6%	×	$\frac{120}{360}$	=	$2,000

Continued on next page

Living in the Real World

The board has shown an interest in diversifying the investment of profits and may decide to contract the manufacturing of steel products while moving into other profitable areas of business.

THINKING CRITICALLY

T-bill
A $10,000 T-bill was purchased at 8 percent interest for 180 days. Write $10,000, $9,600, and $400 on the board along with these terms: face value, maturity date, interest, ordinary interest at exact time, cost, and discount basis. Ask students what each figure represents using these terms. **$10,000 face value of the T-bill; $400 ordinary interest; $9,600 cost of the T-bill on a discount basis.**

National Standards for Business Education	
Standard 1	Mathematical Foundations
Standard 2	Number Relationships and Operations

National Council of Teachers of Mathematics Standards	
Standard 1	Numbers and Operations
Standard 6	Problem Solving
Standard 8	Communication

① FOCUS

Ask students what they do with their extra money. One response may be to put the money into a savings account. In a savings account, the money can be accessed easily if a need arises. Businesses that have extra money generally want to invest the money so that it is liquid, as in a savings account. However, they would want to earn a higher rate of interest. They may choose to invest in Treasury bills.

In-Class Examples

Work through these exercises with students before having them do the Self-Check.

1. $5,000 \div (75,000 \times \frac{90}{360})$ **0.267**
2. $12,390 \div (134,900 \times \frac{6}{360})$ **5.511**
3. $17,682 \div (199,834 \times \frac{180}{360})$ **0.177**

② TEACH

Have students discuss why businesses may invest in short-term investments. Point out that Treasury bills are considered short term. However, the money from a Treasury bill (T-bill) can be reinvested at its maturity date.

It could be higher or lower than the original rate of the T-bill. So, a business would need to reevaluate whether or not to make the investment at the new rate.

In-Class Examples

Find the ordinary interest, cost, and yield of the Treasury bill.

1. Face value: $55,000.
   Interest rate: 5 percent.
   Time in days: 90.
   Bank service fee: None.
   $687.50; $54,312.50; 5.06%

2. Face value: $125,000.
   Interest rate: 6.25 percent.
   Time in days: 180.
   Bank service fee: $40.
   $3,906.25; $121,133.75; 6.45%

Error Analysis

Students may forget to include the bank service fee when they calculate the cost of the T-bill. Remind students that the cost is the face value of the T-bill minus the interest plus the service fee.

Closing Activity

1. Face value: $210,000.
   Interest rate: 8.95 percent.
   Time in days: 110.
   Bank service fee: $37.
   $5,742.92; $204, 294.08; 9.2%

2. Fields Inc., purchased a $225,000 U.S. T-bill at 9.26 percent interest. The T-bill matures in 120 days. The bank service fee is $42. What is the cost of the T-bill? **($218,097)** What is the yield? **9.55%**

STEP 2: Find the cost of the Treasury bill.

Face Value of Bill − Interest + Service Fee
$100,000 − $2,000 + $25 = **$98,025 cost of the Treasury bill**

STEP 3: Find the yield.

Interest ÷ (Cost × Time)
$2,000 ÷ ($98,025 × $\frac{120}{360}$)
= $2,000 ÷ $32,675 = **0.061208 or 6.12% yield for the Treasury bill**

100000 [M+] [×] 6.00 [%] 6000 [×] 120 [÷] 360 [=] 2000
[M−] [RM] 98000 [+] 25 [=] 98025

CONCEPT CHECK

Complete the problems, then check your answers at the end of the chapter.
Find the cost of the Treasury bill.

1. You purchased $120,000 at 4.00 percent interest for 30 days. Service fee is $35.
2. You purchased $200,000 at 3.75 percent interest for 90 days. Service fee is $50.

Use ordinary interest at exact time to solve.

3. Find the yield for the information in Problem 1. **Yield = $400 ÷ ($119,635 × $\frac{30}{360}$) = 0.040122 or 4.012%**
4. Find the yield for the information in Problem 2.
   Yield = $1,875 ÷ ($198,175 × $\frac{90}{360}$) = 0.037845 or 3.785%

SECTION 22-4 PRACTICE

Complete the table.

Face Value of Treasury Bill	Interest Rate	Time in Days	Interest	Bank Service Fee	Cost of Treasury Bill
5. $ 70,000	9.00%	30	a.	$25	b.
6. 100,000	5.75%	120	a.	35	b.
7. 150,000	2.35%	180	a.	No fee	b.
8. 85,000	4.23%	91	a.	30	b.

9. Face value of a Treasury bill is $60,000.
   Interest rate is 6.00 percent.
   Treasury bill matures in 120 days.
   Bank service fee is $30.
   a. What is the interest? **$1,200**
   b. What is the cost of the Treasury bill? **$58,830**
   c. What is the yield? **6.119%**

10. Face value of a Treasury bill is $200,000.
    Interest rate is 8.77 percent.
    Treasury bill matures in 90 days.
    Bank service fee is $40.
    a. What is the interest? **$4,385**
    b. What is the cost of the Treasury bill? **$195,655**
    c. What is the yield? **8.965%**

11. 139.92 12. 60.5475 = 60.548 13. 0.2337 = 0.234 14. 4.58602 = 4.586

MAINTAINING YOUR SKILLS

Multiply. Round answers to the nearest thousandth.

11. 17.49 × 8   12. 7.475 × 8.1   13. 0.57 × 0.41   14. 21.43 × 0.214

Divide. Round answers to the nearest thousandth.

15. 74 ÷ 6   16. 7.47 ÷ 1,000   17. 971 ÷ 40   18. 700 ÷ 32
    12.3333 = 12.333   0.00748 = 0.007   24.275   21.875

SELF-CHECK ✓

1. Interest = $120,000 × 4.00% × $\frac{30}{360}$ = $400
   Cost = $120,000 − $400 + $35 = $119,635

2. Interest = $200,000 × 3.75% × $\frac{90}{360}$ = $1,875
   Cost = $200,000 − $1,875 + $50 = $198,175

5. a. $525
   b. $69,500
6. a. $1,916.67
   b. $98,118.33
7. a. $1,762.50
   b. $148,237.50
8. a. $908.86
   b. $84,121.14

Need Help? Go to...
► Skill 8: Multiplying Decimals, page 735
► Skill 10: Dividing (Decimal Remainder), page 737

WRAP-UP

Go over any problem for which a wrong answer is given.

Assignment Guide
Basic: 5–8
Average: 9–10

20 min.

SECTION ❨22-5❩ Investments— Commercial Paper

Section Objective

Determine the cost and yield for commercial paper.

Your business may invest extra cash in **commercial paper** (CP). CP is an unsecured promissory note issued by various companies. The quality of the CP depends on the credit rating of the issuing company. When your business invests in CP, you are actually lending money to another company. CP earns ordinary interest at exact time from 30 days to 270 days.

Your business (usually) obtains CP through a bank. The bank may charge a service fee. Because CP is a discount investment, it is sold at a price less than its maturity value. That is, the interest is computed and then subtracted from the face value to determine the cost of the CP. The face value of the CP is the amount of money you will receive on the maturity date. CP is generally issued in amounts starting at $500,000.

You might need to calculate the yield on CP. Figure it out the same way you did for Treasury bills. Remember that:

$$\text{Cost of CP} = (\text{Face Value of CP} - \text{Interest}) + \text{Service Fee}$$

$$\text{Yield} = \text{Interest} \div (\text{Cost} \times \text{Time})$$

Living in the Real World

Roundtable Discussion

A Sound Portfolio After more discussion, Zenor board members decide to diversify the investment of the corporation's profits. They suggest including commercial paper in their investment portfolio.

Draw Conclusions What must a company keep in mind as it contemplates lending money to another company?

Continued on page 695

Example 1

Boat Works has a $500,000 cash surplus. The financial manager used the cash to invest in CP issued by Mobile Electric at 6 percent for 45 days. The bank charges a service fee of $50. What is the cost and the yield of the CP?

STEP 1: Find the interest.

Principal	×	Rate	×	Time		
$500,000	×	6%	×	$\frac{45}{360}$	=	$3,750 interest

STEP 2: Find the cost of the CP.

(Face Value of CP − Interest) + Service Fee

($500,000 − $3,750) + $50 = **$496,300 cost of the CP**

Continued on next page

Section 22-5 Investments—Commercial Paper ▶ **693**

National Standards for Business Education

Standard 1	Mathematical Foundations
Standard 2	Number Relationships and Operations

National Council of Teachers of Mathematics Standards

Standard 1	Numbers and Operations
Standard 6	Problem Solving
Standard 8	Communication

❨1❩ FOCUS

Investing in T-bills is not the only option for businesses that want to make a short-term investment. Businesses can also invest in commercial paper (CP).

In-Class Examples

Work through these exercises with students before having them do the Self-Check.

1. $600,000 × 4% × $\frac{45}{360}$ **$3,000**
2. $975,000 × 6% × $\frac{270}{360}$ **$43,875**
3. $1,950,000 × 7.13% × $\frac{120}{360}$ **$46,345**

Living in the Real World

It must be confident in the strength and credit rating of the company it is considering lending money to; to be sure all loans will be repaid in full.

TECHNOLOGY POWER

A company can expand capital by issuing company stock (Initial Public Offering, or IPO) or by being purchased by a public company. The accounting software company Solomon Software was purchased by its biggest competitor— Great Plains Software. One year later Microsoft bought Great Plains. The acquisitions put each company in better financial situations, than if they continued on their own.

② TEACH

Discuss with students why businesses use commercial paper. **(Point out that when a business invests in commercial paper, the business is lending money to another business.)** The business borrowing the money promises to pay a certain amount of money to the investor at a set time.

In-Class Example
Find the cost and the yield for the CP.

1. Face value: $500,000.
   Interest rate: 5 percent.
   Time in days: 270.
   Bank service fee: none.
   $481,250; 5.19%

③ ASSESS

Error Analysis
Remind students that the interest on commercial paper is based on exact time. So, to find the interest, students must multiply the face value of the CP by the rate by the number of days divided by 360. To save calculator keystrokes by avoiding the need to enter a fraction, you may want to teach students some decimal equivalents for common times.

$\frac{30}{360} = 0.83333333$ $\frac{45}{360} = 0.125$

$\frac{90}{360} = 0.25$ $\frac{18}{360} = 0.5$

$\frac{270}{360} = 0.75$

④ CLOSE

Closing Activity
Find the cost and the yield for the CP.

1. Face value: $1,250,000.
   Interest rate: 5.75 percent.
   Time in days: 120.
   Bank service fee: $45.
   $1,226,086.67; 5.86%

694

---

1. Interest =
   $600,000 × 4%
   × $\frac{30}{360}$ = $2,000
   Cost = $600,000
   − $2,000 + $75
   = $598,075

SELF-CHECK✓

2. Interest =
   $1,000,000 ×
   3.75% × $\frac{90}{360}$
   = $9,375
   Cost =
   $1,000,000 −
   $9,375 + $0
   = $990,625

5. a. $3,500
   b. $696,545
   c. 6.030%
6. a. $15,333.33
   b. $784,716.67
   c. 5.862%
7. a. $17,625.00
   b. $1,482,375
   c. 2.378%
8. a. $85,540
   b. $7,914,460
   c. 4.276%

$497,748.33; 5.525% **a.**
$495,248.33; 5.805% **b.**
$492,727.50; 5.969% **c.**
$931,356.67; 6.031% **d.**

Need Help? Go to...
➤ **Skill 8: Multiplying Decimals**, page 735

694 ◂ Chapter 22 Financial Management

STEP 3: Find the yield.

Interest ÷ (Cost × Time)

$3,750 ÷ ($496,300 × $\frac{45}{360}$)

= $3,750 ÷ $62,037.50 = 0.060447 or 6.045% yield of the CP

500000 M+ × 6 % 30000 × 45 ÷ 360 =

3750 M− + 50 = 496300

CONCEPT CHECK

Complete the problems, then check your answers at the end of the chapter. Find the cost of the CP.

1. You invested $600,000 at 4.00 percent interest for 30 days. Service fee of $75.
2. You invested $1,000,000 at 3.75 percent interest for 90 days. No service fee.
3. Find the yield for the information in Problem 1.
4. Find the yield for the information in Problem 2.

3. Yield = $2,000 ÷
($598,075 × $\frac{30}{360}$) =
4.0128% or 4.013%

Yield = $9,375 ÷ ($990,625 × $\frac{90}{360}$) = 3.7854% or 3.785%

SECTION 22-5 PRACTICE

Use ordinary interest at exact time to solve.

	Face Value of CP	Interest Rate	Time in Days	Interest	Bank Service Fee	Cost of CP	Yield
5.	$ 700,000	6.00%	30	a.	$45	b.	c.
6.	800,000	5.75%	120	a.	50	b.	c.
7.	1,500,000	2.35%	180	a.	No fee	b.	c.
8.	8,000,000	4.23%	91	a.	No fee	b.	c.

9. Purchased $750,000 CP for 90 days from the Automobile Corporation. Interest rate is 7.50 percent. Bank service fee is $40.00.
   a. What is the cost? **$735,977.50**
   b. What is the yield? **7.64%**

10. Purchased $500,000 CP for 270 days from U.S. Appliance. Interest rate is 1.75 percent. Bank service fee is $50.00.
    a. What is the cost? **$493,487.50**
    b. What is the yield? **1.77%**

11. The Rural Farm Electric Corporation has a $2,450,000 cash surplus. The financial manager made the following investments in CP:

Wisconsin Energy	$500,000 at 5.50% for 30 days
State Hardware	500,000 at 5.75% for 60 days
Computer Co.	500,000 at 5.85% for 90 days
ABC Financing	950,000 at 5.90% for 120 days

The bank charges a service fee of $40 for each note. What is the cost and the yield for each note?

MAINTAINING YOUR SKILLS

Multiply. Round answers to the nearest hundredth.

12. 52.74 × 1,000
    52,740

13. 0.478 × 0.49
    0.23422 = 0.234

14. 4,173 × 0.005
    20.865

15. 7.165 × 0.047
    0.336755 = 0.337

WRAP-UP

Go over any problem for which a wrong answer is given.

Assignment Guide
  Basic: 5–8
Average: 9–10

20 min.

SECTION 22-6 Growth Expenses

Section Objective
Compute the total cost of expanding a business.

You may expand your business in several different ways. You may purchase another building or build an addition to your present building. You may purchase another business to become part of your business. Your business may **merge**, or combine, with another business to form a new business. **Growth expenses** for your business may include construction fees, consultation fees, legal fees, and so on. Remember that:

Total Cost of Expansion = Sum of Individual Costs

Living in the Real World

Roundtable Discussion

Looking at Last Year The Zenor Steel board of directors now turns its attention to some of the expenses of last year's growth. Although the company is not experiencing growth as strong as it did several years ago, it is nevertheless growing.

Draw Conclusions What are the costs of expanding a business?

Continued on page 699

Example 1

The owner of Posner's Deli plans to expand the business by opening a new store. Growth expenses include the following:

Marketing survey	$ 4,500.00 plus $15.00 per person for 150 people interviewed
Land	80,000.00
Building construction	750,000.00
Architect's fee	7.00% of the cost of construction
Surfacing parking lot	4.90 per square foot for 6,000 square feet
Legal fees	19,975.00
Equipment and fixtures	160,500.00
Additional stock	65,000.00
Miscellaneous expenses	4,000.00

What is the total cost for the expansion of Posner's Deli?

Continued on next page

Living in the Real World

Answers may vary, but could include construction fees, consultation fees, legal fees, etc.

National Standards for Business Education

Standard 1	Mathematical Foundations
Standard 2	Number Relationships and Operations

National Council of Teachers of Mathematics Standards

Standard 1	Numbers and Operations
Standard 6	Problem Solving
Standard 8	Communication

1 FOCUS

When a business decides to expand in some way, there are costs involved. In this section students will learn how to find the total cost of expansion.

In-Class Examples
Work through these exercises with students before having them do the Self-Check.
1. $1,296 + $32,650 + ($15.25 × 400) **$40,046**
2. $110,200 + $56,520 + ($31,875 × 5.5%) **$168,473.13**
3. $88,277 + $2,760 + ($12,675 × 8%) + ($25 × 50) **$93,301**

COMMUNICATION SKILLS

Investigate and Report
Students investigate, then report local costs for:
- Having a marketing survey done.
- Purchasing a plot of land in a commercial area.
- Having an architect draw the plans for a new building.
- Renting a new building (find the cost per month, per square foot).

2 TEACH

Have students discuss the costs listed in Example 1 on pages 695 and 696. Compare these costs to those that students suggested in Motivating the Lesson directly below. Have students try to think of additional costs. You may want to make a master list of the ideas.

In Example 1, have students find the total cost of expansion if the business does not conduct the marketing survey. Discuss how this changes the total. Then, find the total cost of expansion if the marketing survey is only for 100 people.

Motivating the Lesson
Have students work in groups. Ask each group to imagine that they are the owners of a business. Then, have them list ways in which their business could expand. Have students share their ideas with the class. **Answers will vary.**

In-Class Examples
Find the total cost of expansion for the business.
1. Harry's Construction.
   Purchase truck: $52,000.
   Purchase backhoe: $58,000.
   Surveying fees: 2 percent of $325,000. **$116,500**
2. Light Side Cafe.
   Purchase new tables: $1,500.
   Solicit new customers: $255.
   Purchase new tablecloths: $468. **$2,223**
3. Gray Bakery.
   Purchase new display case: $7,200.
   Purchase new lighting: $2,890.
   Install new lighting: 3 hours at $35 per hour. **$10,195**

STEP 1: Find the marketing survey cost.
$4,500 + ($15 \times 150)$
$= $4,500 + \quad $2,250$
$= $6,750 marketing survey cost

STEP 2: Find the architect's fee.
$750,000 \times 7\%$
$= $52,500 architect's fee

STEP 3: Find the cost of surfacing the parking lot.
$6,000 \times 4.90
$= $29,400 surfacing parking lot

STEP 4: Find the total of all items.
Total Cost of Expansion = Sum of Individual Costs
$6,750 + $80,000 + $750,000 + $52,500 + $29,400 + $19,975 + $160,500 + $65,000 + $4,000
$= **$1,168,125 total**

CONCEPT CHECK

SELF-CHECK ✔

Complete the problems, then check your answers at the end of the chapter. Find the total cost of expansion.

1.

Remodeling	$12,560
Permits	350
Equipment	4,480
Stock	14,450
Moving stock	950
Total	**$32,790**

2.

Land	$120,000
Survey	9,560
Construction	980,000
Architect	79,000
Legal fees	9,850
Total	**$1,198,410**

3. Expansion costs for Wyatt Jewelry store: legal fees, $1,500; display cases, $25,000; safe, $10,150; miscellaneous, $3,200. **Total = $39,850**

4. Expansion costs for Harriet's Fashions: new construction, $74,800; display racks, $9,450; clothing stock, $57,500; advertisements, $500.
   Total = $142,250

SECTION 22-6 PRACTICE

5. Housecleaning expansion.
   Solicit new customers for $925.
   Purchase new van for $22,470.
   Additional supplies for $324.
   What is the total cost of expansion? **$23,719**

6. Lawn-care business.
   Purchase new truck for $35,640.
   Purchase supplies for $4,875.
   Exhibit at a trade show for $2,200.
   What is the total cost of expansion? **$42,715**

7. Grandview Farms is opening a new gourmet food outlet in the Green River Mall. Grandview pays rent in advance for 3 months. The rental charge is $2,150 per month. Grandview makes a 20 percent down payment on refrigeration equipment which costs a total of $43,980. Grandview also purchased additional supplies for $15,795. What is the total cost of expansion? **$31,041**

USING CALCULATORS

When your calculator will not display enough digits, perhaps in the case of billions, it is acceptable to move the decimal point to the left any number of places in all numbers keeping count of the **total** number of decimal places. When you have calculated the answer, move the decimal point back to the right the total number of places.

8. Outdoors, Inc., is adding a new department that will specialize in hunting equipment. Outdoors pays $12,775 for redecorating an area of the store. Outdoors also makes a 30 percent down payment on new stock which costs a total of $97,785. What is the total of these growth expenses? **$42,110.50**

9. The Antique Mart is expanding by adding six new stalls available for lease. The Mart is converting a storage area of 1,800 square feet into these stalls. The costs of the expansions are as follows:

Description	Cost
Construction permit	$ 240.00
Removal of two walls	9,800.00
New lighting fixtures and installation	5,785.00
Carpet and installation	18.90 (per square yard)
Down payment on fixtures	25.00% of $8,260

What is the total cost for The Antique Mart to expand? **$21,670**

10. Central National Bank plans to open a new branch office. Central purchased property for $134,500. Construction costs for a new building totaled $875,980. In addition, Central paid an architect's fee of 7.5 percent of the cost of construction. Legal fees for the expansion totaled $6,000. New equipment and fixtures cost $124,675. Other expenses came to $7,215. What was the total cost of the expansion? **$1,214,068.50**

11. JP Industries, Inc., is searching for a new business to buy. Finders, Inc., a company that specializes in locating firms for sale, has located a small machine plant. If JP Industries purchases the firm, it must pay Finders, Inc., a finder's fee of 4.5 percent of the total worth of the machine plant. To acquire the plant, JP Industries must pay the plant its total worth of $2.45 million. JP Industries must pay legal fees amounting to 0.25 percent of the total worth of the machine plant. In addition, JP Industries must pay the debts of the machine plant. The debts amount to $165,850 plus 8.4 percent interest for 1 year. What will be the total cost of the expansion? **$3,071,356.40**

MAINTAINING YOUR SKILLS

Need Help? Go to...
Skill 5: Adding Decimals, page 732

Add.

12.
```
   78.140
+234.854
 312.994
```

13.
```
 571.800
+ 28.912
 600.712
```

14.
```
 747.249
+221.040
 969.089
```

15.
```
 4.718
+0.643
 5.361
```

WRAP-UP

Go over any problem for which a wrong answer is given.

Assignment Guide
  Basic: 5–7
  Average: 8–9

20 min.

 **ASSESS**

Error Analysis
Remind students how to calculate fees for professional services. In Example 1 on pages 695 and 696, the architect's fee is 7 percent of the cost of construction. Students need to identify the cost of construction and then multiply it by 7 percent. Students will also need to recall the formula for area to understand how to find the cost of surfacing the parking lot. Students need to remember to multiply the cost per square foot by the number of square feet in the lot.

4 **CLOSE**

Closing Activity
Find the total cost of expansion for the business.
1. Sunnyside Farms.
   Purchase tractor: $67,000.
   Purchase fertilizer: $310.
   Miscellaneous expenses: $550.
   $67,860
2. Ink Office Supplies.
   Solicit new customers: $2,045.
   Upgrade computer system: $1,099.
   Additional parking: $2,548.
   $5,692
3. Country Candles.
   Purchase materials: $782.
   Hire designer: 24 hours at $37 per hour.
   Window display: $378. **$2,048**
4. Lowell Furniture.
   Purchase new flooring: 1,200 ft^2 at $2.29 per square foot.
   Delivery: $50.
   Floor installation: 7.5 hours at $21 per hour. **$2,955.50**

Quick Quiz

1. Techno Company sold 300,000 shares of stock at $14.625 per share. The investment banker's commission was 4 percent of the value of the stock. The other expenses were 0.75 percent of the value of the stock. What net proceeds did Techno receive? **($4,179,093.75)** What is the selling expense per share? **$0.695**

2. Stella's borrowed $50,000 from a bank that charged 3.15 percent interest over prime on the loan. The term of the loan was 45 days. The prime rate is 5.75 percent. What was the maturity value of the loan? **$50,556.25**

3. The Orange Company purchased a $200,000 U.S. Treasury bill at 6.85 percent interest. The Treasury bill matures in 180 days. The bank service fee is $35. What is the cost of the Treasury bill? **($193,185)** What is the yield? **7.09%**

4. AD Adapts had a cash surplus of $950,000. The company invests in a CP for 30 days. The interest rate is 4 percent. There is a bank service fee of $30. What is the cost? **($946,863.33)** What is the yield? **4.01%**

5. The owner of Renko Electronics plans to expand the business by selling products online. The company pays legal fees of $18,500 and purchases computer equipment for $15,090. A Web designer is hired for 30 hours at $45 per hour. What is the total cost for the expansion? **$34,940**

SECTION 22-1 **CONCEPT CHECK** (p. 683)

1. Taxable income: $145,000 − $60,000 = $85,000
   Tax: $13,750 + 34% of ($85,000 − $75,000) = $13,750 + (0.34 × $10,000) = $13,750 + $3,400 = **$17,150 federal corporate income tax**

2. Taxable income: $219,000 − $154,000 = $65,000
   Tax: $7,500 + 25% of ($65,000 − $50,000) = $7,500 + (0.25 × $15,000) = $7,500 + $3,750 = **$11,250 federal corporate income tax**

SECTION 22-2 **CONCEPT CHECK** (p. 686, 687)

1. Net proceeds: $8,000,000 − $432,000 = **$7,568,000**
2. Net proceeds: $30,000,000 − $1,440,000 = **$28,560,000**
3. Cost per share = $1,112,000 ÷ 1,000,000 = **$1.112**
4. Cost per share = $1,200,000 ÷ 900,000 = **$1.333**

SECTION 22-3 **CONCEPT CHECK** (p. 689)

1. Interest = $100,000 × 0.10 × $\frac{100}{360}$ = $2,777.78
   Maturity Value = $100,000.00 + $2,777.78 = **$102,777.78**

2. Interest = $150,000 × 0.095 × $\frac{140}{360}$ = $5,541.67
   Maturity Value = $150,000.00 + $5,541.67 = **$155,541.67**

3. Interest = $120,000 × (0.06 + 0.02) × $\frac{60}{360}$ = $1,600.00
   Maturity Value = $120,000 + $1,600 = **$121,600**

4. Interest = $150,000 × (0.06 + 0.025) × $\frac{150}{360}$ = $5,312.50
   Maturity Value = $150,000.00 + $5,312.50 = **$155,312.50**

SECTION 22-4 **CONCEPT CHECK** (p. 692)

1. Interest = $120,000 × 4.00% × $\frac{30}{360}$ = $400
   Cost = $120,000 − $400 + $35 = **$119,635**

2. Interest = $200,000 × 3.75% × $\frac{90}{360}$ = $1,875
   Cost = $200,000 − $1,875 + $50 = **$198,175**

3. Yield = $400 ÷ ($119,635 × $\frac{30}{360}$) = **0.040122 or 4.012%**

4. Yield = $1,875 ÷ ($198,175 × $\frac{90}{360}$) = **0.037845 or 3.785%**

SECTION 22-5 **CONCEPT CHECK** (p. 694)

1. Interest = $600,000 × 4% × $\frac{30}{360}$ = $2,000
   Cost = $600,000 − $2,000 + $75 = **$598,075**

2. Interest = $1,000,000 × 3.75% × $\frac{90}{360}$ = $9,375
   Cost = $1,000,000 − $9,375 + $0 = **$990,625**

3. Yield = $2,000 ÷ ($598,075 × $\frac{30}{360}$) = **4.0128% or 4.013%**

4. Yield = $9,375 ÷ ($990,625 × $\frac{90}{360}$) = **3.7854% or 3.785%**

SECTION 22-6 **CONCEPT CHECK** (p. 696)

1. Total = **$32,790**
2. Total = **$1,198,410**
3. Total = **$39,850**
4. Total = **$142,250**

Living in the Real World

Roundtable Discussion

A Historical Perspective Businesspersons and historians can't forget the causes of the Great Depression even to this day. Many people blame corporate greed, overextension of credit, excess debt, and lack of controls on the buying and selling of stock. On "Black Monday," October 29, 1929, more than 16 million shares of stock were traded. It took another 39 years for the volume of trades to reach that number again. The Depression had a profound and long-lasting effect on the life, economic systems, and political relationships of the entire world.

1 Investigate. Use the Internet and magazines to find out what the Dow Jones Industrial average is. What is the Dow Jones average today? If the average fell 100 points in a day before the Crash, what would that mean? If the average falls 100 points today, what does that mean?

2 Critical Thinking. In the 1920s, many people bought stock on margin. That means buyers buy shares with a small down payment, with the balance to follow. In effect, instead of investing money in a company, someone who buys on margin gives the company a small amount of money with the promise to pay more. What are the drawbacks of such a system for individual buyers and companies?

Living in the Real World

1. The current Dow Jones Industrial Average (DJIA) will vary. Suppose it is 7,700. If it fell 100 points to 7,600 then that would be a 1.3 percent drop. On October 28, 1929 the DJIA fell from 298.97 to 260.64, which is a 12.8 percent drop. The next day it fell to 230.07, which is an 11 percent drop. The two-day drop from 298.97 to 230.97 is a drop of 68.9 points or 23 percent.

2. Buying on margin works if the stock increases in price. You can then sell at a higher price and pay for the stock at the original price. If the stock price goes down, the buyer is responsible for the original amount of money.

REVIEW OF KEY WORDS

corporations (p. 682)
taxable income (p. 682)
stocks (p. 685)
bonds (p. 685)
underwriting commission (p. 685)

commercial loans (p. 688)
maturity value (p. 688)
prime rate (p. 689)
Treasury bill (p. 691)
discount (p. 691)

face value (p. 691)
yield (p. 691)
commercial paper (p. 693)
merge (p. 695)
growth expenses (p. 695)

Match one of the key words above with a definition below.

1. an unsecured promissory note issued by various companies. **commercial paper**

2. when a business combines with another business. **merge**

3. the portion of your company's gross income that remains after normal business expenses are deducted. **taxable income**

4. may include construction fees, consultation fees, legal fees, etc. **growth expenses**

5. when these are issued, the buyer is lending money to your business. **bonds**

6. includes the principal borrowed and the interest owed on the loan. **maturity value**

7. a business loan. **commercial loan**

8. when these are issued, the buyer becomes part owner of your business. **stocks**

9. an amount of money paid to the investment banker who helps you distribute the stocks and bonds. **underwriting commission**

10. when you purchase one, you are actually lending money to the government. **Treasury bill**

CHAPTER **Study Guide and Assessment**

22

Skills and Concepts

SECTION OBJECTIVE 22-1 AND EXAMPLES

Compute the taxable income and the corporate income tax.

Use Figure 22.1 on page 682 to find the federal corporate income tax.
  Gross Income: **$175,000**
  Deductions: **$38,000**

STEP 1: Find the taxable income.
    Annual Gross Income − Deductions
        $175,000   − $38,000   = $137,000 taxable income

STEP 2: Find the federal corporate income tax. (Refer to Figure 22.1 on page 682.)
        The tax is $22,250 + 39 percent of the amount over $100,000.
        $22,250 + ($37,000 × 39%) = **$36,680 federal corporate income tax**

REVIEW EXERCISES
Refer to Figure 22.1 on page 682 for federal corporate income tax.

	Annual Gross Income	Deductions	Taxable Income	Total Tax
11.	$ 230,000	$ 82,371	a. $147,629	b. $40,825.31
12.	512,054	209,732	a. $302,322	b. $101,155.58
13.	127,932	85,403	a. $42,529	b. $6,379.35
14.	983,210	356,008	a. $627,202	b. $213,248.68
15.	651,287	410,911	a. $240,376	b. $76,996.64
16.	1,800,529	432,877	a. $1,367,652	b. $465,001.68
17.	341,900	99,812	a. $242,088	b. $77,664.32

SECTION OBJECTIVE 22-2 AND EXAMPLES

Calculate the selling expenses and the net proceeds from an issue of stocks and bonds.

Find the net proceeds and the cost per share for:
    Value of stock: **$7,000,000 for 500,000 shares.**
    Commission: **4.00 percent of the value of the stock.**
    Other selling expenses: **0.3 percent of the value of the stock.**

STEP 1a: Find the underwriting commission.
        Value of Issue × Percent of Underwriting Commission
            $7,000,000 ×   4%   = $280,000 commission
            $7,000,000 ×   0.3%   = $21,000 other selling expenses

STEP 1b: Find the total selling expenses.
        $280,000 + $21,000 = $301,000 total selling expenses

REINFORCEMENT

Section 22-1
Use **Figure 22.1** (page 682) to find the federal corporate tax.
1. Gross income: $73,500.
   Deductions: $8,900. **$11,150**
2. Gross income: $342,879.
   Deductions: $27,875. **$95,351.36**

STEP 2: Find the net proceeds.

Value of Issue − Total Selling Expenses

$7,000,000   − $301,000   = $6,699,000 net proceeds

STEP 3: Find the cost per share.

$301,000 ÷ 500,000 = $0.602 cost per share

REVIEW EXERCISES

Complete the table.

	Value of Issue	Percent	Commission Expenses	Other Expenses	Total Selling Expenses	Net Proceeds	Number of Shares	Selling Cost per Share
18.	$ 1,200,000	5.0%	a.	$ 38,600	b.	c.	35,000	d. $2.82
19.	860,000	7.0%	a.	45,980	b.	c.	27,000	d. $3.93
20.	5,750,000	6.5%	a.	73,500	b.	c.	150,000	d. $2.98
21.	8,900,000	6.0%	a.	120,000	b.	c.	190,000	d. $3.44
22.	32,900,000	8.0%	a.	98,500	b.	c.	1,150,000	d. $2.37
23.	39,800,000	5.5%	a.	110,500	b.	c.	1,500,000	d. $1.53

18. a. $60,000
b. $98,600
c. $1,101,400
19. a. $60,200
b. $106,180
c. $753,820
20. a. $373,750
b. $447,250
c. $5,302,750
21. a. $534,000
b. $654,000
c. $8,246,000
22. a. $2,632,000
b. $2,730,500
c. $30,169,500
23. a. $2,189,000
b. $2,299,500
c. $37,500,500

SECTION OBJECTIVE 22-3 AND EXAMPLES

Determine the maturity value of a commercial loan.

Tristan's Department Store borrowed $130,000 from the bank to pay for a new line of clothing. The bank lent the money at 7 percent ordinary interest for 90 days. What was the maturity value of the loan?

STEP 1: Find the interest owed.

Principal × Rate × Time

$130,000 × 7% × $\frac{90}{360}$ = $2,275 interest owed

STEP 2: Find the maturity value.

Principal + Interest Owed

$130,000 + $2,275   = $132,275 maturity value

24. a. $1,218.75; b. $66,218.75
25. a. $2,200.00; b. $112,200.00
26. a. $1,957.08; b. $87,357.08
27. a. $9,375.00; b. $259,375.00
28. a. $1,716.75; b. $67,116.75
29. a. $10,006.25; b. $810,506.25

REVIEW EXERCISES

Complete the table. Determine the ordinary interest and maturity value.

	Principal	×	Rate	×	Time	=	Interest	Maturity Value
24.	$ 65,000	×	7.50%	×	90 days	=	a.	b.
25.	110,000	×	6.00%	×	120 days	=	a.	b.
26.	85,400	×	8.25%	×	100 days	=	a.	b.
27.	250,000	×	5.00%	×	270 days	=	a.	b.
28.	65,400	×	10.50%	×	90 days	=	a.	b.
29.	800,500	×	7.50%	×	60 days	=	a.	b.

REINFORCEMENT

Section 22-2

Round answers to the nearest tenth of a cent.

1. Find the net proceeds.
   Value of stock: $23,000,000.
   Commission: 4.5 percent of the value of the stock.
   Other selling expenses: 0.4 percent of the value of the stock. **$21,873,000**

2. Find the cost per share.
   Number of shares: 1,200,000
   Total selling expenses: $1,487,000 **$1.239**

Section 22-3

Find the ordinary interest owed and the maturity value.

1. Borrowed $180,000 for 90 days.
   Interest rate: 8.5 percent. **$3,825; $183,825**

2. Borrowed $127,420 for 60 days.
   Interest rate: 2.15 percent over prime.
   Prime rate: 6.75 percent. **$1,890.06; $129,310.06**

CHAPTER 22 Study Guide and Assessment

SECTION OBJECTIVE 22-4 AND EXAMPLES

Work out the cost and yield of a Treasury bill.

Find the cost and the yield of a Treasury bill with a face value of $150,000 that was purchased at 5.5 percent for 60 days. The service fee was $40.

STEP 1: Find the interest.

Principal × Rate × Time

$150,000 × 5.5% × $\frac{60}{360}$ = $1,375 interest

STEP 2: Find the cost.

(Face Value of Bill − Interest) + Service Fee

($150,000 − $1,375) + $40 = $148,665 cost of a Treasury bill

STEP 3: Find the yield.

Interest ÷ (Cost × Time)

$1,375 ÷ ($148,665 × $\frac{60}{360}$) = 5.55% yield of a Treasury bill

30. b. $34,879.17
31. b. $64,325.83
32. b. $99,182.50
33. a. $2,041.17
    b. $123,008.83
34. a. $2,715.00
    b. $72,320.00
35. a. $2,093.82
    b. $95,966.18

REVIEW EXERCISES

Compute the interest, the cost, and the yield of the Treasury bill.

	Face Value of Treasury Bill	Interest Rate	Time in Days	Interest	Bank Service Fee	Cost of Treasury Bill	Yield
30.	$ 35,000	5.00%	30	a. $145.83	$25	b.	c. 5.02%
31.	65,000	6.50%	60	a. $704.17	30	b.	c. 6.57%
32.	100,000	3.43%	90	a. $857.50	40	b.	c. 3.46%
33.	125,000	4.90%	120	a.$2,041.17	50	b.	c. 4.98%
34.	75,000	7.24%	180	a.$2,715.00	35	b.	c. 7.51%
35.	98,000	9.38%	82	a.$2,093.82	60	b.	c. 9.59%

SECTION OBJECTIVE 22-5 AND EXAMPLES

Determine the cost and yield for commercial paper.

Find the cost and yield of the CP. Five hundred thousand dollars is invested at 5 percent interest for 60 days. Service fee of $75.

STEP 1: Find the interest.

Principal × Rate × Time

$500,000 × 5% × $\frac{60}{360}$ = $4,166.67 interest

STEP 2: Find the cost.

(Face Value of CP − Interest) + Service Fee

$500,000 − $4,166.67 + $75 = $495,908.33 cost of the CP

STEP 3: Find the yield.

Interest ÷ (Cost × Time)

$4,166.67 ÷ ($495,908.33 × $\frac{60}{360}$) = 5.04% yield of the CP

REINFORCEMENT

Section 22-4

Find the ordinary interest, cost, and yield of the Treasury bill.

1. Face value: $75,000.
   Interest rate: 8 percent.
   Time in days: 120.
   Bank service fee: $35. **$2,000; $73,035; 8.22%**

2. Face value: $200,000.
   Interest rate: 7.35 percent.
   Time in days: 30.
   Bank service fee: $38. **$1,225; $198,813; 7.39%**

36. a. $2,625.00; b. $597,375.00
37. a. $6,662.50; b. $643,372.50
38. a. $10,057.50; b. $889,987.50
39. a. $18,366.67; b. $931,663.33
40. a. $62,725.00; b. $1,237,300.00
41. a. $114,481.11; b. $6,885,468.89

REVIEW EXERCISES
Use ordinary interest at exact time to solve.

	Face Value of CP	Interest Rate	Time in Days	Interest	Bank Service Fee	Cost of CP	Yield
36.	$ 600,000	5.25%	30	a.	No Fee	b.	c. 5.27%
37.	650,000	6.15%	60	a.	$35	b.	c. 6.21%
38.	900,000	4.47%	90	a.	45	b.	c. 4.52%
39.	950,000	5.80%	120	a.	30	b.	c. 5.91%
40.	1,300,000	9.65%	180	a.	25	b.	c. 10.14%
41.	7,000,000	7.18%	82	a.	50	b.	c. 7.30%

SECTION OBJECTIVE 22-6 AND EXAMPLES

Compute the total cost of expanding a business.

The owner of Digital Designs plans to expand the business by adding some new equipment. Growth expenses include the following:

What is the total cost for the expansion of Digital Designs?

Digital cameras	$ 3,400
Multimedia editing equipment	13,240
Lighting fixtures	8,300
Printers	6,500

STEP: Find the total of all items.   Total Cost of Expansion = Sum of Individual Costs
$3,400 + $13,240 + $8,300 + $6,500 = **$31,440 total**

REVIEW EXERCISES

42. The Fashion Barn is adding a shoe department. Fashion Barn pays $18,560 to convert an area of the store for the shoes. It also pays a 25 percent down payment on new stock that costs a total of $54,300. What is the total of these growth expenses? **$32,135 area of the store for the shoes**

43. The Cranberry Goose Flower Shop is expanding and purchases a new delivery van for $32,000. It also purchases supplies for $6,431 and has additional advertising costs of $1,200. What is the total cost of expansion? **$39,631**

Find the total cost of expansion.

44.

Remodeling	$54,900
Permits	1,900
Computer system	18,700
Phone installation	2,300
Shelving	8,500
Restocking	3,500
Total	**$89,800**

45.

Vehicle	$28,000
Signage	3,500
Additional supplies	4,368
Advertising	5,400
Additional insurance	2,300
Total	**$43,568**

Study Guide and Assessment ▶ **703**

REINFORCEMENT

Section 22-5
Find the cost and the yield for the CP.
1. Face value: $775,000.
   Interest rate: 7 percent.
   Time in days: 120.
   Bank service fee: none. **$756,916.67; 7.17%**

Section 22-6
1. Find the total cost of expansion for the Eastern Draperies business. Purchase machinery: $118,000. Purchase material: $10,000. Install machinery: 6 hours at $25 per hour. **$128,150**

National Standards for Business Education

Section Objectives	1. Mathematical Foundations	2. Number Relationships and Operations	3. Patterns, Functions, and Algebra	4. Measurements	5. Statistics and Probability	6. Problem-Solving Applications	
23-1 Inflation (pp. 706–709) Compute the inflation rate, the current price, and the original price.	X	X					
23-2 Gross Domestic Product (pp. 710–712) Explain and compute the gross domestic product.	X	X					
23-3 Consumer Price Index (pp. 713–715) Calculate the consumer price index, the current cost, and the cost of any given commodity.	X	X					
23-4 Budget (pp. 716–719) Allocate revenue and expenses and analyze a budget.	X	X					

(Source: Reprinted with permission from the National Standards for Business Education, copyright © 2001 by National Business Education Association, 1914 Association Drive, Reston, Virginia 21901-1596)

SCANS Correlation

Foundation Skills

Basic Skills	Reading	Writing	Math	Listening	Speaking	
Thinking Skills	Creative Thinking	Decision Making	Problem Solving	Seeing Things in the Mind's Eye	Knowing How to Learn	Reasoning
Personal Qualities	Responsibility	Self-Esteem	Sociability	Self-Management	Integrity/Honesty	

This chapter's highlighted blocks indicate the chapter's content coverage in the Student Edition and the Teacher Wraparound Edition.

1. Numbers & Operations	2. Algebra	3. Geometry	4. Measurement	5. Data Analysis & Probability	6. Problem Solving	7. Reasoning & Proof	8. Communication	9. Connections	10. Representations
X					X			X	
X					X			X	
X					X			X	
X					X			X	

SCANS Correlation

Workplace Competencies

Resources	Allocating Time	Allocating Money	Allocating Material and Facility Resources	Allocating Human Resources		
Information	Acquiring and Evaluating Information	Organizing and Maintaining Information	Interpreting and Communicating Information	Using Computers to Process Information		
Interpersonal Skills	Participating as a Member of a Team	Teaching Others	Serving Clients/Customers	Exercising Leadership	Negotiating to Arrive at a Decision	Working with Cultural Diversity
Systems	Understanding Systems	Monitoring and Correcting Performance	Improving and Designing Systems			
Technology	Selecting Technology	Applying Technology to Task	Maintaining and Troubleshooting Technology			

What You'll Learn
In this chapter you'll focus on how to plan a corporate budget and how a company takes into account economic trend indicators (such as, inflation, gross domestic product, and the consumer price index).

Why It's Important
Business executives, labor leaders, and other private citizens use the Gross National Product (GNP), Gross Domestic Product (GDP), and Consumer Price Index (CPI) as guides in making economic decisions. The CPI and its components are used to adjust for price changes, inflation, and as a means for adjusting income payments. Some private firms and individuals use the CPI to keep rents, royalties, alimony payments, and child support payments in line with changing prices. Changes in the CPI affect the cost of lunches for the 26.7 million children who eat lunch at school.

Key Word Review
Graphic Organizer
First ask students to make a diagram with four large circles labeled: Inflation, Gross Domestic Product, Consumer Price Index, and Budget. Second, ask students to find each key word in the chapter and note in which part of the chapter it appears. Third, ask students to write each key word in the appropriate circle, and then write their definition.

4.5

7.75

CHAPTER 23
Corporate Planning

What You'll Learn
Section 23-1 Compute the inflation rate, the current price, and the original price.

Section 23-2 Explain and compute the gross domestic product.

Section 23-3 Calculate the consumer price index, the current cost, and the cost of any given commodity.

Section 23-4 Allocate revenue and expenses, and analyze a budget.

When Will You Ever Use This?
To know where you're going, you'll need a plan. In business, it's no different. As a matter of fact, it's extremely important. Corporate planning occurs for strategic short-term and long-range planning. Economic considerations are factored into a corporate budget.

Key Words to Know
- inflation
- gross domestic product (GDP)
- real GDP
- per capita GDP
- consumer price index (CPI)
- budget

Mathematics Online
To learn more about corporate planning, visit the *Mathematics with Business Applications* Web site at www.busmath.glencoe.com.

CLASSROOM RESOURCES

Application and Enrichment
- *Teacher Wraparound Edition*
- *Teacher Resource Binder, Blackline Masters*
- *Interactive Lesson Planner CD-ROM*
- *PowerPoint® Presentations CD-ROM*

Review and Enforcement
- Mathematics Online
  www.busmath.glencoe.com
- *Teacher Resource Binder, Internet Resources*

- *Student Activity Workbook*
- *Student Activity Workbook, Teacher Annotated Edition*
- *School-to-Home Activity Workbook*

Assessment and Evaluation
- *Assessment Binder, Reproducible Tests*
- *Assessment Binder, Alternative Assessment Strategies*
- **Exam**View® *Pro Test Generator* CD-ROM

For the Teacher
- *Student Activity Workbook, Teacher Annotated Edition*
- *Assessment Binder*
- *Interactive Lesson Planner CD-ROM*
- *Teacher Resource Binder*
- Mathematics Online
  www.busmath.glencoe.com

For the Student
- *Student Activity Workbook*
- *School-to-Home Activity Workbook*

Est 1887

Living in the Real World

Vintage Vamp

Vintage Vamp offers its discriminating buyers beautiful vintage and antique dresses and accessories. Customers are treated to tea and cookies and shown the unique and ever-changing collection gathered by owner Joanna Chinen. Chinen scours estate sales, costume-design stores, and even yard sales to find beautiful clothing made from 1900-1955. In this chapter, follow Chinen as she contemplates current sales, buying power, and the store's future.

Read on. Go to . . .

705

Living in the Real World

Story's Summary

Joanna Chinen is the owner of Vintage Vamp, a shop that sells vintage and antique dresses and accessories, but sales have slowed with an increase in inflation, and it's time for Chinen to reconsider her business approach. In this chapter, she contemplates current sales, buying power, and her store's future.

Did You Know...

Using the U.S. Bureau of Labor Statistics inflation calculator, one can compute that $500 in 1982 had the same buying power as $938 in 2002, but $500 in 1952 would be equivalent to $3,415 in 2002.

Think about This

The 1970s in America saw the highest ever rate of peacetime inflation. How might this have affected consumer spending habits?

LOCAL STANDARDS

National Standards for Business Education

Standard 1	Mathematical Foundations
Standard 2	Number Relationships and Operations

National Council of Teachers of Mathematics Standards

Standard 1	Numbers and Operations
Standard 6	Problem Solving
Standard 8	Communication

① FOCUS

Sometimes, businesses have increased costs that are caused by inflation. In this lesson, students will learn how to find the inflation rate, current price, and original price.

In-Class Examples

Work through these exercises with students before having them do the Self-Check.

1. ($900 − $850) ÷ $850 **0.059**
2. $670.75 − ($670.95 × 15%) **$570.31**
3. $3.99 ÷ (1 − 7.8%) **$4.33**

SECTION 23-1 Inflation

○ **Section Objective**

Compute the inflation rate, the current price, and the original price.

Economies go through ups and downs as a result of wars, foreign competition, and changes in technology. One way to measure economic activity is by the rate of inflation. **Inflation** is the general increase in the cost of goods and services. At the corporate level, inflation is observed as increases in (1) wholesale prices, (2) cost of utilities, (3) cost of production and shipping, and (4) demands for scarce materials. Some of the causes of inflation are (1) heavy spending (resulting in high demand), (2) increased production costs while producers try to maintain profit levels, and (3) lack of competition.

Important Questions to Ask Yourself	What Formula Do I Use?
How do you figure out the **inflation rate**?	Inflation Rate $= \dfrac{\text{(Current Price − Original Price)}}{\text{Original Price}}$ [Note: The inflation rate is expressed as a percent increase over a specified time period (usually to the nearest tenth of a percent).]
How do I calculate the **current price**?	Current Price = Original Price + (Original Price × Inflation Rate)
How do I compute the **original price**?	Original Price $= \dfrac{\text{Current Price}}{\text{(1 + Inflation Rate)}}$

Living in the Real World

Vintage Vamp

Peddling Clothes   Until this year many of Chinen's Vintage Vamp customers bought her clothes on a whim. Now, however, inflation is on the rise, and Chinen is considering how to reorient her merchandise to increase slower sales.

Draw Conclusions   What are some causes of inflation?

Continued on page 710

Example 1

Liza Turner works in the summer as a junior staff reporter for the local newspaper. Turner was asked to write a story about changes in the economy. One section was on inflation. She had the following data:

• A two-door car sold for $16,000 two years ago. The same model, comparably equipped, sells for $16,495 today. Find the inflation rate.

BUSINESS NOTES

Comparing

The world's wealthiest countries have a far greater income (at an average annual per capita level of gross domestic product (GDP) of about $16,000), than the rest of the world. Almost 70 percent of the world's population has an average annual per capita level of GDP of less than $4,000. The economic dilemma is how to close the large gap in living standards of the world's population. Discuss this economic dilemma.

Living in the Real World

Inflation is caused by heavy spending that results in high demand and increased production costs, while producers try to maintain profit levels and lack of competition.

- The median sale price of a home in Florida last year was $116,700. The inflation rate for homes in Florida this past year was 10 percent. Find the current median sale price of a home in Florida.
- A single apartment at the local state university rents for $2,110 per semester this year. This reflects a 5.5 percent inflation rate increase over the original rent last year. Find the original rent.

STEP 1: Find the inflation rate for the two-door car.

$$\frac{(\text{Current Price} - \text{Original Price})}{\text{Original Price}}$$

$$\frac{(\$16,495 - \$16,000)}{\$16,000} = \frac{\$495}{\$16,000} = 0.0309 \text{ or } 3.1\% \text{ inflation rate}$$

STEP 2: Find the current median sale price of a home in Florida.

Original Price + (Original Price × Inflation Rate)

$$\$116,700 + (\$116,700 \times 10\%) =$$
$$\$116,700 + \$11,670 = \$128,370 \text{ current median sale price}$$

STEP 3: Find the original rent.

$$\frac{\text{Current Price} \div (1 + \text{Inflation Rate})}{}$$

$$\$2,110 \div (1 + 5.5\%) =$$
$$\$2,110 \div 1.055 = \$2,000 \text{ original rent}$$

16495 [−] 16000 [=] 495 [÷] 16000 [=] 0.0309375

DEFLATION RATE Many factors can lead to inflation. One example is the government printing too much money. When the supply of goods is greater than the demand, the result is deflation. Deflation occurs when prices decrease over a period of time. Although deflation is the opposite of inflation, the calculations are quite similar.

Important Questions to Ask Yourself	What Formula Do I Use?
How do I find the deflation rate?	$\text{Deflation Rate} = \frac{(\text{Current Price} - \text{Original Price})}{\text{Original Price}}$

(**Example 2**)

- Find the deflation rate for a laptop computer that sold for $1,495 last year and is selling for $1,195 this year.
- The deflation rate for handheld calculators has been 25 percent over the past five years. Find the current price of a handheld calculator that sold for $110.96 five years ago.

Continued on next page

Section 23-1 Inflation ▶ **707**

COOPERATIVE LEARNING

Inflation
Group students and assign each an item, such as a loaf of bread, a gallon of milk, a dozen eggs, or a pound of sugar. Ask groups to find the current price of the item and then the prices 5, 10, and 25 years ago. Have them determine if any rise in price is the result of inflation or other factors. Students calculate the percent of increase or decrease for their group's product. Have each group graph its findings and make an oral presentation to explain the graph and inflation. [LS] , [CL]

---

2 TEACH

Have students discuss how increases in wholesale prices, cost of production, cost of shipping, and cost of utilities can affect a business. Sometimes demand increases for materials that are scarce. This also affects businesses.

Sometimes items decrease in price over time instead of increase. Personal computers are a good example. A well-equipped personal computer ten years ago would not be considered so well equipped in today's market. Therefore, the price would be less today than it was ten years ago. Advances in technology cause the market to change.

Motivating the Lesson
Have students work in groups. Give each group the price of an item purchased in different years. Have students create a line graph of the data. Then have students discuss what the line graph shows. **Answers will vary.**

In-Class Examples
1. Original price: $2.00.
   Current price: $4.00.
   Find the inflation rate. **100%**
2. Current price: $12.50.
   Inflation rate: 3 percent.
   Find the original price. **$12.14**
3. Original price: $8.99.
   Inflation rate: 4 percent.
   Find the current price. **$9.35**
4. Original price: $32.75.
   Current price: $30.25.
   Find the deflation rate. **−7.6%**

3 **ASSESS**

Error Analysis

Remind students that a negative symbol in front of the rate shows that it is a deflation rate instead of an inflation rate. Students may forget to write the negative symbol. To reinforce the distinction between rates of inflation and deflation, give students several positive and negative percents. Have them state whether each one could represent an inflation rate or a deflation rate.

- The deflation rate for a gallon of gasoline has been 8.4 percent over the past three years. A gallon of gasoline sells for $1.199 per gallon today. What did a gallon of gasoline sell for three years ago?

STEP 1: Find the deflation rate of the laptop.

$$\frac{(\text{Current Price} - \text{Original Price})}{\text{Original Price}}$$

$$\frac{\$1,195 - \$1,495}{\$1,495} = \frac{-\$300}{\$1,495} = -0.2006 \text{ or } -20.1\% \text{ deflation rate}$$

(The negative sign indicates deflation.)

STEP 2: Find the current price of the calculators.

Original Price − (Original Price × Deflation Rate)

$110.96	−	($110.96	×	25%)	=
$110.96	−			$27.74	= **$83.22 current price of a handheld calculator**

STEP 3: Find the original price of a gallon of gasoline.

Current Price ÷ (1 − Deflation Rate)

$1.199	÷	(1 −	8.4%)	=
$1.199	÷	(1 −	0.084)	=
$1.199	÷	0.916		= **$1.3089 or $1.309 gasoline sold for three years ago**

CONCEPT CHECK

SELF-CHECK✔

Complete the problems, then check your answers at the end of the chapter.

1. ($80 − $75) ÷ $75 = 6.7%
2. ($12,400 × 8.2%) = $1,016.80
   $12,400 + $1,016.80 = $13,416.80
3. (1 + 10%) = 1.10
   $28.05 ÷ 1.10 = $25.50
4. ($350 − $498) = −$148
   −$148 ÷ $498 = −0.2971 = −29.7% or 29.7% deflation

1. Original price was $75. Current price is $80. Find the inflation rate.

2. Original price was $12,400. Inflation rate is 8.2 percent. Find the current price.

3. Current price is $28.05. Inflation rate is 10 percent. Find the original price.

4. Original price was $498. Current price is $350. Find the deflation rate.

SECTION 23-1 PRACTICE

Complete the table.

	Inflation Rate	Current Price	Original Price
5.	6.4%	$ 4,670.00	$ 4,389.80
6.	1.5%	79.99	78.79
7.	5.0%	**$154.35**	147.00
8.	3.6%	**$18,086.49**	17,458.00
9.	0.7%	1.29	**$1.28**
10.	12.4%	243,750.00	**$216,859.43**

GLOBAL PERSPECTIVE

Inflation Trends

In Germany after World War I, inflation was so bad that there are stories of people sitting down to eat in a restaurant and, by the time they got up to leave, the price of the meal had doubled. Students choose a country in Eastern Europe, North America, or South America. Students research and report on inflation in that country. The report could be on a specific time period, such as Mexico around 1990, or Russia in 1998, or a more recent time period. Students include in their report the rate of inflation, inflation trends, and interesting facts and stories.

11. Original price: $16.95.
Current price: $18.49.
Find the inflation rate. **9.1%**

12. Original price: $3.50.
Inflation rate: 12.4 percent.
Find the current price. **$3.93**

13. Current price: $4,370.
Inflation rate: 6.3 percent.
Find the original price. **$4,111.01**

14. Original price: $0.989.
Current price: $0.899. **−9.1%**
Find the deflation rate. **or 9.1% deflation**

15. Original price: $134,980.
Deflation rate: 4.2 percent.
Find the current price. **$129,310.84**

16. Current price: $27,495.
Deflation rate: 14.61 percent.
Find the original price. **$32,199.32**

17. Original price: $3,680.
Current price: $3,680.
Find the inflation rate. **0%**

18. Original price: $0.49.
Inflation rate: 19.8 percent.
Find the current price. **$0.59**

19. The inflation rate over the past year for grocery products is 5.7 percent. How much would a cart of groceries cost today if it cost $72.70 last year? **$76.84**

20. The median sale price of a house in Fort Lauderdale, Florida, was $153,100 last year. This year the median sale price of a house in Fort Lauderdale, Florida, is $172,700. Find the rate of inflation for the median price of a house in Fort Lauderdale, Florida, over the last year. **12.8%**

21. At the grand opening of the Bayview Market in 1938, a 10-ounce box of cereal cost $0.10. Today the box costs $2.99. What is the inflation rate for cereal over that time period? **2,890%**

22. At Bayview Market a quart of milk could be purchased for $0.11 in 1938. The inflation rate for milk since that time is 700 percent. What does a quart of milk cost today? **$0.88**

23. At Bayview Market 2 pounds of coffee cost $5.99 today. The rate of inflation for coffee since 1938 is 1,715.2 percent. What did 2 pounds of coffee cost in 1938? **$0.33**

24. Last year a new car sold for $24,950. A comparably equipped car sells this year for $22,500.
   a. What is the inflation rate? **−9.8% or 9.8% deflation**
   b. What is true of the inflation rate when the current price is less than the original price? **It is negative.**
   c. Instead of inflation, what is this called? **Deflation**

MAINTAINING YOUR SKILLS

Need Help? Go to...
▶ Skill 30: Finding the Percentage, page 757
▶ Skill 31: Finding the Rate, page 758

Find the percentage. Round answers to the nearest cent.

25. 3.7 percent of $436.80
   $16.16

26. 11.5 percent of $48.98
   $5.63

27. 0.4 percent of $1.79
   $0.01

Find the rate. Round answers to the nearest tenth of a percent.

28. $12.85 is what percent of $257.00? **5.0%**

29. $3.79 is what percent of $199.99? **1.9%**

30. $2,500.00 is what percent of $22,387.65? **11.2%**

Closing Activity

1. Original price: $5.00.
Current price: $6.50.
Find the inflation rate. **30%**

2. Current price: $24.75.
Inflation rate: 8 percent.
Find the original price. **$22.92**

3. Original price: $76.99.
Inflation rate: 5.4 percent.
Find the current price. **$81.15**

4. Original price: $198.30.
Current price: $189.20.
Find the deflation rate. **−4.6%**

5. Original price: $1,199.49.
Deflation rate: 14.5 percent.
Find the current price.
$1,025.56

6. Current price: $4,315.99.
Deflation rate: 8.2 percent.
Find the original price.
$4,701.51

PROBLEM SOLVING

Writing Large Numbers as Decimals
Spend ample time having students practice writing large numbers as decimals. For example, $45,800,000,000 can be written as $45.8 billion. Since most calculators can't display some of the large numbers in this lesson, it will be necessary for students to rewrite large numbers as decimals. Be sure students understand that the divisor and the dividend need to be expressed in the same way—that is, either in billions or millions.

WRAP-UP

Go over any problem for which a wrong answer is given.

Assignment Guide
   Basic: 5–10
   Average: 11–18

20 min.

National Standards for Business Education

Standard 1	Mathematical Foundations
Standard 2	Number Relationships and Operations

National Council of Teachers of Mathematics Standards

Standard 1	Numbers and Operations
Standard 6	Problem Solving
Standard 8	Communication

 **FOCUS**

The gross domestic product (GDP) measures a country's economic performance. It is used to determine how well a country is doing compared to other years. The real GDP is adjusted for inflation. The per capita GDP is the GDP divided by the population.

In-Class Examples
Work through these exercises with students before having them do the Self-Check.

1. $30 billion − ($30 billion × 5%) **$28.5 billion**
2. $45 billion ÷ $0.3 billion **150**
3. $1.5 million ÷ $900,000 **1.67**

○ **Section Objective**

Explain and compute the gross domestic product.

SECTION 23-2 Gross Domestic Product

An important measure of the country's economic health is its level of *productivity*, or how much it produces. The total value of the goods and services produced in a country in a given year is called its **gross domestic product (GDP).** Only goods (such automobiles, machinery, food, and clothing) and services (such as haircuts and appliance repairs) add to the national income. The government uses the GDP to monitor the health of the country's economy.

REAL GDP You need to compare GDP over a period of time. The effects of inflation and a change in GDP represent increases in production and income. For these reasons, you need to remove the distortions of inflation. You can do this by computing **real GDP** (or *adjusted GDP*).

POPULATION AND GDP The rate of the population growth influences GDP and economic growth. Labor and size of population are closely linked. Shifts in population can alter economic measures such as GDP. That's why GDP is often measured in a per capita (or per person) basis. The **per capita GDP** indicates the nation's *standard of living*—the amount of goods and services the average citizen can afford to buy. The per capita GDP is the GDP distributed over the population. The United States produces so much more than other countries that it has a higher standard of living.

Important Questions to Ask Yourself	What Formula Do I Use?
How do I calculate **real GDP**?	Real GDP = GDP − (GDP × Inflation Rate)
How do I compute **per capita GDP**?	Per Capita GDP = $\dfrac{\text{GDP}}{\text{Population}}$

Living in the Real World

Vintage Vamp

She Listens to Economists Chinen watches the economic news carefully, both as a businessperson, a consumer, and an investor. She knows that the inflation rate may make the nation's economic performance appear to be better than it is.

Draw Conclusions If the GDP is adjusted for inflation, does this mean it's growing or not?

Continued on page 713

Living in the Real World

Adjusting the GDP for inflation means removing the distortions of inflation to compare GDP over a period of time.

Example 1

The United States has an inflation rate of 1.9 percent and a GDP of $10,253.2 billion. What is the real GDP?

STEP: Find the real GDP.

GDP   −   (GDP   ×   Inflation Rate)

$10,253.2 billion − ($10,253.2 billion ×   1.9%)   =

$10,253.2 billion − $194.8 billion   = **$10,058.4 billion**

Example 2

The United States has a population of 284,796,887 and a GDP of $10,253.2 billion. What is the per capita GDP?

STEP: Find the per capita GDP.

$$\frac{GDP}{Population}$$

$$\frac{\$10,253,200,000,000}{284,796,887} = \textbf{\$36,001.798 or \$36,001.80}$$

10253.2 ÷ 0.284796887 = 36001.79801

CONCEPT CHECK

Complete the problems, then check your answers at the end of the chapter.

1. GDP is $43,800,000.
Inflation rate is 6.4 percent.
Find the real GDP.
($43,800,000 × 6.4%) = **$2,803,200**
$43,800,000 − $2,803,200 = **$40,996,800**

2. GDP is $92.8 million (or $92,800,000).
Population is 78,650.
Find the per capita GDP.
$92,800,000 ÷ 78,650 = **$1,179.91**

SECTION 23-2 PRACTICE

Calculate the real GDP and the per capita GDP.

	GDP	Inflation Rate	Population	Real GDP	Per Capita GDP
3.	$123.6 million	4.3%	0.4 million	a.	b. $309
4.	57,459,650	0.4%	5,365,760	a.	b. $10.71
5.	478.6 billion	6.2%	74.2 million	a.	b. $6,450.13
6.	756,500,000	2.1%	2,586,450	a.	b. $292.49
7.	2,876.7 billion	7.8%	2,456,980,000	a.	b. $1,170.83
8.	98,760,000,000	12.6%	31,478,000	a.	b. $3,137.43

3. a. $118.3 million
4. a. $57,229,811.40
5. a. $448.9 billion
6. a. $740,613,500
7. a. $2,652.3 billion
8. a. $86,316,240,000

Continued on next page

---

② TEACH

The GDP takes into account the total value of all goods produced. Each item is included only once, and it is included at its retail price. You may want to remind students that there are other prices, such as a manufacturer's price to a wholesaler or a wholesaler's price to a retailer. For the year of production, the GDP uses the year in which the item was manufactured instead of the year in which it was sold.

Motivating the Lesson

Give students the GDP, inflation rate, and population for several countries. Walk students through the steps to finding the real GDP and per capita GDP using the data. **Answers will vary.**

In-Class Examples

Find the real GDP.
1. GDP: $34,300,000,000.
Inflation rate: 6 percent.
$32,242,000,000
2. GDP: $12.3 billion.
Inflation rate: 4.5 percent.
$11.7465 billion
3. Find the per capita GDP.
GDP: $76.5 million.
Population: 2.4 million.
$31.875 million

COMMUNICATION SKILLS

Line Graph

Have students express the following figures in a line graph and then answer questions, such as: Which category increased the most between 1960 and 2000? **(Personal consumption.)** Export of goods and services dropped below zero beginning around 1980. What do you think this means? **The U.S. began importing more goods and services than it was exporting.**

Gross Domestic Product (Billions of Dollars)

	1960	1970	1980	1990	2000
Personal Consumption	332.3	648.9	1,762.9	3,831.5	6,709
Private Investment	78.9	152.4	477.9	861.7	1,848.9
Export of Goods & Services	2.4	1.2	−14.9	−71.4	−366.5
Government Consumption	113.8	237.1	569.7	1,181.4	1,746

(Source: Bureau of Labor Statistics, U.S. Department of Labor.)

(3) ASSESS

Error Analysis

In this section, students will need to write large numbers as decimals. Some students may have difficulty with this task. For example, $15,800,000,000 can be written as $15.8 billion. Give students some large numbers to practice writing.

When students are calculating the per capita GDP, there may be different units for the GDP and the population. For instance, the GDP may be expressed in billions and the population may be expressed in millions. Make sure students understand that these both must be expressed in the same unit. Give students some examples to practice converting from one unit to the other.

(4) CLOSE

Closing Activity

Find the real GDP.

1. GDP: $198,700,000,000.
   Inflation rate: 3 percent.
   $192,739,000,000

2. GDP: $289,500,000,000.
   Inflation rate: 0.8 percent.
   $287,184,000,000

Find the per capita GDP.

3. GDP: $72.4 million.
   Population: 3,000,000. **$24.13**

4. GDP: $46.7 million.
   Population: 2.1 billion.
   $46.7 ÷ 2,100 = $0.02

---

9. GDP is $768,000,000.
   Inflation rate is 4.6 percent.
   Find the real GDP. **$732,672,000**

10. GDP is $45,678,000,000.
    Population is 9,670,000.
    Find the per capita GDP. **$4,723.68**

11. Australia has a population of 16,849,496 and a GDP of $289.1 billion. The inflation rate in Australia is 3.6 percent. Find the real GDP and the per capita GDP. **$278,692,400,000; $17,157.78**

12. Greece has a GDP of $76,909,000,000. Its population is 10,538,000, and the inflation rate is 4.7 percent. Find the real GDP and the per capita GDP. **$73,294,277,000; $7,298.25**

13. Canada has a GDP of $618,326,000,000. It has a population of 30,885,000 and an inflation rate of 3.3 percent. Find the real GDP and the per capita GDP. **$597,921,242,000; $20,020.27**

14. The GDP for Israel is $65.6 billion. Its population is 6.283 million. The rate of inflation is 7.2 percent. Find the real GDP and the per capita GDP. **$60,876,800,000; $10,440.87**

15. The GDP for Austria is $191.357 billion. Its population is 8.076 million. The rate of inflation in Austria is 3.1 percent. Find the real GDP and the per capita GDP. **$185,425,000,000; $23,694.53**

16. The population of China is 1,322,141,000. China's GDP is $434,084,000,000, and the inflation rate is 10.3 percent. Find the real GDP and the per capita GDP. **$389,373,348,000; $328.32**

17.

Nation	GDP	Population	Inflation Rate
France	$1,250,699,000,000	59,361,000	2.2%
Italy	1,197,000,000,000	56,877,000	2.8%
U.K.	1,022,000,000,000	56,467,000	3.4%

Using the information above, determine:
   a. Which nation has the highest real GDP. **France: $1,223,183,622,000**
   b. Which nation has the lowest real GDP. **U.K.: $987,252,000,000**
   c. Which nation has the highest per capita GDP. **France: $21,069.37**
   d. Which nation has the lowest per capita GDP. **U.K.: $18,099.07**

18. A few years ago Argentina had a GDP of $289.1 billion and a reported inflation rate of 3,079 percent.
    a. What real GDP do you get using the formula? **−$8,612,289,000,000**
    b. Why is this impossible? **There cannot be a negative GDP and that happens when the inflation rate is greater than 100 percent.**

MAINTAINING YOUR SKILLS

Need Help? Go to...
▶ Skill 30: Finding the Percentage, page 757

Find the percentage. Round answers to the nearest cent.

19. $217,560 × 2.3% **$5,003.88**

20. $416.2 million × 3.1% **$12,902,200**

21. $31,468,917 × 0.4% **$125,875.67**

22. $17.2 billion × 1.6% **$275,200,000**

WRAP-UP

Go over any problem for which a wrong answer is given.

Assignment Guide
   Basic: 3–8
   Average: 9–11

20 min.

SECTION (23-3) Consumer Price Index

Section Objective

Calculate the consumer price index, the current cost, and the cost of any given commodity.

To remove the distortions of inflation, economists construct a statistical series to measure changes in prices over time. They start by selecting a base year. This base year serves as a comparison for all other years. To track inflation, you have to track the price of goods and services at regular intervals and then compare them to the base year. The **consumer price index (CPI)** measures the upward changes on a fixed number of products and services, such as housing, electricity, food, and transportation. It's also known as the cost-of-living index.

The CPI reports on the price change for about 90,000 items in 364 categories. The Bureau of Labor Statistics measures items in terms of their 1982-84 base-period prices. The CPI for 1983 is set at 100. This is important when computing today's CPI.

Important Questions to Ask Yourself	What Formula Do I Use?
How do I calculate the **CPI**?	$CPI = \dfrac{Current\ Cost}{Cost\ in\ 1983} \times 100$
How do I calculate the **current cost**?	$Current\ Cost = \dfrac{Cost\ in\ 1983 \times CPI}{100}$
How do I compute the cost in the **base year**?	$Cost\ in\ Base\ Year = \dfrac{Current\ Cost}{CPI} \times 100$

Living in the Real World

Vintage Vamp

Luxury Items As she reads the economic news, Chinen notices the value of her new collection of wedding gowns has risen more slowly than the average cost of many other "luxury" goods and services such as cars and travel.

Draw Conclusions Explain the importance of 1983 and CPI.

Continued on page 716

▶FYI

In the 1970s, the United States experienced a deep recession. Unemployment was high (8.7 percent) and mortgage interest rates hit 16 percent. By comparison, mortgage rates in the early part of the 21st century hovered around 7 percent.

▶▶▶

Example 1

Claudia Smith was asked to write a story about the CPI. She had the following data:

- The current cost of a briefcase is $74.50. The cost in 1983 was $41.27. What is the CPI for the briefcase?

- The cost in 1983 of a good pair of sport socks was $3.75. The CPI for sport socks is 170. What is the current cost of the sport socks?

- The current cost of a music compact disc is $18.79. The CPI for a classical CD is 145.5. Before CDs there were vinyl albums. What was the cost of the classical album in 1983?

Continued on next page

Living in the Real World

The Bureau of Labor Statistics measures items by their 1982–84 base-period prices; the CPI for 1983 is 100. This number is used to compute today's CPI.

National Standards for Business Education

Standard 1	Mathematical Foundations
Standard 2	Number Relationships and Operations

National Council of Teachers of Mathematics Standards

Standard 1	Numbers and Operations
Standard 6	Problem Solving
Standard 8	Communication

1 FOCUS

Gross Domestic Product is one measure of the economy. Another measure of the economy is the consumer price index (CPI). The CPI measures the change in prices over time. **Point out that the base period is 1983.**

In-Class Examples
Work through these exercises with students before having them do the Self-Check. Round answers to the nearest hundredth.
1. $(15 \div 8) \times 100$ **187.5**
2. $(105.78 \div 79.27) \times 100$ **133.44**
3. $(617.3 \times 144.8) \div 100$ **893.85**

RETEACH / ENRICHMENT

CPI Numbers
Ask students what the following CPI numbers mean. Then, have them find the cost of an item that sold for $240 in 1983 using these numbers:
A. 50 **Cost now is half of what it was in 1983; $120.**
B. 200 **Cost now is twice what it was in 1983; $480.**
C. 100 **Cost now equals what it was in 1983; $240.**
D. 0 **The item must be free now.**

713

STEP 1: Find the CPI for the briefcase.
(Current Cost ÷ Cost in 1983) × 100
($74.50   ÷ $41.27)   × 100 =
1.8051   × 100 = **180.5 CPI for briefcase**

STEP 2: Find the current cost of the sport socks.
(Cost in 1983 × CPI) ÷ 100
($3.75   × 170) ÷ 100 =
$637.50   ÷ 100 = **$6.375 or $6.38 current cost**

STEP 3: Find the cost of the classical album in 1983.
(Current Cost ÷ CPI) × 100
($18.79   ÷ 145.5) × 100 =
$0.12914   × 100 = **$12.91 cost of album**

18.79 ÷ 145.5 × 100 = 12.91408935

(Example 2)

Figure 23.1 gives the CPI for the years 1983 through 2002. Use it to find:
- The cost in 2002 of an auto that sold for $11,980 in 1983.
- The cost in 1983 of a computer that sold for $1,495 in 2002.
- The cost in 1995 of a house that sold for $127,500 in 2002.

Figure 23.1

Year	CPI	Year	CPI
1983	100.0	1993	144.5
1984	103.9	1994	148.2
1985	107.6	1995	152.4
1986	109.6	1996	156.9
1987	113.6	1997	160.5
1988	118.3	1998	163.0
1989	124.0	1999	166.6
1990	130.7	2000	172.3
1991	136.2	2001	177.2
1992	140.3	2002	180.5

STEP 1: Find the cost of the auto in 2002.
($11,980 × 180.5) ÷ 100 =
$2,162,390   ÷ 100 =
$21,623.90 cost of auto

STEP 2: Find the cost of the computer in 1983.
($1,495 ÷ 180.5) × 100 =
$8.28254   × 100 =
$828.25 cost of computer

STEP 3: Find the cost of the house in 1995.

A. Find the cost in 1983 first.
($127,500 ÷ 180.5) × 100 =
$706.37119   × 100 =
$70,637.12 cost for a house

B. Then find the cost in 1995.
($70,637.12 × 152.4) ÷ 100 =
$10,765,097.09 ÷ 100 =
$107,650.97 cost for a house

CONCEPT CHECK

(SELF-CHECK ✔)

Complete the problems, then check your answers at the end of the chapter.

1. The price of a pound of bananas in 1983 was $0.27 a pound. Using the CPI table in Figure 23.1, what was the price in 2000? **($0.27 × 172.3) ÷ 100 = $0.47**

2. In 1992 a sweater vest sold for $24.50. Using the table in Figure 23.1, find the cost in 1987. **($17.46 × 113.6) ÷ 100 = $19.83**

TEACH

2 TEACH

Discuss with students some of the major groups used for the CPI. Some of these are energy, food, housing, apparel, transportation, medical care, and electricity. Have students suggest some items that would fall into each group.

Point out that sometimes the CPI is not greater than 100 for a given item. Students should already be familiar with deflation from the first lesson in this chapter. Compare what it means to have a CPI less than 100 to deflation. Have students suggest some items that may have a CPI less than 100.

Motivating the Lesson

Give students a list of the current CPI and price for several items. Have students compute the cost in 1983. **Answers will vary.**

In-Class Examples

Find the CPI.
1. Current cost: $51.
   Cost in 1983: $28. **182.1**
2. Current cost: $124.99.
   Cost in 1983: $74.79. **167.1**

Find the current cost.
3. Find the current cost.
   Cost in 1983: $24.
   CPI: 110.3. **$26.47**

3 ASSESS

Error Analysis

Students may have difficulty remembering the three formulas presented in this section. You may want to show students how they can use one formula to obtain the other two. For instance, if students can remember the formula for CPI, they can solve the formula for either the current cost or the cost in 1983. Another option is to always use one formula and solve the resulting equation for the missing piece of information.

THINKING CRITICALLY

Increase or Decrease

Have students research Consumer Price Index figures by going online to the Bureau of Labor Statistics (www.bls.gov), or referring to the current *World Almanac.* Have students refer to the table for selected items and groups showing: food and beverages, housing, apparel, transportation, medical care, entertainment, and so on. Ask students questions such as: What groups of items increased in cost the most over the last five years? What groups of items increased in cost the least? Did any groups of items decrease in cost? **LS** , **CL** , **P**

SECTION 23-3 PRACTICE

Complete the table. Round answers to the nearest tenth or to the nearest cent.

	Item	CPI	Current Cost	Cost in 1983
3.	Sport coat	**180.5**	$135.29	$ 74.95
4.	Dinner for two	**212.8**	45.75	21.50
5.	Apartment rent	160.5	**$521.63**	325.00
6.	Lawn mower	130.7	**$556.13**	425.50
7.	Bicycle	180.5	658.78	**$364.98**
8.	Book	172.3	49.97	**$29.00**

9. Current cost is $48. Cost in 1983 was $27. What is the CPI? **177.8**

10. Cost in 1983 was $78. The CPI is 140.3. What is the current cost? **$109.43**

11. The cost in 1995 was $540. Using Figure 23.1, find the cost in 1983. **$354.33**

12. A house sold for $256,890 in 2000. Using Figure 23.1, find the cost of that house in 2002. **$269,115.76**

Use Figure 23.2 of specific CPI indicators for Problems 13–18.

Figure 23.2

Indicators of Specific Items	
Commodity	CPI
Fuel oil	204.8
Gasoline	164.6
Rent	238.9
Home	243.5
Groceries	175.6
Handheld calculator	96.5
VCR	78.2
New car	180.5

13. In 1983 Lucas paid $14,577.13 for a new car. What could he expect to pay today for a similar car? **$26,311.72**

14. In 1983 the Johnson family paid $48,650 for their home. What would a similar home sell for today? **$118,462.75**

15. In 1983 the Johnson family paid $94.70 for their weekly groceries. How much could the Johnsons expect to pay for their weekly groceries today? **$166.29**

16. Last month's fuel oil bill for the Crowleys was $156.36. What would the Crowleys have paid for the same amount of fuel oil in 1983? **$76.35**

17. Juan and Maria Ellias spent $87.95 for a VCR. How much would they have spent in 1983 for the same VCR? **$112.47**

18. Alice McCarty pays $850 per month in rent for her efficiency apartment. What would McCarty have paid in 1983 for a similar apartment? **$355.80**

MAINTAINING YOUR SKILLS

Divide. Round answers to the nearest tenth.

Need Help? Go to...
▶ Skill 11: **Dividing** Decimals, page 738
▶ Skill 8: **Multiplying** Decimals, page 735

19. $234.50 ÷ $78.25 **3.0**

20. $24.79 ÷ $18.45 **1.3**

21. $2.49 ÷ $5.79 **0.4**

Multiply. Round answers to the nearest cent.

22. 234.3 × $45.75 **$10,719.23**

23. 156.8 × $378.89 **$59,409.95**

24. 112.4 × $7.89 **$886.84**

4 CLOSE

Closing Activity
Find the CPI.
1. Current cost: $81.60. Cost in 1983: $49.75. **164**
2. Current cost: $405.28. Cost in 1983: $239.50. **169.2**

Find the current cost.
3. Cost in 1983: $12.99. CPI: 189.2. **$24.58**
4. Cost in 1983: $62.15. CPI: 521.6. **$324.17**
5. The cost in 1983 for a dozen eggs was $0.70. The CPI for eggs is 131.9. What is the current cost of the eggs? **$0.92**

WRAP-UP

Go over any problem for which a wrong answer is given.

Assignment Guide
  Basic: 3–8
  Average: 9–11

20 min.

National Standards for Business Education

Standard 1	Mathematical Foundations
Standard 2	Number Relationships and Operations

National Council of Teachers of Mathematics Standards

Standard 1	Numbers and Operations
Standard 6	Problem Solving
Standard 8	Communication

FOCUS

Discuss with students why a business would want to have a budget. Point out that businesses have income and expenses. Businesses monitor their income and expenses using a budget.

In-Class Examples

Work through these exercises with students before having them do the Self-Check.
1. $899,650 − $875,465 **$24,185**
2. $1,754 − $2,109 **−$355**
3. $5,000,000 × 15% **$750,000**

SECTION 23-4 Budget

○ **Section Objective**

Allocate revenue and expenses, and analyze a budget.

Money is a limited resource. Most people, businesses, and government agencies want more than they can buy with their money. That's why it's important to manage your money by setting a budget—and sticking to it. A **budget** is a plan for using money in a way that best meets your wants and needs. This financial plan identifies what sources are expected to produce revenues (that is, earn money) and what amounts are allocated to various departments or categories for expenses. Revenues and expenses are allocated as a percent of the total income. The main purpose of a budget is to monitor revenues and expenses. The actual amount spent must be compared with the budget allocation.

Important Questions to Ask Yourself	What Formula Do I Use?
How do I perform a **budget allocation?**	Budget Allocation = Total Income × Percent
How do I find the **difference** between the actual amount and the budget allocation?	Difference = Actual Amount − Budget Allocation

Living in the Real World

Vintage Vamp

Planning for Change   Chinen decides to put together two preliminary budgets: one for the shop as it's operating now and one for the shop if she decides to keep an inventory of vintage wedding gowns. That will give her a better idea how much the change in her mission will cost and whether revenues will be greater than the costs.

Draw Conclusions   Why is this a good idea for Chinen to draft the two budgets?

Continued on page 721

Example 1

The Kimberly Auto Company wanted to earn $2,457,890 in revenues for the year. The company expected to earn its revenues from the following sources: 75 percent from sales, 15 percent from services, and 10 percent from return on investments. At the end of the year, a budget analysis was sent to each manager showing the expected amounts and actual amounts from each area. Sales showed revenues of $1,755,965; services showed $369,240; and return on investments showed $245,790. Did the company reach its goal in revenues?

Living in the Real World

It gives her a clear idea of what she can expect in either situation and will help her make important decisions about the direction of her business.

STEP 1: Find the budget allocation.

	Total Income	×	Percent		
Sales	$2,457,890	×	75%	=	$1,843,417.50
Services	2,457,890	×	15%	=	368,683.50
Return on investments	2,457,890	×	10%	=	245,789.00

STEP 2: Find the difference.

	Actual Amount	−	Budget Allocation		
Sales	$1,755,965.00	−	$1,843,417.50	=	−$87,452.50
Services	369,240.00	−	368,683.50	=	+556.50
Return on Investments	245,790.00	−	245,789.00	=	+1.00
Total	$2,370,995.00	−	$2,457,890.00	=	−$86,895.00

The company was $86,895.00 short of its goal for the year.

2457890 M+ × 75 % 1843417.5 RM 2457890 ×
15 % 368683.5 RM 2457890 × 10 % 245789

(Example 2)

Burrito Barn operates on a monthly budget of $25,000. The budget is broken down like this: 50 percent is budgeted for wages and salaries (including all benefits and taxes), 25 percent is for inventory and supplies, 5 percent pays the rent, 10 percent is earmarked for improvements, 3 percent is reserved for miscellaneous, and 7 percent is reinvested.

In analyzing this past month's figures, Carlos Muniz found the expenditures by department as indicated below. Did Burrito Barn operate within its budget? Analyze expenditures by each department.

STEP: Analyze the budget for Burrito Barn.

Department	Actual Amount	−	Budget Allocation			=	Difference
Wages & Salaries	$13,760.00	−	$25,000	× 50%	= $12,500.00	=	$1,260.00
Inventory & Supplies	6,186.00	−	25,000	× 25%	= 6,250.00	−	−64.00
Rent	1,250.00	−	25,000	× 5%	= 1,250.00	=	0.00
Improvements	2,148.80	−	25,000	× 10%	= 2,500.00	=	−351.20
Miscellaneous	345.90	−	25,000	× 3%	= 750.00	=	−404.10
Reinvestment	850.00	−	25,000	× 7%	= 1,750.00	=	−900.00
Total	$24,540.70	−			= $25,000.00	=	−$459.30

NOTE: Pay attention to the negative ("−") signs in the Difference column.

In analyzing this past month's expenditures, Burrito Barn came in $459.30 under budget. You might suggest that Muniz consider budgeting more for wages and salaries and perhaps a little less on improvements, miscellaneous, and reinvestment.

Section 23-4 Budget ▶ **717**

TEACH

Students should already be familiar with budgets from Chapter 3. Corporate budgets are similar to personal budgets. Businesses allocate a certain amount of money for each expense and identify sources that are expected to earn money for the business.

In Example 1 on pages 716 and 717, point out that the difference between the budget allocation and the actual amount can be negative. This indicates that the budgeted item did not meet the expectations of the company. Instead it fell short of the desired amount.

Motivating the Lesson
Have students work in groups. Each group should be given a dollar amount to budget. Give students a list of items that need to be included in the budget. Let students decide the allocation percents. They should be able to justify their choices. Students can present their budgets to the class. **Answers will vary.**

In-Class Examples
1. Allocate $100,000 as shown.
   Sales: 65 percent.
   Services: 20 percent.
   Investments: 15 percent.
   $65,000; $20,000; $15,000
2. Allocate $750,000 as shown.
   Stocks: 57 percent.
   Bonds: 29 percent.
   Interest: 14 percent.
   $427,500; $217,500; $105,000

TECHNOLOGY POWER

The Los Angeles Economic Development Corporation (LAEDC) does an analysis of the Gross Domestic Product for all nations with gross product over $250 billion and includes California and Los Angeles County. This helps put local economies in better perspective. California's economy is larger than the nations of Mexico, India, or Spain. Los Angeles County by itself continues to rank as the world's sixteenth largest economy beating out the countries of Russia, Taiwan, Argentina, and Switzerland with $352 billion in GDP. The LAEDC uses this information to attract, retain, and grow businesses and jobs in the Los Angeles County region.

3 ASSESS

Error Analysis

Point out that the sum of the percents should equal 100. Also, the sum of the budget allocation amounts should equal the expected revenue. Remind students that sometimes this will not be the case due to rounding. Students should already be familiar with this concept from previous chapters.

1. Salaries: $332,000;
   Supplies: $24,000;
   New equipment: $20,000;
   Maintenance: $16,000;
   Miscellaneous: $8,000;
   Total: $400,000
2. Salaries: −$28,000;
   Supplies: +$4,000;
   New equipment: −$6,000;
   Maintenance: +$7,000;
   Miscellaneous: +$5,000;
   Total: −$18,000

CONCEPT CHECK

SELF-CHECK ✔

Complete the problems, then check your answers at the end of the chapter.

Wagner Enterprises had a $400,000 budget. For each category, determine the following:

1. Amount budgeted   **2.** Difference

		Expected Percent	Actual Amount	Budgeted Amount		Difference	
3.	Salaries	83%	$360,000	a.	$332,000	b.	$28,000
4.	Supplies	6%	20,000	a.	$24,000	b.	−$4,000
5.	New equipment	5%	26,000	a.	$20,000	b.	$6,000
6.	Maintenance	4%	9,000	a.	$16,000	b.	−$7,000
7.	Miscellaneous	2%	3,000	a.	$8,000	b.	−$5,000
8.	Total		a. $418,000	b.	$400,000	c.	$18,000

SECTION 23-4 PRACTICE

Determine the budget allocation and the difference.

	Total Revenue	Expected Percent	Actual Amount	Budget Allocation		Difference	
9.	$ 80,000	25%	$ 15,000	a.	$20,000	b.	−$5,000
10.	120,000	60%	74,000	a.	$72,000	b.	$2,000
11.	860,000	7%	64,000	a.	$60,200	b.	$3,800
12.	987,500	80%	760,000	a.	$790,000	b.	−$30,000
13.	5,880,000	64%	3,562,000	a.	$3,763,200	b.	−$201,200
14.	7,644,000	8%	756,253	a.	$611,520	b.	$144,733

15. Allocate $150,000 as shown:
   Sales: 70 percent. **$105,000**
   Services: 20 percent. **$30,000**
   Investments: 10 percent. **$15,000**

16. Allocate $600,000 as shown:
   Interest: 15 percent. **$90,000**
   Stocks: 65 percent. **$390,000**
   Bonds: 20 percent. **$120,000**

17. Find the difference.   **18.** Find the difference.

17. Sales: −$40,000
    Services: −$30,000
    Investments: $10,000
    Total: −$60,000
18. Supplies: $11,400
    Equipment: $60,600
    Services: −$65,320
    Total: $6,680

17. Find the difference.

	Actual Amount	Budget
Sales	$460,000	$500,000
Services	150,000	180,000
Investments	60,000	50,000
Total	**$670,000**	**$730,000**

18. Find the difference.

	Actual Amount	Budget
Supplies	$155,400	$144,000
Equipment	450,600	390,000
Services	90,300	155,620
Total	**$696,300**	**$689,620**

COMMUNICATION SKILLS

Class Discussion

Engage the class in a discussion of the topics presented in this chapter. Focus on how the inflation rate, Gross Domestic Product (GDP), Consumer Price Index (CPI), and budgets are used as tools by businesses to understand the state of the nation's economy and to make business decisions.

19. The Downey Corporation is budgeting total revenues of $15,219,000 next year. Out of the total, 96 percent is expected to come from sales, 2 percent is expected to come from trading profits, and 2 percent is expected to come from other sources. How many dollars has Downey budgeted in expected revenues in each category? **Sales: $14,610,240; Trading profits: $304,380; Other: $304,380**

20. The Downey Corporation from Problem 19 had actual revenues of $14,700,000 from sales, $240,000 from trading profits, and $120,000 from other sources. Did the company reach its revenue goals? How much did Downey differ overall and in each area? **Sales: $89,760; Trading profits: −$64,380; Other: $184,380**

For Problems 21–22, determine the amount budgeted for each source and find the difference between the actual amount and budget allocation.

21. Posy Fruit Farm had planned earnings of $680,000 for the year. The farm expected its revenues to come from the following sources: 60 percent from apple sales, 20 percent from strawberry sales, 15 percent from blueberry sales, and 5 percent from cherry sales. At the end of the season, actual figures showed sales revenues of the following: apples, $420,000; strawberries, $91,320; blueberries, $91,340; and cherries, $39,900. Did Posy Fruit Farm reach its goal in revenues?

22. The City of Miami Beach, Florida, operates on an annual budget of $325 million. They budget as indicated. Actual expenditures are to the right. Analyze the City of Miami Beach's budget by finding the difference between the amount budgeted (nearest tenth of a million) and the actual expenditures. Did the city stay within its budget?

Figure 23.3

City of Miami Beach Budget

City of Miami Beach, Fla.	Budget	Actual Expenditures
General government	17%	$ 55.7 million
Public safety	21%	68.3 million
Transportation	5%	15.2 million
Human services	1%	1.5 million
Culture/Recreation	12%	38.5 million
Physical environment	14%	44.2 million
Economic environment	12%	38.2 million
Debt service	9%	27.7 million
Other	9%	35.9 million
Total	100%	$325.2 million

MAINTAINING YOUR SKILLS

Need Help? Go to... Skill 30: Finding the Percentage, page 757

Find the percentage. Round answers to the nearest cent.

23. 78 percent of $348,970 **$272,196.60**

24. 43 percent of $7,385,450 **$3,175,743.50**

25. 4.6 percent of $23,684,780 **$1,089,499.88**

26. 14.7 percent of $836,712 **$122,996.66**

27. 83.7 percent of $3,769,628 **$3,155,178.64**

28. 1.6 percent of $598,684 **$9,578.94**

22.

Department	Actual	Budget	Difference
Gen. Govt.	$55.7	$55.3	$0.4
Pub. Safety	68.3	68.3	0
Trans.	15.2	16.3	−1.1
H. S.	1.5	3.3	−1.8
Culture/Rec.	38.5	39	0.5
Phys. Envir.	44.2	45.5	−1.3
Econ. Envir.	38.2	39	−0.8
Debt Serv.	27.7	29.3	−1.6
Other	35.9	29.3	6.6
Total	$325.2	$325.3	$0.9

Yes. The City of Miami Beach stayed within its budget by spending $0.1 million or $100,000 less than the amount it had allocated.

WRAP-UP

Go over any problem for which a wrong answer is given.

Assignment Guide

Basic: 9–14

Average: 15–18

20 min.

SECTION 23-4

4 CLOSE

Closing Activity

Find the budget allocation and the difference.

1. Total revenue: $65,000. Expected percent: 20 percent. Actual amount: $13,550. **$13,000; $550**
2. Total revenue: $129,760. Expected percent: 65 percent. Actual amount: $81,748.80. **$84,344; −$2,595.20**
3. Total revenue: $1,452,800. Expected percent: 74 percent. Actual amount: $1,089,600. **$1,075,072; $14,528**
4. Tetley Tile budgeted total revenues of $1,900,000. Out of the total, 84 percent was expected to come from sales, 8.5 percent from investments, and 7.5 percent from other sources. The actual revenues were $1,610,000 from sales, $163,400 from investments, and $143,750 from other sources.
   a. How many dollars did Tetley Tile budget in expected revenues in each category? **Sales $1,596,000; investments $161,500; other sources $142,500**
   b. Did the company reach its revenue goals? **Yes**
   c. What was the difference, if any, in each category? **Sales $14,000; investments $1,900; other sources $1,250**
   d. What was the difference, if any, overall? **$17,150**

21. No

	Actual	Budget Allocation	Difference
Apples	$420,000	$408,000	$+12,000
Strawberries	91,320	136,000	−44,680
Blueberries	91,340	102,000	−10,660
Cherries	39,900	34,000	+5,900
Total	$642,560	$680,000	$−37,440

Quick Quiz

1. The inflation rate for groceries is 4.5 percent. How much would a box of cereal cost today if it cost $2.29 last year? **$2.39**

2. When Jake's Corner Mart opened, a candy bar sold for $0.40. Today it sells for $0.70. What is the inflation rate? **87.5%**

3. A country has a GDP of $45 billion and an inflation rate of 5.8 percent. Find the real GDP. **$42.39 billion**

4. The cost of a gallon of gasoline is $1.40. The CPI for gasoline is 129.3. What was the cost of a gallon of gasoline in 1983? **$1.08**

5. Tetris Industries budgeted total revenues of $8,940,345. Out of the total, 90 percent was expected to come from sales, 7 percent from service, and 3 percent from other sources. How many dollars has Tetris budgeted in expected revenues in each category? **sales $8,046,310.50; service $625,824.15; other sources $268,210.35**

SECTION **23-1** **CONCEPT CHECK** (p. 708)

1. ($80 − $75) ÷ $75 = **6.7%**

2.   ($12,400 × 8.2%) = $1,016.80
   $12,400 + $1,016.80   = **$13,416.80**

3.   (1 + 10%) = 1.10
   $28.05 ÷   1.10   = **$25.50**

4. ($350 − $498)   = −$148
     −$148   ÷ $498 = −0.2971 = **−29.7% or 29.7% deflation**

SECTION **23-2** **CONCEPT CHECK** (p. 711)

1.   ($43,800,000 × 6.4%) = $2,803,200
   $43,800,000 − $2,803,200   = **$40,996,800**

2. $92,800,000 ÷ 78,650 = **$1,179.91**

SECTION **23-3** **CONCEPT CHECK** (p. 714)

1. Cost in Year 2000 = ($0.27 × 172.3) ÷ 100 = **$0.47**

2. Cost in Year 1987 = ($17.46 × 113.6) ÷ 100 = **$19.83**

SECTION **23-4** **CONCEPT CHECK** (p. 718)

1. Salaries: $332,000;
   Supplies: $24,000;
   New equipment: $20,000;
   Maintenance: $16,000;
   Miscellaneous: $8,000;
   Total: $400,000

2. Salaries: −$28,000;
   Supplies: +$4,000;
   New equipment: −$6,000;
   Maintenance: +$7,000;
   Miscellaneous: +$5,000;
   Total: −$18,000

		Expected Percent	Actual Amount	Budgeted Amount	Difference
3.	Salaries	83%	$360,000	a. $332,000	b. $28,000
4.	Supplies	6%	20,000	a. 24,000	b. −4,000
5.	New equipment	5%	26,000	a. 20,000	b. 6,000
6.	Maintenance	4%	9,000	a. 16,000	b. −7,000
7.	Miscellaneous	2%	3,000	a. 8,000	b. −5,000
8.	Total		a. $418,000	b. $400,000	c. $18,000

Living in the Real World

Vintage Vamp

Estimating   Chinen, as a business planner and owner of her own store, uses experience, profiles of current economic conditions, and predictions by government officials and financial experts to put together strategic short-term and long-range plans. If her store is to downsize its inventory, to merge, to relocate, or to expand, it's important that business planning determines the most efficient, effective, and inexpensive way to relocate the store and transfer the inventory.

Strategic Planning. Imagine Chinen hires you, a business relocation specialist, to move Vintage Vamp to a better location, but a smaller store.

- What would you need to find out about the Vintage Vamp move?
- What kinds of emotions might her employees and loyal customers be experiencing about the move of Vintage Vamp? Does the reason for the move make a difference? How so?

Living in the Real World

As a business relocation specialist, you would estimate the cost of physically moving the inventory. You would determine if special packing and handling are required. If there are any large heavy items needing special equipment, and if all doorways at the new location are large enough to accommodate all items.

Emotionally, some employees may be sad about the move, others may see it as an opportunity for growth. A better location should ultimately result in an increase in sales. A smaller store will result in a reduction of inventory, and thereby, reduce capital outlay.

REVIEW OF KEY WORDS

inflation (p. 706)
gross domestic product (GDP) (p. 710)
real GDP (p. 710)

per capita GDP (p. 710)
consumer price index (CPI) (p. 713)
budget (p. 716)

Match one of the key words above with a definition below.

1. a general increase in the cost of goods and services. **inflation**

2. the total value of the goods and services produced in a country in a given year.

3. a plan for using money in a way that best meets your wants and needs. **budget**

4. the gross domestic product of a country distributed over the population, or the GDP per person. **per capita GDP**

5. a measure of the average change in prices of a certain number of goods and services.

6. the gross domestic product adjusted to include the effects of inflation. **real GDP**

2. **gross domestic product (GDP)**

5. **consumer price index (CPI)**

CHAPTER 23 — Study Guide and Assessment

Skills and Concepts

SECTION OBJECTIVE 23-1 AND EXAMPLES

Compute the inflation rate, the current price, and the original price.

The original price was $95. The current price is $125. What is the inflation rate?

STEP: Find the inflation rate.

(Current Price − Original Price) ÷ Original Price

($125 − $95) ÷ $95 = 0.3157 or 31.6% inflation rate

REVIEW EXERCISES
Complete the table.

	Inflation Rate	Current Price	Original Price
7.	10.5%	$5,640.00	$5,104.56
8.	15.6%	103.95	89.95
9.	2.2%	**$1,330.64**	1,302.00
10.	18.0%	**$588.41**	498.65
11.	0.9%	985.40	**$976.61**
12.	6.7%	6,309.65	**$5,913.45**

SECTION OBJECTIVE 23-2 AND EXAMPLES

Explain and compute the gross domestic product.

Norway has an inflation rate of 2.9 percent and a GDP of $124.1 billion. The population of Norway is 4,503,440. What is the real GDP? What is the per capita GDP?

STEP 1: Find the real GDP.　　　GDP − (GDP × Inflation Rate)

($124.1 billion × 2.9%) =

$124.1 billion − $3.6 billion =

$120.5 billion real GDP

STEP 2: Find the per capita GDP.　　　GDP ÷ Population

$124.1 billion ÷ 4,503,440 = **$27,556.71 per capita GDP**

REVIEW EXERCISES
Find the real GDP and per capita GDP.

15. a. $485,616,600,000
18. a. $10,879,050,636

	GDP	Inflation Rate	Population	Real GDP	Per Capita GDP	
13.	$321.8 million	2.10%	63.1 million	a.	b. $5.10	a. $315,042,200
14.	98,567,021	0.85%	45,000,000	a.	b. $2.19	a. $97,729,201.32
15.	548.1 billion	11.40%	2,765,090,900	a.	b. $198.22	
16.	983,409,321	8.10%	42,970,430	a.	b. $22.89	a. $903,753,166
17.	6,340,975,000	3.50%	1,450,040,000	a.	b. $4.37	a. $6,119,040,875
18.	11,089,756,000	1.90%	2.1 billion	a.	b. $5.28	

REINFORCEMENT

Section 23-1

1. Original price: $178.49.
   Deflation rate: 1.5 percent.
   Find the current price. **$175.81**

2. Current price: $1,350.88.
   Deflation rate: 10.25 percent.
   Find the original price. **$1,505.16**

Section 23-2

1. Find the per capita GDP:
   GDP: $14,250,000,000.
   Population: 32 million. **$445.31**

SECTION OBJECTIVE 23-3 AND EXAMPLES

Calculate the consumer price index, the current cost, and the cost of any given commodity.

The current cost of a pair of earrings is $36.99. The cost in 1983 was $21.95. What is the CPI?

STEP: Find the CPI. (Current Cost ÷ Cost in 1983) × 100

($36.99 ÷ $21.95) × 100 = **168.52 CPI**

REVIEW EXERCISES

Complete the table.

	Item	CPI	Current Cost	Cost in 1983
19.	Prom dress	**290.35**	$285.99	$ 98.50
20.	Cup of coffee	**350**	3.50	1.00
21.	Motorcycle	215.7	**$16,166.72**	7,495.00
22.	Sunglasses	150.2	**$9.84**	6.55
23.	Lipstick	146.5	8.95	**$6.11**
24.	Tennis shoes	184.3	85.65	**$46.47**

SECTION OBJECTIVE 23-4 AND EXAMPLES

Allocate revenue and expenses, and analyze a budget.

The Moose Lodge Resort wanted to earn $1,300,000 in revenues for the year. The company expected to earn its revenues from the following sources: 72 percent from room rental, 18 percent from food sales, and 10 percent from gift shop sales. At the end of the year, The Moose Lodge Resort reviewed its actual amounts from each area. Room rentals were $903,000, food sales were $210,000, and gift shop sales were $100,000. Did the company reach its goals in revenues? Find the difference between the actual amount and budget allocation for each source.

STEP: Find the budget allocation and the difference.

Moose Lodge	Actual Amount	−	Budget Allocation			=	Difference
Room rentals	$903,000	−	$1,300,000	× 72%	=	$936,000	= −$33,000
Food sales	210,000	−	1,300,000	× 18%	=	234,000	= −24,000
Gift shop sales	100,000	−	1,300,000	× 10%	=	130,000	− −30,000
Total							−$87,000

REVIEW EXERCISES

Complete the table.

27. a. $152,519.40
b. −$30,554.40

	Total Revenue	Expected Percent	Actual Amount	Budget Allocation	Difference
25.	$ 65,400	45%	$ 50,500	a. $29,430	b. $21,070
26.	109,000	28%	36,540	a. $30,520	b. $6,020
27.	231,090	66%	121,965	a.	b.
28.	543,000	11%	23,900	a. $59,730	b. −$35,830
29.	659,700	82%	435,400	a. $540,954	b. −$105,554
30.	1,200,900	61%	880,650	a. $732,549	b. $148,101

REINFORCEMENT

Section 23-3

1. The cost of a loaf of bread is $0.93. The cost in 1983 was $0.47. What is the CPI for the bread? **197.9**

Section 23-4

1. The Grid Company budgeted total revenues of $22,450,000. Out of the total, 95 percent was expected to come from sales, 3 percent from service, and 2 percent from other sources. The actual revenues were $21,330,000 from sales, $628,600 from service, and $314,300 from other sources.

   a. How many dollars did Grid budget in expected revenues in each category? **Sales $21,327,500; service $673,500; other sources $449,000**

   b. What was the difference, if any, in each category? **Sales $2,500; service −$44,900; other sources −$134,700**

   c. What was the difference, if any, overall? **−$177,100**

Aligned and verified by

The Princeton Review

Cumulative Test Prep

Test-Taking Tip
On some standardized tests, guessing can improve your score if you make educated guesses. First, find out if there is a penalty for incorrect answers. If there is no penalty, a guess can only increase your score, or at worst, leave your score the same. If there is a penalty for guessing, try to eliminate one or more choices to make the probability of a correct guess greater than the probability of an incorrect answer.

SECTION ONE: MULTIPLE CHOICE

This section contains seven multiple-choice questions. After working each problem, write the letter of the correct answer on your paper.

1. The Bellview Corporation had an annual gross income of $834,718 for the year. Business deductions totaled $697,497. What federal corporate tax must Bellview pay for the year? **C**

If Taxable Income Is Over:	But Not Over:	Tax Is:	Of the Amount Over:
$ 75,000	$ 100,000	$ 13,750 + 34%	$ 75,000
100,000	335,000	22,250 + 39%	100,000
335,000	10,000,000	113,900 + 34%	335,000

   (A) $18,430.19   (B) $22,250.19
   (C) $36,766.19   (D) $53,516.19

2. The Temp Company purchased a new copy machine for $7,860. The machine has an estimated life of 4 years. The resale value is expected to be $500. Use the straight-line method to find the annual depreciation. **A**

   (A) $1,840   (B) $1,965
   (C) $2,300   (D) $2,450

3. Find the book value after the second year for the copy machine in Problem 2. **D**

   (A) $1,000   (B) $2,300
   (C) $2,340   (D) $4,180

4. Horton Manufacturing had $250,000.00 in surplus cash. The financial manager decided to invest in a U.S. Treasury bill with a face value of $250,000.00. The bill matured in 126 days. The interest rate was 10.875 percent ordinary interest at exact time. The bank service fee was $35.00. What was the cost of the Treasury bill? **A**

   (A) $240,519.37   (B) $260, 431.37
   (C) $320,900.37   (D) $442,675.37

5. Last year a 2-liter bottle of grapefruit juice cost $1.99. Today it costs $2.79. What is the inflation rate? **D**

   (A) 8.3%   (B) 11.6%
   (C) 21.4%   (D) 40.2%

6. The nation of Aruba has a GDP of $2 billion and a population of 70,000. The inflation rate for Aruba is 4.2 percent. What is the real GDP? **B**

   (A) $84,000,000
   (B) $1,916,000,000
   (C) $2,110,000,000
   (D) $3,410,000,000

7. For one period, The Shoe Box had a beginning inventory of $11,450, receipts of $4,360, and an ending inventory of $10,716. What is the cost of goods sold? **A**

   (A) $5,094   (B) $8,003
   (C) $17,806   (D) $26,526

SECTION TWO: FREE RESPONSE

This section contains seven questions for which you will supply short answers. Write your answer on your paper.

8. The Bright Company sold 45,000 bonds at $85.50 per bond. The underwriting commission was 6.5 percent and the other expenses totaled 0.8 percent. What are the net proceeds? **$3,566,632.50**

9. Freddie's Fishing Supply borrowed $28,000 from Central Bank to finance additional inventory for the summer season. Central Bank charged 7.5 percent ordinary interest on the loan. The term of the loan was 120 days. What was the maturity value of the loan? **$28,700 ordinary interest or $28,690.41 exact interest**

10. A downtown law firm purchased telephone equipment for its office for $32,400. The trade-in value of the equipment is estimated to be $2,400 after 5 years. What is the annual depreciation using the straight-line method? **$6,000**

11. The Campus Bookstore opened a new branch store, which it rents for $1,250 per month. The Campus Bookstore paid the rent in advance for three months. The Campus Bookstore purchased new furniture and store fixtures for $34,175 and additional merchandise for $7,185. Miscellaneous expenses totaled $2,465. What was the total cost of expansion? **$47,575**

12. Ten years ago a ballpoint pen cost $14.95. The inflation rate for the pen since that time is 16.8 percent. What does the pen cost today? **$17.46**

13. A new automobile purchased by the Jones family in 1983 for $11,780 costs $35,400 today. What is the CPI for automobiles? **300.5**

14. The CPI for new homes is 243.5. A new home costing $83,400.00 in 1983 would cost how much today? **$203,079**

SECTION THREE: OPEN-ENDED

This section contains four open-ended questions. Demonstrate your knowledge by giving a clear, concise solution to each problem. Your score on these problems will depend on how well you do on the following:

- Explain your reasoning.
- Show your understanding of mathematics in an organized manner.
- Use charts, graphs, and diagrams in your explanation.
- Show the solution in more than one way or relate it to other situations.
- Investigate beyond the requirements of the problem.

15. Explain why you think federal income tax varies depending on the person's marital status and number of deductions.

16. U.S. Treasury Bills are considered a safe investment. Explain why. **Answers will vary but might mention that they are backed by the federal government.**

17. Describe the difference between a balance sheet and an income statement. What type of information does each provide to the business owner? Explain why you think both are needed.

18. Create a budget for an imaginary business. Determine the expected percent of expenditure. Your budget must include at least five different expenditures. **Answers will vary.**

> ## Mathematics Online
>
> To learn more about corporate planning, visit the *Mathematics with Business Applications* Web site at www.busmath.glencoe.com.

15. Answers will vary but might mention that it rewards people for being married and having children.

17. Answers will vary but might mention that a balance sheet shows the financial position of a company on a certain date. An income statement shows a company's income and operating expenses in detail.

Your Reference Files

SKILLS

Thirty-two computational skills, from whole number and decimal operations through rates and percents, provide the basics you will need as a consumer and future business person.

APPLICATIONS

Twenty-six mathematical applications, covering money, time, measurement, graphs, and more, provide the tools you will need for consumer and business use.

SKILL 1

Numbers

Place Value

In 4,532.869, give the place and value of each digit.

Place:

Ones
Tens .... Tenths
Hundreds .... Hundredths
Thousands ...... Thousandths

4 5 3 2 . 8 6 9

Value:

4000 .... 0.009 or $\frac{9}{1000}$
500 .... 0.06 or $\frac{6}{100}$
30 .... 0.8 or $\frac{8}{10}$
2

Give the place and value of the underlined digit.

1. 6<u>5</u> Ones; 5   **2.** 9<u>6</u> Ones; 6   **3.** 4<u>7</u>2 Tens; 70

4. <u>2</u>3 Tens; 20   **5.** 10<u>8</u> Ones; 8   **6.** <u>5</u>36 Hundreds; 500

7. 1,5<u>0</u>6 Tens; 0   **8.** 2,<u>8</u>21 Hundreds; 800   **9.** 7,<u>7</u>84 Hundreds; 700

10. 1,<u>4</u>92 Thousands; 1,000   **11.** 1,00<u>9</u> Ones; 9   **12.** 1,<u>9</u>26 Hundreds; 900

13. 0.<u>3</u>7 Tenths; 0.3   **14.** 1.6<u>1</u> Hundredths; 0.01   **15.** 2.73<u>9</u> Thousandths; 0.009

16. <u>6</u>.3 Ones; 6   **17.** 9.4<u>2</u> Hundredths; 0.02   **18.** 4.3<u>7</u> Hundredths; 0.07

19. 2<u>4</u>.04 Ones; 4   **20.** 37.<u>3</u>29 Tenths; 0.3   **21.** 1.8<u>2</u>4 Hundredths; 0.02

22. <u>4</u>93.89 Hundreds; 400   **23.** 90.25<u>7</u> Thousandths; 0.007   **24.** 23.<u>5</u>72 Tenths; 0.5

25. 12.76<u>3</u> Thousandths; 0.003   **26.** 0.<u>0</u>78 Tenths; 0.0   **27.** 5.46<u>1</u> Thousandths; 0.001

Numbers as Words

Write each number in words.

Number   Words
105 ⟶ One hundred five
26 ⟶ Twenty-six
17 ⟶ Seventeen
$98.09 ⟶ Ninety-eight and $\frac{9}{100}$ dollars
$33.13 ⟶ Thirty-three and $\frac{13}{100}$ dollars

Write in words.

28. 18 Eighteen   **29.** 34 Thirty-four   **30.** 159   **31.** 78 Seventy-eight   **32.** 103 One hundred three

33. 842   **34.** 207 Two hundred seven   **35.** 5,012   **36.** 6,005 Six thousand five   **37.** 119

38. 72 Seventy-two   **39.** 1,240   **40.** 5,102   **41.** 194   **42.** 6,590

43. $25.00   **44.** $6.24 Six and $\frac{24}{100}$ dollars   **45.** $17.09   **46.** $112.33   **47.** $120.17

48. $4.37   **49.** $7,749   **50.** $65.90   **51.** $0.50 $\frac{50}{100}$ dollars or fifty cents

30. One hundred fifty-nine
33. Eight hundred forty-two
35. Five thousand twelve
37. One hundred nineteen
39. One thousand two hundred forty
40. Five thousand one hundred two
41. One hundred ninety-four
42. Six thousand five hundred ninety
43. Twenty-five and $\frac{00}{100}$ dollars
45. Seventeen and $\frac{9}{100}$ dollars
46. One hundred twelve and $\frac{35}{100}$ dollars
47. One hundred twenty and $\frac{17}{100}$ dollars
48. Four and $\frac{37}{100}$ dollars
49. Seven thousand seven hundred forty-nine dollars
50. Sixty-five and $\frac{90}{100}$ dollars

Numbers as Decimals

Rewrite these large numbers as decimals.

$14,700,000 ┈┈▶ $14.7 million

$245,600 ┈┈▶ $245.6 thousand

Rewrite these decimals as numbers.

$1.2 billion = $1,200,000,000

$43.6 thousand = $43,600

Write in millions.

52. $1,700,000
$1.7 million

53. $71,640,000
$71.64 million

54. $618,700,000
$618.7 million

Write in thousands.

55. 18,400
18.4 thousand

56. $9,640
$9.64 thousand

57. 171,600
171.6 thousand

Write in billions.

58. $16,450,000,000
$16.45 billion

59. 2,135,000,000
2.135 billion

60. $171,200,000,000
$171.2 billion

Write completely in numbers.

61. $3.4 million
$3,400,000

62. 16.2 thousand
16,200

63. $11.2 billion
$11,200,000,000

64. 17.2 million
17,200,000

65. 7.3 billion
7,300,000,000

66. $74.21 thousand
$74,210

67. 0.4 million
400,000

68. $0.5 thousand
$5,000

69. $0.72 billion
$720,000,000

Comparing Whole Numbers

Which number is greater: 5,428 or 5,431?

5,428 = 5,000 + 400 + 20 + 8
5,431 = 5,000 + 400 + 30 + 1

　　　　　↑　　　↑　　　↑
　　　Same　Same　30 is
　　　　　　　　　　greater
　　　　　　　　　　than 20.

So 5,431 is greater than 5,428.

Which number is greater?

70. 23 or 32 **32**

71. 54 or 45 **54**

72. 459 or 462 **462**

73. 741 or 835 **835**

74. 810 or 735 **810**

75. 125 or 211 **211**

76. 3,450 or 6,450
6,450

77. 5,763 or 925
5,763

78. 1,000 or 999
1,000

79. 444 or 4,444
4,444

80. 3,002 or 4,000
4,000

81. 1,236 or 820
1,236

82. 150 or 149
150

83. 493 or 650
650

84. $2,000 or $1,997
$2,000

85. $101 or $99
$101

86. $482 or $600
$600

87. $39 or $93
$93

88. $1,686 or $1,668 **$1,686**

89. $568 or $742 **$742**

90. $86,432 or $101,000
$101,000

91. $791,000 or $768,000
$791,000

Comparing Decimals

Which number is greater 24.93 or 24.86?

24.93 = 20 + 4 + 0.9 + 0.03
24.86 = 20 + 4 + 0.8 + 0.06

　　　↑　　↑　　↑
　Same　Same　0.9 is
　　　　　　　greater
　　　　　　　than 0.8.

So 24.93 is greater than 24.86.

Which number is greater?

92. 3.1 or 1.3 **3.1**

93. 1.2 or 2.0 **2.0**

94. 4.50 or 4.05 **4.50**

95. 25.1 or 20.8 **25.1**

96. 18.43 or 17.88
18.43

97. 56.84 or 58 **58**

98. 0.4 or 0.6 **0.6**

99. 0.01 or 0.1 **0.1**

100. 0.82 or 0.28 **0.82**

101. 0.5 or 0.06 **0.5**

102. 8.739 or 10 **10**

103. 0.002 or 0.020
0.020

104. $5.99 or $5.00
$5.99

105. $10 or $8.50
$10

106. $23.85 or $19.84
$23.85

107. $11.19 or $19
$19

108. $6.98 or $7.50
$7.50

109. $83.59 or $600
$600

110. $4,327.75 or $6,297.86
$6,297.86

111. $8,391.34 or $9,521.39
$9,521.39

112. $4,640.66 or $4,646.40
$4,646.40

113. $2,000.00 or $1,997.98
$2,000.00

Rounding Numbers

Whole Numbers

Round 7,863 to the nearest hundred.

········Hundreds place

7,863

········5 or more? Yes.

········Add 1 to hundreds place.

7,900

········Change the digits to the right to zeros.

Round answers to the place value shown.

Nearest ten:

1. 26 **30**	**2.** 37 **40**		**3.** 68 **70**
4. 195 **200**	**5.** 217 **220**	**6.** 302 **300**	**7.** 8,099 **8,100**

Nearest hundred:

8. 119 **100**	**9.** 649 **600**	**10.** 2,175 **2,200**	**11.** 6,042 **6,000**

Nearest thousand:

12. 7,423 **7,000**	**13.** 15,602 **16,000**	**14.** 22,094 **22,000**	**15.** 750 **1,000**

Decimals

Round 0.6843 to the nearest thousandth.

········Thousandths place

0.6843

········5 or more? No.

········Do not change.

0.684

········Drop the final digit.

Round answers to the place value shown.

Nearest tenth:

16. 0.63 **0.6**	**17.** 0.091 **0.1**	**18.** 0.407 **0.4**	**19.** 0.452 **0.5**

Nearest hundredth:

20. 0.652 **0.65**	**21.** 0.474 **0.47**	**22.** 0.168 **0.17**	**23.** 0.355 **0.36**

Nearest thousandth:

24. 0.4291 **0.429**	**25.** 0.6007 **0.601**	**26.** 0.0097 **0.010**	**27.** 0.2126 **0.213**
28. 6.3942 **6.394**	**29.** 137.4920 **137.492**	**30.** 9.9999 **10.000**	

Mixed Practice

Round answers to the place value shown.

Nearest thousand:

31. 37,874 **38,000**	**32.** 19,266 **19,000**	**33.** 48,092 **48,000**

Nearest ten:

37. 26 **30**	**38.** 6,533 **6,530**	**39.** 575 **580**

Nearest tenth:

43. 189.673 **189.7**	**44.** 10.009 **10**	**45.** 0.07 **0.1**

Nearest thousandth:

49. 0.1791 **0.179**	**50.** 16.0005 **16.001**	**51.** 108.4374 **108.437**

Nearest hundred:

34. 751 **800**	**35.** 919 **900**	**36.** 6,771 **6,800**

Nearest one:

40. 6.2 **6**	**41.** 35.73 **36**	**42.** 17.392 **17**

Nearest hundredth:

46. 0.392 **0.39**	**47.** 152.430 **152.43**	**48.** 0.6974 **0.70**

SKILL 3

Adding Whole Numbers

Without Carrying

Add.

```
  723
  154
+ 212
  ↓

  723
  154
+ 212
1,089
```

1.
```
  65
 +41
 106
```

2.
```
  76
 +32
 108
```

3.
```
  97
 +41
 138
```

4.
```
  32
 +25
  57
```

5.
```
  352
 +837
1,189
```

6.
```
  361
 +834
1,195
```

7.
```
  448
 +351
  799
```

8.
```
  125
 +604
  729
```

9.
```
  864
 + 33
  897
```

10.
```
  721
 + 77
  798
```

11.
```
  423
 + 65
  488
```

12.
```
  108
 + 91
  199
```

13.
```
  9,037
 +1,841
 10,878
```

14.
```
  9,520
 + 1,379
 10,899
```

15.
```
  3,924
 +5,063
  8,987
```

16.
```
  2,840
 + 1,152
  3,992
```

With Carrying

Add.

```
  8,679
+ 9,748
  ↓

 1 11
  8,679
+ 9,748
 18,427
```

17.
```
  32
 +39
  71
```

18.
```
  54
 +48
 102
```

19.
```
  187
 + 23
  210
```

20.
```
  49
 +86
 135
```

21.
```
  728
 +169
  897
```

22.
```
  527
 +284
  811
```

23.
```
  845
 +697
1,542
```

24.
```
  697
 +546
1,243
```

25.
```
  3,046
 +1,592
  4,638
```

26.
```
  7,801
 +3,564
 11,365
```

27.
```
  5,246
 +6,978
 12,224
```

28.
```
  8,347
 +1,528
  9,875
```

29.
```
  8,448
 +3,753
 12,201
```

30.
```
  108
 +7,665
 7,773
```

31.
```
  9,179
 +3,608
 12,787
```

32.
```
  982
 +2,165
 3,147
```

Mixed Practice

33.
```
  1,481
 +2,317
  3,798
```

34.
```
  8,495
 +1,417
  9,912
```

35.
```
  5,783
 +6,535
 12,318
```

36.
```
  3,950
 +1,615
  5,565
```

37.
```
  6,259
 +1,893
  8,152
```

38.
```
  8,347
 +1,528
  9,875
```

39.
```
  6,845
 +2,639
  9,484
```

40.
```
  5,692
 +1,204
  6,896
```

41.
```
  2,642
 +4,135
  6,777
```

42.
```
  7,921
 +2,639
 10,560
```

43.
```
  7,884
 +7,069
 14,953
```

44.
```
  46,234
 +11,325
  57,559
```

45.
```
  17,694
 +15,893
  33,587
```

46.
```
  37,491
 +21,308
  58,799
```

47.
```
  59,641
 +27,840
  87,481
```

48.
```
  9,100
    536
 +2,413
 12,049
```

49.
```
  7,749
  1,240
 +6,010
 14,999
```

50.
```
  6,590
  2,408
 +5,001
 13,999
```

51.
```
  5,783
  6,535
 +2,132
 14,450
```

52.
```
  6,259
    503
 +1,893
  8,655
```

Subtracting Whole Numbers

Without Borrowing

Subtract.

9,876
−7,545

↓

9,876
−7,545
2,331

1. 784 −453 **331**	**2.** 985 −734 **251**	**3.** 693 −542 **151**	**4.** 199 −158 **41**
5. 7,659 −4,217 **3,442**	**6.** 8,436 −6,223 **2,213**	**7.** 5,792 −2,481 **3,311**	**8.** 4,877 −3,614 **1,263**
9. 6,754 −5,643 **1,111**	**10.** 1,866 − 853 **1,013**	**11.** 8,191 − 171 **8,020**	**12.** 1,187 − 145 **1,042**
13. 479 −473 **6**	**14.** 3,987 −3,085 **902**	**15.** 6,358 − 127 **6,231**	**16.** 1,721 − 720 **1,001**

With Borrowing

Subtract.

9,672   8,352
4,136   −1,584

↓   ↓

  6 12   7 12 14 12
9,6͞7͞2͞   8,͞3͞5͞2͞
−4,136   −4,584
5,536   3,768

17. 100 − 36 **64**	**18.** 512 − 43 **469**	**19.** 602 −503 **99**	**20.** 250 −162 **88**
21. 6,932 −4,674 **2,258**	**22.** 8,724 −2,932 **5,792**	**23.** 4,329 −3,163 **1,166**	**24.** 9,721 −6,842 **2,879**
25. 6,123 −4,214 **1,909**	**26.** 9,231 −6,453 **2,778**	**27.** 7,450 −3,783 **3,667**	**28.** 7,734 −3,935 **3,799**
29. 8,121 −6,846 **1,275**	**30.** 9,000 −7,997 **1,003**	**31.** 9,107 −8,248 **859**	**32.** 7,734 −5,935 **1,799**

Mixed Practice

33. 6,140 −3,157 **2,983**	**34.** 8,005 − 6,246 **1,759**	**35.** 7,000 −5,432 **1,568**	**36.** 9,297 9,286 **11**	**37.** 9,811 − 700 **9,111**
38. 9,148 − 954 **8,194**	**39.** 2,625 − 763 **1,862**	**40.** 1,850 − 975 **875**	**41.** 7,469 −5,231 **2,238**	**42.** 6,342 −5,793 **549**
43. 10,743 − 7,842 **2,901**	**44.** 16,947 −14,523 **2,424**	**45.** 22,493 − 5,967 **16,526**	**46.** 64,654 −57,312 **7,342**	**47.** 79,850 −42,347 **37,503**
48. 172,493 − 67,254 **105,239**	**49.** 249,657 −123,254 **126,403**	**50.** 300,692 −147,593 **153,099**	**51.** 647,593 −546,972 **100,621**	**52.** 800,000 −627,351 **172,649**

SKILL 5

Adding Decimals

Same Number of Places

Add.

658.21	658.21
292.73 ⟶	292.73
+832.08	+832.08
	1783.02

1. 423.11
    +983.09
    1,406.20

2. 987.76
    +998.24
    1,986.00

3. 323.35
    +390.04
    713.39

4. 632.37
    +864.87
    1,497.24

5. 456.06
    +443.99
    900.05

6. 763.88
    +980.21
    1,744.09

7. 879.757
    986.752
    +544.847
    2,411.356

8. 57.606
    443.216
    +463.987
    964.809

9. 787.332
    90.887
    +840.783
    1,719.002

Different Number of Places

Add.

0.93	0.930
5.893 ⟶	5.893
8.4	8.400
+81	+81.000
	96.223

Placeholders

10. 34
    + 3.4
    37.4

11. 34.6
    +63.43
    98.03

12. 27.77
    +95.074
    122.844

13. 432.32
    3.644
    +864.876
    1,300.840

14. 4.56
    6.989
    +0.809
    12.358

15. 63.9
    0.01
    +980.09
    1,044.00

16. 65.65
    16.82
    + 5.452
    87.922

17. 0.967
    81.14
    + 9.004
    91.111

18. 7.55
    0.06
    +0.7
    8.31

19. 43.73
    77.8
    +34.724
    156.254

20. 4.787
    76.64
    + 7.983
    89.410

21. 3.7
    9.009
    +7.29
    19.999

Mixed Practice

22. 23.131
    +93.079
    116.210

23. 557.766
    +568.264
    1,126.030

24. 764.5
    + 36.094
    800.594

25. 998.7
    + 84.857
    1,083.557

26. 845.876
    +989.19
    1,835.066

27. 435.745
    67.76
    + 5.09
    508.595

28. 76
    75.879
    +786.87
    938.749

29. 0.678
    0.021
    +0.301
    1.000

30. 0.083
    0.664
    +0.945
    1.692

31. 65.4
    74.042
    + 7.978
    147.420

32. 65.74
    45.78
    54.98
    +54.12
    220.62

33. 654.65
    65.7
    56.982
    + 9.7
    787.032

34. 676.974
    11.743
    456.999
    + 8.7
    1,154.416

35. 765.4
    4.658
    56.46
    +364.9
    1,191.418

36. 765.787
    6.005
    98.89
    + 789
    1,659.682

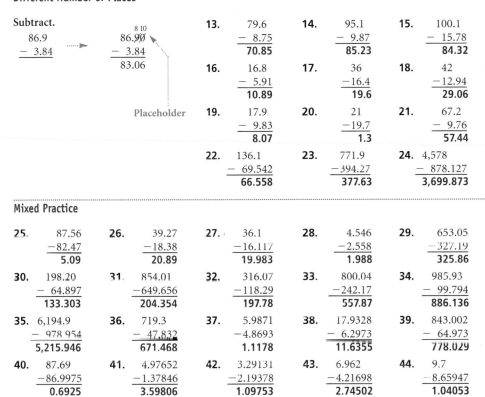

Subtracting Decimals

Same Number of Places

Subtract.

597.18   → $\overset{6\ \ 11}{59\cancel{7}.\cancel{1}8}$
−392.35   −392.35
                204.83

1.	65.46 −14.31 **51.15**	2.	48.58 −15.47 **33.11**	3.	151.02 − 16.13 **134.89**
4.	36.25 −13.67 **22.58**	5.	87.56 −82.47 **5.09**	6.	51.634 −27.849 **23.785**
7.	69.37 −43.86 **25.51**	8.	89.63 − 7.99 **81.64**	9.	109.46 − 29.78 **79.68**
10.	521.52 − 38.56 **482.96**	11.	321.02 −117.18 **203.84**	12.	572.24 −283.35 **288.89**

Different Number of Places

Subtract.

86.9   → $\overset{8\ \ 10}{86.9\cancel{0}}$
− 3.84   − 3.84
              83.06

Placeholder

13.	79.6 − 8.75 **70.85**	14.	95.1 − 9.87 **85.23**	15.	100.1 − 15.78 **84.32**
16.	16.8 − 5.91 **10.89**	17.	36 −16.4 **19.6**	18.	42 −12.94 **29.06**
19.	17.9 − 9.83 **8.07**	20.	21 −19.7 **1.3**	21.	67.2 − 9.76 **57.44**
22.	136.1 − 69.542 **66.558**	23.	771.9 −394.27 **377.63**	24.	4,578 − 878.127 **3,699.873**

Mixed Practice

25.	87.56 −82.47 **5.09**	26.	39.27 −18.38 **20.89**	27.	36.1 −16.117 **19.983**	28.	4.546 −2.558 **1.988**	29.	653.05 −327.19 **325.86**
30.	198.20 − 64.897 **133.303**	31.	854.01 −649.656 **204.354**	32.	316.07 −118.29 **197.78**	33.	800.04 −242.17 **557.87**	34.	985.93 − 99.794 **886.136**
35.	6,194.9 − 978.954 **5,215.946**	36.	719.3 − 47.832 **671.468**	37.	5.9871 −4.8693 **1.1178**	38.	17.9328 − 6.2973 **11.6355**	39.	843.002 − 64.973 **778.029**
40.	87.69 −86.9975 **0.6925**	41.	4.97652 −1.37846 **3.59806**	42.	3.29131 −2.19378 **1.09753**	43.	6.962 −4.21698 **2.74502**	44.	9.7 −8.65947 **1.04053**

SKILL 7

Multiplying Whole Numbers

Without Carrying

Multiply.

```
442  ----->  442
×211         ×211
               442  <----  1 × 442
             4,420  <----  10 × 442
            88,400  <----  200 × 442
            93,262  <----  211 × 442
```

1.	73 ×21 **1,533**	**2.**	42 ×22 **924**	**3.**	212 ×412 **87,344**
4.	311 ×232 **72,152**	**5.**	321 ×312 **100,152**	**6.**	223 ×323 **72,029**
7.	232 ×333 **77,256**	**8.**	7,143 × 102 **728,586**	**9.**	8,643 × 111 **959,373**

With Carrying

Multiply.

```
6,524  --->  6,524
×  273       ×  273
              19,572  <---  3 × 6,524
             456,680  <---  70 × 6,524
           1,304,800  <---  200 × 6,524
           1,781,052  <---  273 × 6,524
```

10.	61 ×76 **4,636**	**11.**	78 ×36 **2,808**	**12.**	437 ×571 **249,527**
13.	465 ×541 **251,565**	**14.**	542 ×168 **91,056**	**15.**	8,023 × 532 **4,268,236**
16.	64 ×27 **1,728**	**17.**	37 ×45 **1,665**	**18.**	68 ×71 **4,828**
19.	836 ×372 **310,992**	**20.**	7,501 × 447 **3,352,947**	**21.**	5,327 × 312 **1,662,024**

Mixed Practice

22.	480 × 10 **4,800**	**23.**	230 ×300 **69,000**	**24.**	641 ×237 **151,917**	**25.**	231 ×122 **28,182**	**26.**	122 × 40 **4,880**
27.	510 ×700 **357,000**	**28.**	8,233 ×2,584 **21,274,072**	**29.**	6,010 ×6,000 **36,060,000**	**30.**	9,000 ×7,011 **63,099,000**	**31.**	2,973 ×1,504 **4,471,392**
32.	19,008 × 8,000 **152,064,000**	**33.**	8,791 ×5,000 **43,955,000**	**34.**	6,743 × 27 **182,061**	**35.**	4,231 × 253 **1,070,443**	**36.**	8,427 × 19 **160,113**
37.	13,010 × 13 **169,130**	**38.**	14,231 × 12 **170,772**	**39.**	17,822 × 35 **623,770**	**40.**	22,300 × 15 **334,500**	**41.**	31,942 × 41 **1,309,622**
42.	27,642 × 321 **8,873,082**	**43.**	13,231 × 212 **2,804,972**	**44.**	14,402 × 121 **1,742,642**	**45.**	49,237 × 321 **15,805,077**	**46.**	64,159 × 347 **22,263,173**

SKILLS

SKILL 8

Multiplying Decimals

Decimals Greater Than One

Multiply.

$$
\begin{array}{r}
17.45 \\
\times\ 2.7 \\
\end{array}
\longrightarrow
\begin{array}{r}
17.45 \\
\times\ 2.7 \\
\hline
47.115 \\
\end{array}
\begin{array}{l}
\longleftarrow\ \text{2 places} \\
\longleftarrow\ \text{+1 place} \\
\longleftarrow\ \text{3 places} \\
\end{array}
$$

1. $\begin{array}{r} 2.5 \\ \times 1.8 \\ \hline 4.5 \end{array}$ **2.** $\begin{array}{r} 8.3 \\ \times 1.5 \\ \hline 12.54 \end{array}$ **3.** $\begin{array}{r} 102 \\ \times 8.61 \\ \hline 878.22 \end{array}$

4. $\begin{array}{r} 15.3 \\ \times\ 5.3 \\ \hline 81.09 \end{array}$ **5.** $\begin{array}{r} 25.14 \\ \times\ 7.5 \\ \hline 188.55 \end{array}$ **6.** $\begin{array}{r} 19.36 \\ \times\ 7.12 \\ \hline 137.8432 \end{array}$

7. $\begin{array}{r} 27.06 \\ \times\ 8.53 \\ \hline 230.8218 \end{array}$ **8.** $\begin{array}{r} 4.367 \\ \times\ 8.5 \\ \hline 37.1195 \end{array}$ **9.** $\begin{array}{r} 5.564 \\ \times\ 7.9 \\ \hline 43.9556 \end{array}$

10. $\begin{array}{r} 32.63 \\ \times\ 9.2 \\ \hline 300.196 \end{array}$ **11.** $\begin{array}{r} 31.20 \\ \times\ 9.21 \\ \hline 287.352 \end{array}$ **12.** $\begin{array}{r} 6.715 \\ \times\ 9.03 \\ \hline 60.63645 \end{array}$

Decimals Less Than One

Multiply.

$$
\begin{array}{r}
0.08 \\
\times 0.4 \\
\end{array}
\longrightarrow
\begin{array}{r}
0.08 \\
\times 0.4 \\
\hline
0.032 \\
\end{array}
\begin{array}{l}
\longleftarrow\ \text{2 places} \\
\longleftarrow\ \text{+1 place} \\
\longleftarrow\ \text{3 places} \\
\end{array}
$$

13. $\begin{array}{r} 0.144 \\ \times\ 0.7 \\ \hline 0.1008 \end{array}$ **14.** $\begin{array}{r} 0.86 \\ \times\ 0.5 \\ \hline 0.43 \end{array}$ **15.** $\begin{array}{r} 0.96 \\ \times\ 0.1 \\ \hline 0.096 \end{array}$

16. $\begin{array}{r} 0.56 \\ \times 0.07 \\ \hline 0.0392 \end{array}$ **17.** $\begin{array}{r} 0.73 \\ \times\ 0.8 \\ \hline 0.584 \end{array}$ **18.** $\begin{array}{r} 0.05 \\ \times\ 0.9 \\ \hline 0.045 \end{array}$

19. $\begin{array}{r} 0.81 \\ \times 0.76 \\ \hline 0.6156 \end{array}$ **20.** $\begin{array}{r} 0.47 \\ \times 0.84 \\ \hline 0.3948 \end{array}$ **21.** $\begin{array}{r} 0.63 \\ \times 0.09 \\ \hline 0.0567 \end{array}$

22. $\begin{array}{r} 0.57 \\ \times 0.03 \\ \hline 0.0171 \end{array}$ **23.** $\begin{array}{r} 1.23 \\ \times 0.07 \\ \hline 0.0861 \end{array}$ **24.** $\begin{array}{r} 0.01 \\ \times 0.05 \\ \hline 0.0005 \end{array}$

Mixed Practice

25. $\begin{array}{r} 41.16 \\ \times\ 100 \\ \hline 4,116 \end{array}$ **26.** $\begin{array}{r} 0.923 \\ \times\ 0.49 \\ \hline 0.45227 \end{array}$ **27.** $\begin{array}{r} 0.12 \\ \times\ 300 \\ \hline 36 \end{array}$ **28.** $\begin{array}{r} 67.32 \\ \times\ 10 \\ \hline 673.2 \end{array}$ **29.** $\begin{array}{r} 7.243 \\ \times\ 121 \\ \hline 876.403 \end{array}$

30. $\begin{array}{r} 557.4 \\ \times\ 100 \\ \hline 55,740 \end{array}$ **31.** $\begin{array}{r} 327.8 \\ \times\ 3.7 \\ \hline 1,212.86 \end{array}$ **32.** $\begin{array}{r} 14.923 \\ \times\ 0.76 \\ \hline 11.34148 \end{array}$ **33.** $\begin{array}{r} 1.125 \\ \times\ 100 \\ \hline 112.5 \end{array}$ **34.** $\begin{array}{r} 0.009 \\ \times 1,000 \\ \hline 9 \end{array}$

35. $\begin{array}{r} 2.014 \\ \times\ 40.7 \\ \hline 81.9698 \end{array}$ **36.** $\begin{array}{r} 2.854 \\ \times\ 0.04 \\ \hline 0.11416 \end{array}$ **37.** $\begin{array}{r} 6,243.78 \\ \times\ 25.9 \\ \hline 161,713.902 \end{array}$ **38.** $\begin{array}{r} 5.9312 \\ \times\ 5.62 \\ \hline 33.333344 \end{array}$ **39.** $\begin{array}{r} 0.534 \\ \times 0.293 \\ \hline 0.156462 \end{array}$

40. $\begin{array}{r} 16.4591 \\ \times\ 51.23 \\ \hline 843.199693 \end{array}$ **41.** $\begin{array}{r} 96.00 \\ \times 0.875 \\ \hline 84 \end{array}$ **42.** $\begin{array}{r} 0.3172 \\ \times 0.2008 \\ \hline 0.06369376 \end{array}$ **43.** $\begin{array}{r} 0.1543 \\ \times 0.4931 \\ \hline 0.07608533 \end{array}$ **44.** $\begin{array}{r} 0.7984 \\ \times 0.0003 \\ \hline 0.00023952 \end{array}$

SKILL 9

Dividing (Fractional Remainder)

Two-Digit Divisor

Divide.

46)703

$$\frac{1}{46)703} \longrightarrow \frac{15}{46)703} \longrightarrow \frac{15\frac{13}{46}}{46)703}$$
$$\frac{-46}{24} \qquad \frac{-46}{243} \qquad \frac{-46}{243}$$
$$\frac{-230}{13} \qquad \frac{-230}{13}$$

1. $2\frac{1}{3}$ 27)63
2. $2\frac{13}{38}$ 38)89
3. $2\frac{2}{41}$ 41)84
4. $13\frac{15}{46}$ 46)613
5. $14\frac{12}{53}$ 53)754
6. $11\frac{14}{61}$ 61)685
7. $84\frac{17}{21}$ 21)1,781
8. $77\frac{38}{55}$ 55)4,273
9. $67\frac{19}{43}$ 43)2,900
10. $54\frac{14}{73}$ 73)3,956
11. $59\frac{12}{23}$ 23)1,369
12. $63\frac{25}{34}$ 34)2,167
13. $71\frac{42}{81}$ 81)5,793
14. $1\frac{5}{26}$ 93)78

Three-Digit Divisor

Divide.

472)9,463

$$\frac{2}{472)9463} \longrightarrow \frac{20\frac{23}{472}}{472)9463}$$
$$\frac{-944}{2} \qquad \frac{-944}{23}$$
$$\frac{-0}{23}$$

15. $16\frac{13}{114}$ 114)1,837
16. $25\frac{17}{216}$ 216)5,417
17. $15\frac{17}{321}$ 321)4,832
18. $21\frac{29}{429}$ 429)9,038
19. $8\frac{792}{892}$ 892)7,928
20. $13\frac{19}{910}$ 910)11,849
21. $23\frac{22}{409}$ 409)9,429
22. $8\frac{421}{900}$ 900)7,621
23. $14\frac{2}{625}$ 625)8,752
24. $22\frac{74}{710}$ 710)15,694
25. $20\frac{831}{843}$ 843)17,691
26. $23\frac{923}{937}$ 937)22,474

Mixed Practice

27. 18 19)342
28. 17 46)782
29. 16 71)1,136
30. $35\frac{13}{279}$ 279)9,778
31. 72 35)2,520
32. $9\frac{508}{509}$ 509)5,089
33. $14\frac{22}{621}$ 621)8,716
34. $101\frac{10}{49}$ 49)4,959
35. $12\frac{349}{549}$ 549)6,937
36. $10\frac{67}{953}$ 953)9,597
37. $5\frac{765}{842}$ 842)4,975
38. $24\frac{17}{29}$ 87)2,139
39. $181\frac{29}{473}$ 473)85,642
40. $478\frac{69}{192}$ 192)91,845
41. $87\frac{527}{622}$ 622)54,641
42. $68\frac{476}{812}$ 812)55,692
43. $1,600\frac{3}{51}$ 51)81,603
44. $1,928\frac{20}{23}$ 23)44,364
45. $252\frac{46}{88}$ 88)22,222
46. $821\frac{31}{34}$ 34)27,945
47. $208\frac{166}{417}$ 417)86,902
48. $1,453\frac{42}{71}$ 71)103,205
49. $1,345\frac{177}{514}$ 514)691,507
50. $3,712\frac{37}{64}$ 64)237,605

SKILL **10**

Dividing (Decimal Remainder)

Exact Quotient

Divide.

$28\overline{)378}$

$$
\begin{array}{r}
13 \\
28\overline{)378} \\
-28 \\
\hline
98 \\
-84 \\
\hline
14
\end{array}
\longrightarrow
\begin{array}{r}
13.5 \\
28\overline{)378.0} \\
-28 \\
\hline
98 \\
-84 \\
\hline
140 \\
-140
\end{array}
$$

1. $8\overline{)89}$ → 11.125

2. $10\overline{)123}$ → 12.3

3. $15\overline{)318}$ → 21.2

4. $16\overline{)264}$ → 16.5

5. $20\overline{)102}$ → 5.1

6. $50\overline{)530}$ → 10.6

7. $12\overline{)237}$ → 19.75

8. $25\overline{)1,310}$ → 52.4

9. $32\overline{)1,104}$ → 34.5

10. $96\overline{)2,988}$ → 31.125

Rounded Quotient

Divide. $39\overline{)818}$

Round to the nearest hundredth.

$$
\begin{array}{r}
20 \\
39\overline{)818} \\
-78 \\
\hline
38
\end{array}
\longrightarrow
\begin{array}{r}
20.974 \\
39\overline{)818.000} \\
78 \\
\hline
380 \\
351 \\
\hline
290 \\
273 \\
\hline
170 \\
156 \\
\hline
14
\end{array}
$$

Thousandths place

20.974 rounded to the nearest hundredth is 20.97 ◄········· Skill 2

Round answers to the place value shown.

Nearest tenth:

11. $14\overline{)319}$ → 22.8

12. $26\overline{)347}$ → 13.4

13. $23\overline{)371}$ → 16.1

14. $46\overline{)9,415}$ → 204.7

15. $47\overline{)9,719}$ → 206.8

Nearest hundredth:

16. $19\overline{)427}$ → 22.47

17. $83\overline{)168}$ → 2.02

18. $47\overline{)432}$ → 9.19

Nearest thousandth:

19. $37\overline{)402}$ → 10.865

20. $24\overline{)643}$ → 26.792

21. $21\overline{)452}$ → 21.524

Mixed Practice

Round answers to the nearest hundredth.

22. $28\overline{)1,022}$ → 36.5

23. $24\overline{)209}$ → 8.71

24. $72\overline{)1,665}$ → 23.13

25. $29\overline{)303}$ → 10.45

26. $85\overline{)1,802}$ → 21.2

27. $24\overline{)747}$ → 31.13

28. $67\overline{)701}$ → 10.46

29. $71\overline{)400}$ → 5.63

30. $23\overline{)273}$ → 11.87

31. $36\overline{)630}$ → 17.5

32. $44\overline{)858}$ → 19.5

33. $59\overline{)852}$ → 14.44

34. $37\overline{)673}$ → 18.19

35. $41\overline{)9,432}$ → 230.05

36. $73\overline{)1,079}$ → 14.78

37. $24\overline{)994}$ → 41.42

38. $27\overline{)3,365}$ → 124.63

39. $35\overline{)894}$ → 25.54

40. $42\overline{)5,264}$ → 125.33

41. $110\overline{)4,345}$ → 39.5

SKILL 11

Dividing Decimals

Divisor Greater Than One

Divide.

$7.2\overline{)16.92}$

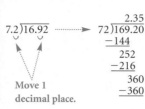

$7.2\overline{)16.92} \longrightarrow 72\overline{)169.20}$

$\phantom{72\overline{)}}\begin{array}{r}2.35\\169.20\\-144\\\hline 252\\-216\\\hline 360\\-360\\\hline\end{array}$

Move 1 decimal place.

Round answers to the nearest hundredth.

1. $2.5\overline{)11.5}$ → **4.6**   **2.** $3.8\overline{)4.56}$ → **1.2**

3. $3.2\overline{)18.272}$ → **5.71**   **4.** $7.5\overline{)27.823}$ → **3.71**

5. $3.15\overline{)53.55}$ → **17**   **6.** $24.12\overline{)369.036}$ → **15.3**

7. $4.08\overline{)26.52}$ → **6.5**   **8.** $3.02\overline{)10.57}$ → **3.5**

9. $4.23\overline{)181.5}$ → **42.91**   **10.** $6.67\overline{)25.963}$ → **3.89**

Divisor Less Than One

Divide.

$0.032\overline{)14.400}$

$0.032\overline{)14.400} \longrightarrow 32\overline{)14400}$

$\phantom{32\overline{)}}\begin{array}{r}450\\14400\\-128\\\hline 160\\-160\\\hline 00\\-00\\\hline\end{array}$

Move 3 decimal places.

Round answers to the nearest hundredth.

11. $0.24\overline{)6.24}$ → **26**   **12.** $0.372\overline{)6.324}$ → **17**

13. $0.154\overline{)4.774}$ → **31**   **14.** $0.48\overline{)2.938}$ → **6.12**

15. $0.37\overline{)9.62}$ → **26**   **16.** $0.21\overline{)1.374}$ → **6.54**

17. $0.51\overline{)4.569}$ → **8.96**   **18.** $0.67\overline{)2.693}$ → **4.02**

19. $0.73\overline{)9.641}$ → **13.21**   **20.** $0.81\overline{)11.632}$ → **14.36**

Mixed Practice

Round answers to the nearest hundredth.

21. $3.12\overline{)4.386}$ → **1.41**   **22.** $0.73\overline{)9.48}$ → **12.99**   **23.** $0.136\overline{)33.32}$ → **245**   **24.** $0.21\overline{)130.2}$ → **620**

25. $6.94\overline{)8.378}$ → **1.21**   **26.** $1.23\overline{)0.3813}$ → **0.31**   **27.** $0.065\overline{)16.64}$ → **256**   **28.** $8.34\overline{)7.416}$ → **0.89**

29. $0.63\overline{)42.51}$ → **67.48**   **30.** $2.91\overline{)5.932}$ → **2.04**   **31.** $1.07\overline{)24.153}$ → **22.57**   **32.** $1.1\overline{)29.9}$ → **27.18**

33. $15.93\overline{)27.931}$ → **1.75**   **34.** $12.12\overline{)36.422}$ → **3.01**   **35.** $0.05\overline{)1.925}$ → **38.5**   **36.** $2.03\overline{)21.249}$ → **10.47**

37. $0.007\overline{)0.692}$ → **98.86**   **38.** $1.05\overline{)25.421}$ → **24.21**   **39.** $0.31\overline{)0.00354}$ → **0.01**   **40.** $15.42\overline{)113.005}$ → **7.33**

41. $5.02\overline{)86}$ → **17.13**   **42.** $0.03\overline{)29}$ → **966.67**   **43.** $5.4\overline{)0.062}$ → **0.01**   **44.** $0.068\overline{)0.009}$ → **0.13**

SKILL 12

Equivalent Fractions

Higher Terms

Complete the equivalent fraction.

$\frac{3}{4} = \frac{?}{20}$

$\times 5$

$\frac{3}{4} = \frac{?}{20} \longrightarrow \frac{3}{4} = \frac{15}{20}$

$\times 5$

Solve.

1. $\frac{5}{6} = \frac{?}{12}$ 10 **2.** $\frac{4}{9} = \frac{?}{27}$ 12 **3.** $\frac{7}{10} = \frac{35}{?}$ 50

4. $\frac{11}{12} = \frac{22}{?}$ 24 **5.** $\frac{8}{17} = \frac{?}{51}$ 24 **6.** $\frac{15}{17} = \frac{90}{?}$ 102

7. $\frac{11}{18} = \frac{?}{36}$ 22 **8.** $\frac{4}{19} = \frac{12}{?}$ 57 **9.** $\frac{16}{17} = \frac{48}{?}$ 51

10. $\frac{11}{13} = \frac{?}{39}$ 33 **11.** $\frac{3}{4} = \frac{?}{32}$ 24 **12.** $\frac{15}{17} = \frac{60}{?}$ 68

13. $\frac{7}{9} = \frac{?}{45}$ 35 **14.** $\frac{11}{12} = \frac{?}{72}$ 66 **15.** $\frac{5}{8} = \frac{45}{?}$ 72

16. $\frac{11}{8} = \frac{33}{?}$ 24 **17.** $\frac{5}{24} = \frac{?}{96}$ 20 **18.** $\frac{23}{73} = \frac{?}{365}$ 115

Lowest Terms

Reduce $\frac{12}{28}$ to lowest terms.

$\div 4$

$\frac{12}{28} = \frac{3}{7} \longrightarrow \frac{12}{28} = \frac{3}{7}$

$\div 4$

Reduce to lowest terms.

19. $\frac{6}{9}$ $\frac{2}{3}$ **20.** $\frac{4}{16}$ $\frac{1}{4}$ **21.** $\frac{9}{18}$ $\frac{1}{2}$

22. $\frac{20}{22}$ $\frac{10}{11}$ **23.** $\frac{18}{27}$ $\frac{2}{3}$ **24.** $\frac{24}{32}$ $\frac{3}{4}$

25. $\frac{16}{48}$ $\frac{1}{3}$ **26.** $\frac{18}{42}$ $\frac{3}{7}$ **27.** $\frac{55}{66}$ $\frac{5}{6}$

28. $\frac{30}{50}$ $\frac{3}{5}$ **29.** $\frac{20}{54}$ $\frac{10}{27}$ **30.** $\frac{21}{27}$ $\frac{7}{9}$

31. $\frac{8}{14}$ $\frac{4}{7}$ **32.** $\frac{19}{57}$ $\frac{1}{3}$ **33.** $\frac{14}{28}$ $\frac{1}{2}$

34. $\frac{15}{25}$ $\frac{3}{5}$ **35.** $\frac{21}{28}$ $\frac{3}{4}$ **36.** $\frac{200}{365}$ $\frac{40}{73}$

37. $\frac{188}{366}$ $\frac{94}{183}$ **38.** $\frac{150}{365}$ $\frac{30}{73}$ **39.** $\frac{180}{360}$ $\frac{1}{2}$

40. $\frac{225}{365}$ $\frac{45}{73}$ **41.** $\frac{190}{360}$ $\frac{19}{36}$ **42.** $\frac{65}{75}$ $\frac{13}{15}$

43. $\frac{72}{468}$ $\frac{2}{13}$ **44.** $\frac{183}{366}$ $\frac{1}{2}$ **45.** $\frac{232}{1,450}$ $\frac{4}{25}$

46. $\frac{1,792}{5,120}$ $\frac{7}{20}$

SKILL 13

Changing Mixed Numbers/Improper Fractions

Mixed Numbers to Improper Fractions

Write $3\frac{7}{8}$ as an improper fraction.

$3\frac{7}{8} = \frac{(3 \times 8) + 7}{8}$

$3\frac{7}{8} = \frac{24 + 7}{8}$

$3\frac{7}{8} = \frac{31}{8}$

Write as an improper fraction.

1. $6\frac{1}{4}$ $\frac{25}{4}$ **2.** $4\frac{3}{4}$ $\frac{19}{4}$ **3.** $7\frac{3}{8}$ $\frac{59}{8}$

4. $9\frac{1}{2}$ $\frac{19}{2}$ **5.** $6\frac{2}{3}$ $\frac{20}{3}$ **6.** $3\frac{5}{6}$ $\frac{23}{6}$

7. $7\frac{4}{5}$ $\frac{39}{5}$ **8.** $3\frac{1}{8}$ $\frac{25}{8}$ **9.** $4\frac{3}{10}$ $\frac{43}{10}$

10. $1\frac{1}{16}$ $\frac{17}{16}$ **11.** $4\frac{7}{32}$ $\frac{135}{32}$ **12.** $4\frac{1}{5}$ $\frac{21}{5}$

13. $5\frac{1}{3}$ $\frac{16}{3}$ **14.** $2\frac{1}{6}$ $\frac{13}{6}$ **15.** $2\frac{9}{10}$ $\frac{29}{10}$

16. $3\frac{1}{10}$ $\frac{31}{10}$ **17.** $3\frac{5}{16}$ $\frac{53}{16}$ **18.** $4\frac{9}{16}$ $\frac{73}{16}$

19. $5\frac{5}{32}$ $\frac{165}{32}$ **20.** $6\frac{3}{5}$ $\frac{33}{5}$ **21.** $7\frac{2}{11}$ $\frac{79}{11}$

22. $8\frac{5}{6}$ $\frac{53}{6}$ **23.** $11\frac{2}{5}$ $\frac{57}{5}$ **24.** $13\frac{1}{3}$ $\frac{40}{3}$

Improper Fractions to Mixed Numbers

Write $\frac{17}{3}$ as a mixed number.

$\frac{17}{3} \longrightarrow \begin{array}{r} 5\frac{2}{3} \longleftarrow \text{Skill 9} \\ 3\overline{)17} \\ -15 \\ \hline 2 \end{array}$

$\frac{17}{3} = 5\frac{2}{3}$

Write as a mixed number. Reduce any fractional parts to lowest terms.

25. $\frac{13}{2}$ $6\frac{1}{2}$ **26.** $\frac{18}{4}$ $4\frac{1}{2}$ **27.** $\frac{46}{8}$ $5\frac{3}{4}$

28. $\frac{19}{4}$ $4\frac{3}{4}$ **29.** $\frac{33}{6}$ $5\frac{1}{2}$ **30.** $\frac{30}{7}$ $4\frac{2}{7}$

31. $\frac{21}{9}$ $2\frac{1}{3}$ **32.** $\frac{28}{8}$ $3\frac{1}{2}$ **33.** $\frac{45}{18}$ $2\frac{1}{2}$

34. $\frac{49}{21}$ $2\frac{1}{3}$ **35.** $\frac{62}{21}$ $2\frac{20}{21}$ **36.** $\frac{23}{3}$ $7\frac{2}{3}$

37. $\frac{35}{6}$ $5\frac{5}{6}$ **38.** $\frac{47}{7}$ $6\frac{5}{7}$ **39.** $\frac{57}{18}$ $3\frac{1}{6}$

40. $\frac{37}{9}$ $4\frac{1}{9}$ **41.** $\frac{49}{8}$ $6\frac{1}{8}$ **42.** $\frac{63}{2}$ $31\frac{1}{2}$

43. $\frac{45}{7}$ $6\frac{3}{7}$ **44.** $\frac{71}{4}$ $17\frac{3}{4}$

Changing Fractions/Decimals

Fraction to Decimal

Write $\frac{5}{12}$ as a decimal. Round to the nearest hundredth.

$\frac{5}{12} \longrightarrow 12\overline{)5.000}^{\,0.416}$ ◄······ Skill 10

0.416 rounded to the nearest hundredth is 0.42. ◄······ Skill 2

$\frac{5}{12} = 0.42$

Write as a decimal. Round answers to the nearest hundredth.

1. $\frac{4}{5}$ 0.8
2. $\frac{7}{20}$ 0.35
3. $1\frac{1}{8}$ 1.13
4. $\frac{3}{4}$ 0.75
5. $2\frac{3}{7}$ 2.43
6. $\frac{7}{12}$ 0.58
7. $1\frac{11}{30}$ 1.37
8. $\frac{2}{5}$ 0.4
9. $\frac{3}{10}$ 0.3
10. $3\frac{4}{25}$ 3.16
11. $4\frac{3}{8}$ 4.38
12. $\frac{7}{10}$ 0.7
13. $3\frac{1}{12}$ 3.08
14. $\frac{1}{15}$ 0.07
15. $\frac{1}{30}$ 0.03
16. $2\frac{9}{10}$ 2.9
17. $5\frac{3}{20}$ 5.15
18. $\frac{9}{20}$ 0.45
19. $2\frac{3}{25}$ 2.12
20. $\frac{1}{8}$ 0.13
21. $7\frac{1}{7}$ 7.14
22. $2\frac{5}{8}$ 2.63
23. $\frac{4}{9}$ 0.44
24. $1\frac{7}{8}$ 1.88

Decimal to Fraction

Write 0.42 as a fraction in lowest terms.

$\overset{\text{Skill 1}}{\downarrow}$

$0.42 = \frac{42}{100} = \frac{21}{50}$ ◄······ Skill 12

$0.42 = \frac{21}{50}$

Write as a fraction in lowest terms.

25. 0.1 $\frac{1}{10}$
26. 3.7 $3\frac{7}{10}$
27. 0.30 $\frac{3}{10}$
28. 2.25 $2\frac{1}{4}$
29. 0.03 $\frac{3}{100}$
30. 0.09 $\frac{9}{100}$
31. 0.53 $\frac{53}{100}$
32. 1.75 $1\frac{3}{4}$
33. 0.003 $\frac{3}{1,000}$
34. 0.010 $\frac{1}{100}$
35. 0.064 $\frac{8}{125}$
36. 4.206 $4\frac{103}{500}$
37. 4.444 $4\frac{111}{250}$
38. 0.732 $\frac{183}{250}$
39. 0.469 $\frac{469}{1,000}$
40. 2.9 $2\frac{9}{10}$
41. 7.5 $7\frac{1}{2}$
42. 0.32 $\frac{8}{25}$
43. 1.08 $1\frac{2}{25}$
44. 0.06 $\frac{3}{50}$
45. 2.83 $2\frac{83}{100}$
46. 1.039 $1\frac{39}{1,000}$
47. 0.105 $\frac{21}{200}$
48. 2.422 $2\frac{211}{500}$
49. 0.0005 $\frac{1}{2,000}$
50. 0.2482 $\frac{1,241}{5,000}$
51. 1.6432 $1\frac{402}{625}$
52. 0.0058 $\frac{29}{5,000}$
53. 0.0002 $\frac{1}{5,000}$
54. 6.66 $6\frac{33}{50}$

Adding Fractions, Like Denominators

Fractions

Add.

Like denominators

$\frac{4}{9}$ ◄—— Add numerators

$+\frac{2}{9}$

$\frac{6}{9} = \frac{2}{3}$ ◄····· Skill 12

Express answers in lowest terms.

1. $\frac{4}{5} + \frac{3}{5}$ $1\frac{2}{5}$

2. $\frac{4}{7} + \frac{2}{7}$ $\frac{6}{7}$

3. $\frac{1}{8} + \frac{5}{8}$ $\frac{3}{4}$

4. $\frac{5}{9} + \frac{7}{9}$ $1\frac{1}{3}$

5. $\frac{5}{7} + \frac{6}{7}$ $1\frac{4}{7}$

6. $\frac{11}{12} + \frac{7}{12}$ $1\frac{1}{2}$

7. $\frac{13}{25} + \frac{16}{25}$ $1\frac{4}{25}$

8. $\frac{11}{30} + \frac{19}{30}$ 1

9. $\frac{15}{32} + \frac{27}{32}$ $1\frac{5}{16}$

10. $\frac{21}{40} + \frac{31}{40}$ $1\frac{3}{10}$

11. $\frac{22}{45} + \frac{31}{45}$ $1\frac{8}{45}$

12. $\frac{11}{50} + \frac{19}{50}$ $\frac{3}{5}$

Mixed Numbers

Add.

$4\frac{5}{7}$

$+8\frac{6}{7}$

$\frac{11}{7} = 1\frac{4}{7}$

Skill 12

$\longrightarrow 1$

$4\frac{5}{7}$

$+8\frac{6}{7}$

$13\frac{4}{7}$

Express answers in lowest terms.

13. $4\frac{1}{3} + 7\frac{1}{3}$ $11\frac{2}{3}$

14. $13\frac{4}{5} + 8\frac{3}{5}$ $22\frac{2}{5}$

15. $5\frac{4}{7} + 8\frac{5}{7}$ $14\frac{2}{7}$

16. $12\frac{3}{8} + 14\frac{1}{8}$ $26\frac{1}{2}$

17. $6\frac{11}{12} + 5\frac{5}{12}$ $12\frac{1}{3}$

18. $2\frac{12}{13} + 7\frac{2}{13}$ $10\frac{1}{13}$

19. $8\frac{9}{16} + 8\frac{11}{16}$ $17\frac{1}{4}$

20. $14\frac{5}{24} + 15\frac{7}{24}$ $29\frac{1}{2}$

21. $4\frac{13}{32} + 5\frac{15}{32}$ $9\frac{7}{8}$

22. $15\frac{19}{45} + 6\frac{28}{45}$ $22\frac{2}{45}$

23. $7\frac{8}{35} + 4\frac{6}{35}$ $11\frac{2}{5}$

24. $9\frac{5}{32} + 14\frac{7}{32}$ $23\frac{3}{8}$

Adding Fractions, Unlike Denominators

Fractions

Add.

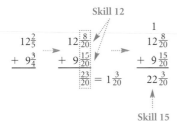

Unlike denominators   Like denominators

Skill 12

$\frac{5}{8}$ $\frac{15}{24}$ $\frac{15}{24}$

$+\frac{2}{3}$ $+\frac{16}{24}$ $+\frac{16}{24}$

Skill 15 $\frac{31}{24} = 1\frac{7}{24}$

Skill 13

Express answers in lowest terms.

1. $\frac{1}{2} + \frac{3}{5}$ $1\frac{1}{10}$ **2.** $\frac{3}{4} + \frac{1}{6}$ $\frac{11}{12}$

3. $\frac{2}{7} + \frac{2}{3}$ $\frac{20}{21}$ **4.** $\frac{3}{8} + \frac{1}{5}$ $\frac{23}{40}$

5. $\frac{5}{6} + \frac{1}{3}$ $1\frac{1}{6}$ **6.** $\frac{7}{12} + \frac{3}{7}$ $1\frac{1}{84}$

7. $\frac{9}{11} + \frac{3}{10}$ $1\frac{13}{110}$ **8.** $\frac{13}{16} + \frac{9}{8}$ $1\frac{15}{16}$

9. $\frac{7}{20} + \frac{19}{30}$ $\frac{59}{60}$ **10.** $\frac{5}{18} + \frac{19}{24}$ $1\frac{5}{72}$

11. $\frac{1}{25} + \frac{13}{30}$ $\frac{71}{150}$ **12.** $\frac{2}{15} + \frac{29}{30}$ $1\frac{1}{10}$

Mixed Numbers

Add.

Skill 12

$12\frac{2}{5}$ $12\frac{8}{20}$ $12\frac{8}{20}$

$+ 9\frac{3}{4}$ $+ 9\frac{15}{20}$ $+ 9\frac{15}{20}$

$\frac{23}{20} = 1\frac{3}{20}$ $22\frac{3}{20}$

Skill 15

Express answers in lowest terms.

13. $5\frac{1}{2} + 3\frac{2}{3}$ $9\frac{1}{6}$ **14.** $4\frac{3}{8} + 9\frac{3}{4}$ $14\frac{1}{8}$

15. $7\frac{5}{6} + 8\frac{1}{2}$ $16\frac{1}{3}$ **16.** $9\frac{7}{8} + 10\frac{7}{16}$ $20\frac{5}{16}$

17. $11\frac{2}{13} + 9\frac{15}{26}$ $20\frac{19}{26}$ **18.** $18\frac{2}{3} + 5\frac{7}{11}$ $24\frac{10}{33}$

19. $12\frac{4}{7} + 15\frac{7}{9}$ $28\frac{22}{63}$ **20.** $16\frac{5}{6} + 10\frac{6}{7}$ $27\frac{29}{42}$

21. $16\frac{5}{8} + 12\frac{1}{7}$ $28\frac{43}{56}$ **22.** $11\frac{4}{9} + 13\frac{3}{8}$ $24\frac{59}{72}$

23. $4\frac{2}{3} + 24\frac{7}{16}$ $29\frac{5}{48}$ **24.** $15\frac{5}{8} + 9\frac{4}{7}$ $25\frac{11}{56}$

SKILLS

SKILLS ▶

○ **SKILL 17**

Subtracting Fractions, Like Denominators

Fractions

Subtract.

Like denominators

$$\frac{11}{12}$$
$$-\frac{7}{12}$$

$$\frac{11}{12}$$
$$-\frac{7}{12}$$
$$\frac{4}{12} = \frac{1}{3}$$

Skill 13 ·······

Subtract numerators

Express answers in lowest terms.

1. $\frac{4}{9} - \frac{2}{9}$ **$\frac{2}{9}$**　　　　2. $\frac{9}{8} - \frac{3}{8}$ **$\frac{3}{4}$**

3. $\frac{11}{12} - \frac{1}{12}$ **$\frac{5}{6}$**　　　　4. $\frac{5}{6} - \frac{1}{6}$ **$\frac{2}{3}$**

5. $\frac{5}{7} - \frac{1}{7}$ **$\frac{4}{7}$**　　　　6. $\frac{19}{27} - \frac{1}{27}$ **$\frac{2}{3}$**

7. $\frac{11}{16} - \frac{9}{16}$ **$\frac{1}{8}$**　　　　8. $\frac{16}{25} - \frac{6}{25}$ **$\frac{2}{5}$**

9. $\frac{37}{40} - \frac{29}{40}$ **$\frac{1}{5}$**　　　　10. $\frac{29}{36} - \frac{11}{36}$ **$\frac{1}{2}$**

11. $\frac{7}{10} - \frac{3}{10}$ **$\frac{2}{5}$**　　　　12. $\frac{19}{36} - \frac{5}{36}$ **$\frac{7}{18}$**

13. $\frac{19}{24} - \frac{13}{24}$ **$\frac{1}{4}$**　　　　14. $\frac{13}{28} - \frac{7}{28}$ **$\frac{3}{14}$**

15. $\frac{29}{60} - \frac{8}{60}$ **$\frac{7}{20}$**

Mixed Numbers

Subtract.

$$8\frac{11}{16}$$
$$-5\frac{9}{16}$$

$$8\frac{11}{16}$$
$$-5\frac{9}{16}$$
$$\frac{2}{16} = \frac{1}{8}$$

$$8\frac{11}{16}$$
$$-5\frac{9}{16}$$
$$3\frac{1}{8}$$

Skill 12

Express answers in lowest terms.

16. $7\frac{3}{4} - 6\frac{1}{4}$ **$1\frac{1}{2}$**　　　　17. $8\frac{6}{7} - 7\frac{5}{7}$ **$1\frac{1}{7}$**

18. $10\frac{4}{5} - 6\frac{1}{5}$ **$4\frac{3}{5}$**　　　　19. $12\frac{5}{8} - 9\frac{3}{8}$ **$3\frac{1}{4}$**

20. $2\frac{16}{21} - 1\frac{5}{21}$ **$1\frac{11}{21}$**　　　　21. $7\frac{11}{24} - 5\frac{7}{24}$ **$2\frac{1}{6}$**

22. $14\frac{17}{20} - 8\frac{9}{20}$ **$6\frac{2}{5}$**　　　　23. $15\frac{15}{32} - 10\frac{9}{32}$ **$5\frac{3}{16}$**

24. $14\frac{7}{8} - 9\frac{3}{8}$ **$5\frac{1}{2}$**　　　　25. $12\frac{11}{13} - 10\frac{4}{13}$ **$2\frac{7}{13}$**

26. $18\frac{17}{20} - 15\frac{9}{20}$ **$3\frac{2}{5}$**　　　　27. $35\frac{39}{40} - 27\frac{19}{40}$ **$8\frac{1}{2}$**

28. $74\frac{41}{75} - 29\frac{16}{75}$ **$45\frac{1}{3}$**　　　　29. $103\frac{11}{35} - 78\frac{1}{35}$ **$25\frac{2}{7}$**

Subtracting Fractions, Unlike Denominators

Fractions

Subtract.

Unlike denominators   Like denominators

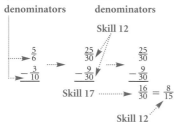

Express answers in lowest terms.

1. $\frac{3}{4} - \frac{3}{8}$ **$\frac{3}{8}$**

2. $\frac{1}{3} - \frac{2}{9}$ **$\frac{1}{9}$**

3. $\frac{9}{10} - \frac{3}{4}$ **$\frac{3}{20}$**

4. $\frac{4}{5} - \frac{2}{3}$ **$\frac{2}{15}$**

5. $\frac{5}{6} - \frac{7}{9}$ **$\frac{1}{18}$**

6. $\frac{5}{8} - \frac{5}{12}$ **$\frac{5}{24}$**

7. $\frac{3}{5} - \frac{8}{15}$ **$\frac{1}{15}$**

8. $\frac{11}{12} - \frac{3}{4}$ **$\frac{1}{6}$**

9. $\frac{4}{5} - \frac{13}{20}$ **$\frac{3}{20}$**

10. $\frac{6}{7} - \frac{10}{21}$ **$\frac{8}{21}$**

11. $\frac{1}{2} - \frac{2}{5}$ **$\frac{1}{10}$**

12. $\frac{3}{4} - \frac{11}{16}$ **$\frac{1}{16}$**

Mixed Numbers

Subtract.

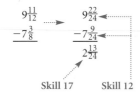

Express answers in lowest terms.

13. $9\frac{3}{4} - 5\frac{1}{2}$ **$4\frac{1}{4}$**

14. $7\frac{5}{6} - 4\frac{2}{3}$ **$3\frac{1}{6}$**

15. $14\frac{4}{9} - 8\frac{1}{6}$ **$6\frac{5}{18}$**

16. $15\frac{3}{7} - 10\frac{1}{3}$ **$5\frac{2}{21}$**

17. $34\frac{11}{12} - 29\frac{4}{5}$ **$5\frac{7}{60}$**

18. $48\frac{4}{7} - 37\frac{5}{9}$ **$11\frac{1}{63}$**

19. $12\frac{5}{8} - 9\frac{1}{2}$ **$3\frac{1}{8}$**

20. $2\frac{16}{21} - 1\frac{2}{3}$ **$1\frac{2}{21}$**

21. $13\frac{3}{4} - 11\frac{3}{5}$ **$2\frac{3}{20}$**

22. $21\frac{5}{6} - 19\frac{5}{8}$ **$2\frac{5}{24}$**

23. $7\frac{11}{24} - 5\frac{1}{3}$ **$2\frac{1}{8}$**

24. $20\frac{15}{38} - 20\frac{1}{19}$ **$\frac{13}{38}$**

SKILL 19

Subtracting Mixed Numbers, Borrowing

Whole Number and a Mixed Number

Subtract.

$$\begin{array}{c} 8 \\ -4\frac{3}{5} \end{array} \longrightarrow \begin{array}{c} 7\frac{5}{5} \\ -4\frac{3}{5} \\ \hline 3\frac{2}{5} \end{array}$$

Like denominators

Express answers in lowest terms.

1. $3 - 1\frac{1}{2}$ $1\frac{1}{2}$ **2.** $4 - 2\frac{3}{4}$ $1\frac{1}{4}$

3. $10 - 7\frac{9}{10}$ $2\frac{1}{10}$ **4.** $6 - 4\frac{3}{8}$ $1\frac{5}{8}$

5. $12 - 9\frac{5}{11}$ $2\frac{6}{11}$ **6.** $15 - 12\frac{7}{16}$ $2\frac{9}{16}$

Mixed Numbers with Unlike Denominators

Subtract.

Skill 12

$$\begin{array}{c} 6\frac{2}{3} \\ -2\frac{4}{5} \end{array} \longrightarrow \begin{array}{c} 6\frac{10}{15} \\ -2\frac{12}{15} \end{array} \longrightarrow \begin{array}{c} 5\frac{25}{15} \\ -2\frac{12}{15} \\ \hline 3\frac{13}{15} \end{array}$$

Express answers in lowest terms.

7. $5\frac{1}{2} - 2\frac{4}{9}$ $3\frac{1}{18}$ **8.** $8\frac{1}{2} - 3\frac{5}{8}$ $4\frac{7}{8}$

9. $18\frac{3}{4} - 5\frac{5}{6}$ $12\frac{11}{12}$ **10.** $27\frac{2}{7} - 13\frac{3}{4}$ $13\frac{15}{28}$

11. $28\frac{3}{7} - 26\frac{9}{10}$ $1\frac{37}{70}$ **12.** $40\frac{19}{30} - 39\frac{3}{4}$ $\frac{53}{60}$

13. $6\frac{3}{4} - 3\frac{7}{8}$ $2\frac{7}{8}$ **14.** $16\frac{1}{12} - 9\frac{3}{10}$ $6\frac{47}{60}$

Mixed Practice

15. $4 - 2\frac{5}{8}$ $1\frac{3}{8}$ **16.** $9 - 5\frac{11}{12}$ $3\frac{1}{12}$ **17.** $12 - 11\frac{7}{8}$ $\frac{1}{8}$ **18.** $16 - 7\frac{5}{11}$ $8\frac{6}{11}$

19. $8\frac{1}{3} - 4\frac{5}{9}$ $3\frac{7}{9}$ **20.** $13\frac{1}{2} - 7\frac{3}{5}$ $5\frac{9}{10}$ **21.** $14\frac{1}{5} - 13\frac{3}{4}$ $\frac{9}{20}$ **22.** $13 - 6\frac{5}{8}$ $6\frac{3}{8}$

23. $27\frac{1}{4} - 15\frac{15}{16}$ $11\frac{5}{16}$ **24.** $38\frac{3}{7} - 29\frac{9}{10}$ $8\frac{37}{70}$ **25.** $18\frac{1}{12} - 3\frac{11}{36}$ $14\frac{7}{9}$ **26.** $17\frac{8}{9} - 5\frac{3}{8}$ $12\frac{37}{72}$

27. $19 - 5\frac{2}{7}$ $13\frac{5}{7}$ **28.** $16\frac{4}{5} - 6\frac{3}{4}$ $10\frac{1}{20}$ **29.** $19\frac{11}{32} - 7\frac{3}{16}$ $12\frac{5}{32}$ **30.** $25 - 8\frac{7}{10}$ $16\frac{3}{10}$

SKILL 20

Multiplying Fractions/Mixed Numbers

Fractions

Multiply.

$$\frac{5}{8} \times \frac{2}{3} = \frac{5 \times 2}{8 \times 3} = \frac{10}{24} = \frac{5}{12}$$

↑
Skill 12

Express answers in lowest terms.

1. $\frac{1}{2} \times \frac{2}{3}$ $\frac{1}{3}$ **2.** $\frac{1}{4} \times \frac{3}{5}$ $\frac{3}{20}$

3. $\frac{5}{6} \times \frac{3}{4}$ $\frac{5}{8}$ **4.** $\frac{8}{9} \times \frac{2}{7}$ $\frac{16}{63}$

5. $\frac{11}{12} \times \frac{5}{11}$ $\frac{5}{12}$ **6.** $\frac{4}{13} \times \frac{8}{9}$ $\frac{32}{117}$

7. $4 \times \frac{1}{2}$ 2 **8.** $17 \times \frac{2}{5}$ $6\frac{4}{5}$

9. $21 \times \frac{3}{7}$ 9

Mixed Numbers

Multiply.

$$4\frac{1}{3} \times 2\frac{1}{4} - \frac{13}{3} \times \frac{9}{4} - \frac{117}{12} - 9\frac{3}{4}$$

Skill 13

Express answers in lowest terms.

10. $1\frac{1}{2} \times 1\frac{1}{3}$ 2 **11.** $3\frac{2}{3} \times 4\frac{2}{5}$ $16\frac{2}{15}$

12. $\frac{1}{8} \times 4\frac{4}{5}$ $\frac{3}{5}$ **13.** $7 \times 8\frac{1}{3}$ $58\frac{1}{8}$

14. $12\frac{1}{2} \times 1\frac{1}{2}$ $18\frac{3}{4}$ **15.** $20\frac{1}{2} \times 2\frac{1}{4}$ $46\frac{1}{8}$

Mixed Practice

Express answers in lowest terms.

16. $\frac{2}{5} \times \frac{4}{7}$ $\frac{8}{35}$ **17.** $\frac{3}{8} \times \frac{4}{9}$ $\frac{1}{6}$ **18.** $\frac{2}{3} \times 1\frac{1}{8}$ $\frac{8}{27}$ **19.** $3\frac{2}{3} \times \frac{1}{4}$ $4\frac{1}{8}$

20. $6 \times \frac{4}{5}$ $4\frac{4}{5}$ **21.** $\frac{3}{4} \times 8$ 6 **22.** $3\frac{1}{3} \times 4\frac{2}{5}$ $14\frac{2}{3}$ **23.** $2\frac{1}{4} \times 1\frac{2}{3}$ $3\frac{3}{4}$

24. $\frac{3}{4} \times 2\frac{5}{6}$ $2\frac{1}{8}$ **25.** $6 \times 3\frac{1}{4}$ $19\frac{1}{2}$ **26.** $18\frac{1}{2} \times 2\frac{2}{3}$ $49\frac{1}{3}$ **27.** $1\frac{3}{5} \times 5\frac{2}{6}$ $8\frac{8}{15}$

28. $5 \times 15\frac{1}{2}$ $77\frac{1}{2}$ **29.** $10 \times 6\frac{2}{5}$ 64 **30.** $2\frac{2}{7} \times 1\frac{1}{9}$ $2\frac{34}{63}$ **31.** $3\frac{4}{9} \times 7\frac{3}{8}$ $25\frac{29}{72}$

32. $\frac{7}{10} \times \frac{5}{9}$ $\frac{7}{18}$ **33.** $11\frac{3}{4} \times 8\frac{1}{3}$ $97\frac{11}{12}$ **34.** $\frac{11}{12} \times \frac{4}{33}$ $\frac{1}{9}$ **35.** $6\frac{7}{8} \times 10\frac{1}{3}$ $71\frac{1}{24}$

Dividing Fractions/Mixed Numbers

Fractions

Divide.

$$\frac{2}{3} \div \frac{3}{8} = \frac{2}{3} \times \frac{8}{3} = \frac{16}{9} = 1\frac{7}{9}$$

Skill 20

Express answers in lowest terms.

1. $\frac{1}{4} \div \frac{1}{8}$ 2

2. $\frac{3}{8} \div \frac{1}{4}$ $1\frac{1}{2}$

3. $\frac{3}{4} \div \frac{2}{5}$ $1\frac{7}{8}$

4. $5 \div \frac{5}{6}$ 6

5. $7 \div \frac{14}{15}$ $7\frac{1}{2}$

6. $8 \div \frac{4}{11}$ 22

7. $\frac{3}{4} \div \frac{1}{8}$ 6

8. $\frac{2}{5} \div \frac{5}{6}$ $\frac{12}{25}$

9. $\frac{4}{7} \div \frac{1}{28}$ 16

Mixed Numbers

Divide.

Skill 13

$$5\frac{1}{6} \div 1\frac{1}{4} = \frac{31}{6} \div \frac{5}{4}$$
$$= \frac{31}{6} \times \frac{4}{5}$$
$$= \frac{124}{30}$$
$$= 4\frac{2}{15} \longleftarrow \text{Skill 20}$$

Express answers in lowest terms.

10. $3\frac{2}{3} \div 1\frac{1}{2}$ $2\frac{4}{9}$

11. $3\frac{5}{6} \div 1\frac{1}{5}$ $3\frac{7}{36}$

12. $2\frac{1}{6} \div 3\frac{1}{3}$ $\frac{13}{20}$

13. $4\frac{2}{3} \div 1\frac{3}{5}$ $2\frac{11}{12}$

14. $\frac{3}{4} \div 3\frac{1}{2}$ $\frac{3}{14}$

15. $\frac{5}{8} \div 2\frac{1}{2}$ $\frac{1}{4}$

16. $16 \div 1\frac{1}{8}$ $14\frac{2}{9}$

17. $11\frac{1}{3} \div 2\frac{1}{5}$ $5\frac{5}{33}$

18. $12 \div 2\frac{12}{17}$ $4\frac{10}{23}$

19. $13\frac{1}{17} \div 3\frac{1}{6}$ $4\frac{40}{323}$

Mixed Practice

Express answers in lowest terms.

20. $7\frac{1}{2} \div 1\frac{1}{4}$ 6

21. $8\frac{1}{4} \div 5\frac{1}{2}$ $1\frac{1}{2}$

22. $\frac{5}{11} \div 2\frac{1}{5}$ $\frac{25}{121}$

23. $\frac{9}{10} \div \frac{3}{5}$ $1\frac{1}{2}$

24. $\frac{7}{12} \div \frac{1}{6}$ $3\frac{1}{2}$

25. $1\frac{3}{8} \div 2\frac{1}{16}$ $\frac{2}{3}$

26. $13\frac{1}{3} \div \frac{1}{10}$ $133\frac{1}{3}$

27. $8\frac{1}{3} \div \frac{5}{9}$ 15

28. $\frac{19}{21} \div 3\frac{1}{2}$ $\frac{38}{147}$

29. $3\frac{5}{7} \div \frac{13}{21}$ 6

30. $8 \div 1\frac{3}{5}$ 5

31. $20 \div \frac{2}{3}$ 30

32. $2\frac{1}{16} \div 11$ $\frac{3}{16}$

33. $5\frac{3}{8} \div 22$ $\frac{43}{176}$

34. $22 \div \frac{3}{5}$ $36\frac{2}{3}$

35. $\frac{11}{15} \div 1\frac{12}{13}$ $\frac{143}{375}$

36. $\frac{11}{12} \div \frac{11}{12}$ 1

37. $2\frac{11}{14} \div \frac{3}{7}$ $6\frac{1}{2}$

38. $\frac{15}{16} \div \frac{5}{32}$ 6

39. $19\frac{1}{2} \div 19\frac{1}{2}$ 1

Writing Ratios

Compare Two Numbers

What is the ratio of desks to computers?

Office Inventory		
Computers	Calculators	Desks
12	5	15

Ratio of desks to computers:

15 to 12 or 15:12 or $\frac{15}{12}$

Write the ratio.

Department Sales		
Meat	Produce	Dairy
$1,500	$600	$1,200

1. Ratio of meat to produce **1,500:600**

2. Ratio of meat to dairy **1,500:1,200**

3. Ratio of produce to dairy **600:1,200**

4. Ratio of dairy to produce **1,200:600**

5. Ratio of produce to meat **600:1,500**

6. Ratio of dairy to meat **1,200:1,500**

Ratios as Fractions

Write the ratio of tables to chairs as a fraction in lowest terms.

A restaurant has 40 chairs and 16 tables.

Ratio of tables to chairs is $\frac{16}{40}$.

$\frac{16}{40} = \frac{2}{5}$ ◄----- Skill 12

Write the ratio as a fraction in lowest terms.

7. Nurse-to-patient ratio in a hospital is 6 nurses to 30 patients. $\frac{1}{5}$

8. Teacher-to-student ratio in a school is 8 teachers to 160 students. $\frac{1}{20}$

9. Door-to-window ratio in a house is 3 doors to 45 windows. $\frac{1}{15}$

10. Width-to-length ratio of a box is 22 centimeters to 30 centimeters. $\frac{11}{15}$

11. Room-to-desk ratio in a school is 40 rooms to 1,000 desks. $\frac{1}{25}$

12. Land area-to-people ratio in a county is 6 square kilometers to 138 people. $\frac{1}{23}$

13. Car-to-people ratio in a town is 4,000 cars to 10,000 people. $\frac{2}{5}$

14. Hit-to-strikeout ratio of a batter is 15 hits to 25 strikeouts. $\frac{3}{5}$

SKILL 23

Proportions

Checking Proportions

Is this proportion true?

$\frac{5}{9} \overset{?}{=} \frac{35}{63}$

Cross multiply.

$\frac{5}{9} \overset{?}{=} \frac{35}{63}$ ┈┈► $5 \times 63 \overset{?}{=} 9 \times 35$

$315 = 315$

True. The products are equal.

1. $\frac{1}{3} \overset{?}{=} \frac{4}{12}$ **T**

2. $\frac{2}{5} \overset{?}{=} \frac{4}{10}$ **T**

3. $\frac{4}{5} \overset{?}{=} \frac{16}{19}$ **F**

4. $\frac{5}{6} \overset{?}{=} \frac{25}{29}$ **F**

5. $\frac{3}{4} \overset{?}{=} \frac{6}{9}$ **F**

6. $\frac{1}{2} \overset{?}{=} \frac{11}{24}$ **F**

7. $\frac{3}{8} \overset{?}{=} \frac{9}{24}$ **T**

8. $\frac{2}{7} \overset{?}{=} \frac{14}{49}$ **T**

9. $\frac{16}{32} \overset{?}{=} \frac{1}{2}$ **T**

10. $\frac{13}{23} \overset{?}{=} \frac{1}{2}$ **F**

11. $\frac{10}{15} \overset{?}{=} \frac{5}{8}$ **F**

12. $\frac{22}{30} \overset{?}{=} \frac{11}{15}$ **T**

Solving Proportions

Solve for the number that makes the proportion true.

$\frac{7}{8} = \frac{28}{a}$

Cross multiply.

$\frac{7}{8} = \frac{28}{a}$ ┈┈► $7 \times a = 28 \times 8$

$7 \times a = 224$

$a = \frac{224}{7}$

$a = 32$

Solve.

13. $\frac{1}{2} = \frac{9}{h}$ **18**

14. $\frac{2}{3} = \frac{12}{y}$ **18**

15. $\frac{6}{a} = \frac{9}{11}$ **$7\frac{1}{3}$**

16. $\frac{8}{y} = \frac{12}{15}$ **10**

17. $\frac{t}{6} = \frac{1}{11}$ **$\frac{6}{11}$**

18. $\frac{a}{7} = \frac{2}{19}$ **$\frac{14}{19}$**

19. $\frac{5}{9} = \frac{n}{10}$ **$5\frac{5}{9}$**

20. $\frac{4}{11} = \frac{x}{33}$ **12**

21. $\frac{8}{13} = \frac{y}{20}$ **$12\frac{4}{13}$**

22. $\frac{42}{66} = \frac{y}{11}$ **7**

23. $\frac{11}{33} = \frac{c}{60}$ **20**

24. $\frac{8}{40} = \frac{5}{n}$ **25**

25. $\frac{n}{7} = \frac{15}{21}$ **5**

26. $\frac{2}{3} = \frac{18}{n}$ **27**

27. $\frac{96}{16} = \frac{n}{4}$ **24**

28. $\frac{13}{42} = \frac{65}{c}$ **210**

29. $\frac{16}{3} = \frac{t}{12}$ **64**

30. $\frac{h}{25} = \frac{15}{125}$ **3**

31. $\frac{27}{y} = \frac{81}{45}$ **15**

32. $\frac{a}{21} = \frac{9}{27}$ **7**

33. $\frac{121}{11} = \frac{550}{h}$ **50**

SKILL 24

Solving a Rate Problem

Equal Rates as a Proportion

Write the proportion.

Three hundred words keyboarded in 5 minutes. How many words in 3 minutes?

$$\frac{300 \text{ words}}{5 \text{ minutes}} = \frac{n \text{ words}}{3 \text{ minutes}}$$

$$\frac{300}{5} = \frac{n}{3}$$

2. $\dfrac{84 \text{ kilometers}}{7 \text{ liters}} = \dfrac{n}{13 \text{ liters}}$

3. $\dfrac{5 \text{ cm}}{40 \text{ kilometers}} = \dfrac{17 \text{ cm}}{n}$

Write the proportion.

1. Five oranges cost $0.99. How much does it cost for 7 oranges? $\dfrac{5 \text{ oranges}}{\$0.99} = \dfrac{7 \text{ oranges}}{n}$

2. A car travels 84 kilometers on 7 liters of gas. How many kilometers can it go on 13 liters of gas?

3. Five centimeters on a map represents 40 kilometers. How many kilometers does 17 centimeters represent?

4. A machine uses 50 kilowatt-hours in 6 hours. How many kilowatt-hours does it use in 45 hours? $\dfrac{50 \text{ kilowatts}}{6 \text{ watts}} = \dfrac{n}{45 \text{ hours}}$

Solve a Rate Problem

Find the number of boxes.

5,000 envelopes in 10 boxes. 3,000 envelopes in how many boxes?

$$\frac{5,000 \text{ envelopes}}{10 \text{ boxes}} = \frac{3,000 \text{ envelopes}}{n \text{ boxes}}$$

$$\frac{5,000}{10} = \frac{3,000}{n}$$

$$n = 6 \ \blacktriangleleft\text{----- Skill 23}$$

Solve.

5. Four apples cost $0.79. How much for 22 apples?
   $4.35

6. A machine produces 121 bolts in 3 hours. How many bolts in 15 hours?
   605 bolts

7. Thirty-six pages keyboarded in 4 hours. How many pages in 13 hours?
   117 pp.

8. A car travels 19 kilometers on 2 liters of gas. How many kilometers on 76 liters of gas?
   722 km

Mixed Practice

Write the proportion and solve.

9. A machine produces 660 wheels in 4 hours. How many wheels are made in 9 hours?
   1,485 wheels

10. Fuel costs $1.23 cents for 3 liters. How much would it cost to fill a car with an 84 liter tank?
    $34.44

11. The telephone rate to Europe is $6.00 for 3 minutes. How much for 14 minutes?
    $28.00

12. Carlotta can run 11 kilometers in 60 minutes. How far can she run in 105 minutes?
    19.25 km

13. Juan can read 6 pages in 5 minutes. How long will it take him to read 40 pages?
    $33\frac{1}{3}$ minutes

Comparing Rates

Find the Unit Rate.

Find the number of books.

4,200 books in 200 boxes.
How many books in 1 box?

$$\frac{4{,}200 \text{ books}}{200 \text{ boxes}} = \frac{n \text{ books}}{1 \text{ box}}$$

$$n = 21 \quad \longleftarrow \text{ Skill 24}$$

The unit rate is 21 books per box.

Find the unit rate.

1. There are 3,456 oranges in 12 crates. How many oranges in 1 crate? **288**

2. Ida prints 4,950 words in 9 minutes. How many words in 1 minute? **550**

3. Lou drives 560 kilometers in 7 hours. How many kilometers in 1 hour? **80**

4. For $14.25 you can buy 15 dozen eggs. How much for 1 dozen? **$.95**

5. Sam drives 384 kilometers in 6 hours. How far does he drive in 1 hour? How far in 10 hours? **64; 640**

6. There are 2,500 sheets of bond paper that weigh 100 pounds. How many sheets weigh 1 pound? What will 10,000 sheets weigh? **25; 400 lb.**

Compare Unit Rates

Which is faster?

Car A: 280 kilometers in 4 hours
Car B: 455 kilometers in 7 hours

Car A   **Car B**
$\frac{280}{4} = 70$ $\frac{455}{7} = 65$

70 km/h   65 km/h

$\cdots\cdots$ is greater than $\cdots\cdots$

Car A is faster.

Compare the unit rates.

7. Which uses less fuel per kilometer? **A**
Car A: 52 kilometers on 6 liters
Car B: 59 kilometers on 7 liters

8. Which costs less per kilogram? **B**
Carton A: $89.25 for 15 kilograms
Carton B: $117.00 for 20 kilograms

9. Which shipment holds more per crate? **B**
Shipment A: 1,584 apples in 11 crates
Shipment B: 1,937 apples in 13 crates

10. Which makes more cogs per hour? **A**
Machine A: 288 cogs in 4 hours
Machine B: 414 cogs in 6 hours

11. Which gets more kilometers per liter? **B**
Car A: 162 kilometers on 18 liters of fuel
Car B: 220 kilometers on 20 liters of fuel

Writing Decimals as Percents

Two or More Decimal Places

Write 0.037 as a percent.

0.037 = ?%

0.037 ┈┈► 0.037

Move decimal
2 places to the right.

0.037 = 3.7%

Write as a percent.

1. 0.10 **10%**	**2.** 0.15 **15%**	**3.** 0.25 **25%**
4. 0.74 **74%**	**5.** 0.82 **82%**	**6.** 0.93 **93%**
7. 2.13 **213%**	**8.** 4.212 **421.2%**	**9.** 5.753 **575.3%**
10. 0.267 **26.7%**	**11.** 0.391 **39.1%**	**12.** 0.914 **91.4%**
13. 12.104 **1,210.4%**	**14.** 0.625 **62.5%**	**15.** 10.82 **1,082%**
16. 0.007 **0.7%**	**17.** 0.106 **10.6%**	**18.** 0.008 **0.8%**
19. 0.04 **4%**	**20.** 0.001 **0.1%**	**21.** 0.503 **50.3%**

Fewer Than Two Decimal Places

Write 0.5 as a percent.

0.5 — ?%

Use zero as a placeholder.

0.5 ┈┈► 0.50%

Move decimal
2 places to the right.

0.5 = 50%

Write as a percent.

22. 0.4 **40%**	**23.** 0.7 **70%**	**24.** 0.9 **90%**
25. 7.1 **710%**	**26.** 9.3 **930%**	**27.** 10.5 **1,050%**
28. 11.0 **1,100%**	**29.** 12.6 **1,260%**	**30.** 17.1 **1,710%**
31. 22.5 **2,250%**	**32.** 29.0 **2,900%**	**33.** 37.2 **3,720%**
34. 0.1 **10%**	**35.** 7.5 **750%**	**36.** 1.8 **180%**
37. 16.3 **1,630%**	**38.** 0.3 **30%**	**39.** 6.2 **620%**

Mixed Practice

Write as a percent.

40. 0.57 **57%**	**41.** 3.80 **380%**	**42.** 0.001 **0.1%**	**43.** 0.67 **67%**	**44.** 20.7 **2,070%**
45. 8.8 **880%**	**46.** 0.2915 **29.15%**	**47.** 0.32 **32%**	**48.** 17.4 **1,740%**	**49.** 3.003 **300.3%**
50. 139.25 **13,925%**	**51.** 0.2187 **21.87%**	**52.** 9.1 **910%**	**53.** 25.00 **2,500%**	**54.** 12.004 **1,200.4%**
55. 0.14 **14%**	**56.** 2.185 **218.5%**	**57.** 0.51 **51%**	**58.** 9.3 **930%**	**59.** 1.868 **186.8%**
60. 8.554 **855.4%**	**61.** 0.003 **0.3%**	**62.** 3.246 **324.6%**	**63.** 0.26 **26%**	**64.** 0.07 **7%**
65. 0.0032 **0.32%**	**66.** 3.642 **364.2%**	**67.** 0.29 **29%**	**68.** 0.052 **5.2%**	**69.** 3.42 **342%**
70. 0.30 **30%**	**71.** 2.1 **210%**	**72.** 0.0001 **0.01%**	**73.** 1.67 **167%**	**74.** 1.0 **100%**
75. 2.5 **250%**	**76.** 0.005 **0.5%**	**77.** 2.077 **207.7%**	**78.** 1.5 **150%**	**79.** 0.19 **19%**

○ SKILL 27

Writing Fractions/Mixed Numbers as Percents

Fractions

Write $\frac{3}{5}$ as a percent.

$\frac{3}{5} = ?\%$

$\frac{3}{5} = 0.6 = 60\%$

↗ Skill 14   ↖ Skill 26

Write as a percent.

1. $\frac{1}{4}$ 25%   2. $\frac{2}{5}$ 40%   3. $\frac{3}{4}$ 75%

4. $\frac{7}{10}$ 70%   5. $\frac{1}{8}$ 12.5%   6. $\frac{3}{20}$ 15%

7. $\frac{7}{20}$ 35%   8. $\frac{12}{25}$ 48%   9. $\frac{7}{50}$ 14%

10. $\frac{7}{40}$ 17.5%   11. $\frac{5}{8}$ 62.5%   12. $\frac{11}{16}$ 68.75%

Mixed Numbers

Write $2\frac{3}{8}$ as a percent.

$2\frac{3}{8} = ?\%$

$2\frac{3}{8} = \frac{19}{8} = 2.375 = 237.5\%$

↗ Skill 13   ↑ Skill 14   ↖ Skill 26

Write as a percent.

13. $2\frac{3}{4}$ 275%   14. $4\frac{5}{8}$ 462.5%   15. $6\frac{2}{3}$ 666.7%

16. $7\frac{1}{6}$ 716.7%   17. $8\frac{5}{9}$ 855.6%   18. $5\frac{4}{15}$ 526.7%

19. $8\frac{7}{40}$ 817.5%   20. $14\frac{3}{16}$ 1,418.8%   21. $7\frac{11}{50}$ 722%

Mixed Practice

Write as a percent.

22. $\frac{3}{5}$ 60%   23. $5\frac{3}{8}$ 537.5%   24. $12\frac{5}{6}$ 1,283.3%   25. $\frac{7}{12}$ 58.3%   26. $\frac{1}{9}$ 11.1%

27. $15\frac{3}{10}$ 1,530% 28. $\frac{9}{40}$ 22.5%   29. $20\frac{4}{5}$ 2,080%   30. $10\frac{6}{25}$ 1,024%   31. $18\frac{5}{8}$ 1,862.5%

32. $9\frac{3}{40}$ 907.5%   33. $\frac{15}{16}$ 93.8%   34. $8\frac{19}{50}$ 838%   35. $11\frac{5}{14}$ 1,135.7%   36. $16\frac{9}{20}$ 1,645%

37. $\frac{7}{9}$ 77.8%   38. $7\frac{3}{16}$ 718.8%   39. $5\frac{11}{15}$ 573.3% 40. $\frac{11}{30}$ 36.7%   41. $17\frac{7}{20}$ 1,735%

SKILL 28

Writing Percents as Decimals

Percent in Decimal Form

Write 8.75% as a decimal.

Drop % sign.

8.75% ⤏ 0̬08.75

Move 2 places to the left.

8.75% = 0.0875

Write as a decimal.

1. 10.5% **0.105**   **2.** 15.7% **0.157**   **3.** 40% **0.40**

4. 85% **0.85**   **5.** 120% **1.20**   **6.** 137% **1.37**

7. 6.7% **0.067**   **8.** 7.1% **0.071**   **9.** 8.9% **0.089**

10. 95% **0.95**   **11.** 119% **1.19**   **12.** 7.9% **0.079**

13. 17.2% **0.172**   **14.** 85.6% **0.856**   **15.** 100% **1.00**

16. 1.35% **0.0135** **17.** 5.3% **0.053**   **18.** 142% **1.42**

Percent in Fractional Form

Write $\frac{3}{20}$% as a decimal.

$\frac{3}{20}$% = 0.15% ⤏ 0̬00.15

↑
Skill 14

$\frac{3}{20}$% = 0.0015

Write as a decimal.

19. $\frac{7}{10}$% **0.007**   **20.** $\frac{11}{20}$% **0.0055**   **21.** $\frac{5}{8}$% **0.00625**

22. $\frac{2}{25}$% **0.0008**   **23.** $5\frac{3}{5}$% **0.056**   **24.** $7\frac{1}{10}$% **0.071**

25. $6\frac{4}{5}$% **0.068**   **26.** $22\frac{3}{4}$% **0.2275** **27.** $30\frac{3}{5}$% **0.306**

28. $89\frac{13}{20}$% **0.8965** **29.** $57\frac{21}{25}$% **0.5784** **30.** $12\frac{3}{4}$% **0.1275**

Mixed Practice

31. 74.25% **0.7425** **32.** $6\frac{1}{4}$% **0.0625** **33.** $18\frac{4}{5}$% **0.1880** **34.** 0.97% **0.0097** **35.** $14\frac{9}{20}$% **0.1445**

36. $28\frac{3}{40}$% **0.28075** **37.** 0.125% **0.00125** **38.** 6.25% **0.0625** **39.** $\frac{7}{50}$% **0.0014** **40.** 6.63% **0.0663**

41. 8.79% **0.0879** **42.** 100% **1.00** **43.** $\frac{19}{20}$% **0.0095** **44.** 127% **1.27** **45.** $\frac{1}{40}$% **0.00025**

46. $20\frac{1}{4}$% **0.2025** **47.** $22\frac{1}{2}$% **0.225** **48.** 14.6% **0.146** **49.** $25\frac{1}{5}$% **0.252** **50.** 18.9% **0.189**

Writing Percents as Fractions

Percent in Decimal Form

Write 37.5% as a fraction.

$37.5\% = 0.375 = \frac{3}{8}$

    Skill 28 Skill 14

Write as a fraction in lowest terms.

1. 45% $\frac{9}{20}$ 2. 80% $\frac{4}{5}$ 3. 175% $1\frac{3}{4}$

4. 200% 2   5. 11.7% $\frac{117}{1,000}$ 6. 0.1% $\frac{1}{1,000}$

7. 0.15% $\frac{3}{2,000}$ 8. 67.3% $\frac{673}{1,000}$ 9. 10.6% $\frac{53}{500}$

10. 78.55% $\frac{1,571}{2,000}$ 11. 37.63% $\frac{3,763}{10,000}$ 12. 51.42% $\frac{2,571}{5,000}$

13. 50% $\frac{1}{2}$ 14. 75% $\frac{3}{4}$ 15. 10.1% $\frac{101}{1,000}$

16. 0.12% $\frac{3}{2,500}$ 17. 80.9% $\frac{809}{1,000}$ 18. 42.1% $\frac{421}{1,000}$

Percent in Fractional Form

Write $16\frac{2}{3}\%$ as a fraction.

$16\frac{2}{3}\% = 16\frac{2}{3} \div 100$

$\qquad = \frac{50}{3} \div 100$

$\qquad = \frac{50}{300} \longleftarrow$ Skill 21

Skill 13 $\; = \frac{1}{6} \longleftarrow$ Skill 12

Write as a fraction in lowest terms.

19. $6\frac{1}{4}\%$ $\frac{1}{16}$ 20. $37\frac{1}{2}\%$ $\frac{3}{8}$ 21. $43\frac{3}{4}\%$ $\frac{7}{16}$

22. $3\frac{1}{2}\%$ $\frac{7}{200}$ 23. $\frac{1}{4}\%$ $\frac{1}{400}$ 24. $10\frac{1}{3}\%$ $\frac{31}{300}$

25. $15\frac{1}{2}\%$ $\frac{31}{200}$ 26. $20\frac{1}{2}\%$ $\frac{41}{200}$ 27. $25\frac{1}{2}\%$ $\frac{51}{200}$

28. $15\frac{3}{4}\%$ $\frac{63}{400}$ 29. $16\frac{2}{3}\%$ $\frac{1}{6}$ 30. $33\frac{1}{3}\%$ $\frac{1}{3}$

Mixed Practice

Write as a fraction in lowest terms.

31. 30% $\frac{3}{10}$ 32. 57.2% $\frac{143}{250}$ 33. $31\frac{1}{4}\%$ $\frac{5}{16}$ 34. 63.5% $\frac{127}{200}$ 35. $12\frac{1}{2}\%$ $\frac{1}{8}$

36. $13\frac{1}{3}\%$ $\frac{2}{15}$ 37. $26\frac{2}{3}\%$ $\frac{4}{15}$ 38. 64.75% $\frac{259}{400}$ 39. $11\frac{1}{9}\%$ $\frac{1}{9}$ 40. 78.55% $\frac{1,571}{2,000}$

41. 50% $\frac{1}{2}$ 42. 75% $\frac{3}{4}$ 43. $1\frac{1}{4}\%$ $\frac{1}{80}$ 44. 100% $\frac{1}{1}$ or 1   45. $12\frac{3}{4}\%$ $\frac{51}{400}$

46. $4\frac{3}{4}\%$ $\frac{19}{400}$ 47. $5\frac{3}{8}\%$ $\frac{43}{800}$ 48. 75.91% $\frac{7,591}{10,000}$ 49. $6\frac{2}{3}\%$ $\frac{1}{15}$ 50. 121% $1\frac{21}{100}$

SKILL 30

Finding the Percentage

Decimal Percents

Find 15.5% of 36.

15.5% of 36 $= n$

Skill 28

$0.155 \times 36 = n$

$5.58 = n$

15.5% of 36 $= 5.58$

Find the percentage.

1. 15% of 60 **9**

2. 30% of 72 **21.6**

3. 4% of 96 **3.84**

4. 9% of 122 **10.98**

5. 6.5% of 120 **7.8**

6. 8.3% of 150 **12.45**

7. 17.8% of 80 **14.24**

8. 31.2% of 140 **43.68**

9. 5.81% of 60 **3.486**

10. 7.32% of 45 **3.294**

11. 67.7% of 67 **45.359**

12. 8.92% of 35 **3.122**

Fractional Percents

Find $\frac{3}{4}$% of 1,600.

$\frac{3}{4}$% of 1,600 $= n$

Skill 29

$\frac{3}{400} \times 1,600 = n$

$12 = n$

$\frac{3}{4}$% of 1,600 $= 12$

Find the percentage.

13. $2\frac{1}{2}$% of 400 **10**

14. $4\frac{1}{2}$% of 200 **9**

15. $33\frac{1}{3}$% of 120 **40**

16. $3\frac{5}{6}$% of 600 **23**

17. $\frac{3}{4}$% of 800 **6**

18. $\frac{3}{5}$% of 50 **0.30**

19. $\frac{3}{8}$% of 600 **2.25**

20. $\frac{7}{8}$% of 80 **0.70**

Mixed Practice

Find the percentage.

21. 80% of 160 **128**

22. $8\frac{1}{3}$% of 72 **6**

23. 9.1% of 90 **8.19**

24. $15\frac{4}{5}$% of 90 **14.04**

25. $16\frac{2}{3}$% of 90 **15**

26. 45% of 72 **32.4**

27. $\frac{1}{4}$% of 800 **2**

28. 0.75% of 1,000 **7.5**

29. 125% of 64 **80**

30. $12\frac{1}{4}$% of 65 **7.9625**

31. 7.2% of 127 **9.144**

32. $6\frac{1}{4}$% of 1,600 **100**

33. $4\frac{1}{6}$% of 600 **25**

34. 16.5% of 84 **13.86**

35. $8\frac{1}{2}$% of 75 **6.375**

36. 24.7% of 80 **19.76**

SKILL 31

Finding the Rate

Percent Less Than Base

What percent of 75 is 60?

$n\%$ of 75 = 60

Write as a proportion and solve.

$$\frac{n}{100} = \frac{60}{75}$$

$$75 \times n = 6,000$$

$$n = 80 \blacktriangleleft \cdots \text{Skill 23}$$

80% of 75 = 60

Solve. Round answers to the nearest tenth of a percent.

1. $n\%$ of 40 = 20 **50%**   **2.** $n\%$ of 60 = 15 **25%**

3. $n\%$ of 90 = 18 **20%**   **4.** $n\%$ of 60 = 9 **15%**

5. $n\%$ of 70 = 25 **35.7%**   **6.** $n\%$ of 90 = 65 **72.2%**

7. $n\%$ of 65 = 58 **89.2%**   **8.** $n\%$ of 84 = 75 **89.3%**

9. $n\%$ of 113 = 79 **69.9%**   **10.** $n\%$ of 410 = 295.5 **72.1%**

11. $n\%$ of 94 = 82 **87.2%**   **12.** $n\%$ of 296 = 239.76 **81%**

Percent Greater Than Base

What percent of 90 is 162?

$n\%$ of 90 = 162

Write as a proportion and solve.

$$\frac{n}{100} = \frac{162}{90}$$

$$90 \times n = 16,200$$

$$n = 180$$

180% of 90 = 162

Solve. Round answers to the nearest tenth of a percent.

13. $n\%$ of 20 = 30 **150%**   **14.** $n\%$ of 36 = 45 **125%**

15. $n\%$ of 50 = 60 **120%**   **16.** $n\%$ of 70 = 91 **130%**

17. $n\%$ of 60 = 80 **133.3%**   **18.** $n\%$ of 72 = 96 **133.3%**

19. $n\%$ of 24 = 31 **129.2%**   **20.** $n\%$ of 56 = 77 **137.5%**

21. $n\%$ of 37 = 148 **400%**   **22.** $n\%$ of 60 = 90 **150%**

23. $n\%$ of 81 = 415.75 **513.3%**   **24.** $n\%$ of 110 = 130 **118.2%**

Mixed Practice

Solve. Round answers to the nearest tenth of a percent.

25. $n\%$ of 125 = 100 **80%**   **26.** $n\%$ of 100 = 115 **115%**   **27.** $n\%$ of 130 = 60 **46.2%**

28. $n\%$ of 56 = 96 **171.4%**   **29.** $n\%$ of 89 = 49 **55.1%**   **30.** $n\%$ of 84 = 108 **128.6%**

31. $n\%$ of 115 = 92 **80%**   **32.** $n\%$ of 42 = 52.5 **125%**   **33.** $n\%$ of 64 = 76.8 **120%**

34. $n\%$ of 64 = 24 **37.5%**   **35.** $n\%$ of 204 = 51 **25%**   **36.** $n\%$ of 42 = 6.72 **16%**

37. $n\%$ of 36 = 50 **138.9%**   **38.** $n\%$ of 173 = 136.25 **78.8%**   **39.** $n\%$ of 18 = 36 **200%**

40. $n\%$ of 21 = 63 **300%**   **41.** $n\%$ of 120 = 80 **66.7%**   **42.** $n\%$ of 15.5 = 62 **400%**

43. $n\%$ of 90 = 4.5 **5%**   **44.** $n\%$ of 125 = 18.75 **15%**   **45.** $n\%$ of 75 = 110 **146.7%**

SKILL 32

Finding the Base

Decimal Percents

42 is 37.5% of what number?

37.5% of $n = 42$

$\downarrow$

$0.375 \times n = 42$

$n = 42 \div 0.375$

Skill 28 $n = 112$

37.5% of 112 = 42

Find the number. Round to the nearest tenth.

1. 12.5% of $n = 9$ **72**

2. 62.5% of $n = 55$ **88**

3. 8.25% of $n = 664$ **8,048.5**

4. 7% of $n = 3.5$ **50**

5. 5.75% of $n = 92$ **1,600**

6. 9% of $n = 8.2$ **91.1**

7. 11% of $n = 37$ **336.4**

8. 3% of $n = 8.7$ **290**

9. 5% of $n = 3$ **60**

10. 12.5% of $n = 21$ **168**

11. 37.3% of $n = 50$ **134**

12. 81% of $n - 14$ **17.3**

Fractional Percents

3 is $6\frac{1}{4}$% of what number?

$6\frac{1}{4}$% of $n = 3$

$\downarrow$

$\frac{1}{16} \times n = 3$

$n = 3 \div \frac{1}{16}$

Skill 29 $n = 48$

$6\frac{1}{4}$% of 48 = 3

Find the number.

13. $2\frac{1}{2}$% of $n = 4$ **160**

14. $3\frac{1}{8}$% of $n = 2$ **64**

15. $33\frac{1}{3}$% of $n = 20$ **60**

16. $\frac{1}{4}$% of $n = 2$ **800**

17. $37\frac{1}{2}$% of $n = 34$ **$90\frac{2}{3}$**

18. $\frac{3}{5}$% of $n = 6$ **1,000**

19. $45\frac{1}{2}$% of $n = 25$ **$54\frac{86}{91}$**

20. $\frac{3}{4}$% of $n = 7$ **$933\frac{1}{3}$**

Mixed Practice

Find the number.

21. 80% of $n = 60$ **75**

22. 12.5% of $n - 39$ **312**

23. 116% of $n = 2.9$ **2.5**

24. 10% of $n = 2.9$ **29**

25. 8% of $n = 4.2$ **52.5**

26. 40% of $n - 6.8$ **17**

27. $16\frac{2}{3}$% of $n = 13$ **78**

28. 145% of $n = 6.38$ **4.4**

29. $66\frac{2}{3}$% of $n - 120$ **180**

30. 25% of $n = 36$ **144**

31. $2\frac{2}{3}$% of $n = 6$ **225**

32. 90% of $n = 72$ **80**

33. 6% of $n = 3.3$ **55**

34. 7.8% of $n - 9$ **115.4**

35. $16\frac{3}{4}$% of $n = 33$ **$197\frac{1}{67}$**

APPLICATIONS

APPLICATION **A**

Formulas

Substituting in a Formula

To use a formula to solve a problem, substitute known values in the formula. Then solve. Remember to perform any computations within parentheses first.

▶ **An airplane travels at a rate of 960 kilometers per hour. How far can the plane travel in 7 hours?**

Formula: Distance = Rate × Time

Substitute: Distance = 960 × 7

Solve: Distance = 6,720

The plane travels 6,720 kilometers in 7 hours.

Find the distance.

	Rate	Time	Distance
1.	100 mi/h	6 h	**600 mi**
2.	55 km/h	4 h	**220 km**
3.	14 m/s	32 s	**448 in**
4.	30 mi/h	6 h	**180 mi**
5.	42 m/s	5 s	**210 m**

Rate × Time = Distance

Find the area of the triangle.

$\frac{1}{2}$ × Base × Height = Area of Triangle

	Base	Height	Area
6.	1 m	0.5 m	**0.25 sq m**
7.	64 ft	38 ft	**1,216 sq ft**
8.	18 in	5 in	**45 sq in**
9.	30 km	24 km	**360 sq km**

Find the percent of sales made. Round to the nearest tenth.

$\frac{\text{Sales Made}}{\text{Possible Sales}}$ × 100 = % of Sales

	Possible Sales	Sales Made	Percent
10.	$ 4,600	$ 1,900	**41.3**
11.	19,100	6,000	**31.4**
12.	23,000	13,000	**56.5**
13.	64,000	15,000	**23.4**
14.	8,200	3,000	**36.6**

Find the price of the sound system.

Amp + CD Player + Speakers = Price

	Amp	CD Player	Speakers	Price
15.	$199.00	$ 99.95	$139.00	**$437.95**
16.	395.00	119.99	259.00	**$773.99**
17.	685.00	249.00	495.00	**$1,429.00**
18.	449.00	188.00	350.00	**$987.00**

Find the long-distance telephone charge.

Cost per Minute × Minutes = Charge

	Minutes	Cost per Minute	Charge
19.	15	$0.35	**$5.25**
20.	9	1.12	**$10.08**
21.	31	1.49	**$46.19**
22.	22	0.54	**$11.88**
23.	38	1.32	**$50.16**

More Formulas

Multiplying or Dividing to Solve Formulas

To solve some formulas after substituting, you may have to multiply or divide both sides of the equation by the same number.

▶ **An airplane cruising at a rate of 575 kilometers per hour has traveled 2,645 kilometers. How long did it take to make this trip?**

Formula: $\text{Distance} = \text{Rate} \times \text{Time}$

Substitute: $2{,}645 = 575 \times \text{Time}$

Divide: $\dfrac{2{,}645}{575} = \dfrac{575 \times \text{Time}}{575}$

Solve: $4.6 \text{ hours} = \text{Time}$

Find the missing amount.

	Rate × Time = Distance		
	Rate	**Time**	**Distance**
1.	88 in/min	3.5 min	**308 in**
2.	60 km/h	**3.25 h**	195 km
3.	675 yd/h	13 h	**8,775 yd**
4.	**45 km/h**	1.75 h	78.75 km
5.	24 km/h	**8 h**	192 km
6.	**55 ft/h**	$4\frac{1}{2}$ h	$247\frac{1}{2}$ ft
7.	3.2 m/s	**30 s**	96 m

Adding or Subtracting to Solve Formulas

To solve some formulas after substituting, you may have to add the same number to, or subtract it from, both sides of the equation.

▶ **The temperature of a solution is 212°F (degrees Fahrenheit). What is this in degrees Celsius (°C)?**

Formula: $°F = (1.8 \times °C) + 32$

Substitute: $212 = (1.8 \times °C) + 32$

Subtract: $\dfrac{-32 \qquad = \qquad\quad -32}{180 = (1.8 \times °C)}$

Divide: $\dfrac{180}{1.8} = \dfrac{(1.8 \times °C)}{1.8}$

Solve: $100 = °C$

Find the missing amount.

	(1.8 × °C) + 32 = °F	
	Degrees Celsius	**Degrees Fahrenheit**
8.	50	**122**
9.	**30**	86
10.	**0**	32
11.	120	**248**
12.	**35**	95
13.	20	68
14.	144	**291.2**
15.	10	**50**
16.	**−15**	5

Tables and Charts

Reading Tables and Charts

To read a table or chart, find the row containing one of the conditions of the information that you seek. Run down the column containing the other condition until it crosses that row. Read the answer.

▶ **How many sales were made at the Lincoln office?**

The table shows that there were 537 sales made at the Lincoln office.

Imag Corp. Sales Report

Office	Agents	Sales	Income
Bronx	252	640	$12,000,000
Calgary	204	307	1,800,000
Columbus	92	778	1,200,000
Dallas	50	761	1,300,000
Denver	76	398	1,500,000
Lincoln	35	537	1,500,000
San Diego	128	813	14,300,000
Toronto	710	390	7,900,000

1. $1,200,000

Find the income for each of the following offices:

1. Columbus   **2.** Denver **$1,500,000**   **3.** Toronto **$7,900,000**   **4.** Bronx **$12,000,000**

5. Which offices made more than 500 sales?
Bronx, Columbus, Dallas, Lincoln, San Diego

6. Which offices have less than 200 agents?
Columbus, Dallas, Denver, Lincoln, San Diego

Using Tables and Charts

To classify an item, find the row or column that contains the data you are looking for. Then read the classification from the head of the row or column.

▶ **An order weighing 5 pounds 5 ounces cost $9.25 in shipping charges. To which zone was it delivered?**

The table shows that the order was delivered in Zone 2.

Delivery Chart	Delivery Zones		Custom Delivery	
Weight	Zone 1	Zone 2	Express	Express Plus
Find Your State at Right ▶	AL, AR, DC, DE, IA, IL, IN, KS, KY, MD, MI, MN, MO, MS, NC, NE, ND, OH, OK, PA, SC, SD, TN, VA, WI, WV	AK, AZ, CA, CO, CT, FL, GA, HI, ID, LA, MA, ME, MT, NH, NJ, NM, NV, NY, OR, RI, TX, UT, VT, WA,WY	Ordered Delivered Mon. Thur. Tue. Fri. Wed. Mon. Thur. Tue. Fri. Wed. Sat. Wed. Sun. Wed.	Ordered Delivered Mon. Wed. Tue. Thur. Wed. Fri. Thur. Mon. Fri. Tue. Sat. Tue. Sun. Tue.
Shipping Weight ▼				
Minimum Charge	$ 4.00	$ 4.50	$ 9.00	$19.00
2 lb 1 oz to 4 lb	6.50	6.75	11.00	21.00
4 lb 1 oz to 8 lb	9.00	9.25	15.75	25.75
8 lb 1 oz to 14 lb	11.25	11.75	22.25	32.25
14 lb 1 oz to 20 lb	13.00	15.00	28.25	38.25

Find the missing information.

7. An order weighing 16 pounds cost $38.25 in shipping charges. How was the order sent? **Express Plus**

8. An order weighing 9 pounds 12 ounces cost $11.25 in shipping charges. To what zone was it delivered? **Zone 1**

9. An order weighing 10 pounds cost $22.25 in shipping charges.
   a. How was the order sent? **Express**
   b. When would the order be delivered if it was ordered on a Wednesday? **Mon.**

Making Change

Making Change: Building Up

To make change, build up to the next nickel, dime, quarter, and so on, until the amount presented is reached.

▶ **Compute the change from $5.00 for a purchase of $3.67.**

CHANGE

	$3.67
3 pennies ············▶	+ .03
	3.70
1 nickel ············▶	+ .05
	3.75
1 quarter ············▶	+ .25
	4.00
1 dollar ············▶	+ 1.00
Amount presented ············▶	$5.00

Making Change: Loose Coins

The amount presented may contain loose coins so that fewer coins and bills are returned in the change.

▶ **Compute the change from $5.02 for a purchase of $3.67.**

a. Subtract the loose change.

Amount Presented	Purchase
$5.02	$3.67
− .02	− .02
$5.00	$3.65

b. Now compute the change from $5.00 for a purchase of $3.65.

CHANGE

	$3.65
1 dime ············▶	+ .10
	3.75
1 quarter ············▶	+ .25
	4.00
1 dollar ············▶	+ 1.00
	$5.00

Compute the change from $10 using the fewest coins and bills.

1. $3.75   **2.** $7.78

3. $1.99   **4.** $3.47

5. $5.63   **6.** $9.19

Compute the change using the fewest coins and bills.

7. Amount spent: $15.05   **2 dimes, 3 quarters,**
Amount presented: $20   **4 dollars**

8. Amount spent: $3.37   **3 pennies, 1 dime,**
Amount presented: $20   **2 quarters, 1 dollar,**
1 $5 bill, 1 $10 bill

9. Amount spent: $2.29   **1 penny, 2 dimes,**
Amount presented: $3   **2 quarters**

Compute the change using the fewest coins and bills.

10. Amount spent: $5.26   **3 quarters**
Amount presented: $6.01

11. Amount spent: $7.79   **1 quarter,**
Amount presented: $10.04   **2 dollars**

12. Amount spent: $1.07   **4 dollars**
Amount presented: $5.07

13. Amount spent: $3.92   **1 dime, 1 dollar,**
Amount presented: $10.02   **1 $5 bill**

14. Amount spent: $15.21   **1 nickel, 3 quar-**
Amount presented: $20.01   **ters, 4 dollars**

15. Amount spent: $7.81   **1 quarter,**
Amount presented: $10.06   **2 dollars**

16. Amount spent: $6.03   **1 $5 bill,**
Amount presented: $21.03   **1 $10 bill**

17. Amount spent: $9.62   **2 quarters,**
Amount presented: $21.12   **1 dollar, 1 $10 bill**

1. **1 quarter, 1 dollar, 1 $5 bill**
2. **2 pennies, 2 dimes, 2 dollars**
3. **1 penny, 3 dollars, 1 $5 bill**
4. **3 pennies, 2 quarters, 1 dollar, 1 $5 bill**
5. **2 pennies, 1 dime, 1 quarter, 4 dollars**
6. **1 penny, 1 nickel, 3 quarters**

Applications ▶ **763**

○─ **APPLICATION** **E**

Rounding Time: Nearest Quarter Hour

To round to the nearest quarter hour, find the quarter-hour interval that the given time is between. Subtract the earlier quarter from the given time. Subtract the given time from the later quarter. Round to whichever is closer.

▶ **Round 6:19 to the nearest quarter hour.**

6:19	6:30
− 6:15	− 6:19
4 minutes	11 minutes

4 is less than 11; round to 6:15

Round to the nearest quarter hour.

1. 8:39 **8:45**   2. 10:40 **10:45** 3. 6:55 **7:00**
4. 1:23 **1:30**   5. 11:17 **11:15** 6. 3:11 **3:15**
7. 12.09 **12:15** 8. 4:44 **4:45**   9. 3:32 **3:30**
10. 11:11 **11:15**   11. 8:51 **8:45** 12. 1:50 **1:45**
13. 7:35 **7:30** 14. 5:04 **5:00** 15. 9:40 **9:45**
16. 10:34 **10:30** 17. 12:39 **12:45** 18. 6:41 **6:45**
19. 6:01 **6:00** 20. 3:49 **3:45** 21. 11:36 **11:30**
22. 8:05 **8:00** 23. 10:10 **10:15**   24. 2:15 **2:15**

○─ **APPLICATION** **F**

Elapsed Time (Hours)

Finding Elapsed Time in Hours

To find the elapsed time, subtract the earlier time from the later time. If it is necessary to "borrow," rewrite the later time by subtracting 1 from the hours and by adding 60 to the minutes.

▶ **How much time has elapsed between 11:45 A.M. and 12:23 P.M.?**

12:23 =	11:23 + :60 =	11:83
− 11:45 =	− 11:45	= − 11:45
		38 min

Finding Elapsed Time Spanning 1 O'Clock.

To find the elapsed time when the period spans 1 o'clock, add 12 hours to the later time before subtracting.

▶ **How much time has elapsed between 7:45 P.M. and 2:52 A.M.?**

2:52 =	2:52 + 12:00 =	14:52
− 7:45 =	− 7:45	= − 7:45
		7h:7 min

Find the elapsed time.

1. From 6:05 P.M. to 8:51 P.M. **2 h:46 min**
2. From 4:18 A.M. to 6:52 A.M. **2 h:34 min**
3. From 8:30 A.M. to 11:45 A.M. **3 h:15 min**
4. From 6:45 P.M. to 11:59 P.M. **5 h:14 min**
5. From 10:45 A.M. to 11:36 A.M. **51 min**
6. From 3:45 P.M. to 5:30 P.M. **1 h:45 min**

Find the elapsed time.

7. From 8:15 A.M. to 1:30 P.M. **5 h:15 min**
8. From 4:55 A.M. to 1:00 P.M. **8 h:5 min**
9. From 11:30 P.M. to 7:50 A.M. **8 h:20 min**
10. From 9:45 P.M. to 8:00 A.M. **10 h:15 min**
11. From 3:30 A.M. to 2:15 P.M. **10 h:45 min**

Elapsed Time (Days)

To find the number of days **between** two dates, or **from** one date **to** the next, use the table on page 796. Find the position of each date in the year. When the date runs from one year to the next year, add 365 to the later date. Then subtract the earlier date from the later. To find the number of days **from** one date through another, find the elapsed time between the dates and add 1 day.

Day No.	Jan.	Feb.	Mar.	Apr.	May	June	July	Aug.	Sept.
1	1	32	60	91	121	152	182	213	244
2	2	33	61	92	122	153	183	214	245
3	3	34	62	93	123	154	184	215	246
4	4	35	63	94	124	155	185	216	247
5	5	36	64	95	125	156	186	217	248
6	6	37	65	96	126	157	187	218	249

▶ **How many days have elapsed between April 4 and January 6?**

Jan. 6: (6 + 365) = 371
Apr. 4: − 94 = − 94
  277 days

Find the elapsed time. Use the table on page 796.

1. Between August 10 and December 25 **137 days**
2. From March 21 through September 30 **193 days**
3. Between June 1 and December 30 **212 days**
4. From May 21 to July 2 **42 days**
5. From September 5 through May 20 **258 days**

APPLICATION H

Determining Leap Years

A year is a leap year if it is exactly divisible by 4. Exceptions are years that end in '00' (1900, 2000, and so on); they must be divisible by 400.

▶ **Was 1848 a leap year?**

1848 ÷ 4 = 462; 1848 was a leap year.

Find the leap years.

1. 1949 **No**
2. 1980 **Yes**
3. 2000 **Yes**
4. 1912 **Yes**
5. 2100 **No**
6. 1954 **No**
7. 1992 **Yes**
8. 1951 **No**
9. 2400 **Yes**
10. 1882 **No**
11. 1920 **Yes**
12. 2004 **Yes**

APPLICATION I

Elapsed Time in a Leap Year

When the dates include February 29 in a leap year, add 1 day to the later date.

▶ **How many days elapsed between January 5, 1980 and September 3, 1980?**

Sept. 3, 1980: (246 + 1) = 247
Jan. 5, 1980: − 5 = − 5
  242 days

Find the elapsed time. Use the table on page 796.

1. January 12, 1978, to April 1, 1978 **79 days**
2. July 1, 1979, through March 21, 1980 **265 days**
3. February 5, 1984, to September 23, 1984 **231 days**
4. January 9, 1988, through July 2, 1988 **176 days**
5. February 21, 2000, to September 30, 2000 **222 days**

APPLICATION J

Fractional Parts of a Year

Changing Months into a Part of a Year

To change months into a part of a year, write as a fraction with denominator 12. Express answers in lowest terms.

▶ **6 months is what part of a year?**

6 months $= \frac{6}{12}$ year $= \frac{1}{2}$ year

Change each term to a part of a year.

1. 9 months $\frac{3}{4}$ yr
2. 7 months $\frac{7}{12}$ yr
3. 12 months **1 yr**
4. 20 months $1\frac{2}{3}$ yr
5. 36 months **3 yr**
6. 18 months $1\frac{1}{2}$ yr
7. 21 months $1\frac{3}{4}$ yr
8. 8 months $\frac{2}{3}$ yr
9. 14 months $1\frac{1}{6}$ yr

Changing Days into a Part of a Year

To change days into a part of a year, write as a fraction with denominator 365 when using the exact year or 360 when using the ordinary year. Express answers in lowest terms.

▶ **240 days is what part of an exact year?**

240 days $= \frac{240}{365}$ year $= \frac{48}{73}$ year

▶ **240 days is what part of an ordinary year?**

240 days $= \frac{240}{360}$ year $= \frac{2}{3}$ year

Change each term to a part of a year.

10. 90 days as an exact year $\frac{18}{73}$ yr
11. 300 days as an ordinary year $\frac{5}{6}$ yr
12. 120 days as an exact year $\frac{24}{73}$ yr
13. 175 days as an exact year $\frac{35}{73}$ yr
14. 146 days as an ordinary year $\frac{73}{180}$ yr
15. 250 days as an exact year $\frac{50}{73}$ yr

APPLICATION K

Chronological Expressions

Changing Months into a Part of a Year

▶ **Monthly payments for 30 years. How many payments in all?**

Monthly: 12 times a year

In 30 years: $12 \times 30 = 360$ payments

Common Chronological Expressions		
(number of occurrences per year)		
	Weekly (52)	Biweekly (26)
Semimonthly (24)	Monthly (12)	Bimonthly (6)
	Quarterly (4)	
Semiannually (2)	Annually (1)	

Find the number of occurrences. Use the table above.

1. Weekly for 1 year **52**
2. Biweekly for 2 years **52**
3. Quarterly for 4 years **16**
4. Semimonthly for 1 year **24**
5. Bimonthly for 2 years **12**
6. Annually for 25 years **25**
7. Monthly for $\frac{1}{2}$ year **6**
8. Weekly for 1.5 years **78**
9. Semimonthly for $2\frac{1}{2}$ years **60**

APPLICATION L

The Complement of a Number

To find the complement of a percent or decimal less than 1, subtract the percent from 100% or the decimal from 1.

▶ **What is the complement of 65%?**

The complement of 65% =
100% − 65% = 35%

▶ **What is the complement of 0.25?**

The complement of 0.25 =
1 − 0.25 = 0.75

Find the complement.

1. 0.15 **0.85**	**2.** 0.72 **0.28**	**3.** 0.35 **0.65**
4. 0.50 **0.50**	**5.** 0.80 **0.20**	**6.** 0.34 **0.66**
7. 91% **9%**	**8.** 85% **15%**	**9.** 47% **53%**
10. 66% **34%**	**11.** 7% **93%**	**12.** 45% **55%**
13. 3.5% **96.5%**	**14.** 56.6% **43.4%**	**15.** 75.9% **24.1%**

APPLICATION M

Reading Bar Graphs

To read a bar graph, find the bar that represents the information you seek. Trace an imaginary line from the top of the bar to the scale on the left. Read the value represented by the bar from the scale.

Average Hourly Earnings

▶ **In 1992, what were the average hourly earnings for manufacturing workers?**

The bar graph shows that the average hourly earnings for manufacturing workers were about $11.00 per hour in 1992.

Answer the following. Use the bar graph shown.

1. In 1992, what were the average hourly earnings for mining workers? **$11.00**

2. In 2012, what are the projected average hourly earnings for manufacturing workers? **$20.00**

3. In 1992, what were the average hourly earnings for transportation workers? **$13.00**

4. Did any of the wages decrease over time? **No**

5. Estimate how much wages increased from 1992 to 2002 for the mining workers. **About $4.00**

6. How much more would a transportation worker earn in 2012 as compared to 1992? **About $10.00**

APPLICATIONS

Reading Line Graphs

To read a line graph, find the point that represents the information you seek. Trace an imaginary line from the point to the scale on the left. Read the value represented by the point from the scale.

▶ **What were the predicted and the actual amount of sales for the month of May?**

The line graph shows that the predicted amount of sales was $10,000. The actual amount was $8,000.

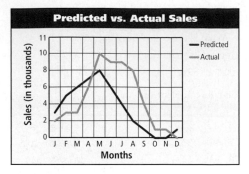

Answer the following. Use the line graph shown.

1. What was the predicted amount of sales for the month of August? **$8,000**

2. What was the actual amount of sales for the month of October? **$0.00**

3. Which month(s) actually had the least amount of sales? **October and November**

4. In which month was the actual amount predicted? **None**

Reading Pictographs

To read a pictograph, find the scale to see how much each picture represents. Then multiply that amount times the number of pictures on each line to get the total amount.

▶ **How many hours did it take to build a Toyota automobile?**

Each picture represents 5 hours.
The Toyota row has 7.5 pictures.

$7.5 \times 5 = 37.5$ hours

Hours to Build an Automobile	
🕐 = **5 hours**	
General Motors	🕐 🕐 🕐 🕐 🕐 🕐 🕐 🕐
Ford	🕐 🕐 🕐 🕐 🕐 🕐 🕐
Daimler-Chrysler	🕐 🕐 🕐 🕐 🕐 🕐 🕐 🕐 🕐
Toyota	🕐 🕐 🕐 🕐 🕐 🕐 🕐 🕐
Honda	🕐 🕐 🕐 🕐 🕐 🕐
Nissan	🕐 🕐 🕐 🕐 🕐 🕐

Answer the following. Use the pictograph shown.

1. How many hours did it take to build a Daimler-Chrysler automobile? **45 hours**

2. How many hours did it take to build a Honda automobile? **35 hours**

3. How much longer did it take to build a General Motors automobile than a Toyota? **2.5 hours**

Circle Graphs

Reading Circle Graphs

A circle graph is used to compare the parts to the whole. To find what part of the whole each section represents, multiply the amount, or percent, per section times the total amount.

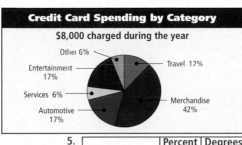

Credit Card Spending by Category

$8,000 charged during the year

Other 6%
Entertainment 17%
Services 6%
Automotive 17%
Travel 12%
Merchandise 42%

▶ **How much of the annual budget was spent on entertainment?**

Entertainment = 17 percent of the total

$0.17 \times \$8,000 = \$1,360$

Answer the following. Use the circle graph shown.

1. How much was spent on automotive? **$1,360**

2. How much of the credit card spending went for travel? **$960**

3. How much was spent on services? **$480**

4. Is more spent on merchandise than on all other categories? **No, 42% < 58%**

Constructing Circle Graphs

To construct a circle graph, find the percent of the total each section represents. Multiply each percent times 360° to find the measure of the angle for each proportion of the circle graph. Use a protractor to draw each portion.

▶ **Construct that portion of a circle graph that represents the Bradford family spending 40 cents out of every dollar for food.**

$\frac{40}{100} = 40\%$; $0.40 \times 360° = 144°$

5. Complete the circle graph shown. Use the following information. The Bradford family budgets the rest of each dollar as follows: rent 30 percent; entertainment 15 percent, clothing and personal items 10 percent, and all other expenses 5 percent.

6. Draw a circle graph. Use the following information. A factory budgets each dollar spent as follows: salaries 60 cents; raw materials 20 cents; utilities 10 cents; plant maintenance 5 cents; and research and development 5 cents.

5.

	Percent	Degrees
Food	40%	144
Rent	30%	108
Entertainment	15%	54
Clothing etc.	10%	36
Other	5%	18
	100%	360

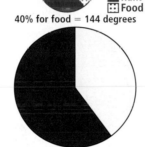

☐ Clothing etc.
☐ Entertainment
■ Other
■ Rent
▦ Food

40% for food = 144 degrees

6.

	Percent	Degrees
Salaries	60%	216
Materials	20%	72
Utilities	10%	36
Maintenance	5%	18
R & D	5%	18
	100%	360

☐ Maintenance
☐ Utilities
■ R & D
■ Materials
▦ Salaries

APPLICATIONS

Mean

To find the mean (average) of a group of numbers, find the sum of the group and divide it by the number of items in the group.

▶ **What is the mean of the following: 454, 376, 416, 472?**

$$\text{Mean} = \frac{(454 + 376 + 416 + 472)}{4}$$

$$= \frac{1,718}{4} = 429.5$$

Find the mean for each group.

1. 43, 19, 61, 72, 81, 50 **54.3**
2. 116, 147, 136, 151, 123, 117, 120 **130**
3. 4,615, 5,918, 7,437, 8,937 **6,726.75**
4. 4.0, 3.5, 4.0, 3.0, 3.5, 3.0, 2.0, 0.5, 4.6, 5.0 **3.31**
5. $580,000; $625,000; $105,583; $733,358; $5,750,000; $255,000; $600,000 **$1,235,563**

Median

To find the median of a group of numbers, arrange the items in order from smallest to largest. The median is the number in the middle. If there is an even number of items, find the mean of the two middle numbers.

▶ **What is the median of the following: 454, 376, 416, 472?**

Arrange in order: 376, <u>416</u>, <u>454</u>, 472

$$\text{Median} = \frac{(416 + 454)}{2} = 435$$

Find the median for each group.

1. 141, 136, 191, 187, 149, 148 **148.5**
2. 17, 21, 30, 35, 27, 25, 15 **25**
3. 91, 92, 85, 98, 100, 76, 80, 75 **88**
4. 4.2, 3.7, 3.1, 4.8, 2.4, 3.0, 2.9 **3.1**
5. 0.07, 0.05, 0.10, 0.12, 0.09, 0.17, 0.01 **0.09**
6. $121,500; $49,750; $72,175; $65,449 **$68,812**
7. 2.08, 2.04, 2.00, 2.10, 2.08, 2.24, 1.55, 2.04, 2.13, 2.08, 2.09 **2.08**

Mode

To find the mode of a group of numbers, look for the number that appears most often. A group may have no mode, or it may have more than one mode.

▶ **What is the mode of the following: 92, 98, 76, 84, 92, 1,200?**

The number that appears most often, the mode, is 92.

Find the mode for each group.

1. $51, $13, $24, $62, $55, $57, $24 **$24**
2. 800, 600, 800, 500, 600, 700 **600; 800**
3. 4.1, 4.7, 4.5, 4.3, 4.2, 4.4 **None**
4. 3, 3, 5, 3, 4, 2, 3, 2, 4, 4, 4 **3; 4**
5. 0.01, 0.1, 0.01, 1.0, 0.01, 0.11, 1.00 **0.01**
6. $45, $63, $27, $91, $65, $8, $43, $90 **None**

APPLICATION T

Metric Length

The common units of length in the metric system are the millimeter, centimeter, meter, and the kilometer.

A millimeter (mm) is about the thickness of a U.S. dime.

A centimeter (cm) is about the thickness of a sugar cube.

A meter (m) is about the length of a baseball bat.

A kilometer (km) is 1,000 m and is used to measure large distances. It is 3,400 kilometers from Toronto to Vancouver.

Name the unit that is most commonly used to measure the object.

1. The length of a tennis court **meter**
2. The distance between Detroit and Montreal **kilometer**
3. The thickness of a magazine **millimeter**
4. The length of a standard paper clip **centimeter**
5. The length of your living room **meter**
6. The thickness of a soda straw **millimeter**
7. The length of a postage stamp **centimeter**
8. The width of your foot **centimeter**

APPLICATION U

Metric Mass and Volume

The common units of mass and volume in the metric system are the gram, kilogram, metric ton, and kiloliter.

A gram (g) is about the mass of a paper clip.

A kilogram (kg) is about the mass of a hammer.

A metric ton (t) is 1,000 kilograms and is used to measure very heavy objects.

A liter (L) is about the amount of liquid in a can of motor oil.

A kiloliter (kL) is 1,000 liters and is used to measure large volumes, such as that of a railroad tank car.

Name the unit that is most commonly used to measure the object.

1. The mass of your best friend **kilogram**
2. The amount of gas in a car's tank **liter**
3. The mass of a nickel **gram**
4. The volume of helium in a blimp **kiloliter**
5. The mass of an adult blue whale **metric ton**
6. The mass of a baseball **kilogram**
7. The volume of a large fuel tank **kiloliter**
8. The mass of a dime **gram**
9. The mass of a gumdrop **gram**
10. The volume of a milk container **liter**

APPLICATION V

Perimeter

The distance around a shape is its perimeter. To find the perimeter of a shape, add the lengths of all its sides.

► **What is the perimeter of the triangle at the right?**

10 cm, 15 cm, 20 cm

Perimeter:

10 cm + 15 cm + 20 cm = 45 cm

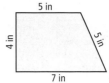

Find the perimeter.

1. 10.5 cm	**2.** 21 in	**3.** 2.6 ft
4. 6.1 m	**5.** 162 mi	**6.** 55.8 m

1.

3.8 cm

2.
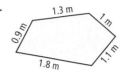
5 in
4 in
5 in
7 in

3.

0.65 ft
0.65 ft
0.65 ft
0.65 ft

4.

1.3 m
1 m
0.9 m
1.1 m
1.8 m

5.
34 mi
34 mi
34 mi
30 mi
30 mi

6.
9.3 m
9.3 m
9.3 m
9.3 m
9.3 m
9.3 m

APPLICATION W

Circumference

The length of a diameter of a circle is twice the length of its radius. The circumference is the distance around a circle. The circumference is estimated by multiplying 3.14 times the length of a diameter.

circumference
diameter = 23 mm
radius
center

► **The diameter of a circle is 23 millimeters. What is its circumference?**

Circumference = 3.14 × Diameter

Circumference = 3.14 × 23 millimeters

= 72.22 millimeters

Find the circumference.

1. Diameter: 4 miles **12.56 mi**	**2.** Diameter: 3.5 centimeters **10.99 cm**	**3.** Diameter: 0.8 meters **2.5 m**
4. Radius: 35 millimeters **219.8 mm**	**5.** Radius: 0.75 feet **4.71 ft**	**6.** Radius: 13 inches **81.64 in**
7. Diameter: 18 feet **56.52 ft**	**8.** Radius: 120 kilometers **753.6 km**	**9.** Diameter: 12.5 miles **39.25 mi**

Area of a Rectangle or Square

To find the area of a rectangle, multiply length by width. In a square, the length and the width are equal.

▶ **What is the area of a rectangular board that measures 3.5 meters by 1.9 meters?**

Area = Length × Width

Area = 3.5 m × 1.9 m = 6.65 m²

Find the area.

1. Rectangle: 25 inches long, 6 inches wide **150 in²**
2. Square: 45.4 centimeters per side **2061.16 cm²**
3. Rectangle: 0.9 meters long, 0.75 meters wide **0.675 m²**
4. Square: $3\frac{1}{2}$ yards per side **12.25 yd²**
5. Rectangle: $4\frac{2}{3}$ feet long, $2\frac{1}{6}$ feet wide **10.11 ft²**

Area of a Triangle or Circle

To find the area of a triangle or circle, use the formulas below.

Area of Triangle = $\frac{1}{2}$ × Base × Height

Area of Circle = 3.14 × Radius²

▶ **What is the area of a circle with a radius of 27 meters?**

Area of Circle = 3.14 × Radius²

Area of Circle = 3.14 × 27²

= 3.14 × 729

Area of Circle = 2,289.06 m²

Find the area.

13.5 in² 1. Triangle: base is 3 inches, height is 9 inches
2. Circle: radius is 5 centimeters **78.5 cm²**
3. Triangle: base is 16 meters, height is 25 meters **200 m²**
4. Triangle: base is 132 meters, height is 9.6 meters **633.6 m²**
5. Circle: radius is $2\frac{1}{2}$ yards **19.625 yd²**

$15\frac{1}{6}$ ft² 6. Triangle: base is $9\frac{1}{3}$ feet, height is $3\frac{1}{4}$ feet
7. Circle: radius is 86 millimeters **23,223 mm²**

Volume of a Rectangular Solid

To find the volume of a rectangular solid, multiply length by width by height.

▶ **What is the volume of a rectangular box that is 6 meters long, 4 meters wide, and 2 meters deep?**

Volume = Length × Width × Height

Volume = 6 m × 4 m × 2 m

Volume = 48 m³

Find the volume.

1. 36 meters long, 44 meters wide, 32 meters high **50,688 m³**
2. 1.6 m long, 0.55 m wide, 0.8 m high **0.704 m³**
3. 11 centimeters long, 12 centimeters wide, 3 centimeters high **396 cm³**
4. 60 inches long, 18 inches wide, 18 inches high **22,032 in³**

$157\frac{1}{4}$ yd³ 5. $12\frac{1}{3}$ yards long, $4\frac{1}{4}$ yards wide, 3 yards high
6. $7\frac{1}{2}$ feet long, $3\frac{1}{2}$ feet wide, $5\frac{5}{8}$ feet high **$147\frac{21}{32}$ ft³**

Glossary

A

account statement A bank statement that shows all deposits, withdrawals, and interest credited to an account.

accumulated depreciation The total depreciation of an item to date.

amount financed The portion of the cash price that is owed on an item after making the down payment.

amount of change When comparing income statements, the difference between the base figure on the earlier statement and the corresponding figure on the current statement.

annual expenses Expenses which occur once a year, such as insurance premiums and real estate taxes.

annual interest rate The percent of the principal in a bank account earned as interest based on one year.

annual percentage rate (APR) An index showing the cost of borrowing money on a yearly basis, expressed as a percent.

annual yield The rate at which money earns simple interest in one year.

annuity An equal amount of money deposited into an account at equal periods of time.

annuity due An account in which regular deposits are made at the beginning of each interest period and start earning interest immediately.

apportion To distribute expenses among different departments.

assessed value The dollar value assigned to property by a tax assessor for tax purposes, which is found by multiplying the market value times the rate of assessment.

assets The total of your cash, the items that you have purchased, and any money that your customers owe you.

automated teller machine (ATM) A bank machine that allows you to deposit or withdraw money electronically using a card.

average-cost method Calculating the value of an inventory based on the average cost of items in stock.

average-daily-balance method Computing the finance charge on a credit account based on the average of the account balance at the end of each day of the billing period.

B

balance The amount of money you have in an account.

balance sheet A statement that shows your total assets, total liabilities, and owner's equity.

base figure When comparing income statements, the dollar amount on the earlier income statement.

base price The price of a vehicle's engine, chassis, and any other standard equipment for a particular model.

beneficiary A person who receives the money from life insurance if the insured dies.

bonds Certificates issued by a business that indicate the buyer has lent the business money; written pledges issued by governments and corporations to repay a specific amount of money with interest at a certain time in return for lending them the money.

book value The approximate value of an item after it has been owned and depreciated for a period of time.

break-even analysis Determining how many units of a product must be made and sold to cover the cost of producing it.

break-even point The point where income from sales on a product equals what it cost to produce the product.

budget A plan for using money in a way that best meets your wants and needs.

budget sheet A record of monthly expenditures.

C

capital The amount of your owner's equity.

cash discount A discount a supplier grants if a bill is paid within a certain number of days.

cash value Monetary value that a life insurance policy builds up, like a savings account, that can be cashed in or borrowed.

certificate of deposit A kind of savings account that requires a specific deposit for a specified period of time, and which earns a higher rate of interest than a regular savings account.

chain discounts A series of trade discounts a supplier may offer to sell out a discontinued item or to encourage a customer to place a larger order.

charge account An existing line of credit, often at a particular business.

check register A record you keep of your checking account deposits, withdrawals, and transfers.

GLOSSARY

closing costs The costs of transferring ownership of property, such as credit checks and title searches, to the buyer by the seller.

co-insurance A percent of medical expenses a person with health insurance must pay beyond the deductible.

collision insurance Insurance that pays to repair a vehicle if it's involved in an accident.

commercial loans Loans made to businesses rather than individuals.

commercial paper A promissory note issued by various companies that pay interest. They are actually loans to a company.

commission An amount of money paid to an employee for selling a product or service.

commission rate A specified amount of money paid to an employee for each sale made or a percent of the total value of sales made.

complement method A way to find the net price of a discounted item by subtracting the discount rate from 100 percent.

compound interest Interest earned not only on the principal in a bank account, but also on the interest earned on the account, or interest on interest.

comprehensive insurance Insurance protection from losses due to fire, vandalism, theft, and other causes.

consultants Professional advisers hired by businesses to solve particular problems.

consultant's fee Payment to a consultant for professional services, it may be in the form of a flat fee, a percent of the cost of a project, or an hourly charge.

consumer price index (CPI) A measure of the average change in prices of a certain number of goods and services.

co-payment An amount a person with health insurance must pay for a service, such as a prescription or a doctor's visit, along with the insurance company.

corporations Businesses with many owners called stockholders.

cost The actual amount paid for a product, as opposed to its selling price, and which can include expenses such as freight charges and taxes.

cost of goods sold The value of a beginning inventory, plus the cost of any goods received, minus the value of the ending inventory.

cost-of-living adjustment A raise in salary to keep up with the rate of inflation.

coupons Discounts offered by businesses in the form of tickets that are redeemed at the time of purchase.

credit card A card that allows the cardholder to purchase goods and services on demand by presenting it.

current ratio The ratio of total assets to total liabilities.

D

daily compounding Interest on an account that is computed each day and added to the account balance.

dealer's cost The price actually paid for a vehicle by a dealer, usually expressed as a percent. The dealer's cost is not negotiated.

deductible An amount of money someone with insurance must pay before the insurance company pays anything.

deductible clause An insurance clause that requires the insured to pay a certain amount before the insurance company pays.

defective What manufactured items that are broken, damaged, the wrong size, or otherwise faulty are classified as.

demand charge The cost of electricity based on the peak load, or greatest number of kilowatts used by a business at one time during the month.

deposit Money put into a bank account.

depreciation A decrease in the value of an item or vehicle because of its age or condition.

destination charge The cost of shipping a vehicle from the factory to the dealer.

direct labor cost The cost of the labor used to make a product, such as wages paid to employees.

direct material cost The cost of the goods or materials used to make a product.

disability insurance Insurance that pays benefits to individuals who must miss work because of an illness or injury.

discount The difference between the face value and the maturity value of a bond or Treasury bill.

dividend Money received for being a shareholder in a corporation.

double time An overtime pay rate of two times the regular hourly rate, often paid for working on Sundays and holidays.

down payment A portion of the cash price of an item that has to be paid before financing the rest on credit.

E

emergency fund Extra monies set aside to be used for unpredictable expenses, such as medical bills and vehicle repairs.

employee benefits Services offered by businesses to employees beyond salary, or wages, such as paid vacations, health insurance, and sick leave.

end-of-month dating Terms of payment on an invoice from supplier which grants a cash discount if a bill is paid within a certain numbers of days after the end of the month when the invoice is issued.

energy charge The cost of electricity based on the total number of kilowatt-hours used by a business during the month.

estimated life The length of time, usually in years, an item is expected to last.

exact interest Interest on a loan calculated by basing the time of the loan on a 365-day year.

expenditures Items you spend money on.

expense summary A monthly report that compares the amounts you spend to the amounts you have budgeted.

F

face value The amount of money printed on a bond or Treasury bill that you receive on its maturity date.

factor A company's present share of the market for a product or service.

factor method Projecting a company's sales by multiplying the company's present market share by the projected sales for the entire market for the coming year.

federal income tax Money withheld by an employer from an employee's paycheck to pay federal government taxes.

final payment Payment on a simple interest loan that consists of the remaining balance plus the current month's interest.

finance charge Interest that is charged to a credit account if the account holder does not pay off the balance in full.

fire protection class A number assigned to property based on how safe it is from fire, and whether a house is made of wood or brick, used to determine the cost of insuring it.

first in, first out (FIFO) A method of valuing inventory that assumes the first items received are the first items shipped out.

fixed costs Production or vehicle costs that remain the same no matter how much you produce or drive, such as building rent or vehicle registration.

fixed expenses Regular expenses that do not vary from month to month, such as rent and car payments.

fuel adjustment charge A charge added to an electricity bill to cover increases in the cost of fuel needed to produce electricity.

G

graduated commission Pay in which the commission rate is different for different levels of sales.

graduated income tax An income tax in which the tax rate increases at different levels of income.

gross domestic product (GDP) The total value of the goods and services produced in a country in a given year.

gross profit The amount of money a supplier makes on a product when it sells it for more than it costs.

group insurance Insurance offered by many businesses to employees, paid in part by the business and in part by deductions from employees' paychecks.

growth expenses Expenses from expanding a business, such as construction fees and consultation fees.

H

health insurance Protection against the costs of medical expenses.

health maintenance organization (HMO) A group program that provides health care at its own center with its own doctors for a fixed fee per month.

homeowners insurance Financial protection for homeowners against fire, theft of contents, personal liability, and other damages.

horizontal analysis The comparison of two or more income statements for different periods.

hourly rate A fixed amount of money paid for each hour of work.

I

income statement A statement that shows in detail the income and operating expenses of a business, also called a profit-and-loss statement.

inflation A general increase in the cost of goods and services.

installment loan A loan repaid in equal payments over a specified period of time.

interest The amount of money paid for the use of a lender's money.

inventory The number of each item that a business has in stock.

inventory card A record of each item a business has in stock.

invoice A bill listing the quantities and costs of items purchased.

K

kilowatt A unit of electrical power equal to 1,000 watts, used by power companies to measure energy usage.

L

labor charge The cost of paying people to do a job.

last in, first out (LIFO) A method of valuing inventory that assumes the last items received are the first items shipped out.

lease An agreement for the use of property, such as a building or a vehicle, usually on an annual basis.

liabilities The total amount of money that you owe to creditors.

liability insurance Financial protection against accidents that cause bodily injury and property damage.

life insurance Financial protection for a family in case a family member dies.

limited payment policy Life insurance that is paid up after a specified number of years, or until the insured reaches a certain age, but offers lifetime protection.

list price The price at which a business generally sells an item, also call the catalog price.

living expenses Routine expenses, such as food, utilities, and clothing, that vary from month to month.

loss The amount of money lost on an investment, such as stocks.

loss-of-use coverage Insurance coverage for homeowners that pays for the costs of living away from home while the home is being repaired.

M

manufactures Makes, or produces, a product.

markdown The difference between the regular selling price of an item and its sale price, also called the amount of the discount.

markdown rate The discount on an item expressed as a percent of its regular selling price, such as 20 percent off.

market The total number of people who might purchase a type of product.

market share The total number of people who might purchase a specific product.

market value The price at which a house can be bought or sold.

markup The difference between the cost of a product and the selling price when the selling price is higher.

markup rate The markup on an item expressed as a percent of its selling price.

maturity value The total amount that must be repaid on a loan, including the principal borrowed and the interest owed.

medical coverage Insurance for homeowners that pays medical expenses if someone is injured in their home.

Medicare A federal government program to provide medical insurance, financed by taxes.

merge To combine one business with another business to form a new business.

merit increase A raise in salary to reward an employee for the quality of his or her work.

modified accelerated cost recovery system (MACRS) A method of computing depreciation that allows businesses to depreciate assets fully over a set period of time.

monthly service charge Base amount charged by a utility, such as a phone company, to its customers for use of its services.

mortgage loan A real estate loan that gives the lender the right to seize and sell the property if the borrower fails to make the payments on the loan.

N

net income Any money left over after expenses have been deducted from gross profits, also called net profit.

net pay The amount of money you actually receive in your paycheck after deductions, also called take-home pay.

net price The price actually paid for a discounted item.

net-price rate The percent of the price paid for an item, found by multiplying the complements of the chain discounts.

net profit Any money left after expenses have been deducted from gross profits, also called net income.

net-profit rate The net profit on an item expressed as a percentage of the selling price.

net worth The amount by which your assets exceed your liabilities.

O

online banking Doing bank transactions, such as loan payments and funds transfers, electronically over the Internet.

operating expenses The costs of running a business, such as salaries, rent, utilities, and taxes, also called overhead.

opinion research firm A business that specializes in product testing and opinion surveys.

opinion survey A series of questions about a new product submitted to a group of volunteers to find out how well the product will sell.

options Extra equipment on a vehicle not included in the base price, such as a sunroof, air conditioning, and tinted glass.

ordinary annuity An account in which equal deposits are made at the end of each interest period and start earning interest at the beginning of the next interest period.

ordinary dating Terms of payment on an invoice from a supplier which grants a cash discount if a bill is paid within a certain numbers of days.

ordinary interest Interest on a loan calculated by basing the time of the loan on a 360-day year.

overtime pay Extra pay for hours worked beyond regular hours.

owner's equity The difference between your assets and your liabilities.

P

packaging Placing a product in a container for shipment, or the actual containers themselves.

payroll register A record of the gross income, deductions, and net income of a company's employees.

peak load The greatest number of kilowatts of electricity a business uses at one time during the month.

per capita GDP The gross domestic product of a country distributed over the population, or the GDP per person.

personal exemptions The number of people an employee supports, on which taxes are based, also called withholding allowances.

personal identification number (PIN) A personal number on a bankcard that gives you access to your bank account electronically.

personal liability Insurance coverage for homeowners if someone is injured in their home.

piecework A specified amount of money paid to an employee for each item of work completed.

preferred provider organization (PPO) A group of selected health care providers who offer comprehensive services at preset reimbursement levels.

premium The amount paid to an insurance company for insurance.

prime cost The total of the direct material cost and the direct labor cost used to make a product, often expressed on a per-unit basis.

prime rate The lowest rate of interest available for commercial loans at a given time.

principal The amount borrowed on a loan or put into an account, on which interest is based.

product test A test to see how well a new product is likely to sell by asking a group of people to try the product.

profit Money made on a product or an investment over and above the amount spent on it.

profit-and-loss statement A statement that shows in detail the income and operating expenses of a business, also called an income statement.

promissory note A written promise to pay a certain sum of money on a certain date in the future.

Q

quality control Inspecting mass-produced items for defects.

quality control chart A chart that shows the percent of defective products that is allowable in manufacturing.

quick ratio The ratio of total assets minus inventory to total liabilities, sometimes called the acid-test ratio.

R

rate of assessment Percent of the market value of property that is taxed.

real estate taxes Taxes collected by the city or county from homeowners to pay for roads, parks, schools, and other public services.

real GDP The gross domestic product adjusted to include the effects of inflation.

rebates Discounts offered by businesses in the form of money given back to the customer, usually through the mail.

reconcile To compare your check register with the bank statement of your checking account to make sure they agree.

recordkeeping Keeping track of monthly expenses by recording them in a budget sheet.

recruiting The act of soliciting qualified people to work for a company.

release time Time an employee spends away from a job for which a business will still pay a regular salary, such as for a training program.

rent Payment for the use of property, such as a building or vehicle, often on a daily, weekly, or monthly basis.

repayment schedule A schedule showing the distribution of interest and principal payments on a loan over the life of the loan.

replacement value The amount required to reconstruct a home if it's destroyed, used to determine the amount of insurance a home should have.

S

salary A fixed amount of money earned on a regular basis, received weekly, bi-weekly, semimonthly, or monthly.

salary scale A table of wages or salaries used to compare various jobs in a company.

sale price The regular selling price of an item minus the discount or markdown on the price.

sales potential An estimate of the sales volume of a product during a specified period of time.

sales projection An estimate of the dollar volume or unit sales of a product that might occur during a future time period.

sales receipt Proof of purchase of a good or service from a store.

sales tax A tax charged by most states on the selling price of a good or service, usually expressed as a percent.

salvage value The estimated trade-in, resale, or scrap value of an item at the end of its expected life.

sample A selected group of people (who are representative of a much larger group) that try out a new product to find out how well the product will sell.

savings account A special bank account for storing money for future use.

selling price What a product actually sells for in the store, also called retail price.

simple interest installment loan A loan repaid with equal monthly payments.

simple interest Interest paid only on the principal in a bank account.

single equivalent discount One discount that is equal to a chain discount.

single-payment loan A loan that has to be repaid with one payment after a specified period of time.

Social Security A federal government program to pay for retirement and disability benefits, financed by taxes.

sticker price The total price of a vehicle, including the base price, options, and destination charge.

stock certificate Proof of ownership in a corporation.

stocks Shares of ownership in a corporation.

straight commission Pay that consists only of money earned on sales.

straight-line method A method of determining the annual depreciation of an item which assumes that the depreciation is the same from year to year.

straight-time pay The total amount of money earned for a pay period at the regular hourly rate.

T

tax rate The percent of income, sales, or property value collected in taxes. The tax rate on property is sometimes expressed in mills per dollar.

taxable income The amount of gross income that remains after normal business expenses are deducted, upon which taxes are based.

term The amount of time for which a loan is granted before it has to be repaid.

term life insurance Life insurance for a specified term, such as five years, or to a specified age, that ends unless the policy is renewed. The cost of the insurance is based on the age of the insured.

time and a half An overtime pay rate of $1\frac{1}{2}$ times the regular hourly rate.

time study Determining the average time a task should take to do.

total purchase price The selling price of an item plus the sales tax.

trade discount A discount off the list price or catalog price of an item.

trade-discount rate The amount of the discount of an item expressed as a percent of the list price or catalog price.

travel expenses Expenses required to travel for a business, for which the business will usually pay.

Treasury bill A bill that can be purchased from the federal government in various amounts and that pays interest. It is actually a loan to the government. Also known as a "T-bill."

U

underwriting commission An amount of money paid to an investment banker for helping a business distribute stocks or bonds.

unemployment insurance A federal and state program that provides financial aid to qualified persons who, through no fault of their own, become unemployed.

unit pricing The cost of an item per unit of measure or count, such as dollars per pound or cents per dozen.

universal life insurance A combination of a life insurance policy and a savings plan. It covers the insured for a lifetime, and any amount the insured pays over the minimum goes into an investment account that earns interest.

unpaid-balance method Computing the finance charge on a credit account based on the portion of the previous balance that has not been paid.

used-vehicle guides Guides published monthly that give the average prices for vehicles that were purchased from dealers during the previous month.

utilities Public services such as electricity, water, and gas.

utility costs The costs of public services such as electricity, water, and gas.

V

variable costs The costs of producing a product that vary directly with the number of units produced, such as raw materials and packaging. Also, vehicle costs that increase the more you drive, such as gasoline and tires.

W

warehouse A storage space for a business to keep materials or products until it's ready to use them, sell them, or ship them.

weekly time card A record of the time you report for work and the time you depart each day of the week.

whole life insurance Insurance that offers financial protection throughout one's lifetime and costs a specific amount, also known as permanent insurance.

withdrawal Money taken out of a bank account.

withholding allowances The number of people an employee supports, on which taxes are based, also called personal exemptions.

workers compensation insurance Insurance that covers employees' medical expenses and lost wages if they're hurt on the job.

Y

yield Rate of return on a stock, a bond or Treasury Bill, or savings account earned by an investor after a certain period of time.

Appendix

Table of Contents

SINGLE Persons—WEEKLY Payroll Period

(For Wages Paid)

If the wages are—		And the number of withholding allowances claimed is—										
At least	But less than	0	1	2	3	4	5	6	7	8	9	10
		The amount of income tax to be withheld is—										
$0	$55	$0	$0	$0	$0	$0	$0	$0	$0	$0	$0	$0
55	60	1	0	0	0	0	0	0	0	0	0	0
60	65	1	0	0	0	0	0	0	0	0	0	0
65	70	2	0	0	0	0	0	0	0	0	0	0
70	75	2	0	0	0	0	0	0	0	0	0	0
75	80	3	0	0	0	0	0	0	0	0	0	0
80	85	3	0	0	0	0	0	0	0	0	0	0
85	90	4	0	0	0	0	0	0	0	0	0	0
90	95	4	0	0	0	0	0	0	0	0	0	0
95	100	5	0	0	0	0	0	0	0	0	0	0
100	105	5	0	0	0	0	0	0	0	0	0	0
105	110	6	0	0	0	0	0	0	0	0	0	0
110	115	6	0	0	0	0	0	0	0	0	0	0
115	120	7	1	0	0	0	0	0	0	0	0	0
120	125	7	1	0	0	0	0	0	0	0	0	0
125	130	8	2	0	0	0	0	0	0	0	0	0
130	135	8	2	0	0	0	0	0	0	0	0	0
135	140	9	3	0	0	0	0	0	0	0	0	0
140	145	9	3	0	0	0	0	0	0	0	0	0
145	150	10	4	0	0	0	0	0	0	0	0	0
150	155	10	4	0	0	0	0	0	0	0	0	0
155	160	11	5	0	0	0	0	0	0	0	0	0
160	165	11	5	0	0	0	0	0	0	0	0	0
165	170	12	6	0	0	0	0	0	0	0	0	0
170	175	13	6	1	0	0	0	0	0	0	0	0
175	180	13	7	1	0	0	0	0	0	0	0	0
180	185	14	7	2	0	0	0	0	0	0	0	0
185	190	15	8	2	0	0	0	0	0	0	0	0
190	195	16	8	3	0	0	0	0	0	0	0	0
195	200	16	9	3	0	0	0	0	0	0	0	0
200	210	17	10	4	0	0	0	0	0	0	0	0
210	220	19	11	5	0	0	0	0	0	0	0	0
220	230	20	12	6	0	0	0	0	0	0	0	0
230	240	22	13	7	1	0	0	0	0	0	0	0
240	250	23	15	8	2	0	0	0	0	0	0	0
250	260	25	16	9	3	0	0	0	0	0	0	0
260	270	26	18	10	4	0	0	0	0	0	0	0
270	280	28	19	11	5	0	0	0	0	0	0	0
280	290	29	21	12	6	0	0	0	0	0	0	0
290	300	31	22	14	7	1	0	0	0	0	0	0
300	310	32	24	15	8	2	0	0	0	0	0	0
310	320	34	25	17	9	3	0	0	0	0	0	0
320	330	35	27	18	10	4	0	0	0	0	0	0
330	340	37	28	20	11	5	0	0	0	0	0	0
340	350	38	30	21	12	6	1	0	0	0	0	0
350	360	40	31	23	14	7	2	0	0	0	0	0
360	370	41	33	24	15	8	3	0	0	0	0	0
370	380	43	34	26	17	9	4	0	0	0	0	0
380	390	44	36	27	18	10	5	0	0	0	0	0
390	400	46	37	29	20	11	6	0	0	0	0	0
400	410	47	39	30	21	13	7	1	0	0	0	0
410	420	49	40	32	23	14	8	2	0	0	0	0
420	430	50	42	33	24	16	9	3	0	0	0	0
430	440	52	43	35	26	17	10	4	0	0	0	0
440	450	53	45	36	27	19	11	5	0	0	0	0
450	460	55	46	38	29	20	12	6	0	0	0	0
460	470	56	48	39	30	22	13	7	1	0	0	0
470	480	58	49	41	32	23	15	8	2	0	0	0
480	490	59	51	42	33	25	16	9	3	0	0	0
490	500	61	52	44	35	26	18	10	4	0	0	0
500	510	62	54	45	36	28	19	11	5	0	0	0
510	520	64	55	47	38	29	21	12	6	0	0	0
520	530	65	57	48	39	31	22	14	7	1	0	0
530	540	67	58	50	41	32	24	15	8	2	0	0
540	550	68	60	51	42	34	25	17	9	3	0	0
550	560	70	61	53	44	35	27	18	10	4	0	0
560	570	71	63	54	45	37	28	20	11	5	0	0
570	580	74	64	56	47	38	30	21	12	6	0	0
580	590	76	66	57	48	40	31	23	14	7	1	0
590	600	79	67	59	50	41	33	24	15	8	2	0

SINGLE Persons—WEEKLY Payroll Period
(For Wages Paid)

If the wages are—		And the number of withholding allowances claimed is—										
At least	But less than	0	1	2	3	4	5	6	7	8	9	10
		The amount of income tax to be withheld is—										
$600	$610	$82	$69	$60	$51	$43	$34	$26	$17	$9	$3	$0
610	620	84	70	62	53	44	36	27	18	10	4	0
620	630	87	72	63	54	46	37	29	20	11	5	0
630	640	90	74	65	56	47	39	30	21	13	6	1
640	650	92	77	66	57	49	40	32	23	14	7	2
650	660	95	80	68	59	50	42	33	24	16	8	3
660	670	98	82	69	60	52	43	35	26	17	9	4
670	680	101	85	71	62	53	45	36	27	19	10	5
680	690	103	88	72	63	55	46	38	29	20	12	6
690	700	106	90	75	65	56	48	39	30	22	13	7
700	710	109	93	77	66	58	49	41	32	23	15	8
710	720	111	96	80	68	59	51	42	33	25	16	9
720	730	114	98	83	69	61	52	44	35	26	18	10
730	740	117	101	86	71	62	54	45	36	28	19	11
740	750	119	104	88	73	64	55	47	38	29	21	12
750	760	122	107	91	75	65	57	48	39	31	22	13
760	770	125	109	94	78	67	58	50	41	32	24	15
770	780	128	112	96	81	68	60	51	42	34	25	16
780	790	130	115	99	83	70	61	53	44	35	27	18
790	800	133	117	102	86	71	63	54	45	37	28	19
800	810	136	120	104	89	73	64	56	47	38	30	21
810	820	138	123	107	92	76	66	57	48	40	31	22
820	830	141	125	110	94	79	67	59	50	41	33	24
830	840	144	128	113	97	81	69	60	51	43	34	25
840	850	146	131	115	100	84	70	62	53	44	36	27
850	860	149	134	118	102	87	72	63	54	46	37	28
860	870	152	136	121	105	90	74	65	56	47	39	30
870	880	155	139	123	108	92	77	66	57	49	40	31
880	890	157	142	126	110	95	79	68	59	50	42	33
890	900	160	144	129	113	98	82	69	60	52	43	34
900	910	163	147	131	116	100	85	71	62	53	45	36
910	920	165	150	134	119	103	87	72	63	55	46	37
920	930	168	152	137	121	106	90	75	65	56	48	39
930	940	171	155	140	124	108	93	77	66	58	49	40
940	950	173	158	142	127	111	96	80	68	59	51	42
950	960	176	161	145	129	114	98	83	69	61	52	43
960	970	179	163	148	132	117	101	85	71	62	54	45
970	980	182	166	150	135	119	104	88	72	64	55	46
980	990	184	169	153	137	122	106	91	75	65	57	48
990	1,000	187	171	156	140	125	109	93	78	67	58	49
1,000	1,010	190	174	158	143	127	112	96	81	68	60	51
1,010	1,020	192	177	161	146	130	114	99	83	70	61	52
1,020	1,030	195	179	164	148	133	117	102	86	71	63	54
1,030	1,040	198	182	167	151	135	120	104	89	73	64	55
1,040	1,050	200	185	169	154	138	123	107	91	76	66	57
1,050	1,060	203	188	172	156	141	125	110	94	78	67	58
1,060	1,070	206	190	175	159	144	128	112	97	81	69	60
1,070	1,080	209	193	177	162	146	131	115	99	84	70	61
1,080	1,090	211	196	180	164	149	133	118	102	87	72	63
1,090	1,100	214	198	183	167	152	136	120	105	89	74	64
1,100	1,110	217	201	185	170	154	139	123	108	92	76	66
1,110	1,120	219	204	188	173	157	141	126	110	95	79	67
1,120	1,130	222	206	191	175	160	144	129	113	97	82	69
1,130	1,140	225	209	194	178	162	147	131	116	100	85	70
1,140	1,150	227	212	196	181	165	150	134	118	103	87	72
1,150	1,160	230	215	199	183	168	152	137	121	105	90	74
1,160	1,170	233	217	202	186	171	155	139	124	108	93	77
1,170	1,180	236	220	204	189	173	158	142	126	111	95	80
1,180	1,190	238	223	207	191	176	160	145	129	114	98	82
1,190	1,200	241	225	210	194	179	163	147	132	116	101	85
1,200	1,210	244	228	212	197	181	166	150	135	119	103	88
1,210	1,220	246	231	215	200	184	168	153	137	122	106	91
1,220	1,230	249	233	218	202	187	171	156	140	124	109	93
1,230	1,240	252	236	221	205	180	174	168	143	127	112	06
1,240	1,250	254	239	223	208	192	177	161	145	130	114	99

MARRIED Persons—WEEKLY Payroll Period
(For Wages Paid)

If the wages are—		And the number of withholding allowances claimed is—										
At least	But less than	0	1	2	3	4	5	6	7	8	9	10
		The amount of income tax to be withheld is—										
$0	$130	$0	$0	$0	$0	$0	$0	$0	$0	$0	$0	$0
130	135	1	0	0	0	0	0	0	0	0	0	0
135	140	1	0	0	0	0	0	0	0	0	0	0
140	145	2	0	0	0	0	0	0	0	0	0	0
145	150	2	0	0	0	0	0	0	0	0	0	0
150	155	3	0	0	0	0	0	0	0	0	0	0
155	160	3	0	0	0	0	0	0	0	0	0	0
160	165	4	0	0	0	0	0	0	0	0	0	0
165	170	4	0	0	0	0	0	0	0	0	0	0
170	175	5	0	0	0	0	0	0	0	0	0	0
175	180	5	0	0	0	0	0	0	0	0	0	0
180	185	6	0	0	0	0	0	0	0	0	0	0
185	190	6	1	0	0	0	0	0	0	0	0	0
190	195	7	1	0	0	0	0	0	0	0	0	0
195	200	7	2	0	0	0	0	0	0	0	0	0
200	210	8	2	0	0	0	0	0	0	0	0	0
210	220	9	3	0	0	0	0	0	0	0	0	0
220	230	10	4	0	0	0	0	0	0	0	0	0
230	240	11	5	0	0	0	0	0	0	0	0	0
240	250	12	6	1	0	0	0	0	0	0	0	0
250	260	13	7	2	0	0	0	0	0	0	0	0
260	270	14	8	3	0	0	0	0	0	0	0	0
270	280	15	9	4	0	0	0	0	0	0	0	0
280	290	16	10	5	0	0	0	0	0	0	0	0
290	300	17	11	6	0	0	0	0	0	0	0	0
300	310	18	12	7	1	0	0	0	0	0	0	0
310	320	19	13	8	2	0	0	0	0	0	0	0
320	330	20	14	9	3	0	0	0	0	0	0	0
330	340	21	15	10	4	0	0	0	0	0	0	0
340	350	22	16	11	5	0	0	0	0	0	0	0
350	360	23	17	12	6	0	0	0	0	0	0	0
360	370	25	18	13	7	1	0	0	0	0	0	0
370	380	26	19	14	8	2	0	0	0	0	0	0
380	390	28	20	15	9	3	0	0	0	0	0	0
390	400	29	21	16	10	4	0	0	0	0	0	0
400	410	31	22	17	11	5	0	0	0	0	0	0
410	420	32	23	18	12	6	0	0	0	0	0	0
420	430	34	25	19	13	7	1	0	0	0	0	0
430	440	35	26	20	14	8	2	0	0	0	0	0
440	450	37	28	21	15	9	3	0	0	0	0	0
450	460	38	29	22	16	10	4	0	0	0	0	0
460	470	40	31	23	17	11	5	0	0	0	0	0
470	480	41	32	24	18	12	6	0	0	0	0	0
480	490	43	34	25	19	13	7	1	0	0	0	0
490	500	44	35	27	20	14	8	2	0	0	0	0
500	510	46	37	28	21	15	9	3	0	0	0	0
510	520	47	38	30	22	16	10	4	0	0	0	0
520	530	49	40	31	23	17	11	5	0	0	0	0
530	540	50	41	33	24	18	12	6	1	0	0	0
540	550	52	43	34	26	19	13	7	2	0	0	0
550	560	53	44	36	27	20	14	8	3	0	0	0
560	570	55	46	37	29	21	15	9	4	0	0	0
570	580	56	47	39	30	22	16	10	5	0	0	0
580	590	58	49	40	32	23	17	11	6	0	0	0
590	600	59	50	42	33	24	18	12	7	1	0	0
600	610	61	52	43	35	26	19	13	8	2	0	0
610	620	62	53	45	36	27	20	14	9	3	0	0
620	630	64	55	46	38	29	21	15	10	4	0	0
630	640	65	56	48	39	30	22	16	11	5	0	0
640	650	67	58	49	41	32	23	17	12	6	0	0
650	660	68	59	51	42	33	25	18	13	7	1	0
660	670	70	61	52	44	35	26	19	14	8	2	0
670	680	71	62	54	45	36	28	20	15	9	3	0
680	690	73	64	55	47	38	29	21	16	10	4	0
690	700	74	65	57	48	39	31	22	17	11	5	0
700	710	76	67	58	50	41	32	24	18	12	6	0
710	720	77	68	60	51	42	34	25	19	13	7	1
720	730	79	70	61	53	44	35	27	20	14	8	2
730	740	80	71	63	54	45	37	28	21	15	9	3
740	750	82	73	64	56	47	38	30	22	16	10	4

MARRIED Persons—WEEKLY Payroll Period
(For Wages Paid)

If the wages are—		And the number of withholding allowances claimed is—										
At least	But less than	0	1	2	3	4	5	6	7	8	9	10
		The amount of income tax to be withheld is—										
$750	$760	$83	$74	$66	$57	$48	$40	$31	$23	$17	$11	$5
760	770	85	76	67	59	50	41	33	24	18	12	6
770	780	86	77	69	60	51	43	34	26	19	13	7
780	790	88	79	70	62	53	44	36	27	20	14	8
790	800	89	80	72	63	54	46	37	29	21	15	9
800	810	91	82	73	65	56	47	39	30	22	16	10
810	820	92	83	75	66	57	49	40	32	23	17	11
820	830	94	85	76	68	59	50	42	33	24	18	12
830	840	95	86	78	69	60	52	43	35	26	19	13
840	850	97	88	79	71	62	53	45	36	27	20	14
850	860	98	89	81	72	63	55	46	38	29	21	15
860	870	100	91	82	74	65	56	48	39	30	22	16
870	880	101	92	84	75	66	58	49	41	32	23	17
880	890	103	94	85	77	68	59	51	42	33	25	18
890	900	104	95	87	78	69	61	52	44	35	26	19
900	910	106	97	88	80	71	62	54	45	36	28	20
910	920	107	98	90	81	72	64	55	47	38	29	21
920	930	109	100	91	83	74	65	57	48	39	31	22
930	940	110	101	93	84	75	67	58	50	41	32	24
940	950	112	103	94	86	77	68	60	51	42	34	25
950	960	113	104	96	87	78	70	61	53	44	35	27
960	970	115	106	97	89	80	71	63	54	45	37	28
970	900	116	107	90	90	81	73	64	56	47	38	30
980	990	118	109	100	92	83	74	66	57	48	40	31
990	1,000	120	110	102	93	84	76	67	59	50	41	33
1,000	1,010	122	112	103	95	86	77	69	60	51	43	34
1,010	1,020	125	113	105	96	87	79	70	62	53	44	36
1,020	1,030	128	115	106	98	89	80	72	63	54	46	37
1,030	1,040	130	116	108	99	90	82	73	65	56	47	39
1,040	1,050	133	118	109	101	92	83	75	66	57	49	40
1,050	1,060	136	120	111	102	93	85	76	68	59	50	42
1,060	1,070	138	123	112	104	95	86	78	69	60	52	43
1,070	1,080	141	126	114	105	96	88	79	71	62	53	45
1,080	1,090	144	128	115	107	98	89	81	72	63	55	46
1,090	1,100	147	131	117	108	99	91	82	74	65	56	48
1,100	1,110	149	134	118	110	101	92	84	75	66	58	49
1,110	1,120	152	136	121	111	102	94	85	77	68	59	51
1,120	1,130	155	139	123	113	104	95	87	78	69	61	52
1,130	1,140	157	142	126	114	105	97	88	80	71	62	54
1,140	1,150	160	144	129	116	107	98	90	81	72	64	55
1,150	1,160	163	147	132	117	108	100	91	83	74	65	57
1,160	1,170	165	150	134	119	110	101	93	84	75	67	58
1,170	1,180	168	153	137	121	111	103	94	86	77	68	60
1,180	1,190	171	155	140	124	113	104	96	87	78	70	61
1,190	1,200	174	158	142	127	114	106	97	89	80	71	63
1,200	1,210	176	161	145	130	116	107	99	90	81	73	64
1,210	1,220	179	163	148	132	117	109	100	92	83	74	66
1,220	1,230	182	166	150	135	119	110	102	93	84	76	67
1,230	1,240	184	169	153	138	122	112	103	95	86	77	69
1,240	1,250	187	171	156	140	125	113	105	96	87	79	70
1,250	1,260	190	174	159	143	127	115	106	98	89	80	72
1,260	1,270	192	177	161	146	130	116	108	99	90	82	73
1,270	1,280	195	180	164	148	133	118	109	101	92	83	75
1,280	1,290	198	182	167	151	136	120	111	102	93	85	76
1,290	1,300	201	185	169	154	138	123	112	104	95	86	78
1,300	1,310	203	188	172	157	141	125	114	105	96	88	79
1,310	1,320	206	190	175	159	144	128	115	107	98	89	81
1,320	1,330	209	193	177	162	146	131	117	108	99	91	82
1,330	1,340	211	196	180	165	149	133	118	110	101	92	84
1,340	1,350	214	198	183	167	152	136	121	111	102	94	85
1,350	1,360	217	201	186	170	154	139	123	113	104	95	87
1,360	1,370	219	204	188	173	157	142	126	114	105	97	88
1,370	1,380	222	207	191	175	160	144	129	116	107	98	90
1,380	1,390	225	209	194	178	163	147	131	117	108	100	91
1,390	1,400	228	212	196	181	165	150	134	119	110	101	93

Form **1040EZ**

Department of the Treasury—Internal Revenue Service

Income Tax Return for Single and Joint Filers with No Dependents   (99)

OMB No. 1545-0675

Label

Use the IRS label. Otherwise, please print or type.

L A B E L   H E R E

| Your first name and initial | Last name | Your Social Security number |
| If a joint return, spouse's first name and initial | Last name | Spouse's Social Security number |

Home address (number and street).   Apt. no.

City, town or post office, state, and ZIP code.

▲ **Important!** ▲

You **must** enter your SSN(s) above.

Presidential Election Campaign ▶

Note. Checking "Yes" will not change your tax or reduce your refund.

Do you, or your spouse if a joint return, want $3 to go to this fund? . . . . . . ▶

You   Spouse

☐ Yes ☐ No   ☐ Yes ☐ No

Income

Attach Form(s) W-2 here.
Enclose, but do not attach, any payment.

Note. You **must** check Yes or No.

1 Total wages, salaries, and tips. This should be shown in box 1 of your W-2 form(s). Attach your W-2 form(s).   1

2 Taxable interest. If the total is over $1,500, you cannot use Form 1040EZ.   2

3 Unemployment compensation and Alaska Permanent Fund dividends   3

4 Add lines 1, 2, and 3. This is your **adjusted gross income.**   4

5 Can your parents (or someone else) claim you on their return?

   Yes. Enter amount from   **No.** If **single,** enter $7,700.
   ☐ worksheet on back.   ☐ If **married,** enter $13,850.
                     See back for explanation.   5

6 Subtract line 5 from line 4. If line 5 is larger than line 4, enter -0-. This is your **taxable income.**   ▶   6

Payments and tax

7 Federal income tax withheld from box 2 of your W-2 form(s).   7

8 **Earned income credit (EIC).**   8

9 Add lines 7 and 8. These are your **total payments.**   ▶   9

10 **Tax.** Use the amount on **line 6 above** to find your tax in the tax table. Then, enter the tax from the table on this line.   10

Refund

Have it directly deposited!

11a If line 9 is larger than line 10, subtract line 10 from line 9. This is your **refund.**   ▶   11a

▶ **b** Routing number ☐☐☐☐☐☐☐☐☐   ▶ **c** Type: ☐ Checking ☐ Savings

▶ **d** Account number ☐☐☐☐☐☐☐☐☐☐☐☐☐☐☐☐☐

Amount you owe

12 If line 10 is larger than line 9, subtract line 9 from line 10. This is the **amount you owe.**   ▶   12

Third party designee

Do you want to allow another person to discuss this return with the IRS?   ☐ **Yes.** Complete the following.   ☐ **No**

Designee's name ▶ _____   Phone no. ▶ (   )   Personal identification number (PIN) ☐☐☐☐☐

Sign here

Keep a copy for your records.

Under penalties of perjury, I declare that I have examined this return, and to the best of my knowledge and belief, it is true, correct, and accurately lists all amounts and sources of income I received during the tax year. Declaration of preparer (other than the taxpayer) is based on all information of which the preparer has any knowledge.

| Your signature | Date | Your occupation | Daytime phone number (   ) |
| Spouse's signature. If a joint return, **both** must sign. | Date | Spouse's occupation | |

Paid preparer's use only

Preparer's signature ▶	Date	Check if self-employed ☐	Preparer's SSN or PTIN
Firm's name (or yours if self-employed), address, and ZIP code ▶		EIN	
		Phone no. ( )	

Form **1040EZ**

Form 1040EZ

Use this form if

- Your filing status is single or married filing jointly.
- You (and your spouse if married) were under 65 and not blind at the end of 20--. If you were born on January 1, 1938, you are considered to be age 65 at the end of 20--.
- You do not claim any dependents.
- Your taxable income (line 6) is less than $50,000.
- You do not claim a deduction for educator expenses, the student loan interest deduction, or the tuition and fees deduction.
- You do not claim an education credit, the retirement savings contributions credit, or the health insurance credit for eligible recipients.
- You had **only** wages, salaries, tips, taxable scholarship or fellowship grants, unemployment compensation, or Alaska Permanent Fund dividends, and your taxable interest was not over $1,500. **But** if you earned tips, including allocated tips, that are not included in box 5 and box 7 of your W-2, you may not be able to use Form 1040EZ.
- You did not receive any advance earned income credit payments.

Filling in your return

If you received a scholarship or fellowship grant or tax-exempt interest income, such as on municipal bonds, see the booklet before filling in the form. Also, see the booklet if you received a Form 1099-INT showing Federal income tax withheld or if Federal income tax was withheld from your unemployment compensation or Alaska Permanent Fund dividends.

Remember, you must report all wages, salaries, and tips even if you do not get a W-2 form from your employer. You must also report all your taxable interest, including interest from banks, savings and loans, credit unions, etc., even if you do not get a Form 1099-INT.

Worksheet for dependents who checked "Yes" on line 5

(keep a copy for your records)

Use this worksheet to figure the amount to enter on line 5 if someone can claim you (or your spouse if married) as a dependent, even if that person chooses not to do so. To find out if someone can claim you as a dependent.

A. Amount, if any, from line 1 on front

+ 250.00   Enter total ▶ **A.** _____

B. Minimum standard deduction . . . . **B.** 750.00

C. Enter the **larger** of line A or line B here . . . . **C.** _____

D. Maximum standard deduction. If **single,** enter $4,700; if **married,** enter $7,850 . . . . **D.** _____

E. Enter the **smaller** of line C or line D here. This is your standard deduction . . . . **E.** _____

F. Exemption amount.

- If single, enter -0-.
- If married and—

—both you and your spouse can be claimed as dependents, enter -0-.

—only one of you can be claimed as a dependent, enter $3,000. } **F.** _____

G. Add lines E and F. Enter the total here and on line 5 on the front . . **G.** _____

If you checked "No" on line 5 because no one can claim you (or your spouse if married) as a dependent, enter on line 5 the amount shown below that applies to you.

- Single, enter $7,700. This is the total of your standard deduction ($4,700) and your exemption ($3,000).
- Married, enter $13,850. This is the total of your standard deduction ($7,850), your exemption ($3,000), and your spouse's exemption ($3,000).

Mailing return

Mail your return by **April 15.** Use the envelope that came with your booklet. If you do not have that envelope or if you moved during the year, see the back cover for the address to use.

✿   Form **1040EZ**

Annual Percentage Rate Table for Monthly Payment Plans

# of Pmts. ▼	Annual Percentage Rate (Finance Charge per $100 of Amount Financed)									
	2.00%	2.25%	2.50%	2.75%	3.00%	3.25%	3.50%	3.75%	4.00%	4.25%
6	$ 0.58	$ 0.66	$ 0.73	$ 0.80	$ 0.88	$ 0.95	$ 1.02	$ 1.10	$ 1.17	$ 1.24
12	1.09	1.22	1.36	1.50	1.63	1.77	1.91	2.04	2.18	2.32
18	1.59	1.79	1.99	2.19	2.39	2.59	2.79	2.99	3.20	3.40
24	2.10	2.36	2.62	2.89	3.15	3.42	3.69	3.95	4.22	4.49
30	2.60	2.93	3.26	3.59	3.92	4.25	4.58	4.92	5.25	5.58
36	3.11	3.51	3.90	4.30	4.69	5.09	5.49	5.89	6.29	6.69
42	3.62	4.08	4.54	5.00	5.47	5.93	6.40	6.86	7.33	7.80
48	4.14	4.66	5.19	5.72	6.24	6.78	7.31	7.84	8.38	8.92
54	4.65	5.24	5.83	6.43	7.03	7.63	8.23	8.83	9.44	10.04
60	5.17	5.82	6.48	7.15	7.81	8.48	9.15	9.82	10.50	11.18
	4.50%	4.75%	5.00%	5.25%	5.50%	5.75%	6.00%	6.25%	6.50%	6.75%
6	$ 1.32	$ 1.39	$ 1.46	$ 1.54	$ 1.61	$ 1.68	$ 1.76	$ 1.83	$ 1.90	$ 1.98
12	2.45	2.59	2.73	2.87	3.00	3.14	3.28	3.42	3.56	3.69
18	3.60	3.80	4.00	4.21	4.41	4.61	4.82	5.02	5.22	5.43
24	4.75	5.02	5.29	5.56	5.83	6.10	6.37	6.64	6.91	7.18
30	5.92	6.25	6.59	6.92	7.26	7.60	7.94	8.28	8.61	8.96
36	7.09	7.49	7.90	8.30	8.71	9.11	9.52	9.93	10.34	10.75
42	8.27	8.74	9.91	9.69	10.16	10.64	11.12	11.60	12.08	12.56
48	9.46	10.00	10.54	11.09	11.63	12.18	12.73	13.28	13.83	14.39
54	10.65	11.26	11.88	12.49	13.11	13.73	14.36	14.98	15.61	16.23
60	11.86	12.54	13.23	13.92	14.61	15.30	16.00	16.70	17.40	18.10
	7.00%	7.25%	7.50%	7.75%	8.00%	8.25%	8.50%	8.75%	9.00%	9.25%
6	$ 2.05	$ 2.13	$ 2.20	$ 2.27	$ 2.35	$ 2.42	$ 2.49	$ 2.57	$ 2.64	$ 2.72
12	3.83	3.97	4.11	4.25	4.39	4.52	4.66	4.80	4.94	5.08
18	5.63	5.84	6.04	6.25	6.45	6.66	6.86	7.07	7.28	7.48
24	7.45	7.73	8.00	8.27	8.55	8.82	9.09	9.37	9.64	9.92
30	9.30	9.64	9.98	10.32	10.66	11.01	11.35	11.70	12.04	12.39
36	11.16	11.57	11.98	12.40	12.81	13.23	13.64	14.06	14.48	14.90
42	13.04	13.52	14.01	14.50	14.98	15.47	15.96	16.45	16.95	17.44
48	14.94	15.50	16.06	16.62	17.18	17.75	18.31	18.88	19.45	20.02
54	16.86	17.50	18.13	18.77	19.41	20.05	20.69	21.34	21.98	22.63
60	18.81	19.52	20.23	20.94	21.66	22.38	23.10	23.82	24.55	25.28
	9.50%	9.75%	10.00%	10.25%	10.50%	10.75%	11.00%	11.25%	11.50%	11.75%
6	$ 2.79	$ 2.86	$ 2.94	$ 3.01	$ 3.08	$ 3.16	$ 3.23	$ 3.31	$ 3.38	$ 3.45
12	5.22	5.36	5.50	5.64	5.78	5.92	6.06	6.20	6.34	6.48
18	7.69	7.90	8.10	8.31	8.52	8.73	8.93	9.14	9.35	9.56
24	10.19	10.47	10.75	11.02	11.30	11.58	11.86	12.14	12.42	12.70
30	12.74	13.09	13.43	13.78	14.13	14.48	14.83	15.19	15.54	15.89
36	15.32	15.74	16.16	16.58	17.01	17.43	17.86	18.29	18.71	19.14
42	17.94	18.43	18.93	19.43	19.93	20.43	20.93	21.44	21.94	22.45
48	20.59	21.16	21.74	22.32	22.90	23.48	24.06	24.64	25.23	25.81
54	23.28	23.94	24.59	25.25	25.91	26.57	27.23	27.90	28.56	29.23
60	26.01	26.75	27.48	28.22	28.96	29.71	30.45	31.20	31.96	32.71

Annual Percentage Rate Table for Monthly Payment Plans

# of Pmts. ▼	Annual Percentage Rate (Finance Charge per $100 of Amount Financed)									
	12.00%	12.25%	12.50%	12.75%	13.00%	13.25%	13.50%	13.75%	14.00%	14.25%
6	$ 3.53	$ 3.60	$ 3.68	$ 3.75	$ 3.83	$ 3.90	$ 3.97	$ 4.05	$ 4.12	$ 4.20
12	6.62	6.76	6.90	7.04	7.18	7.32	7.46	7.60	7.74	7.89
18	9.77	9.98	10.19	10.40	10.61	10.82	11.03	11.24	11.45	11.66
24	12.98	13.26	13.54	13.82	14.10	14.38	14.66	14.95	15.23	15.51
30	16.24	16.60	16.95	17.31	17.66	18.02	18.38	18.74	19.10	19.45
36	19.57	20.00	20.43	20.87	21.30	21.73	22.17	22.60	23.04	23.48
42	22.96	23.47	23.98	24.49	25.00	25.51	26.03	26.55	27.06	27.58
48	26.40	26.99	27.58	28.18	28.77	29.37	29.97	30.57	31.17	31.77
54	29.91	30.58	31.25	31.93	32.61	33.29	33.98	34.66	35.35	36.04
60	33.47	34.23	34.99	35.75	36.52	37.29	38.06	38.83	39.61	40.39
	14.50%	14.75%	15.00%	15.25%	15.50%	15.75%	16.00%	16.25%	16.50%	16.75%
6	$ 4.27	$ 4.35	$ 4.42	$ 4.49	$ 4.57	$ 4.64	$ 4.72	$ 4.79	$ 4.87	$ 4.94
12	8.03	8.17	8.31	8.45	8.59	8.74	8.88	9.02	9.16	9.30
18	11.87	12.08	12.29	12.50	12.72	12.93	13.14	13.35	13.57	13.78
24	15.80	16.08	16.37	16.65	16.94	17.22	17.51	17.80	18.09	18.37
30	19.81	20.17	20.54	20.90	21.26	21.62	21.99	22.35	22.72	23.08
36	23.92	24.35	24.80	25.24	25.68	26.12	26.57	27.01	27.46	27.90
42	28.10	28.62	29.15	29.67	30.19	30.72	31.25	31.78	32.31	32.84
48	32.37	32.98	33.59	34.20	34.81	35.42	36.03	36.65	37.27	37.88
54	36.73	37.42	38.12	38.82	39.52	40.22	40.92	41.63	42.33	43.04
60	41.17	41.95	42.74	43.53	44.32	45.11	45.91	46.71	47.51	48.31
	17.00%	17.25%	17.50%	17.75%	18.00%	18.25%	18.50%	18.75%	19.00%	19.25%	19.50%
6	$ 5.02	$ 5.09	$ 5.17	$ 5.24	$ 5.32	$ 5.39	$ 5.46	$ 5.54	$ 5.61	$ 5.69	$ 5.76
12	9.45	9.59	9.73	9.87	10.02	10.16	10.30	10.44	10.59	10.73	10.87
18	13.99	14.21	14.42	14.64	14.85	15.07	15.28	15.49	15.71	15.93	16.14
24	18.66	18.95	19.24	19.53	19.82	20.11	20.40	20.69	20.98	21.27	21.56
30	23.45	23.81	24.18	24.55	24.92	25.29	25.66	26.03	26.40	26.77	27.14
36	28.35	28.80	29.25	29.70	30.15	30.60	31.05	31.51	31.96	32.42	32.87
42	33.37	33.90	34.44	34.97	35.51	36.05	36.59	37.13	37.67	38.21	38.76
48	38.50	39.13	39.75	40.37	41.00	41.63	42.26	42.89	43.52	44.15	44.79
54	43.75	44.47	45.18	45.90	46.62	47.34	48.06	48.79	49.51	50.24	50.97
60	49.12	49.92	50.73	51.55	52.36	53.18	54.00	54.82	55.64	56.47	57.30
	19.75%	20.00%	20.25%	20.50%	20.75%	21.00%	21.25%	21.50%	21.75%	22.00%	22.25%
6	$ 5.84	$ 5.91	$ 5.99	$ 6.06	$ 6.14	$ 6.21	$ 6.29	$ 6.36	$ 6.44	$ 6.51	$ 6.59
12	11.02	11.16	11.31	11.45	11.59	11.74	11.88	12.02	12.17	12.31	12.46
18	16.36	16.57	16.79	17.01	17.22	17.44	17.66	17.88	18.09	18.31	18.53
24	21.86	22.15	22.44	22.74	23.03	23.33	23.62	23.92	24.21	24.51	24.80
30	27.52	27.89	28.26	28.64	29.01	29.39	29.77	30.14	30.52	30.90	31.28
36	33.33	33.79	34.25	34.71	35.17	35.63	36.09	36.56	37.02	37.49	37.95
42	39.30	39.85	40.40	40.95	41.50	42.05	42.60	43.15	43.71	44.26	44.82
48	45.43	46.07	46.71	47.35	47.99	48.64	49.28	49.93	50.58	51.23	51.88
54	51.70	52.44	53.17	53.91	54.65	55.39	56.14	56.88	57.63	58.38	59.13
60	58.13	58.96	59.80	60.64	61.48	62.32	63.17	64.01	64.86	65.71	66.57

Amount of $1.00 at 5.5 Percent, Compounded Daily (365-Day Year)

Day	Amount	Day	Amount	Day	Amount	Day	Amount	Day	Amount
1	1.00015	11	1.00165	21	1.00316	31	1.00468	50	1.00755
2	1.00030	12	1.00180	22	1.00331	32	1.00483	60	1.00907
3	1.00045	13	1.00196	23	1.00347	33	1.00498	70	1.01059
4	1.00060	14	1.00211	24	1.00362	34	1.00513	80	1.01212
5	1.00075	15	1.00226	25	1.00377	35	1.00528	90	1.01364
6	1.00090	16	1.00241	26	1.00392	36	1.00543	100	1.01517
7	1.00105	17	1.00256	27	1.00407	37	1.00558	110	1.01670
8	1.00120	18	1.00271	28	1.00422	38	1.00574	120	1.01823
9	1.00135	19	1.00286	29	1.00437	39	1.00589	130	1.01977
10	1.00150	20	1.00301	30	1.00452	40	1.00604	140	1.02131

Elapsed Time Table

The Number of Each Day of the Year

Day No.	Jan.	Feb.	Mar.	Apr.	May	June	July	Aug.	Sept.	Oct.	Nov.	Dec.
1	1	32	60	91	121	152	182	213	244	274	305	335
2	2	33	61	92	122	153	183	214	245	275	306	336
3	3	34	62	93	123	154	184	215	246	276	307	337
4	4	35	63	94	124	155	185	216	247	277	308	338
5	5	36	64	95	125	156	186	217	248	278	309	339
6	6	37	65	96	126	157	187	218	249	279	310	340
7	7	38	66	97	127	158	188	219	250	280	311	341
8	8	39	67	98	128	159	189	220	251	281	312	342
9	9	40	68	99	129	160	190	221	252	282	313	343
10	10	41	69	100	130	161	191	222	253	283	314	344
11	11	42	70	101	131	162	192	223	254	284	315	345
12	12	43	71	102	132	163	193	224	255	285	316	346
13	13	44	72	103	133	164	194	225	256	286	317	347
14	14	45	73	104	134	165	195	226	257	287	318	348
15	15	46	74	105	135	166	196	227	258	288	319	349
16	16	47	75	106	136	167	197	228	259	289	320	350
17	17	48	76	107	137	168	198	229	260	290	321	351
18	18	49	77	108	138	169	199	230	261	291	322	352
19	19	50	78	109	139	170	200	231	262	292	323	353
20	20	51	79	110	140	171	201	232	263	293	324	354
21	21	52	80	111	141	172	202	233	264	294	325	355
22	22	53	81	112	142	173	203	234	265	295	326	356
23	23	54	82	113	143	174	204	235	266	296	327	357
24	24	55	83	114	144	175	205	236	267	297	328	358
25	25	56	84	115	145	176	206	237	268	298	329	359
26	26	57	85	116	146	177	207	238	269	299	330	360
27	27	58	86	117	147	178	208	239	270	300	331	361
28	28	59*	87	118	148	179	209	240	271	301	332	362
29	29		88	119	149	180	210	241	272	302	333	363
30	30		89	120	150	181	211	242	273	303	334	364
31	31		90		151		212	243		304		365

*Add one day for February 29 for leap year. (Leap years are 2004, 2008, and so on.)

Compound Interest—Amount of $1.00

Period "n"	Rate per Period									
	1.000%	1.250%	1.375%	1.500%	2.000%	2.500%	2.750%	2.875%	3.000%	3.125%
1	1.01000	1.01250	1.01375	1.01500	1.02000	1.02500	1.02750	1.02875	1.03000	1.03125
2	1.02010	1.02516	1.02769	1.03023	1.04040	1.05063	1.05576	1.05833	1.06090	1.06348
3	1.03030	1.03797	1.04182	1.04568	1.06121	1.07689	1.08479	1.08875	1.09273	1.09671
4	1.04060	1.05095	1.05614	1.06136	1.08243	1.10381	1.11462	1.12006	1.12551	1.13098
5	1.05101	1.06408	1.07067	1.07728	1.10408	1.13141	1.14527	1.15226	1.15927	1.16633
6	1.06152	1.07738	1.08539	1.09344	1.12616	1.15969	1.17677	1.18538	1.19405	1.20277
7	1.07214	1.09085	1.10031	1.10984	1.14869	1.18869	1.20913	1.21946	1.22987	1.24036
8	1.08286	1.10449	1.11544	1.12649	1.17166	1.21840	1.24238	1.25452	1.26677	1.27912
9	1.09369	1.11829	1.13078	1.14339	1.19509	1.24886	1.27655	1.29059	1.30477	1.31909
10	1.10462	1.13227	1.14633	1.16054	1.21899	1.28008	1.31165	1.32770	1.34392	1.36032
11	1.11567	1.14642	1.16209	1.17795	1.24337	1.31209	1.34772	1.36587	1.38423	1.40283
12	1.12683	1.16075	1.17807	1.19562	1.26824	1.34489	1.38478	1.40514	1.42576	1.44666
13	1.13809	1.17526	1.19427	1.21355	1.29361	1.37851	1.42287	1.44553	1.46853	1.49187
14	1.14947	1.18995	1.21069	1.23176	1.31948	1.41297	1.46199	1.48709	1.51259	1.53849
15	1.16097	1.20483	1.22733	1.25023	1.34587	1.44830	1.50220	1.52985	1.55797	1.58657
16	1.17258	1.21989	1.24421	1.26899	1.37279	1.48451	1.54351	1.57383	1.60471	1.63615
17	1.18430	1.23514	1.26132	1.28802	1.40024	1.52162	1.58596	1.61908	1.65285	1.68728
18	1.19615	1.25058	1.27866	1.30734	1.42825	1.55966	1.62957	1.66563	1.70243	1.74001
19	1.20811	1.26621	1.29624	1.32695	1.45681	1.59865	1.67438	1.71351	1.75351	1.79438
20	1.22019	1.28204	1.31407	1.34686	1.48595	1.63862	1.72043	1.76278	1.80611	1.85046
21	1.23239	1.29806	1.33213	1.36706	1.51567	1.67958	1.76774	1.81346	1.86029	1.90828
22	1.24472	1.31429	1.35045	1.38756	1.54598	1.72157	1.81635	1.86559	1.91610	1.96792
23	1.25716	1.33072	1.36902	1.40838	1.57690	1.76461	1.86630	1.91923	1.97359	2.02942
24	1.26973	1.34735	1.38784	1.42950	1.60844	1.80873	1.91763	1.97441	2.03279	2.09284
25	1.28243	1.36419	1.40693	1.45095	1.64061	1.85394	1.97036	2.03117	2.09378	2.15824
26	1.29526	1.38125	1.42627	1.47271	1.67342	1.90029	2.02455	2.08957	2.15659	2.22568
27	1.30821	1.39851	1.44588	1.49480	1.70689	1.94780	2.08022	2.14964	2.22129	2.29523
28	1.32129	1.41599	1.46576	1.51722	1.74102	1.99650	2.13743	2.21144	2.28793	2.36696
29	1.33450	1.43369	1.48592	1.53998	1.77584	2.04641	2.19621	2.27502	2.35657	2.44093
30	1.34785	1.45161	1.50635	1.56308	1.81136	2.09757	2.25660	2.34043	2.42726	2.51721
31	1.36133	1.46976	1.52706	1.58653	1.84759	2.15001	2.31866	2.40772	2.50008	2.59587
32	1.37494	1.48813	1.54806	1.61032	1.88454	2.20376	2.38242	2.47694	2.57508	2.67699
33	1.38869	1.50673	1.56935	1.63448	1.92223	2.25885	2.44794	2.54815	2.65234	2.76065
34	1.40258	1.52557	1.59092	1.65900	1.96068	2.31532	2.51526	2.62141	2.73191	2.84692
35	1.41660	1.54464	1.61280	1.68388	1.99989	2.37321	2.58443	2.69677	2.81386	2.93588
36	1.43077	1.56394	1.63498	1.70914	2.03989	2.43254	2.65550	2.77431	2.89828	3.02763
37	1.44508	1.58349	1.65746	1.73478	2.08069	2.49335	2.72852	2.85407	2.98523	3.12224
38	1.45953	1.60329	1.68025	1.76080	2.12230	2.55568	2.80356	2.93612	3.07478	3.21981
39	1.47412	1.62333	1.70335	1.78721	2.16474	2.61957	2.88066	3.02054	3.16703	3.32043
40	1.48886	1.64362	1.72677	1.81402	2.20804	2.68506	2.95987	3.10738	3.26204	3.42419
41	1.50375	1.66416	1.75051	1.84123	2.25220	2.75219	3.04127	3.19671	3.35990	3.53120
42	1.51879	1.68497	1.77458	1.86885	2.29724	2.82100	3.12491	3.28862	3.46070	3.64155
43	1.53398	1.70603	1.79898	1.89688	2.34319	2.89152	3.21084	3.38317	3.56452	3.75535
44	1.54932	1.72735	1.82372	1.92533	2.39005	2.96381	3.29914	3.48043	3.67145	3.87270
45	1.56481	1.74895	1.84880	1.95421	2.43785	3.03790	3.38986	3.58050	3.78160	3.99373
46	1.58046	1.77081	1.87422	1.98353	2.48661	3.11385	3.48309	3.68344	3.89504	4.11853
47	1.59626	1.79294	1.89999	2.01328	2.53634	3.19170	3.57887	3.78933	4.01190	4.24723
48	1.61223	1.81535	1.92611	2.04348	2.58707	3.27149	3.67729	3.89828	4.13225	4.37996
49	1.62835	1.83805	1.95260	2.07413	2.63881	3.35328	3.77842	4.01035	4.25622	4.51683
50	1.64463	1.86102	1.97944	2.10524	2.69159	3.43711	3.88232	4.12565	4.38391	4.65798

APPENDIX

Future Value of an Ordinary Annuity for $1.00 per Period

Period "n"	Rate per Period									
	0.50%	1.00%	1.50%	2.00%	3.00%	4.00%	5.00%	6.00%	7.00%	8.00%
1	$ 1.00000	$ 1.00000	$ 1.00000	$ 1.00000	$ 1.00000	$ 1.00000	$ 1.00000	$ 1.00000	$ 1.00000	$ 1.00000
2	2.00500	2.01000	2.01500	2.02000	2.03000	2.04000	2.05000	2.06000	2.07000	2.08000
3	3.01502	3.03010	3.04522	3.06040	3.09090	3.12160	3.15250	3.18360	3.21490	3.24640
4	4.03010	4.06040	4.09090	4.12161	4.18363	4.24646	4.31013	4.37462	4.43994	4.50611
5	5.05025	5.10101	5.15227	5.20404	5.30914	5.41632	5.52563	5.63709	5.75074	5.86660
6	6.07550	6.15202	6.22955	6.30812	6.46841	6.63298	6.80191	6.97532	7.15329	7.33593
7	7.10588	7.21354	7.32299	7.43428	7.66246	7.89829	8.14201	8.39384	8.65402	8.92280
8	8.14141	8.28567	8.43284	8.58297	8.89234	9.21423	9.54911	9.89747	10.25980	10.63663
9	9.18212	9.36853	9.55933	9.75463	10.15911	10.58280	11.02656	11.49132	11.97799	12.48756
10	10.22803	10.46221	10.70272	10.94972	11.46388	12.00611	12.57789	13.18079	13.81645	14.48656
11	11.27917	11.56683	11.86326	12.16872	12.80780	13.48635	14.20679	14.97164	15.78360	16.64549
12	12.33556	12.68250	13.04121	13.41209	14.19203	15.02581	15.91713	16.86994	17.88845	18.97713
13	13.39724	13.80933	14.23683	14.68033	15.61779	16.62684	17.71298	18.88214	20.14064	21.49530
14	14.46423	14.94742	15.45038	15.97394	17.08632	18.29191	19.59863	21.01507	22.55049	24.21492
15	15.53655	16.09690	16.68214	17.29342	18.59891	20.02359	21.57856	23.27597	25.12902	27.15211
16	16.61423	17.25786	17.93237	18.63929	20.15688	21.82453	23.65749	25.67253	27.88805	30.32428
17	17.69730	18.43044	19.20136	20.01207	21.76159	23.69751	25.84037	28.21288	30.84022	33.75023
18	18.78579	19.61475	20.48938	21.41231	23.41444	25.64541	28.13238	30.90565	33.99903	37.45024
19	19.87972	20.81090	21.79672	22.84056	25.11687	27.67123	30.53900	33.75999	37.37896	41.44626
20	20.97912	22.01900	23.12367	24.29737	26.87037	29.77808	33.06595	36.78559	40.99549	45.76196
21	22.08401	23.23919	24.47052	25.78332	28.67649	31.96920	35.71925	39.99273	44.86518	50.42292
22	23.19443	24.47159	25.83758	27.29898	30.53678	34.24797	38.50521	43.39229	49.00574	55.45676
23	24.31040	25.71630	27.22514	28.84496	32.45288	36.61789	41.43048	46.99583	53.43614	60.89330
24	25.43196	26.97346	28.63352	30.42186	34.42647	39.08260	44.50200	50.81558	58.17667	66.76476
25	26.55912	28.24320	30.06302	32.03030	36.45926	41.64591	47.72710	54.86451	63.24904	73.10594
26	27.69191	29.52563	31.51397	33.67091	38.55304	44.31174	51.11345	59.15638	68.67647	79.95442
27	28.83037	30.82089	32.98668	35.34432	40.70963	47.08421	54.66913	63.70577	74.48382	87.35077
28	29.97452	32.12910	34.48148	37.05121	42.93092	49.96758	58.40258	68.52811	80.69769	95.33883
29	31.12439	33.45039	35.99870	38.79223	45.21885	52.96629	62.32271	73.63980	87.34653	103.96594
30	32.28002	34.78489	37.53868	40.56808	47.57542	56.08494	66.43885	79.05819	94.46079	113.28321
31	33.44142	36.13274	39.10176	42.37944	50.00268	59.32834	70.76079	84.80168	102.07304	123.34587
32	34.60862	37.49407	40.68829	44.22703	52.50276	62.70147	75.29883	90.88978	110.21815	134.21354
33	35.78167	38.86901	42.29861	46.11157	55.07784	66.20953	80.06377	97.34316	118.93343	145.95062
34	36.96058	40.25770	43.93309	48.03380	57.73018	69.85791	85.06696	104.18375	128.25876	158.62667
35	38.14538	41.66028	45.59209	49.99448	60.46208	73.65222	90.32031	111.43478	138.23688	172.31680
36	39.33610	43.07688	47.27597	51.99437	63.27594	77.59831	95.83632	119.12087	148.91346	187.10215
37	40.53279	44.50765	48.98511	54.03425	66.17422	81.70225	101.62814	127.26812	160.33740	203.07032
38	41.73545	45.95272	50.71989	56.11494	69.15945	85.97034	107.70955	135.90421	172.56102	220.31595
39	42.94413	47.41225	52.48068	58.23724	72.23423	90.40915	114.09502	145.05846	185.64029	238.94122
40	44.15885	48.88637	54.26789	60.40198	75.40126	95.02552	120.79977	154.76197	199.63511	259.05652
41	45.37964	50.37524	56.08191	62.61002	78.66330	99.82654	127.83976	165.04768	214.60957	280.78104
42	46.60654	51.87899	57.92314	64.86222	82.02320	104.81960	135.23175	175.95054	230.63224	304.24352
43	47.83957	53.39778	59.79199	67.15947	85.48389	110.01238	142.99334	187.50758	247.77650	329.58301
44	49.07877	54.93176	61.68887	69.50266	89.04841	115.41288	151.14301	199.75803	266.12085	356.94965
45	50.32416	56.48107	63.61420	71.89271	92.71986	121.02939	159.70016	212.74351	285.74931	386.50562
46	51.57578	58.04589	65.56841	74.33056	96.50146	126.87057	168.68516	226.50812	306.75176	418.42607
47	52.83366	59.62634	67.55194	76.81718	100.39650	132.94539	178.11942	241.09861	329.22439	452.90015
48	54.09783	61.22261	69.56522	79.35352	104.40840	139.26321	188.02539	256.56453	353.27009	490.13216
49	55.36832	62.83483	71.60870	81.94059	108.54065	145.83373	198.42666	272.95840	378.99900	530.34274
50	56.64516	64.46318	73.68283	84.57940	112.79687	152.66708	209.34800	290.33590	406.52893	573.77016

APPENDIX

Monthly Payment for a $1,000 Loan

Interest Rate	Length of Loan in Years						
	10	15	20	25	30	35	40
5.00%	$10.61	$ 7.91	$ 6.60	$ 5.85	$ 5.37	$ 5.05	$ 4.82
5.50%	10.85	8.17	6.88	6.14	5.68	5.37	5.16
6.00%	11.10	8.44	7.16	6.44	6.00	5.70	5.50
6.50%	11.35	8.71	7.46	6.75	6.32	6.04	5.85
7.00%	11.61	8.99	7.75	7.07	6.65	6.39	6.21
7.50%	11.87	9.27	8.06	7.39	6.99	6.74	6.58
8.00%	12.13	9.56	8.36	7.72	7.34	7.10	6.95
8.50%	12.40	9.85	8.68	8.05	7.69	7.47	7.33
9.00%	12.67	10.14	9.00	8.39	8.05	7.84	7.71
9.50%	12.94	10.44	9.32	8.74	8.41	8.22	8.10
10.00%	13.22	10.75	9.65	9.09	8.78	8.60	8.49
10.50%	13.49	11.05	9.98	9.44	9.15	8.98	8.89
11.00%	13.78	11.37	10.32	9.80	9.52	9.37	9.28
11.50%	14.06	11.68	10.66	10.16	9.90	9.76	9.68
12.00%	14.35	12.00	11.01	10.53	10.29	10.16	10.08
12.50%	14.64	12.33	11.36	10.90	10.67	10.55	10.49
13.00%	14.93	12.65	11.72	11.28	11.06	10.95	10.90

Monthly Payment on a Simple Interest Installment Loan of $100

Term in Months	Annual Percentage Rate										
	8.00%	9.00%	10.00%	11.00%	12.00%	13.00%	14.00%	15.00%	16.00%	17.00%	18.00%
6	17.06	17.11	17.16	17.21	17.25	17.30	17.35	17.40	17.45	17.50	17.55
12	8.70	8.75	8.79	8.84	8.88	8.93	8.98	9.03	9.07	9.12	9.17
18	5.91	5.96	6.01	6.05	6.10	6.14	6.19	6.24	6.29	6.33	6.38
24	4.52	4.57	4.61	4.66	4.71	4.75	4.80	4.85	4.90	4.94	4.99
30	3.69	3.73	3.78	3.83	3.87	3.92	3.97	4.02	4.07	4.11	4.16
36	3.13	3.18	3.23	3.27	3.32	3.37	3.42	3.47	3.52	3.57	3.62
42	2.74	2.78	2.83	2.88	2.93	2.98	3.03	3.07	3.12	3.18	3.23
48	2.44	2.49	2.54	2.58	2.63	2.68	2.73	2.78	2.83	2.89	2.94
54	2.21	2.26	2.31	2.36	2.41	2.46	2.51	2.56	2.61	2.66	2.72
60	2.03	2.08	2.12	2.17	2.22	2.28	2.33	2.38	2.43	2.49	2.54

APPENDIX

Amount of $1.00 Invested—Daily, Monthly, and Quarterly Compounding						
Annual Rate	Interest Period—1 Year			Interest Period—4 Years		
	Daily	Monthly	Quarterly	Daily	Monthly	Quarterly
0.50%	1.005012	1.005011	1.005009	1.020201	1.020197	1.020189
0.75%	1.007528	1.007526	1.007521	1.030454	1.030445	1.030426
1.00%	1.010050	1.010046	1.010038	1.040810	1.040793	1.040759
1.25%	1.012578	1.012572	1.012559	1.051270	1.051244	1.051189
1.50%	1.015113	1.015104	1.015085	1.061835	1.061797	1.061717
1.75%	1.017654	1.017641	1.017615	1.072506	1.072453	1.072344
2.00%	1.020201	1.020184	1.020151	1.083285	1.083215	1.083071
2.25%	1.022754	1.022733	1.022691	1.094171	1.094082	1.093898
2.50%	1.025314	1.025288	1.025235	1.105167	1.105056	1.104827
2.75%	1.027881	1.027849	1.027785	1.116273	1.116138	1.115858
3.00%	1.030453	1.030416	1.030339	1.127491	1.127328	1.126992
3.25%	1.033032	1.032989	1.032898	1.138822	1.138628	1.138230
3.50%	1.035618	1.035567	1.035462	1.150266	1.150039	1.149574
3.75%	1.038210	1.038151	1.038031	1.161825	1.161563	1.161023
4.00%	1.040808	1.040742	1.040604	1.173501	1.173199	1.172579
4.25%	1.043413	1.043338	1.043182	1.185293	1.184949	1.184242
4.50%	1.046025	1.045940	1.045765	1.197204	1.196814	1.196015
4.75%	1.048643	1.048548	1.048353	1.209235	1.208796	1.207897
5.00%	1.051267	1.051162	1.050945	1.221386	1.220895	1.219890
5.25%	1.053899	1.053782	1.053543	1.233659	1.233113	1.231994
5.50%	1.056536	1.056408	1.056145	1.246056	1.245451	1.244211
5.75%	1.059180	1.059040	1.058752	1.258577	1.257909	1.256541
6.00%	1.061831	1.061678	1.061364	1.271224	1.270489	1.268986
6.25%	1.064489	1.064322	1.063980	1.283998	1.283193	1.281546
6.50%	1.067153	1.066972	1.066602	1.296900	1.296020	1.294222
6.75%	1.069824	1.069628	1.069228	1.309932	1.308974	1.307017
7.00%	1.072501	1.072290	1.071859	1.323094	1.322054	1.319929
7.25%	1.075185	1.074958	1.074495	1.336389	1.335262	1.332962
7.50%	1.077876	1.077633	1.077136	1.349817	1.348599	1.346114
7.75%	1.080573	1.080313	1.079782	1.363380	1.362067	1.359389
8.00%	1.083278	1.083000	1.082432	1.377079	1.375666	1.372786
8.25%	1.085989	1.085692	1.085088	1.390916	1.389398	1.386306
8.50%	1.088706	1.088391	1.087748	1.404892	1.403265	1.399952
8.75%	1.091431	1.091096	1.090413	1.419008	1.417267	1.413723
9.00%	1.094162	1.093807	1.093083	1.433266	1.431405	1.427621
9.25%	1.096900	1.096524	1.095758	1.447667	1.445682	1.441648
9.50%	1.099645	1.099248	1.098438	1.462212	1.460098	1.455803
9.75%	1.102397	1.101977	1.101123	1.476904	1.474655	1.470089
10.00%	1.105156	1.104713	1.103813	1.491743	1.489354	1.484506
10.25%	1.107921	1.107455	1.106508	1.506731	1.504196	1.499055
10.50%	1.110694	1.110203	1.109207	1.521870	1.519184	1.513738
10.75%	1.113473	1.112958	1.111912	1.537160	1.534317	1.528556
11.00%	1.116260	1.115719	1.114621	1.552604	1.549598	1.543509
11.25%	1.119053	1.118486	1.117336	1.568203	1.565028	1.558600
11.50%	1.121853	1.121259	1.120055	1.583959	1.580608	1.573829
11.75%	1.124660	1.124039	1.122779	1.599873	1.596341	1.589197
12.00%	1.127475	1.126825	1.125509	1.615947	1.612226	1.604706
12.25%	1.130296	1.129617	1.128243	1.632182	1.628266	1.620357
12.50%	1.133124	1.132416	1.130982	1.648580	1.644463	1.636151
12.75%	1.135960	1.135221	1.133727	1.665143	1.660817	1.652089
13.00%	1.138802	1.138032	1.136476	1.681872	1.677330	1.668173
13.25%	1.141652	1.140850	1.139230	1.698769	1.694005	1.684403

Conversion Tables

Time	
60 seconds (s) = 1 minute (min)	52 weeks = 1 year
60 minutes = 1 hour (h)	12 months = 1 year
24 hours = 1 day	100 years = 1 century
7 days = 1 week	

Metric System	
Length	**Volume**
10 millimeters (mm) = 1 centimeter (cm)	1,000 milliliters (mL) = 1 liter (L)
100 centimeters = 1 meter (m)	1,000 cubic centimeters (cm^3) = 1 liter
1,000 meters = 1 kilometer (km)	10 milliliters = 1 centiliter (cL)
	10 deciliters (dL) = 1 liter
Area	**Mass**
100 square millimeters (mm^2) = 1 square centimeter (cm^2)	1,000 milligrams (mg) = 1 gram (g)
10,000 square centimeters = 1 square meter (m^2)	1,000 grams = 1 kilogram (kg)
10,000 square meters = 1 hectare (ha)	1,000 kilograms = 1 metric ton (t)

Customary System	
Length	**Volume**
12 inches (in) = 1 foot (ft)	8 fluid ounces (oz) = 1 cup (c)
3 feet = 1 yard (yd)	2 cups = 1 pint (pt)
5,280 feet = 1 mile (mi)	2 pints = 1 quart (qt)
	4 quarts = 1 gallon (gal)
Area	**Weight**
144 square inches (in^2) = 1 square foot (ft^2)	16 ounces = 1 pound
9 square feet = 1 square yard (yd^2)	2,000 pounds = 1 ton (t)
4,837 square yards = 1 acre (A)	

Selected Answers

Workshop Answers

Workshop 1 *Self-Check* **1.** 24,366 **2.** 436.785
3. hundreds and thousandths **4.** Standard form: 5,456.68; Word form: five thousand four hundred fifty-six and sixty-eight hundredths; Point form: five four five six point six eight
5. Standard form: 56.817; Word form: fifty-six and eight hundred seventeen thousandths; Point form: five six point eight one seven **6.** Word form: eight hundred seventy-five and forty-eight one hundredth dollars or eight hundred seventy-five and $\frac{48}{100}$ dollars or eight hundred seventy-five dollars and forty-eight cents
Practice **7.** millions **9.** Word form: five hundred forty-three thousand, six hundred ninety-eight; Short word form: 543 thousand, 698 **11.** Standard form: 654,321; Word form: six hundred fifty-four thousand, three hundred twenty-one
13. $4,000 + 600 + 70 + 8$

Workshop 2 *Self-Check* **1.** 6,000 **2.** 5,693.3 **3.** 5,700
4. 5,693 **5.** $21.28 **6.** $967.46 **7.** $138.78 **8.** $647.56
Practice **9.** 16,000,000 **11.** 15,749,000 **13.** 15,750,000
15.

	Football Game	Number	Nearest Thousand	Nearest Hundred	Nearest Ten
a.	Austin Peavey	18,971	19,000	19,000	18,970
b.	Bowling Green	25,687	26,000	25,700	25,690
c.	Ohio University	20,119	20,000	20,100	20,120
d.	Western Michigan	24,567	25,000	24,600	24,570
e.	Central Michigan	19,424	19,000	19,400	19,420

Workshop 3 *Self-Check* **1.** 8,891 **2.** 7,521 **3.** 284.4
4. 0.06 *Practice* **5.** 29 **7.** 2.65 **9.** 0.4 **11.** 0.03
13. 1.36, 1.37, 1.39 **15.** 7.18, 7.38, 7.58 **17.** 40.004, 40.04, 40.4 **19.** 365.15, 365.490, 365.51 **21. a.** Science: 513.12, 519.03, 532.626, 571.113, 587.41 **b.** Literature: 11.7, 32.615, 34.9, 67.192, 94.79 **c.** Religion: 15.04, 18.7, 26.311, 46.94, 71.21 **d.** Language: 22.5, 38.9, 48.275, 67.21, 93.047

Workshop 4 *Self-Check* **1.** 70.88 **2.** 178.44 **3.** 222.86
4. 183.76 **5.** 365.475 **6.** 1,282.842 **7.** $597.36 **8.** $579.84
Practice **9.** 133.49 **11.** 871.76 **13.** 175.364 **15.** 14.082
17. 201.38 **19.** 22.4009 **21.** 601.234 **23.** 649.647
25. 1,128.894 **27.** 191.968 **29.** 124.03 **31.** 302.6016
33. $123.96 **35.** $289.17

Workshop 5 *Self-Check* **1.** 53.61 **2.** 38.3 **3.** 610.08
4. 68.76 *Practice* **5.** 63.30 **7.** 11.33 **9.** 39.30
11. 4.639 **13.** $67.69 **15.** $665.90 **17.** $264.03
19. $16,681.07 **21.** 117.5 **23.** 4.50 **25.** $863.15
27. a. $0.06 **b.** $0.88 **c.** $0.03 **d.** $2.00 **e.** $0.00
f. $1.89 **g.** $0.10 **h.** $2.58 **i.** $1.00 **j.** $0.16

Workshop 6 *Self-Check* **1.** 8.151 **2.** 89.452
3. 0.0858 **4.** 0.0592 **5.** $35.275 = $35.28 **6.** 714
7. 4,186.1 *Practice* **9.** 23.52 **11.** 37.224 **13.** 34.639
15. 0.0592 **17.** $437.75 **19.** $25.46 **21.** 57.1
23. 4,178.6 **25.** 7,195.6 **27.** 34,287.6

Workshop 7 *Self-Check* **1.** 6.2 **2.** 4.29 **3.** 36
4. $1.36 **5.** 0.79 **6.** 1.389 **7.** 9.8628 *Practice*
9. 3.5 **11.** 1.83 **13.** 12.002 = 12.00 **15.** 1.442
17. 4.298 **19.** 84.6265 **21.** 0.32129 **23.** 6.365218
25. 0.041549

Workshop 8 *Self-Check* **1.** $\frac{3}{4} \times \frac{5}{8} = \frac{3 \times 5}{4 \times 8} = \frac{15}{32}$
2. $\frac{7}{8} \times \frac{3}{8} = \frac{7 \times 3}{8 \times 8} = \frac{21}{64}$ **3.** $\frac{2}{3} \times 600 = \frac{2}{3} \times \frac{600}{1} = \frac{1,200}{3} = 400$ **4.** $\frac{3}{4} \times \frac{5}{9} = \frac{3 \times 5}{4 \times 9} = \frac{3 \times 5}{2 \times 2 \times 3 \times 3} = \frac{5}{12}$
5. $\frac{2}{15} \times \frac{5}{8} = \frac{2 \times 5}{3 \times 5 \times 2 \times 2 \times 2} = \frac{1}{3 \times 2 \times 2} = \frac{1}{12}$
6. $\frac{5}{6} \times 180 = \frac{5}{6} \times \frac{180}{1} = \frac{5 \times 6 \times 30}{6} = 150$
7. $4\frac{1}{2} \times 8 = \frac{9}{2} \times \frac{8}{1} = \frac{9 \times 2 \times 4}{2} = 36$
8. $3\frac{3}{5} \times 2\frac{2}{9} = \frac{18}{5} \times \frac{20}{9} = \frac{2 \times 9 \times 5 \times 4}{5 \times 9} = \frac{8}{1} = 8$
9. $4\frac{1}{2} \times 3\frac{1}{3} = \frac{9}{2} \times \frac{10}{3} = \frac{3 \times 3 \times 2 \times 5}{2 \times 3} = 15$
Practice **11.** $\frac{21}{40}$ **13.** $\frac{27}{50}$ **15.** 15 **17.** 440 **19.** $1\frac{1}{2}$
21. $\frac{6}{25}$ **23.** $27\frac{5}{8}$ **25.** $59\frac{3}{8}$ **27.** 238

Workshop 9 *Self-Check* **1.** $\frac{1}{5}$ **2.** $\frac{8}{9}$ **3.** $\frac{1}{10}$ **4.** $\frac{2}{5}$ **5.** $\frac{5}{6}$
6. $\frac{3}{8}$ **7.** $\frac{7}{5}$ **8.** 5 *Practice* **9.** $\frac{4}{3}$ **11.** $\frac{16}{3}$ **13.** $\frac{10}{1}$ **15.** $\frac{1}{15}$
17. $\frac{2}{3}$ **19.** $\frac{7}{24}$ **21.** $2\frac{5}{8}$ **23.** 16 **25.** $\frac{7}{128}$ **27.** 4 **29.** $7\frac{12}{13}$
31. 98 bags **33.** $3\frac{1}{2}$ quarts

Workshop 10 *Self-Check* **1.** $\frac{3}{3}$ or 1 **2.** $\frac{23}{18}$ or $1\frac{5}{18}$
3. $\frac{14}{7}$ or 2 **4.** $\frac{12}{9}$ or $1\frac{1}{3}$ **5.** $\frac{9}{8}$ or $1\frac{1}{8}$ **6.** $\frac{11}{6}$ or $1\frac{5}{6}$ **7.** $\frac{53}{30}$ or $1\frac{23}{30}$
8. $\frac{79}{60}$ or $1\frac{19}{60}$ *Practice* **9.** $\frac{22}{15}$ or $1\frac{7}{15}$ **11.** $\frac{19}{18}$ or $1\frac{1}{18}$ **13.** $\frac{65}{42}$ or $1\frac{23}{42}$ **15.** $\frac{65}{44}$ or $1\frac{21}{44}$ **17.** $\frac{59}{63}$ **19.** $\frac{193}{120}$ or $1\frac{73}{120}$ **21.** $\frac{16}{15}$ or $1\frac{1}{15}$
23. $\frac{13}{6}$ or $2\frac{1}{6}$ **25.** $\frac{41}{24}$ or $1\frac{17}{24}$ **27.** $\frac{77}{36}$ or $2\frac{5}{36}$ **29.** $\frac{101}{66}$ or $1\frac{35}{66}$
31. $\frac{89}{28}$ or $3\frac{5}{28}$ **33.** 2 **35.** $\frac{9}{10}$ **37.** $\frac{59}{60}$

Workshop 11 *Self-Check* **1.** $\frac{1}{2}$ **2.** $\frac{2}{3}$ **3.** $\frac{11}{12}$ **4.** $\frac{2}{29}$
5. $\frac{1}{4}$ **6.** $\frac{11}{24}$ **7.** $\frac{7}{60}$ **8.** $\frac{29}{60}$ **9.** $3\frac{3}{8}$ **10.** $4\frac{1}{4}$ **11.** $7\frac{5}{36}$ **12.** $\frac{1}{16}$
Practice **13.** $\frac{1}{3}$ **15.** $\frac{11}{17}$ **17.** $\frac{5}{24}$ **19.** $\frac{5}{24}$ **21.** $\frac{31}{63}$ **23.** $\frac{13}{30}$
25. $2\frac{5}{12}$ **27.** $7\frac{3}{10}$ **29.** $\frac{1}{24}$ **31.** $\frac{1}{12}$ **33.** $\frac{1}{5}$

Workshop 12 *Self-Check* **1.** $\frac{5}{8} < \frac{7}{8}$ **2.** $\frac{11}{12} > \frac{7}{12}$
3. $\frac{2}{3} > \frac{1}{3}$ **4.** $\frac{49}{50} > \frac{41}{50}$ **5.** $\frac{5}{8} < \frac{7}{8}$ **6.** $\frac{7}{9} > \frac{5}{9}$ **7.** $\frac{3}{7} < \frac{7}{15}$
8. $\frac{45}{47} > \frac{89}{93}$ **9.** $\frac{8}{11} < \frac{15}{19}$ **10.** $\frac{1}{23} < \frac{2}{45}$ **11.** $\frac{5}{13} > \frac{9}{25}$
12. $\frac{147}{347} > \frac{440}{1,039}$ *Practice* **13.** $\frac{4}{5} > \frac{3}{5}$ **15.** $\frac{347}{498} > \frac{299}{498}$
17. $\frac{5}{8} > \frac{3}{18}$ **19.** $\frac{43}{45} < \frac{22}{23}$ **21.** $\frac{14}{19} > \frac{27}{37}$ **23.** $\frac{23}{23} > \frac{45}{49}$
25. $\frac{3}{11} < \frac{7}{23}$ **27.** $\frac{12}{17} > \frac{26}{57}$ **29.** Clothing Hut **31.** Dow Jones Industrials **33.** Texas

Workshop 13 *Self-Check* **1.** 0.4286 = 0.429 **2.** 0.875
3. $0.4 = \frac{4}{10} = \frac{2}{5}$ **4.** $7\frac{82}{100} = 7\frac{41}{50}$ **5.** 0.375 **6.** 0.09 **7.** 85%
8. 7% **9.** 30% **10.** 155% *Practice* **11.** 0.260
13. 0.889 **15.** 0.56 **17.** $\frac{3}{8}$ **19.** $\frac{287}{20}$ or $14\frac{7}{20}$ **21.** 8.17
23. 35% **25.** 412.5%

Workshop 14 *Self-Check* **1.** 28 **2.** 30 **3.** 1.5
4. 290 **5.** $24.50 discount **6.** 57 tons *Practice* **7.** 10.8

9. 140.7 11. 100.8 13. 3.8 15. $3.30 17. $2.33
19. $12.00 21. $6.27 23. 243 feet

Workshop 15 *Self-Check* 1. 16 2. −12 3. −17.5
4. −1$\frac{2}{5}$ 5. 4 6. 15 7. 4 8. −13 9. −2.3 10. −$30
11. −2 12. −7 13. −9 14. 12 *Practice* 15. −11
17. −7 19. −30 21. 2 23. −4 25. 7 27. 214° F

Workshop 16 *Self-Check* 1. 5 2. 5.1 3. 130
4. $41.33 *Practice* 5. 10 7. 80 9. 140 11. 743
13. 4.38 15. 3.05 17. $14.20 19. 6.7 21. 33.9
23. 40.04 25. 150 27. $2.56 29. $425.40 31. 85
33. No

Workshop 17 *Self-Check* 1. 2 h:0 min 2. 3 h:20 min
3. 7 h:5 min 4. 8 h:5 min 5. 3 h:45 min 6. 7 h:30 min
7. 1 h:45 min 8. 9 h:50 min 9. 8 h:0 min 10. 8 h:15 min
11. 8 h:15 min 12. 8 h:50 min *Practice* 13. 7 h:15 min
15. 5 h:55 min 17. 8 h:30 min 19. 3 h:53 min 21. 4 h:45 min 23. 8 h:27 min 25. 3 h:30 min 27. 4:15 P.M.

Workshop 18 *Self-Check* 1. $36 2. $55 3. $107
4. $111 5. Size 38 or 39 6. Size 42 *Practice* 7. $126
9. $187 11. $104 13. $91 15. $123 17. $55
19. a. 12.0 lb b. 3.0 lb c. 11.0 lb d. 6.0 lb e. 13.0 lb
f. 1.0 lb 21. Size 36 or 37

Workshop 19 *Self-Check* 1. Year I. Look at the bars for
the shortest bar. 2. No. 3. Just over 60,000. Look
at the height of the bar and then look at the vertical scale.
Practice 5. Statoil ASA and Prudential 7. service
9. manufacturing 11. J 13. H 15. $100

Workshop 20 *Self-Check*
1.
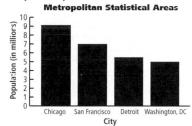
Metropolitan Statistical Areas

2.
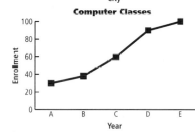
Computer Classes

Practice
3.
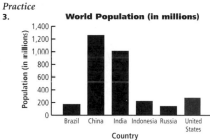
World Population (in millions)

5.
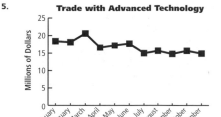
Trade with Advanced Technology

Workshop 21 *Self-Check* 1. 108 in 2. 150 ml 3. 8 yd
4. 3.5 m *Practice* 5. 27 ft 7. 112 oz 9. 96 oz
11. 3,800 m 13. 3,200 g 15. 2.25 gal 17. 3.5 gal 19. 2 kg
21. 3.3 L 23. 72,100 g 25. 0.723 kg 27. 180 mm 29. 40 in
31. 11 pt 33. 10 qt 35. 20 qt 37. 8 c 39. 240 in
41. 3,900 43. 2.13 L 45. a. 36 ft b. 36 ft, 48 ft, 84 ft
c. 21 ft, 18 ft 8 in, 39 ft 8 in d. 22 ft 6 in, 15 ft 4 in, 37 ft 10 in
e. 22 ft 8 in, 26 ft 4 in, 49 ft f. 35 ft 4 in, 25 ft 6 in, 60 ft 10 in
g. 16 ft 10 in, 15 ft 6 in, 32 ft 4 in; **Total:** 381 ft 8 in

Workshop 22 *Self-Check* 1. 280 cm 2. 1.5 dm
3. 2.61 m 4. 3.26 km 5. 2.5 m 6. 0.098 hm
7. 3,870 mL 8. 2,000 g *Practice*

	Kilo	Hecto	Deka	Base	Deci	Centi	Milli
9.	9	90	900	9,000	90,000	900,000	9,000,000
11.	0.02	0.20	20	200	2,000	20,000	200,000
13.	0.033	0.33	3.3	33	330	3,300	33,000

15. 200 17. 20 19. 4 21. 0.25 23. 500 25. 10
27. 38,000 29. 0.736 31. 5 33. 8 35. 32,000
37. 0.0321 39. 3,170 g 41. 76,200 mm, 0.304 m 43. 2.27 kg

Workshop 23 *Self-Check* 1. 188.5 2. 41,343.75
3. 679.61 4. 63,747.9 *Practice* 5. 30,013.5 7. $13,951.40
9. 36,361.625 = 36,361.63 11. $1,652.665 = $1,652.67
13. $3.532 = $3.53

Workshop 24 *Self-Check* 1. 40 − 30 = 10; 16.495
2. 42 ÷ 7 − 6; 5.894 3. 5 × 5 = 25; 23$\frac{11}{17}$ 4. 64 × 10 =
640; 628.2353 *Practice* 5. 6,000 + 2,000 = 8,000; 7,789
7. 16 − 14 = 2; 2.14 9. 9 × 8 = 72; 73.9728 11. 49 ÷ 7 =
7; 7.135 13. 3 × 2 = 6; 4$\frac{1}{8}$ 15. $\frac{1}{4}$ × 12 = 3; 3$\frac{1}{8}$ 17. $\frac{7}{10}$ ×
$50 = $35; $34.97 19. $\frac{1}{2}$ × 160 = 80; $83.20 21. 800 ÷ 40
− 20; $18.76 23. $\frac{1}{3}$ × 36 = 12; $11.86

Workshop 25 *Self-Check* 1. 900; 1,100 2. 15,000;
1,631 3. 6,000; 7,338 4. 800; 871.75 5. 600 + 200 =
800; 1,195 6. 700 + 200 = 900; 1,006 7. 1,700 + 200 =
1,900; 1,900 8. 2,200 + 300 = 2,500; 2,582.61 *Practice*
9. 15,000; 16,784 11. 8,000; 8,946 13. 1,500; 1,505
15. $102; $104.26 17. 21,000; 21,647

Workshop 26 *Self-Check* 1. 640 ÷ 80 = 8; 8.07
2. 9,000 ÷ 300 = 30; 27.3 3. 50 ÷ 5 = 10; 9.33 4. 300 ÷
6 = 5; 54.99 5. $\frac{1}{4}$ × 12 = 3; 3$\frac{1}{32}$ 6. $\frac{1}{2}$ × 30 = 15; 19$\frac{1}{8}$
7. $\frac{1}{3}$ × $900 = $300; $324.10 8. $\frac{1}{4}$ × $800 = $200; $221.40
Practice 9. 1,000; 1,103 11. 1,200; 1,219 13. 30, 28
15. 100; 108.23 17. 3; 2$\frac{5}{6}$ 19. $215; $215 21. 14,000;
14,095.42 23. 7; 6$\frac{5}{6}$ 25. 5,000; 5,500 27. $3,000; $3,025
29. $500; $484.62 31. $15,300; $17,680 33. $18; $17.88

Workshop 27 *Self-Check* 1. 600 × 4 = 2,400; 2,332
2. $30 × 4 = $120; $119.09 3. (3 × $2) + $1 = $6 + $1
= $7; $6.34 *Practice* 5. 500 × 4 = 2,000; 2,063

7. $40 \times 4 = \$160; \$161.24$ **9.** $(8 \times 4) + 4 = 32 + 4 = 36;$ 35.87 **11.** $(2 \times 4) + 9 = 8 + 9 = 17; 18.28$ **13.** $\$7 \times 5 =$ $\$35; \$35.09$ **15.** $(\$26 \times 3) + (\$40 \times 2) = \$78 + \$80 = \$158;$ $\$157.60$ **17.** $(\$18 \times 4) + \$40 = \$72 + \$40 = \$112; \$110.05$ **19.** $\$50,000 + (\$90,000 \times 3) = \$50,000 + \$270,000 =$ $\$320,000; \$323,610$ **21.** $\$125; \$122.80$

Workshop 28 *Self-Check* **1.** 1,375,000 or One million three hundred seventy-five thousand **2.** 386,420,000 or Three hundred eighty-six million four hundred twenty thousand **3.** 712.3 or Seven hundred twelve and three tenths **4.** 0.00000047945 or Forty-seven thousand nine hundred forty-five hundred billionths **5.** 9.3×10^7 **6.** 3.86×10^{-8} **7.** 7.000216×10^6 **8.** 4.021×10^{-1} *Practice* **9.** 739,100 or Seven hundred thirty-nine thousand one hundred **11.** 0.000871 or Eight hundred seventy-one millionths **13.** 292,651,000,000 or Two hundred ninety-two billion six hundred fifty-one million **15.** 1.262038×10^7 **17.** 2.86×10^{-5} **19.** 19.475×10^6 **21.** 2,600,000,000 or Two billion six hundred million **23.** 10,400,000 or Ten million four hundred thousand **25.** 0.000096 or Ninety-six millionths **27.** $\$2.0 \times 10^6$

Workshop 29 *Self-Check* **1.** \$4,200 *Practice* **3.** \$139.88 **5.** \$11,984 **7.** \$868.50 **9.** Approximately 1,495 rotations **11.** 224 miles

Workshop 30 *Self-Check* **1.** Problem cannot be solved. Need number of payments. *Practice* **3.** Cannot be solved. Need relationship between pints and pounds. **5.** \$74 **7.** Cannot be solved. Need weight of watermelons. **9.** 5' 11" **11.** Cannot be solved. Need the cost of the tennis balls. **13.** 19 **15.** One mile per hour

Workshop 31 *Self-Check* **1.** $\$50.00 - (\$7.95 + \$15.20$ $+ \$12.47) = \$14.38$ **2.** 17 **3.** \$231.00 **4.** \$2.68 *Practice* **5.** \$29.60 **7.** \$310.00 **9.** 28.5 degrees C **11.** 223 **13.** \$2,250 **15.** \$4.55

Workshop 32 *Self-Check* **1.** No, he used 93 instead of \$0.93. Answer is \$9.30. **2.** About \$18.00; 36" = 3 ft and 3 × \$6 = \$18 *Practice* **3.** Yes; No error **5.** No; Decimal point; estimate: \$70 **7.** Yes; No error **9.** No; Used 10 sq ft instead of 1 sq yd; estimate: \$15 **11.** about \$500 **13.** about \$1,600 **15.** about \$200 **17.** about \$3 **19.** about 25

Workshop 33 *Self-Check* **1.** 7 bicycles; 4 unicycles **2.** 9 high school; 5 college *Practice* **3.** 6 bicycles; 3 tricycles **5.** 20 nickels; 20 quarters **7.** 25 **9.** 12 **11.** 4 pennies; 4 dimes; 1 quarter

Workshop 34 *Self-Check* **1.** 81, 243, 729 **2.** 16, 22, 29 *Practice* **3.** 34, 40, 46 **5.** 18, 15, 12 **7.** 25, 36, 49 **9.** 1,093, 3,280, 9,841 **11.** 8 dimes; 12 quarters **13.** 33 **15.** 2:30 P.M. **17.** $4 \times 4; 6 \times 3$ **19.** 11

Workshop 35 *Self-Check* **1.** 7, 8, and 9 *Practice* **3.** 15 letters and 6 postcards. **5.** All sums are 12. **7.** 2 **9.** Green van: 10 years old; white van: 8 years old; blue van: 4 years old. **11.** Many different ways. Here are two: $888+8+8+8+8+8+8+8+8+8+8+8+8$ or $888+88+8+8+8$. **13.** 378 bicycles and 108 tricycles.

Workshop 36 *Self-Check* **1. a.** Add 4, divide by 6: $m = 5$ **b.** Subtract 12, multiply by 3: $n = 9$ **c.** Add 3, multiply by 5, divide by 2: $p = 30$ *Practice* **3.** $s = 15$ **5.** $u = 9$ **7.** $w = 8$ **9.** 150 **13.** 3:00 P.M. **15.** 15

Workshop 37 *Self-Check* **1.** 29 days *Practice* **3.** 5 cartons **5.** \$15,000 **7.** 56 dozen **9.** 62

11. 6 couples **13.** 128 games if the champion is undefeated; 129 games if the champion has one loss.

Workshop 38 *Self-Check* **1.** 11 *Practice* **3.** Cork: \$0.05; bottle: \$1.05 **5.** 54 yards **7.** \$3,695.33 **9.** Holstein **11.** 7, 9, 11 **13.** $B = 3A - 2$; 118 **15.** Harry = 197; Jerry = 210; Darrel = 192

Workshop 39 *Self-Check* **1.** Width = 7 feet; Length = 14 feet; Area = 98 square feet *Practice* **3.** $g = 8, f = 1$ **5.** $p =$ 4, $q = 3$ **7.** $v = 53$, $w = 19$ **9.** 32 copies of the *New York Times* and 27 copies of the *Washington Post* **11.** Forty-two \$21,500 model and thirty-five \$28,500 model in the first quarter; Twenty-one \$21,500 model and seventy \$28,500 model in the second quarter.

Workshop 40 *Self-Check* **1.** $3" + \frac{1}{4}" + \frac{1}{4}" + 3" + \frac{1}{4}" =$ $6\frac{3}{4}"$ **2.** (18 in + 7 in) − 10 in *Practice* **3.** 2 blocks west and 8 blocks south **5.** 20 ft **7.** 16 feet; 19 feet; 25 feet **9.** 28 minutes **11.** 3.8 cm **13.** Cedric or Clare in Canton or Cincinnati; Connie—Cleveland; Charles—Toledo; Carol—Columbus

Workshop 41 *Self-Check* **1.** 3 *Practice* **3.** 12 **5.** none **7. a.** 182 **b.** 198

Workshop 42 *Self-Check* **1.** $42,390 \div 5,280 = 8.028$ miles *Practice* **3.** $25^2 = 625$ **5. a.** 15 **b.** 99 **7. a.** $60 \text{ mph} \times 4 \text{ sec} \times \left(\frac{1 \text{ hr}}{3,600 \text{ sec}}\right) \times \left(\frac{5,280 \text{ ft}}{1 \text{ mile}}\right) = 352 \text{ feet}$ **b.** $60 \text{ mph} \times 50 \text{ sec} \times \left(\frac{1 \text{ hr}}{3,600 \text{ sec}}\right) \times \left(\frac{5,280 \text{ ft}}{1 \text{ mile}}\right) = 4,400 \text{ feet}$ **9.** Borrow one horse from neighbor, then $18 \times \frac{1}{2} = 9$ for Rick, $18 \times \frac{1}{3} = 6$ for Mike, and $18 \times \frac{1}{9} = 2$ for Peter, and then return horse to neighbor. **11.** 53

Chapter 1 Gross Income

Section 1-1 **3.** \$288.00 **5.** \$486.00 **7.** $\$452.090625 =$ \$452.09 **9.** \$195.00 **11.** \$812.50 **13.** \$435.20 **15.** \$657.00 **17.** \$85.00 **19.** 0.5 **21.** $\$136.125 = \$136.13$ **23.** \$471.25 **25.** 140 **27.** 100 **29.** 14,400 **31.** 1,000

Section 1-2 **3. a.** \$240 **b.** \$72 **c.** \$312 **5. a.** \$272.00 **b.** \$40.80 **c.** \$312.80 **7. a.** \$680 **b.** \$442 **c.** \$1,122 **9.** \$392.20; \$127.20; \$519.40 **11.** $\$280 + \$96 = \$376$ **13.** \$67.26 **15.** \$20.41 **17.** \$88.20 **19.** \$67.50

Section 1-3 **3.** $3\frac{3}{4} + 4 = 7\frac{3}{4}$ **5.** $4\frac{1}{4} + 3\frac{1}{2} = 7\frac{3}{4}$ **7.** $4\frac{3}{4} +$ $3\frac{3}{4} = 8\frac{1}{2}$ **9.** \$336.00 **11. a.** 8 **b.** 8 **c.** 8 **d.** 8 **e.** $7\frac{3}{4}$ **f.** $39\frac{3}{4}$ **13.** $\frac{7}{8}$ **15.** $\frac{23}{24}$ **17.** 7:45 **19.** 40,000 **21.** 68,000 **23.** 300

Section 1-4 **3.** \$720.00 **5.** \$516.75 **7.** \$60.30 **9.** \$93.11 **11.** \$20.47 **13.** \$251.52 **15.** \$119.60 **17.** \$231.00 **19.** 117 **21.** 9.68 **23.** 334,146.5

Section 1-5 **5.** \$432.69 **7.** Annual = \$42,120; Semimonthly = \$1,755 **9.** \$4,866.67; \$1,123.08 **11.** \$1,332.50 **13.** 285.80 **15.** 13.01 **17.** 72

Section 1-6 **5.** \$285.00 **7.** \$362.00 **9.** \$117.99 **11.** \$690.48 **13. a.** \$2,240.00 **b.** \$2,240.00 **15. a.** \$2,867.50 **b.** \$3,140.00 **17. a.** \$2,475.00 **b.** \$2,475.00 **19.** \$274.69 **21.** \$790 is greater **23.** 5.50 **25.** 9.25 **27.** \$365.50 **29.** \$331.20 **31.** 123.1 **33.** 0.6

Section 1-7 **3.** \$482 **5.** \$243.63 **7.** \$142.50 **9.** \$1,748.75 **11.** \$1,034.31 **13.** 0.055 **15.** 0.15 **17.** \$319.20

Study Guide and Assessment **1.** True **3.** True **5.** False **7.** False **9.** False **11.** False *Section 1-1* **13.** $40 \times \$9.45 = \$378$ **15.** $17.50 \times \$9.45 = \$165.38$ **17.** \$262 **19.** \$250.58 *Section 1-2* **21.** $\$9.17 \times 40 = \$366.80$

straight-time pay; $(1.5 \times \$9.17) \times 7 = \$96.29$ overtime pay;
$\$366.80 + \$96.29 = \$463.09$ **23.** $414.10 **25.** $481.00
Section 1-3

	Date	In	Out	In	Out	Total
27.	9/1	6:45 A.M.	11:30 A.M.	12:00 P.M.	3:45 P.M.	8.50
29.	9/3	6:56 A.M.	11:45 A.M.	12:30 P.M.	4:00 P.M.	8.25
31.	9/5	7:10 A.M.	11:30 A.M.	12:30 P.M.	4:20 P.M.	8.25

Section 1-4 **33.** $125 \times 11 = \$1,375; \$18 \times 9 = \$162$;
$\$1,375 + \$162 = \$1,537$ **35.** $414.80 *Section 1-5*
37. 156 **39.** 96 **41.** $703.37 **43.** $2,696.25 *Section 1-6* **45.** $304 **47.** $1,224.86 **49.** $246.35; $246.35
51. $191.25; $1,500.00 *Section 1-7* **53.** $5,000 \times 0.05 =$
$250; \$15,000 \times 0.065 = \$975; \$3,458 \times 0.07 = \$242.06; \$250$
$+ \$975 + \$242.06 = \$1,467.06$ **55.** $925 **57.** $9.89

Chapter 2 Net Income
Section 2-1 **9.** $15 **11.** $17 **13.** $12 **15.** $7
17. a. $55.77 **b.** $736.25 **c.** $(\$736.25 - \$415.00) \times 28\% +$
$\$58.65 = \$148.60$ **19.** thousands **21.** hundreds **23.** ones
25. $118.56 **27.** $1.55 **29.** $5,934.59 **31.** $801.69

Section 2-2 **5.** $496 **7.** $11,000; $385 **9.** $2,377.60
personal exemption; $4,400 tax withheld **11. a.** $2,200
b. $752.50 **13.** $897.40 **15.** $3,796 FIT + $780 state =
$4,576 **17.** 26.98 **19.** 173.8 **21.** 6.25
Section 2-3 **3.** $1,238 **5.** $101.69 **7.** 241.143
9. 20.49 **11.** 16 **13.** $365 \times 4 = 1,460; (365 \times 4) + 1 -$
1,461 for the leap year
Section 2-4 **3. a.** $7.75 **b.** $1.81 **c.** $9.56 **5. a.** $14.94
b. $3.49 **c.** $18.43 **7. a.** $156.30 **b.** $36.55 **c.** $192.85
9. $117.39; $27.45; $144.84 **11.** Fed: $36.00; S.S.: $34.10;
Med: $7.98; Total: $78.08 **13.** 48.33 **15.** 448.63 **17.** 620
19. 8,200 **21.** 623,200
Section 2-5 **5.** $158.33 **7.** $159.83 **9.** 1.12 **11.** 0.02
13. 727.16
Section 2-6 **3.** See table below. **5.** See table below.
7. See table below. **9.** 61.732 **11.** 399.25 **13.** −2.21
15. $100.45 **17.** $5.31 **19.** $129.31 **21.** $36.06
Study Guide and Assessment **1.** False **3.** False
5. True **7.** False **9.** True *Section 2-1* **11.** $38 **13.** $11
Section 2-2 **15.** $797.54 **17.** $43.38 *Section 2-3*
19. $27.02 **21.** $23.61 *Section 2-4* **23. a.** $394.90
b. $92.36 **25. a.** $52.27 **b.** $12.23 *Section 2-5*
27. $29.17 **29.** $13.27 *Section 2-6* **31.** See table below.

Section 2-6 **3.**

Dept	Employee	Check Number	Gross Pay	Net Pay
23	Terence Hall	463	$598.00	$428.82

	Tax Deductions				Other Deductions		
FIT	FICA	Medicare	State	Local	Medical	Union Dues	Others
67.00	37.08	8.67	11.96	8.97	15.50	14.00	6.00

Section 2-6 **5.**

Dept	Employee	Check Number	Gross Pay	Net Pay
SPDI	Rhonda Dakar	1574	$425.00	$304.61

	Tax Deductions				Other Deductions		
FIT	FICA	Medicare	State	Local	Medical	Union Dues	Others
25.00	26.35	6.16	8.50	6.38	18.00	10.00	20.00

Section 2-6 **7.**

Dept	Employee	Check Number	Gross Pay	Net Pay
PAYR	Lynn Golding	355-5887-01	$720.00	$553.52

	Tax Deductions				Other Deductions		
FIT	FICA	Medicare	State	Local	Medical	Union Dues	Others
27.00	44.64	10.44	21.60	10.80	35.00	17.00	0.00

Study Guide and Assessment
Section 2-6 **31.**

	General Check Information				
Dept.	Employee	Check #	Week Ending	Gross Pay	Net Pay
23	Chapman, D.	432	3/5/--	$640.00	$481.64

	Tax and Personal Deductions						
FIT	FICA	Medicare	State	Local	Medical	Union Dues	Others
77.00	39.68	9.28	12.80	9.60	10.00	—	—

Alternative Assessment **33.** Gross Pay — Total Deductions = Net Pay **35.** Filing status, allowances, any other deductions, such as state or medical

Chapter 3 Recordkeeping

Section 3-1 **5. a.** $3,440.00 **b.** $688.00
7. a. $8,802.34 **b.** $1,760.47 **9. a.** $545.45 **b.** 109.09
11. $131.23 **13.** $675.00 **15.** No; do not know their monthly net income. **17.** $69.29 **19.** $17.53
Section 3-2 **5.** $751.50 **7.** $1,742 **9.** $1,796.67
11. Rent, life insurance, car insurance, car registration (i.e., fixed expenses, annual expenses) **13.** $1,008.75 **15.** $226.79
17. No **19.** $241 **21.** $25.74 **23.** $2,014.61 **25.** $60.25
27. $6.44
Section 3-3 **5.** Food, telephone, water, gasoline, pocket money **7.** $100.00; More; $16.70 **9.** Less; $12.86 **11.** No
13. $1,796.66 budgeted; $1,740.09 expenses; $56.57 less
15. $174.85 **17.** $2,231.61 **19.** $3.64 **21.** $3.97
23. $129.84
Study Guide and Assessment **1.** True **3.** True
5. True **7.** False **9.** False *Section 3-1* **11.** $2,334.09 + $2,567.33 + $3,451.96 + $1,988.78 = $10,342.16; $10,342.16 ÷ 4 = $2,585.54 **13.** $110.55 *Section 3-2* **15.** $847.01
17. $173.90 **19.** Yes *Section 3-3* **21.** $125.00 + $50.00 + $45.00 + $60.00 = $280.00 budgeted for personal expenses. Actual personal expenses: $73.89 + $50.00 + $39.85 + $75.12 = $238.86. $280.00 − $238.86 = $41.14. They spent less than the amount budgeted by $41.14. **23.** Yes; car registration.
25. $5,278.71 *Alternative Assessment* **27.** Answers will vary. **29.** Answers will vary.

Chapter 4 Checking Accounts

Section 4-1 **5. a.** $41.80 **b.** $41.80 **7. a.** $178.20
b. $168.20 **9. a.** $1,275.55 **b.** $1,240.55 **11.** $151.45
13. $1,238.03 **15.** $1,556.46 **17.** $659.40 **19.** $653.32
Section 4-2 **9.** Forty and $\frac{40}{100}$ dollars **11.** Sixty-three and $\frac{74}{100}$ dollars **13.** Thirty-four and $\frac{06}{100}$ dollars **15.** One thousand nine hundred seventeen and $\frac{00}{100}$ dollars **17.** Two hundred one and $\frac{09}{100}$ dollars **19.** Five thousand two hundred twenty-seven and $\frac{17}{100}$ dollars **21.** No, two hundred forty-seven and $\frac{25}{100}$ dollars **23.** No, should be written ninety-eight and $\frac{72}{100}$ dollars
25. $35.15 **27.** Nineteen and $\frac{25}{100}$ dollars **29.** Four hundred thirty-five and $\frac{00}{100}$ dollars **31.** Five thousand two hundred seventy-four and $\frac{19}{100}$ dollars
Section 4-3 **5.** 401.43 **7.** 366.72 **9.** $269.30
11. a. 103.42 **b.** 317.22 **c.** 300.28 **d.** 225.03
13. $680.35 **15.** $305.28 **17.** $2,863.29 **19.** $366.63
21. $253.38 **23.** $2,792.20
Section 4-4 **5.** $47.66 **7.** $6,287.68 **9.** $684.66
11. $1,066.70 **13.** $47,082.74 **15.** $600.82 **17.** $1,362.97
Section 4-5 **5. a.** $496.05 **b.** $496.05 **7. a.** $4,604.53
b. $4,604.53 **9.** $411.05 **11.** $93.78 **13.** $243.77
Section 4-6 **5.** $45.45 **7. a.** $1,593.97 **b.** $3,640.46
c. $1,831.19 **d.** $800.92 **9.** $15,359.29 **11.** $884.07
13. $89,650.10 **15.** $281.31
Study Guide and Assessment **1.** reconcile **3.** balance
5. bank statement **7.** check register **9.** online banking
Section 4-1 **11.** $256.00 + $194.55 − $39.30 = $411.25

13. $1,121.91 *Section 4-2* **15.** One hundred twenty-three and $\frac{45}{100}$ dollars **17.** Fifty-four and $\frac{33}{100}$ dollars **19.** Three hundred eighty-seven and $\frac{21}{100}$ dollars *Section 4-3*
21. $472.25 **23.** $314.87 *Section 4-4* **25.** $176.93
27. $1,344.62 *Section 4-5* **29.** $172.21 **31.** $172.21
Section 4-6 **33.** $23.45

Chapter 5 Savings Accounts

Section 5-1 **5.** $77.18 **7.** $902.90 **9. a.** $129.65
b. $129.65 **11. a.** $296.16 **b.** $146.16 **13.** $500.03
15. $256.48 **17.** $1,609.50 **19.** $58.78 **21.** $697.97
23. $657.17 **25.** $612.28
Section 5-2 **7.** One hundred fifty and $\frac{00}{100}$ dollars **9.** Sixty-eight and $\frac{74}{100}$ dollars **11.** One hundred thirty-seven and $\frac{51}{100}$ dollars **13.** $932.25 **15.** $7,585.00 **17. a.** 13-122-541
b. $2,460.00 **c.** Two thousand four hundred sixty and $\frac{00}{100}$ dollars **19. a.** 17594179 **b.** $831.95 **c.** Eight hundred thirty-one and $\frac{95}{100}$ dollars **21.** Ninety-four and $\frac{78}{100}$ **23.** One hundred sixty-two and $\frac{05}{100}$ **25.** $39.41 **27.** $6,340.22
Section 5-3 **5.** $411.95 **7.** $7,442.26 **9.** $1,947.25
11. a. $236.75 **b.** $572.35 **c.** $574.63 **d.** $577.24
e. $579.86 **f.** $15.59 **13.** $1,267.52 **15.** $1,047.62
17. $1,874.56 **19.** $29,569.33
Section 5-4 **5. a.** $43.20 **b.** $10.80 **7. a.** $26.16
b. $13.08 **9. a.** $256.45 **b.** $5.62 **11.** $9.50
13. $20.00 **15.** 0.5 **17.** 0.25 **19.** 6.25 **21.** 0.055
23. 0.095 **25.** 0.10625
Section 5-5 **3. a.** $13.70 **b.** $927.20 **5. a.** $2,413.10
b. $54.29 **c.** $2,467.39 **7. a.** $2,637.10 **b.** $30,358.10
c. $2,887.97 **d.** $33,246.07 **9. a.** $836.54 **b.** $36.54
11. $4,957.69 **13. a.** $3,799.36 **b.** $179.36 **15.** 0.0525
17. 0.0575 **19.** $49.40 **21.** 0.30 **23.** 0.63
Section 5-6 **5. a.** $678.98 **b.** $38.98 **7. a.** $8,273.43
b. $2,042.03 **9.** $320.94 **11.** $12,092.02 **13.** $896.04;
$96.04 **15.** 0.02 **17.** 0.005 **19.** 0.0425
Section 5-7 **5. a.** $904.21 **b.** $4.21 **7. a.** $3,851.83
b. $51.83 **9.** $38.57 **11.** $79.04 **13.** $2,303.05
15. $9,012.15 **17.** $1,442.63 **19.** $1,431.00
21. $41,688.99 **23.** $390.17 **25.** $327.83
Section 5-8 **5. a.** 1.50 **b.** 8 **c.** 8.43284
d. $42,164.20 **e.** 1.0150 **f.** $42,796.66 **7. a.** 4.00
b. 10 **c.** 12.00611 **d.** $24,012.22 **e.** 1.0400
f. $24,972.71 **9. a.** 2.00 **b.** 40 **c.** 60.40198
d. $31,711.04 **e.** 1.0200 **f.** $32,345.26 **11.** $10,354.72
13. $135,352.95 **15.** $971.09 **17.** $11,616.80
19. $15,241.71 **21.** $9,641.82 **23.** $324,170.24
Study Guide and Assessment **1–13.** Answers will vary. *Section 5-1* **15. a.** $208.68 **b.** $173.18
17. a. $213.28 **b.** $98.28 **19. a.** $187.89 **b.** $112.89
Section 5-2 **21.** Twenty-one and $\frac{44}{100}$ dollars **23.** Seventy-six and $\frac{60}{100}$ dollars **25. a.** 045-8996 **b.** $985.40
c. Nine hundred eighty-five and $\frac{40}{100}$ dollars *Section 5-3*
27. $2,086.43 **29.** $21,395.65 + $14.39 + ($498.88 + $98.10) − $8,498.23 = $13,508.79 *Section 5-4*
31. $22.25 **33. a.** $1,250 × 0.0425 × $\frac{20}{365}$ = $2.9109
= $2.91 **b.** ($1,250 + $450) × 0.0425 × $\frac{10}{365}$ = $1.9789 =
$1.98 **c.** ($1,700 − $300) × 0.0425 × $\frac{8}{365}$ = $1.3030 =
$1.30; Total Interest for the Month = $6.19; Account at end of month: $1,406.19 *Section 5-5* **35. a.** $18.00
b. $1,218.00 **c.** $18.27 **d.** $1,236.27 **37. a.** $7.84

b. $972.84 **c.** $7.90 **d.** $980.74 *Section 5-6*
39. a. $1,273.08 **b.** $73.08 **41. a.** $1,358.51 (or
rounded $1,358.52) **b.** $128.51 (or rounded $128.52)
Section 5-7 **43. a.** $8,551.34 **b.** $51.34 **45.** Find
the number of days from June 30 to August 1. Use the Elapsed
Time table on page 796. August 1 is day 213. June 30 is day
181. 213 − 181 = 32 days. Find the amount of $1.00 for
32 days. It is 1.00483. $1,500 × 1.00483 = $1,507.25;
$1,507.25 − $1,500 = $7.25 *Section 5-8* **47. a.** 1%
b. 8 **c.** $8.28567 **d.** $24,857.01 **49. a.** 2% **b.** 12
c. $13.41209 **d.** $33,530.22 (or rounded $33,530.23)

Chapter 6 Cash Purchases

Section 6-1 **3.** $2.44 **5.** $1.09 **7.** $157.61 **9.** $90.34;
$4.52 **11.** $5.75 **13.** $2.39 **15.** $108 **17.** 4,000
19. 440 **21.** 90 **23.** $279.54 **25.** 37.6 **27.** 131.0
Section 6-2 **3.** $1.77 **5. a.** $0.87 **b.** $22.62
7. $64.14 **9.** $77.88 **11.** $121.02 **13.** $33.02
15. $22.48; $413.48 **17.** 142.6152 **19.** 500.81
21. 351.75 **23.** 943.584
Section 6-3 **3.** $0.08 **5.** $0.66 **7.** $0.12 **9.** $1.50
11. $84.79 **13.** $0.28 **15.** 2.51 **17.** 3.58 **19.** 20
21. 21.8 **23.** 2.3 **25.** 87.16
Section 6-4 **3. a.** $0.0169 or 1.7¢ **b.** $0.004 or 0.4¢
c. 300 for $1.27 **5.** 946 mL can is better buy. She must
consider if the stain will go bad before it is all used up.
7. 66-ounce jar **9.** Four 4-packs for $7.95 **11.** 2-pack of
$5\frac{3}{4}$ oz **13.** 0.05 **15.** 0.01 **17.** $0.2349
Section 6-5 **5.** $3.45 **7.** $6.89 **9.** $4.19 **11.** $4.09
13. $4.29 **15.** $79.99 **17.** $100.61 **19.** $8.65
Section 6-6 **5.** $70.00 **7.** $20.45 **9.** $15.00 **11.** $9.25
13. $15.00 **15.** $104.99 **17.** $6.66/ream; $3.33 per ream
19. $600.05 **21.** $69.53 **23.** 303.19 **25.** 0.9699
27. $36.00 **29.** $2.13
Section 6-7 **5.** $20.99 **7. a.** 80% **b.** $18.39
9. $112.49 **11.** $49.99 **13.** ($44.00 − $14.95) ÷
$44.00 = 0.66 = 66%; ($152 − $76) ÷ $152 = 0.50 = 50%
15. $18.70 **17.** 25.76 **19.** 10.679
Study Guide and Assessment **1.** markdown
3. markdown rate **5.** unit pricing **7.** rebate **9.** coupons
Section 6 1 **11.** $32.72 **13.** $0.93 *Section 6-2*
15. a. $1.27 **b.** $20.77 **17.** $63.88 *Section 6-3*
19. $\frac{1.99}{32}$ = $0.062187 = $0.062 = 6.2¢ per ounce
21. $6.25 per L *Section 6-4* **23.** 100 envelopes: $2.19
÷ 100 = $0.0219 = 2¢ per envelope; 150 envelopes: $2.59
÷ 150 = $0.0172 = 1.7¢ per envelope; 200 envelopes: $2.99
÷ 200 = $0.0149 = 1.4¢ per envelope; The 200 envelopes
per box is the best buy. **25.** small size *Section 6-5*
27. $19.99 − $2.50 = $17.49 **29.** $14.72 *Section 6-6*
31. $899 × 35% = $314.65 **33.** $38.24 *Section 6-7*
35. a. $87.44 **b.** $262.31 **37. a.** $43.21 **b.** $80.24
39. $21.76; $41.75; $6.68 **41.** The 10-oz size is the best buy.
Cumulative Test Prep **1.** B **3.** B **5.** B **7.** D
9. $50.00 **11.** $1,046.14 **13.** $574.68 **15.** 8-oz = $0.411;
12-oz = $0.324 **17.** They may wish to put money in the bank
to collect interest until the tax money is due. **19.** A higher
interest rate can give you considerably more interest because of
the compounding so it is important to get the highest rate. The
interest periods are also important—the more times your money
compounds the more interest you get.

Chapter 7
Charge Accounts and Credit Cards

Section 7-1 **5.** $649.00 **7.** $337.65 **9.** $416.34
11. $323.72 **13.** $796.35 **15. a.** payments & credits:
$109.90 **b.** new purchases: $188.73 **c.** new balance: $369.04
17. $405.04 **19.** $309.30
Section 7-2 **5. a.** $400.00 **b.** $6.00 **c.** $486.00
7. a. $275.00 **b.** $4.13 **c.** $369.13 **9. a.** $380.00
b. $5.70 **c.** $608.20 **11. a.** $372.87 **b.** $5.59
c. $526.40 **13.** $1,197.28 **15.** $817.72 **17.** unpaid
balance: $374.29; finance charge: $7.49; new balance: $461.09
19. $497.58 **21.** $410.93 **23.** $369.10 **25.** 4.80
Section 7-3 **9. a.** 19 **b.** $7,600 **c.** 1 **d.** $300 **e.** 11
f. $3,300 **g.** 31 **h.** $11,200 **i.** average daily balance:
$361.29 **11. a.** average daily balance: $82.73 **b.** finance
charge: $1.65 **c.** new balance: $152.95 **13.** 2,400
15. 825 **17.** 120 **19.** 72
Section 7-4 **11. a.** 12 days **b.** $7,200 **13. a.** $740
b. 6 days **c.** $4,440 **15. a.** $620 **b.** 10 days **c.** $6,200
17. a. $19,200 **b.** 30 days **c.** $640.00 **19.** 1,015
21. 1,743.13 **23.** 42.90 **25.** 49.80
Study Guide and Assessment **1.** average-daily-balance
method **3.** credit card **5.** finance charge *Section 7-1*
7. $1,934.16 **9.** $863.48 *Section 7-2* **11.** $75.06 × 2% =
$1.50; $75.06 + $1.50 + $432.11 = $508.67 **13. a.** $354.99
b. $4.44 **c.** $435.88 *Section 7-3* **15. a.** $2.86
b. $109.76 **17. a.** $31.47 **b.** $0.47 **c.** $38.58 *Section
7-4* **19. a.** $261.02 **b.** $5.22 **c.** $301.01

Chapter 8 Loans

Section 8-1 **5. a.** $4.50 **b.** $904.50 **7. a.** $34.50
b. $3,484.50 **9. a.** $164.00 **b.** $4,964.00 **11. a.** $21.00
b. $1,021.00 **13.** $24,864 **15.** $3,257.18 **17.** 0.40
19. 0.07 **21.** $\frac{1}{2}$ **23.** 0.667 **25.** 0.35
Section 8-2 **5. a.** $120 **b.** $520 **7. a.** $1,500
b. $8,274 **9. a.** $1,422 **b.** $8,058 **11.** $1,165
13. $7,115.68 **15.** $3,216 **17.** $3,190.36 **19.** 25%
21. 0.32 **23.** 0.25 **25.** 65 **27.** $49.96 **29.** $414.00
Section 8-3 **3. a.** $17.16 **b.** $171.60 **c.** $1,029.60
d. $29.60 **5. a.** $4.52 **b.** $253.12 **c.** $6,074.88
d. $474.88 **7. a.** $3.13 **b.** $298.92 **c.** $10,761.12
d. $1,211.12 **9. a.** $57.63 **b.** $133.12 **11. a.** $4,000
b. $16,000 **c.** $619.20 **d.** $2,576.00 **13.** $178.64
15. $56.26 **17.** $2,467.20 **19.** Save $136.80 w/15%
21. Save $456.66 w/18% for 24 months **23.** 25.246
25. 1,224.50
Section 8-4 **5.** $1,105.44 **7. a.** $28.83 **b.** $179.12
c. $3,280.88 **9. a.** $90.00 **b.** $259.20 **c.** $6,940.80
11. $1,236.53 **13. a.** $10.36 **b.** $202.76 **c.** $833.02
15. a. $6.28 **b.** $206.84 **c.** $421.39 **17. a.** $214.60
b. $2.12 **c.** $212.48 **d.** $0.00; You need to adjust the last
payment to $214.60 in order to zero out the loan. **19.** $900
21. $282.07 **23.** $91.24 **25.** $1,476.78
Section 8-5 **5. a.** $37.50 **b.** $3,037.50 **7. a.** $59.81
b. $4,047.41 **9.** $42.35; $5,124.56; $407.44 **11.** $619.98;
$6.42 **13.** $22.36 **15.** 1,625.70 **17.** 320.57
Section 8-6 **5. a.** 18.09 **b.** 16.5% **7. a.** $30.59
b. 18.25% **9.** 15.75% **11.** 7.75% **13.** 14.25%
15. 21.5% **17.** 15% **19.** 11.24% **21.** 16.25%
23. ABC: 22.25%; Atco: 22.50% **25.** Computer: FC: $501.52;

APR: 17.5%; TP: $3,750.81; Small business loan: FC: $343.72; APR: 16%; TP: $3,593.01; Based on APR the loan should be a small business loan. Based on finance charge the loan should come from the computer company. The times are different so you really cannot compare. **27.** $12.42 **29.** 30 **31.** 56.21
Study Guide and Assessment **1.** True **3.** True **5.** False **7.** False **9.** False *Section 8-1* **11.** $22,006.33 **13. a.** $12.66 **b.** $1,552.66 *Section 8-2* **15.** $587.33 − $147.00 = $440.33 **17. a.** $300 **b.** $489 *Section 8-3* **19.** ($3,500 ÷ 100) × $3.87 = $135.45; 30 × $135.45 = $4,063.50; $4,063.50 − $3,500 = $563.50 **21. a.** $17.06 **b.** $255.90 **c.** $1,535.40 **d.** $35.40 *Section 8-4* **23. a.** $39.00 **b.** $264.55 **c.** $3,635.45 **25. a.** $8.67 **b.** $96.76 **c.** $1,203.24 **27.** $3,733.55 × 14% × $\frac{1}{12}$ = $43.558 or $43.56 *Section 8-5* **29. a.** $30.00 **b.** $3,630.00 **31. a.** $48.61 **b.** $4,909.41 *Section 8-6* **33. a.** $2.26 **b.** 7.75% **35. a.** $15.99 **b.** 19.25%

Cumulative Test Prep **1.** C **3.** B **5.** C **7.** Interest: $15.40; payment to principal: $121.35; new principal: $1,418.65 **9.** 15% **11.** To check for accuracy, check to see if the payments and new purchases are covered. **13.** Credit cards are important today, since most people do not like to carry a lot of cash. However, the pervasive use of credit cards has riddled the nation in debt, causing an increase in personal bankruptcy. The cost of keeping a high balance can be expensive. Generally, answers will vary.

Chapter 9 Vehicle Transportation
Section 9-1 **5.** $11,000.00 **7.** $23,145.00 **9.** $54,128.00 **11.** $19,390.00 **13.** $803.45 **15.** 9,064 **17.** 13,306 **19.** 9,609.70
Section 9-2 **3.** $8,410 **5.** $13,127 **7.** $28,286.48 **9.** $33,374.44 **11.** $81,393.05 **13.** 147 **15.** 364.8 **17.** 2,683.2
Section 9-3 **3. a.** $13,050 **b.** $13,700 **5. a.** $14,675 **b.** $15,465 **7.** $17,975 **9.** $12,690 **11.** 8,635 **13.** 1,360
Section 9-4 **3. a.** $642.80 **b.** $835.64 **5.** Annual Base Premium: $622.40; Annual Premium: $622.40 **7.** Annual Base Premium: $683.60; Annual Premium: $1,469.74 **9.** Annual Base Premium: $472.40; Annual Premium: $1,488.06 **11.** 597.2 **13.** 99.875 **15.** 264.03
Section 9-5 **5. a.** $2,805 **b.** $0.255 = $0.26 **7. a.** $2,518.35 **b.** $0.370 = $0.37 **9. a.** $3,200 **b.** $0.336 = $0.34 **11.** $0.263 = $0.26 **13.** $0.513 = $0.51 **15.** 15.35 **17.** 15.91 **19.** 0.32 **21.** 3
Section 9-6 **5. a.** $9,552 **b.** $10,331 **7. a.** $9,720 **b.** $11,051 **9.** $23,425 **11.** $12,787 **13.** Total lease cost: $23,010; Total cost to purchase: $32,456 **15.** $16,799.60 to lease; $14,563.08 to purchase; best to purchase **17.** 119.8
Section 9-7 **5. a.** $224.88 **b.** $0.362 = $0.36 **7. a.** $76.89 **b.** $0.320 = $0.32 **9. a.** $183.02 **b.** $0.384 = $0.38 **11. a.** $304.38 **b.** $0.585 = $0.59 **13.** $361.64; $0.861 = $0.86 **15.** $0.513 = $0.51 **17.** 508.35 **19.** 23.818 = 23.82 **21.** 1.39
Study Guide and Assessment **1.** depreciation **3.** deductible clause **5.** sticker price **7.** used-vehicle guides **9.** variable costs *Section 9-1* **11.** $13,700 **13.** $19,102 *Section 9-2* **15.** $15,575 **17.** $21,832 *Section 9-3* **19.** $14,500 + $150 + $700 − $600 − $560 = $14,190 **21.** $14,690 **23.** $9,025 *Section 9-4* **25.** $272.40 + $122.00 + $307.60 = $702 annual base premium; $702 × 3.85 = $2,702.70 **27. a.** $642.80 **b.** $771.36 *Section 9-5* **29. a.** $4,587.33 **b.** $0.48 **31. a.** $3,440.33 **b.** $0.24

Section 9-6 **33. a.** $4,992 **b.** $5,636 **35. a.** $6,660 **b.** $8,314 *Section 9-7* **37. a.** $168.82 **b.** $0.20 **39. a.** $170.24 **b.** $0.19

Chapter 10 Housing Costs
Section 10-1 **3.** $69,600 **5. a.** $74,700 **b.** $224,100 **7.** $61,920 **9.** $69,200 **11.** $70,560 **13.** $6,000 **15.** $18,000 **17.** 76,000
Section 10-2 **3. a.** $540.40 **b.** $162,120.00 **c.** $92,120.00 **5. a.** $2,151.00 **b.** $387,180.00 **c.** $162,180.00 **7. a.** $644.00 **b.** $193,200.00 **c.** $113,200.00 **9.** $146,232 **11.** $556.20; $100,116.00 **13.** 11.5% for 25 years; $44,286 **15.** 15,523.2 **17.** 53,300 **19.** 353,821.50
Section 10-3 **3.** $3,665 **5. a.** $14,715 **b.** $434,715 **7.** $2,811.25; $89,311.25 **9.** 1,350 **11.** 17,640 **13.** 2,739 **15.** 276 **17.** 8.92
Section 10-4 **7.** $49,855.33 **9. a.** $475.00 **b.** $84.80 **c.** $59,915.20 **11. a.** $1,875.00 **b.** $543.75 **c.** $224,456.25 **13.** $700 **15. a.** $612.50 **b.** $73.50 **c.** $97,926.50 **17.** $1,500; $80.40; $179,919.60 **19.** 47,970.54 **21.** 24,376.88 **23.** 18,139.89
Section 10-5 **5.** $63,920 **7.** $4,743.60 **9.** $13,570.20 **11.** 2,924.32 **13.** 58.121 **15.** 63,000
Section 10-6 **5.** $95,000 **7. a.** $115,200 **b.** $23,040 **9. a.** $259,200 **b.** $129,600 **c.** $51,840 **d.** $25,920 **11.** $24,000
Section 10-7 **3.** $183 **5.** $662 **7.** Mortgage payment: $1,003.20 per month; insurance: $459 ÷ 12 = $38.25 per month; taxes: $2,707.95 ÷ 12 = $222.66 per month **9.** 112,000 **11.** 35,000 **13.** 10,710
Section 10-8 **3.** $1,365 **5.** $1,499 **7.** $2,780 **9. a.** $1,103.90 **b.** Yes; $1,103.90 < $1,120.00 **11.** $994.71; No; $875 **13.** Mortgage: $880.80; insurance: $52.08; taxes: $357.85; total: $1,538.18; FHA: Yes **15.** 74,846.50 **17.** 515.13 **19.** 1,840
Study Guide and Assessment **1.** premium **3.** closing costs **5.** principal **7.** market value **9.** replacement value *Section 10-1* **11. a.** $33,150 **b.** $99,450 **13. a.** $53,585 **b.** $252,615 *Section 10-2* **15. a.** $463.57 **b.** $139,071.00 **c.** $63,571.00 **17. a.** $836.33 **b.** $250,899.00 **c.** $126,999.00 *Section 10-3* **19.** $8,946.80 **21.** $4,929.28 *Section 10-4* **23. a.** $425.00 **b.** $58.14 **c.** $59,941.86 **25. a.** $1,455.00 **b.** $41.63 **c.** $145,458.37 *Section 10-5* **27.** $95,000 × 45% = $42,750 assessed value; 54.5 ÷ 1,000 = 0.0545 tax rate as decimal; 0.0545 × $42,750 = $2,329.88 real estate tax **29.** $7,095.61 *Section 10-6* **31.** $112,050 **33. a.** $212,500 **b.** $21,250 *Section 10-7* **35.** $241 **37.** $391 *Section 10-8* **39.** $889 **41.** $454.30

Chapter 11 Insurance
Section 11-1 **3. a.** 40% **b.** $1,192.00 **c.** $99.33 **5. a.** 25% **b.** $1,516.50 **c.** $126.38 **7. a.** 15% **b.** $2,190 **c.** $182.50 **9. a.** $2,975.00 **b.** $123.96 **11.** $23.92 **13.** $370.50 **15.** 40% **17.** 35% **19.** 133.48 **21.** 168.35
Section 11-2 **3. a.** $400 **b.** $4,800 **c.** $5,400 **5. a.** $320 **b.** $21,600 **c.** $22,520 **7.** Deductible: $1,800; Co-pay: $976.50; Hospital charges: $4,730; Total paid: $7,506.50 **9.** $498 **11.** 113 **13.** 54,465 **15.** 49,355

Section 11-3 5. a. $2.13 **b.** $127.80 **7. a.** 95
b. $2.29 **c.** $217.55 **9.** 27.5% **11.** $138.45 **13. a.** $540
b. $45 **c.** $1,543.75 **d.** $2,700 **15.** 544.714 **17.** 21.624
19. 18.400 **21.** 0.152 **23.** 1,402.14 **25.** 3,481
Section 11-4 5. a. 50 **b.** $6.25 **c.** $312.50 **d.** $26.56
7. a. 200 **b.** $25.00 **c.** $5,000 **d.** $425 **9. a.** $725.00
b. $366.13 **11.** $29.00; $348.00 **13.** $228.00; $1,572.00
15. 3.05 **17.** 0.26 **19.** 0.33
Study Guide and Assessment 1–9. Definitions will vary.
Evaluate based on the students' understanding of the term and
their ability to put the definition into their own words. *Section
11-1 **11. a.** 35% **b.** $1,052.10 **c.** $87.68 **13. a.** 25%
b. $1,458 **c.** $121.50 **15. a.** 15% **b.** $384 **c.** $32
Section 11-2 **17. a.** $150 **b.** $3,000 **c.** $3,650
19. a. $450 **b.** $10,000 **c.** $10,650 **21. a.** $410
b. $15,750 **c.** $16,310 *Section 11-3* **23.** $125,000 ÷
1,000 = 125 units purchased; $5.84 premium per $1,000;
125 × $5.84 = $730 annual premium **25. a.** 50 **b.** $2.47
c. $123.50 **27. a.** 80 **b.** $4.17 **c.** $333.60 **29. a.** 200
b. $9.71 **c.** $1,942.00 *Section 11-4* **31. a.** 50
b. $11.75 **c.** $587.50 **d.** $49.94 **33. a.** 150 **b.** $13.75
c. $2,062.50 **d.** $175.31 *Alternative Assessment*
35. Doctor can take a vacation and can share cost of equipment
and office. **37.** Answers will vary.

Chapter 12 Investments

Section 12-1 5. a. 1.050945 **b.** $4,729.25 **c.** $229.25
7. a. 1.208796 **b.** $10,879.16 **c.** $1,879.16 **9.** $27,393.95
quarterly; $27,422.50 daily; $28.55 difference **11.** $9,998.80
Interest on Granite; $9,772.90 interest on Hancock; $225.90 more
at Granite **13.** 140 **15.** 0.067 **17.** 4.641 **19.** 2,191.06
Section 12-2 5. a. $6,446.97 **b.** $446.97 **c.** 7.450%
7. a. 1.096524 **b.** $5,482.62 **c.** $482.62 **d.** 9.652%
9. 8.25% compounded daily **11.** 6% daily: $618.31 (interest);
6.1831% (effective annual yield); 6% monthly: $616.78 (interest);
6.1678% (effective annual yield) **13.** $11,734.98 vs. $11,735.01
(the amount is about the same) **15.** 125.64% **17.** 30,000
19. 33,960
Section 12-3 3. a. $11,050.00 **b.** $11,059.99
5. a. $17,800.00 **b.** $17,845.50 **7. a.** $16,450.00
b. $16,515.00 **9.** $18,900; $18,960 **11.** $21,805.37
13. It costs $2.39 more to buy $6,999 of stock than to
buy $7,000 of stock. **15.** $5,882.95 **17.** $18,200
19. $22,952
Section 12-4 3. 0.01690 = 1.69% **5.** 0.01088 = 1.09%
7. 9.53% **9. a.** $608.00 **b.** 2.71% **11.** $203; 1.36%
13. 6.34%; 4.75% **15.** 0.12 **17.** 65.22 **19.** 25.83%
21. 3.126%

Section 12-5 3. a. $7,170 **b.** $1,970 profit
5. a. $6,480 **b.** $280 loss **7.** $848 profit **9.** $11,942.05
sale; $3,457.10 profit **11.** $73,000.00 + ($49.95 + $40.00) =
$73,089.95; $96,500.00 − ($49.95 + $40.00) = $96,410.05; Net
amount of sale: $96,410.05; Profit: $23,320.10 **13.** $2,430.00
+ $48.60 = $2,478.60; $5,670.00 − $170.10 = $5,499.90;
Profit: $3,021.30 **15.** 381.6 **17.** $219.84 **19.** 14.92
21. 16.492 **23.** 108.4176
Section 12-6 5. a. $7,025 **b.** $800 **c.** 11.39%
7. a. $10,400 **b.** $790 **c.** 7.60% **9. a.** $700 **b.** $9,950
c. 7.04% **11.** $1,500; $47,187.50; 3.18% **13.** $33,819.19
total purchase; $2,175.00 yearly earnings; 2013 bond matures
15. 13,987.50 **17.** 1,080 **19.** 1,034 **21.** 31.34
Study Guide and Assessment 1–7. Definitions will
vary. *Section 12-1* **9. a.** 1.030416 **b.** $6,697.70
c. $197.70 **11. a.** 1.053899 **b.** $3,688.65 **c.** $188.65
13. a. 1.172579 **b.** $41,040.27 **c.** $6,040.27 *Section
12-2* **15. a.** 1.082432 **b.** $4,870.94 **c.** $370.94
d. 8.243% **17. a.** 1.427621 **b.** $36,404.33 **c.** $10,904.33
d. 9.381% **19. a.** 1.096524 **b.** $10,965.24 **c.** $965.24
d. 9.652% *Section 12-3* **21. a.** $7,318.50 **b.** $7,368.50
23. a. $135,907 **b.** $135,946.50 **25. a.** $120,020
b. $120,042 *Section 12-4* **27.** Annual yield on high price:
$\frac{\$2.31}{\$54.54} = 0.04235$ or 4.24%; Annual yield based on low price:
$\frac{\$2.31}{\$44.45} = 0.05196$ or 5.20%; Total annual dividend: 200 × $2.31
= $462 **29.** 2.441% **31.** 2.034% *Section 12-5*
33. a. $7,756.50 **b.** $1,956.50 profit **35. a.** $513.50
b. $1,286.50 loss **37. a.** $2,918 **b.** $332 loss *Section
12-6* **39. a.** $3,105 **b.** $195 **c.** 6.3% **41. a.** $3,762.50
b. $400 **c.** 10.6% **43. a.** $10,100 **b.** $900 **c.** 8.9%

Chapter 13 Personnel

Section 13-1 3. $979.10 **5.** $2,417.90 **7.** $12,880.70
9. $6,128.65 **11.** $47,492.55 **13.** $2,325 **15.** $17,698
17. $5,380.40
Section 13-2 3. $69,160 **5.** $38,220 **7.** $33,930
9. a. $893 **b.** $917 **c.** $942.30 **11.** $47,500
13. $55,000 **15.** $1,849.86
Section 13-3 3. 27.1% **5.** 20% **7.** 32% **9. a.** See
table below. **b.** 18.2% **11.** $1,854.97 **13.** $951.05
15. 40%
Section 13-4 3. a. $20,000 **b.** $1,666.67
5. a. $20,563.20 **b.** $1,713.60 **7. a.** $21,932.40
b. $1,827.70 **9.** $531 **11. a.** $26,380.73 **b.** $2,198.39
13. $1,381.71 **15.** 35 **17.** 39 **19.** 38 **21.** $959.30
23. $525.17

Section 13-3 9. a.

Position	Annual Wage	2-Week Vacation	3.6% Workers Comp.	8-Day Sick Leave	6.2% FICA	1.45% Medicare	Total Benefits
Manager	$47,580	$1,830.00	$1,712.88	$1,464.00	$2,949.96	$689.91	$8,646.75
Counter 1	27,560	1,060.00	992.16	848.00	1,708.72	399.62	5,008.50
Counter 2	22,620	870.00	814.32	696.00	1,402.44	327.99	4,110.75
Cleanup	14,560	560.00	524.16	448.00	902.72	211.12	2,646.00

Section 13-5 **3.** $48.02 **5.** $479.46 **7.** $296.14
9. a. $7,000 **b.** $490.00 **c.** 0.8% **d.** $56.00
11. a. $4,800 **b.** $105.60 **c.** 4.0% **d.** $192.00
13. a. $7,000 **b.** $70.00 **c.** 5.2% **d.** $364.00
15. Koster: **a.** $7,000 **b.** $56.00 **c.** $637.00; Ahmed:
a. $7,000 **b.** $56.00 **c.** $637.00; Morales: **a.** $7,000
b. $56.00 **c.** $637.00; Gallos: **a.** $7,000 **b.** $56.00
c. $637.00; Haddad: **a.** $7,000 **b.** $56.00 **c.** $637.00; Brown:
a. $6,850.00 **b.** $54.80 **c.** $623.35; Lopez: **a.** $6,240.00
b. $49.92 **c.** $567.84; Woo: **a.** $4,650.00 **b.** $37.20
c. $423.15 **17.** $3,594.24 **19.** $1,127.07 **21.** $293.11
Section 13-6 **3. a.** $25.60 **b.** $72.50 **5. a.** $57.60
b. $338.00 **7. a.** $199.36 **b.** $1,008.15 **9.** $524.70
11. $1,184.52 **13.** $73.50 **15.** $136.40 **17.** $108.00
19. $139.26 **21.** $332.40 **23.** $280.41 **25.** $345
27. $410.27
Section 13-7 **3.** $915 **5.** $2,838 **7.** $1,455 **9.** $5,390.00
11. $5,508 **13.** $5,732 **15.** $580 **17.** $592 **19.** $916.35
21. $110.17 **23.** $1,849 **25.** $3,391.06
Study Guide and Assessment **1.** salary scale
3. employee benefits **5.** travel expenses **7.** disability insurance
Section 13-1 **9.** $1,012.14 **11.** $2,949.75 *Section 13-2*
13. $31,140 **15.** $60,176 **17.** $109,060 *Section 13-3*
19. a. $2,511.54 **b.** $2,350.80 **c.** $2,260.35 **d.** $4,048.60
e. $946.85 **f.** $12,118.17 **g.** 18.6% **21. a.** $846.15
b. $792 **c.** $761.54 **d.** $1,364.00 **e.** $319 **f.** $4,082.69
g. 18.6% **23. a.** $1,361.54 **b.** $1,274.40 **c.** $1,225.38 **d.**
$2,708.10 **e.** $513.30 **f.** $7,082.65 **g.** 18.6%
Section 13-4 **25. a.** $27,360 **b.** $2,280 **27. a.** $41,470
b. $3,455.83 **29. a.** $22,411.20 **b.** $1,867.60 *Section*
13-5 **31.** $99.23 **33.** $37.20; $251.10 *Section 13-6*
35. a. $32.96 **b.** $169.61 **37. a.** $62.08 **b.** $191.64
39. a. $237.44 **b.** $613.22 *Section 13-7* **41.** $5,020.00
43. $1,760 **45.** $540 **47.** Answers will vary.
Cumulative Test Prep **1.** A **3.** B **5.** C **7.** B
9. $830.50 **11.** $13,344 **13–15.** Answers will vary.

Chapter 14 Production

Section 14-1 **3.** $0.092 **5. a.** $0.014 **b.** $0.022
c. $0.036 **7.** $0.003 **9.** $0.058 **11.** $0.033 **13.** $0.061
15. $0.215 **17.** $0.007 **19.** $0.072 **21.** $0.05 **23.** $0.077
25. $0.147 **27.** $0.038 **29.** $0.041 **31.** $0.023
Section 14-2 **3.** 95,000 **5.** 450,000 **7.** 19,281
9. 28,986 **11.** 230,941 **13.** 480,000 **15.** $5.36
17. $6.75 **19.** $37.59 **21.** 190,000 **23.** 274,039
Section 14-3 **3.** 4%; In **5.** 8%; Out **7.** 5%; In **9.** In
(5%) **11.** 8%; Out **13.** 9 A.M. 2%; 11 A.M. 0%; 1 P.M. 6%;
3 P.M. 4%; 5 P.M. 4%; Out of control at 1 P.M. **15.** 1.3%; 2.7%;
1.3%; 0%; 2.7%; 1.3%; 4%; 5.3%; 1.3%; 0%; Out of control at
checkpoint 7. **17.** 4% **19.** 16% **21.** 5.3% **23.** 4%
Section 14-4 **5.** 75.5 = 76 **7.** 490.9 = 491 **9.** 140.1 =
140 **11.** 115 **13.** 70 **15.** 5 **17.** 1,250 **19.** 67
Section 14-5 **5.** 0.375 = 37.5% **7.** 0.125 = 12.5%
9. 0.3125 = 31.25% **11.** 0.37333 = 37.33% **13.** 0.3 = 30%
15. Loading truck 0.14444 = 14.44%; Driving truck 0.34444 =
34.44%; Delivering bread 0.24444 = 24.44%; Recording sale 0.05555
= 5.56%; Checking out 0.03333 = 3.33%; Break and miscellaneous
0.06666 = 6.67%; Lunch 0.11111 = 11.11%; 73.32% spent
loading, driving, and delivering **17.** 10 **19.** 0.23333 = 23.33%
Section 14-6 **5.** 0.8 cm **7.** 12.8 cm **9.** 0.4 cm
11. 25.2 cm **13.** 0.6 cm **15.** 49.4 cm **17.** Without top and

bottom flaps: 21 (W) × 20.25 (L) × 19.75 (H); With top and
bottom flaps: 21 (W) × 20.25 (L) × 20.50 (H) **19.** Height =
$13\frac{5}{8}$ in; Length = $22\frac{1}{8}$ in; Width = $18\frac{3}{4}$ in **21.** $\frac{5}{8}$ **23.** $\frac{7}{16}$ **25.** $\frac{3}{4}$
27. 3 **29.** $\frac{5}{16}$ **31.** $4\frac{1}{2}$
Study Guide and Assessment **1–13.** Answers will vary.
Section 14-1 **15. a.** $0.03750 **b.** $0.01250 **c.** $0.05
17. a. $0.02167 **b.** $0.03590 **c.** $0.06 **19. a.** $0.11000
b. $0.01893 **c.** $0.13 *Section 14-2* **21.** 75,000
23. 164,935 **25.** 18,238 *Section 14-3* **27. a.** 6.67%
b. Out **29. a.** 2.22% **b.** In **31. a.** 4.44% **b.** Out
Section 14-4 **33.** 57 **35.** 77 **37.** 76 *Section*
14-5 **39.** 25% **41.** 15.63% **43.** 21.88% *Section 14-6*
45. 15.6 cm **47.** 28 cm **49.** 0.8 cm **51.** 28 cm **53.** 0.8 cm

Chapter 15 Purchasing

Section 15-1 **3. a.** $105 **5. a.** $140.00 **b.** $260.00
7. a. $55.68 **b.** $118.32 **9. a.** $8.53 **b.** $86.22
11. $127.02 **13. a.** $4.53; $8.42 **b.** $0.90; $8.09
c. $8.84; 50.11 **15.** $11.86; $1.07; $34.10; $200.96;
$106.93; $71.56 **17.** $16.45 **19.** $9.73 **21.** $915.18
23. $333.28
Section 15-2 **5. a.** $90.00 **7. a.** 65% **b.** $206.36
9. a. 76% **b.** $241.64 **11. a.** 40% **b.** $167.16
13. $1,590.60 **15. a.** $191.98; $113.27 **b.** $94.00; $55.46
c. $239.60; $141.36 **d.** $769.50; $454.01 **17. a.** $11.32;
$407.52 **b.** $2.47; $61.75 **c.** $4.21; $25.26 **d.** $12.76;
$76.56 **19.** 50% **21.** 78% **23.** $116.57 **25.** $7.32
27. $96.00
Section 15-3 **3. a.** 20% **5. a.** $18 **b.** 30.0%
7. a. $85.10 **b.** 75.6% **9. a.** $888.89 **b.** 17.3%
11. a. $400 **b.** Compute: $\frac{400}{2,000}$ = 20% **13.** WH: 35%; BL:
25%; AVO: 33%; GLD: 20% **15.** 40%; 33%; 25% **17.** $6.56
19. $11.46 **21.** $499.91 **23.** 0.4 **25.** 0.2 **27.** 0.5
Section 15-4 **3. a.** $70 **b.** $280 **5. a.** $248
b. $992 **c.** $148.80 **d.** $843.20 **7. a.** $868
b. $1,302 **c.** $325.50 **d.** $976.50 **9.** $60.24
11. $46.93; $41.44; $35.02 **13.** $349.91; $100.77; $40.24;
$5.36 **15.** $114 **17.** $8,178.14 **19.** $51 **21.** $56.61
23. $425.91 **25.** $13,530.44 **27.** $167.61 **29.** $1,025.27
31. $5,614.77
Section 15-5 **5. a.** 44% **b.** $272.80 **7. a.** 48%
b. $209.28 **c.** 52% **d.** $226.72 **9. a.** 50.4%
b. $74.49 **c.** 49.6% **d.** $73.31 **11. a.** $1,644.75
b. $505.25 **13. a.** $74.15; 50.50% **b.** $108.65; 50.50%
c. $14.85; 50.50% **15. a.** $31.77; $46.68 **b.** $181.85;
$159.97 **c.** $35.35; $23.02 **d.** $101.14; $46.72
17. $19.72 **19.** $912.41 **21.** 70% **23.** 75%
25. 90% **27.** $175.29
Section 15-6 **7. a.** $725.20 **9. a.** 9/18 **b.** 10/3
c. 0 (no discount) **d.** $348.64 **11. a.** 10/17 **b.** 11/06
c. $6,447.17 **13.** $505.68 **15.** $3,051.28 **17.** $9,295.31
19. $8.30 **21.** $843.40
Section 15-7 **5.** $602.70 **7. a.** 10/10 **b.** 10/30
c. $287.39 **d.** $6,897.34 **9. a.** 10/10 **b.** 10/30
c. $907.24 **11.** 9/15; 9/30; $723.78 **13.** $16.42
15. $1,011.45 **17.** $8,356.07
Study Guide and Assessment **1.** ordinary dating
3. chain discount **5.** net price **7.** list price **9.** net-price rate
11. single equivalent discount *Section 15-1* **13. a.** $39.60
b. $92.40 **15. a.** $39.57 **b.** $356.08 **17. a.** $32.07
b. $305.48 *Section 15-2* **19.** 100% − 47% = 53%

complement of trade-discount rate   **a.** 9 × $36.54 = $328.86 total list; $328.86 × 53% = $174.30 net price   **b.** 30 × $95.41 = $2,862.30 total list; $2,862.30 × 53% = $1,517.02 net price   **c.** 100 × 2.99 = $299; $299 × 53% = $158.47 net price   **21. a.** 63%   **b.** $59.54   **23. a.** 55%   **b.** $357.57   **25. a.** 25%   **b.** $0.82   *Section 15-3*   **27. a.** $25.45   **b.** 29.8%   **29. a.** $65.00   **b.** 18.5%   **31. a.** 1,303.13   **b.** 20.6%   *Section 15-4*   **33. a.** $160   **b.** $480   **c.** $48   **d.** $432   **35. a.** $1,418   **b.** $2,127   **c.** $319.05   **d.** $1,807.95   **37. a.** $591   **b.** $2,364   **c.** $354.60   **d.** $2,009.40   *Section 15-5*   **39. a.** 48.75%   **b.** $112.13   **c.** 51.25%   **d.** $117.87   **41. a.** 63.75%   **b.** $2,539.80   **c.** 36.25%   **d.** $1,444.20   **43. a.** 57.38%   **b.** $8.86   **c.** 42.62%   **d.** $6.59   *Section 15-6*   **45. a.** July 7   **b.** July 27   **c.** $4.07   **d.** $131.53   **47. a.** March 23   **b.** April 12   **c.** $0   **d.** $941.22   **49. a.** June 10   **b.** June 25   **c.** $7.31   **d.** $358.13   *Section 15-7*   **51. a.** March 10   **b.** March 30   **c.** $10.95   **d.** $354.17   **53. a.** Aug. 10   **b.** Aug. 30   **c.** $48.39   **d.** $1,161.42   **55. a.** Dec. 15   **b.** Jan. 4   **c.** $11.99   **d.** $227.88

Chapter 16 Sales

Section 16-1   **5.** $1,465.00   **7.** $164.89   **9.** $61.95   **11.** $70.86   **13.** $28.11   **15.** $4.71   **17.** $3.85   **19.** $39.40   **21.** $10.89   **23.** $86.78   **25.** $1.22   **27.** $3.25   **29.** $4,406.32

Section 16-2   **5.** Markup $80.75; Markup rate 0.4821 = 48.2%   **7.** 0.4384 = 43.8%   **9.** 0.3807 = 38.1%   **11.** 0.3802 = 38.0%   **13.** $15.90   **15.** 0.2408 = 24.1%   **17.** 0.9999 = 100.0%

Section 16-3   **5.** $8   **7.** $27   **9.** $29.96   **11.** $246,461.75   **13.** $1.11   **15.** $0.46   **17.** $0.35   **19.** $48.00   **21.** $44.72

Section 16-4   **5. a.** $25.00   **b.** 50%   **7. a.** $29.07   **b.** 19%   **9. a.** $3,976.60   **b.** 47%   **11.** 16.2%   **13.** 30.2%   **15. a.** 23.8%   **b.** 20.2%   **17.** 42.2%   **19.** $1.96   **21.** 29.6%   **23.** 15.0%

Section 16-5   **5. a.** $10.00   **7. a.** 50%   **b.** $173.48   **9. a.** 62.5%   **b.** $76.54   **11.** $18.70   **13.** $6.95   **15. a.** $1.21   **b.** $0.21   **c.** $0.71   **d.** $0.37   **e.** $0.42   **17.** 65%   **19.** 50%   **21.** $60.00

Section 16-6   **5. a.** $0.50   **b.** 40.0%   **7. a.** $38.00   **b.** 80.0%   **9. a.** $0.91   **b.** 700.0%   **11.** 150.0%   **13.** 205.1%   **15.** 123.6%   **17. a.** 150.0%   **b.** 66.7%   **c.** 100.0%   **d.** 185.7%   **e.** 144.7%   **f.** 68.4%   **g.** 68.1%   **h.** 83.7%   **i.** 12.9%   **19.** $89.69   **21.** 150.0%   **23.** 25.0%

Section 16-7   **5. a.** $81.00   **7. a.** $129.60   **b.** $216.00   **9. a.** $657.83   **b.** $1,409.63   **11.** $178.99   **13.** $33.48   **15.** $295.70   **17.** $0.82   **19. a.** 2.29   **b.** 62.4%   **21.** $129.00   **23.** $1,919.49   **25.** $180.00

Section 16-8   **5. a.** $5.00   **b.** 20.0%   **7. a.** $97.88   **b.** 39.5%   **9.** 40.4%   **11.** 14.4%   **13.** 25.3%   **15.** 33.3%   **17.** $60.00   **19.** 30.0%   **21.** 20.2%   **23.** 34.9%   **25.** 15.0%   **27.** 33.3%   **29.** 25.0%

Study Guide and Assessment   **1.** markdown   **3.** net profit   **5.** markdown rate   **7.** operating expenses   **9.** gross profit   *Section 16-1*   **11.** $0.20   **13.** $30.74   **15.** $24.15   **17. a.** $1.51   **b.** $54.36   *Section 16-2*   **19. a.** $6.14   **b.** 48.8%   **21. a.** $400.47   **b.** 30.8%   **23. a.** $10.45   **b.** 40.3%   *Section 16-3*   **25.** $53.26   **27.** $55.90

29. $7.96   *Section 16-4*   **31. a.** $33.31   **b.** 45.4%   **33. a.** $27.76   **b.** 25.2%   **35. a.** $160.27   **b.** 8.2%   *Section 16-5*   **37. a.** 78%   **b.** $135.26   **39. a.** 68%   **b.** $122.40   **41. a.** 81.5%   **b.** $1,238.22   *Section 16-6*   **43. a.** $11.42   **b.** 61.6%   **45. a.** $30.00   **b.** 37.5%   **47. a.** $34.25   **b.** 61.7%   *Section 16-7*   **49. a.** $185.50   **b.** $371   **51. a.** $126.30   **b.** $189.45   **53. a.** $759.02   **b.** $1,600.04   *Section 16-8*   **55. a.** $65.55   **b.** 39.6%   **57. a.** $895.50   **b.** 47.2%   **59. a.** $7.17   **b.** 56.6%   **61.** Answers will vary.

Chapter 17 Marketing

Section 17-1   **3.** 80.0%   **5.** 60.0%   **7.** 89.0%   **9. a.** Definitely: 405; Probably: 602; Possibly: 451; No: 282   **b.** Under 25: 306; 25–34: 527; 35–49: 513; 50 and over: 394   **c.** 1,740   **d.** Definitely: 23.3%; Probably: 34.6%; Possibly: 25.9%; No: 16.2%   **e.** Under 25: 13.1%; 25–34: 37.3%; 35–49: 31.1%; 50 and over: 18.5%   **f.** 25–34   **g.** Under 25: 32.3%; 25–34: 20.2%; 35–49: 19.1%; 50 and over: 28.4%   **h.** Under 25   **11.** 56

Section 17-2   **3. a.** 200,000   **5. a.** 20.0%   **b.** 1,140,000   **7. a.** 2.5%   **b.** 8,150,000   **9.** 500,000   **11.** 2,250,000   **13.** 0.45

Section 17-3   **3.** 40.0%   **5.** 28.0%   **7.** 6.0%   **9.** 10.0%   **11.** 9.1%   **13.** 36.5%   **15.** 4.3%   **17.** 4.8%   **19.** 14.0%   **21.** 70.0%   **23.** 23.0   **25.** 0.7

Section 17-4   **3.** $37,000   **5.** $44,000   **7.** $50,000   **9.** 2005: $15 million; 2010: $16 million; 2015: $17 million   **11.** $44,286.00   **13.** 17.600   **15.** Fifty-two

Section 17-5   **3.** $400,000   **5.** $4,050,000   **7.** $324,000   **9.** $617,500   **11.** $130,224   **13.** 44,650   **15.** $3,188.25   **17.** 1,015.00   **19.** $480.00   **21.** $850.00

Section 17-6   **3. a.** $385.65   **5. a.** $37.52   **b.** $375.20   **7. a.** $49.50   **b.** $247.50   **9.** $744.00   **11.** $3,517.20   **13.** $3,892.91   **15.** $2,424.75

Section 17-7   **5.** $110,000   **7.** $345,000   **9.** $3,858,250   **11.** $307,500   **13.** $\frac{1}{8}$

Section 17-8   **3.** $120,000   **5. a.** $17.14   **b.** $38.14   **c.** $258,020   **7.** Selling price of $3.75: $0.53; $1.58; $2,061,500; Selling price of $4.50: $0.71; $1.76; $1,918,000; Selling price of $8.50: $1.67; $2.72; $1,734,000; Selling price of $10.25: $2.00; $3.05; $1,800.000; Selling price of $3.75 yields greatest possible profit of $2,061,500.; 950,000 units should be produced.   **9.** 11.877

Study Guide and Assessment   **1–9.** Students' definitions will vary. Make sure they use their own words and show an understanding of the definition.   *Section 17-1*   **11.** 11%   **13.** 30.6%   **15.** 20.8%   *Section 17-2*   **17. a.** 33.3%   **b.** 99,900   **19. a.** 50%   **b.** 3,000,000   **21. a.** 35.7%   **b.** 44,625   *Section 17-3*   **23.** 50%   **25.** 36%   **27.** 7.5%   *Section 17-4*   **29.** Approximately $9.0 million.

Sales Projections

31. Approximately $5.5 million.

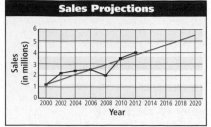

Sales Projections

Section 17-5   **33.** $1,560,000   **35.** $1,676,400
37. $16,500,000   **Section 17-6**   **39. a.** $26.13
b. $783.90   **41. a.** $50.40   **b.** $756.00   **43. a.** $19.45
b. $1,945   **Section 17-7**   **45.** $144,000   **47.** $325,000
49. $33,750   **Section 17-8**   **51.** $12.50 selling price results
in net profit of $76,250; $16.00 selling price results in net profit
of $89,000; $22.00 selling price results in net profit of $104,250;
$26.00 selling price results in net profit of $39,500   **53. a.** $25
b. $43   **c.** $88,000   **55. a.** $1.00   **b.** $19.00
c. $16,500,000

Cumulative Test Prep   **1.** A   **3.** A   **5.** A   **7.** C
9. 68.1%   **11.** 20%   **13.** $550.63   **15.** $66,500
17. Answers may vary. Defective items could result in loss of
customers.   **19.** It can be hard to collect money. Offering cash
discounts is an incentive to pay. It is not always advantageous
to pay early if the money is invested somewhere making more
money than the discount.

Chapter 18 Warehousing and Distributing
Section 18-1   **5.** 1,313 cu ft   **7. a.** 4   **b.** 80 cu ft
9. a. 20   **b.** 240 cu ft   **11. a.** 2,056.25   **b.** 17.8 =
18 cu ft   **13.** 4,800 cu ft   **15.** 25 cu ft   **17.** 840 cu meters
19. 4,536,000 cu in; 2,625 cu ft   **21.** 1.12 cu meters
23. 2,430 cu meters   **25.** 2.3625 cu yd
Section 18-2   **7. a.** 119   **b.** 82   **c.** 6   **d.** 6   **9. a.** 128
b. 74   **c.** 34   **d.** 158   **e.** 115   **11. a.** 40   **b.** 184   **c.** 126
13. 90
15.

Date	Receipts	Shipments	Balance
8/01			47
8/06		24	23
8/16	40		63
8/27		36	27
8/31	50		77

17. 195   **19.** 94   **21.** 142   **23.** 8,685
Section 18-3   **5. a.** $22.15   **b.** $509.45
7. a.

Date	Units Received	Unit Cost	Total Cost
3/10	1,152	$0.89	$1,025.28
4/22	936	0.94	879.84
Total	2,088	—	$1,905.12

7. b. $0.91   **c.** $236.60   **9.** $40.61

11. a.

Date	Units Received	Unit Cost	Total Cost
5/01	100	$9.65	$ 965.00
5/08	65	9.75	633.75
5/19	145	9.90	1,435.50
Total	310		$3,034.25

11. b. $1,550   **c.** $1,484.25

100 at $9.65	=	$ 965	5 at $9.75	=	$ 48.75
60 at $9.75	=	$ 585	145 at $9.90	=	$1,435.50
160 Total		$1,550	150 Total		$1,484.25

13. $420   **15.** $2,656.80   **17.** $31.32   **19.** $8.37
21. $3.42   **23.** $0.87
Section 18-4   **3.** $240   **5.** $1,170   **7.** $38,414.01
9. $32,680.80

11. a.

4.0%	$15,200
8.0%	30,400
10.0%	38,000
2.0%	7,600
0.5%	1,900
0.5%	1,900
25.0%	95,000

11. b. $23,750
13. $24,000
15. $43,990
17. $25,070.50

Section 18-5   **5. a.** $196.00   **b.** $1,176.00   **7. a.** $160.10
b. $1,215.16   **9.** $770.80; $554.60   **11. a.** $384.95
b. $271.33   **13.** $73.01   **15.** $22.61   **17.** $892.04
Section 18-6   **5. a.** $165.30   **b.** $165.30   **7. a.** $1.95
b. $167.70   **c.** $442.70   **9. a.** $3.11   **b.** $1,216.01
c. $1,216.01   **11.** $632.56   **13.** $364.42   **15.** $236.64
17. $460.34   **19.** $216.87   **21.** $365.50
Study Guide and Assessment   **1.** average-cost method
3. warehouse   **5.** first in, first out   **Section 18-1**   **7.** 360
cubic ft   **9.** 105 cubic ft   **11.** 1,320 cubic ft   **Section 18-2**
13. a. 599   **15. a.** 539   **b.** 464   **17. a.** 434   **b.** 503
Section 18-3   **19.** $733.88 ÷ 510 = $1.44 average cost per
unit; $1.44 × 12 = $17.28 inventory value   **21.** FIFO: $2,717.50;
LIFO: $277.50   **Section 18-4**   **23.** $3,628.50   **25.** $3,570
27. $223,125   **Section 18-5**   **29. a.** $127.75   **b.** $1,277.50
31. a. $46   **b.** $552   **33. a.** $146.75   **b.** $1,323.69
Section 18-6   **35. a.** $1.95   **b.** $193.05   **c.** $243.05
37. a. $2.69   **b.** $742.44   **c.** $1,067.44   **39. a.** $4.30
b. $709.50   **c.** $959.50

Chapter 19 Services
Section 19-1   **3. a.** 450 sq ft   **b.** $300   **5. a.** 1,500 sq ft
b. $1,250   **7.** $319   **9.** $1,560   **11.** $1,525   **13.** $2,150
15. $756
Section 19-2   **3. a.** $168.00   **b.** $593.00   **5. a.** $196.00
b. $1,143.56   **7.** $153.60   **9.** $962.50   **11.** $6.56
13. $146.25   **15.** $95.06
Section 19-3   **3. a.** $94.78   **b.** $394.28   **5. a.** $102.76
b. $655.11   **7.** $1,231.65   **9.** $469.90   **11. a.** $18,316.26
b. Rent for 12 months, $18,316.26 for 12 months vs. $18,655.45
for 11 months (no discount). Rent for 12 months and save.
13. $2.90

Section 19-4 3. $97.84 **5.** $123.59 **7.** $123.59
9. $141.29 **11.** $160.62 **13.** $63.93 **15.** $36.81
17. $44.44
Section 19-5 3. $2,223.90 **5.** $647.00 **7.** $548.10
Section 19-6 5. $1,500.00 **7.** $5,000.00
9. $18,450.00 **11.** $2,160.00 **13.** $63,375.00;
$911,625.00 **15.** $4,888.20 **17.** $21,753.85
19. $65,030.00 **21.** $211,962.50
Study Guide and Assessment 1–11. Definitions will
vary. *Section 19-1* **13. a.** 200 **b.** $150 **15. a.** 875
b. $765.63 **17. a.** 540 **b.** $281.25 *Section 19-2*
19. a. $236.25 **b.** $558.23 **21. a.** $158.40 **b.** $780.30
23. a. $58.80 **b.** $771.70 *Section 19-3* **25. a.** $625.30
b. $3,995.68 **27. a.** $152.96 **b.** $663.85 **29. a.** $811.27
b. $10,319.35 *Section 19-4* **31.** $153.39 **33.** $173.54
35. $88.64 *Section 19-5* **37.** $2,485 **39.** $2,303.50
41. $4,494.00 *Section 19-6* **43.** $1,875 **45.** $937.50
47. $31,850

Cumulative Test Prep 1. B **3.** D **5.** D **7.** D
9. Receipts are incoming items; issues are outgoing items
11. $2,940 **13.** Demand charge is based on the peak load
during the month; energy charge is based on the total number
of kilowatt-hours that the business uses during the month.
15. $1,832.73 **17.** It is important so that a business can meet
sales demands while not keeping excessive quantities. **19.** If
they only need the furniture for a short time.

Chapter 20 Accounting
Section 20-1

	Name	Gross Pay	FIT	SS	Medicare	Total Ded.	Net Pay
3.	Abbot	$485.00	$ 43.00	$30.07	$ 7.03	$ 80.10	$404.90
5.	Jackson	795.00	117.00	49.29	11.53	177.82	617.18
7.	Murakami	643.00	67.00	39.87	9.32	116.19	526.81

9. $12,563.68 **11.** See table below. **13.** See table below.
15. $26.40 **17.** $410.30 **19.** $463.92
Section 20-2 3. 3% **5.** 31.5% **7.** 26.6% **9.** 3.8%
11. 66.7% **13. a.** 47.9% **b.** 2% **c.** 17.1% **d.** 22.3%
e. 4% **f.** 2.1% **g.** 4.6% **h.** $301,705 **15.** $202,783
17. 25.0%
Section 20-3 3. $1,250 **5.** $19,531.25 **7.** $2,204.44
9. See table below. **11.** 0.021 **13.** 0.005

Section 20-1 11.

Payroll Register for Goldstone Swimming Complex Date: June 8, 20--

Name	Hours	Gross Pay	FIT	SS	Medicare	CIT	Total Ded.	Net Pay
Banks	24	$ 180.00	$ 7.00	$ 11.16	$ 2.61	$ 2.52	$ 23.29	$ 156.71
Drake	34	255.00	25.00	15.81	3.70	3.57	48.08	206.92
Faust	36	270.00	19.00	16.74	3.92	3.78	43.44	225.56
Harakis	38	285.00	29.00	17.67	4.13	3.99	54.79	230.21
Kendrick	36	270.00	28.00	16.74	3.92	3.78	52.44	217.56
Reese	38	285.00	21.00	17.67	4.13	3.99	46.79	238.21
Segura	30	225.00	20.00	13.95	3.26	3.15	40.36	184.64
Total		$1,770.00	$149.00	$109.74	$25.67	$24.78	$309.19	$1,460.81

Section 20-1 13.

Name	Sales	Gross Pay	FIT	SS	Med.	Total Ded.	Net Pay
Aguilar	$ 4,200.00	$ 454.50	$ 46.00	$ 28.18	$ 6.59	$ 84.77	$ 369.73
Grant	2,786.00	369.66	41.00	22.92	5.36	73.28	296.38
Iskersky	3,865.00	474.90	24.00	29.44	6.89	64.33	410.57
Melendez	4,500.00	540.00	60.00	33.48	7.83	105.31	436.69
Quinn	1,430.00	254.55	25.00	15.78	3.69	48.47	206.08
Valdez	5,184.00	581.04	32.00	36.02	8.43	80.45	500.59
Xerxes	3,146.00	418.26	40.00	25.93	6.06	75.99	342.27
Total	$25,111.00	$3,092.91	$268.00	$191.75	$44.85	$532.60	$2,560.31

Section 20-3 9.

Shop	Sq. Ft.	Base Rent	Security	Taxes	Insurance	Maint.	Assoc. Fee	Total
								$ 19.66
Ken's Carry Out	4,000	$ 52,000	$ 3,000	$ 5,400	$1,440	$13,800	$ 3,000	78,640
The Jean Place	3,000	39,000	2,250	4,050	1,080	10,350	2,250	58,980
Pan's Pizza	2,500	32,500	1,875	3,375	900	8,625	1,875	49,150
World Travel	3,000	39,000	2,250	4,050	1,080	10,350	2,250	58,980
Kay Jewelers	2,500	32,500	1,875	3,375	900	8,625	1,875	49,150
Total	15,000	$195,000	$11,250	$20,250	$5,400	$51,750	$11,250	$294,900

Section 20-4 **3.** $4,000 **5.** $1,275 **7.** $48,500 **9.** $12,747 **11.** $48,333.33 **13.** $1,974.37 **15.** $611.43 **17.** $48.1745

Section 20-5 **5. a.** $800 **b.** $3,200 **c.** $1,800 **7. a.** $2,000 **b.** $6,000 **c.** $9,000 **9. a.** $2,000 **b.** $10,000 **c.** $5,000 **11. a.** $2,000 **b.** $14,000 **c.** $1,000 **13. a.** $4,330 **b.** $8,660 **c.** $4,330 **15.**

End of Year	Original Cost	Depreciation	Accumulated Depreciation	Book Value
1	$1,880	$240	$ 240	$1,640
2	1,880	240	480	1,400
3	1,880	240	720	1,160
4	1,880	240	960	920
5	1,880	240	1,200	680
6	1,880	240	1,440	440
7	1,880	240	1,680	200

17. $6,200 **19.** $17,500 **21.** $49,050

Section 20-6 **3–5.** See table below. **7.**

Year	Original Cost	Fixed Percent	Annual Depreciation
1	$164,500.00	33.33%	$ 54,827.85
2	164,500.00	44.45%	73,120.25
3	164,500.00	14.81%	24,362.45
4	164,500.00	7.41%	12,189.45
		100.00%	164,500.00

9. See table below. **11.** $28,310 **13.** $118

Study Guide and Assessment **1–9.** Definitions will vary. *Section 20-1* **11. a.** $34.80 **b.** $8.14 **c.** $104.94 **d.** $456.31 **13. a.** $19.28 **b.** $4.51 **c.** $48.79 **d.** $262.21 **15. a.** $67.61 **b.** $15.81 **c.** $280.42 **d.** $810.08 **17.** $418.75 *Section 20-2* **19.** 9.4% **21.** 8.1% **23.** 13.3% *Section 20-3* **25–27.** See table below. *Section 20-4* **29.** $3,800 **31.** $15,200 **33.** $4,250 *Section 20-5* **35. a.** $5,290 **b.** $550 **c.** $550 **d.** $5,290 **37. a.** $5,290 **b.** $550 **c.** $1,650 **d.** $5,290 **39. a.** $5,290 **b.** $550 **c.** $2,750 **d.** $5,290 **41. a.** $5,290 **b.** $550 **c.** $3,850 **d.** $5,290 *Section 20-6* **43. a.** $86,500 **b.** $17,300 **c.** $17,300 **d.** $69,200 **45. a.** $86,500 **b.** $12,283 **c.** $44,115 **d.** $42,385 **47. a.** $86,500 **b.** $8,520.25 **c.** $63,188.25 **d.** $23,311.75 **49. a.** $86,500 **b.** $7,802.30 **c.** $78,905.30 **d.** $7,594.70

Chapter 21 Accounting Records

Section 21-1 **3.** $77,000 **5.** $36,250 **7.** $17,450 **9.** Assets: $221,797; Liabilities: $142,257; Owner's equity: $79,540 **11.** $17,704.22 **13.** $72,958.00

Section 21-2 **3.** Total assets: $33,000; Total liabilities: $12,300; Owner's equity: $20,700 **5.** Total assets: $52,500; Bank loan: $22,500; Total liabilities: $27,500 **7. a.** Total assets: $99,800 **b.** Total liabilities: $65,000 **c.** Owner's equity: $34,800 **9.** Total assets: $80,467.50; Total liabilities: $51,013.20; Owner's equity: $29,454.30; Total liabilities and Owner's equity: $80,467.50 **11.** Total assets: $199,504,200; Total liabilities: $142,599,410; Owner's equity: $56,904,790; Total liabilities and Owner's equity: $199,504,200 **13.** $27,970 **15.** $5,072,400

Section 20-6

Item	Year 1	2	3	4	5	6
3. Taxi	$3,200.00	$ 5,120.00	$3,072.00	$1,843.20	$1,843.20	$ 921.60
5. Computers	6,960.00	11,136.00	6,681.60	4,008.96	4,008.96	2,004.48

Section 20-6 **9.**

Year	Original Cost	Fixed Percent	Annual Depreciation	Accumulated Depreciation	Book Value
1	$48,260.00	20.00%	$ 9,652.00	$ 9,652.00	$38,608.00
2	48,260.00	32.00%	15,443.20	25,095.20	23,164.80
3	48,260.00	19.20%	9,265.92	34,361.12	13,898.88
4	48,260.00	11.52%	5,559.55	39,920.67	8,339.33
5	48,260.00	11.52%	5,559.55	45,480.22	2,779.78
6	48,260.00	5.76%	2,779.78	48,260.00	0
		100.00%	48,260.00		

Study Guide and Assessment *Section 20-3*

	Sq. Ft.	Base	Sec.	Taxes	Insur.	Maint.	Assoc.	Total
		12.5	0.85	1.55	0.065	2.1	0.9	
25.	3,400	$42,500	$2,890	$5,270	$221	$7,140	$3,060	$61,081
27.	2,100	26,250	1,785	3,255	137	4,410	1,890	37,727

Section 21-3 **3.** $96,600 **5.** $17,950 **7.** $58,127
9. $7,871.68 **11.** $9,921.32 **13.** $1,164.92 **15.** $17,847.80
17. $16,596.26 **19.** $2,853.46 **21.** $95.76
Section 21-4 **3.** $4,685 **5. a.** $3,675 **b.** $1,935
c. $1,107 **7. a.** $673,642 **b.** $255,726 **c.** $159,307
9. a. $388,125 **b.** $157,125 **c.** $85,209 **11.** Net sales:
$3,080; Gross profit: $3,080; Total operating expenses: $2,209;
Net income: $871 **13.** Gross profit: $58.3 million; Total
operating expenses: $38.7 million; Net income: $19.6 million
15. $218,695.25 **17.** $455.06
Section 21-5 **5.** 50.0% **7.** 44.5% **9. a.** 2.0:1.0
b. 1.2:1.0 **11. a.** $3,553 **b.** 46.2% **13. a.** 1.6:1.0
b. 1.3:1.0 **15.** 25% **17.** 1.0:1.0
Section 21-6 **3.** 15.3% **5.** $23,090; 20.1%
7. a. −$775 **b.** −16.7% **9. a.** $8,943 **b.** 21.1%
11. a. −$7.5; −6.4% **b.** −$2.2; −3.9% **c.** −$5.3; −8.8%
d. $0.5; 1.4% **e.** −$5.8; −23.4% **13.** 50.0% **15.** 29.6%
Study Guide and Assessment **1.** income statement
3. amount of change **5.** assets **7.** quick ratio **9.** cost of
goods sold **Section 21-1** **11.** $47,144 **13.** $32,870
15. $96,500 **Section 21-2** **17. a.** $132,800
b. $113,400 **c.** $19,400 **19. a.** $287,954 **b.** $5,600
c. $216,200 **21. a.** $113,192 **b.** $56,890 **c.** $68,390
23. a. $181,337.10 **b.** $80,500.68 **c.** $81,483.89
Section 21-3 **25.** $136,134 **27.** $43,715.10
29. $85,114.90 **Section 21-4** **31. a.** $36,250
b. $27,709.80 **c.** $9,209.80 **33. a.** $84,009.89
b. $68,109.55 **c.** $26,909.55 **35. a.** $38,393.03
b. $17,183.72 **c.** $752.75 **Section 21-5** **37. a.** 1.7:1
b. 1.5:1 **39. a.** 2.2:1 **b.** 1.8:1 **Section 21-6**
41. a. $128,100 **b.** 22.8% **43. a.** $66,931 **b.** 61.1%
45. a. −$99,030 **b.** −3.1% **47. a.** −$77,553.64
b. −70.2%

Chapter 22 Financial Management

Section 22-1 **3.** $5,511.90 **5. a.** $64,823
b. $11,205.75 **7. a.** $194,884 **b.** $59,254.76
9. $742.35 **11.** 4.44 **13.** 12.48 **15.** 1,645
17. $12,434 **19.** $58.084
Section 22-2 **5. a.** $408,000 **b.** $455,500 **c.** $6,344,500
d. $1.14 **7. a.** $1,050,000 **b.** $1,104,650 **c.** $19,895,350
d. $1.10 **9.** $653,360 **11.** $31,249,125; $1.48 **13.** $63,700
15. $44,580
Section 22-3 **5. a.** $1,050 **b.** $71,050 **7. a.** $1,562.50
b. $39,062.50 **9. a.** $1,066.67 **b.** $65,066.67
11. $202,468.75 **13.** $718,250 **15.** 0.127 **17.** 0.006
19. 0.0005
Section 22-4 **5. a.** $525 **b.** $69,500 **7. a.** $1,762.50
b. $148,237.50 **9. a.** $1,200 **b.** $58,830 **c.** 6.119%
11. 139.92 **13.** 0.2337 = 0.234 **15.** 12.3333 = 12.333
17. 24.275
Section 22-5 **5. a.** $3,500 **b.** $696,545
c. 6.030% **7. a.** $17,625.00 **b.** $1,482,375 **c.** 2.378%
9. a. $735,977.50 **b.** 7.64% **11. a.** $497,748.33;
5.525% **b.** $495,248.33; 5.805% **c.** $492,727.50; 5.969%
d. $931,356.67; 6.031% **13.** 0.23422 = 0.234
15. 0.336755 = 0.337
Section 22-6 **5.** $23,719 **7.** $31,041 **9.** $21,670
11. $3,071,356.40 **13.** 600.712 **15.** 5.361

Study Guide and Assessment **1.** commercial
paper **3.** taxable income **5.** bonds **7.** commercial loan
9. underwriting commission **Section 22-1** **11. a.** $147,629
b. $40,825.31 **13. a.** $42,529 **b.** $6,379.35
15. a. $240,376 **b.** $76,996.64 **17. a.** $242,088
b. $77,664.32 **Section 22-2** **19. a.** $60,200
b. $106,180 **c.** $753,820 **d.** $3.93 **21. a.** $534,000
b. $654,000 **c.** $8,246,000 **d.** $3.44 **23. a.** $2,189,000
b. $2,299,500 **c.** $37,500,500 **d.** $1.53 **Section 22-3**
25. a. $2,200.00 **b.** $112,200.00 **27. a.** $9,375
b. $259,375 **29. a.** $10,006.25 **b.** $810,506.25
Section 22-4 **31. a.** $704.17 **b.** $64,325.83
c. 6.57% **33. a.** $2,041.47 **b.** $123,008.83 **c.** 4.98%
35. a. $2,093.82 **b.** $95,966.18 **c.** 9.59% **Section**
22-5 **37. a.** $6,662.50 **b.** $643,372.50 **c.** 6.21%
39. a. $18,366.67 **b.** $931,663.33 **c.** 5.91%
41. a. $114,481.11 **b.** $6,885,468.89 **c.** 7.30%
Section 22-6 **43.** $39,631 **45.** $43,568

Chapter 23 Corporate Planning

Section 23-1 **5.** 6.4% **7.** $154.35 **9.** $1.28
11. 9.1% **13.** $4,111.01 **15.** $129,310.84 **17.** 0%
19. $76.84 **21.** 2,890% **23.** $0.33 **25.** $16.16
27. $0.01 **29.** 1.9%
Section 23-2 **3. a.** $118.3 million **b.** $309 **5. a.** $448.9
billion **b.** $6,450.13 **7. a.** $2,652.3 billion **b.** $1,170.83
9. $732,672,000 **11.** $278,692,400,000; $17,157.78
13. $597,921,242,000; $20,020.27 **15.** $185,425,000,000;
$23,694.53 **17. a.** France: $1,223,183,622,000 **b.** U.K.:
$987,252,000,000 **c.** France: $21,069.37 **d.** U.K.: $18,099.07
19. $5,003.88 **21.** $125,875.67
Section 23-3 **3.** 100.5 **5.** $521.63 **7.** $364.98
9. 177.8 **11.** $354.33 **13.** $26,311.72 **15.** $166.29
17. $112.47 **19.** 3.0 **21.** 0.4 **23.** $59,409.95
Section 23-4 **9. a.** $20,000 **b.** −$5,000
11. a. $60,200 **b.** $3,800 **13. a.** $3,763,200
b. −$201,200 **15.** Sales: $105,000; services: $30,000;
investments: $15,000 **17.** Sales: −$40,000; services:
−$30,000; investments: $10,000; total: −$60,000 **19.** Sales:
$14,610,240; trading profits: $304,380; other: $304,380
21.

	Actual	Budget Allocation	Difference
Apples	$420,000	$408,000	$+12,000
Strawberries	91,320	136,000	−44,680
Blueberries	91,340	102,000	−10,660
Cherries	39,900	34,000	+5,900
Total	$642,560	$680,000	$−37,440

23. $272,196.60 **25.** $1,089,499.88 **27.** $3,155,178.64
Study Guide and Assessment **1.** inflation
3. budget **5.** consumer price index **Section 23-1**
7. 10.5% **9.** $1,330.64 **11.** $976.61 **Section 23-2**
13. a. $315,042,200 **b.** $5.10 **15. a.** $485,616,600,000
b. $198.22 **17. a.** $6,119,040,875 **b.** $4.37 **Section**
23-3 **19.** 290.35 **21.** $16,166.72 **23.** $6.11 **Section**
23-4 **25. a.** $29,430 **b.** $21,070 **27. a.** $152,519.40
b. −$30,554.40 **29. a.** $540,954 **b.** −$105,554
Cumulative Test Prep **1.** C **3.** D **5.** D **7.** A
9. $28,700 ordinary interest or $28,690.41 exact interest

11. $47,575 **13.** 300.5 **15.** Answers will vary but might mention that it rewards people for being married and having children. **17.** Answers will vary but might mention that a balance sheet shows the financial position of a company on a certain date. An income statement shows a company's income and operating expenses in detail.

Skills Answers

Skill 1 **1.** Ones; 5 **3.** Tens; 70 **5.** Ones; 8 **7.** Tens; 0 **9.** Hundreds; 700 **11.** Ones; 9 **13.** Tenths; 0.3 **15.** Thousandths; 0.009 **17.** Hundredths; 0.02 **19.** Ones; 4 **21.** Hundredths; 0.02 **23.** Thousandths; 0.007 **25.** Thousandths; 0.003 **27.** Thousandths; 0.001 **29.** Thirty-four **31.** Seventy-eight **33.** Eight hundred forty-two **35.** Five thousand twelve **37.** One hundred nineteen **39.** One thousand two hundred forty **41.** One hundred ninety-four **43.** Twenty-five and $\frac{00}{100}$ dollars **45.** Seventeen and $\frac{9}{100}$ dollars **47.** One hundred twenty and $\frac{17}{100}$ dollars **49.** Seven thousand seven hundred forty-nine dollars **51.** $\frac{50}{100}$ dollars or fifty cents **53.** $71.64 million **55.** 18.4 thousand **57.** 171.6 thousand **59.** 2.135 billion **61.** $3,400,000 **63.** $11,200,000,000 **65.** 7,300,000,000 **67.** 400,000 **69.** $720,000,000 **71.** 54 **73.** 835 **75.** 211 **77.** 5,763 **79.** 4,444 **81.** 1,236 **83.** 650 **85.** $101 **87.** $93 **89.** $742 **91.** $791,000 **93.** 2.0 **95.** 25.1 **97.** 58 **99.** 0.1 **101.** 0.5 **103.** 0.020 **105.** $10 **107.** $19 **109.** $600 **111.** $9,521.39 **113.** $2,000.00

Skill 2 **1.** 30 **3.** 70 **5.** 220 **7.** 8,100 **9.** 600 **11.** 6,000 **13.** 16,000 **15.** 1,000 **17.** 0.1 **19.** 0.5 **21.** 0.47 **23.** 0.36 **25.** 0.601 **27.** 0.213 **29.** 137.492 **31.** 38,000 **33.** 48,000 **35.** 900 **37.** 30 **39.** 580 **41.** 36 **43.** 189.7 **45.** 0.1 **47.** 152.43 **49.** 0.179 **51.** 108.437

Skill 3 **1.** 106 **3.** 138 **5.** 1,189 **7.** 799 **9.** 897 **11.** 488 **13.** 10,878 **15.** 8,987 **17.** 71 **19.** 210 **21.** 897 **23.** 1,542 **25.** 4,638 **27.** 12,224 **29.** 12,201 **31.** 12,787 **33.** 3,798 **35.** 12,318 **37.** 8,152 **39.** 9,484 **41.** 6,777 **43.** 14,953 **45.** 33,587 **47.** 87,481 **49.** 14,999 **51.** 14,450

Skill 4 **1.** 331 **3.** 151 **5.** 3,442 **7.** 3,311 **9.** 1,111 **11.** 8,020 **13.** 6 **15.** 6,231 **17.** 64 **19.** 99 **21.** 2,258 **23.** 1,166 **25.** 1,909 **27.** 3,667 **29.** 1,275 **31.** 859 **33.** 2,983 **35.** 1,568 **37.** 9,111 **39.** 1,862 **41.** 2,238 **43.** 2,901 **45.** 16,526 **47.** 37,503 **49.** 126,403 **51.** 100,621

Skill 5 **1.** 1,406.20 **3.** 713.39 **5.** 900.05 **7.** 2,411.356 **9.** 1,719.002 **11.** 98.03 **13.** 1,300.840 **15.** 1,044.00 **17.** 91.111 **19.** 156.254 **21.** 19.999 **23.** 1,126.030 **25.** 1,083.557 **27.** 508.595 **29.** 1.000 **31.** 147.420 **33.** 787.032 **35.** 1,191.418

Skill 6 **1.** 51.15 **3.** 134.89 **5.** 5.09 **7.** 25.51 **9.** 79.68 **11.** 203.84 **13.** 70.85 **15.** 84.32 **17.** 19.6 **19.** 8.07 **21.** 57.44 **23.** 377.63 **25.** 5.09 **27.** 19.983 **29.** 325.86 **31.** 204.354 **33.** 557.87 **35.** 5,215.946 **37.** 1.1178 **39.** 778.029 **41.** 3.59806 **43.** 2.74502

Skill 7 **1.** 1,533 **3.** 87,344 **5.** 100,152 **7.** 77,256 **9.** 959,373 **11.** 2,808 **13.** 251,565 **15.** 4,268,236 **17.** 1,665 **19.** 310,992 **21.** 1,662,024 **23.** 69,000 **25.** 28,182 **27.** 357,000 **29.** 36,060,000 **31.** 4,471,392

33. 43,955,000 **35.** 1,070,443 **37.** 169,130 **39.** 623,770 **41.** 1,309,622 **43.** 2,804,972 **45.** 15,805,077

Skill 8 **1.** 4.5 **3.** 878.22 **5.** 188.55 **7.** 230.8218 **9.** 43.9556 **11.** 287.352 **13.** 0.1008 **15.** 0.096 **17.** 0.584 **19.** 0.6156 **21.** 0.0567 **23.** 0.0861 **25.** 4,116 **27.** 36 **29.** 876.403 **31.** 1,212.86 **33.** 112.5 **35.** 81.9698 **37.** 161,713.902 **39.** 0.156462 **41.** 84 **43.** 0.07608533

Skill 9 **1.** $2\frac{1}{3}$ **3.** $2\frac{2}{41}$ **5.** $14\frac{12}{53}$ **7.** $84\frac{17}{21}$ **9.** $67\frac{19}{43}$ **11.** $59\frac{12}{23}$ **13.** $71\frac{42}{81}$ **15.** $16\frac{13}{114}$ **17.** $15\frac{17}{321}$ **19.** $8\frac{792}{892}$ **21.** $23\frac{22}{409}$ **23.** $14\frac{2}{625}$ **25.** $20\frac{831}{843}$ **27.** 18 **29.** 16 **31.** 72 **33.** $14\frac{22}{621}$ **35.** $12\frac{349}{549}$ **37.** $5\frac{765}{842}$ **39.** $181\frac{29}{473}$ **41.** $87\frac{527}{622}$ **43.** $1,600\frac{3}{51}$ **45.** $252\frac{46}{88}$ **47.** $208\frac{166}{417}$ **49.** $1,345\frac{177}{514}$

Skill 10 **1.** 11.125 **3.** 21.2 **5.** 5.1 **7.** 19.75 **9.** 34.5 **11.** 22.8 **13.** 16.1 **15.** 206.8 **17.** 2.02 **19.** 10.865 **21.** 21.524 **23.** 8.71 **25.** 10.45 **27.** 31.13 **29.** 5.63 **31.** 17.5 **33.** 14.44 **35.** 230.05 **37.** 41.42 **39.** 25.54 **41.** 39.5

Skill 11 **1.** 4.6 **3.** 5.71 **5.** 17 **7.** 6.5 **9.** 42.91 **11.** 26 **13.** 31 **15.** 26 **17.** 8.96 **19.** 13.21 **21.** 1.41 **23.** 245 **25.** 1.21 **27.** 256 **29.** 67.48 **31.** 22.57 **33.** 1.75 **35.** 38.5 **37.** 98.86 **39.** 0.01 **41.** 17.13 **43.** 0.01

Skill 12 **1.** 10 **3.** 50 **5.** 24 **7.** 22 **9.** 51 **11.** 24 **13.** 35 **15.** 72 **17.** 20 **19.** $\frac{2}{3}$ **21.** $\frac{1}{2}$ **23.** $\frac{2}{3}$ **25.** $\frac{1}{3}$ **27.** $\frac{5}{6}$ **29.** $\frac{10}{27}$ **31.** $\frac{4}{7}$ **33.** $\frac{1}{3}$ **35.** $\frac{3}{4}$ **37.** $\frac{94}{183}$ **39.** $\frac{1}{2}$ **41.** $\frac{19}{36}$ **43.** $\frac{2}{3}$ **45.** $\frac{4}{25}$

Skill 13 **1.** $\frac{25}{4}$ **3.** $\frac{59}{8}$ **5.** $\frac{20}{3}$ **7.** $\frac{39}{4}$ **9.** $\frac{43}{10}$ **11.** $\frac{135}{32}$ **13.** $\frac{16}{3}$ **15.** $\frac{29}{10}$ **17.** $\frac{53}{16}$ **19.** $\frac{165}{32}$ **21.** $\frac{79}{11}$ **23.** $\frac{57}{5}$ **25.** $6\frac{1}{2}$ **27.** $5\frac{3}{4}$ **29.** $5\frac{1}{2}$ **31.** $2\frac{1}{3}$ **33.** $2\frac{1}{2}$ **35.** $2\frac{20}{21}$ **37.** $5\frac{5}{6}$ **39.** $3\frac{1}{6}$ **41.** $6\frac{1}{8}$ **43.** $6\frac{3}{7}$

Skill 14 **1.** 0.8 **3.** 1.13 **5.** 2.43 **7.** 1.37 **9.** 0.3 **11.** 4.38 **13.** 3.08 **15.** 0.03 **17.** 5.15 **19.** 2.12 **21.** 7.14 **23.** 0.44 **25.** $\frac{1}{10}$ **27.** $\frac{3}{100}$ **29.** $\frac{3}{100}$ **31.** $\frac{53}{100}$ **33.** $\frac{3}{1,000}$ **35.** $\frac{8}{125}$ **37.** $4\frac{111}{250}$ **39.** $\frac{469}{1,000}$ **41.** $7\frac{1}{2}$ **43.** $1\frac{2}{25}$ **45.** $2\frac{83}{100}$ **47.** $\frac{21}{200}$ **49.** $\frac{1}{2,000}$ **51.** $1\frac{402}{625}$ **53.** $\frac{1}{5,000}$

Skill 15 **1.** $1\frac{2}{5}$ **3.** $\frac{3}{4}$ **5.** $1\frac{4}{7}$ **7.** $1\frac{4}{5}$ **9.** $1\frac{1}{6}$ **11.** $1\frac{8}{45}$ **13.** $11\frac{2}{3}$ **15.** $14\frac{2}{7}$ **17.** $12\frac{1}{3}$ **19.** $17\frac{1}{4}$ **21.** $9\frac{7}{8}$ **23.** $11\frac{7}{2}$

Skill 16 **1.** $1\frac{1}{3}$ **3.** $\frac{20}{21}$ **5.** $1\frac{1}{2}$ **7.** $1\frac{13}{110}$ **9.** $\frac{59}{60}$ **11.** $\frac{71}{150}$ **13.** $9\frac{1}{6}$ **15.** $16\frac{1}{3}$ **17.** $20\frac{19}{26}$ **19.** $28\frac{22}{63}$ **21.** $28\frac{43}{56}$ **23.** $29\frac{5}{48}$

Skill 17 **1.** $\frac{2}{6}$ **3.** $\frac{5}{6}$ **5.** $\frac{4}{7}$ **7.** $\frac{1}{8}$ **9.** $\frac{2}{5}$ **11.** $\frac{2}{5}$ **13.** $\frac{1}{4}$ **15.** $\frac{7}{20}$ **17.** $1\frac{1}{7}$ **19.** $3\frac{1}{4}$ **21.** $2\frac{1}{6}$ **23.** $5\frac{3}{16}$ **25.** $2\frac{7}{13}$ **27.** $8\frac{1}{2}$ **29.** $25\frac{2}{7}$

Skill 18 **1.** $\frac{3}{8}$ **3.** $\frac{3}{20}$ **5.** $\frac{1}{18}$ **7.** $\frac{1}{15}$ **9.** $\frac{3}{20}$ **11.** $\frac{1}{10}$ **13.** $4\frac{1}{4}$ **15.** $6\frac{5}{18}$ **17.** $5\frac{7}{60}$ **19.** $3\frac{1}{8}$ **21.** $2\frac{3}{20}$ **23.** $2\frac{1}{8}$

Skill 19 **1.** $1\frac{1}{2}$ **3.** $2\frac{1}{10}$ **5.** $2\frac{6}{11}$ **7.** $3\frac{1}{18}$ **9.** $12\frac{11}{12}$ **11.** $1\frac{37}{70}$ **13.** $2\frac{7}{8}$ **15.** $1\frac{3}{8}$ **17.** $\frac{1}{8}$ **19.** $3\frac{7}{9}$ **21.** $\frac{9}{20}$ **23.** $11\frac{5}{6}$ **25.** $14\frac{7}{9}$ **27.** $13\frac{5}{7}$ **29.** $12\frac{5}{32}$

Skill 20 **1.** $\frac{1}{3}$ **3.** $\frac{5}{8}$ **5.** $\frac{5}{12}$ **7.** 2 **9.** 9 **11.** $16\frac{2}{15}$ **13.** $58\frac{1}{3}$ **15.** $46\frac{1}{8}$ **17.** $\frac{1}{6}$ **19.** $4\frac{1}{8}$ **21.** 6 **23.** $3\frac{3}{4}$ **25.** $19\frac{1}{2}$ **27.** $8\frac{8}{15}$ **29.** 64 **31.** $25\frac{49}{72}$ **33.** $97\frac{11}{12}$ **35.** $71\frac{1}{24}$

Skill 21 **1.** 2 **3.** $1\frac{7}{8}$ **5.** $7\frac{1}{2}$ **7.** 6 **9.** 16 **11.** $3\frac{7}{36}$ **13.** $2\frac{11}{12}$ **15.** $\frac{1}{4}$ **17.** $5\frac{5}{33}$ **19.** $4\frac{40}{323}$ **21.** $1\frac{1}{2}$ **23.** $1\frac{1}{2}$ **25.** $\frac{2}{3}$ **27.** 15 **29.** 6 **31.** 30 **33.** $\frac{43}{176}$ **35.** $\frac{143}{375}$ **37.** $6\frac{1}{2}$ **39.** 1

Skill 22   **1.** 1,500:600   **3.** 600:1,200   **5.** 600:1,500   **7.** $\frac{1}{5}$
9. $\frac{1}{15}$ **11.** $\frac{1}{25}$ **13.** $\frac{2}{5}$
Skill 23   **1.** T   **3.** F   **5.** F   **7.** T   **9.** T   **11.** F   **13.** 18
15. $7\frac{1}{3}$ **17.** $\frac{6}{11}$ **19.** $5\frac{5}{9}$ **21.** $12\frac{4}{13}$ **23.** 20   **25.** 5   **27.** 24
29. 64   **31.** 15   **33.** 50
Skill 24   **1.** 5 oranges/$0.99 = 7 oranges/$n$ **3.** 5 cm/40
kilometers = 17 cm/n **5.** $4.35   **7.** 117 pp.   **9.** 1,485 wheels
11. $28.00   **13.** $33\frac{1}{3}$ minutes
Skill 25   **1.** 288   **3.** 80   **5.** 64; 640   **7.** A   **9.** B   **11.** B
Skill 26   **1.** 10%   **3.** 25%   **5.** 82%   **7.** 213%
9. 575.3%   **11.** 39.1%   **13.** 1,210.4%   **15.** 1,082%
17. 10.6%   **19.** 4%   **21.** 50.3%   **23.** 70%   **25.** 710%
27. 1,050%   **29.** 1,260%   **31.** 2,250%   **33.** 3,720%
35. 750%   **37.** 1,630%   **39.** 620%   **41.** 380%
43. 67%   **45.** 880%   **47.** 32%   **49.** 300.3%   **51.** 21.87%
53. 2,500%   **55.** 14%   **57.** 51%   **59.** 186.8%   **61.** 0.3%
63. 26%   **65.** 0.32%   **67.** 29%   **69.** 342%   **71.** 210%
73. 167%   **75.** 250%   **77.** 207.7%   **79.** 19%
Skill 27   **1.** 25%   **3.** 75%   **5.** 12.5%   **7.** 35%   **9.** 14%
11. 62.5%   **13.** 275%   **15.** 666.7%   **17.** 855.6%
19. 817.5%   **21.** 722%   **23.** 537.5%   **25.** 58.3%
27. 1,530%   **29.** 2,080%   **31.** 1,862.5%   **33.** 93.8%
35. 1,135.7%   **37.** 77.8%   **39.** 573.3%   **41.** 1,735%
Skill 28   **1.** 0.105   **3.** 0.40   **5.** 1.20   **7.** 0.067   **9.** 0.089
11. 1.19   **13.** 0.172   **15.** 1.00   **17.** 0.053   **19.** 0.007
21. 0.00625   **23.** 0.056   **25.** 0.068   **27.** 0.306   **29.** 0.5784
31. 0.7425   **33.** 0.1880   **35.** 0.1445   **37.** 0.00125
39. 0.0014   **41.** 0.0879   **43.** 0.0095   **45.** 0.00025
47. 0.225   **49.** 0.252
Skill 29   **1.** $\frac{9}{20}$ **3.** $1\frac{3}{4}$ **5.** $\frac{117}{1,000}$ **7.** $\frac{3}{2,000}$ **9.** $\frac{53}{500}$
11. $\frac{3,763}{10,000}$ **13.** $\frac{1}{2}$ **15.** $\frac{101}{1,000}$ **17.** $\frac{809}{1,000}$ **19.** $\frac{1}{10}$ **21.** $\frac{7}{10}$
23. $\frac{1}{400}$ **25.** $\frac{31}{200}$ **27.** $\frac{51}{200}$ **29.** $\frac{1}{6}$ **31.** $\frac{3}{10}$ **33.** $\frac{5}{16}$ **35.** $\frac{1}{8}$
37. $\frac{4}{15}$ **39.** $\frac{1}{9}$ **41.** $\frac{1}{2}$ **43.** $\frac{1}{80}$ **45.** $\frac{51}{400}$ **47.** $\frac{43}{800}$ **49.** $\frac{1}{15}$
Skill 30   **1.** 9   **3.** 3.84   **5.** 7.8   **7.** 14.24   **9.** 3.486
11. 45.359   **13.** 10   **15.** 40   **17.** 6   **19.** 2.25   **21.** 128
23. 8.19   **25.** 15   **27.** 2   **29.** 80   **31.** 9.144   **33.** 25
35. 6.375
Skill 31   **1.** 50%   **3.** 20%   **5.** 35.7%   **7.** 89.2%   **9.** 69.9%
11. 87.2%   **13.** 150%   **15.** 120%   **17.** 133.3%   **19.** 129.2%
21. 400%   **23.** 513.3%   **25.** 80%   **27.** 46.2%   **29.** 55.1%
31. 80%   **33.** 120%   **35.** 25%   **37.** 138.9%   **39.** 200%
41. 66.7%   **43.** 5%   **45.** 146.7%
Skill 32   **1.** 72   **3.** 8,048.5   **5.** 1,600   **7.** 336.4   **9.** 60
11. 134   **13.** 160   **15.** 60   **17.** $90\frac{2}{3}$ **19.** $54\frac{86}{91}$ **21.** 75
23. 2.5   **25.** 52.5   **27.** 78   **29.** 180   **31.** 225   **33.** 55
35. $197\frac{1}{67}$

Applications Answers

Application A   **1.** 600 mi   **3.** 448 in   **5.** 210 m   **7.** 1,216
sq ft   **9.** 360 sq km   **11.** 31.4   **13.** 23.4   **15.** $437.95
17. $1,429.00   **19.** $5.25   **21.** $46.19   **23.** $50.16
Application B   **1.** 308 in   **3.** 8,775 yd   **5.** 8 h   **7.** 30 s
9. 30   **11.** 248   **13.** 20   **15.** 50
Application C   **1.** $1,200,000   **3.** $7,900,000   **5.** Bronx,
Columbus, Dallas, Lincoln, San Diego   **7.** Express Plus
9. a. Express   **b.** Mon.
Application D   **1.** 1 quarter, 1 dollar, 1 $5 bill   **3.** 1 penny,
3 dollars, 1 $5 bill   **5.** 2 pennies, 1 dime, 1 quarter, 4 dollars

7. 2 dimes, 3 quarters, 4 dollars   **9.** 1 penny, 2 dimes, 2 quarters
11. 1 quarter, 2 dollars   **13.** 1 dime, 1 dollar, 1 $5 bill
15. 1 quarter, 2 dollars   **17.** 2 quarters, 1 dollar, 1 $10 bill
Application E   **1.** 8:45   **3.** 7:00   **5.** 11:15   **7.** 12:15
9. 3:30   **11.** 8:45   **13.** 7:30   **15.** 9:45   **17.** 12:45
19. 6:00   **21.** 11:30   **23.** 10:15
Application F   **1.** 2 h:46 min   **3.** 3 h:15 min   **5.** 51 min
7. 5 h:15 min   **9.** 8 h:20 min   **11.** 10 h:45 min
Application G   **1.** 137 days   **3.** 212 days   **5.** 258 days
Application H   **1.** No   **3.** Yes   **5.** No   **7.** Yes   **9.** Yes
11. Yes
Application I   **1.** 79 days   **3.** 231 days   **5.** 222 days
Application J   **1.** $\frac{3}{4}$ yr   **3.** 1 yr   **5.** 3 yr   **7.** $1\frac{3}{4}$ yr
9. $1\frac{1}{6}$ yr   **11.** $\frac{5}{6}$ yr   **13.** $\frac{35}{73}$ yr   **15.** $\frac{50}{73}$ yr
Application K   **1.** 52   **3.** 16   **5.** 12   **7.** 6   **9.** 60
Application L   **1.** 0.85   **3.** 0.65   **5.** 0.20   **7.** 9%
9. 53%   **11.** 93%   **13.** 96.5%   **15.** 24.1%
Application M   **1.** $11.00   **3.** $13.00   **5.** About $4.00
Application N   **1.** $8,000   **3.** October and November
Application O   **1.** 45 hours   **3.** 2.5 hours
Application P   **1.** $1,360   **3.** $480
5.

	Percent	Degrees
Food	40%	144
Rent	30%	108
Entertainment	15%	54
Clothing etc.	10%	36
Other	5%	18
	100%	360

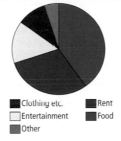

■ Clothing etc.   ■ Rent
□ Entertainment   ■ Food
■ Other

Application Q   **1.** 54.3   **3.** 6,726.75   **5.** $1,235,563
Application R   **1.** 148.5   **3.** 88   **5.** 0.09   **7.** 2.08
Application S   **1.** $24   **3.** None   **5.** 0.01
Application T   **1.** meter   **3.** millimeter   **5.** meter
7. centimeter
Application U   **1.** kilogram   **3.** gram   **5.** metric ton
7. kiloliter   **9.** gram
Application V   **1.** 10.5 cm   **3.** 2.6 ft   **5.** 162 mi
Application W   **1.** 12.56 mi   **3.** 2.5 m   **5.** 4.71 ft
7. 56.52 ft   **9.** 39.25 mi
Application X   **1.** 150 in^2 **3.** 0.675 m^2 **5.** 10.11 ft^2
Application Y   **1.** 13.5 in^2 **3.** 200 m^2 **5.** 19,625 yd^2
7. 23,223 mm^2
Application Z   **1.** 50,688 m^3 **3.** 396 cm^3 **5.** $157\frac{1}{4}$ yd^3

Index

INDEX

INDEX

Photo Credits

David Ball/Getty Images 704–705, xii(t to b)–3; Paul Barton/CORBIS 550–551, xi(t to b)–1;
Rob Brimson/Getty Images 140; Myrleen Ferguson Cate/PhotoEdit 656–657, xii(t to b)–1;
Steve Chenn/CORBIS 608–609, xi(t to b)–3; Francisco Cruz/SuperStock 680–681, xii(t to b)–2;
Amy Etra/PhotoEdit 342–343, ix(t to b)–2;
David R. Frazier/David R. Frazier Photolibrary, Inc. 312–313, 580–581, ix(t to b)–1, xi(t to b)–2;
Lowell Georgia/CORBIS 456–457, x(t to b)–2;
Helen King/CORBIS 422–423, 484–485, x(t to b)–1, x(t to b)–3;
Michael Krasowitz/Getty Images 144–145, vii(t to b)–3; Jon Miller/Hedrich Blessing, Ltd. Cover;
David Muench/CORBIS 282–283, viii(t to b)–4; Richard T.Nowitz/CORBIS 420–421;
Jose Luis Pelaez, Inc./CORBIS 114–115, vii(t to b)–2; David Samuel Robbins/CORBIS 2–3;
Rick Rusing/Getty Images 392–393, ix(t to b)–4; Wendy Shattil/Index Stock Imagery 88–89;
Adam/Woolfitt/CORBIS 256–257, viii(t to b)–3.
Ian Shaw/Stone/Getty Images xxi; Matthias Kulka/CORBIS xxix.